THE GARDENER'S BUG BOOK

THE GARDENER'S BUG BOOK

Third Edition
Completely Rewritten and Reset

CYNTHIA WESTCOTT

With Full-Color Illustrations of 102 Pests
by Eva Melady

GARDEN CITY, NEW YORK

Doubleday & Company, Inc.

1964

Library of Congress Catalog Card Number 64-15311
Copyright © 1946, 1956, 1964 by Cynthia Westcott
All Rights Reserved
Printed in the United States of America

PESTS

The rose-bug on the rose
Is evil—so are those
Who see the rose-bug
Not the rose.

Ella M. Boult

PREFACE

During the many years that I have doctored gardens and studied their pests a major source of help has been *Insects of Western North America* by Professor E. O. Essig. This was published in 1926, but not until I started to write the preface to the present edition of *The Gardener's Bug Book* did I stop to read the title page of Dr. Essig's exhaustive manual. Belatedly I learn that the book was introduced as a "Manual and Textbook for Students in Colleges and Universities and a Handbook for County, State and Federal Entomologists and Agriculturists as well as for Foresters, Farmers, Gardeners, Travelers, and Lovers of Nature."

Now I hopefully address my own book to exactly the same audience as envisioned by Dr. Essig, nearly forty years ago. It is for the student, of course—for anyone working in entomology, plant pathology or horticulture, including floriculture, pomology, vegetable culture, and landscape design.

Primarily, however, this book is oriented toward the serious gardener and those who serve him, from the farmer who grows his food to the County Agricultural Agent who advises him on growing his own food. It is for the forester who provides wood for his shelter and woods for his recreation; for the nurseryman who produces the trees and shrubs for home planting, and for the tree expert who keeps them healthy. It is for the florist who provides the material for home arrangements and for the flower lover who wants to grow her own decorative material.

This book is for the manufacturing chemist and for the dealer who sells chemicals in small packages and must aid the home gardener in using them wisely. And because it includes friendly insects as well as pests and discusses alternative control methods, this book is even for the organic gardener who shuns all chemicals and for the wildlife enthusiast who is worried about them.

Because previous editions have been increasingly used by professional entomologists, this revision is a bit more scientific, giving the authors of scientific names and some other items of interest to taxonomists. Such details need not worry the gardener.

Because so many people have said, "I can't find my bug in your book," this revision includes many more insects—nearly 1900, as against 1100 in the second edition. Of course this by no means exhausts the possibilities; there are still many, many more injurious insects in the United States than can be mentioned here, but I hope there is a reasonable representation of the more important pests that occur in various sections of the country.

Because the field of nematology has expanded so rapidly since 1956, much more attention has been paid to nematodes. In the previous edition, for instance, there were no nematodes in the check list of pests of Lawn Grasses. In this edition twenty types of nematodes that may injure turf are included.

Because the *Bug Book* has been used in warm climates and because travelers are interested in exotic plants, the Host Plants have been expanded from 450 to 700. Many of the additions are subtropical, but some are cover crops that the gardener or nurseryman might use. We still do not include grains and other plants that would have no place in a home garden.

There has been no attempt to increase the number of illustrations, the space being used for information. Eva Melady's exquisite color paintings have been retained, as have many of the line drawings. Nor has there been any attempt at changing the general format, for gardeners continue to find it easy to use for finger-tip reference. Although the additions have made this third edition a more ponderous tome, it should not be more difficult. However, if this increased array of pests and hosts seems too formidable, and perhaps too extensive, try instead *Are You Your Garden's Worst Pest?* (Doubleday, 1961), which deals only with the more common problems of the more important ornamental plants.

CYNTHIA WESTCOTT

Springvale
Croton-on-Hudson, New York
November, 1963

CONTENTS

PREFACE   vii

LIST OF COLOR PLATES   xiii

LIST OF LINE DRAWINGS   xv

HOW TO USE THIS BOOK   xix

I. INSECTS IN THE GARDEN   1

    Are Insects Increasing?   2

    Insects as Friends of Man   2

    Insects as Enemies of Man   3

    Ways of Controlling Insect Pests   4

        Natural Control   4

        Biological Control   4

        Control by Exclusion   5

        Cultural Control   6

II. GARDEN CHEMICALS   8

    Steps in the Introduction of a New Chemical   9

    Insecticides, Acaricides, Nematocides, Attractants,

        Chemosterilants, and Synergists (an alphabetical list)   10

    Chemicals in Combination   22

    Stop, Look, and Listen! (safety measures)   23

III. SPRAYING AND DUSTING   25

    The Art of Spraying   25

    Choosing a Sprayer   25

Making up Spray Mixtures   30

Manipulating the Spray Rod   32

Timing the Spray   32

Cleaning the Sprayer   33

Dusting Preferred?   34

Advantages of Dusting   36

IV. INSECTS IN ORDER   38

Insect Morphology   39

How Insects Grow   41

Insect Orders   43

Names of Insects   44

V. GARDEN PESTS (AND A FEW FRIENDS)   45

Ant-lions   46

Ants   46

Aphids   51

Armyworms   82

Bagworms   84

Bees   85

Beetles   87

Billbugs   133

Bollworms   133

Borers   134

Budworms (Bud Moths)   159

Bugs   162

Butterflies   178

Cankerworms   182

Casebearers   184

Caterpillars   187

Centipedes and Symphylans   206

Cicadas   207

Crickets   209

Curculios   212

Cutworms   215

Earthworms   219

Earwigs   220

Earworms   221

Flies   223

Fruitworms   230

Galls   232

Grasshoppers   232

Horntails   234

Hornworms   236

Katydids   237

Lacewings   238

Leaf Crumpler   239

Leaf Cutters   240

Leaf Folder   240

Leafhoppers   241

Leaf Miners   247

Leaf Rollers   256

Leaf Skeletonizers   260

Leaf Tiers   262

Maggots   264

Mantids   266

Mealybugs   267

Midges   273

Millipedes   277

Mites   278

Moths 292

Nematodes 312

   Nematocides for Soil Treatment 331

Orthezia 332

Planthoppers 333

Psyllids 334

Rootworms 337

Sawflies 339

Scale Insects 349

Slugs and Snails 385

Sowbugs and Pillbugs 388

Spanworms 389

Spittlebugs 390

Springtails 392

Termites 393

Thrips 395

Treehoppers 403

Walkingsticks 404

Wasps 405

Webworms 410

Weevils 415

Whiteflies 427

Wireworms 432

VI. HOST PLANTS AND THEIR PESTS 436

LIST OF AGRICULTURAL EXPERIMENT STATIONS 561

GLOSSARY 562

SELECTED BIBLIOGRAPHY 566

INDEX 571

LIST OF COLOR PLATES

(Following Page 290)

I Melon Aphid; Bean Aphid

II Aphids: Rosy Apple; Potato; Woolly Apple; Melon; Eastern Spruce Gall; Cooley Spruce Gall; Snowball

III Bagworms. European Pine Shoot Moth

IV Asparagus Beetle; Spotted Asparagus Beetle; Colorado Potato Beetle

V Blister Beetles: Clematis; Margined; Striped. Tarnished Plant Bug

VI Gypsy Moth. Elm Leaf Beetle

VII Flea Beetles: Potato; Pale-striped; Eggplant; Striped; Grape; Spinach. Garden Fleahopper

VIII Japanese Beetle; June Beetle

IX Mexican Bean Beetle; Asiatic Garden Beetle

X Bark Beetles: Smaller European Elm; Native Elm; Western Pine Beetle

XI Rose Chafer; Rose Curculio; Imported Willow Leaf Beetle; Black-legged Tortoise Beetle; Green June Beetle; Rhinoceros Beetle

XII Squash Bug. Striped Cucumber Beetle; Spotted Cucumber Beetle

XIII European Corn Borer. Corn Earworm

XIV Roundheaded Apple Tree Borer; Flatheaded Apple Tree Borer. Potato Leafhopper

XV Iris Borer; Lilac Borer

XVI Squash Borer; Peach Tree Borer

XVII Chinch Bug; Hairy Chinch Bug. Rhododendron Lace Bug

XVIII Fall Webworm. Eastern Tent Caterpillar. Fall Cankerworm

(Following Page 314)

    XIX   Tomato Hornworm. Celeryworm

     XX   Banded Woollybear; Red-humped Caterpillar

    XXI   Northern Mole Cricket; Snowy Tree Cricket

   XXII   Plum Curculio. Pear Psylla

  XXIII   Variegated Cutworm; Dingy Cutworm; Wireworm

   XXIV   Beet Leafhopper; Six-spotted Leafhopper

    XXV   Codling Moth. Apple Maggot

   XXVI   Imported Cabbageworm. Cabbage Maggot

  XXVII   Two-spotted Mite (Red Spider). Mealybugs

 XXVIII   Rose Midge; Chrysanthemum Gall Midge

   XXIX   Millipedes. Slugs. Sowbugs

    XXX   Gladiolus Thrips. Cyclamen Mite

   XXXI   Red-headed Pine Sawfly; Introduced Pine Sawfly; Willow Sawfly

  XXXII   Imported Currantworm; Bristly Rose-slug; Curled Rose Sawfly

 XXXIII   Juniper Scale; Pine Needle Scale; Euonymus Scale

  XXXIV   San Jose Scale; Scurfy Scale; Oystershell Scale; Cottony Maple
          Scale

   XXXV   Bean Weevil; Black Vine Weevil

  XXXVI   Pickleworm; Melonworm

LIST OF LINE DRAWINGS

1. *Sprayers, assorted sizes and types.*   26

2. *More sprayers.*   27

3. *Various types of dusters.*   35

4. *Diagram of an insect.*   39

5. *Mouth parts of sucking and chewing insects.*   40

6. *Insect metamorphosis.*   42

7. *Ant-lion.*   46

8. *Diagram of an ant.*   47

9. *Aphid feeding.*   52

10. *Parasitic wasp on aphid.*   54

11. *Wasp and parasitized aphids.*   54

12. *Aphid gall on blue spruce.*   60

13. *Aphid galls on Norway spruce.*   63

14. *Grape phylloxera.*   65

15. *Green peach aphid.*   67

16. *Snowball leaves curled by aphids.*   76

17. *Fall armyworm.*   83

18. *Leaf-cutter and small carpenter bee on rose.*   86

19. *Diagram of a beetle.*   88

20. *Black blister beetle.*   94

21. *Elm calligrapha and elm leaf beetle.*   100

22. *Flea beetles.*   104

23. *Fuller rose beetle.*   104

24. Ground beetle.   106

25. Japanese beetle.   109

26. Lady beetles.   113

27. Cucumber beetles.   125

28. Tortoise beetles.   129

29. White-fringed beetle.   131

30. Carpenterworm.   138

31. Flatheaded apple tree borer.   142

32. Shot-hole borer.   155

33. Spruce budworm.   161

34. Azalea lace bug.   165

35. Boxelder bug.   166

36. Four-lined plant bug.   169

37. Harlequin bug.   171

38. Leaf-footed bug.   172

39. Mourning-cloak butterfly.   180

40. Cankerworms.   183

41. Pistol casebearer.   187

42. Diagram of a caterpillar.   187

43. California oakworm.   190

44. Garden symphylan.   206

45. Periodical cicada.   208

46. Cutworm.   216

47. European earwig.   220

48. Mediterranean fruit fly.   226

49. Green fruitworm.   231

50. Horntail.   235

51. Angular-winged katydid.   237

52. Golden-eye lacewing.   238

53. *Rose leafhopper.*   245

54. *Birch leaf miner.*   248

55. *Boxwood leaf miner.*   249

56. *Columbine leaf miner.*   251

57. *Holly leaf miners.*   252

58. *Hydrangea leaf tier.*   263

59. *Mealybugs.*   269

60. *Rose midge.*   276

61. *Millipede.*   278

62. *Spruce spider mite.*   289

63. *Leopard moth.*   303

64. *Oriental fruit moth.*   305

65. *White-marked tussock moth.*   311

66. *Typical nematode.*   313

67. *Nematode injury.*   317

68. *Root-knot nematode.*   326

69. *Greenhouse orthezia.*   333

70. *Boxwood psyllid.*   335

71. *Elm sawfly.*   341

72. *European pine sawfly.*   342

73. *Red-headed pine sawfly.*   347

74. *Rose-slug.*   348

75. *Cottony-cushion scale.*   357

76. *European fruit lecanium.*   361

77. *Fern scale.*   362

78. *Florida red scale.*   363

79. *Hemispherical scale.*   367

80. *Purple scale.*   376

81. *Tea scale.*   382

82. *Spotted garden slug.*   387

83. *Spittlebug.*   391

84. *Garden springtail.*   393

85. *Termites.*   394

86. *Flower thrips.*   398

87. *Buffalo treehopper.*   403

88. *Walkingstick.*   405

89. *Tomato hornworm parasitized by wasp.*   406

90. *Cicada killer.*   408

91. *Giant hornet.*   409

92. *Imported long-horned weevil.*   421

93. *Greenhouse whitefly.*   430

94. *Mulberry whitefly.*   431

95. *Wireworm.*   433

HOW TO USE THIS BOOK

The Gardener's Bug Book is not designed to be swallowed whole. It is not meant to floor you with so many pests that you decide not to garden at all. It is a reference manual to be consulted as problems arise. You will never have, in one place, all the pests presented here, but you will have your fair share and after you have gardened long enough to know that insects are facts of life not to be completely ignored, you will start trying to identify them and to keep them at a minimum with the least effort.

Before using this book as a manual, before attempting to look up information on any specific pest, please read Chapter I for a general picture of insects in gardens and types of control measures.

Next read the first part of Chapter II, on garden chemicals, carefully and thoroughly. Skim through the alphabetical list of insecticides, acaricides, nematocides et al., starting on page 10, so that you will know the types of chemicals available and their general functions, but don't worry about the long chemical names. Common names or trade names will be sufficient for most of you. Plan to return to this list of chemicals before using any particular one. No one expects you to remember the specific information. Be sure and read, most attentively, the words under Stop, Look, and Listen page 23, *before* opening any package and *before* using any material on any plant at any time.

Chapter III helps you in choosing, manipulating, and cleaning a sprayer, in making up spray mixtures. If you prefer dusting, check its advantages and disadvantages, the types of dusters available.

Chapter IV orients insects in the animal kingdom, tells how they are made and grow, how they are named, prerequisites to later identification.

With this background information there are two methods by which you can locate the information you need about a plant enemy.

(1.) If you know the common name of the insect or other pest, look it up directly in Chapter V, "Garden Pests (and a Few Friends)." Here groups are in alphabetical order under common names: ANT-LIONS, ANTS, APHIDS, ARMYWORMS, BAGWORMS, BEES, BEETLES, and so on. Consult the table of contents for the complete list of 65 such groups. Under each heading a general discussion of group characteristics is followed by specific insects arranged alphabetically by their common names. For instance, if you want information on the rhododendron lace bug, turn to BUGS for characters common to all true bugs and distinguishing family characteristics and then thumb your way along to *R* for **Rhododendron Lace Bug*** for detailed information. The common name is given in boldface type, marked with an asterisk if it is one presently accepted by the Entomological Society of America, followed by the scientific name in italics. If there is another name in rather common use it is also given, and capitalized. For example, the **Mourning-cloak Butterfly***, *Nymphalis antiopa* (Linnaeus), is treated under BUTTERFLIES because that is the approved common name. Linnaeus first named the species and so his name is given as the author, but put in parentheses because some later scientist transferred it to a different genus. This insect, however, may be more familiar to you as the Spiny Elm Caterpillar and so this name is also given, both in the description and in the Index.

(2.) If you do not know the name of the pest, look up, in the alphabetical treatment of Host Plants, Chapter VI, the plant or plants attacked and note the most likely prospect—**Borer** or **Caterpillar, Mealybug** or **Aphid.** There may be only a few listed, so that checking back is simple. There may be many kinds of aphids or borers in the check list and so you will have to skim through the description of each one to find yours. Your particular species may not be in this book at all, for the nearly 1900 pests included are still less than twenty per cent of those that might possibly be damaging. But you can find its type described and you can probably control it without knowing its full name. In a few cases an insect is listed under a host and is not specifically described in Chapter V. If it is not in the Index, don't waste time hunting for it.

Color plates 1–18 follow page 290; color plates 19–36 follow page 314. The plate number is referred to in the description of the pest and in the Index. Line drawings are indicated by boldface in the Index. Insect size is indicated by a line on the color plate.

THE GARDENER'S BUG BOOK

Chapter I

INSECTS IN THE GARDEN

Insects are not new! They have been around for three hundred million years, according to one estimate; at least fifty million years are quoted by another authority. Either figure far surpasses the less than one million years during which man has evolved. Insects, therefore, are well ahead of man in the race for survival, and ever since the beginning of his existence man has had to try to tip the balance of nature in his favor.

There is a lament in the Bible (Joel 1:4) which sounds very modern: "That which the palmerworm hath left hath the locust eaten; and that which the locust hath left hath the cankerworm eaten; and that which the cankerworm hath left hath the caterpillar eaten." Sometimes, however, the locust leaves nothing for either the cankerworm or man, for insects may appear in incredible numbers. In some countries vast swarms of locusts, measuring several hundred square miles and containing three hundred million individuals (weighing five tons) per mile, devour every bit of edible vegetation.

Chemicals for pest control are not new! Homer wrote of "pest-averting sulfur" 1000 B.C. But *organized* chemical warfare against insects is relatively new. The year 1954 marked the centennial of professional entomology in the United States. Our public fight began in 1854, when the New York State Legislature appropriated funds and Dr. Asa Fitch was employed to study injurious insects and their control. The next month Dr. Townsend Glover was appointed as the first federal entomologist.

In 1962 the Entomological Society of America had 4731 members, distributed in federal and state departments of agriculture, in state experiment stations, in public health services, in the armed forces, or working as pest-control operators or conducting research for industry. This really small number of entomologists means that not too much individual help is available to the more than thirty million gardeners in this country. Many gardeners take their problems to the clerks in seed stores or garden centers. These usually have no professional training and their advice may or may not be helpful. This book is planned so that each gardener may learn for himself enough about insects to profit from the investigations made by the professionals; and it provides finger-tip reference for those who advise the gardener or are engaged in the commercial production or maintenance of ornamentals or food crops.

ARE INSECTS INCREASING?

Gardeners are always complaining about the numbers of insects now compared to the good old days. They say our grandfathers did not have to be continually concerned with pests. Grandfather, however, was not accustomed to the unblemished fruits and vegetables of today's market and he did not worry too much about the holes in the foliage of ornamentals. But he had plenty of pests and so did great-grandfather. Many of the insects we fear today are mentioned in a book, *Insects Injurious to Vegetation,* published in 1841 by T. W. Harris in Massachusetts. As far back as 1933 the plum curculio could totally destroy the plum, apricot, and nectarine crops. The codling moth, first mentioned by name in 1868, was recorded in 1898 as causing an annual loss of one fourth to one half of our apple crop. Serious codling-moth invasions in the West have occurred since 1922. Our native eastern grape phylloxera became a major pest in California in 1863. The cottony-cushion scale from Australia nearly wrecked the citrus industry in the 1870s.

It is, however, quite true that insects are increasing. One reason is that we continue to introduce new insects along with foreign plants. Despite the Plant Quarantine Act, created in 1912 to regulate the movement of nursery stock, insects still sneak through quarantine and inspection, often aided by unthinking gardeners who want a plant souvenir of their travels. Every seventeen minutes around the clock a foreign pest is intercepted at quarantine, but occasionally one escapes detection.

Within our own country our present rapid transportation greatly facilitates insect spread. Despite precautions, Japanese beetles do get a foothold in a new area near an airport. And despite the Federal Plant Pest Act of 1957, which prohibits the movement of plant pests into or through the country, gardeners continue to exchange and to transport plants and unnoticed insects, mites, and nematodes.

Mechanized farming, with large areas devoted to a single crop, has vastly increased insect populations, and so has our habit of planting streets or other areas with large numbers of a single ornamental species. Both the farmer and the home gardener have, paradoxically, increased some pests by the too generous use of broad-spectrum insecticides, thereby killing many insect parasites and predators as well as the pest species.

INSECTS AS FRIENDS OF MAN

No one knows exactly how many kinds of insects there are, and figures vary widely even on the number already described. The fourth (1962) edition of *Destructive and Useful Insects* by Metcalf, Flint and Metcalf gives 686,000 as the estimated number of living described species of true insects. Around 100,000 of these are in North America, but probably not more than a tenth can be designated as public enemies. The rest are either harmless or decidedly beneficial. Without insects, life as we know it today would not exist. We depend on insects for the pollination of 85 per cent of our fruits and many of our vegetables. They play a large role as scavengers. They provide food for birds and fishes. They give us honey and wax, shellac, cochineal, and silk; they have a minor role in surgery and medicine. Practically every insect order contains some useful species that live on destructive insects and it is only within the last twenty years, when some chemicals have reached such a high degree of non-selective efficiency, that we have learned the extent of the role played by parasites and predators in reducing harmful insects and mites.

INSECTS AS EMEMIES OF MAN

In 1868 our crop loss due to insects was figured at 300 million. Today the annual figure is something over 4 billion, and without control measures the figure would be astronomical. In general, we feed about 1/10 of our crops each year to insects, but this can vary, with the crop and the location and the season, from 0 to 100 per cent. The newer chemicals have, in many cases, drastically reduced losses. Greenhouse operators who used to average 15 per cent have, with proper methods, cut that loss to 1 or 2 per cent. Figures are not available for home-garden losses, but some of the nurseryman's profit comes from plants sold to replace those killed by insects in home plantings.

Besides their direct effect on plants, insects are often even more injurious as disseminators of plant disease. Leafhoppers spread the viruses causing curly top, aster yellows, peach yellows, cranberry false blossom, elm phloem necrosis, peach X disease, and Pierce's disease of grape. Aphids transmit viruses causing bean, cucumber, and crucifer mosaics, potato leaf roll, onion yellow dwarf, citrus tristeza. Several species of thrips carry the virus of tomato spotted wilt and a mite is the vector of peach mosaic. Bark beetles spread the Dutch-elm-disease fungus; the peach tree borer helps to distribute the plum-wilt fungus; the plum curculio aids the fungus causing brown rot of peach, plum, and cherry; and the cabbage maggot spreads the blackleg disease of that host. Flies, bees, and aphids are all vectors of bacterial fire blight and the iris borer is intimately connected with vile-smelling soft rot. Cucumber beetles transmit the bacteria of cucurbit wilt and flea beetles transmit those causing Stewart's disease of corn. Insects are also, of course, enormously important as vectors of human diseases, but these are outside the scope of this garden manual.

WAYS OF CONTROLLING INSECT PESTS

Control of plant pests has never been limited to spraying and dusting operations, but the multitude of modern chemicals has, in recent years, made some overlook the fact that chemical control is only one facet of an integrated program. Now the pendulum is swinging back, with too much emphasis on possible adverse effects from chemicals and a tendency to believe that if we let Nature alone everything will be all right. Maybe so, but that depends on whose side you are on. The much quoted "balance of nature" is merely a continuing struggle to the death, and if man does not use all the resources at his command, including chemicals, the insects will certainly come out on top. To keep our exploding population fed, clothed, and housed chemicals are an absolute necessity. They must, however, be used with restraint and discretion, and fitted into a program that also makes full use of natural, biological, legal, mechanical, and cultural measures.

Natural control comes from the climate and physical characteristics of a region and the presence there of natural enemies. Not many insects live in all climatic zones—arctic, temperate, and tropical. Winter temperatures restrict the range of some; summer heat limits others. Some insects prefer a warm, moist climate; others like it warm and dry. Some insects can fly or be carried by the wind long distances; others can crawl only a short distance. Large lakes, rivers, and mountain ranges check the natural spread of insects. The character of the soil limits certain pests, wireworms flourishing in poorly drained soil, nematodes in sandy soil.

Birds, moles, shrews, skunks, snakes, lizards, newts, salamanders, and toads eat many insects. Birds consume enough to more than pay for the cherries, strawberries, grapes, and corn they also eat. Skunks eat a lot of grubs—compensation for the rather conspicuous holes they leave in lawns.

Biological control is a sort of artificial restoration of the balance of nature, bringing in insect predators and parasites, encouraging birds and useful animals, introducing nematodes or bacteria or fungi which will work on the undesirable insects and other pests.

When, despite quarantines and inspection, a foreign pest gets established in this country, we send scientists abroad, often to many countries, in a search for its natural enemies. When such enemies are brought to this country, under strict security, exhaustive tests must be made to ensure that they will not themselves become pests. Then methods must be found for mass rearing in quantities and for effective distribution, often by repeated releases at suitable colonization sites under proper conditions of temperature and humidity.

There are many failures, a few spectacular successes, such as the complete control of cottony-cushion scale on California citrus by Vedalia, an

Australian lady beetle, and a fairly large number of partial successes where biological control is used along with other methods. Almost all insect orders include some beneficial members, and these are most important for forage crops where chemical residues have a zero tolerance.

Microbial insecticides are coming into wider use as potent weapons for biological control. Spores of the bacteria causing milky disease of the Japanese beetle, applied to sod as a powder at frequent intervals, will in time give an excellent kill of grubs, but it may take several years. Commercial preparations of *Bacillus thuringiensis* are applied with an ordinary sprayer for the control of cabbage loopers and similar caterpillars. The action is essentially chemical in nature, the toxin coming from crystals formed in the bacterial cells, and the same precautions for dosage are necessary.

Macerated bodies of cabbage caterpillars infected with a polyhedrosis virus can be disseminated by airplane at the low rate of 5 to 10 larvae per acre for good control. Another virus, also dispensed from planes, takes care of sawflies on pines around reservoirs where chemicals may not be used. So far as we know at this time, such virus diseases offer no harm to man or wildlife, but there is always the possibility of future complications.

Fungi also have a place in biological control. At least fifteen species of Entomophthora attack aphids; one species has markedly decreased brown-tail moths and another is the most important natural control of the grape leafhopper. Some fungi trap nematodes in the soil, but as yet no practical application of this ability has been developed. Most nematodes are pests but some devour other nemas and so may be classed as beneficial.

The most startling new development in biological control is the release of male insects, sterilized by irradiation, to mate with normal females and so render the eggs infertile. This method, used to eradicate screw-worms, a livestock pest in the South, is now being tried for certain crop pests. We are also developing chemical sterilants and these are included in the next chapter, on garden chemicals.

Control by exclusion may be either legal or voluntary. The Plant Quarantine Act of 1912 authorizes the Secretary of Agriculture to impose quarantines and restrictions on plants and plant products and any other articles necessary to prevent the spread of insect infestations of plant diseases. The Act authorizes inspectors of the Department of Agriculture to search, without a warrant, persons coming into the United States and any vehicles coming from any country or moving interstate.

The Insect Pest Act, passed by Congress in 1905, was superseded in 1957 by the Federal Plant Pest Act, prohibiting the movement from any foreign country into the United States, or interstate, of any insect in a live state that is notoriously injurious to cultivated crops.

It is not expected that a quarantine can keep out a pest forever, but the expense of the inspection service is justified if the insect is prohibited for a period sufficiently long to enable us to learn its life history, to develop control measures, and to introduce its parasites.

Home gardeners should make their own voluntary exclusion laws. Why, for instance, borrow trouble by introducing into the garden a delphinium crippled by cyclamen mites, or a Norway spruce with aphid galls, or a juniper covered with scale?

Cultural control, including sanitation, is usually free from expense except for labor costs. Sometimes it does not even require labor, merely a little planning based on knowledge of life histories of particular insects. Diversified planting is of primary importance; mixing types and species in the garden keeps increase of pests at a minimum. Crop rotation is a fundamental principle in good culture, although it is not always possible in a small garden. Most insects attack a small group of related plants. Cabbage worms chew members of the cabbage family; the squash vine borer sticks to the cucurbit group; Mexican bean beetles don't like much except beans. By switching locations for crops you can either starve out certain pests or keep them from building up huge populations.

Soil cultivation during the season destroys some insects. Spading up the vegetable patch in the fall, leaving the ground rough, exposes some larvae and pupae to death by freezing. Garden sanitation—destruction of crop residues, weeds, and trash—is always important, but even this supposedly foolproof method of pest control requires a bit of thought. On land subject to erosion over the winter it may be wiser to let some corn roots remain to anchor the soil even if an occasional borer may hibernate in the old stalk.

Control by mechanical measures depends on barriers erected between the plant and the pest. A cardboard cylinder keeps cutworms away from young transplants; Hotkaps keep cucumber beetles off seedlings; a square of tar paper on the ground keeps the cabbage maggot from depositing eggs too close to young broccoli or cabbage.

Timing of planting is another cultural measure. In Connecticut snap beans planted in early June often mature between broods of Mexican bean beetles. Early summer squash may come along ahead of the squash vine borer; late corn is less apt to be injured by the European corn borer.

In addition to such "escape" methods there is also the possibility of resistant varieties. Long used in disease control, resistance is also becoming a weapon against insect pests, being somewhat successful against corn borers, earworms, rootworms, and a few potato insects. Unfortunately, as soon as a resistant variety is developed the pest usually produces another race or strain to which the host is susceptible.

Advocates of organic gardening claim that plants grown without chemical fertilizer but with proper organic culture are resistant to pests. Vigorous plants may more readily survive the devastating effects of pests, but on the other hand some pests, such as aphids, are attracted to lush, succulent tissue. In a few cases some relation between nutrition and susceptibility to insects or mites has been demonstrated, but this field is largely unexplored. Entomologists looking for insects can usually find them even on plants produced "organically."

Control by chemicals makes up the bulk of this book on garden pests. The list of materials available today is given in the next chapter, and the application of these chemicals for the control of specific pests in Chapter V.

Chapter II

GARDEN CHEMICALS

Beginning with World War II and the spectacular debut of DDT, there has been tremendous activity in the development of chemicals for the control of plant pests. Before the 1940s chemical control was limited and simple; now it is decidedly complex.

In 1854 tobacco, soap, and sulfur were about the only materials tried as insecticides. In 1865 Paris green, brushed onto vines with a broom to halt the Colorado potato beetle, became the first successful stomach poison. About 1880 kerosene emulsion was tried as a contact insecticide and in another quarter of a century was largely replaced by oil sprays. The proprietary miscible oil Scalecide, which appeared on the market in 1905, is still sold under that brand name. Lead arsenate became available commercially in 1903 and calcium arsenate came into use, chiefly for cotton pests, about ten years later. Rotenone became popular about 1933.

That was the year I started out as a doctor to gardens. I used a miscible oil or lime-sulfur as a dormant spray, lead arsenate for chewing insects, and nicotine sulfate for sucking insects on ornamentals and rotenone on fruits and vegetables. When I retired from such active pursuits, in 1960, there was a choice of many hydrocarbons besides DDT, including benzene hexachloride, lindane, methoxychlor, TDE, chlordane, toxaphene, aldrin, dieldrin, helptachlor, and endrin; many phosphates, varying from TEPP—so poisonous that a drop of undiluted chemical on your skin can kill you—to safe malathion; nitrophenyl derivatives such as Elgetol; carbamates such as Sevin; some synthesized botanicals along with pyrethrum and rotenone. There were fumigants of varying degrees of safety, poisonous systemic insecticides, and relatively safe synergists, attractants and miticides.

There are perhaps a hundred basic new chemicals that are now marketed under trade names, in thousands of different formulations and combinations and under prescribed safeguards.

For each new chemical an average of six years has been spent in research and at least a million dollars, more likely $2 to $3 million which does not include plant development and marketing.

In 1938 the Federal Food, Drug and Cosmetic Act made provision for the pesticide residues in food. In 1947 the old Insecticide Act, passed in 1910, became the Federal Insecticide, Fungicide and Rodenticide Act, requiring that economic poisons (pesticides) shipped in interstate commerce be registered with the U. S. Department of Agriculture.

In 1954 the Miller Amendment to the Food, Drug and Cosmetic Act required tolerances for pesticide residues in or on raw agricultural products and made it illegal to sell food products with residues in excess of stipulated tolerances in interstate commerce.

In 1959 an amendment to the Federal Insecticide, Fungicide and Rodenticide Act expanded coverage to include nematocides, defoliants, dessicants, and plant-growth regulators.

Although federal legislation applies only to pesticides in interstate commerce, forty-three of the fifty states have adopted a "Uniform State Act" for controlling distribution and sale of pesticides within their borders.

Here are the steps leading to the introduction of a new chemical and its registration:

1. *Preliminary screening.* Controlled greenhouse experiments show whether the new chemical has more or less activity than a standard (such as DDT) for a cross section of insect species.

2. *Secondary screening.* About 5 per cent of the synthesized compounds show promise for additional evaluation. The selected chemical then is tested on rats for acute oral toxicity and for hazards of handling. It is investigated more extensively in the greenhouse and on a wider range of insects. Analytical methods are developed for determining the amount of residue.

3. *Preliminary field testing.* On crops in a few areas of expected insect infestation, with tests on persistence of residue, influence of weather etc.

4. *Secondary field testing.* The material is screened for cost as compared to standard chemicals, and extensive toxicity studies are made on several species of experimental animals.

5. *Large-scale field testing.* This must yield all information necessary for proper labeling and include long-term toxicity studies to show the safe level of the pesticide as a residue on edible crops. From these data the Food and Drug Administration is requested to set a tolerance for specific crops. This is expressed in parts per million (ppm), a term expressing the weight of the residue in relation to the product weight; this is set at only 1/100 of the amount that might be harmful under maximum consumption. The amount of permissible residue has been explained as equivalent to a dash of vermouth in a martini made with 20,000 gallons of gin.

6. *Marketing.* The label registered with the U. S. Department of Agriculture is a legal document. It must spell out the purposes and effects of the chemical as well as necessary precautions, detailed instructions for use, first-aid information, and antidotes.

The label must contain:

a. Name and address of the manufacturer or person for whom manufactured.

b. The name, brand or trademark under which the article is marketed or distributed.

c. The net weight, volume or measure of contents.

d. An ingredient statement. Each active ingredient is listed with the correct percentage by weight and the total percentage of inert ingredients.

e. Poison labeling (skull and crossbones) on products highly toxic to man. Antidotes are listed; safety equipment.

f. A warning or caution statement as necessary to prevent injury to man, animals, or plants.

g. Adequate directions for use. The petition presented to the U.S.D.A. for label registration must show that the product is useful for the control of specific pests and that it can be handled safely if all directions are followed.

So much for the manufacturer! He has gone through a lot of time, money, worry, and red tape to get that label on his product so it can be included in the array on the shelves of your local garden-supply store. The next step is yours. If you are like nine out of ten gardeners you will grab the package off the shelf, merely glancing at the brand name and not looking at the fine print on the label. You will take it home, put it on the kitchen table, open it up, scattering some of the contents, and then—possibly—look at the label just enough to learn if the dose is 1 teaspoon or 2 tablespoons per gallon of water. Meanwhile you can inhale enough vapor to kill you, or you can spill enough on your skin to kill you, or you can scatter specks of lethal powder around the kitchen.

As a safety measure everyone should read *every word* on a label before a pesticide container is opened. The material may be so poisonous that it requires respirator, special clothing and rubber gloves. If so, take it back to the store unopened. Such a product is not for an amateur without experience. If there is no skull and crossbones, no list of protective clothing, then read the warning and caution statements and proceed according to directions.

INSECTICIDES, ACARICIDES, NEMATOCIDES, ATTRACTANTS, CHEMOSTERILANTS, AND SYNERGISTS

The following list of chemicals is in alphabetical order according to approved common name, where such has been designated, otherwise by trade name. Common names are written in lower case; trade names are capitalized. The chemical name is given in parentheses. The LD_{50} values refer to the dosage, in milligrams per kilogram of body weight, lethal to 50 per cent of the white rats used to test acute oral toxicity. The lower this value, the more precautions should be taken in handling the chemical. Where a tolerance has been given, this is expressed in parts per million (ppm) of the weight of the commodity at harvest. Some chemicals are considered safe enough to be exempt from tolerance.

aldrin (not less than 95% of 1,2,3,4,10,10,hexachloro-1,4,4a,5,8,8a-hexahydro-1,4-*endo-exo*-5,8-dimethanonaphthalene). Highly poisonous fumigant, contact and stomach insecticide. Hazardous to fish, birds, bees, but not to soil microorganisms. LD_{50} 50 mg/kg; tolerance 0.1 to 0.25 but zero for forage crops. Compatible with most other pesticides. Widely used for grasshoppers, at 2 to 4 ounces per acre, and for grubs and other soil insects, broadcast before planting at 3 pounds per acre. It may no longer be used in soil for potatoes but is allowed for many vegetables.

allethrin (*dl*-2-allyl-4-hydroxy-3-methyl-2-cyclopenten-1-one esters of *cis* and *trans* *dl*-chrysanthemum monocarboxylic acids). A synthetic pyrethrum, allyl homolog of Cinerin I, contact insecticide of very low toxicity to mammals. Exempt from tolerance on vegetables before harvest; 2 to 4 ppm post-harvest on fruits.

apholate (2,2,4,4,6,6-hexahydro-2,2,4,4,6,6-hexakis (1-aziridinyl)-1,3,5,2, 4,6-triazatriphosphorine). A chemosterilant.

Aramite® (2-(*p-tert*-butylphenoxy) isopropyl 2-chloroethyl sulfite). Alkyl aryl sulfite, acaricide (miticide). Excellent for mite control on ornamentals, safe to handle, and with little hazard for wildlife but possible carcinogenic. LD_{50} 3900; zero tolerance on fruits and vegetables. Not compatible with alkaline materials. Normal dosage is 1 tablespoon of 15% wettable powder to 1 gallon of water. Aramite is included in many combination sprays and dusts sold under trade names for roses and other ornamentals.

azobenzene (diphenyl diimide). Acaricide, used as a greenhouse fumigant, vaporized from hot steam pipes. Poisonous, to be handled carefully, not to be used in houses with food crops; zero tolerance. Under some conditions may cause plant injury.

Bacillus thuringiensis Berliner. **Thuricide®**. A microbial pesticide, presumably non-toxic to mammals, useful in control of certain caterpillars. Exempt from tolerance. This bacterial preparation, available as a powder or in liquid form, is used like any chemical insecticide.

barthrin (6-chloropiperonyl chrysanthemumate). A botanical derivative of very low mammalian toxicity.

BHC (benzene hexachloride, gammexane; 1,2,3,4,5,6-hexachloro-cyclohexane). Contact insecticide, stomach poison and fumigant, toxicity varying with isomers present; tolerance 5 ppm. Of unpleasant odor; may impart off-flavor to root crops; not to be used on food crops near harvest. Not compatible with alkaline materials, questionable with nicotine and fixed copper fungicides.

Bichloride of mercury. See mercuric chloride.

Bidrin® (3-(dimethoxyphosphinyloxy)-*N,N*-dimethyl-*cis*-crotonamide). A poisonous phosphate, used for cotton, crops for seed, some ornamentals.

binapacryl (2-*sec*-butyl-4,6-dinitrophenyl 3-methyl-2-butenoate). Morocide®, a promising acaricide. It is recommended for apples, at 1 pound per 100 gallons of water, to control various species of mites but not more than 3 times or within 60 days of harvest.

Black Leaf 40. See nicotine sulfate.

Bladan. See HETP.

Bladafume. See sulfotepp.

Bromofume. See ethylene dibromide.

Bulan® (2-nitro-1,1-bis (*p*-chlorophenyl) butane). One constituent of Dilan.

Calcium arsenate. Stomach poison dangerous to wildlife, bees, and many beneficial insects. LD_{50} 40 to 100 mg/kg; tolerance 3.5 ppm. Not compatible with many pesticides but can be combined with coppers, sulfur, and glyodin. Sometimes recommended for potatoes and a few other vegetables, rarely for ornamentals.

Calcium cyanide. Fumigant, intensely poisonous, hazardous to all life; zero tolerance on fresh fruits and vegetables. Sold as Cyanogas, a dust to blow into wasp and ant nests, and as granules for greenhouses. Do not use this fumigant if the greenhouse is attached to a dwelling.

Calomel. See mercurous chloride.

carbaryl (1-naphthyl-N-methyl-carbamate). Sevin®. Broad-spectrum insecticide of low mammalian toxicity but highly toxic to bees and many beneficial insects; tolerance 5 to 12 ppm. Highly effective for Japanese beetles, recommended for tent caterpillars, leaf miners, lace bugs, bagworms, sawflies, and webworms but may seriously increase mites. Dosage is 2 tablespoons of 50 per cent wettable powder to 1 gallon of water. Do not use on Boston ivy or Virginia-creeper.

Carbon disulfide. Insecticide fumigant, dangerous because of extreme inflammability, poisonous if inhaled. Exempt from tolerance when used as a fumigant for most grains.

Carbon tetrachloride. Insecticide fumigant; poisonous; avoid prolonged exposure to vapors. Exempt from tolerance when used for grains.

carbophenothion (S-[(*p*-chlorophenylthio) methyl] O-*O*-diethyl phosphorodithioate). Trithion®. Insecticide, highly poisonous. LD_{50} 30 mg/kg; tolerance 0.2 to 2 ppm.

chlorbenside (*p*-chlorobenzyl *p*-chlorophenyl sulfide). Mitox®. Acaricide. Tolerance 3 ppm for various fruits and vegetables.

chlordane (1,2,4,5,6,7,8,8-octachloro-3a,4,7,7a-tetrahydro-4,7-methanoindane). Contact insecticide for ants, beetle grubs, chinch bugs, mole crickets, grasshoppers, bagworms, taxus weevil, and other pests. LD_{50} 457-500 mg/kg acute oral, but quite toxic by skin contact; tolerance 0.3 ppm for fruits and vegetables. Not compatible with alkaline materials.

chlorobenzilate (ethyl 4,4'-dichlorobenzilate). Acaricide of very low mammalian toxicity. LD_{50} 3.1 g/kg; tolerance 5 ppm for fruits.

Chloropicrin (nitrochloroform). Tear gas, sold as Larvacide or Picfume. Insecticide fumigant for soil insects, nematodes, weed seeds, and some fungi.

Not safe around living plants; gas is highly poisonous to man and wildlife but leaves no harmful residue. Exempt from tolerance. Inject ½ teaspoon 6 inches deep at 10-inch intervals and apply water seal immediately.

Cinerin I and **II.** See pyrethrum.

Corrosive sublimate. See mercuric chloride.

Cryolite (sodium fluoaluminate or sodium alumino fluoride). Protective insecticide, of some mammalian toxicity; tolerance 7 ppm for fruits and vegetables.

Cube. A tropical plant used as a source of rotenone.

cue-lure (acetate of 4-(p-hydroxyphenyl)-2-butanone). Insect attractant, used in bait sprays; low mammalian toxicity.

Cyanogas. See calcium cyanide.

cyclethrin (dl-2-(2-cyclopentenyl)-4-hydroxy-3-methyl-2-cyclopenten-1-one-esters of cis and trans dl-chrysanthemummonocarboxylic acids). An analog of allethrin.

Cygon®. See dimethoate.

Cynem (O,O-diethyl 0-2-pyrazinyl phosphorothioate). Zinophos, Nemaphos. Acaricide, systemic insecticide and nematocide.

D-D Mixture® (1,3-dichloropropene and 1,2-dichloropropane). Dowfume N. An excellent soil fumigant for nematodes, wireworms, some other soil insects, some weeds. It is applied in holes 6 inches deep staggered 18 inches apart, at the rate of ⅓ ounce per hole. Apply only to fallow soil; wait 2 to 4 weeks before planting. Toxic to mammals by ingestion or inhalation but irritating enough to minimize danger; little hazard to wildlife if used as directed; LD_{50} 140 mg/kg; zero tolerance.

DDT (1,1,1-trichloro-2,2-bis (p-chlorophenyl)ethane). Broad-spectrum insecticide with long residual effect, the first of the organic insecticides to come into wide use. Although first synthesized in 1874, by a German chemist, it was 1939 before it was put to practical use—in Switzerland against the Colorado potato beetle. Coming into its own as an aid in public health during World War II, DDT is credited with saving five million lives and preventing a hundred million illnesses by controlling mosquitoes, lice, flies, and other vectors of human disease. DDT is mildly toxic to mammals, LD_{50} values being given as 113 to 250 mg/kg, and is less harmful to bees than some other pesticides, but it is toxic to many beneficial insects, is hazardous to fish at low dosage and to birds at more than 2 pounds per acre. The widespread use of DDT has increased populations of spider mites, and certain scale insects and some insects are now resistant to it. The usual dosage for caterpillars, beetles, leafhoppers and other foliage pests is 2 tablespoons of 50 per cent wettable powder to 1 gallon of water; for beetle grubs 6 pounds of 6 per cent dust to 1000 square feet of lawn area; for treating gladiolus corms after harvest, 5 per cent dust. Applications via airplane for control of gypsy moths and other pests are usually only ½ to 1 pound actual DDT, in oil, per acre. DDT may injure camellias, Japanese maples, and some cucurbits. It is not compatible with alkaline materials. Residue tolerances vary from zero for milk, 1 ppm for apricots and plums, 3 ppm for apples and grapes, 5 ppm for cranberries and citrus, to 30 ppm for asparagus.

DDVP. See Vapona®.

Delnav® (2,3-*p*-dioxanedithiol S,S-bis (*O,O*)-diethyl phosphorodithioate). Acaricide and insecticide. LD_{50} 110 mg/kg; tolerance 2.8 ppm for citrus fruits, 4.9 ppm for apples, pears, quinces.

demeton (*O,O*-diethyl *O* (and *S*(-2-(ethylthio) ethyl phosphorothioates). Often sold as Systox®, a highly poisonous systemic insecticide and acaricide, to be used only with respirator and protective clothing. LD_{50} 1.7 to 7.5 mg/kg; tolerance 0.3 ppm for beans to 1.25 ppm for grapes. Applied to soil, demeton helps plants resist mites, aphids, and thrips.

Derris. A plant with insecticidal properties. Two species, *Derris elliptica* and *D. malaccensis* from Malaya and the East Indies, have 4 to 5 per cent rotenone in their dried roots. See rotenone.

diazinon (*O,O*-diethyl *O*-(2-isopropyl-6-methyl-4-pyrimidyl) thiophosphate). An organic phosphate, less dangerous than some others. LD_{50} 150 to 220 mg/kg; tolerance 0.75 ppm. Recommended for control of chinch bugs, bagworms, azalea leaf miner, whiteflies, clover aphid, apple maggot and other insects.

Dibrom®. See naled.

dicapthon (*O*-(2-chloro-4-nitrophenyl)*O,O*-dimethyl phosphorothioate). Acaricide, insecticide. LD_{50} 500 mg/kg.

dichloroethyl ether (bis-(2-chloroethyl)ether). A soil fumigant sometimes used for sod webworms, also in corn earworm oils. Strongly irritating; LD_{50} 105 mg/kg.

dieldrin (not less than 85% of 1,2,3,4,10,10-hexachloro-6,7-epoxy-1,4, 4a,5,6,7,8,8a-octahydro-1,4-*endo-exo*-5,8-dimethanonaphthalene).   Contact and stomach insecticide, poisonous. LD_{50} 60 mg/kg; tolerance 0.1 ppm to 0.25. Recommended for wireworms, white-fringed beetles, black vine weevils, grasshoppers, armyworms, borers, plum and apple curculios, sawflies, thrips, and other insects. Compatible with most other insecticides.

Dilan®. Mixture of Bulan and Prolan, sometimes used for Mexican bean beetles.

Dimecron. See phosphamidon.

dimefox (bis (dimethylamino) fluorophosphine oxide). Systemic acaricide, insecticide, sold as Pestox 14®. Highly poisonous; LD_{50} 5 mg/kg.

dimetan (5,5-dimethyldihydroresorcinol dimethylcarbamate). Systemic insecticide; LD_{50} 150 mg/kg.

dimethoate (*O,O*-dimethyl *S* (*N*-methylcarbamoylmethyl) phosphorodithioate). Sold as Cygon®, systemic acaricide, insecticide, less hazardous to use than most other phosphates. LD_{50} 245 mg/kg. May be used on ornamentals and non-bearing fruit trees for aphids, mites, leafhoppers, thrips, bagworms and scale insects, being especially useful for tea scale on camellias. The dosage is 1 teaspoon of Cygon 4E to 1 gallon of water. Do not use on chrysanthemums.

dimethrin (2,4-dimethylbenzyl chrysanthemumate). Non-toxic insecticide.

Dimetilan® (2-dimethylcarbamyl-3-methylpyrazolyl-(5)-dimethyl-carbamate). Insecticide, poisonous; LD_{50} 47 to 71 mg/kg.

Dimite® (1,1-bis(p-chlorophenyl)ethanol). Acaricide only, particularly useful for cyclamen mite on delphinium and African violet; use on food crops only early in the season. LD_{50} 500 mg/kg; zero tolerance.

dinitrobutylphenol (4,6-dinitro-o-sec-butylphenol, triethanolamine salt). Dinoseb, DN-289, DNSOBP, DNBP. Herbicide, insecticide. LD_{50} 37 to 60 mg/kg; zero tolerance for fruits and vegetables.

dinitrocresol (4,6-dinitro-o-cresol, sodium salt). Elgetol®. Poisonous insecticide used as a dormant spray for some scale insects and aphid eggs. LD_{50} 40 to 65 mg/kg; zero tolerance. Incompatible with many other pesticides.

dinitrocyclohexylphenol (4,6-dinitro-o-cyclohexylphenol). Dinex, DN-Dry Mix No. 1, DNOCHP. Contact insecticide, fungicide, herbicide. LD_{50} 180 mg/kg; tolerance 1 ppm. Incompatible or questionable with many other pesticides.

Di-Syston® (O,O-diethyl S-2-(ethylthio)ethyl phosphorodithioate). Systemic acaricide, insecticide, highly poisonous. LD_{50} 6.5 mg/kg; tolerance 0.3 to 0.5 ppm. Also sold as Syston® in 2% granules.

endosulfan (6,7,8,9,10,10-hexachloro-1,5,5a,6,9,9a-hexahydro-6,9-methano-2,4,3-benzodioxathiepin 3-oxide). Thiodan®. Insecticide useful for various fruit and vegetable pests. LD_{50} 100 mg/kg; tolerance 2 ppm.

endothion (S[(5-methoxy-4-oxo-4H-pyran-2-yl)methyl]O,O-dimethyl phosphorothioate). Insecticide.

endrin (1,2,3,4,10,10-hexachloro-6-7-epoxy-1,4,4a,5,6,7,8,8a-octahydro-1,4-endo endo-5,8-dimethanonaphthalene). Highly poisonous insecticide; concentrates must be handled with great care; LD_{50} 5 to 45 mg/kg; zero tolerance. Recommended for control of cyclamen mite and for some insects on food crops but use should be limited to professionals.

EPN® (O-ethyl O-p-nitrophenol phenylphosphonothioate). Acaricide, insecticide. LD_{50} 9 to 45 mg/kg; tolerance 3 ppm for most fruits and vegetables.

ethion (O,O,O',O'-tetraethyl S,S'-methylene bis phosphorodithioate). Nialate®. Acaricide, insecticide. LD_{50} 96 to 208 mg/kg; tolerance 1 to 2 ppm.

Ethylene bromide (1,2-dibromoethane) EDB. Fumigant, nematocide, for soil treatment. LD_{50} 117 to 146 mg/kg; tolerance 5 to 10 ppm.

Ethylene chlorobromide (1-bromo-2-chloroethane). Insecticide fumigant and nematocide. LD_{50} 64 mg/kg.

Ethylene dichloride (1,2-dichloroethane). Fumigant. Reasonably safe but toxic if inhaled in quantity; LD_{50} 770 mg/kg; exempt from tolerance used as a fumigant for grains.

Ethylene oxide (1,2-epoxyethane). Insecticide fumigant. Poisonous if inhaled for long periods; tolerance 50 ppm for some nuts.

eugenol (4-allyl-2-methoxyphenol). Attractant, used in some beetle traps.

Fumazone. See Nemagon.

furethrin (3-furfuryl-2-methyl 4-oxo-2-cyclopenten-1-yl chrysanthemumate). Insecticide of low mammalian toxicity.

gamma BHC. See lindane.

Genicide® (9-xanthenone). Acaricide, ovicide, insecticide.

Genite® (2,4-dichlorophenyl ester of benzenesulfonic acid). Genitol. Acaricide. LD_{50} 1400 to 1900 kg/mg.

Guthion® (O,O-dimethyl S-4-oxo-1,2,3-benzotriazin-3(4H)-ylmethyl phosphorodithioate). Highly poisonous insecticide useful for fruits, controlling plum curculio, red-banded leaf roller, and other insects. LD_{50} 16 to 80 mg/kg; tolerance 2 ppm for most fruits and vegetables, 5 ppm for grapes.

gyplure (cis-9-octadecene-1,12-diol 12-acetate). Synthetic attractant, useful in gypsy-moth traps.

heptachlor (1,4,5,6,7,8,8-heptachloro-3a,4,7,7a-tetrahydro-4,7-methanoindene). Poisonous insecticide. LD_{50} 130 mg/kg; tolerance zero for most food crops. Used in control of ants, grasshoppers, and beetle grubs but toxic to game birds and bees until the residue wears off—about 3 weeks.

HETP (hexaethyl tetraphosphate). Similar to TEPP, which see.

Hydrogen cyanide (hydrocyanic acid gas). HCN. Insecticide fumigant. Violent poison; use gas mask; 10 ppm in air can be fatal.

Isolan® (dimethyl 5-(1-isopropyl-3-methyl-pyrazolyl)carbamate). Insecticide. LD_{50} 54 mg/kg.

Karathane® (dinitro (1-methylheptyl) phenyl crotonate). Also known as Arathane, Mildex, and Iscothan. Efficient fungicide for powdery mildew and also of value as an acaricide. LD_{50} 1000 mg/kg.

Kelthane® (1,1-bis(p-chlorophenyl) 2,2,2-trichloroethanol). Acaricide safe for home-garden use. LD_{50} 575 mg/kg; tolerance 5 to 10 ppm for fruits and vegetables. Recommended for cyclamen mite as well as spider mites.

Kepone® (decachlorooctahydro-1,3,4-metheno-2H-cyclobuta [cd] pentalen-2-one). Insecticide, fungicide. LD_{50} 126 to 132 mg/kg. Used as a stomach poison for ants and grasshoppers.

Larvacide. See chloropicrin.

Lead arsenate. Stomach poison for chewing insects, highly toxic to mammals if ingested. LD_{50} 100 mg/kg; tolerance 7 ppm for most fruits and vegetables, 1 ppm for citrus.

Lethane 60® ($beta$-thiocyanoethyl laurate(coconate). Insecticide of low mammalian toxicity. LD_{50} 500 mg/kg.

Lime sulfur (calcium polysulfides). Fungicide, acaricide, insecticide, used as a dormant spray for scale insects, especially rose, juniper, and pine needle scales. Of low mammalian toxicity; exempt from tolerance.

lindane (gamma isomer of 1,2,3,4,5,6-hexachlorocyclohexane of 99% purity). Purified form of benzene hexachloride, recommended for lace bugs, aphids, leaf rollers, wireworms and other insects. LD_{50} 125 to 230 mg/kg, but toxic on skin contact; tolerance 10 ppm for most fruits and vegetables.

Compatible with most pesticides, questionable with alkaline materials. Usual dosage is 1 tablespoon of 25% wettable powder to 1 gallon of water.

Lonchocarpus. Plant in Central and South America, principal source of rotenone.

London purple. Mixture of calcium arsenite and calcium arsenate. Mostly outmoded as an insecticide.

Loro® (n-dodecyl thiocyanate). Insecticide of very low mammalian toxicity. LD_{50} 1250 mg/kg.

Magnesium arsenate. Has been used for some insects not controlled by lead or calcium arsenates. Tolerance 3.5 ppm for beans, black-eyed peas.

malathion (O,O-dimethyl dithiophosphate of diethyl mercaptosuccinate). Broad-spectrum phosphate insecticide of relatively low toxicity to mammals (100 times less than parathion) but more harmful than DDT to bees and some beneficial insects. LD_{50} 1500 mg/kg; tolerance 8 ppm for most fruits and vegetables, 2 ppm for corn. Sometimes phytotoxic in certain formulations; the wettable powder is safer than an emulsion in hot weather.

Marlate. See methoxychlor.

medlure (sec-butyl 4 (or 5)-chloro-2-methylcyclohexanecarboxylate). Attractant of low mammalian toxicity; used in baits for control of the Mediterranean fruit fly.

menazon (S-(4,6-diamino-1,3,5-triazin-2-ylmethyl)dimethyl phosphorothiolothionate). Saphos, Saphizon. Systemic acaricide, insecticide. LD_{50} 890 mg/kg.

Mercuric chloride. Bichloride of mercury, corrosive sublimate. Mostly used as a fungicide or bactericide; highly toxic to mammals.

Mercurous chloride. Calomel. Insecticide, fungicide of low mammalian toxicity, but there is a zero tolerance for any mercury compound. Has been recommended for control of onion and cabbage maggots.

Metacide® (O,O-dimethyl O-p-nitrophenyl phosphorothioate, parathion mixture). Mixture of parathion and methyl parathion; highly poisonous.

Metaldehyde (Metacetaldehyde). Attractant and toxicant for slugs and snails; used in baits and sprays.

Meta-Systox®. See methyl demeton.

metepa (tris-[1-(2-methylazidinyl)]phosphine oxide). Chemosterilant.

methiotepa (tris(2-methyl-1-aziridinyl) phosphine sulfide). Metapside. Chemosterilant.

methotrexate (N-(p-[(2,4-diamino-6-pteridyl)methyl]methylamino-benzoyl (glutamic acid). A chemosterilant.

methoxychlor (1,1,1-trichloro-2,2-bis (p-methoxyphenyl) ethane). Marlate®. Methoxy DDT. Analog of DDT, safer for mammals but with about the same effect on bees and beneficial insects. LD_{50} 6000 mg/kg; tolerance 14 ppm for fruits and vegetables. Usual dosage is 2 tablespoons of 15 per cent wettable powder to 1 gallon of water.

methyl apholate (2,2,4,4,6,6-hexahydro-2,2,4,4,6,6-hexakis (2-methyl-1-aziridinyl)-1,3,5,2,4,6-triazatriphosphorine). Chemosterilant.

Methyl bromide. Bromethane. Highly toxic fumigant for soil insects and nematodes; extremely hazardous by inhalation and without special odor to give warning; to be used only by expert operators. Not very phytotoxic and is used in special chambers to fumigate potted plants and outdoors under special covers. LD_{50} 9 mg/kg; tolerance 5 to 30 ppm for fruits and vegetables.

Methyl chloride (chloromethane). Aerosol propellant of rather low mammalian toxicity.

methyl demeton (O,O-dimethyl O (and S) (2-ethylthio) ethyl phosphorothioates). Meta-Systox. Another phosphate, slightly less hazardous than demeton. LD_{50} 40 to 180 mg/kg.

methyl parathion (O,O-dimethyl O-p-nitrophenyl phosphorothioate). Highly toxic insecticide. LD_{50} 9 to 25 mg/kg; tolerance 1 ppm.

Methyl Trithion® (O,O-dimethyl S[(p-chlorophenylthio)methyl] phosphorodithioate). Acaricide, insecticide. LD_{50} 200 mg/kg.

mipafox (N,N'-diisopropyldiamidophosphoryl fluoride). Pestox 15®. Systemic insecticide. LD_{50} to rabbits 100 mg/kg.

mirex (dodecachlorooctahydro-1,3,4-metheno-$2H$ -cyclobuta (c,d) pentalene. Insecticide of relatively low mammalian toxicity, of special use for control of the imported fire ant.

Mitox®. See chlorbenside.

Morocide. See binapacryl.

morzid (bis (1-aziridinyl) morpholinophosphine sulfide). Chemosterilant.

naled (1,2-dibromo-2,2-dichloroethyl dimethyl phosphate). Dibrom. Used for aphids, mites, certain caterpillars and leafhoppers on fruits and vegetables. LD_{50} 430 mg/kg; zero tolerance.

Naphthalene. Fumigant, of no mammalian toxicity.

Natriphene (o-phenylphenol). Dowicide®. Fungicide and acaricide of low mammalian toxicity. LD_{50} 1160 mg/kg.

Nemagon® (1,2-dibromo-3-chloropropane). Fumazone®. Fumigant nematocide that can be used around living plants; useful for home gardens.

Neotran® (di(4-chlorophenoxy) methane. Acaricide of low mammalian toxicity.

Nialate. See ethion.

Nicotine (l-1-methyl-2-(3-pyridyl)-pyrrolidine). Nicotine sulfate contains 40 per cent of the alkaloid and is commonly sold as Black Leaf 40®. Contact insecticide, highly toxic if inhaled, ingested, or spilled on skin, but with little residual effect; not harmful to bees and most beneficial insects. LD_{50} 50 to 60 mg/kg; tolerance 2 ppm. The usual dosage for aphids and other sucking insects is 1 teaspoon of the sulfate and 1 ounce of soap to 1 gallon of water.

Octochlor®. See chlordane.

Oils. Sometimes animal or vegetable oils, as fish oil or lemon oil, but usually petroleum products in an emulsion, when the oil is broken into fine globules in water, and miscible oils that mix readily with water. Oils are safe for the operator and are exempt from tolerance, but they may be phytotoxic if used when the temperature is below 45° F. or above 85°. Oil sprays should not be used on sugar and Japanese maples, on Japanese and black walnut, on butternut or beech; they should be used with caution on magnolia and some evergreens.

ovex (*p*-chlorophenyl *p*-chloro-benzenesulfonate). Ovotran®. Acaricide effective for the egg stage of spider mites, safe for the user, harmless to bees, slightly phytotoxic to roses, recommended for evergreens. LD_{50} 2000; tolerance 3 to 5 ppm.

para-dichlorobenzene. Paracide®. Insecticide fumigant, used on soil around peach trees to control borers. Not toxic as commonly applied.

parathion (*O,O*-diethyl *O-p*-nitrophenyl phosphorothioate). Acaricide and insecticide, a violent poison to be used with all precautions. LD_{50} 5 mg/kg; tolerance 1 ppm. Readily absorbed through skin and lungs, but the residual toxic effect on food crops is short.

para-oxon. Oxygen analog of parathion.

Paris green (copper acetoarsenite). One of the earliest insecticides, a stomach poison of high mammalian toxicity and toxic to some plants. Formerly used for potatoes and in grasshopper and cutworm baits.

Pentac® (Bis(pentachloro-2,4-cyclopentadien-1-yl)). Acaricide proving helpful in mite control on roses and other greenhouse crops.

Perthane® (1,1-dichloro-2,2-bis(*p*-ethylphenyl) ethane). Insecticide of great safety. LD_{50} 8200 mg/kg; tolerance 15 ppm. Effective for some fruit and vegetable pests.

Pestox III. See schradan.

Phenothiazine (thiodiphenylamine). Insecticide, fungicide of low toxicity to man but may cause dermatitis. Tolerance 7 ppm for apples, pears, quinces.

phorate (*O,O*-diethyl *S*-ethylthiomethyl phosphorodithioate). Thimet®. Systemic acaricide, insecticide; acutely poisonous. LD_{50} 3.7 mg/kg. Used for control of aphids, birch-leaf miners and other pests but only by professionals with proper protection.

Phosdrin® (2-methoxycarbonyl-1-methylvinyl dimethyl phosphate). Extremely poisonous systemic insecticide. LD_{50} 6.8 mg/kg; tolerance 0.25 to 1 ppm.

phosphamidon (2-chloro-2-diethylcarbamoyl-1-methylvinyl dimethyl phosphate). Dimecron. Acaricide, systemic insecticide. LD_{50} 16.8 mg/kg.

Phostex® (bis(dialkophosphinothioyl) disulfides). A rather safe acaricide and insecticide. LD_{50} 2500 mg/kg.

piperonyl butoxide (a[2-(2 butoxy)ethoxy]-4,5-methylenedioxy-2-propyltoluene). Insecticide synergist of very low mammalian toxicity. LD_{50} 7500 mg/kg; tolerance 8 ppm. Often used with pyrethrum in "bombs" for house plants.

piperonyl cyclonene (mixture of 3-alkyl-6-carbethoxy-5-(3,4-methylene dioxyphenyl)-2-cyclohexen-1-one and 3-alkyl-5-(3,4-methylenedioxyphenyl) 2-cyclohexen-1-one). Synergist of very low mammalian toxicity; exempt from tolerance when applied to growing crops but not post harvest.

propyl isome (di-n-propyl-3-methyl-6,7-methylenedioxy-1,2,3,4-tetra-hydronaphthalene-1,2-dicarboxylate). Synergist of very low mammalian toxicity; LD_{50} 1500 mg/kg.

Pyrethrin I (ester of chrysanthemum monocarboxylic acid and the alcohol pyrethrolone). Active principle in pyrethrum.

Pyrethrin II (ester of chrysanthemum dicarboxylic acid and the alcohol pyrethrolone). A constituent of pyrethrum.

Pyrethrum. Dried flower heads of *Chrysanthemum cineraefolium* and some other members of this genus, active principles being Cinerin I and II (esters of chrysanthemum monocarboxylic acid and dicarboxylic acid with the alcohol cinerolone) and Pyrethrins I and II. Contact insecticide of very low mammalian toxicity, with little hazard to bees and beneficial insects but toxic to fish; exempt from tolerance.

Rhothane®. See TDE.

rotenone. Derived from plants, species of *Derris* and *Lonchocarpus,* the latter, found in Central and South America, a principal source. Contact and stomach insecticide highly toxic to fish but of low toxicity to most mammals. In the form of ground derris it may kill nestling birds. LD_{50} varies from 100 to 1000 mg/kg according to form in which it is used; exempt from tolerance. Incompatible with alkaline materials.

ryania. From ground stem and root of *Ryania speciosa,* a South American shrub. Contact and protective insecticide of low toxicity to mammals. LD_{50} 750 mg/kg; exempt from tolerance. Effective for the European corn borer and some other pests of food crops.

sabadilla. From seeds of *Schoenocaulon officinale.* A South American plant of the lily family. Irritating to the eyes and respiratory tract but relatively harmless. LD_{50} 4000; exempt from tolerance. Used for squash bugs, stink bugs and similar insects.

schradan (octamethylpyrophosphoramide). Pestox III®; OMPA. Systemic acaricide and insecticide; highly poisonous, requiring extreme care. LD_{50} 20 to 30 mg/kg; tolerance 0.75 for English walnuts. Particularly effective for aphids and mites.

Selenium. See sodium selenate.

sesamex (2-(3,4-methylenedioxyphenoxy)-3,6,9-trioxaundecane). Synergist. LD_{50} 2000 mg/kg.

sesamin (2,6-bis(3,4-methylenedioxyphenyl)-3,7-dioxabicyclo[3.3.0]octane). Synergist for pyrethrins.

sesamolin (2-(3,4-methylenedioxyphenyl)-6-(3,4-methylene-dioxyphenoxy)-3,7-dioxabicyclo [3.3.0] octane). Synergist.

Sevin®. See carbaryl.

siglure (*sec*-butyl-6-methyl 3-cyclohexene-1-carboxylate). Insect attractant of low mammalian toxicity.

Sodium arsenate. Highly toxic insecticide and herbicide; tolerance 3.5 ppm for grapes.

Sodium arsenite. Highly poisonous herbicide and ingredient of insect baits. LD_{50} 10–50 mg/kg.

Sodium fluoride. Ingredient of insect baits; not used on living plants; poisonous.

Sodium fluosilicate. See cryolite.

Sodium selenate. Systemic insecticide of high mammalian toxicity; must not be applied to land that may later be used for food crops. LD_{50} for rabbits 4 mg/kg; zero tolerance. Useful against the cyclamen mite, and chrysanthemum leaf nematode. Apply, in water, at rate of ¼ gram per square foot of soil. Available in capsules for potted plants.

sulfotepp (tetraethyl dithiopyrophosphate). Insecticide, acaricide of very high mammalian toxicity and zero tolerance. Used in commercial greenhouses for aphids and mites.

sulfoxide (1,2-methylenedioxy-4-[2-(octylsulfinyl)propyl]benzene). Synergist, of low mammalian toxicity.

Sulfur. Fungicide and somewhat of an acaricide, controlling some mites. Non-toxic to mammals but harmful to some beneficial insects. Exempt from tolerance. Incompatible with oils and dinitro sprays; phytotoxic to *Viburnum carlesi;* may burn rose foliage in hot weather.

Sulphenone® (*p*-chlorophenyl phenyl sulfone and related sulfones). Insecticide, acaricide used on fruits, particularly in the Northwest. LD_{50} 1400 to 4000 mg/kg; tolerance 8 ppm. Compatible with most pesticides.

Synthetic pyrethrins. See allethrin, barthrin, cyclethrin, furethrin.

Systox®. See demeton.

Tartar emetic (antimony potassium tartrate). Insecticide, formerly recommended, with brown sugar, for thrips control. LD_{50} 600 mg/kg.

TDE (2,2-bis(*p*-chlorophenyl)-1,1-dichloroethane). Rhothane®, DDD. Contact insecticide with same general properties as DDT but much safer for man, and so recommended for vegetables, but more toxic to fish. LD_{50} 3400 mg/kg; tolerance 7 ppm.

Tedion®. See tetradifon.

TEPP (tetraethyl pyrophosphate). Violently poisonous contact insecticide, very toxic to mammals dermally and orally. LD_{50} 2 mg/kg; zero tolerance. Used by commercial growers on food crops because residue is quickly dissipated.

Telone®. (dichloropropenes mixture). Nematocide and soil fumigant.

tetradifon (*p*-chlorophenyl 2,4,5-trichlorophenyl sulfone). Tedion®. Acaricide useful in home gardens, a constituent of various all-purpose sprays and dusts. Of very low mammalian toxicity with no deaths in test rats fed up to 14000 mg/kg. Tolerance from 1 to 5 ppm for most fresh fruits and vegetables.

Thimet®. See phorate.

Thiodan®. See endosulfan.

Thuricide®. See *Bacillus thuringiensis*.

toxaphene (chlorinated camphene containing 67–69% chlorine). Contact insecticide. LD_{50} 69 mg/kg; tolerance 3 to 7 ppm. Not compatible with alkaline materials.

trimedlure (*tert*-butyl 4(or 5)-chloro-2-methylcyclohexanecarboxylate). Attractant of low mammalian toxicity.

Trithion®. See carbophenothion.

Vapona®. DDVP (2,2-dichlorovinyl dimethyl phosphate). For aphids, mites, mealybugs, whiteflies in greenhouses. Poisonous!

Vapam® (sodium methyldithiocarbamate). Soil fumigant and nematocide of low mammalian toxicity. LD_{50} 820 mg/kg. Use as preplanting treatment only; not safe around living plants.

V-C-13 Nemacide (*O,O*-diethyl *O*-2,4-dichlorophenyl phosphorothioate). Acaricide, insecticide, nematocide for soil treatment; can be used around some living plants and on turf. LD_{50} 270 mg/kg.

WARF (*N,N*-di-*n*-butyl-*p*-chlorobenzenesulfonamide). Synergist antiresistant for DDT.

Zectran® (4-dimethylamino-3,5-xylyl methylcarbamate). Systemic insecticide. LD_{50} 15 to 63 mg/kg. Excellent for slugs and various other pests.

CHEMICALS IN COMBINATION

There are thousands of all-purpose sprays and dusts now on the market that combine several different chemicals. A fungicide (sulfur, copper, captan, dichlone, ferbam, folpet (Phaltan), glyodin, maneb, zineb, or ziram) is usually included to take care of plant diseases in the same application as that intended for insects and mites. It is seldom possible to solve all problems with one mixture, but usually you can find one that will do fairly well for ornamentals, another for vegetables, and another for fruit trees, with a few supplementary treatments for special pests.

In choosing the right combination you must make sure that both the active ingredients and the diluents used in making up the mixture are safe on the plants you want to protect. Rotenone is non-toxic to most plants but sometimes sulfur is combined with it, both as a diluent and as a fungicide, and sulfur is decidedly toxic to most melon varieties and to some other cucurbits.

Dust mixtures containing DDT may markedly reduce squash yields, and tomatoes are sometimes sensitive to it. DDT in a mixture can kill or seriously injure some varieties of camellias, though others are little affected. DDT in a rose spray or dust without an acaricide may encourage so many spider mites that the results may be worse than no treatment. Mixtures with

DDT must be formulated for use on plants, not for mosquitoes and household pests. I have seen severe injury to rose foliage when DDT was applied with a mist blower for mosquito control. The injury was not from the DDT itself but from the kerosene or other oil solvent.

A spray containing lead arsenate planned for shade trees is not usually safe on the tender foliage of peaches and other stone fruits, or for flowering cherries or ornamental plums. For these, lead arsenate is used at a weaker strength and lime or zinc sulfate is added as a safener.

The mixing of incompatible chemicals may cause injury to a plant that would be safe with either one alone, or one chemical may inactivate another so that the spray loses its potency. Until recently, gardeners were almost always urged to add a good spreader-sticker to their spray mixture, but now we know that that may be bad advice. Some additives seem to increase plant injury, perhaps by increasing plant absorption, and some seem to decrease efficiency, perhaps by increasing runoff, perhaps by actual chemical change. Unless a manufacturer directs that a specific spreader-sticker be added to his product, it might be wise to use it without an additive.

STOP, LOOK, AND LISTEN!

Before using *any* chemical or combination, in *any* form, at *any* time, on *any* plant, ask yourself these questions:

(1.) *Is it safe for me?* Before opening any package or bottle READ THE LABEL. See if you are to take special precautions against inhalation or skin contact. The very moment of opening a bag or can of toxic dust presents the grave danger of getting poison into your lungs. The moment of opening a bottle presents a chance of spilling concentrated liquid on your skin.

If you are an amateur gardener, avoid using chemicals that require respirator and protective clothing and that come with directions to wash clothing after each use. But after using *any* chemical, wash your face and hands. Never smoke while spraying or dusting. You get the chemical from your hands to the cigarette and thence into your mouth. Avoid use of chemicals on a windy day; work so that the spray or dust blows away from you.

(2.) *Have I safeguarded my neighbor's children and pets?* Children do trespass and they sometimes find discarded containers with a trace of poison left inside. There have been tragic fatal accidents. It is not easy to dispose of leftover poisons and their containers. Some liquids can be flushed down the toilet and the bottles carefully rinsed before being put out for the trash man. Some bags and cardboard cartons can be burned, but with others the burning itself creates a hazard. Some can be buried deeply, but few of us have enough unused land for this.

At the end of any spraying operation there is some unused liquid. This can be poured into a gravel drive where it will be absorbed instantly, or down a drain, but should not stand in gutters or in hollows in a concrete drive long enough for birds or a dog to take a drink.

Under no circumstances should a chemical be divided and part given away without the original label with all warnings.

(3.) *Do I know the active ingredient in this material and is it formulated for use on plants?* Is there any danger of injuring my plant at the dilution needed to kill the insect?

(4.) *Is there any diluent in this dust or spreader in this spray that may harm my plant?*

(5.) *Is it specifically recommended for the pest I want to kill?*

(6.) *Are the weather conditions right for this chemical on this plant at this time?* Oil sprays injure all plants somewhat and evergreens severely if used when it is too cold; copper puts red spots on rose leaves in cold weather; sulfur and malathion may burn tender foliage in too hot weather.

(7.) *Have I used anything on this plant in the recent past that would either inactivate this chemical or be injurious to the plant when mixed with this chemical?* Don't lime your lawn the same spring you use chlordane for control; don't follow summer oils with sulfur.

(8.) *Have I used any other material in this sprayer recently and forgotten to clean it out?* The sprayer should be rinsed between different chemical mixtures and at the end of each day. Weed killers, however, should be used in a separate sprayer, for it is almost impossible to clean a sprayer that has been used for 2,4-D sufficiently for protective spraying.

(9.) *Have I measured or weighed the amounts correctly?* If you need only 1 teaspoon and spill enough more to make 2, you are doubling the dosage and vastly increasing the chance of injury. Worse yet, that amount you may remember as 1 tablespoon is only 1 teaspoon in the manufacturer's directions and so you are tripling the dose and perhaps killing your plant. Always reread the label just before mixing up a pesticide.

(10.) *Have I compensated for possible harm from this chemical?* Have you added a miticide to DDT to take care of the red spiders it will encourage? Are you remembering to save the bees by not spraying fruit trees in full bloom? Are you leaving some of your garden unsprayed as a haven for beneficial insects?

If you can answer these questions, go ahead and apply your chemical. If you don't know the answers, stop and think again before spraying or dusting. You can do more harm in 10 thoughtless minutes than the bugs can do in a whole season. If you don't know *what* you are doing and *why* you are doing it, don't do anything in the line of chemicals. Stick to sanitary and cultural measures and encourage the beneficial insects and birds to work for you.

Chapter III

SPRAYING AND DUSTING

THE ART OF SPRAYING

Spraying is a fine art and one which all too few gardeners ever acquire. It takes a lot of common sense and a modicum of brains. It takes a sense of timing and a sense of responsibility to plants. It takes a little mechanical skill but not necessarily too much brawn. We used to be able to hire the brawn but with the scarcity and present cost of garden help some of us are turning thankfully to hose-end sprayers and letting water pressure take the place of hand pumping. Lack of common sense in selecting and applying chemicals (which includes neglecting to read labels) and inability or unwillingness to keep up regular treatments throughout the growing season are the chief obstacles to maintaining a vigorous, reasonably pest-free garden.

CHOOSING A SPRAYER

Sprayers vary in size and type from those suitable for a few house plants to large trucks for farmers and shade-tree experts and airplanes for large-scale operations.

Aerosol "Bombs." True aerosols are air suspensions of solid or liquid particles of ultramicroscopic size. They remain suspended in air for hours and are very effective in fogging operations for mosquitoes but are not so useful for plant pests. The so-called aerosol sprays have somewhat larger particles, which deposit readily on foliage. The insecticide is dissolved in liquefied gas and held under pressure in a metal container known as a bomb. When a valve is opened, the chemical is dispersed in a fine mist spray from which the solvent gas immediately evaporates. Greenhouse aerosols containing TEPP or parathion have to be used with gas masks and other safety measures, but there are small bombs containing pyrethrum and rotenone that are safe to use indoors on house plants and there are others formulated for garden plants. Do not ever use on plants bombs sold for household pests. Be sure to hold the bomb 12 to 18 inches away from the plant. Otherwise the solvent does not evaporate fast enough and may cause severe burning. Always use the bomb in short bursts with a sweeping motion; do not visibly wet the foliage.

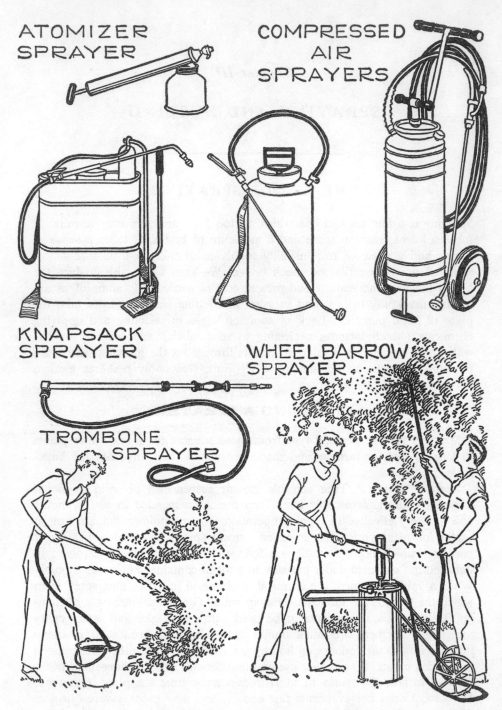

ATOMIZER SPRAYER

COMPRESSED AIR SPRAYERS

KNAPSACK SPRAYER

WHEELBARROW SPRAYER

TROMBONE SPRAYER

1. Sprayers of assorted sizes and types.

POWER SPRAYERS

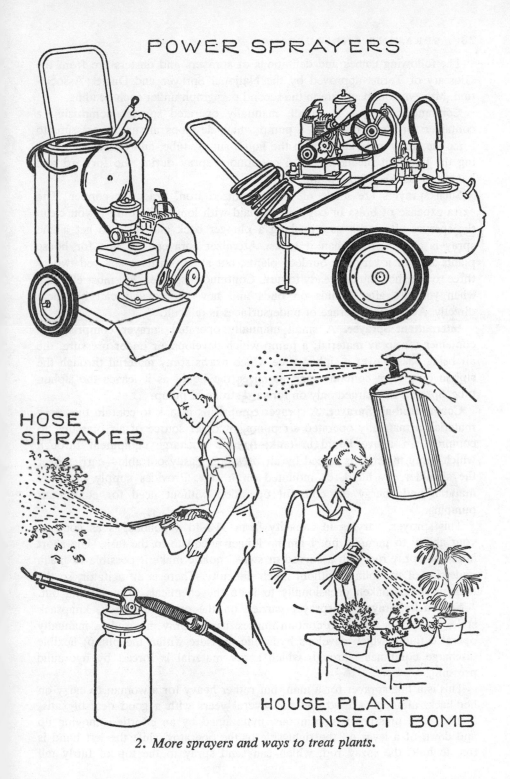

HOSE SPRAYER

HOUSE PLANT INSECT BOMB

2. More sprayers and ways to treat plants.

The following names and definitions of sprayers and dusters are from the Glossary of Terms approved by the National Sprayer and Duster Association. My own comments are in the second paragraph under each heading.

Continuous Sprayer. A small, manually operated sprayer comprising a container for spray material; a pump which develops air under pressure to force the spray material through the liquid supply tube, and assist in atomizing the liquid at the nozzle as a continuous spray during the forward and backward strokes of the pump.

Such sprayers are made of tin, galvanized iron, brass, or copper. The extra expense of brass or copper is repaid with longer life only if you clean the sprayer after each use. Pushing a plunger back and forth to get a fine spray is a lot harder than it looks. Atomizer sprayers are fine for house plants and for a very few outdoor plants, but after you have sprayed two or three rosebushes you are ready to quit. Continuous sprayers are most effective when you are after aphids on buds and new shoots and can hit them directly. Adequate coverage of undersurfaces is difficult.

Intermittent Sprayer. A small manually operated sprayer comprising a container for spray material; a pump which develops air under pressure, the air being passed over a siphon tube which draws spray material through the siphon tube from container and atomizes the liquid as it leaves the siphon tube. Spray is discharged only on forward stroke of pump.

Compressed-air Sprayer. A sprayer comprising a tank to contain the spray material; a manually operated air pump, or other source of air pressure, to compress air above liquid in tank; flexible discharge equipment through which spray material is forced by air pressure. Easily portable—carries over the shoulder, by hand, or mounted on a cart. Provides supply of spray material and energy for constant operation without need for continuous pumping.

This sprayer, varying in capacity from 1½ to 4 gallons, is as good as your ability to pump it up. I am no longer adequate to the task. The short hose and spray rod with a curved or swivel nozzle make it possible to reach underside of the foliage without much difficulty. There is no agitator, so the tank must be shaken occasionally to keep the chemicals from settling out.

Knapsack Sprayer. A sprayer carried on the operator's back, knapsack style. Comprises a tank to contain unpressurized spray material; a manually operated pump which develops hydraulic pressure within the pump; flexible discharge equipment through which spray material is forced by hydraulic pressure.

This is a fine sprayer for a man, but rather heavy for a woman to carry on her back, although I used one for several years with a good deal of satisfaction. The pressure is continuous, maintained by an effortless moving up and down of a lever on the right side of the operator while the left hand is free to hold the spray rod, which can send spray to the top of fairly tall bushes or underneath low plants. The spray mixture is kept agitated and comes out in fine droplets.

Slide Sprayer (Trombone Sprayer). A manually operated hydraulic sprayer with telescoping plunger, operated by two hands. Draws material from attached or separate container and discharges it as a spray under pressure on either forward and back strokes of the plunger or on forward strokes only.

This type allows you to send a stream of spray up into small trees, but it is a nuisance to keep moving the bucket around, and working the slide back and forth is fairly arduous.

Bucket Pump (Barrel Pump). A manually operated hydraulic piston-type pump which may be held or mounted in a container holding the spray material. Draws spray material into the pump when plunger is operated and discharges it in a continuous spray through the discharge equipment. Provides flexibility in size and type of container and high pressures.

Wheelbarrow Sprayer. A manually operated hydraulic sprayer mounted on frame with wheelbarrow-type handles and one or two wheels. Comprises a container holding spray material; a manually operated barrel pump, mounted within, which draws spray material into the pump when plunger is operated and discharges it as a continuous spray through the discharge equipment. Provides portability, large capacity, and high pressures.

I used a sprayer of this general type (12-gallon Paragon) in spraying other people's gardens, all day, every day, for over a quarter of a century. In those days my chief requirement of an assistant was that he have a strong right arm, and the chief disadvantage of this type of sprayer is that it takes two people to operate it efficiently. My helper did the pumping and pushed the heavy truck around the garden; I concentrated on operating the spray rod. This comes in 3 sections and for trees all are put together, but for most garden work 2 sections are best. A 10-foot hose comes with the sprayer, but I had this replaced with a 25-foot length of heavy-duty spray hose to reach easily all sides of shrubbery and to get into garden beds at some distance from paths. This type of sprayer is quite easily cleaned and costs little more than a good knapsack sprayer. It provides a fine mist with little visible residue to mar the beauty of ornamentals.

Hose-end Sprayer. An applicator attached to garden hose, operated by water pressure, which mixes liquid or solid spray materials in water stream and discharges the mixture.

Now that I no longer doctor other gardens and no longer have an assistant to help in my own, I have adopted the lazy hose method and find it surprisingly effective with the right equipment. I use the *Hayes 6 Spray Gun* (also sold as the *Ortho Queen Size Sprayette*). This type has an extension tube as deflector which allows good coverage of underleaf surfaces, and it also has a shutoff at the jar. The type of sprayer used for applying fertilizers and weed killers to lawns, where you have to keep your thumb over an air vent, is not adequate for pest control on flowers and shrubs. A single mixing will serve for 1 to 6 gallons of spray. I use wettable powders or liquids with equal success, but I do make my mixtures in a separate jar and then strain into the hose jar through a wire tea strainer.

Power Sprayer, Hydraulic Type. A sprayer with hydraulic pump (piston, gear, roller, etc.) driven by gasoline engine or electric motor. Comprises a tank or other container for spray material; a power-driven pump which draws spray material into the pump and discharges the spray material under pressure through the discharge system.

Power sprayers are available now in all sizes, from the 5-gallon affair, which seems to me too small to be worth the cost, to the large 300-gallon tank on a truck which delivers from 5 to 50 gallons a minute under 200 to 800 pounds pressure. For estates, sprayers of 15-, 25-, or 50-gallon capacity are practical if you can afford the initial investment and will keep them clean so they last long enough to give adequate return on that investment. Power spraying usually takes more spray solution than hand spraying for the same amount of protection.

Mist blowers or low-gallonage sprayers are used by commercial operators in addition to hydraulic equipment but seldom entirely replace it. The spray is very concentrated; air instead of water is used as the carrier so that a fog-like mist comes out of the machine.

Airplanes and helicopters are used for custom spraying of large acreages— farms, for routine spraying of field crops, or forests, to control outbreaks of spruce budworm, gypsy moth, and other pests of great economic importance.

MAKING UP SPRAY MIXTURES

Measurements must be exact. Keep with your spray materials a set of plastic measuring spoons and a glass measuring cup marked in ounces. Remember your household measurements:

> 3 level teaspoons are 1 level tablespoon.
> 2 tablespoons are 1 fluid ounce.
> 16 tablespoons are 1 cup (8 fluid ounces).
> 2 cups are 1 pint.
> 4 cups are 1 quart.
> 16 cups (4 quarts) are 1 gallon.

By a little figuring you can save much time in measuring. If directions call for 1⅔ tablespoons, you can be exact by measuring 1 tablespoon and 2 teaspoons. But if you need 8 tablespoons, it is a lot quicker to measure out ½ cup. If you are making up dormant spray oil at a 1 to 15 dilution, put in 1 cup of oil and add water to make 1 gallon. But if you want a summer spray of about 1 to 50 dilution, you add 3 gallons (48 cups) of water to the 1 cup of oil. The actual dilution is then 1 to 49, but that is near enough at such a great dilution.

If directions in bulletins call for 1 pint in 100 gallons, just figure that that means 1 pint in 800 pints or a 1 to 800 dilution; 1 quart to 100 gallons is a 1 to 400 dilution. The following table will help in transposing figures for any amount of spray you wish.

DILUTION TABLE FOR SPRAYS

Desired Amount of Finished Spray	Amount of Concentrated Spray for Dilution			
	1–200	1–400	1–600	1–800
1 quart	1 tsp.	½ tsp.	⅓ tsp.	¼ tsp.
1 gallon	4 tsps.	2 tsps.	1½ tsps.	1 tsp.
5 gallons	6 tbsps.	3 tbsps.	2¼ tbsps.	1½ tbsps.
50 gallons	1 quart	1 pint	1½ cups	1 cup
100 gallons	2 quarts	1 quart	1½ pints	1 pint

When it comes to mixing sprays from dry materials, directions are usually given in pounds per chemical per 100 gallons of water—e.g., 3 pounds lead arsenate to 100; 1 pound actual DDT (which means 2 pounds of the 50 per cent wettable powder) to 100. Translating pounds to tablespoons for small amounts of spray is difficult because of the difference in weight of various compounds. One ounce of lead arsenate is 5½ tablespoons, but 1 ounce of calomel is only 1¾ tablespoons; wettable sulfur is about 3 tablespoons to an ounce; hydrated lime 4 to 5 tablespoons; 50 per cent wettable DDT about 6. The measurement also varies according to whether the material is fluffed up or packed down hard.

Chemicals marketed in small packages for home gardeners usually give the dosage per gallon in teaspoons or tablespoons. In purchasing commercial amounts for garden use, I read the label to see how many pounds are recommended to 100 gallons of water and then I figure how many grams or ounces that means for 1 gallon. I weigh that amount out and then see how many tablespoons it fills and mark the figure on the package for subsequent use. My small scales weigh in grams, but it is easy to transpose from the metric system by knowing that 28.35 grams equal 1 ounce; 453.6 grams equal 1 pound.

In making up sprays the usual method is to make a slurry by adding water very slowly to the dry material, stirring constantly, but some chemicals work better sprinkled on top of the pail of water. The directions on the package sometimes tell you; sometimes you find it out by trial and error. Some compounds work better if a spreader, such as Household Dreft, or DuPont Spreader-sticker, or Triton B-1956 is added to the diluted spray. But in some instances such additives are harmful, so manufacturer's directions should be carefully noted. Dry mixes usually have some inert materials which do not go into solution, so the diluted spray should always be strained into the tank through cheesecloth or a special strainer.

MANIPULATING THE SPRAY ROD

Handling the spray rod to get complete coverage, yet not to drench the plants so the spray runs off or builds up too much residue, is where the fine art of spraying comes in.

The type of spray droplets and the amount of unsightly residue depend somewhat on the hole in the nozzle. A very small hole is required for the fine spray we usually want for ornamentals. Since almost all chemicals have an abrasive action which constantly enlarges the hole, a new nozzle should replace the old whenever the droplets get larger, or it takes more spray to cover the same number of plants.

In spraying, work from several different positions—first from one side, then the other, then around from the back, keeping the rod constantly in motion and sending the spray from the underside of the lowest leaves up through the bush. You can end up with a swipe over the top of plants to get aphids on buds and new shoots but ordinarily if you do a good job from underneath, with the nozzle turned up, enough spray falls back on top of the leaves to take care of that surface. Work rapidly; don't stay in one place long enough for water to run off the leaves or collect at the tip of the leaves to produce burning. Apply a fine, even mist.

If possible, wait until the foliage is dry in the morning before spraying, but if it rains every few hours get out and do the best you can between showers. With an even distribution of droplets you don't have to worry about spraying in full sun, even in hot weather, unless the chemical you are using, like sulfur or oil, is one that is itself injurious at high temperatures. For beetles chewing flowers or thrips inside petals, you have to direct the full force of the spray into the flower. For such purposes it is wiser not to have an ingredient in the spray that will leave a dark residue.

There is a widespread belief that rain washes off the spray and the application must be repeated after the shower. That is seldom true. Modern pesticides are formulated to stand a good bit of weathering, and the important thing is to have the protective spray in place before the insect pest or the disease pathogen arrives. So I always advise spraying roses and other plants with continuing problems more or less regularly every week, which means that there is always sufficient residue to take care of the enemy regardless of weather.

TIMING THE SPRAY

Exact timing may be somewhat more important in applying fungicides than in dealing with insects, but it does play a large part in the successful use of all pesticides. The life histories given under the specific pests often suggest the proper timing of control measures. Scale insects must be killed when plants are dormant or with a summer spray during the brief period when vulnerable young crawlers are moving. To be effective, the spray for boxwood leaf miner should be in place before the orange fly emerges. The most important time to spray apples for codling moth is when most of the petals have fallen but before the calyx closes. Japanese-beetle sprays on roses have to be repeated weekly to keep new growth protected. Unless you plan an early spray for rose-slugs and pine sawflies, most of the damage will be done before you know the pests are out. On the other hand, it is foolish to waste money spraying for pests that have already finished their season. If there is only 1 brood, as with cankerworms, and the caterpillars chew for only a month or so, a spray near the end of that month is scarcely justified whereas one near the beginning of the period would be highly desirable.

CLEANING THE SPRAYER

The best way to clean a sprayer is to *keep it clean*. Strain all mixtures into the spray tank through close-mesh cheesecloth to avoid clogging nozzles and thoroughly rinse the sprayer at the end of *every operation*. This is necessary for the longevity of the plants as well as for the apparatus. Left-over solutions have unpredictable and often injurious results. Never, never put away a sprayer without discarding all liquid left in the tank and pumping at least 2 changes of water through the entire system. Don't just dump water in and pour it out again; keep on pumping until water comes out of the nozzle crystal-clear.

Once or twice during the season, and at the end before putting away for winter, more strenuous cleaning is indicated. Pour a pail of warm water with a handful of trisodium phosphate (available at hardware stores) into the tank; let it soak, then scrub with a stiff brush. Soak the small metal parts— nozzle, strainer, etc—in kerosene; poke wire through the rods. Reassemble, rinse with water containing a cupful or two of vinegar, and finally rinse with pure water.

If the sprayer has been used for killing weeds with 2,4-D it is next to impossible to clean it sufficiently for general spraying. If you want to try, rinse spray tank and hose with water; fill tank with water containing 2 teaspoons household ammonia per quart; stir and pump a little into hose and nozzle; let stand at least 18 hours; drain, rinse at least twice, pumping water through hose and nozzle; rinse again, pumping water through the whole system, immediately before putting in a spray mixture, for faint traces of 2,4-D will still be present.

DUSTING PREFERRED?

Dusting has a place in every garden. In my own, I have dusted vegetables and ornamentals I care little about and guinea-pig plants, which get all kinds of combinations tried out on them, but I much prefer spraying for roses and other flowers that are too glowingly beautiful to have their colors dimmed by even the finest film of dust.

I don't subscribe to the theory that you do not have to wear old clothes for dusting and can do it any time you have a few spare moments. Dusts are harder on my shoes than sprays; I have to tie up my hair and cover up my arms and clothes. If I use sulfur I have to cry myself to sleep at night to get the particles washed off my eyeballs. Of course I should wear goggles but I dislike them more than the sulfur.

There is also a theory that you can dust plants between showers if necessary, and so get protection from a dust when there would be no chance to spray. But for ornamentals I believe just the opposite. If you dust a rose when the leaves are wet with either rain or dew, the dust goes on in lumps and stays in unsightly blotches that are an eyesore all summer. If you spray a rose when it is wet, you may not get the best control and you may have to make a second application a little sooner than usual but you have not spoiled the beauty of that rosebush for the rest of the season. If, however, dust can be applied to a dry plant and can be blown up through the foliage from underneath so that only a fine film settles on the upper surfaces, then dusts need not be too unsightly for the majority of plants.

In very early days dusts were sometimes applied by beating a cheesecloth bag with a stick. The modern cans or cartons, with holes punched in the top to be used as salt shakers and the contraptions where you purchase the dust inside one cardboard cylinder telescoped within another are not even as good as the cheesecloth bag. If you must dust, by all means purchase a reliable duster.

Plunger Duster. Dust Gun. A small manually operated duster comprising a container for the dust material; a plunger pump which develops a current of air at each forward stroke which picks up dust from the dust container and discharges it through the discharge equipment. Volume of dust discharged and range of carry controlled by size of pump and speed of stroking.

Plunger dusters are satisfactory for small gardens if the dust is discharged through an extension tube having a deflector which can send the dust up through the foliage.

Crank Duster. A manually operated duster which comprises a hopper or container for the dust; an agitating device; a high-velocity, gear-driven fan, driven by a hand-operated crank which develops a continuous current of air which carries the dust through the discharge equipment. Volume of dust

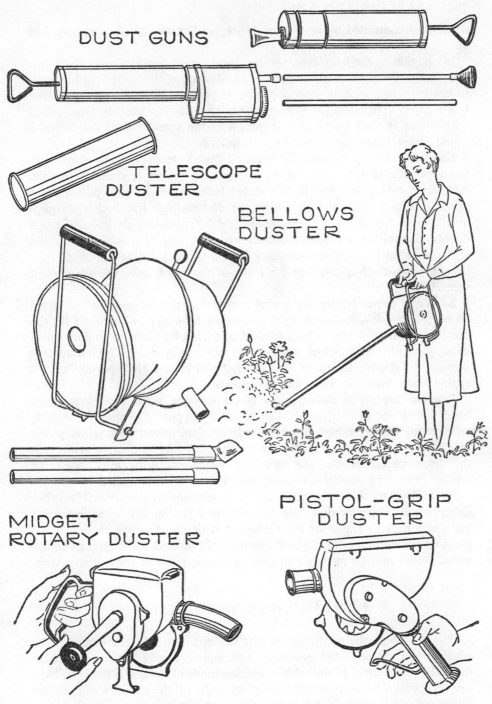

DUST GUNS

TELESCOPE
DUSTER

BELLOWS
DUSTER

MIDGET
ROTARY DUSTER

PISTOL-GRIP
DUSTER

3. Various types of dusters.

discharged controlled by regulating device, and range of carry by speed of fan.

In addition to the large crank dusters used by market gardeners there is a midget rotary duster, made of lightweight aluminum, that is delightfully easy to operate. Used with an extension tube, it provides adequate coverage, and I can highly recommend it from personal experience. Another type, which applies only its own very fine dust from a carton screwed onto the duster, I found rather heavy for a woman to handle.

Knapsack Duster. A manually operated duster designed to be carried on the operator's back, knapsack style. Comprises a hopper or container for the dust; an agitating device; a lever-actuated bellows which develops a current of air at each stroke which discharges the dust through the discharge equipment. Volume of dust discharged controlled by regulating device, and range of carry by rapidity of actuating operating lever.

A somewhat smaller bellows duster is held in the hand and operated as a fireside bellows. It is excellent for roses or for quick coverage of rows of vegetables.

Knapsack Power Duster. An engine-powered duster designed to be carried on operator's back, knapsack style. Comprises a hopper or container for the dust; an agitating device; a high-speed fan, driven by gasoline engine, which develops an air current which picks up the dust and discharges it continuously through the flexible discharge equipment. Provides complete portability and engine power instead of manpower to operate.

Traction Duster. A duster mounted on a frame with wheelbarrow-type handles and one or two wheels. Comprises a hopper or container for dust; an agitating device; a high-speed, gear-driven fan, driven by traction power from the ground wheel, which picks up the dust and discharges it through the discharge equipment. The unit may be propelled by man, horse, or tractor. Provides greater dust capacity and wider area of coverage.

Power Duster. A duster powered by a gasoline engine or PTO drive. Comprises a copper or dust compartment; an agitating device; a high-speed fan which may be engine or PTO driven and develops an air current which picks up the dust and discharges it continuously through the discharge equipment. Duster may be mounted on tractor, trailer, truck or other conveyance.

ADVANTAGES OF DUSTING

One big advantage of dusting is that the apparatus does not have to be emptied and cleaned after each use, although it should be cleaned out at the end of the season. If you wish to use two kinds of dust, it is better to have two inexpensive plunger dusters than to try to get all the particles of one kind blown out of the duster before putting in the other mixture.

Dusting is usually quicker than spraying and probably somewhat more foolproof, if you use prepared mixtures and don't try to roll your own. I mean that "roll" literally, for in making dust mixtures at home, you put the ingredients in a tin with some round stones and roll back and forth, round and round. However, it is difficult to do a good job of mixing and few of us know enough about compatibility and diluents and fluxers to make our own mixtures.

Chapter IV

INSECTS IN ORDER

The entomologist says an insect is a very special creature with body divided into three sections, only three pairs of legs, and usually with wings. He also says that a bug is a very special kind of sucking insect. The layman says that any small crawling or flying animal is an insect and any insect is a bug. The dictionary says both are right. In former editions of this *Bug Book* we stretched several points to include rabbits, dogs, squirrels, mice, moles and other creatures in one alphabetical treatment of garden pests. In this edition we are devoting all the space available to animals that the layman might consider a "bug."

Exact figures are unobtainable, but there are probably a million different species of animals in the world that have already been classified, and many more unclassified. These are divided into a few main groups known as Phyla and then subdivided into Classes, Orders, Families, Genera, and Species. Man belongs in the phylum Chordata, which includes all the vertebrates (creatures with a backbone), in the class Mammalia, which includes animals with hair and mammary glands, in the order Primates, which also includes monkeys, in the family Hominidae, which does not include monkeys, the genus *Homo* and the species *sapiens*. Man is not always as wise as his species name would indicate, and I definitely include him among the garden pests. For more on this subject, please see my book ARE YOU YOUR GARDEN'S WORST PEST? (Doubleday, 1961).

Slugs and snails are in the phylum Mollusca, along with clams and oysters. Earthworms, which are not often pests, are in the phylum Annelida and roundworms are in the phylum Nemathelminthes. Nematodes have been included here but have now become so important that many nematologists put them in a separate phylum, Nematoda.

At least three fourths of all animals are in the phylum Arthropoda, which means they have segmented bodies, bilateral symmetry, paired jointed appendages usually terminating in claws, chitinous exoskeleton, ventral nervous system, and heart dorsal when present. The classes listed below have members that are garden pests.

CLASSES OF THE PHYLUM ARTHROPODA

Insecta (Hexapoda). All true insects, about 90 per cent of all species in the Arthropoda. They have only 3 pairs of legs.

Arachnida. The spiders, ticks, and mites, with only 4 pairs of legs.

Crustacea. Crayfish, lobsters, crabs, and sowbugs, with 5 to 7 pairs of legs; most species aquatic in habitat.

Chilopoda. Centipedes, "hundred-legged worms," but not quite literally. They have 1 pair of legs on each segment.

Symphyla. Garden centipedes, with 12 pairs of legs.

Diplopoda. Millipedes, "thousand-legged worms" with 2 pairs of legs on each segment.

INSECT MORPHOLOGY

Insects have an exoskeleton—a protective shell on the outside of soft body parts—rather than the internal skeleton of higher animals. The chief chemical in this outer covering is chitin. The surface of the body consists of a number of hardened plates, separated by membranous areas.

The segmented body is divided into 3 main sections—head, thorax, and abdomen. Six of the body segments are fused into the head, which is usually hard, heavily sclerotized. Most insects have a pair of large compound eyes made up of hexagonal facets. They also usually have 3 simple eyes, *ocelli,*

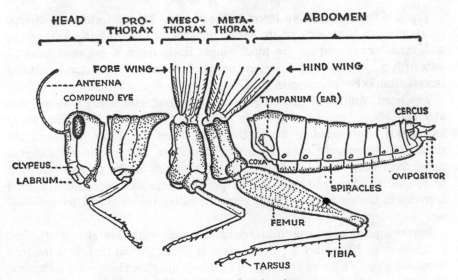

4. Diagram of an insect showing important parts.

located on the upper part of the head between the compound eyes. The head also bears a pair of *antennae,* feelers, which arise in front of the compound eyes. In chewing insects with biting mouth parts we have a *labrum,* upper lip, just below a plate called the *clypeus; mandibles,* the first pair of jaws; *maxillae,* second pair of jaws; and *labium,* lower lip. The mandibles act as teeth, cutting or tearing off leaf portions and then masticating the food. In sucking insects there is a long slender beak with the labium on the outside and inside, 4 sharp *stylets* which pierce the plant and draw out the sap. These stylets are the mandibles and maxillae greatly modified. The labrum in this case is merely a short flap covering the groove in the labium.

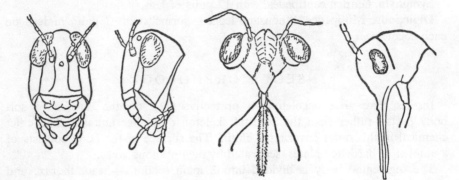

5. *Mouth parts, front and side views: left, chewing insect; right, sucking insect.*

The middle section of an insect is the *thorax.* This is further subdivided into *prothorax,* just back of the head; *mesothorax,* bearing the fore wings; and *metathorax,* bearing the hind wings. Each thoracic segment bears 1 pair of legs. This total of 6 legs is the chief diagnostic character separating insects from other arthropods.

The word "arthropod" means jointed leg or foot; insects are able to jump and hop about because of the way their legs are jointed. The first heavy leg section, corresponding to the thigh, is called the *femur,* the next, the *tibia.* The segmented foot is known as the *tarsus,* and insects are differentiated from each other by the number of segments in the tarsus, usually 2 to 5, and the claws and pads on the pretarsus, the last segment. The tibia is joined to the thorax by 2 small segments called the *coxa* and the *trochanter.*

Insects are the only winged invertebrates; their wings are always attached to the thorax. When only 1 pair of wings is present, as in flies, it is the fore wings, attached to the mesothorax. The wings are thin sheets of parchment-like cuticle with ribs known as *veins.* The number, branching, and arrangement of the veins are very important to entomologists classifying insects but are of little import to laymen.

The third section of the insect, the *abdomen,* typically has 11 segments, but the last is much reduced so there appear to be but 10. The apex of the abdomen often bears a pair of structures called *cerci* (singular *cercus*), and the female usually has an *ovipositor,* the egg-laying apparatus. In wasps and bees this is modified into a stinger and drawn up into the body when not in use. The abdomen never has true legs but may have fleshy, jointed append-ages known as *prolegs.*

Insects breathe by means of *spiracles,* pores along the side of the body opening into tubes called *tracheae.* The number of tracheae varies, but there is usually a pair on the mesothorax, one on the metathorax, and a pair on each of the first 7 or 8 abdominal segments. Contact poisons work largely because of the way they affect this respiratory system.

Insects do not have a true ear but have various organs for the perception of sound waves. In grasshoppers there is an oval plate, *tympanum,* on each side of the first segment of the abdomen, which serves as an ear. In crickets the "ears" are on the front tibiae.

HOW INSECTS GROW

Because insects live inside a chitinous exoskeleton which cannot be ex-panded as they grow, they progress by a series of molts, splitting and casting off the old shell or *cuticulum.* Such discarded shells are known as *exuviae,* which means clothes. Between the time the insect pulls free from its old covering and before the new form is heavily chitinized, there is a chance for expansion in size. The stages between molts are called *instars.* The egg hatches into the first instar, terminated by the first molt; this molt produces the second instar where the young insect is larger and sometimes of different appearance. There may be 3, 4, 5, or even 20 molts, depending on the species.

The adult insect never increases in size; growth is always in the life stage that follows directly from the egg. Some insects have a simple or *gradual metamorphosis,* with the young resembling adults except for size and posses-sion of wings. Such young are called *nymphs* during their growing period. Figure 6 shows insect metamorphosis in diagrammatic form. The bug hatches from an egg into a nymph and grows in size through different instars (the number shown here does not represent the exact number for each species), acquires external wing pads, and then, without any prolonged resting stage, molts again into the adult form with wings, never growing after that.

Other insects have a *complete metamorphosis,* with the adult totally different from the young insect, often living in a different habitat. In the life stage following the egg the immature insect, usually wormlike, is called

INSECT METAMORPHOSIS

INSECT	EGG	INSTARS PERIOD OF GROWTH				PERIOD OF TRANSFORMATION	ADULT
SQUASH BUG	HATCHING	NYMPH	MOLT NYMPH	MOLT NYMPH	MOLT NYMPH MOLT		BUG
JAPANESE BEETLE	HATCHING	GRUB	MOLT GRUB	MOLT GRUB	MOLT GRUB MOLT	PUPA MOLT	BEETLE MOLT
SPHINX MOTH	HATCHING	CATERPILLAR	MOLT CATERPILLAR	MOLT CATERPILLAR	MOLT CATERPILLAR MOLT	PUPA MOLT	MOTH MOLT

6. Metamorphosis or growth stages of a sucking insect (squash bug) with gradual metamorphosis; and of a beetle and a moth (chewing insects) with complete metamorphosis.

a *larva*. The wings, if any, are developed internally during the immature stages, and there is a resting or pupal stage before the final molt.

The larva of a beetle is known as a *grub*. It increases in size in different instars but does not change much in appearance. In the resting stage the pupa is naked with the form of the legs showing on the outside of the pupa case.

The larva of a moth or butterfly is a *caterpillar* and may change considerably in size and appearance during different instars. The pupa may be a chrysalid attached to a twig by a strand of silk, or may be enclosed in a cocoon, or may be a naked pupa in the soil.

The larva of a fly is known as a *maggot,* and it transforms to the adult stage in a *puparium*.

INSECT ORDERS

The orders of insects whose individuals are commonly found in gardens, either as friends or enemies, are:

Collembola. Springtails: wingless; without metamorphosis; chewing mouth parts.

Orthoptera. Crickets, mole crickets, grasshoppers, katydids, mantids, walkingsticks: gradual metamorphosis; 4 wings; nymphs with compound eyes; chewing mouth parts.

Dermaptera. Earwigs: beetlelike but with simple metamorphosis; 4 wings; nymphs with compound eyes; chewing mouth parts.

Isoptera. Termites, "white ants": gradual metamorphosis; chewing mouth parts.

Thysanoptera. Thrips: rasping-sucking mouth parts; simple metamorphosis; 4 wings; nymphs with compound eyes.

Hemiptera. With piercing-sucking mouth parts; gradual metamorphosis.

Heteroptera. True bugs, including flower bugs, plant bugs, lace bugs, chinch bugs, stink bugs: with "half wings"—part hard, part membranous.

Homoptera. Aphids, scale insects, whiteflies, leafhoppers, plant hoppers, spittlebugs, mealybugs, psyllids: with 4 uniform wings.

Neuroptera. Lacewings, ant-lions: chewing mouth parts in larvae and adults; 4 wings; larvae carnivorous.

Lepidoptera. Butterflies, moths, skippers: chewing mouth parts in larvae, siphoning in adults; complete metamorphosis; 4 wings; larvae lack compound eyes.

Coleoptera. Beetles and weevils: chewing mouth parts in larvae and adults; complete metamorphosis; 4 wings, the fore pair hardened into a sheath; larvae lack compound eyes.

Hymenoptera. Bees, wasps, ants, sawflies: chewing or reduced mouth parts in larvae and chewing-lapping in adults; complete metamorphosis; 4 wings; larvae lack compound eyes.

Diptera. Flies: chewing or reduced mouth parts in larvae, sponging in adults: complete metamorphosis; 2 wings; larvae lack compound eyes.

NAMES OF INSECTS

The only sure way to identify any particular insect is by its scientific name. Common names vary widely, not only in different parts of the country but with different gardeners in the same section. Insects are named by the universal system of binomial nomenclature, which means they have two names. The first is the genus name, corresponding to your own last name; the second is the species name, which really corresponds to a person's first name, for there can be several species in a genus just as there are several children in a family, all with the same last name but with different given names.

If you ask me what to do for your "aster beetles" I can't tell you, for I don't know whether you have the Asiatic garden beetle, whose name, *Autoserica castanea,* identifies it beyond doubt, or the black blister beetle, *Epicauta pennsylvanica.* Perhaps you have the striped blister beetle, *Epicauta vittata,* or maybe the Oriental beetle, *Anomala orientalis.*

You will notice in these examples that the species names is usually descriptive. *Castanea* refers to the lovely chestnut color; *orientalis* and *pennsylvanica* refer to places of origin; while *vittata* means striped. In fact, the names often tell you a great deal about the insects, and you often need the scientific names to get more information from books and other sources.

In citing insects by scientific name, the species is usually followed by the name of the author who first described it. In the first two editions of the *Bug Book* authors were omitted because they have little import for the backyard gardener. They are included in this edition to aid the professionals who, apparently, also turn to this manual for quick reference.

Unfortunately, with insects as with plants, names get shifted around a bit. A species is put into another genus, or the original name for a genus is revived, or one genus is split in two and so on.

In compiling this revision I have used the latest (1960) compilation of "Common Names of Insects" approved by the Entomological Society of America, revising some of the scientific names to accord with recent taxonomic studies, and using my own best judgment where a pest has no approved common name. Approved names are marked with an asterisk.

Chapter V

GARDEN PESTS (AND A FEW FRIENDS)

Here are the bugs and other insects, the slugs, snails, sowbugs, millipedes, mites, and nematodes, in alphabetical order according to their common names.

A borer may be either a moth or a beetle, but if it is commonly called a borer it is discussed under Borers. For instance, the shot-hole borer is a beetle (*Scolytus rugulosus*), but you will find it by looking under Borers and then thumbing your way along to S—Shot-hole. But it is sometimes called the fruit-tree bark beetle and so you will find a cross reference to it under Beetles, in the *F* section. The adult of the rhododendron borer is a moth, but because it is not commonly referred to by its adult name, it is listed only under Borers without any cross reference.

With the aid of the Index you can probably find the pest you want quite quickly if you know some common name for it, even if it is not the one presently approved by the Entomological Society of America. So far as possible, insects are treated under their "official" common names, but other names are given in the text and in the Index. The scientific names, brought up to date so far as I am able, are given in parentheses and in italics, after the common names printed in boldface. The name of the author first describing a species is given with the Latin name.

You may not, however, recognize an insect enough to guess at a common name. If all you know is that you have a caterpillar on a cherry, turn to Chapter VI (Host Plants and Their Pests) and look up Cherry. There you will find a long list of pests with a few brief comments on some of the more important. If your caterpillar is officially known as a caterpillar, you will find it in the list of insects following the word "Caterpillar" in boldface. Then you can turn back to the section on caterpillars in this chapter and read up on the ones you think might be your specimen. If you live in New Jersey you obviously do not have the California Tent Caterpillar, but you may have the Eastern Tent Caterpillar.

Your caterpillar, however, may be better known by its adult form—perhaps codling moth, found under Moths, or a bud moth, found under Budworms (Bud Moths). Or it may be called a Cankerworm, Leaf Crumpler, or Leaf Roller. Perhaps it isn't a caterpillar at all but the larval stage of a Sawfly, or the maggot of a Fly or the grub of a Beetle. You may have to explore several possibilities before you can, by a process of elimination, arrive at the probable classification of your caterpillar.

I have given a rather involved example. Under many hosts you will find very few possibilities listed and will not have to do much checking back and forth. Although we have fairly good check lists for common fruits and vegetables and some other economic plants, for many ornamentals, the readily available information is rather sketchy and so my lists of known possibilities are quite short.

ANT-LIONS

Ant-lion (*Myrmeleon* sp.). The larva of an adult similar to a dragonfly, in the order Neuroptera, family Myrmeleontidae. The adults have 4 long,

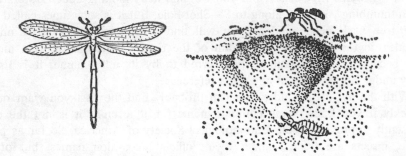

7. *Ant-lion larva waiting at the bottom of a pit dug for its ant victim, and winged adult ant-lion.*

slender wings, about equal in size, marked with many small branching veins and cross veins, a long, narrow, very soft abdomen, and short, threadlike antennae knobbed at the tip. The larvae, queer creatures with sickle-shaped jaws, are called doodlebugs in the South. They dig conical pits in sandy soil, up to 2 inches across and nearly as deep, and there lie in wait for ants and other victims to fall in. Sand adheres to the hairs covering the broad abdomen of the doodlebug and helps to conceal it from its prey. It is definitely not a garden pest although its useful role may be rather minor.

ANTS

Ants belong to the order Hymenoptera, along with bees and wasps, and are in the family Formicidae. They are social insects, living in colonies all over the world, outnumbering almost all other terrestrial animals and comprising some 6000 kinds.

The body of an ant is sharply constricted into its 3 divisions—head, thorax, and abdomen. The antennae, with the first segment very long, are hinged like an elbow and have a club at the tip. The gaster, soft part of the abdomen, is attached to the thorax by a pedicel—a movable link which, in the subfamily Formicinae, has only 1 segment but in the Myrmicinae has 2 parts. Besides the digestive organs the abdomen contains a device for releasing poison. Species in the Myrmicinae have a real stinger like that of a bee. This releases poison in the wound, causing considerable burning and pain. Members of the Formicinae have a poison bladder; they first bite their enemy, then squirt poison into the bite.

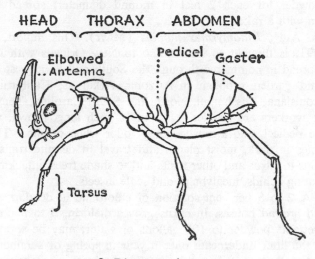

8. Diagram of an ant.

Each ant colony has 3 castes—males, females, and wingless, sterile workers. After mating, the males die and the females shed their wings to found new colonies as queens. The queen raises the first brood of workers, feeding them with her saliva; after that the workers feed the queen and tend the young, maggotlike larvae. They build new galleries for the nest and forage for food. Some ants live on household sweets or greasy proteins, some on honeydew of aphids, mealybugs, or scale insects; some feed on seeds, grains, or vegetable roots, some on fungi cultivated in their nests, and some on other insects.

Some ants make disfiguring mounds, disturb plant roots, and occasionally act as vectors of plant disease. Fire-blight bacteria may be disseminated by ants, and they probably distribute spores of the fungus causing Botrytis blight of peonies. Ants are attracted to the sticky secretion on peony buds but do no direct harm. Many ants are useful as scavengers and pollinators and some as predators. The first known application of biological control, antedating recorded history, was the practice in the Orient of placing bamboo poles between trees to facilitate movement of a predatory ant feeding on citrus pests.

Allegheny Mound Ant*, *Formica exsectoides* Forel. The mound-building ant common in eastern U.S., particularly damaging to forest stands. The large mounds, 2 to 3 feet high, up to 8 feet across, contain thousands of individual ants. Small trees and shrubs within 35 feet of such mounds are killed by the injection of formic acid into the tissues near the ground, resulting in a sunken band girdling the stem. The ants have reddish-brown head and thorax, blackish-brown abdomen, 1-segmented pedicel; they feed chiefly on insect honeydew. Chlordane is effective in control: 2 ounces of wettable powder for each 2 feet in mound diameter, spread evenly and scratched in with a rake.

Argentine Ant*, *Iridomyrmex humilis* (Mayr). This import, first noted here in 1891, is thought to have come to New Orleans with coffee from Brazil. It spread in commerce through the South and Southwest and is now a house and garden problem in Arizona, Arkansas, California, Florida, Georgia, Louisiana, Mississippi, North and South Carolina, Tennessee, and Texas. The workers are slender, 1/12 to ⅛ inch long, brown, with 1 segment in the pedicel, and a musty, greasy odor when crushed. They nest in large colonies in dark, moist places and travel in definite trails. They are very injurious to citrus and other fruits and to shade trees, attacking blossoms and distributing aphids, mealybugs, and scale insects.

Control. A 2 to 5 per cent solution of chlordane in deodorized kerosene can be used around houses. In citrus groves dieldrin, 6 to 8 pounds of 25 per cent wettable powder to 100 gallons of water, may be sprayed on tree trunks and the litter underneath once a year in spring or summer. A special Argentine Ant Bait, distributed in small containers on a community-wide basis, has eliminated the pest in some towns. Directions are: 1. Boil together for 30 minutes and then cool: 1¼ pounds granulated sugar, 1¼ pints water, 1 gram tartaric acid (crystallized), 1 gram benzoate of soda. 2. Dissolve ⅛ ounce sodium arsenite in 1 fluid ounce of hot water; cool. 3. Add second mixture to first, stir, and add ⅔ pounds strained honey. 4. Place in aluminum or plastic ant cups. These are covered but have indentations to admit the ants. Place 20 to 25 feet apart, out of reach of children.

Big-headed Ant*, *Pheidole megacephala* (Fabricius). Common in warmer areas, sometimes a nuisance in seedbeds. Similar to fire ants but with 12-jointed antennae and 3-jointed antennal club.

Black Carpenter Ant*, *Camponotus pennsylvanicus* (De Geer). A large native species, ¼ to ½ inch long, dark brown to black, nesting entirely in wood—trees, buildings, stumps, and telephones poles—in the eastern half of the country. It makes honeycomb galleries and signals its presence by sawdust protruding from the holes. In this species the tip of the abdomen has a circlet of hairs, the pedicel is 1-segmented, and a freshly crushed worker has a formic acid odor. It is fond of sweets and can bite but not sting. Control by injecting chlordane or malathion into the holes, preferably with an oil gun of the type used for automobiles. Keep ants from entering trees by pruning carefully and painting the cuts.

California Harvester Ant*, *Pogonomyrmex californicus* (Buckley). The most common agricultural ant in California, clearing large areas around nests. Widespread in Texas, Arizona, New Mexico, and Nevada, reported recently from Utah. This pale-red ant, ¼ inch long, bites and stings severely, collects seeds, and interferes with planting operations. See Red Harvester Ant for habits and control.

Cornfield Ant*, *Lasius alienus* (Förster). A native species, present in much of the U.S., nesting in soil or rotten wood, making objectionable nests (small mounds) in lawns, especially in the Northeast. It is small, 1/12 to 1/10 inch long, stout, soft-bodied, light to dark brown; the anal opening is surrounded by a fringe of hairs; the pedicel is 1-segmented; there is no antennal club; there is a formic acid odor. The sweets-loving workers caress root aphids to stimulate the production of honeydew, protect them in their nests over the winter, and ward off their enemies. See also Corn Root Aphid. Apply chlordane spray or dust to nests in lawns.

Crazy Ant*, *Paratrechina longicornis* (Latreille). A household pest.

Fire Ant*, *Solenopsis geminata* (Fabricius). Formerly called tropical fire ant. This is a yard ant entering houses to feed on meat, milk, sweets, and cereals. The workers have a larger head than other species. The bite and sting are painful. Mounds may be numerous in Texas peanut fields, hindering harvest. See Imported Fire Ant.

Florida Carpenter Ant*, *Camponotus abdominalis floridanus* (Buckley). Common in Florida, similar to the Black Carpenter Ant.

Florida Harvester Ant*, *Pogonomyrmex badius* (Latreille). An agricultural ant similar to the Red Harvester Ant.

Imported Fire Ant*, *Solenopsis saevissima richteri* Forel. A South American species, first identified in Mobile, Alabama, in 1929 but probably present for some years previously and unnoticed because of its resemblance to native fire ants. Transported on logs in streams, by cars, trucks, trains, airplanes, and in nursery stock, the imported fire ant is now a menace to 9 southern states—Alabama, Arkansas, Florida, Georgia, Louisiana, Mississippi, North and South Carolina, and Texas. It has been eradicated from Tennessee and probably will not survive in colder regions.

The ants feed on young succulent vegetables, may attack and kill ground birds, young quail especially, and newborn animals, and may sting people with very painful and sometimes serious results. But their chief damage is from their hard mounds, from 15 inches to 3 feet high, which interfere with farm operations. There may be up to 60 mounds per acre, and an average mound may contain 25,000 to 100,000 ants. The workers are ⅛ to ¼ inch long, reddish to blackish red, with a 2-segmented pedicel and 2-segmented antennal club.

A federal-state eradication program, started in 1957, brought criticism because heptachlor, applied at 2 pounds per acre, seriously injured wildlife. The amount was reduced to ½ pound per acre and recent programs have substituted a bait, mirex, non-hazardous to wildlife, which is mixed with corncob grits and soybean oil. Individual mounds in home gardens can be treated with chlordane (4 tablespoons of 45 per cent emulsion to 3 gallons of water, or 5 per cent dust), first breaking up the hard surface of the mound and treating this and an area 3 feet beyond. A physician should treat the sores or pustules caused by stings. People especially sensitive to fire-ant venom should be inoculated against allergic reactions.

Larger Yellow Ant*, *Ancanthomyops* (Lasius) *interjectus* (Mayr). A common soil species fostering mealybugs and aphids on plant roots. The yellow workers, 1/10 to ⅛ inch long, have a lemon-verbena odor. See Cornfield Ant.

Little Black Ant*, *Monomorium nimimum* (Buckley). A native house pest but usually nesting outdoors in soil. The slender workers are 1/12 to 1/10 inch long, jet-black and shiny. They are fond of honeydew and other sweets, fruits, vegetables, meats, and cereals.

Little Fire Ant*, *Wasmannia auropunctata* (Roger). A common house pest in parts of Florida.

Odorous House Ant*, *Tapinoma sessile* (Say). A native species, sometimes making shallow nests outdoors. The workers are deep brown to black, 1/10 to ⅛ inch long, soft-bodied, with 1-segmented pedicel, and have a rotten coconut odor when crushed. This species is omnivorous in its food habits and attends honeydew-excreting insects.

Pavement Ant*, *Tetramorium caespitum* (Linnaeus). An imported species, common in lawns along the Atlantic seaboard, nesting under stones or edges of pavements. It is a frequent garden and greenhouse pest, gnawing at roots and tubers and stealing seeds. Treat individual ant hills with chlordane, ⅛ teaspoon of wettable powder put in the center of a mound and watered in, or use chlordane emulsion, 1 ounce to 1 gallon of water, or 5 per cent dust.

Pharaoh Ant*, *Monomorium pharaonis* (Linnaeus). A tiny, slow-moving ant, same genus as the Little Black Ant.

Pyramid Ant*, *Dorymyrmex pyramicus* (Roger). Common in Florida and California, in lawns and houses. This small species, with black abdomen and reddish-black head and thorax, is named for a pyramidlike projection on the thorax.

Red Carpenter Ant*, *Camponotus ferrugineus* (Fabricius).

Red Harvester Ant*, *Pogonomyrmex barbatus* (F. Smith). Also known as Texas Harvester Ant and Agricultural Ant. This species causes heavy losses in cultivated crops in the Southwest, clearing areas 3 to 35 feet in diameter bare of all vegetation. The nest is a deep cone, going down to 10 feet at the small end, and is a honeycomb of tunnels and chambers. The colony consists of a queen and innumerable workers, reddish brown, ¼ to ½ inch long, vicious if molested. The ant colonies may kill trees and shrubs and there is a direct loss of seeds, either newly planted or ready for harvest. To control, apply a continuous band, 4 to 6 inches wide, of 2 per cent dieldrin dust or 5 per cent chlordane dust, in a circle 5 to 6 feet in diameter, centering on the nest entrance. Rubber boots offer some protection from ant stings while the chemical is being applied.

Silky Ant*, *Formica fusca* Linnaeus.

Smaller Yellow Ant*, *Acanthomyops claviger* Roger.

Southern Fire Ant*, *Solenopsis xyloni* McCook. A native species common in the Gulf States, recently found as far north as North Carolina, and with subspecies in California and the Southwest. The workers are variable in size, 1/16 to ¼ inch long, and in color, shining yellowish red or darker. The body is hard and the pedicel and antennal club are 2-segmented. These ants steal planted seeds, infest houses, and sting severely, killing young quail on hatching. They nest in open places, in loose mounds.

Texas Leaf-cutting Ant*, *Atta texana* (Buckley). A pest of most species of plants in Texas and Louisiana and a serious defoliator of young pines. Foliage is removed in pieces and carried to subterranean nests as a substrate on which the ants grow a fungus for food, much as we cultivate mushrooms. The soil may be mounded several inches high over the burrows, which extend for many feet below the surface. Adjoining colonies may cover 1000 square feet or more. The workers are reddish brown, 1/16 to ½ inch long, with many spines on head and thorax, a 2-segmented pedicel. Methyl bromide is the most effective fumigant, introduced 2 feet or more below soil surface, at the rate of 1 pound to 600 square feet.

Another leaf-cutting ant, *Trachymyrmex septentrionalis,* is found along the Atlantic Coast in open pine woods, making crescent-shaped mounds of sand.

Thief Ant*, *Solenopsis molesta* (Say). A native species, nesting outdoors in soil or wood, and a common house pest, with a preference for protein foods, sometimes injuring germinating corn seeds. The workers are small, 1/15 to 1/10 inch long, light yellow to bronze, with 2 segments in the pedicel and in the antennal club.

Western Harvester Ant*, *Pogonomyrmex occidentalis* (Cresson).

Western Thatching Ant*, *Formica obscuripes* Forel.

APHIDS

Aphids, plant lice, are sucking insects in the order Hemiptera, Homoptera group. There are a great many species abundant on, and injurious to, all forms of vegetation. At least a few species are inevitable in every home garden, and it is often easier to control aphids than to understand their complicated life histories and to distinguish between species.

True aphids are in the family Aphididae, members of which are viviparous (bearing living young) during part of their life cycle. Bark aphids, gall aphids, and phylloxeras are in the family Chermidae where all the females are oviparous (depositing eggs) and none bear living young.

Typical aphids (subfamily Aphinae) are small, soft-bodied, pear-shaped, with a pair of cornicles—wax-secreting tubes—projecting from the 5th or 6th abdominal segment; a cauda, projection from the tip of the abdomen; antennae with 4 to 6 segments; and 2-segmented tarsi (feet). The mouth parts form a hollow beak (rostrum) which arises far back on the underside of the head. The beak encloses 4 needlelike stylets, which pierce plant tissue so that the sap can be sucked out. All aphids secrete honeydew from

9. Aphid getting ready to feed and in process of sucking sap.

the anus. This is really plant sap, rich in sugars, attracting ants and forming a medium for the growth of a black fungus known as sooty mold. Wings, when present, are usually clear, with few veins, and are held vertically over the body when at rest.

Aphids are of all colors—black, green, pink, red, yellow, lavender, brown, or grayish—and the young nymphs may differ in color from the wingless adult and the latter may differ from the winged form. Some aphids live out their lives on a single plant; others infest several to many different plant species. Some aphids require an alternate host, wintering on one type of plant, usually woody, then migrating to one or more herbaceous species for the summer.

The life history of an aphid is complicated even for the single-host type. In a typical case, overwintering eggs hatch in spring into wingless females called stem mothers (fundatrix). These are parthenogenetic, viviparous females, reproducing without fertilization by a male and holding eggs in their bodies to give birth to living young. Their progeny are similar females but some develop wings and migrate to other plants of the same species when the colony gets too dense. Many more such generations may be produced during the summer, but toward autumn male and female wingless forms are born. These mate and the oviparous females lay fertilized eggs for overwintering. Males may be either winged or wingless; oviparous females are usually wingless. In warm climates living young may be produced continually with no overwintering egg stage.

Alternate-host aphids also winter as eggs and hatch into wingless females, but in the third or fourth generation they produce winged females which migrate to the summer food plant. There may be 6 or more generations of wingless females on this host before winged males and females appear for the trek back to the woody winter host. There winged females give birth to wingless females which mate with the winged males and then lay fertilized eggs on the bark. Males thus appear in the life cycle but once a year, at the approach of cold weather.

In the subfamily Eriosomatinae, the woolly and gall-making aphids, cornicles are lacking, or are mere pores, and the cauda is inconspicuous, but abundant wax glands cover the body with white, cottony threads. Many such species have an alternate host, on which the galls are formed. The sexual forms lack mouth parts and the ovipositing female lays a single egg.

Members of the family Chermidae lack cornicles, have a reduced wing venation, and have only egg-laying females. Species in the subfamily Cherminae feed only on conifers, living on needles, twigs, or in galls. Their antennae are 5-segmented in winged forms, 4-segmented in sexual forms, 3-segmented in wingless females. Wings at rest are held rooflike over the body, which is often covered with waxy threads. The Cooley and Eastern Spruce Gall Aphids are important members of the Cherminae.

In the subfamily Phylloxerinae the antennae are 3-segmented in all forms, the wings at rest are held flat over the abdomen, and waxy threads are not produced. The grape phylloxera is the most economically important member of this group.

Aphids cause loss of plant vigor and sometimes stunting, deformation of buds and flowers, curling or puckering of leaves. The honeydew, substratum for sooty mold, is attractive to ants which herd destructive root aphids. Of chief importance, perhaps, is the role of aphids as vectors (transmitters) of mosaic and other virus diseases, the bacteria of fire blight, and other disease-producing organisms.

Most aphids are readily controlled by applying a contact insecticide at the proper time. Old reliable nicotine sulfate (Black Leaf 40) is still good. Use 1 to 1½ teaspoons with 1 ounce of liquid soap or 1 cubic inch of soap flakes to 1 gallon of water. Rotenone and pyrethrum are still effective and, because of their low toxicity to humans, particularly useful in small aerosol bombs for house plants. Dinitro compounds are sometimes used in a dormant spray to kill aphid eggs. Currently widely recommended are malathion and lindane, the latter being especially useful for woolly and gall aphids. Dimethoate, a reasonably safe phosphate, is of value. TEPP, parathion, and other highly poisonous phosphates are used by commercial growers on vegetables because the residue is quickly dissipated. DDT kills aphids but it is not recommended because it kills so many of the beneficial insects that keep aphids in check.

Parasites, insects which live part of their lives in or on other insects without killing them, and predators, which kill and devour other insects, are important in aphid control. Parasitic wasps are common and whenever you find a dead aphid with a hole in the back you know that it has been parasitized and a young wasp has emerged from that hole. Lady beetles, aphid-lions (larvae of lacewings) and the sluglike larvae of syrphid flies all help in reducing aphid populations.

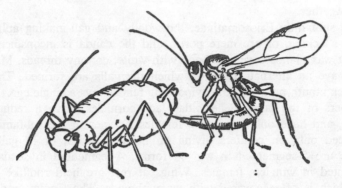

10. Parasitic wasp laying an egg in an aphid.

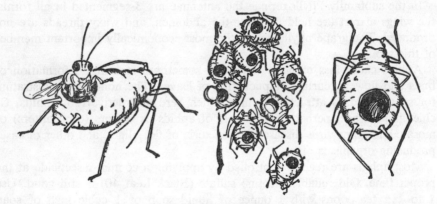

11. Young wasp emerging from parasitized aphid and dead aphids showing emergence holes (greatly enlarged).

In the following pages aphids are taken up alphabetically under common names, those officially recognized by the Entomological Society of America being marked with an asterisk. Important aphids are treated in some detail, others are dismissed in a line or two. Though the list is long, it includes but a fraction of the thousands of plant lice in the world—a fraction intended to be representative of aphids injuring trees, flowers, or vegetables on home properties in different sections of the United States.

Alder Aphid, *Oestlundiella flava* (Davidson). Pale yellow with dark-brown cornicles and markings, more or less woolly, on alder leaves; not too common. Another species, *Euceraphis gillettei* Davidson, pale apple-green with pale cornicles, is common on twigs and leaves of alder and birch in the Rocky Mountain region.

Alder Blight Aphid. See Woolly Alder Aphid.

Alfalfa Aphid, *Macrosiphum creelii* Davis. Pale green, with antennae longer than body, on alfalfa leaves.

American Maple Aphid, *Periphyllus americanus* (Baker). Summer forms pale green, on maple leaves.

Apple Aphid* (Green Apple Aphid), *Aphis pomi* De Geer. Common and widespread on apple, sometimes on pear, wild crab apple, hawthorn, and mountain-ash, more injurious to nursery than to orchard trees. Terminals may be entirely covered by aphids in midsummer and growth halted. Leaves may be loosely curled, but not tightly as by the rosy apple aphid; young apples may be deformed; there is a copious amount of honeydew with resultant sooty mold. The apple aphid winters as shiny black eggs on bark and the dark-green nymphs appear as buds are swelling in early spring. The adults, yellow green with dark cornicles, head, and legs, remain through the summer, not migrating to an alternate host.

Use a dormant dinitro spray, or add a dinitro to the dormant oil spray, or spray with lindane during the season.

Apple Grain Aphid*, *Rhopalosiphum fitchii* (Sanderson). Abundant on small grains and grasses during the summer but not seriously injuring the winter hosts—apple, pear, wild crab apples, and hawthorn. Control measures for apple and rosy apple aphids will take care of this species on apple.

Arborvitae Aphid, *Cinara tujafilina* (Del Guercio). Widely distributed, perhaps more important in warmer states, feeding in colonies on twigs, branches, and roots, often seriously weakening arborvitae, Italian cypress, and retinospora, also reported on redcedar. The small, reddish-brown lice with a whitish bloom feed all year on roots, attended by ants, and on aerial parts spring and fall. Treat the soil with chlordane; spray branches with lindane.

Artemisia Aphid, *Macrosiphum artemisiae* (Fonscolombe). Metallic dark green or blackish, in dense colonies on shoots of artemisia, also reported on yarrow, oxeye-daisy, and costmary; in western states. Other aphids on artemisia include *Macrosiphum coweni* (Hunter), dark brown to blackish green; *Artemisaphis artemisicola* (Williams), shining reddish black; and *Microsiphum artemisiae* (Gillette), dark brown.

Aster Aphids, *Macrosiphum anomalae* Hottes and Frison, *M. asterifoliae* Strom, and *M. breviscriptum* Palmer. Green, common on New England aster, particularly *M. anomalae*.

Aucuba Aphid, *Macrosiphum aucubae* Bartholomew.

Azalea Aphid, *Vesiculaphis caricis* Fullaway. Reported on azalea in California.

Balsam Twig Aphid*, *Mindarus abietinus* Koch. Pale green, covered with white wax, curling and roughening balsam fir and spruce twigs from New England to the Pacific Coast, with migrants sometimes going to pine. Spray with malathion or lindane in late spring.

Balsam Woolly Aphid*, *Chermes piceae* Ratzenburg. An introduced species attacking balsam and other firs in New England, New York, New Jersey, North Carolina, Washington and Oregon. It causes gouty swellings at tip of twigs, abnormal growth of sapwood on main trunks, sometimes death. The very small blue-black body is covered with long waxy threads. Long slender stylets pierce the bark, injecting a toxin. The wood becomes reddish and brittle, needle growth is reduced, and the foliage gradually dies. There is no alternate host, the aphids wintering as nymphs on bark. Spread is mostly by wind, winged forms being rare.

A predaceous beetle, *Laricobius erichsoni,* has been released in the hope of biological control in forest areas. Spray ornamental trees with lindane or malathion.

Bamboo Aphid, *Myzocallis arundinariae* Essig. Yellow, with black markings, common on leaves of bamboo in California.

Banana Aphid, *Pentalonia nigronervosa* Coquerel. A tropical species, reddish brown to nearly black with clouded wings, introduced with bananas and sometimes found in greenhouses. Reported on caladium indoors in Oklahoma and Washington, D.C.

Barberry Aphid, *Rhopalosiphum berberidis* (Kaltenbach). Small, yellowish green, usually found in groups on underside of leaves and on shoots of barberry and mahonia.

Bean Aphid*, *Aphis fabae* Scopoli. A common and important species, congregating in great numbers on succulent plant parts, causing general debility and yellowing foliage. The young nymphs are green, spotted with white wax, very small; the adults are dark green to dull, sooty black. The winter host is chiefly euonymus, sometimes highbush cranberry, deutzia and snowball. The summer forms frequent various vegetables—bean, asparagus, globe artichoke, beet, carrot, corn, lettuce, parsnip, rhubarb, spinach, squash, watercress—and many ornamentals. It is practically inevitable on nasturtium, clustering on underside of leaves, and occurs on dahlia, calendula, elderberry, globe thistle, hibiscus, mockorange, oleander, poppy and zinnia.

Control. Spray or dust ornamentals with malathion or lindane; use nicotine or malathion on vegetables. Commercial growers may use more dangerous phosphate sprays.

Beech Aphid, *Phyllaphis fagi* (Linnaeus). Dark green, covered with loose white flocculence, infesting undersides of leaves of practically all species of beech in the Northeast and also important on ornamental plantings in Oregon and California. This aphid is particularly noticeable, and sometimes decorative, on copper beech.

Beech Blight Aphid*, *Prociphilus imbricator* (Fitch). Large, bluish, covered with white wool, on underside of branches and sometimes on trunks of beech from New England west to Illinois and south to Georgia, also reported on sycamore. It may be abundant enough to kill twigs or even young trees. Spray with lindane if necessary.

Birch Aphids. Several species are rather common and generally distributed. The **European Birch Aphid,** *Euceraphis betulae* (Linnaeus), considered one of the most annoying pests of ornamentals in Alaska, appears on various species of birch across the country, particularly on white birch. It is a large green-and-black species, with a flocculent waxy covering.

A large green aphid with short cornicles and no wax, *Calaphis betulaecolens* Fitch, and its near relative, *C. betulella* Walsh, produce quantities of honeydew on birch foliage.

Blackberry Aphid, *Aphis rubifolii* (Thomas). Minute, yellowish green, tightly curling leaves of wild and cultivated blackberries in New York; reported on red raspberry in Rocky Mountain region.

Black Cherry Aphid*, *Myzus cerasi* (Fabricius). Commonly injurious to sweet cherries, occasionally serious on sour cherries. Shiny black eggs winter on branches near buds and hatch as buds are opening. The large black aphids reproduce rapidly, curling leaves of terminal shoots and fruit clusters. The fruit is dwarfed and sooty mold growing in the copious honeydew makes it unmarketable.

Control. Use a dinitro spray in fall after all leaves have fallen or in spring before buds break. If this dormant spray is neglected, nicotine sulfate in the green-tip stage will give fair control.

Black Citrus Aphid*, *Toxoptera aurantii* (Fonscolombe). Small, 1/15 inch, reddish brown to nearly black, with long legs, important on citrus in California, Florida, and other warm climates. Camellias are often infested and sometimes ixora, clusia, seagrape, and other tropical ornamentals. This aphid has been found on English holly as far north as Maryland, possibly introduced on nursery stock. Leaves are cupped, curved, and distorted but not tightly curled; they are covered with sooty mold. The species is also a vector of the Tristeza disease virus, though not as efficient as some other aphids.

Control. Normally the black citrus aphid is held in check by predators, parasites, and fungus diseases. Spraying with nicotine, malathion or rotenone is sometimes necessary. Commercial growers may use phosphates such as parathion or demeton. Control ants which disseminate the aphids.

Black-margined Aphid*, *Monellia costalis* (Fitch). On hickory, pecan, and walnut; reported important on pecans in New Mexico.

Black Peach Aphid*, *Anuraphis persicaeniger* (Smith). Shiny black with immature forms reddish brown, with short wartlike cauda, antennae as long as body. Native in Eastern states and occasionally serious where it has been introduced in the West. This species infests roots, tender shoots, and fruit of peaches, almonds, apricots, sometimes plums. Black wingless forms live on roots through the year, some migrating in spring to new growth. Paradichlorobenzene has controlled the root forms; Nicotine or malathion can be used on foliage.

Black Pecan Aphid*, *Melanocallis caryaefoliae* (Davis). A pest of hickory in the North, destructive to all pecan varieties in the South, causing premature defoliation and reducing the nut crop. Nymphs are pale green, adults darker green with black spots. Bright yellow spots appear on the leaves, which turn brown and drop by midsummer. There may be 15 generations before eggs are deposited in bark crevices for the winter. Populations are said to be increased when bordeaux mixture or DDT is used in the orchard. Commercial growers should spray, as soon as first yellow spots appear, with nicotine sulfate in summer oil, or with parathion.

Bow-legged Fir Aphid, *Cinara curvipes* Patch. On balsam, white, alpine, noble and Spanish firs, Engelmann spruce, and deodar. This species is brownish black with long, curved tibia, the "bow-legs."

Boxelder Aphid*, *Periphyllus negundinis* (Thomas). A pale green species, with long hairs, on leaves and twigs of boxelder and sycamore maple. Another green species, *Drepanosiphum braggii* Gillette, may also infest boxelder foliage. It is larger, with antennae longer than body.

Brown Ambrosia Aphid, *Dactynotus* (Macrosiphum) *ambrosiae* (Thomas). Brown to dark blood-red, rather large, common and widespread on a number of plants, including goldenrod, aster, lettuce, endive, eupatorium, rudbeckia, and sunflower. Especially important on lettuce and endive in the West.

Buckthorn Aphid*, *Aphis nasturtii* Kaltenbach (*A. abbreviata* Patch). One of four common potato aphids, more important in the Northeast. This species winters in the egg stage on buckthorn, winged migrants flying in summer to potatoes, some other vegetables, nasturtium and a few other ornamentals. The aphid is small, yellow to dark green to nearly black, and is a vector of potato leaf roll and mild mosaic viruses. DDT is recommended for control on potatoes, applied when 25 per cent of the stand is present; or a phosphate insecticide in July.

Cabbage Aphid*, *Brevicoryne brassicae* (Linnaeus). Common throughout North America on cabbage, broccoli, cauliflower, brussels sprouts, kohlrabi, collards, kale, radish. Small gray-green lice with a powdery, waxy covering congregate in dense clusters on underside of leaves, causing them to cup and curl, and on flower heads. Broccoli in home gardens is frequently infested. Plants are dwarfed, seedlings may be killed. This species winters in the North as small black eggs on stems and old leaves of cabbage and other crucifers. In the South, it continues to produce living young with no sexual stage and up to 30 generations a year. Some cabbage fields may be 100 per cent infested.

Control. In home gardens use malathion, nicotine, or rotenone dust or spray. Commercial growers may use demeton in the transplant water or parathion or TEPP spray, but these are hazardous for the operator.

California-laurel Aphid, *Thoraphis umbellulariae* Essig. On this host.

Canadian Fleabane Aphid, *Dactynotus erigeronensis* (Thomas). Yellowish green on erigeron (fleabane); also reported on goldenrod.

Ceanothus Aphid, *Aphis ceanothi* Clarke. Reddish brown and black, infesting limbs, twigs, leaves of ceanothus and soapbush in California.

Chokecherry Aphid, *Aphis cerasifoliae* Fitch. Tightly curling terminal leaves of chokecherry. Summer hosts are grains and grasses.

Chrysanthemum Aphid*, *Macrosiphoniella sanborni* (Gillette). Shiny dark brown, almost black, with short cornicles, occurring in great numbers on tender terminal shoots and on underside of chrysanthemum leaves. Growth is stunted, leaves are slightly curled and plants may die. Common and widespread. If infested cut flowers are brought into the house, the aphids may cause dark stains. Spray or dust with malathion.

Clover Aphid*, *Anuraphis bakeri* (Cowen). Primarily on clover but summering also on related plants, wintering on hawthorn, apple, pear, quince, reported on myrtle. Generally distributed but more serious in the Northwest, where crops are lost because of honeydew causing seeds to stick together. This species may be green with a black patch or pinkish or yellow green mottled with dark green or rusty flecks; it has short cornicles. Seed treatment with demeton before planting is less likely to kill beneficial insects than foliage sprays.

Columbine Aphid, *Pergandeidia trirhoda* (Walker). Small, cream-colored lice appear in late summer; plants may be stunted and covered with honeydew. The Black-backed Columbine Aphid, *Kakimia essigi* Gillette and Palmer, is small, green and pinkish, with a dark patch on the back.

Cooley Spruce Gall Aphid*, *Chermes cooleyi* Gillette. Occurring wherever spruces are grown, common on ornamental Colorado blue spruce, also infesting Engelmann, Sitka, and oriental spruces, with Douglas-fir as an alternate host. Immature stem mothers winter on spruce, mature in early spring and lay eggs in masses of white, cottony wax. On hatching, the nymphs migrate to new growth. Their feeding at the base of needles introduces a toxin, causing the formation of conelike galls, about 2½ inches long, at the tips of twigs. Each gall contains many chambers with several nymphs in each. The galls open in midsummer (around July 1 in New Jersey) and the aphids migrate to Douglas-fir, there to deposit eggs on needles. The nymphs wintering here are covered with fluffs of cotton. A winged stage in spring takes the aphid back to spruce, but cycles may continue on either host. No galls are formed on Douglas-fir.

Control. Avoid planting spruce and Douglas-fir together; cut off galls be-

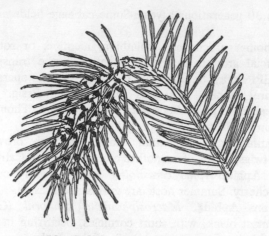

12. Aphid gall on blue spruce.

fore they open in summer. Spray needles with lindane, or malathion, lime sulfur or Sevin, in April and/or late summer or early fall.

Coreopsis Aphid, *Aphis coreopsidis* (Thomas). On coreopsis, eupatorium, cosmos, also reported distorting foliage of sourgum and covering ground with honeydew.

Corn Leaf Aphid*, *Rhopalosiphum maidis* (Fitch). Small, bluish green, densely congregated in the curl of corn leaves, in the upper part of stalk, and in tassels, where the honeydew interferes with pollination and attracts corn-earworm moths. This aphid is common in all corn-growing areas but more abundant in the South, feeding also on sugarcane and wintering on barley.

Lady beetles, lacewings and other predators are effective in control. Planting early and fertilizing to hasten maturity is helpful.

Corn Root Aphid*, *Anuraphis maidiradicis* (Forbes). A serious pest, dependent for its existence on ants, especially the cornfield ant. Roots of corn, clover, beet, carrot, cotton, and grasses are infested with myriads of pinhead size, bluish-green powdery lice with short legs. Ants collect the aphid eggs in autumn, store them in their nests over winter, then transport the young in spring to smartweed and grass roots where the stem mothers mature and produce 2 or 3 generations before the ants carry them to corn roots for another 10 to 20 generations. If winged forms are produced to fly to other cornfields, the migrants are seized by the ants and carried back down underground.

The corn root aphid and other species also infest roots of many ornamentals, including aster, browallia, buttercup, calendula, chrysanthemum, cosmos, dahlia, erigeron, primrose, sweetpea, and zinnia. Plants turn yellow, stop growing, and wilt in bright sun.

Control. Use chlordane to control the ants and cultivate to break up their nests before planting annuals. Treat aphids at roots of growing plants by pouring 1 to 2 cups of lindane spray (1 tablespoon to 1 gallon of water) into a depression around the stem.

Cotton Aphid. See Melon Aphid.

Cowpea Aphid, *Aphis craccivora* Koch. This species was long considered identical with the European *A. medicaginis,* but the latter is not known in America. The nymphs are slaty gray, the adults shiny black with white legs. They are common on laburnum (goldenchain), locust, rose-acacia, deutzia, honey-locust, and other ornamentals as well as cowpea, beans and clovers. Spraying with malathion or other aphicide may be necessary to keep the aphids from ruining the new growth.

Crapemyrtle Aphid*, *Myzocallis kahawaluokalani* Kirkaldy. Confined to crapemyrtle and abundant wherever this host is grown. Foliage is often covered with sooty mold growing in the copious honeydew. Spray early and thoroughly with lindane, malathion or nicotine sulfate.

Crescent-marked Lily Aphid*, *Neomyzus circumflexus* (Buckton). Yellow, with a black U-shaped patch on the back. Common on lily and other ornamentals, including asparagus fern, aster, California-laurel, calla lily, columbine, crocus, cyclamen, ferns, freesia, fuchsia, gladiolus, gloxinia, hydrangea, iris, myrtle, rose, penstemon, snowberry, violet and wallflower, also celery and potato. This species is important as a vector of mosaic and other virus diseases. Commercial growers often use a systemic insecticide—e.g., 80 pounds of 10 per cent phorate granules applied in the furrow at time of planting. Home gardeners must be content with foliage sprays of malathion or other safe aphicide.

Currant Aphid*, *Capitophorus ribis* (Linnaeus). Common on currant throughout the United States, occasional on gooseberry, recorded on deutzia and snowball. Leaves curl, crinkle, and hump up into half galls above the portions where stem mothers are producing their numerous yellow-green progeny. Such humped areas turn red and leaves may drop. Glossy black eggs on twigs hatch into wingless females which continue to reproduce parthenogenetically on currant while winged females migrate to various weeds for the summer. The aphids return to currant in autumn, produce males and females, and overwintering eggs.

Control. Spray with nicotine or malathion early in the season, being sure to cover underleaf surfaces. A dormant dinitro spray is said to give control.

There are other currant aphids. The **Variable Currant Aphid,** *Aphis varians* Patch, may curl leaves of golden and black currant but is not common. The **Ornamental Currant Aphid,** *Amphorophora ribiella* (Davis) is a pale yellow-green species on leaves and twigs of ornamental (golden) currant. Also green on golden currant is *Aphis ribiensis* Gillette and Palmer. Terminal leaves of currant and gooseberry may be curled by *A. ribi-gillettei* Allen and Knowlton.

Cypress Aphid, *Siphonatrophia cupressi* (Swain). A rather large green aphid with convex abdomen, large cauda, and short cornicles infesting blue and Monterey cypress in California.

Daylily Aphid. See Sand Lily Aphid.

Delphinium Aphid. Russet-colored Larkspur Aphid, *Aphis rociadae* Cockerell. Common on annual larkspur and perennial delphinium, clustering between buds in the flower spikes or on underside of leaves, which are cupped downward. The shoots are dwarfed, florets fail to open. The aphids, a striking orange red with dull-black head, dusky brown legs and antennae, have been confused by amateurs with the red goldenglow aphid. Spray with malathion, directing it toward underside of foliage and between buds of flower spikes.

Dock Aphid, *Aphis rumicis* Linnaeus. A black aphid heavily infesting dock and apparently confined to this host, although it has been confused with the bean aphid. It has been reported on citrus and avocado in California.

Dogberry Aphid, *Kakimia cynosbati* (Oestlund). Yellow to green, on leaves of currant and gooseberry.

Dogwood Aphid, *Aphis cornifoliae* Fitch. Greenish black, on leaves and stems of dogwood. Another dark-green aphid, *Aphis neogillettei* Palmer, curls dogwood leaves. It is rather rare but when it occurs, infestations are heavy.

Dogwood or Sunflower Aphid, *Aphis helianthi* Monell. Greenish yellow mottled with darker green. It winters on dogwood and migrates to wild and cultivated sunflower for the summer, often seriously curling leaves.

Douglas-fir Aphid, *Cinara pseudotaxifoliae* Palmer. Pale brownish yellow, fairly common on bark of Douglas-fir twigs. Eggs are laid end to end on the needles. A similar species, *Cinara splendens* (Gillette and Palmer) is also reported on twigs of this host.

Dusky-veined Walnut Aphid, *Panaphis juglandis* (Goeze). A relatively new walnut pest, first noticed in California in 1952. It is larger than the walnut aphid and is clustered in colonies on upper surface of leaves, along midribs. See Walnut Aphid for control.

Eastern Spruce Gall Aphid*, *Chermes abietis* Linnaeus. A European insect widely distributed in the Northeast on Norway spruce, also attacking white, red, black, and Engelmann spruce. Pineapple-shaped galls, ½ to 1 inch long, are formed at base of new shoots (Plate II). Greenish immature females hibernate on twigs near terminal buds, feed and mature in spring, then deposit a mass of eggs under a waxy cover. These hatch in a week and the nymphs feed at base of developing needles, their saliva causing the bases to enlarge into bulblike hollows. Fifty such cells may be joined together into a typical gall, each cell holding up to a dozen aphids. New galls are green with the closed mouth of each cell marked with a red or purple line; old galls are brown. The galls open in midsummer, releasing aphids which develop wings at maturity and fly to needles of the same or another

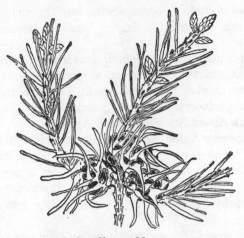

13. Aphid galls on Norway spruce.

spruce tree but not to an alternate host. Eggs deposited at the bases of new growth produce the overwintering females. There are no males in this species. Infested branches often die. Individual trees show a marked difference in susceptibility, some eventually dying, some with retarded growth, and some almost immune from attack.

Control. Propagation from immune individuals is the best long-range control measure. The galls can seldom be cut out without spoiling the symmetry of the tree. Spray infested trees in spring at start of terminal-shoot enlargement and/or in late summer or early fall with lindane; second choice, nicotine sulfate and soap. An early April dormant spray of lime sulfur or oil is an older recommendation.

Elaeagnus Aphid. See Russian-olive Aphid.

Elder Aphid, *Aphis sambucifoliae* Fitch. Dull blackish green, often abundant on underside of elder leaves.

Elm Cockscomb Gall Aphid*, *Colopha ulmicola* (Fitch). General on elm. The galls, a series of elevations growing out of the leaf, green with red tips resembling cocks' combs, ½ inch high by ¾ inch broad, are filled with small greenish or brownish aphids which drip honeydew onto walks, people, and cars parked under trees. Shiny brown eggs winter in bark crevices, hatching in spring when leaves are half grown. The first 3 generations are passed on elm, then winged forms migrate to roots of grasses during the summer. There is a return to elm in autumn, each female laying a single egg. To prevent deformation, spray in spring as soon as leaves are fully expanded with lindane or malathion.

Elm Leaf Aphid*, *Myzocallis ulmifolii* (Monell). Small, yellow to green, sometimes abundant and dropping honeydew from underside of foliage of American elm.

Elm Sack Gall Aphid, *Colopha ulmisacculi* (Patch). Forms bladderlike galls on upper side of leaves of English elm and summers on grass roots, attended by ants.

English Grain Aphid*, *Macrosiphum granarium* (Kirby). Generally distributed on wheat and other grains, on wild and cultivated grasses, and on corn. Grass green or pink lice on Kentucky bluegrass make this species of interest to home gardeners. It is usually held in check by natural enemies.

European Birch Aphid. See under Birch Aphids.

European Raspberry Aphid. See under Raspberry Aphids.

Fern Aphid, *Idiopterus nephrolepidis* Davis. Small, black, with whitish legs and black areas in wings. It infests ferns in houses and greenhouses and outdoors in California. Boston fern is a favorite host. Ferns are injured by some sprays; malathion or nicotine sulfate sprays or dips may be helpful.

Flocculent Fir Aphid, *Cinara occidentalis* (Davidson). Olive green with powdery wax and long hairs on appendages. It infests bark of twigs; eggs are usually only one to a needle.

Four-spotted Hawthorn Aphid, *Amphorophora crataegi* (Monell). Pale yellow with 4 green spots, common on hawthorn leaves.

Foxglove Aphid*, *Acyrthosiphon solani* (Kaltenbach). An important pest of potatoes but common in the flower garden on campanula, gladiolus, lily, pansy, penstemon, physostegia, scarlet sage, verbena, violet, and reported on African violet indoors. The aphids, shining light green with a dark patch around the base of the cornicles, about 1/15 inch long, winter in the egg stage on foxglove and other hosts, migrating to lower leaves and stems of potato in summer. Feeding on the flower hosts results in yellowed or blanched spots, sometimes leaf curling or a distortion resembling a virus disease. Spray or dust with malathion.

Geranium (Pelargonium) **Aphid,** *Arcythosiphon pelargonii* (Kaltenbach). Grape-green, with antennae longer than body, on leaves of geranium (Pelargonium), calceolaria, calla lily, chrysanthemum, cineraria, verbena, and viola.

The **Wild Geranium Aphid,** *Amphorophora geranii* Gillette and Palmer, is found on true geranium, not Pelargonium. It is dull yellow green with sooty markings.

Giant Bark Aphid* (Hickory Aphid), *Longistigma caryae* (Harris). Our largest aphid species, ½ inch long, occurring only in trees—beech, birch, chestnut, elm, hickory, linden, maple, oak, pecan, sycamore, walnut, and willow—in the eastern half of the country, New England to Florida and west to Minnesota. Wingless forms are ash-gray with black spots on the thorax; winged forms have all-black thorax. They feed on bark of twigs and small branches and when abundant may cause injury or death. There are several generations a year. It may pay to have trees sprayed with malathion, lindane, or nicotine when aphids first appear.

Giant Willow Aphid, *Lachnus salignus* (Gmelin). Large, blackish but appearing gray from its many hairs, with a conspicuous tubercle on the back. In large colonies on bark of various willows, often near the ground.

Gillette's Blue Grass Aphid, *Rhopalosiphum poae* Gillette. Dusky brown to black with pale cornicles, infesting lawn and wild grasses. Common on roots of grasses, including Kentucky bluegrass, is a sordid yellow to olive-green species, *Forda olivacea* Rohwer.

Goldenglow Aphid*, *Dactynotus rudbeckiae* (Fitch). Bright-red lice with long legs, body ⅙ inch, are practically inevitable on goldenglow or cone-flower (Rudbeckia) wherever grown. They seem to stick straight out from the stems and may also cluster on flower buds. The same species may also appear on chrysanthemum, goldenrod, Fuller's teasel, sunflower, and lettuce. A similar red aphid on larkspur and delphinium is a different species; see Delphinium Aphid.

Goldenrod Aphid, *Aphis solidaginifoliae* Williams. Black to reddish or greenish brown, folding goldenrod leaves along the midrib so they look like pods. See Brown Ambrosia Aphid for another species on goldenrod.

Gooseberry Witchbroom Aphid, *Kakimia houghtonensis* (Troop). Gooseberry leaves are tightly curled by pale yellow-green lice.

Grape Phylloxera*, *Phylloxera vitifoliae* (Fitch). A common, injurious, gall-forming species. A native of eastern United States, this is the most destructive grape pest in western America and in Europe. It nearly wrecked the

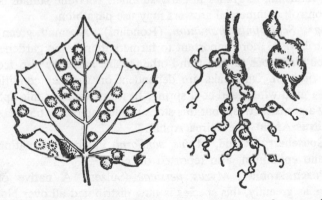

14. Grape phylloxera, showing galls on leaf and roots, and root gall enlarged.

grape industry when introduced into France, and has been devastating in Italy and Germany. In its original home varieties have acquired resistance so that eastern vineyards are seldom seriously injured.

The life history varies according to location. In the East, young lice, hatching from overwintering eggs on canes, settle on grape leaves, producing, by their feeding, pea-shaped galls open on the underside. One female in each gall becomes a stem mother, laying 400 to 600 eggs. Young yellow-green nymphs, hatching from these eggs in 7 to 10 days, migrate to form new galls on other leaves. Several such generations occur during the season but about every third generation some of the aphids move down to the roots to form nodules there. There may be 5 or more generations of the root-gall type, but finally some of the root forms acquire wings and migrate to vines where they deposit 2 kinds of eggs. The small eggs produce males, the larger eggs, females; both are wingless. They mate and each female deposits a single overwintering egg under the bark of the cane.

In California vineyards the leaf form is extremely rare and the sex forms seldom mature. Nymphs winter on grape roots and summer generations succeed each other on the roots, although winged migrants may appear to establish new colonies or wingless individuals may crawl to other vines. Feeding roots are destroyed; plants frequently die.

Control. The most practical control is the grafting of desirable European varieties onto resistant native understock. Where European rootstocks are used, as in parts of California, the vineyards may be flooded at certain times to kill the root forms or the soil fumigated before new vines are set. Lindane is recommended for controlling phylloxera on leaves.

Grapevine Aphid*, *Aphis illinoisensis* Shimer. Very small, dark brown, common east of the Mississippi River. The lice may be abundant in dry weather, covering new shoots. They also infest fruit clusters, causing some drop, but often disappear after a heavy rain. In autumn the aphids migrate to black haw, returning to grapes in early summer. Nicotine sulfate is the usual chemical control; commercial growers may use parathion.

Greenbug*, *Schizaphis graminum* (Rondani). A small green aphid of general distribution, more important to farmers than home gardeners. Greenbugs may be disastrous to wheat and other grains and may also feed on rice, corn, and sorghum. Outbreaks are dependent on weather conditions, being favored by a mild winter and cool spring. In warm weather this aphid is held in check by a parasitic wasp, but this stops producing below 65° F.

Green Citrus Aphid. See Spirea Aphid.

Green Gooseberry Aphid, *Aphis sanborni* Patch. Alternating between *Ribes* sp. and epilobium, also reported on elder.

Green Peach Aphid*, *Myzus persicae* (Sulzer). A native of Europe, known there as greenfly, this species is now distributed all over North America. Often called the Spinach Aphid, it is most injurious to spinach, and to potatoes and peaches, but it also infests beet, celery, eggplant, lettuce, tomato, pepper, crucifers, cucurbits; and many ornamentals, including aster, calendula, crocus, carnation, chrysanthemum, dahlia, dianthus, English ivy, forget-me-not, freesia, iris, lily, nasturtium, poppy, pittosporum, primrose, rose, snapdragon, tulip, verbena, and violet; and some fruits—citrus, apricot, cherry, plum, and prune—besides peach. The green peach aphid is a dangerous vector of tomato and tobacco mosaic, beet mosaic, lettuce, dahlia, and canna mosaics, leaf roll of potatoes, and other virus diseases.

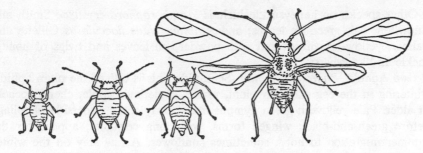

15. Stages in development of the green peach aphid.

Shiny black eggs winter on bark of fruit trees and hatch into pale, yellowish green aphids, with 3 dark lines on the back, about the time peaches come into bloom. Living young are produced for 2 or 3 generations and these suck sap from twigs; migrants then go to garden plants. In autumn winged females return to peach and give birth to true sexual females which mate with males flying over from spinach and other summer hosts.

Control. Use malathion or nicotine sulfate and soap on vegetables and ornamentals in home gardens. Commercial growers may prefer parathion, TEPP, or phosdrin.

Green and Pink Willow Aphid, *Aphis saliceti* Kaltenbach. Various forms are apple-green, pink or rust-red, with long, pale cornicles, on willow leaves and twigs.

Green Spruce Aphid*, *Cinara fornacula* Hottes. Light green, with some white powder, on Colorado spruce.

Grindelia Aphid, *Atarsos grindelliae* Gillette. Pale yellow to green, without feet (tarsi); on gumweed and aster.

Hawthorn Aphid, Long-beaked Clover Aphid, *Aphis crataegifoliae* Fitch. On hawthorn from New England to Illinois, also on Japanese quince, apple, pear, with clover and other legumes as summer hosts. The aphids are pinkish to yellowish green and their sucking causes young hawthorn leaves to curl tightly, older leaves to crinkle. Spray with malathion or lindane when leaves are first unfolding. See also Four-spotted Hawthorn Aphid.

Hemlock Woolly Aphid, *Chermes tsugae* (Annand). White tufts on bark and needles of western hemlock, sometimes killing ornamentals in the Pacific Northwest.

Hickory Aphid. See Giant Bark Aphid.

Hickory Leaf Aphid. See Black Pecan Aphid.

Hollyhock Aphid, *Macrosiphum eoessigi* Knowlton. Reddish brown with black appendages, on hollyhock.

Honeysuckle and Parsnip Aphid, *Rhopalosiphum conii* (Davidson). Yellowish, on honeysuckle and snowberry as winter hosts, migrating to dill, celery, carrot, and parsnip for the summer.

Other species on honeysuckle include *Amphorophora crystleae* Smith and Knowlton, pale-green on leaves; and *Amphicercidus flocculosus* Gillette and Palmer, yellow-brown covered with powder, on leaves and twigs of honeysuckle and snowberry.

Hop Aphid*, *Phorodon humuli* (Schrank). This is one of the plum aphids, wintering in the egg stage on plum, prune, sometimes apple, cherry, peach, or alder. Pale yellowish-green nymphs may nearly cover underside of foliage before green-and-black winged forms, with long cornicles, appear for the summer migration to hops, sometimes sunflower. A few stay on the winter host. Use a dormant oil or dinitro spray or malathion or nicotine as the leaves unfold.

Horsemint Aphid, *Myzus monardi* (Davis). Yellow brown, tightly rolling leaves of horsemint.

Impatiens Aphids, *Aphis impatientis* Thomas, and *Macrosiphum impatiensicolens* Patch, *M. impatientis* Williams.

Iris Root Aphid. See Tulip Bulb Aphid.

Ivy Aphid*, *Aphis hederae* Kaltenbach. A dark purplish-green, brown or black species common on growing tips of English ivy; also reported on euonymus, viburnum and aralia. Also known as the Ivy Aphid, but less common, is *Aphis pseudohederae* Theobald, which is dark maroon-brown.

Juniper Aphids. The **Rocky Mountain Juniper Aphid,** *Cinara sabinae* (Gillette and Palmer) is commonly injurious. It is light yellow-brown marked with black and appears in colonies on bark, often killing twigs.

The **Hemispherical Juniper Aphid,** *Siphonatrophia gravida* (Knowlton), appears as a minute green drop on the upper side of needles.

Larch Aphid*, *Cinara laricis* (Hartig). Dark brown to black, with brown spots on abdomen, infesting twigs and needle bases.

Larch is also the alternate host for two spruce gall aphids. See Spruce Gall Aphids.

Larkspur Aphid. See Delphinium Aphid.

Latania Aphid, *Cerataphis lataniae* (Boisduval). Frequently called the Lantana Aphid, but that is a perpetuation of an old mistake. This Latania or palm species is rather rare and may not even occur in the United States. It has been confused with *C. orchidearum,* which infests orchids, and *C. variabilis,* confined to palms. The latter two are common here and are similar to the latania aphid. The nymphs are dark, disklike, with a white fringe; the winged forms are dull brown to black. See also Orchid Aphid and Palm Aphid.

Leaf-curl Ash Aphid, *Prociphilus fraxinifolii* (Riley). Leaves are tightly folded and curled into a mass, a pseudo-gall, at tips of twigs. The species is common on white, red, and Modesto ash, especially in California.

Leaf-curl Plum Aphid, *Anuraphis helichrysi* (Kaltenbach). Pest of plum and prune, the winter hosts, especially in western states. Summer hosts include aster, carrot, celery, chrysanthemum, cynoglossum, cineraria, eupatorium, gerbera, heliotrope, lobelia, marguerite, mertensia, sunflower. The summer forms are pale green to lemon-yellow, the others are dark green to brownish. Plum leaves are tightly curled. A dormant spray is the best preventive.

Lettuce Aphids. The Brown Ambrosia Aphid, which see, is important on lettuce and endive in some western and southern states. A green aphid, *Acyrthosiphon barri* (Essig) damages lettuce in Arizona, California and other western states.

Lettuce Root Aphid, *Pemphigus bursarius* (Linnaeus). Yellowish white or dull green with wax glands. Wintering in petiole galls on poplar, summering on roots of lettuce, carrot, grasses, aster, and goldenrod.

Another lettuce root aphid, *Pemphigus brevicornis* Hart, is a very small, oval, white to pale yellow species, with dusky legs and white powder. Other hosts include aster, erigeron, achillea, euphorbia.

Lily Aphids. See Crescent-marked Lily Aphid and Purple-spotted Lily Aphid for the more common species. *Myzus lilii* is reported on nursery lilies and *Macrosiphum scopioli* on Easter lilies in California.

Linden Aphid, *Myzocallis tiliae* (Linnaeus). A yellow-and-black species with clouded wings, often abundant on linden leaves.

Little Black-veined Aster Aphid, *Aphis asterensis* Gillette and Palmer. Mottled greenish yellow, in heads of New England aster reported from New York, on leaves and stems of heath aster in Colorado; rather rare.

Locust Aphid, *Myzocallis robiniae* (Gillette). Yellow to greenish with long antennae, on locust leaves.

Lupine Aphid, *Macrosiphum albifrons* Essig. Also called Essig's Lupine Aphid. A large green species entirely covered with white powdery wax, with long legs and cornicles. It infests tips of annual and perennial lupines in spring and early summer.

Malaheb Cherry Aphid, *Myzus lythri* (Schrank). Green; on leaves and shoots of *Prunus malaheb* as winter host, on epilobium and lythrum as summer hosts.

Manzanita Leaf-gall Aphid, *Tamalia coweni* (Cockerell). Dull yellow to blackish, marked with dark green, on manzanita and bearberry. Inside pod-shaped galls formed by one third the leaf's being folded lengthwise on the rest. Galls are green or red.

Mealy Plum Aphid*, *Hyalopterus pruni* (Geoffroy). An alternate-host species wintering in the egg stage on plum and prune twigs, migrating to reed grass or cattails. This is a pale-green aphid with a mealy or powdery coating, native of Europe, especially important in the West. It may infest apple, apricot, and peach as well as plum, curling foliage, causing general stunting, fruit splitting, and spoilage by excrement and sooty mold. Use a dormant dinitro or oil spray, or nicotine or parathion or malathion when aphids appear.

Melon Aphid*, Cotton Aphid*, *Aphis gossypii* Glover. One of our most destructive species, distributed throughout the country but more serious in the South, where there may be 50 or more generations. There are upward of 100 possible hosts. A partial list includes, besides melon and cotton, asparagus, avocado, bean, beet, celery, cucumber, pumpkin, spinach, squash for vegetables; citrus fruits, pomegranate, strawberry, loquat; and aster, begonia, buckthorn, catalpa, chrysanthemum, cineraria, cyclamen, gardenia, dogwood, gourd, hibiscus, hydrangea, ironwood, lily, nemesia, rose, seagrape, sunflower, syringa, tabebuia, thistle, verbena, and wisteria.

The aphid is small, 1/16 inch long, usually very dark green but varying from pale yellow to brown or nearly black, with black cornicles. In the South living young are produced through the year, each female averaging more than 80 young. When a colony gets too dense, winged forms migrate to start another. In the North there is an egg stage on live-forever and other weeds with migration to garden plants in early summer.

The first sign of aphid infestation in the melon or cucumber patch is the wilting and curling of leaves (Plate I) accompanied by visits of ants, bees, wasps, and flies to get the honeydew. This aphid is a vector of cucumber and melon mosaic, a strain of which is responsible for the serious mosaic disease of lilies. On cucurbits, the mosaic shows as mottled dark- and light-green foliage with stunting of vines. The melon aphid is the worst watermelon pest in Florida, large acreages often being destroyed before the melons can be shipped. On orange, grapefruit and other citrus trees the aphids distort and curl young twigs. They are vectors of tristeza, a virus disease.

Control. This is difficult after the leaves and tender tips start curling. A malathion or nicotine dust is recommended for food plants in home gardens but the former may be injurious if applied to wet foliage. Commercial growers often use parathion, Thiodan or Trithion. Lindane is useful for ornamentals. In normal seasons natural parasites and predators are quite efficient in keeping this aphid in check, but if a cool wet spring, unfavorable for beneficial insects, is followed by a hot dry summer, favorable for aphid reproduction, there may be trouble.

Mint Aphid, *Ovatus crataegarius* Walker, formerly *Phorodon menthae* (Buckton). Yellow-green mottled with darker green, on mint foliage.

Monell's Sumac Aphid, *Rhopalosiphum rhois* (Monell). Light rusty brown to greenish yellow, common on terminal shoots and leaves of sumac.

Monterey-pine Aphid, *Essigella californica* Essig. Green, slender, with long hind legs, on needles of Monterey pine; also reported on lodgepole and white pine.

Norway-maple Aphid*, *Periphyllus lyropictus* (Kessler). A nuisance to large numbers of people, most of whom have never seen or heard of it. This is a large, hairy, green to brown aphid infesting underside of Norway- and sometimes sugar-maple foliage through the summer, dropping copious quantities of honeydew to smear windshields and bodies of automobiles parked under street trees. Heavy aphid infestations may be followed by heavy summer leaf drop and a sticky mess on sidewalks. Spray early in summer with lindane or malathion, wetting undersurface of leaves thoroughly.

Oak Aphids. There are many species. *Hoplochaitophorus quercicola* (Monell) is yellowish with black hairs, sometimes injurious to foliage of young oaks. *Therioaphis bellus* (Walsh) is small, bright yellow, with cloudy wings, infesting many eastern oaks and live oak in California. *Stegophylla quercicola* (Monell), green to yellow or brown with flocculent wax, lives exposed on oak leaves or twigs or in galls on edges of leaves. The Eastern Dusky-winged Aphid, *Myzocallis discolor* (Monell) is reported common on white oaks.

Oat Bird-cherry Aphid, *Rhopalosiphum padi* (Linnaeus). Nymph green with posterior orange, adult blackish green, similar to the apple grain aphid.

Oenothera Aphid, Evening Primrose Aphid, *Aphis oenotherae* Oestlund. Variable in color, green to slate to rusty, on evening primrose and epilobium.

Oleander Aphid, *Aphis nerii* Fonscolombe. A pretty yellow-and-black species common in Florida and California and occurring in other states. It appears in spring on young oleander shoots and later migrates to milkweed, although it can stay on oleander the entire year.

Oleaster-thistle Aphid, *Capitophorus braggii* (Gillette). Also called Artichoke Aphid. Pale yellow and green with darker-green markings, often abundant on globe artichoke in California and Louisiana. It winters on elaeagnus (Russian olive) and shepherdia. Various thistles are summer hosts.

Orchid Aphid, *Cerataphis orchidearum* (Westwood). On orchids. See Latania Aphid.

Ornate Aphid, *Myzus ornatus* Laing. A pest of fuchsia in California.

Ornamental Currant Aphid, *Amphorophora ribiella* (Davis). Pale yellowgreen, on golden and black currant.

Painted Maple Aphid*, *Drepanaphis acerifoliae* (Thomas). Greenish or brownish with dark borders on wings; on leaves of various species of maple.

Pale Chrysanthemum Aphid, *Amphorophora rufomaculatum* (Wilson). Reported on chrysanthemum and artemisia.

Palm Aphid, *Cerataphis variabilis* Hille Ris Lambers. On palms. See Latania Aphid.

Pea Aphid*, *Macrosiphum pisi* (Harris). A smooth, pale-green species with black tarsi, generally distributed but of special importance to large growers and the pea-canning industry. In large pea fields aphids may be so abundant that plants and ground appear white from cast skins; vines wilt and die. Even when less abundant the quality of the peas is affected. The aphid is also a vector of the virus causing pea enation and yellow bean mosaic. It winters on clovers and alfalfa, migrating to peas, including sweetpea, about May 1, there to produce 7 to 20 generations depending on the weather. There is some migration to other legumes in summer but aphids are again abundant on the fall crop of peas.

Control. Phosphate sprays or dusts are recommended for peas—malathion, parathion, TEPP, or phosdrin. Some pea varieties are resistant but there are several biological races of the pea aphid so that maintaining plant resistance is difficult. On forage crops control is largely by beneficial insects—lady beetles, lacewings, and larvae of syrphid flies.

Pecan Leaf Phylloxera*, *Phylloxera notabilis* Pergande. Galls on pecan leaves.

Pecan Phylloxera*, *Phylloxera devastatrix* Pergande. Galls on pecan stems.

Pine Bark Aphid*, *Pineus strobi* (Hartig). Principally on white pine, occasionally on Scotch, Austrian and other pines over most of the country. This is a small dark louse covered with wax, congregating in conspicuous white, flocculent colonies on underside of larger limbs or on main trunk, giving a whitewashed appearance. The immature forms winter under the felty white masses or under the bark, maturing and laying eggs in April or May, from which come both winged and wingless forms. Most of the former migrate to other pines; the latter lay eggs for a brood of adults appearing in August and September, whose young are the hibernating nymphs. This aphid is more unsightly than injurious on older trees but may damage unthrifty young trees in ornamental plantings.

Control. A dormant spray, miscible oil or lime-sulfur, has been standard and is still recommended, but if this is omitted, spray with lindane, second choice malathion, in late April or May.

Pine Leaf Aphid, *Pineus pinifoliae* Fitch. On white and lodgepole pines and red, Engelmann, black and Sitka spruces. The woolly nymphs winter on pine, migrate to spruce in spring where they produce compact terminal galls with only 1 or 2 aphids per chamber. The galls open in June and the aphids migrate back to old pine needles, where they give birth to nymphs which move to the new growth and are covered with white wax for the winter. Needles may turn yellow and new growth appear sickly. Spray pines with lindane. Break the galls off ornamental spruces and destroy them before the cells open.

Other **Pine Aphids.** Many other species are listed on pine. Among those infesting needles are the **Woolly Pine Needle Aphid,** *Schizolachnus piniradiatae* (Davidson) on Scotch, red, and yellow pine and a sister species, *S. pineti* (Fabricius) on Scotch and mugho pines; the **Powdery Pine Needle Aphid,** *Eulachnus rileyi* (Williams) on longleaf and yellow pine; *E. agilus* (Kaltenbach) abundant in some red-pine plantations; and the **Green and Brown Pine Needle Aphid,** *Essigella fusca* Gillette and Palmer, common on piñon pine. On bark of various pines there are a dozen or more species of *Cinara,* mostly brown or black, covered with a white powder and with short antennae. See also White-pine Aphid.

Poplar Petiole Gall Aphid*, *Pemphigus populitransversus* Riley. Globular galls on leaf stems have transverse mouths. The greenish yellow, small, stout aphids have poplar as a winter host and summer on roots of cruciferous plants. This species is important on Lombardy poplar.

Poplar Twig Gall Aphid*, *Pemphigus populiramulorum* Riley. Dark-green aphids causing globular galls with transverse mouths on twigs.

Poplar Vagabond Aphid*, *Mordwilkoja vagabunda* (Walsh). Green powdery aphids live clustered together in a bladderlike leaf gall composed of crumpled leaves of a terminal bud.

Other **Poplar Aphids.** Among the numerous other species on aspen, cottonwood, and poplar are: the **Folded Leaf Poplar Aphid,** *Thecabius populiconduplifolius* (Cowen) which winters in a folded pseudo-gall but summers on leaf bases of ranunculus; *T. populi-monilis* (Riley), making beadlike galls on underside of cottonwood leaves; **Poplar Leaf-purse Aphid,** *Asiphum pseudo-byrsum* (Walsh), with leaf folded downward on midrib; **Poplar Leaf-petiole Gall Aphid,** *Pemphigus populi-caulis* Fitch, with the gall formed at the leaf base; **Poplar Sugar-beet Root Aphid,** *Pemphigus balsamiferae* Williams, wintering in yellow green to reddish pocket galls on underside of leaves, summering on roots of beet, aster, and other plants; the **Reddish Brown Poplar Aphid,** *Pterocomma populifoliae* (Fitch) on bark; the **Crescent-gall Poplar Aphid,** *Cornaphis populi* Gillette, in crescent-shaped galls composed of folded edges of leaves; the **Clear-winged Aspen Aphid,** *Chaitophorus populifoliae* Davis, green and black with hyaline wings, on aspen leaves and twigs; the **Clear-winged Cottonwood Leaf Aphid,** *C. populellus* Gillette and Palmer, light green to yellowish, on leaves; the **Black Cloudy-winged Poplar Leaf Aphid,** *Periphyllus bruneri* (Williams), having wings with black borders, on leaves and twigs; the **Cloudy-winged Cottonwood Leaf Aphid,** *P. populicolus* (Thomas); the **Spotted Poplar Aphid,** *Aphis maculatae* Oestlund, black with white patches, on leaves and twigs; and the **American Poplar Bark Aphid,** *Pterocomma pseudo-populea* Palmer, yellow to olive-brown, on bark.

Potato Aphid*, *Macrosiphum euphorbiae* (Thomas). Common throughout North America (Plate II). This aphid is a menace as a vector of mosaic and other virus diseases of potato and tomato. Years of great abundance, when the aphid is present in epidemic proportions, are followed by lean years. Rose is the winter host, occasionally apple, agrimonia and potentilla. Black eggs on rose canes hatch into glistening pink-and-green lice, about ⅙ inch long, with long cornicles. These feed on rose buds and succulent young leaves, but in early summer migrates fly or crawl to potatoes and other summer hosts, including amaranthus, asparagus, aster, bean, cineraria, citrus, columbine, corn, currant, eggplant, euphorbia, fuchsia, geranium, gladiolus, groundcherry, iris, Jerusalem-cherry, lettuce, oxalis, pea, penstemon, pepper, poppy, pumpkin, raspberry, squash, sunflower, sweetpotato, tomato, tulip, turnip, and many weeds.

Potato foliage is curled and distorted by aphid feeding; the vines often turn brown and die. On tomatoes the blossom clusters are so devitalized that no fruit is set. Generations develop every 2 or 3 weeks, with vines rapidly covered with lice. On a single tomato plant 24,688 aphids were once counted.

In September and October the aphids return to roses, there to produce egg-laying females which mate with males flying over from summer hosts.

Control. Commercial growers may use DDT, diazinon, endrin, parathion or Thiodan on potatoes; home gardeners should play safe with malathion or pyrethrum-rotenone spray or dust, adding lindane as a possibility for roses. Pyrethrum-rotenone in aerosol bombs may be used for aphids on rose buds between regular combination-spray applications.

Privet Aphid, *Myzus ligustri* (Mosley). Privet (Ligustrum) sometimes has new leaves tightly curled lengthwise. The aphids leave in midsummer but return in autumn to lay eggs.

Purple-spotted Lily Aphid*, *Macrosiphum lilii* (Monell). Yellow with a purple patch on the back, ⅛ inch long, common in eastern United States. It feeds on underside of lower leaves, on stems, buds, and seed pods of regal, formosanum, speciosum, and other late-flowering garden lilies, causing yellowed foliage, sometimes premature death. Spray or dust with malathion; cut off and burn infested stems in early fall before females deposit eggs.

Raspberry Aphids. The large green **European Raspberry Aphid,** *Amphorophora rubi* (Kaltenbach) is rather common on underside of leaves of red and black raspberries, and loganberries. It is important as a vector of raspberry mosaic. The **Spotted-winged Raspberry Aphid,** *A. rubicola* (Oestlund), is occasional on leaves of red raspberry. It is greenish with a dusky spot on tip of fore wings. Also rather rare is *A. sensoriata* Mason. A small greenish aphid, *Aphis rubicola* (Oestlund), sometimes appears on leaves and tips of red and black raspberry, and a small pale-yellow relative, *A. rubifolii* (Thomas) is infrequent on red raspberry. Use malathion as necessary for control.

Red and Black Cherry Aphid, *Aphis feminea* Hottes. Red, with black head, clustering on cherry; rather rare, reported from Massachusetts, New York, Illinois, and District of Columbia.

Rhododendron Aphid, *Macrosiphum rhododendri* Wilson. Pale pink-and-green species infesting this host in the Pacific Northwest.

Rose Aphid*, *Macrosiphum rosae* (Linnaeus). A large green species with black appendages, with a pink form in some areas. Common and widespread on cultivated roses, reported as sometimes injurious to pyracantha. This is a single-host species, continuing to breed on roses through the season. It injures tender leaves, stems, and buds, and deposits eggs for the winter on canes. There are several predators and parasites and when the lady-beetle larvae or aphid-lions are at work, it is sometimes better to stop spraying temporarily and give the beneficial insects a chance. Malathion, lindane, nicotine sulfate, or pyrethrum and rotenone can usually be included in a spray aimed at other insects as well.

Other Rose Aphids. The **Small Green Rose Aphid,** *Myzaphis rosarum* (Kaltenbach) is smaller than the rose aphid, has no pink forms, and is not restricted to succulent new growth. The **Black and Red Rose Aphid,** *Macro-*

siphum nigromaculosum Macdougall, may infest rose leaves and stems but is rather rare. Another species, *M. pseudodirhodum* Patch, has been reported on greenhouse roses. The **Rose and Bearberry Aphid,** *Amphorophora nervata* (Gillette) is found on leaves and twigs of cultivated roses and on bearberry. The **Hairy Rose Aphid,** *Lachnus rosae* Cholodkovsky, a dark species with hairs, is occasional on canes of wild roses. *Myzaphis bucktoni,* found on swamp rose in Maine, is a new record for North America.

Rose Grass Aphid, *Acyrthosiphon dirhodum* (Walker). Yellow to pale green, wintering on twigs and leaves of rose, summering on celery, oats, and various grasses.

Rosy Apple Aphid*, *Anuraphis rosea* Baker. An important apple pest, curling leaves and deforming young fruit, producing "aphis apples" (Plate II). This species is present throughout apple-growing sections and may also feed on pear, hawthorn, and mountain-ash. It winters as dark-green shiny eggs attached to twigs or in bark crevices, hatching over a period of 2 weeks when buds are opening. The stem mothers, purplish or rose with a waxy coating, feed on the outside of buds until the leaves start to unfold, then work their way down into the cluster. When their sucking makes the leaves curl around them, they are well protected from sprays. Stem mothers continue to produce living young through spring and early summer, but around July winged forms, rosy with black head and thorax, migrate to stems of narrow-leaved plantain. The aphids return to apple and deposit eggs from October to November.

Control. Efforts are best directed at the overwintering eggs by means of dormant dinitro sprays, but parathion, TEPP, and other phosphate sprays seem able to kill aphids even after leaves are curled. Malathion or lindane may prevent curling on hawthorn if applied early enough. Syrphid flies, lady beetles, lacewings, and parasitic wasps are very helpful in warm seasons but when the weather is cold and wet, aphids get the upper hand unless man steps in.

Russet-colored Larkspur Aphid. See Delphinium Aphid.

Russian-olive Aphid, *Capitophorus shepherdiae* Gillette and Bragg. Yellow-green, marked with darker green, on Russian-olive, sea-buckthorn and buffaloberry. Another species, the **Polygonum Aphid,** *C. hippophaes* (Walker), greenish yellow with reddish streaks, winters on sea-buckthorn and Russian-olive, summers on polygonum.

Rusty Plum Aphid*, *Hysteroneura setariae* (Thomas). A rust-brown aphid common on plums in the East and west to Colorado. It also feeds on corn, grasses, sugarcane, and Virginia-creeper. Use a dormant dinitro spray or malathion or nicotine sulfate later.

Sand Lily Aphid, *Myzus leucocrini* Gillette and Palmer. Nymphs are light green, adults are brownish green with 2 rust-orange blotches. On leucocrinum, sand lily, and recently injurious to daylilies in Florida.

Sedum Aphid, *Aphis sedi* Kaltenbach. On various species of sedum; similar to the melon aphid.

Snowball Aphid*, *Anuraphis viburnicola* (Gillette). Cause of the familiar curling and deforming of new leaves of the common snowball (*Viburnum opulis*) in early spring (Plate II). The aphids vary in color from ash-gray to dark green and start curling the leaves long before they are expanded. Control is difficult because the lice are protected almost from the beginning,

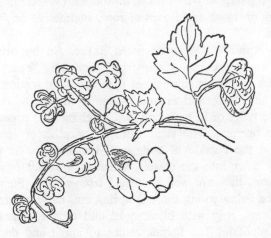

16. Snowball leaves curled by aphids.

inside the curled portions. Use a dormant dinitro or oil spray and/or spray or dust with malathion, lindane, or nicotine, starting as the leaf buds break. It may be easier to replace the common snowball with resistant *Viburnum tomentosum*. See also Viburnum Aphid.

Snowberry Aphid, *Brevicoryne symphoricarpi* (Thomas). Yellow, maturing to black or dusky green with white, powdery patches; curling snowberry leaves. Another species, *Aphis incognita* Hottes and Frison, yellowish green, less common but sometimes found with the snowberry aphid, lives on leaves in summer, on roots spring and winter. The **Pulverulent Snowberry Aphid,** *Amphicercidus pulverulens* (Gillette) is sordid brown or green, powdery, on bark at base of stems.

Solanum Root Louse, *Trifidaphis radicicola* (Essig); probably a synonym of *T. phaseoli* (Passerini) and the name recently changed to *Smynthurodes betae* (Westwood). Pale pinkish yellow with brown head and appendages, powdery; on roots of potato, bean, sweetpea, beet, carrot, aster, goldenrod, vinca, and grass.

Sowthistle Aphid, *Amphorophora sonchi* (Oestlund). Greenish, with pale appendages. Winter hosts, leaves of golden and black currant; summer hosts celery, sowthistle, and wild lettuce.

Spinach Aphid. See Green Peach Aphid.

Spirea Aphid*, *Aphis spiraecola* Patch. Also known as the Green Citrus Aphid. Green with black cornicles, 1/10 inch long. This is a common species on spirea, covering new growth with myriads of green lice. On citrus it curls and stunts leaves and twigs, deforms fruit, and covers everything with honey-dew, medium for sooty mold. The eggs and sexual forms appear on spirea, the viviparous forms on citrus and other hosts. The life cycle is only 6 to 10 days, with the possibility of large populations built up in a short time. In addition to spirea and citrus this aphid infests many shrubs, trees and herbaceous ornamentals, including Japanese quince, hawthorn, apple, pear, cherry-laurel, jacaranda, viburnum, and various herbs. Newly planted trees suffer most.

Citrus growers may use dangerous phosphate sprays if natural enemies are not adequate, but homeowners will use malathion, lindane or nicotine sulfate.

The **Brown Spirea Aphid,** *Aphis spiraephila* Patch, hazel to chestnut green, covered with powder, also infests leaves and twigs of spirea but is less common than the green species.

Spotted Alfalfa Aphid*, *Therioaphis maculata* (Buckton). An import from the Middle East, first noted in New Mexico in 1954. By 1957 it had spread from coast to coast, a serious menace to forage crops, alfalfa and clovers. The aphid is small, pale yellow or grayish with dark spots. It reproduces rapidly, killing foliage by its sucking, and clogging baling machinery with sticky honeydew. The introduction of 3 imported parasites and the action of native predators and entomophagous fungi has brought this pest largely under control, although chemicals may be necessary on young seedlings.

Spruce Aphid*, *Aphis abietina* Walker. Serious on all species of spruce wherever grown; very destructive to Sitka spruce, having killed millions of board feet in forests. The aphids, yellowish to dull green, 3/16 inch long, feed on needles, causing them to turn brown and drop. The lice disappear in summer, the alternate host being unknown. Spray ornamentals with malathion, lindane, or nicotine.

Other Spruce Aphids. Many species of Cinara infest spruce. The **Powdery Spruce Aphid,** *Cinara braggi* (Gillette), yellowish, marked with dark brown and lightly covered with powder, is rather common on bark of ornamental blue spruce in parks; the honeydew may damage automobiles in the vicinity. The **Black Polished Spruce Aphid,** *C. coloradensis* (Gillette) is also fairly common in parks on blue and Engelmann spruce, as is the **Spotted Spruce Aphid,** *Cinara palmerae* (Gillette), dark brown with a spotted pattern of pulverulence. The **Dark Brown Spruce Aphid,** *C. piceicola* (Cholodkovsky), is reported on twigs of spruce nursery stock. The **Light Brown Spruce Aphid,** *C. engelmanniensis* (Gillette and Palmer), is rather rare on Engelmann spruce.

Gall aphids on spruce include *Pineus similis* (Gillette) which produces loose terminal galls on current year's growth, from New England to Minnesota, and *P. floccus* Patch, which galls the entire new growth on spruce and goes to pine as an alternate host. Larch is the alternate host for *Chermes strobilobius* Kaltenbach, which makes small galls, and *C. laricatus* Patch, which stimulates galls with very short needles.

See Cooley Spruce Gall Aphid and Eastern Spruce Gall Aphid for the most important gall formers on this host.

Strawberry Aphid*, *Pentatrichopus fragaraefolii* (Cockerell). A small, pale-yellow species occurring in dense populations on strawberry leaves and stems, but with a marked preference for younger leaves. A pale-green form of this species occurs on leaves and stems of wild rose and another on potentilla. Winged forms migrate from rose to strawberry and reproduce abundantly on the latter. This aphid is particularly important as a vector of strawberry yellows, crinkle, and other virus diseases. Control with malathion spray or dust, or parathion for commercial growers.

Strawberry Root Aphid*, *Aphis forbesi* Weed. On roots and crown of strawberries, particularly injurious in Central Atlantic States. Black, shiny eggs, overwintered on leaves and stems, hatch in early spring into dark, bluish-green aphids which feed on new leaves. They are found there by the little brown cornfield ant and carried to strawberry roots. There are several generations, keeping the ants in honeydew, but in autumn winged forms fly to the leaves and give birth to sexual males and females which mate and provide overwintering eggs. In mild winters the root forms also persist. Strawberry plants lack vigor, have pale foliage; the fruit dries up or fails to mature properly.

Control. Phosphate sprays are recommended for the leaf forms. In preparing new beds, cultivate the ground deeply in early spring to drive out the ants and set uninfested plants. Chlordane may be used to drench the soil around established plants if no fruit is present.

Sugar-beet Root Aphid*, *Pemphigus betae* Doane. Found in the western half of the country on roots of sugar beets, beets, mangels, and many weeds. The aphids are yellow, with a mass of white waxy cotton toward the rear of the abdomen. They appear as bits of white mold on roots. A winged form, black with a white waxy covering, migrates to poplar for the winter, depositing eggs on the bark, and returns to beet in July, after feeding on poplar leaves during the spring. When beets are grown on irrigated land, root aphids can be reduced by irrigations at 10-day intervals.

Sumac Gall Aphid, *Melaphis rhois* Fitch. Red ball-like galls on sumac leaves.

Sunflower Aphid, *Aphis debilicornis* (Gillette and Palmer). Dark olive-buff on curled leaves and stems of sunflower and Jerusalem artichoke. See also Dogwood or Sunflower Aphid.

Sweetclover Aphid*, *Therioaphis riehmi* (Börner). A European species that recently appeared in North America on sweetclover and is now present from the Atlantic to the Pacific, from Canada to the Gulf of Mexico. It does not injure other legumes. It is pale yellow with black spots, somewhat resembling the spotted alfalfa aphid.

Sycamore Aphid, *Drepanosiphum platanoides* (Schrank). A large, common aphid in various shades of yellow, red, or green, with black markings; on Norway, English, and sycamore maples.

Thistle Aphid*, *Anuraphis cardui* (Linnaeus). A large, shiny green to yellowish species, with a black patch and bands, long cornicles; summering on thistles, chrysanthemum and weeds, wintering on apricot, prune, and plum.

Tulip Bulb Aphid*, *Anuraphis tulipae* (Fonscolombe). Also called Iris Root Aphid. A whitish powdery species with the wingless form pinkish or green with dusky markings. The winged form has black head and thorax, yellow or green body, short cauda and cornicles, is 1/10 inch long. The aphids infest bases of plants at or below ground level and hide in flower stems, under leaf sheaths, or in seed pods. They attack all varieties of bearded and beardless iris and continue to feed on stored rhizomes. They are common and abundant on stored bulbs or corms of tulip, lily, freesia, crocus, gladiolus, and are reported on roots of celery, carrot, and blackberry-lily. Plants are stunted, distorted, or killed. Dust bulbs with lindane before storage; treat growing plants with malathion or lindane.

Tulip Leaf Aphid, *Rhopalosiphoninus tulipaella* (Theobald). Small, green, 1/16 inch long, clustering on leaves and shoots of iris and tulip. Leaves and flowers may fail to open and plants may die. This species also winters on dormant bulbs which should be dusted with lindane before storing. Dust or spray plants with malathion.

Tuliptree Aphid*, *Macrosiphum liriodendri* (Monell). A small green species abundant on underside of leaves and secreting copious quantities of honeydew. Leaves of tuliptrees and foliage of broad-leaved evergreens growing underneath are often densely coated with black sooty mold. Use a dormant oil spray in spring and nicotine or malathion in July.

Turnip Aphid*, *Rhopalosiphum pseudobrassicae* (Davis). Also called False Cabbage Aphid and Turnip Louse. It resembles the common cabbage aphid but does not have the waxy body covering. It is pale green and the winged form has black spots, a black head, and transparent wings marked by black veins. This species is generally distributed but causes more serious losses in the South. It feeds chiefly on turnip, mustard and radish but may infest other crucifers—cabbage, cauliflower, collards, kale, kohlrabi, rutabaga—and lettuce. Full-grown females give birth to 50 to 100 living young during a period of 20 to 30 days, and in the Gulf States as many as 46 generations have been observed in a single year. Commercial growers use parathion, TEPP, diazinon, Phosdrin, or malathion. Amateurs should stick to malathion, nicotine, or rotenone.

Viburnum Aphid*, *Anuraphis viburniphila* Patch. Reddish brown, mottled, with black head and hairy legs. Fairly common on leaves and stems of *Viburnum opulis* and var. *sterile*. See also Snowball Aphid.

Violet Aphid*, *Micromyzus violae* (Pergande). A wine-red species, with clouded wing veins and swollen cornicles. Infests shoots, buds, and leaves of wild and cultivated violets in California and is present in greenhouses elsewhere.

Walnut Aphid*, *Chromaphis juglandicola* (Kaltenbach). On English walnut; abundant and serious in Pacific States in summer. The color varies from lemon-yellow to salmon-pink to brown. Injury comes from loss of sap from aphids feeding on underside of leaves, and from sooty mold growing in the honeydew. DDT used to control codling moth on walnut has markedly increased aphid populations by killing off beneficial predators. Phosphate sprays are usually used by orchardists, the first application in spring, the second in July or August. Nicotine or malathion dust is also used. A braconid wasp parasite (*Trioxys pallidus*), introduced from Europe in 1959, has spread rapidly over coastal areas and is most promising for control.

Other **Walnut Aphids.** The **American Walnut Aphid,** *Monellia caryae* (Monell), is yellow with dusky spots, found on leaves of walnut and hickory. The **European Walnut Aphid,** *Panaphis juglandis* (Goeze), is yellow with brown to black markings and occurs on upper surface of walnut leaves.

Waterlily Aphid*, *Rhopalosiphum nymphaeae* (Linnaeus). Small, olive green to golden brown, on waterlily, water plantain, cattail, pondweed, and knotweed for summer hosts. On its winter fruit-tree hosts—almond, apricot, cherry, plum—the aphid is larger and covered with white powder. Waterlily leaves are disfigured and decayed, flowers discolored and stems distorted. Japanese cherry grown near waterlily ponds may be injured.

Control. In pools with fish, remove fish, lower water level to expose foliage, and spray with malathion or nicotine. Change water before replacing the fish. If fish cannot be removed, fill pool to overflowing and wash aphids onto lawn with the hose. Spray plums with malathion in spring, before aphids migrate to waterlilies.

Western Aster Root Aphid, *Aphis armoraciae* Cowen. Pale to olive green, with powder, common on roots of aster, erigeron, salsify, parsley, horseradish and other plants. For control see Corn Root Aphid.

White Aster Root Aphid, *Prociphilus erigeronensis* (Thomas). Yellow-buff, woolly; on roots of aster, China aster, primrose, lettuce, evening primrose, sunflower; winter host is unknown.

White-pine Aphid*, *Cinara strobi* Fitch. Found on eastern white pine from New England to Illinois and south to the Carolinas, feeding on twigs and branches. Small trees may be heavily damaged or killed. Eggs are laid in lines on the needles with sooty mold developing in the honeydew. Spray with a dormant oil in April, or use nicotine or lindane later, or wash off the aphids with a strong stream of water from the hose.

Willow Aphids. Many species are recorded, some quite common. *Peri-*

phyllus salicorticis (Essig) is greenish yellow or rust-brown with darker spots. It occurs on bark of older limbs and often at or beneath surface of the ground. The **Black Willow Aphid,** *Pterocomma smithiae* (Monell), pink or salmon as a nymph, rusty brown with bluish powder as an adult, commonly infests bark of twigs of willow and poplar. A related species, *P. bicolor* (Oestlund), also reddish brown with powdery markings, is likewise common on willow bark. Willow is winter host to two green aphids, *Cavariella aegopodii* (Scopoli) and *C. essigi* (Gillette and Bragg). The former summers on dill, celery, caraway, carrot, and parsnip; the latter goes to cow parsnip. The **Little Black-and-green Willow Aphid,** *Chaitophorus viminalis* Monell, commonly infests willow leaves in large colonies.

See also Giant Willow Aphid.

Witch-hazel Leaf Gall Aphid, *Hormaphis hamamelidis* (Fitch). Forming conical galls on upper surface of leaves, found from New England to North Carolina and Illinois. Birch is an alternate host. The **Spiny Witch-hazel Gall Aphid,** *Hamamelistes spinosus* Shimer, forms galls on stem buds of witch-hazel and goes on to birch.

Woolly Alder Aphid*, *Prociphilus tessellatus* (Fitch). Also known as Alder Blight Aphid and Maple Leaf Aphid. Widely distributed, with maple considered the primary host, alder the secondary. Leaves are folded downward over large woolly masses covering blue-black aphids. In early fall males and females, the latter small and orange, migrate from alder to maple to mate and lay eggs on the bark. At the same time a wingless hibernating form on alder crawls down the trunk to spend the winter under leaves on the ground. Lady beetles and the sluglike caterpillar of an orange butterfly (*Feniseca tarquinius*) feed on these aphids, but ants protect them in exchange for honeydew.

Woolly Apple Aphid*, *Eriosoma lanigerum* (Hausmann). Of world-wide distribution, wherever apples are grown, also attacking pear, hawthorn, mountain-ash, and elm. It covers trunk and branches with white cottony masses enclosing purplish brown lice and forms knots on the roots, causing many fibrous roots, stunting, and sometimes death of young apple trees (Plate II).

The life history is complicated. This woolly aphid winters in several forms—eggs on the bark of elm trees, immature nymphs on apple roots, or, in warm climates, as egg-laying females on apple bark. The eggs on elm hatch in spring into wingless forms which feed on elm buds and leaves for 2 generations, turning young leaves into curled rosettes that protect the aphids. The next generation has wings and migrates to apple, hawthorn, and mountain-ash, where some of the lice feed in wounds on trunk and branches and others work their way down to the roots, where the most important injury is produced. In autumn winged migrants return to elm while other, wingless aphids remain to produce living young on apple roots.

Control. An effective parasite, *Aphelinus mali,* has been distributed to many countries, but it works best at fairly high temperatures and is killed when DDT, TDE, or methoxychlor is used in the spray schedule. However, its numbers are not decreased by parathion and TEPP, which are effective for the aphids. Orchardists also use diazinon, Guthion, or malathion. Root forms may be killed on nursery stock by dipping in a strong nicotine solution before planting.

Woolly Beech Aphid. See Beech Blight Aphid.

Woolly Elm Aphid*, *Eriosoma americanum* (Riley). Attacks only American elm, with roots of shadbush or serviceberry the alternate host. One side of the leaf is rolled under to enclose woolly dark-green to black lice. Another species, the **Woolly Elm Bark Aphid,** *Eriosoma rileyi* (Thomas), powdery flesh-colored to brownish, is found on bark or trunk and roots of American and slippery elm. No alternate host is known.

Woolly Hawthorn Aphid, *Eriosoma crataegi* (Oestlund). A large black species with wax in 2 long white filaments, on bark of hawthorn and curling leaves of elm. It has been confused with the woolly apple aphid; it is parasitized by the same wasp.

Another Woolly Hawthorn Aphid, *Prociphilus corrugatans* (Sirrine) is less common. It is olive-green and lives inside curled leaves of hawthorn and shadbush. The summer host is not known.

Woolly Honeysuckle Aphid, *Prociphilus xylostei* (De Geer). Yellow, with black head and thorax, woolly; inside partly curled honeysuckle leaves.

Woolly Larch Aphid, *Chermes strobilobius* Kaltenbach. On larch, appearing as white woolly masses on needles and as dark aphids on underside of twigs and clustered at base of needles. It migrates to spruce, forming small galls at tip of current growth. Spray with malathion or lindane.

Woolly Pear Aphid*, *Eriosoma pyricola* Baker and Davidson. Similar to the woolly apple aphid, established on the Pacific Coast and in limited locations farther east. The life cycle is completed on elm, where leaf galls are formed.

Woolly Pine Needle Aphid. See under Pine Aphids.

Yellow Clover Aphid*, *Therioaphis trifolii* (Monell). Fairly common but not often significant on clovers.

Yellow Rose Aphid*, *Myzus porosus* Sanderson. Pale, on rose, wild and cultivated, and strawberry.

ARMYWORMS

Armyworms are related to cutworms, in the family Noctuidae, order Lepidoptera. They are the larvae of night-flying moths and work in armies, devouring everything in their paths.

Armyworm*, *Pseudaletia unipuncta* (Haworth). Common in all parts of the country, especially injurious east of the Rocky Mountains, and an ancient native pest. The Pilgrim fathers reported damage to corn as early as 1632, and this species has been intermittently disastrous ever since. It reaches epidemic proportions at varying intervals of years, usually being more serious after a cold spring. The caterpillars are 1½ inches long, smooth, greenish, with dark stripes and with a fine, broken, light-colored stripe down the back. They travel in dense armies, devouring all crops along the line of march, wheat, corn, oats, and rye being favorite food plants. They winter mainly as larvae, then form dark-brown pupae in the soil, whence emerge brownish-gray moths. These "millers" have a small white dot in the center of each front wing; they are 1½ inches across the wings. The moths fly only at night; they are attracted to lights and decaying fruits. The females deposit greenish-white eggs in long rows on lower leaves of grasses. There may be 2 or 3 generations a year, with the first most injurious.

Control. Spraying or dusting with DDT or toxaphene is recommended for seedlings but not on forage crops. Poison baits, same as for grasshoppers, may be used across the line of march. Many insects, especially tachinid flies and wasplike egg parasites, are helpful in control. The caterpillars are also eaten by birds, skunks, and toads.

Beet Armyworm*, *Spodoptera exigua* (Hübner). Also known as Asparagus Fern Caterpillar. The larvae are green above, yellow underneath, with a dark stripe on the back and yellowish stripes on each side. They eat corn, cotton, peas, peppers, tomatoes, as well as beets and asparagus fern. Adults are a mottled gray.

Fall Armyworm*, *Laphygma frugiperda* (J. E. Smith). So named because it does not appear before fall in northern states. It is a tropical insect, winter-

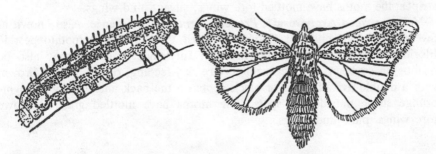

17. Fall armyworm, larva and adult moth.

ing in southern Florida and along the Gulf Coast, migrating north in summer as far as New England and Michigan. Called the Southern Grassworm in Florida, it eats all grass in easy range (lawns as well as meadows) before moving to corn, second choice. On corn, it is sometimes called budworm and acts like the corn earworm. It is particularly injurious following a cold wet spring and may feed on many vegetables—bean, cabbage, cowpea, cucumber, peanut, potato, sweetpotato, spinach, tomato, turnip—as well as on grass, corn, clover, and grains.

The caterpillars are light tan to green or black, with 3 yellowish hairlines down the back, then a darker stripe next to a waxy yellow stripe splotched with red. They have a conspicuous V-shaped white mark on the head. When they have eaten all the food in one garden, they start a forced march on the next. Because they start feeding near the ground, they do a lot of feeding before being noticed.

The moths—1½ inches across, with grayish-white hind wings, dark mottled fore wings with a whitish spot at the tip—fly northward in swarms, mostly at night. A single female may deposit up to 1000 eggs, in clusters of 150 each, on green plants. There may be 5 or 6 generations in the South but only 1 that is important in the North.

Control. This armyworm is rather resistant to DDT; toxaphene is more effective. Dieldrin, heptachlor, and chlordane are possibilities. Cultivate soil in gardens to expose pupae to their many natural enemies.

Lawn Armyworm, *Spodoptera mauritia acronyctoides* Guenée. A new pest in Hawaii; on Bermuda grass in lawns.

Southern Armyworm*, *Prodenia eridania* (Cramer). Also called Semitropical Armyworm. This species is prevalent in Florida and has been noted as far north as South Carolina. It is a major pest of celery and sweetpotato, attacks cotton and some other plants. The larvae are black, or yellow with black markings.

Western Yellow-striped Armyworm*, *Prodenia praefica* Grote. A problem in western states on alfalfa, also damaging tomato, rhubarb, melons, grapevines and a variety of plants. The caterpillars are velvety black with yellow stripes; the moths have mottled fore wings, silvery hind wings.

Yellow-striped Armyworm*, *Prodenia ornithogalli* Guenée. Also known as Sweetpotato Caterpillar or Cotton Cutworm. This is a sweetpotato pest in Florida, often defoliating whole fields in July and August. It may also be serious on soybeans. The caterpillars are day-feeding, olive-green to brown, with a double row of green or black spots on the back and usually a bright-orange stripe outside the spots. The moths have mottled gray or brown fore wings, pale hind wings.

BAGWORMS

Bagworms are caterpillars that carry their baglike houses around with them. They are larvae of moths, family Psychidae, order Lepidoptera, with wingless, almost legless females that practically never leave their bags. Of the 20 species in this country only one is commonly mentioned.

Bagworm*, *Thyridopteryx ephemeraeformis* (Haworth). Distributed from Massachusetts to Florida and west well into Texas and Oklahoma. Although called the Evergreen Bagworm and a frequent pest of conifers, it is a general feeder, sometimes defoliating sycamores, Norway and soft maples, locust, boxelder, linden, citrus trees, as well as arborvitae, juniper, hemlock, larch and pine. It seems to be more devastating in the South. I have seen miles of redcedars in Virginia and many arborvitae in Texas killed by bagworms, but never such total destruction in northern states.

The spindle-shaped bag, 1 to 2 inches long, of unbelievably tough silk, is covered with bits of leaves and twigs from the host plant, a bag hanging on a juniper being of quite different appearance from one on pine (Plate III). The eggs winter in the bag and the larvae hatch in late spring—perhaps April in Florida, late May and early June in New Jersey. The larvae, dark brown to black with white to yellowish head and thorax spotted with black, immediately set about making new cases as they feed, enlarging at the top as they grow, thus accounting for the spindle shape. The caterpillar, ¾ to 1 inch long when grown, moves freely about with this bag. When it wants to eat, or to molt, which it does 4 times, it fastens the bag to a twig with a silken thread. The bagworm pupates in late summer and the black male moth, with furry body and feathered antennae, wingspread about 1 inch, flies to mate with the maggotlike yellowish female through an opening at the base of the bag. The female lays 500 to 1000 eggs in the pupal case inside the bag and then dies.

Control. When there is a light infestation, picking off the bags in winter or spring is the easiest control. Some recommend burning these; others suggest placing the bags in deep open containers near the infested trees. The larvae, unable to crawl for food, will die, but their beneficial parasites will be liberated. For heavy infestations spray in late spring, as soon as the caterpillars start feeding. Use lead arsenate, 3 to 4 level tablespoons per gallon, or malathion, chlordane, or Sevin. DDT is not effective. Sometimes woodpeckers and sapsuckers help to reduce bagworms.

BEES

Bees, of the order Hymenoptera, are tremendously important for pollination in orchard and garden. Apples rarely set fruit unless they are fertilized by pollen from some other variety. Honeybees accomplish 90 per cent of the pollen transfer in apple orchards, but bumblebees, solitary bees, and other insects also help. Pears, cherries, plums, peaches, strawberries, and some vegetables need bees for a good crop or to set seed. Commercial orchardists frequently rent hives of bees for the flowering period, and broad-spectrum insecticides such as DDT and Sevin used in the vicinity may poison the bees.

In one section of California there is a warning system, and when there is to be large-scale spraying, owners have time to remove the hives.

Even older insecticides such as lead arsenate may kill bees, and that is one reason why fruit-spray schedules are so carefully timed. The pre-pink spray is put on before blossoms open, and the calyx spray is applied when most of the petals have fallen. No poison should be used while the bees are coming to flowers for nectar.

A few bees have injurious as well as beneficial habits. Leaf-cutter and carpenter bees, in the family Aphidae, are among these.

Carpenter Bee*, *Xylocopa virginica* (Linnaeus). Often called large carpenter bee. Large, robust, about 1 inch long, similar to a bumblebee but with the upper part of the abdomen largely bare. This species excavates galleries in solid wood.

Leaf-cutter Bee, *Megachile* spp. Moderate-sized, stout-bodied, solitary bee, nesting in wood or hollow stems of woody plants. The bees are hairy, black or metallic blue, green or purple, with short, elbowed antennae. The long

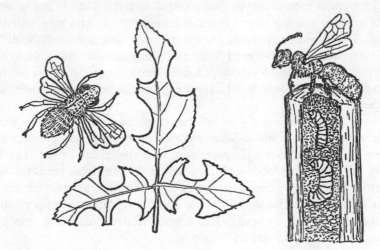

18. Leaf-cutter bee, left; small carpenter bee, right.

legs are not equipped with pollen baskets, the pollen being carried on brushes under the abdomen. All members of this group are important pollinators and many are particularly useful with alfalfa, clovers, and other forage crops. The female cuts very precise ovals and circles from margins of leaves, frequently rose leaves. The ovals line the bottom and sides of her nest; the circles cap each cell after an egg has been laid inside. These nests are in cavities of dead twigs, in broken ends of branches, or in the pithy stem of plants such as dahlia. There is no control except to cut out wilted or dying shoots containing the nests. And although rose foliage all over the country may be disfigured somewhat by these bees, one should not begrudge a few leaves required by this primarily beneficial insect. It is better to admire the perfection of their tailoring.

Small Carpenter Bee, *Ceratina* spp. These bees are known to most rose lovers as pith borers and are a source of great concern, but they are not entirely bad. There are several species, most of them black, with faint metallic highlights, and small, seldom more than ⅓ inch long. They nest in tunnels in the pith of various woody shrubs, with rose a special favorite. When the cut stem shows a hole in the pith, slitting it lengthwise usually reveals a half dozen or so yellowish, curved maggots, lined up in cavities.

Control. At spring pruning, cut rose canes below infested portions; during the season cut back a cane showing wilting or sawdust protruding from the stem. Some recommend putting a thumbtack into the end of the cut stem, or covering it with grafting wax, putty, paraffin, or tree-wound paint. Some paints, however, injure the cane, and those now available in aerosol form disfigure more than the cut end of the stem. Orange shellac is perhaps the safest and least conspicuous covering for the cut stem. My personal solution is to be meticulous about pruning and to keep a sharp watch during the season but not to paint the pruning cuts. I think it takes more time than is warranted by the amount of control effected, and too many materials are unsightly and cause the cane to die back an inch or more.

BEETLES

Beetles belong to the order Coleoptera, which means "sheath wings." This order comprises 40 per cent of all insects, with a quarter of a million species already described. More than 26,000 species occur in the United States. Some beetles are predaceous, preying on other insects, some are scavengers, cleaning up rotting animal and plant refuse, but many feed on healthy plant tissue. They are doubly injurious because both larvae and adults have chewing mouth parts.

The chief characteristic of members of the order Coleoptera is the modification of the first pair of wings into hard, tough or horny sheaths (elytra) commonly called wing covers. These meet, in most cases, in a straight line down the middle of the back and in flight are held stiffly out at the sides. All movement is by the membranous hind wings, which are folded transversely under the elytra when at rest. Some running ground beetles and some weevils lack hind wings and have the hard elytra grown together down the back.

Beetles have complete metamorphosis. The egg hatches into a soft grub, usually with 6 legs, occasionally legless, then turns into a pupa with the sacs holding the appendages freely movable, and finally transforms into the adult beetle. The mouth parts often indicate beetle habits. Short, chunky mandi-

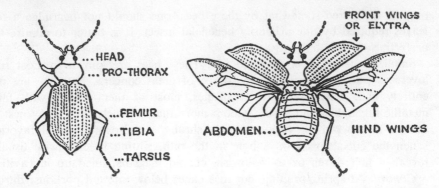

19. Diagram of a beetle with wings in normal position and spread for flight.

bles usually belong to a plant-eating species, while a predator more often has long, pointed jaws right for grasping other insects. If the mandibles lack distinct teeth and are covered with stiff hairs, the beetle is likely a harmless pollen feeder. Snout beetles and weevils have the head prolonged forward and downward into a cylindrical snout that may be shorter than the head or much longer than the body. Beetles called curculios have a long, curved snout with the mouth parts at the tip of this projection.

Adult beetles have compound eyes but no ocelli (simple eyes), while the larvae have a small group of ocelli on each side of the head but no compound eyes. The antennae have 10 to 11 segments, the tarsi 3 to 5.

There are 122 beetle families reported in the United States, divided by many technical taxonomic characters such as structure of antennae, form of legs, number of tarsal segments, mouth parts. The relatively few families considered here are those containing individuals injurious to garden plants or predators especially helpful to gardeners. They are grouped under 2 suborders.

Suborder ADEPHAGA. Predaceous beetles mostly beneficial to us; tarsi with 5 segments; antennae filiform; hind wings with veins; ventral part of first segment of abdomen divided into 2 areas by the hind coxae. The larvae are active and carnivorous; each leg has 6 segments with 2 claws at the end.

Carabidae. Ground beetles; common on surface of ground, lurking under stones and rubbish.

Cicindellidae. Tiger beetles, beautifully colored adults with ugly larvae waiting in burrows for prey. Many forms are semiaquatic.

Suborder POLYPHAGA. Beetles varying in form, habit; legs of larvae with not more than 5 segments, ending in a single claw; hind wings with reduced venation; first ventral segment of abdomen in a single piece.

Anthicidae. Antlike flower beetles. With small, antlike bodies; occasional on flowers and foliage.

Bostrichidae. False powder post beetles. Wood borers; in branches and twigs. Elongate, somewhat cylindrical, with deflexed head; ⅛ to ½ inch long; antennal club 3-segmented; abdominal sternites (segments) of about equal length.

Brentidae. Brentid beetles. Primitive weevils with long narrow body, sides almost parallel, and prothorax almost as long as the elytra; females smaller than males but with a more elongate snout, projecting straight forward.

Bruchidae. Seed beetles. Bean and pea weevils. Short, stout-bodied, mostly less than ¼ inch long; short elytra not covering tip of abdomen; short broad snouts; prominent eyes; usually gray or brown.

Buprestidae. Flatheaded or metallic wood borers. Hard-bodied, flat, with striking iridescent blue or bronze coloring; head very short; eyes large; antennae short; tarsi 5-segmented. Larvae long, legless, with small head and very broad, flat thorax; working beneath bark of various trees and shrubs.

Byturidae. Fruitworm beetles. Small, hairy, with clubbed antennae and 5-segmented tarsi, reddish yellow, brown or black. Adults feed on raspberry or blackberry flowers; larvae damage berries.

Cantharidae. Soldier beetles. Elongate, soft-bodied, similar to lightning beetles but without light-producing organs; adults often found on flowers; larvae predaceous on other insects.

Cerambycidae. Long-horned beetles or roundheaded wood borers. Very large family with all species feeding on plants, adults on flowers, foliage, or bark, larvae boring in wood. Adults are elongate, cylindrical, mostly over ½ inch long; very long filiform antennae; tarsi apparently 4-segmented, the 5th segment being small and concealed.

Chryptophagidae. Silken fungus beetles. Very small, yellowish brown with silky hairs, found under bark or in flowers but feeding on decaying matter.

Chrysomelidae. Leaf beetles. Feeding mostly on flowers and foliage; closely related to Cerambycidae but with shorter antennae; smaller, more oval in shape. Some larvae feed on foliage, others mine inside leaves, some bore in stems or feed on roots. This family includes many serious plant pests—flea beetles, Colorado potato beetle, asparagus and cucumber beetles.

Cleridae. Checkered beetles. Brightly marked, densely covered with short hairs, ⅛ to ½ inch long; predaceous as larvae and adults, preying on wood borers and on small insects in flowers.

Coccinellidae. Lady beetles. Very useful predators; small, oval, convex, often bright-colored; antennae club-shaped; tarsi 3-segmented. Larvae elongate, somewhat flattened, covered with tubercles or spines, often with colored spots.

Cucujidae. Flat bark beetles. Very flat, reddish, brownish, or yellow; found under bark; predaceous on mites and other small insects.

Curculionidae. Snout beetles, curculios, or weevils. Head prolonged into a long or short snout; clubbed and elbowed antennae arising from the snout; tarsi apparently 4-segmented. Adults drill holes in fruits, nuts, or other plant tissue; larvae feed inside fruits, buds, nuts, seeds, or stems.

Dermestidae. Dermestid or skin beetles. Feeding on leather, silk, rugs, etc. but many species feeding on flowers. Small, oval, convex, with short, clubbed antennae, 1/16 to ½ inch long, usually hairy or covered with scales; larvae brownish with long hairs.

Elateridae. Click beetles, wireworms. Having a special joint at union of prothorax and mesothorax, enabling them to snap back into position when placed on their backs. Body elongate, usually parallel-sided, rounded at each end; eyes large; antennae serrate; tarsi 5-segmented; mostly black or brown; feeding on flowers or foliage. The slender, hard wireworm larvae work on seeds and roots.

Histeridae. Hister beetles. Scavengers on dung, fungi, decaying matter but also predaceous on other insects. Small, broadly oval, usually shiny black; cut off square at the apex, exposing 1 or 2 abdominal segments.

Lampyridae. Fireflies, lightning bugs. Soft-bodied, elongate, with pronotum extending over the head; flattish, with luminous segments near the end of the abdomen; antennae slender; tarsi 5-segmented. Larvae (glowworms) are predaceous on smaller insects, slugs, and snails.

Languriidae. Lizard beetles. Narrow, elongate, with reddish pronotum and black elytra; feeding on leaves and stems of goldenrod, clovers, various other common plants and weeds.

Lucanidae. Stag beetles, pinching bugs. Large, brownish, with mandibles on the male half as long as the body and branched like antlers; antennae elbowed; attracted to lights at night. Larvae live in decaying wood.

Lycidae. Net-winged beetles. Elongate, soft-winged, with network of raised lines on the elytra; often found in woods on trunks and foliage but feeding on decaying matter and other insects. Larvae are predaceous.

Lyctidae. Powder post beetles. So named because they bore into dry wood and reduce it to powder, occurring also in woody fungi and dead limbs of trees. Similar to members of Bostrichidae.

Meloidae. Blister beetles. Elongate, soft-bodied, usually cylindrical; large head, set off from thorax; fairly short filiform antennae; 5 segments in tarsi of front and middle legs, 4 in hind tarsi; body fluid containing cantharidin, causing blisters. Adults are injurious, larvae somewhat beneficial.

Mordellidae. Tumbling flower beetles. Usually small, with wedgeshaped, humpback body, head bent down, abdomen pointed and extending beyond tips of elytra; black, covered with dense white hairs sometimes making a white pattern. Often found in flowers and some forms predaceous on small insects; tumbling when disturbed.

Nitulidae. Sap beetles. Feeding on dried fruit and sap; usually small, elongate or oval, active; elytra shorter than abdomen; head large; eyes conspicuous; antennae club-shaped, 11-segmented; tarsi 5-segmented. Attracted to fermenting or souring fluids.

Oedermeridae. Oedermerid beetles. Slender, soft-bodied, occasional on flowers and foliage; eastern forms yellow brown with tip of elytra black; western forms bright blue with red pronotum, common on ceanothus.

Ostomatidae. Grain and bark-gnawing beetles. Head and pronotum large, and union between pronotum and elytra narrow; larvae feed on grain and also other insects in grain.

Phalacridae. Shiny flower beetles. Minute, round, shiny, convex, very small, mostly dark brown. Quite common on flowers of goldenrod and other composites. Larvae develop in heads of flowers.

Scarabaeidae. Scarabs. A very large family with some dung beetles beneficial as scavengers but with many plant feeders—chafers, June beetles, Japanese beetle etc. Adults are oval, robust, with short, usually elbowed antennae, having clubs made of several thin plates pressed together; tarsi 5-segmented; larvae are plump, whitish, usually C-shaped.

Scolytidae (Ipidae). Bark beetles, engraver beetles. Mining on the surface of hardwood and making patterns under the bark. Small cylindrical beetles, brownish or black, with a small head and large first-thoracic segment; antennae short, with a club; tarsi apparently 4-segmented. This family also includes ambrosia or timber beetles which penetrate sapwood and heartwood of dead trees and feed on fungi growing on the walls of their tunnels.

Silphidae. Carrion beetles. Beneficial insects working on bodies of dead animals, sometimes burying small mice by excavating under the body. Large, often brightly colored, soft, somewhat flattened; antennae clubbed; tarsi 5-segmented.

Staphylinidae. Rove beetles. A large group of predators; rather flat, elongate; head as wide as thorax; fore wings much shortened; tip of abdomen elevated when disturbed; mandibles long, slender, sharp, sometimes crossing in front of the head.

Stylopidae. Twisted-wing insects, placed by some in a separate order, Strepsiptera. Minute parasites on other insects, resembling beetles; females wingless, often legless, males free-living, winged.

Tenebrionidae. Darkling beetles. Similar to ground beetles, more common in arid areas under stones and rubbish. Some species are destructive pests of stored grain and flour, the larvae being called mealworms.

In considering the specific beetles, I am following the entirely artifical system set up for this book as a whole—i.e., treating them alphabetically under approved common names. If a beetle is officially named a borer, from its larval state, then it is discussed under Borers; if its approved name is curculio, then it is considered under Curculios; and if it is called a weevil, it is treated under Weevils.

Alaska Spruce Beetle*, *Dendroctonus borealis* Hopkins. Bark beetle in British Columbia and Alaska, sometimes killing Sitka, Engelmann and Canada spruces; black, or with reddish-brown elytra, ¼ inch long.

Alder Bark Beetle*, *Alniphagus aspericollis* (LeConte). Commonly destructive to western alders, attacking weakened or dying trees. Small, black, robust beetles, ⅛ inch long, bore through bark in pairs, usually at base of branches, and construct longitudinal egg galleries 2 to 5 inches long. Larvae pupate in the soft inner bark. There are 2 generations a year.

Alder Flea Beetle*, *Altica ambiens* LeConte. Feeding on foliage of alders, also poplar and willow, from Maine to New Mexico, normally scarce but periodically epidemic and defoliating the host. Color cobalt to greenish blue, shiny; ⅕ inch long; elytra wider at the base, finely punctate. Adults hibernate in protected places, lay orange eggs on leaves in spring. Larvae, dark brown with black heads, eat everything but veins in July and August. Pupation is in the ground. There is 1 generation in Maine, sometimes 2 farther south. Spray ornamentals with DDT or lead arsenate.

Alfalfa Snout Beetle*, *Brachyrhinus ligustici* (Linnaeus). A European pest first noted in this country near Oswego, New York, in 1933 feeding on raspberries. Since then it has been found on rhubarb and strawberry, as well as alfalfa, its chief host.

Allegheny Spruce Beetle*, *Dendroctonus punctatus* LeConte. A bark beetle.

Ambrosia Beetles, *Xyleborus, Platypus* and other genera. Small, cylindrical, brown to black insects resembling bark beetles, making pinholes in dead wood, occasionally in weakened or dying fruit and shade trees, including avocado. The beetles live on fungi cultured in their tunnels.

American Aspen Beetle*, *Gonioctena americana* (Schaeffer). A leaf beetle.

Apple Twig Beetle*, *Stephanoderes obscurus* (Fabricius). A bark beetle; borer in dying apple bark or dead twigs.

Argus Tortoise Beetle*, *Chelymorpha cassidea* (Fabricius). A tortoise-shaped, yellow to bright-red beetle with black spots, very convex, ⅓ inch long, with long marginal spines holding a mass of excrement. This species is present throughout the East and as far west as New Mexico, feeding on morning-glory, moonflower, sweetpotato, and related plants. Spray or dust with malathion.

Arizona Pine Beetle*, *Dendroctonus arizonicus* Hopkins. Dark-brown bark beetle, making transversely winding egg galleries in yellow pine.

Ash Bark Beetle, *Leperisinus aculeatus* Say. Common wherever ash grows but attacking only weakened and dying trees. The beetle is very small, dark brown, with tan scales. The **White-banded Ash Beetle** (*L. fasciatus*) is also small, black with white markings.

Ash-gray Blister Beetle*, *Epicauta fabricii* (LeConte). A common eastern species but abundant as far west as Arizona and Idaho. Destructive to forest and forage crops and to young trees in nurseries; recently reported defoliating small honeylocust trees in Virginia. The larvae feed on grasshopper eggs. See Black Blister Beetle for life history and control.

Asiatic Beetle. See Oriental Beetle.

Asiatic Garden Beetle*, *Maladera* (*Autoserica*) *castanea* (Arrow). Native of the Orient, first found in New Jersey in 1921 and now serious along the Atlantic seaboard from Massachusetts through South Carolina, also present in Ohio near Lake Erie, and in West Virginia. Apparently this beetle does not survive in regions of low summer rainfall. It resembles the Japanese beetle in shape and size but it is a uniform cinnamon-brown and comes out to feed *only at night*.

It is attracted to lights, bangs into screens, flies into automobiles. About 80 plants are attacked, including: flowers, aster, azalea, chrysanthemum, dahlia, delphinium, rose, strawflower, sunflower, viburnum, zinnia; for vegetables, beet, carrot, corn, eggplant, kohlrabi, parsnip, pepper, and turnips; fruits, cherry, peach, and strawberry. The beetles strip the foliage, especially that near the ground, sometimes severely damaging nursery seedlings of pine, hemlock, yew, barberry, and others. The larvae cut grass roots by their feeding, causing brown patches in lawns, and may feed on roots of many garden plants.

There is only 1 generation a year. Eggs are laid in the soil, at depths to 4 inches, from mid-July to mid-August. They hatch in about 10 days and the grubs start feeding on roots. In mid-October they move down several more inches in the soil for the winter, becoming active again, in the top 5 inches, in mid-April. The grubs pupate in June and the adults emerge in about 10 days, being most abundant between mid-July and mid-August. Full-grown larvae are grayish with light-brown heads, ¾ inch long, found in a curved position. They differ from Japanese-beetle grubs chiefly in having the spines at the tip of the abdomen arranged in a semicircle rather than a V.

Control. Grubproof lawns, as for Japanese beetles, with granular chlordane or dieldrin. The bacterial milky disease has some effect on this species as well as on Japanese-beetle grubs. Spray foliage with DDT, Sevin, or lead arsenate.

Asparagus Beetle*, *Crioceris asparagi* (Linnaeus). Introduced from Europe about 1856 and now present in most asparagus regions. The beetles are slender, ¼ inch long, metallic blue-black with 3 yellow squares along each wing cover; reddish margins, prothorax, and head (Plate IV). Adults winter in protected places around the garden, feed on asparagus shoots when they come up in spring, and lay dark-brown eggs attached at one end. These hatch into olive-green or dark-gray, soft, wrinkled larvae with black heads, ½ inch long, which gnaw stems and leaves for 10 to 12 days.

Asparagus can be almost defoliated and is often stained by a dark fluid. The larvae pupate in cells in the soil. The life cycle takes 3 to 8 weeks and there are at least 2 generations in the North, 3 or more in the South.

Control. Use Sevin, rotenone, or malathion in the cutting field; after harvest, dust with 10 per cent DDT or with calcium or lead arsenate. Lady-beetle larvae and predaceous plant bugs keep this beetle in bounds; a chalcid wasp is a parasite. See also Spotted Asparagus Beetle.

Aspen Leaf Beetle*, *Chrysomela crotchi* Brown. On cottonwood.

Banded Cucumber Beetle*, *Diabrotica balteata* LeConte. A southern pest, from South Carolina around to California, primarily on beans, also on soy-beans, and not so important on cucumbers. The adult is light green with 3 bands of darker green.

Bean Leaf Beetle*, *Cerotoma trifurcata* (Forster). Abundant in south-eastern states, occasional elsewhere. The beetle is yellow buff to dull red, ¼ inch long, with 3 or 4 spots on the inner edge of wing covers and a black band near outer margins. The adults chew holes in leaves, feeding from the underside, but slender white larvae feed on roots and nodules, chewing stems under the soil line, sometimes girdling them. There are 1 or 2 broods a year on beans, peas, cowpeas, soybeans and various weeds. See Mexican Bean Beetle for control.

Beet Leaf Beetle*, *Erynephala puncticollis* (Say). A western pest now extending east to the Atlantic States, injuring table and sugar beets, spinach, clovers and other legumes. The adult is ⅓ inch long, dull yellow with black margins and black spots on the thorax. The grayish or olive-brown larvae are marked with raised tubercles and yellow spots resembling those of lady beetles. Both larvae and adults feed on foliage, with the former more injurious. Destroying weed hosts and cleaning up winter shelters may be sufficient control.

Birch Bark Beetle*, *Dryocoetes betulae* Hopkins. Breeding in beech, wild cherry and red gum as well as birch, with irregular egg galleries.

Black-bellied Clerid, *Enocleris lecontei* (Wolcott). One of the checkered beetle predators of bark beetles.

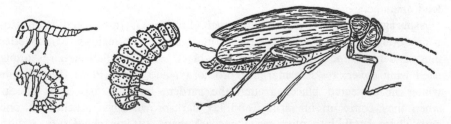

20. *Black blister beetle: triungulin, instars 2 and 6, and adult.*

Black Blister Beetle*, *Epicauta pennsylvanica* (De Geer). An all-black species common in the East. A special pest of asters and Japanese anemone in late summer but also feeding on flowers and foliage of calendula, chrysanthemum, gladiolus, clematis, dahlia, dianthus, delphinium, ivy, phlox, zinnia; and may be abundant on corn. This species is typical of all blister beetles. They are rather long, ½ to ¾ inch, slender, with the prothorax narrower than the soft and flexible wing covers. The name comes from the cantharidin in their bodies; this will blister the skin if beetles are crushed upon it. This powerful agent, obtained from the "Spanish Fly," a European blister beetle, was formerly used in much the same fashion as a mustard plaster and also as an aphrodisiac. Cantharidin still has a few uses in modern medicine and animal breeding.

Other names for blister beetles are Old-fashioned Potato Bug and Yankee Bug. Their life history is peculiar, to say the least. They differ from most beetles in being predaceous, and therefore helpful, in the larval state, but plant-eating as adults. The beetle winters as a partly transformed larva, pseudopupa, in a cell in the soil. More than one winter may be spent in this suspended state, but some spring the pseudopupa molts, acquires functional legs, moves about for a while, then goes into the true pupal state, which lasts about 2 weeks. The beetles appear in swarms in June or July or later and feed gregariously. The females lay yellow eggs in clusters of about 100 in holes in the soil. In 10 to 21 days active, strong-jawed larvae start burrowing through the soil until they find the egg mass of a grasshopper. They gnaw into the egg pod and eat the eggs. The larvae molt 4 times, going through a series of changes in form. The first larval state is called a triungulin and the active triungulins specialize in eating eggs of the two-striped and differential grasshoppers. Some ascend to flowers and may be carried thence by bees to their nests. When the triungulin sheds its skin after the first molt, it looks more like a grub. After the last molt the larva burrows into the soil to form the cell in which it turns into the hard-shelled, immobile pseudopupa.

There are about 250 species of blister beetles in this country. They are black or gray, brown or yellow, sometimes striped or margined. They feed on many vegetables, flowers, young trees and vines.

Control. Spray or dust with DDT; handpick beetles, but be sure to wear gloves. Cover valuable ornamentals with mosquito netting if necessary in late summer.

Black Hills Beetle*, *Dendroctonus ponderosae* Hopkins. The worst enemy of ponderosa pine in the Rocky Mountain region, attacking other pines when epidemic. In such cases it kills trees of all sizes and conditions, although normally it infests only weakened trees. The beetles are reddish brown, up to ⅜ inch. Egg galleries are longitudinal and straight; the larval mines are short, broad, packed with reddish boring dust. As with all bark beetles, infested wood should be burned, normal trees kept growing vigorously.

Black Lady Beetle*, *Rhizobius ventralis* (Erichson). Black, with reddish abdomen, ⅛ inch long, found in egg masses of mealybugs and under shells of scales. Introduced from Australia in 1892; a valuable destroyer of black scale.

Black-legged Tortoise Beetle*, *Jonthonota nigripes* (Oliver). Golden yellow with 3 black dots arranged in a triangle on each wing cover. Larvae are straw yellow with 2 dark spots behind the head (Plate XI). See Tortoise Beetles.

Black Turpentine Beetle, *Dendroctonus terebrans* (Olivier). An eastern bark beetle working near the base of pine and spruce, especially on pitch pine. In some areas 10 to 25 per cent of trees are killed in a year. Very broad (½ to 1 inch) egg galleries extend downward from entrance holes a few inches to several feet. Beetles are ⅕ to ⅜ inch long, robust, reddish brown to black. The larvae have prominent spines on 8th and 9th abdominal segments.

Control. Spray base of trees with benzene hexachloride, 1 per cent by weight in No. 2 fuel oil, after removing rough bark. Salvage attacked trees as soon as possible and spray stumps.

Blueberry Flea Beetle, *Altica sylvia* Malloch. Reported as causing heavy damage in Maine. See also Flea Beetles.

Bumble Flower Beetle*, *Euphoria inda* (Linnaeus). An eastern species ranging west into New Mexico. The adult resembles a bumblebee, is ½ inch long, broadly oval, yellowish brown mottled with black. It feeds on ears of ripening corn, sometimes on apples, grapes, and peaches. Larvae develop in dung and rotting fruit, which should be cleaned up.

Cabbage Flea Beetle, *Phyllotreta cruciferae* (Goeze). An introduced beetle recorded on cabbage in Delaware and Wisconsin.

California Five-spined Ips*, *Ips confusus* (LeConte). Small engraver beetle on pines.

Caragana Blister Beetle*, *Epicauta subglabra* (Fall). Defoliating caragana stock in nurseries. See also Black Blister Beetle.

Carrot Beetle*, *Bothynus gibbosus* (De Geer). Occurring over most of the country except far northern states. The beetles, ½ inch long, broad, reddish brown with stout legs, gouge out roots and base of stems of amaranthus, carrot, beet, celery, corn, cotton, dahlia, elm, Japanese iris, lily, oak, parsnip, potato, sunflower and weeds. The nocturnal adults winter in the soil, laying eggs there in spring. The larvae—bluish white, curved, with brown heads—feed on roots of grasses and other plants. There is only one generation. Clean up decaying plant material. Use chlordane dust in soil for grubs, 4 pounds of 6 per cent dust to each 1000 square feet, and work it into the top 3 inches.

Cedar Bark Beetle, *Phloeosinus cupressi* Hopkins. Mining inner bark and girdling twigs of weakened Monterey and other cypresses and oriental and incense cedar, and redcedar. Another species, *P. dentatus* (Say) injures western juniper, Alaska cedar and redcedar, making larval galleries at right angles to egg galleries. The **Western Cedar Bark Beetle***, *P. punctatus* Lee, infests normal, injured, and dead cedars and giant arborvitae in the Pacific Northwest.

Cereal Leaf Beetle, *Oulema melanopa* (Linnaeus). A European pest, potentially destructive, reported first from Michigan in 1962, also present in Indiana. Known areas are under quarantine and everyone is asked to watch for this beetle, which has caused 50 per cent loss in Europe. The adult is ¼ inch long, with black head, reddish brown midsection, and metallic blue back. The larvae, dark brown, shaped like potato bugs, pupate in the soil. This beetle feeds heavily on corn and grains. It is forbidden to move from quarantined areas grains, grass, or straw fodder.

Cherry Leaf Beetle*, *Galerucella cavicollis* (LeConte). Present in the East in large numbers at intervals of several years. Adults are small red beetles, less than ¼ inch long, feeding on foliage of cherry and peach, sometimes plum, occasionally apple. Brown larvae with yellow and black spots feed only on wild cherry. There is only one generation a year, and attacks are so sudden that protective sprays are usually too late.

Chinese Rose Beetle*, *Adoretus sinicus* Burmeister. A Hawaiian pest, frequently intercepted in shipments destined for California; in flowers, including orchids, in stems, and plant cuttings.

Clematis Blister Beetle*, *Epicauta cinerea* (Forster). Gray, with a yellowish tinge, found on clematis, sometimes aster, verbena and other ornamentals and on potatoes. See also Black Blister Beetle.

Colorado Pine Beetle*, Larger Mexican Pine Beetle*, *Dendroctonus parallelocollis* Chapuis. (*D. approximatus*). Roundheaded, shining reddish brown, ⅓ inch long. On pines in the Southwest, attacking injured trees and preventing recovery.

Colorado Potato Beetle*, *Leptinotarsa decemlineata* (Say). An example of a native insect which suddenly became dangerous to cultivated plants (Plate IV). For many years this beetle lived on the sandbur weed on high plateaus at the base of the Rocky Mountains. It was described in 1824 and had probably been around as an obscure beetle for a long time. But the pioneer settlers of the West brought with them the potato, which the beetle found much to its taste. In a short time this almost unknown insect became, under the title of "potato bug," the best-known insect in America. It migrated eastward at the rate of about 85 miles a year, following potato plantings, appearing in Nebraska in 1859, Illinois in 1864, Ohio in 1869, reaching the Atlantic coast by 1874. Eventually it made its way to Europe, where it is well established in France, Holland, Belgium, Spain, parts of Italy, and in other countries. It appeared in England but was eradicated there. It is now a problem throughout the United States except in parts of Florida, Nevada, and California.

The Colorado potato beetle is hard-shelled, very broad (⅜ by ¼ inch), very convex, yellow with 10 longitudinal lines and black spots on the thorax.

It winters as an adult in the ground, emerging as soon as potatoes are up to deposit bright orange-yellow eggs in small clusters on undersurface of leaves. These hatch in 4 to 7 days into very humpbacked, fat red grubs which feed for 2 or 3 weeks, then pupate in the ground. Beetles emerge in another week or two to lay eggs for the second generation. Adults appear early in autumn to feed for a time, then to enter the soil for hibernation. In the South there may be 3 generations, in the extreme North, only 1. Both beetles and larvae completely ravage potato foliage, often destroying whole fields. Although potato is preferred, the beetles may go to other members of the nightshade family, such as eggplant, tomato, pepper, petunia, nicotiana, groundcherry.

Control. Handpicking was the first control measure tried, and most farm boys a century ago had to pick their quota of potato bugs. Paris green was the first poison, developed in 1865 specifically for this pest. This was followed by London purple, calcium or lead arsenate, and sometimes cryolite. DDT marked a great advance in control and has been widely used as a spray— 2 to 3 pounds of 50 per cent wettable in 100 gallons of water—or as a dust—3 per cent in the East, 5 per cent in the West. Other presentday recommendations for farmers include dieldrin, Guthion, and Thiodan. Home gardeners should spray with methoxychlor or Sevin, materials safer to handle. Make the first application when potatoes are only a few inches high. Keep foliage covered during periods of most rapid growth.

Columbian Timber Beetle*, *Corythylus columbianus* Hopkins. One of the ambrosia beetles, boring in the bark of living hardwoods, including red and silver maples. A stain, produced by the fungi on which the beetles feed, extends 3 to 6 inches above and below each egg gallery.

Convergent Lady Beetle. See under Lady Beetles.

Corn Flea Beetle*, *Chaetocnema pulicaria* Melsheimer. A small, brassy beetle more dangerous for its ability to disseminate bacterial wilt of corn (Stewart's disease) than for its feeding on corn foliage, which results in small perforations. The beetles inoculate the corn with bacteria which have overwintered in their alimentary tracts. Control with DDT or malathion.

Corn Sap Beetle*, *Carpophilus dimidiatus* (Fabricius). A very small brown scavenger beetle that also eats corn kernels, getting into the ear when the husk is loosened by birds, or following after earworms. It is also a pest of dates and other dried fruit. Spray corn with malathion 6 days after silks appear and repeat 10 days later.

Corn Silk Beetle*, *Luperodes brunneus* (Crotch). A chrysomelid (leaf beetle) feeding on corn silks.

Cottonwood Leaf Beetle*, *Chrysomela scripta* Fabricius. Occurring from coast to coast, often more injurious to willows than to cottonwood and other poplars. The beetle, ¼ inch long, has black head and thorax, the latter bordered with orange red, and gold wing covers with a purplish line at the inner edge, each bearing 7 purple-black spots. The larvae are black when young, later dirty yellow, with black legs, brown heads. They emit drops of pungent milky fluid when disturbed. They skeletonize leaves and may partially defoliate trees, especially in the West. Basket willows are particularly subject to attack. The pupae hang downward from the trees. Spray with lead arsenate or DDT early in the season when larvae are young.

Cranberry Beetle, *Lichnanthe vulpina* (Hentz). One of several beetle grubs working on roots, this species causes a serious annual crop reduction in Massachusetts. Most grubs can be killed by treating bogs with dieldrin after harvest.

Cuban May Beetle, *Phyllophaga bruneri* Chapin. A scarab beetle from Cuba, first found in Florida in 1959 and now common on 22 species of host plants in the vicinity of Miami. The adults are smaller than most May beetles, under ½ inch; light golden tan with a slight metallic luster; antennae with 9 segments (other Phyllophaga species in the U.S. have 10-segmented antennae); strictly nocturnal. The larvae are C-shaped white grubs feeding on roots of grasses, especially St. Augustine grass. Preferred host of the adult is Florida trema (*Trema micrantha*). It also infests satinwood and mahogany, two other Florida natives, and shaving-brush tree, pecan, bauhinia, golden shower, senna, royal poinciana, coral bean, madre, Chinese hibiscus, Spanish lime, and sapote. DDT is fairly effective as a spray for adults; control of grubs is difficult.

Darkling Beetles. Black or brown nocturnal beetles, common in the West, acting as scavengers, but sometimes becoming serious pests. The **Small Darkling Ground Beetle,** *Metoponium abnorme* (LeConte) is smooth, black or dark brown, ⅓ inch long, with legs slightly reddish. It may injure grapevine buds, bark of young citrus trees, fruit of strawberries and tomatoes. Another species, *Coniontis subpubescens* LeConte, shining black and brown, ⅓ inch long, flies into sugar-beet fields and sometimes attacks young avocados.

Desert Corn Flea Beetle*, *Chaetocnema ectypa* Horn. Very small, metallic bronze, injuring corn, sorghum, small grains in the arid Southwest, breeding on wild grasses. The adults feed on foliage, the grubs on roots.

Diabrotica Beetles. The name popularly given to the spotted species of cucumber beetles when they infest flowers in the garden. See Western Spotted Cucumber Beetle.

Douglas-fir Beetle*, *Dendroctonus pseudotsugae* Hopkins. The most important bark beetle enemy of Douglas-fir, also attacking western larch and big-cone spruce. The small, reddish to dark-brown beetle, ⅕ inch long, covered with hairs, usually works in injured or dying trees but may feed on healthy specimens. Keep trees growing vigorously; cut down seriously weakened trees. In forests, fire-injured timber should be salvaged rapidly to avoid build-up of beetle populations.

Douglas-fir Engraver*, *Scolytus unispinosus* LeConte. Present in the West on weakened Douglas-fir and big-cone spruce. The beetle is very small, shiny black, with a stout spine.

Dried-fruit Beetle*, *Carpophilus hemipterus* (Linnaeus). A small, broad, flat beetle, brown with pale spots, elytra shorter than body. This is one of the scavenger beetles, a special pest of dried fruit, figs, and dates, found on any fermenting tree fruit in orchards, distributing fig smut and other diseases; reported on orange blossoms. Found chiefly in warm climates—California and the Gulf States. Dusting with 5 per cent malathion helps to control the beetles, as does prompt collection of all fallen fruit and destruction of culls. Many beetles can be attracted to traps baited with fermenting fruit. Packages of dried fruits can be fumigated.

Dusky Sap Beetle*, *Carpophila lugubris* Murray. In corn ears and tassels, sometimes damaging uninjured sweet corn but usually associated with damage by other insects.

Eastern Larch Beetle*, *Dendroctonus simplex* LeConte. A small, dark-red to brown beetle infesting dying or injured living larches; no other host. The bark galleries are long, longitudinal, and slightly winding.

Eastern Spruce Beetle*, *Dendroctonus piceaperda* Hopkins. A most injurious eastern bark beetle, killing native red, white, and black spruces. The adult is ¼ inch long, black with reddish-brown wing covers. The female, after making a 6-inch egg gallery in one tree, may repeat in another. Red boring dust, pitch tubes on the bark, fading and dropping of needles indicate beetles at work.

Eggplant Flea Beetle*, *Epitrix fuscula* Crotch. Very small, 1/16 inch, black, riddling foliage of eggplant. Control with DDT or Sevin.

Elm Calligrapha*, *Calligrapha scalaris* (LeConte). Also known as Lin-

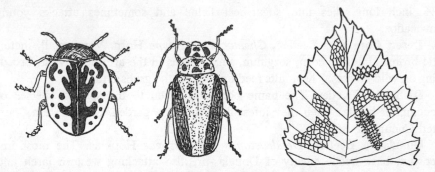

21. Elm calligrapha, left; elm leaf beetle, right.

den Leaf Beetle. The beautifully colored adult feeds on elm, linden, alder, and willow. It is oval, convex, ⅜ inch long; head and thorax dark coppery green; wing covers yellowish with a pattern of 2 branched stripes down the inside and 11 green dots. The larvae are dirty white with yellow heads, humped like the Colorado potato beetle. Both larvae and adults feed on foliage. Spray with lead arsenate or DDT in midsummer.

Elm Flea Beetle, *Altica ulmi* Woods. Very small, metallic blue or green; larvae and adults feeding on elm foliage in eastern states south to Florida.

Elm Leaf Beetle*, *Galerucella luteola* (Müller). A very serious elm pest, import from Europe, first found near Baltimore, Maryland, in 1838, apparently having arrived here some years before that. The beetle attacks American, English, Scotch, Chinese, and Camperdown elms but does not much bother slippery, rock, and winged elms. It is present throughout the United States, but some areas are more heavily infested than others.

The beetles are about ¼ inch long, rather slender, yellow to olive green with a dark line near the outer edge of each wing cover (Plate VI). As they grow older and get ready to hibernate, they darken so that the lines are scarcely visible. Hordes of sluggish beetles crawl into houses in late summer, often through cracks around cellar windows and doors. The elm leaf beetle is chiefly a pest in towns and cities where buildings offer dry winter hiding places.

The adults come out from attics and cellars in early spring, mate, and start eating small holes in elm leaves as they unfold. During late May and early June (in the vicinity of New York City) they lay clusters of lemon-shaped yellow eggs, 5 to 25 in a cluster, on underside of leaves. The egg-laying period may last several weeks, until 500 or more eggs have been deposited. These hatch in 5 or 6 days into ½-inch-long larvae. They are yellow but so striped and spotted with black that they appear dark. The larvae skeletonize the leaves, eating everything but veins and upper cuticle. Maturing in 15 to 20 days, each larva drops or crawls to the ground and transforms into a yellow pupa at the base of the tree. Beetles emerge in 6 to 10 days to lay eggs for a second generation. The number of generations depends on the season and locality. There are usually 2, sometimes 1 and a partial 2nd, or 2 and a partial 3rd. In California, where this beetle is a most important pest, there may be 4 generations.

Unsprayed trees are covered with brown leaves which look like lace or are completely defoliated by midsummer, becoming a terrible eyesore. Often the elms put out new leaves in late summer, a devitalizing process. Complete defoliation for 3 consecutive years may result in death. Weakened trees are host to elm bark beetles carrying spores of the Dutch elm disease fungus, so neglect of the leaf beetle may have tragic results.

Control. DDT in a hydraulic spray, 2 pounds of 50 per cent wettable powder per 100 gallons of water, gives excellent control of the leaf beetle but may be followed by a tremendous build-up of mites, which turn foliage dusty, and often by a marked increase in aphid and scale populations. DDT in a mist blower, 6 per cent emulsion, does not have quite such disastrous aftereffects. Many arborists continue to use lead arsenate, 4 pounds per 100 gallons of water, plus 1 pint of fish oil or other suitable sticker. This has no such harmful effect as DDT on the beneficial insects that keep mites, aphids, and scales in check. It is quite satisfactory if applied early enough. Two sprays are preferable: one, which will also take care of cankerworms, is applied when the leaves are nearly expanded and overwintering beetles are starting to feed; the second, is applied when eggs are hatching, about 3 weeks later. If only one spray is possible, it should be in late May or early June (in the New York area).

Engelmann Spruce Beetle*, *Dendroctonus engelmanni* Hopkins. A small, ¼-inch dark reddish-brown bark beetle, with sparse long hairs, at intervals vastly destructive to Engelmann spruce, sometimes damaging other spruces and lodgepole pine in the vicinity. Found throughout the Rocky Mountain region, preferring mature trees and infesting the lower parts of trees. The beetles breed in forests on windfall trees and may reach epidemic proportions. In 1949 in Colorado the air was full of beetles. A fraction that fell in a small lake formed a drift of dead beetles a foot deep, 6 feet wide, and 2 miles long. The survivors killed 400,000 previously uninfested trees in a mass attack. Large-scale treatment has consisted of spraying the lower 30 to 35 feet of tree boles with orthodichlorobenzene or ethylene dibromide emulsion or oil solution. Woodpeckers have at times greatly reduced the beetle population. Very low temperatures kill most of the beetles above the snow line. Rapid salvage of wind-thrown or damaged timber is the best prevention.

European Chafer*, *Amphimallon majalis* (Razoumowski). A European beetle first noted in New York in 1940, now present also in Massachusetts, Connecticut, New Jersey, and West Virginia, despite quarantines against it. The European chafer causes a turf injury similar to that of Japanese beetles. It has a similar life history. The adult, a typical scarab, is light brown or tan, with dark bands at the inner edge of wing covers, oval, ½ inch long. It feeds on leaves of some trees at dusk, but this injury is negligible. Chief damage is from grubs, which prefer grass roots but also feed on roots of chrysanthemum, strawberry, gladiolus, and evergreen seedlings. The grubs—C-shaped, white with brown head, ¾ inch long when grown—burrow below the frost line for winter, resuming feeding before pupation in spring. The beetles start emerging from soil in mid-June.

Control. Federal and state quarantines restrict movements of plants, sod, soil and other material which might harbor the beetles. But the adults can fly 2 miles, so peripheral spread from infested areas is to be expected. Turf can be treated with chlordane or dieldrin as for Japanese beetle grubs.

European Ground Beetle, *Calosoma sycophanta* Linnaeus. Imported from Europe to aid in control of gypsy and brown-tail moths. It is a brilliant iridescent golden green with a dark-blue thorax, about 1¼ inches long. Adults hibernate in cells in the ground, emerging in late spring. Eggs are laid in the soil in June and July. The active larvae—elongate, dark, chitinized—run over the ground or climb trees in search of caterpillars or pupae. Do not destroy this beautiful friend.

European Spruce Beetle*, *Dendroctonus micans* (Kugelann).

Eyed Click Beetle*, *Alaus oculatus* (Linnaeus). A very large, shiny black beetle with 2 conspicuous eyelike spots on the thorax, sometimes called the Owl Beetle. Like all click beetles, this can snap itself upright when placed on its back. The larval stage is a wireworm. The adult is carnivorous and is often found in trunks of old apple trees.

False Potato Beetle*, *Leptinotarsa juncta* (Germar). Plentiful on potatoes in Alabama home plantings; related to the Colorado potato beetle.

False Powder Post Beetle. See Branch and Twig Borer.

Fiery Hunter*, *Calosoma candidum* (Fabricius). A friend; a black ground beetle with 3 rows of large copper-colored pits in each wing cover. It is often seen searching for cutworms, potato beetle grubs, and other succulent larvae. It secretes a fiery, burning acid.

Fig Beetle, *Cotinus texana* Casey. Also called Green Fruit or Peach Beetle. A large, flat, broad beetle over 1 inch long, usually green varying to copper and violet; a fruit pest in Arizona, New Mexico and Texas. It prefers ripe peaches but also feeds on apricot, apple, fir, grape, muskmelon, nectarine, pear, tomato, and fruit of cacti. The larvae breed in dung of old corrals, which should be thoroughly cleaned in late winter and early spring.

Fir Engraver*, *Scolytus ventralis* LeConte. On all true firs in the West, also Douglas-fir, Engelmann spruce, and mountain hemlock but especially destructive to white fir in California. Mature trees are infested, mostly in the upper part of the bole, by typical brownish bark beetles, ⅛ inch long. Narrow egg galleries extend across the grain.

FIREFLIES. Lightning Bugs or Glowworms, family Lampyridae, known for their luminescence at night. They are a delight to see and are equally delightful to gardeners for their predilection for slugs and snails, sometimes cutworms. Adults, larvae, and eggs are all luminous in some species. True nocturnal fireflies are found chiefly east of the Rockies. In the West the forms are of the glowworm type; the female is like the larva but emits light; the male has wings but is not phosphorescent.

Fireflies are soft-bodied beetles of medium size, with light-producing organs on the underside of the abdomen. According to Fabre, the contortions of the female which result in flashes of light are signals for the male. But because the light is often present in larvae as well as adults, its exact function is in doubt. It is produced by oxidation of a substance called luciferin in a heatless reaction.

FLEA BEETLES. A very large group of very small leaf beetles, family Chrysomelidae, named for their habit of jumping like fleas when disturbed. They usually feed on plants early in the season, often on seedlings set out from greenhouses, sometimes on ornamentals like forget-me-not, perforating foliage with tiny shot holes. The various species go under such names as corn, eggplant, grape, horseradish, mint, pale-striped, potato, sinuate-striped, spinach, strawberry and sweetpotato flea beetles, some of which are

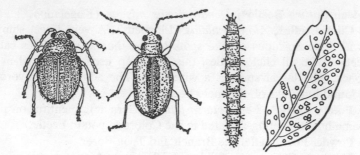

22. *Potato flea beetle, left; pale-striped flea beetle, right, and leaf showing typical shot holes.*

treated separately in this section. Flea beetles can be controlled with DDT, lead arsenate, Sevin, or rotenone.

Fruit Tree Bark Beetle. See Shot-hole Borer, under Borers.

Fuller Rose Beetle*, *Pantomorus godmani* (Crotch). A grayish brown weevil, probably from South America; ⅓ inch long with a short, broad snout, a white diagonal stripe across each wing cover, eating ragged areas

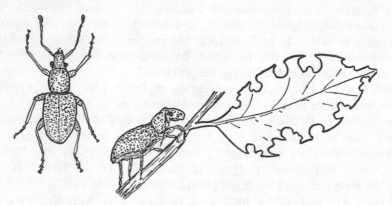

23. *Fuller rose beetle and feeding pattern on leaf.*

from margins of leaves at night. A greenhouse pest in the North, it is numerous outdoors in the South and in California, feeding on abutilon, acacia, apple, apricot, avocado, azalea, bean, begonia, blackberry, camellia, canna, cape jasmine, carnation, chrysanthemum, cissus, citron, crapemyrtle, currant, deutzia, dracaena, fuchsia, gardenia, geranium, goldenglow, grapefruit, hibiscus, honeysuckle, lemon, lilies, oak, orange, palms, peach, pear, penstemon, persimmon, plum, plumbago, potato, prune, primrose, raspberry, rose, scabiosa, strawberry, tangerine, and vinca.

The larvae are white or yellowish, legless grubs, with a brown head, feeding on roots of young citrus trees and of other plants, and causing the foliage to turn yellow. Pupation is in the soil and the wingless parthenogenic females lay eggs in late summer in crevices of tree bark or under buttons of citrus fruit or at the base of plants. There is 1 generation a year.

Control. Formerly dusting with cryolite and applying a sticky band around young trees were the chief control measures. Now dusting with malathion or chlordane is easier and quite effective. For potted greenhouse plants, soils can be treated with dieldrin.

Giant Stag Beetle*, *Lucanus elaphus* Fabricius. A very large, dark scavenger beetle, 2 or more inches long with mandibles, in the male, taking a third of this length and formed like antlers of a stag.

Golden Buprestid*, *Buprestis aurulenta* Linnaeus. Throughout western North America on injured, dying and dead Douglas-fir, redcedar, spruces, pines, especially in the mountains. The beetle is ½ to ⅞ inch long, metallic, iridescent yellow to green or blue-green; edges of wing covers colored copper, with 4 ridges on each. The larva is a flatheaded borer, 1½ inches long. The life cycle is 2 to 4 or more years.

Golden Tortoise Beetle*, *Metriona bicolor* (Fabricius). A small, tortoise-shaped beetle, looking like a drop of burnished gold, sometimes called a gold bug. The larvae are dull brown, spiny, and carry their excrement and cast skins in a mass on their backs. They feed on morning-glory, sweetpotato, and bindweed. Spray or dust with DDT or malathion.

Goldsmith Beetle, *Cotalpa lanigera* (Linnaeus). Related to June beetles, feeding on leaves of aspen or cottonwood, willow, oak and other hardwoods. The beetle is large, about 1 inch, lemon-yellow above, bronze underneath, with gold head and thorax. The underside of the body is covered with white hairs. The larvae, resembling white grubs, feed at roots of rose, chrysanthemum, canna, sometimes young conifers. The life cycle takes 2 or 3 years.

Grape Bud Beetle, *Glyptoscelis squamulata* Crotch. Light gray, ¼ inch long, found on grape buds in California vineyards, usually at dusk in early spring. The larvae feed on grape roots. Canes may be smeared with tanglefoot for control.

Grape Colaspis*, *Maecolaspis flavida* (Say). The Clover Rootworm, distributed from eastern states into Arizona. The adults are very small, pale brown, elliptical beetles covered with rows of punctures. They are general feeders, making long, curved feeding marks, sometimes in a zigzag pattern, on apple, bean, cowpea, clover, dahlia, grape, melons, okra, potato, rose, or strawberry. In summer eggs are laid at roots of timothy, grape, clover, sometimes other plants; the larvae—small, fat, short-legged grubs—winter there. There is only 1 generation a year. Most severe injury occurs on corn planted in clover sod, larvae at the roots often causing wilting when plants are 6 to 10 inches high. Plow or spade in fall rather than spring; do not plant corn after clover.

Grape Flea Beetle*, *Altica chalybea* (Illiger). A small, metallic dark-blue beetle feeding on unfolding leaves of grape in spring. Light brown, black-spotted grubs also feed on buds and chew foliage ragged. Distributed through the eastern two thirds of the country, the beetles feed also on apple, beech, elm, plum, quince, and Virginia-creeper. The adults hibernate near vineyards; the larvae pupate in soil. To control adults, spray or dust with DDT as buds are swelling; repeat when shoots are 6 to 8 inches long to kill the grubs.

Gray Willow Leaf Beetle*, *Galerucella decora* (Say). Relative of the elm leaf beetle, common on willows and poplars. The eastern form is pale, the western is dark.

Green June Beetle*, *Cotinus nitida* (Linnaeus). An eastern species related to the fig beetle of the Southwest, occurring east of the Mississippi and from Long Island south. The adult is rather flat, green with bronze or yellow margins, nearly an inch long and half as broad. The beetles feed on foliage of various trees and shrubs and many fruits—fig, peach, various berries, apple, apricot, nectarine, pear, plum, prune—sometimes on corn and other vegetables. The thick, dirty-white grubs feed on roots of grasses in lawns and golf courses and various ornamentals. The adults are around in July and August and lay eggs in soil rich in decaying vegetable matter. Avoid piles of grass clippings or manure near lawn or orchard.

Green Rose Chafer*, *Dichelonyx backi* (Kirby). One of several greenish species feeding largely on conifers. This one is reported as causing heavy damage to Douglas-fir Christmas-tree stock in Montana.

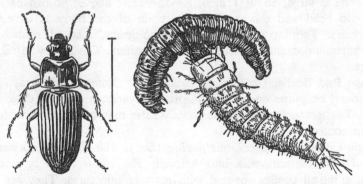

24. *Ground beetle: adult and larva working on a caterpillar.*

GROUND BEETLES. Members of the family Carabidae; feed chiefly on insects, sometimes on earthworms and snails. One or two species may be injurious to plants—e.g., *Harpalus pennsylvanicus,* which may be abundant in soil around grapevines and may attack strawberries. By and large, however, ground beetles are decidedly worth-while additions to the garden, and it ill behooves the gardener to step on one. Ground beetles are found most often lurking under stones; they do not fly but they can run very fast, and many climb trees in search of prey.

The shield-shaped elytra are hard, with fine longitudinal ridges and rows of punctures, and are grown together down the back. A common native species, *Calosoma frigidum* (Fabricius) is black, but some are brownish and some are beautifully iridescent. See also European Ground Beetle and Fiery Hunter. All are large, with ferocious-looking jaws and a very definite indentation between thorax and elytra. Many secrete an offensive liquid for defense.

Ground beetles hibernate in the soil, some passing through 2 winters there, although the cycle is usually 1 year. Eggs are laid in soil. Larvae are flat, heavily chitinized, black and white, with sharp, projecting jaws and a pair of bristly appendages at the posterior end of the body. They are shy, less frequently seen than the adults, but equally predaceous. Ground beetles sometimes scurry into buildings in search of their prey, especially those with stone floors. DON'T STEP ON GROUND BEETLES; THEY ARE YOUR FRIENDS.

Hackberry Engraver*, *Scolytus muticus* Say. A bark beetle breeding in dying hackberry limbs; black, with long ashen hairs on the elytra. Clean up and burn infested material.

Helenium Snout Beetle, *Baris confinis* (LeConte). A very small (to 3/16 inch) black snout beetle commonly found on growing tips of helenium (sneezeweed) in May and June, sometimes later in the season. White grubs with brown heads bore into stems, killing plants or preventing flowering. Spray or dust with DDT at weekly intervals.

Hickory Bark Beetle*, *Scolytus quadrispinosus* Say. The most injurious pest of hickories, found from Quebec to Georgia, Mississippi and Texas. Breeding normally in broken or weakened trees, the beetles will attack and kill healthy trees in epidemics, which may come after droughts. The beetle is small, ⅛ to ¼ inch, dark brown, with 4 spines on abdomen of the male. The grub is white, legless, ¼ inch. The grubs mine in sapwood and inner bark, sometimes girdling trunk and branches. Adults bore into bases of leaf stems, terminal buds, or green nuts. Infested trees lose leaves early in summer; tops and branches may die back. The bark is covered with small perforations, exit holes of the beetles.

Larvae hibernate in the bark, pupate in wood in spring. The beetles, emerging in early summer, fly to living hickories, feeding on young twigs. The female bores through the bark to sapwood and makes her longitudinal egg gallery, with eggs deposited in niches along the sides of the straight tunnel. Grubs burrow out at right angles. There is 1 generation a year in the North, often 2 in the South.

Control. Because injury is more severe in a dry summer, trees kept well watered are more resistant. Spraying with DDT or lead arsenate while beetles are feeding may give some control. Cut and burn badly infested trees between October and May, while the larvae are in their burrows, to prevent beetles from invading other hickories. There are several hymenopterous parasites.

Hickory Saperda, *Saperda discoidea* Fabricius. In eastern and central states. The female is ¾ inch long with brownish wing covers, yellow hairs, and a crescent-shaped marking. The male is smaller, blackish, with 3 lines of gray hairs on the thorax. Large grubs bore in the sapwood of weakened hickories and butternut, often following bark beetles.

Hop Flea Beetle*, *Psylliodes punctulata* Melsheimer. Small, elongate-oval, shining metallic black or dull green. On hops but also on beets, cabbage, cucumber, potato, radish, rhubarb, tomato, turnip, and watermelon. Feeding by adults injures young plants; larvae feed on roots.

Hoplia Beetles, *Hoplia oregona* LeConte and other species. Grapevine Hoplia. Robust scarab beetles, to ⅓ inch, reddish brown with dark head, silvery underside, a problem on the West Coast. The adults feed on blossoms, favoring white, of rose, lily, ceanothus, azalea, orange, peach, and grape, and on tender grape foliage. The grubs, resembling Japanese-beetle larvae, feed on roots of roses and lawn grasses. There is only 1 generation; lindane dust gives satisfactory control.

Horseradish Flea Beetle*, *Phyllotreta armoraciae* (Koch). Small, ⅛ inch long, black with a yellow stripe on wing cover. It deposits eggs in clusters on leaf petioles and larvae burrow into petioles on hatching. It attacks mustard as well as horseradish.

Imbricated Snout Beetle*, *Epicaerus imbricatus* (Say). A brownish gray weevil about ½ inch long, with 2 pale zigzag lines across the wing covers, occurring over most of the United States. It is a general feeder on apple, blackberry, cabbage, cherry, clover, corn, cucumber, gooseberry, muskmelon, onion, pea, potato, raspberry, squash, sugar beet, and watermelon. It injures apples by eating out the buds or cutting off young fruit and leaves. Strawberries may be defoliated. Eggs are laid on foliage and larvae live in roots or stems of legumes and other field crops. Adults appear on apples in late May or June, feeding for about a month; there is 1 generation a year. A general fruit spray schedule should take care of this pest. The beetles can also be jarred from young trees onto a sheet laid underneath.

Imported Willow Leaf Beetle*, *Plagiodera versicolora* (Laicharteg). First recorded in this country in 1915 and now abundant in the Northeast from Washington, D.C., to Maine. It is common on weeping willow but all willows are attacked, the smooth-leaf types most severely, and Lombardy poplar occasionally. The shining metallic blue adult, 3/6 inch long, resembles a flea beetle. The larvae are bluish black, sluglike, with abdomen tapering toward the end. The beetles eat holes in leaves but the larvae rapidly skeletonize them, feeding from the underside. Adults hibernate under bark, emerge in late April or May to lay clusters of lemon-yellow eggs on underside of leaves. They hatch in 4 to 8 days, then the larvae feed for 2 weeks or so before pupating on the leaf. There may be 2 to 4 broods a season.

Control. Spray in late May with lead arsenate, DDT or Sevin. Repeat if necessary the first of July.

Iris Blister Beetle, *Lytta cyanipennis* (LeConte). Reported as damaging commercially grown iris in Idaho.

Japanese Beetle*, *Popillia japonica* Newman. A horrible example of an introduced pest which has cost untold millions for lack of a little money and prompt eradication measures when it was first discovered. It probably came

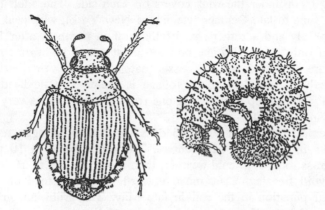

25. *Japanese beetle: adult and grub.*

from Japan as a grub in soil around plant roots prior to 1912, the year when earth balls around imported plants were prohibited. It was first noticed in 1916, in a nursery near Riverton, New Jersey. The next year it had covered 3 square miles with a half mile heavily infested; in 1918 the infested area was 48 square miles. Now most of the East has been taken over. The Japanese beetle is present in Connecticut, Delaware, Georgia, Illinois, Indiana, Iowa, Kentucky, Maine, Maryland, Massachusetts, Michigan, Missouri, New Hampshire, New Jersey, New York, North Carolina, Ohio, Pennsylvania, Rhode Island, South Carolina, Tennessee, Vermont, Virginia and West Virginia. It has been taken in traps near airfields in other areas. It became established near Sacramento, California, in 1961 but eradication measures were immediately started and are apparently succeeding.

Adult Japanese beetles feed on about 275 kinds of deciduous fruits, shade trees, shrubs and garden flowers, but only a few vegetables—chiefly asparagus, corn, rhubarb, and soybeans. The beetles are exceedingly fond of Boston ivy and Virginia-creeper, birch, canna, chestnut, elm, hollyhock, horsechestnut, linden, kerria, mallow, marigold (African but not French), grape, peach, plum, quince, Japanese quince, rose, rose-of-Sharon, sassafras, turquoise vine, zinna, to name a mere handful of ornamentals on which the beetles can be expected. They feed on apple and cherry but not as severely as on grape, raspberry, and peach, massing on ripening fruit as well as eating foliage. Evergreens are seldom ravaged and phlox, chrysanthemum, gladiolus, iris and some other flowers are not favored. Lawns are often wrecked by grubs feeding on roots.

A Japanese beetle is a most beautiful insect, until you see it hanging in a cluster of 100 or so around a peach or over a rose bloom (Plate VIII). It is oval, just under ½ inch long, a gorgeous metallic green with coppery wing covers which are striated with fine longitudinal lines. There are 2 patches of white hairs at the tip of the abdomen and 5 tufts of white hairs projecting from under the wing covers on each side. The adult beetles feed from late June to late October (vicinity of New York), with peak abundance usually in July and a rather sharp falling off in numbers after Labor Day. They feed only in the daytime and are most active on warm, sunny days. Flowers are devoured and leaf tissue eaten between veins, so the foliage looks like lace. Succulent young foliage is preferred. The beetles are gregarious, a whole group demolishing one rose, sometimes in a very short time, before trying the next.

Each female lives from 30 to 45 days, lays 40 to 60 eggs, mostly under grass roots in lawns and golf courses. The grubs hatch in 10 to 12 days, feed on grass roots until cold weather, then move down 8 to 10 inches in the soil to avoid freezing. They move upward in spring, feed on grass roots again until pupation in the soil in late May. The grubs are grayish white with brown heads, ¾ to 1 inch long when full-grown, usually found in a curved position and distinguished from similar white grubs by a V-shaped row of spines in the underside of the last segment of the body. They chew off grass roots so that the turf can be rolled back like a carpet.

Control of Adults. In regions of serious beetle infestation, summer spraying or dusting is almost obligatory. DDT, at 2 pounds of 50 per cent wettable powder per 100 gallons (2 level tablespoons per gallon) or as a 5 per cent dust has been effective but the more recent Sevin is even more efficient. Use it at 2 pounds 50 per cent wettable powder per 100 gallons or ⅔ tablespoon to 1 gallon. Both DDT and Sevin are broad-spectrum insecticides which also kill the beneficial insects keeping aphids and mites under control, so a miticide should be added to the spray. If mites are a problem, lead arsenate may be preferred for ornamental trees and shrubs, using 3 tablespoons to 1 gallon of water. For vegetables and fruits methoxychlor or rotenone sprays or dusts are safer, although commercial growers may use parathion.

Malathion and lindane are sometimes recommended for roses and other flowers. Weekly treatment is necessary to protect the foliage, and nothing will keep beetles from feeding on flowers opening between sprays. Some confirmed rosarians cover the blooms with cellophane protectors or erect a frame over the plants. Most of us cut our best buds in the morning and enjoy them in the house during the peak beetle season. The finest roses bloom before and after the Japanese beetles are active, so they need be no deterrent to planting roses.

Control of Larvae. Lawns may be grubproofed with chlordane, 5 pounds of 5 per cent dust per 1000 square feet, or 4 ounces of 75 per cent emulsion in 25 gallons of water as a spray; or with dieldrin, 4¼ pounds of a 1½ per cent dust or 6 ounces of an 18.6 per cent emulsion; or DDT, 6 pounds of 10 per cent dust or 1¼ pounds of 50 per cent wettable powder as a spray; or lead arsenate, 10 pounds per 1000 square feet. DDT has a long residual effect, up to 5 years. Chlordane and dieldrin are now more often used on home lawns, applied in granular form according to manufacturer's directions. Aldrin and helptachlor have been used in some eradication programs but offer some hazard to wildlife. Chemicals may be applied to turf in either fall or spring.

Insect parasites have been brought from Asia; two Tiphia wasps have become established and are quite effective. The most promising natural control is a bacterial milky disease, disseminated by applying a spore-dust mixture made from inoculated grubs. This is available under trade names, such as *Doom* or *Japidemic,* and is applied at 3- to 5-foot intervals, about a teaspoon per dose. This takes about 3 years to effect much control, and there must be a sufficient number of grubs in the soil for the bacteria to live on, but the end results are good.

All plants leaving nurseries in beetle areas during their season must be certified. Special control measures are taken around airports; planes departing in summer months are treated to avoid unwelcome hitchhikers. Once in a while a plane does transport a live beetle to an uninfested area, and undoubtedly private automobiles are responsible for some spread. There are many traps to check such infestations; eradicant measures are necessary immediately to prevent the beetle from getting established in yet another state.

Jeffrey Pine Beetle*, *Dendroctonus jeffreyi* Hopkins. Dark brown or black bark beetles, ⅓ inch long, in dying Jeffrey, sugar, and yellow pines in mountains along the Pacific Coast.

June Beetles, *Phyllaphaga* spp. Familar large, reddish-brown or black beetles, an inch or more long, also known as May Beetles, June Bugs or Daw Bugs, and as White Grubs in the larval state. There are about 200 species, not to be distinguished by the layman, with similar life histories. They are distributed over the country, probably more serious in the Middle West and South than in the East. The life cycle takes from 1 to 4 years, with a 3-year cycle more common in the North. Adults appear in May, June, or July—earlier in the South—and fly at night, feeding on foliage of ash, birch, butternut, elm, hickory, poplar, oaks, tuliptree, willow and other ornamentals. Most species prefer hardwoods, but some southern forms feed on pine and cypress and some infest roses. The beetles are attracted to lights and try to enter houses; during the day they remain hidden under grass or in debris. The females enter the soil for egg laying, depositing each egg in a separate ball of earth 1 to several inches below the surface of sod land. The eggs hatch in 2 or 3 weeks and the young grubs feed on roots and underground plant parts until fall, when they burrow downward. The next spring they move up to feed on roots of grass, corn, cereals, potatoes and other crops. That autumn they again move down in the soil, coming up to feed for a short time in spring prior to forming a pupal cell in the soil. The adults are formed but stay in the cell until the next spring when they emerge to feed as beetles. Most grub damage comes the year after heavy beetle flights. The grubs look like Japanese beetle grubs but are larger, ½ to 1½ inches, and the spines on the underside of the tip of the abdomen are in the pattern of an elongated diamond.

Control. Valuable shade trees can be sprayed with lead arsenate or Sevin during beetle years. Previous records in a locality show when to expect injury. Lawns and golf courses can be grubproofed with lead arsenate, 10 pounds to a 1000 square feet, or with chlordane or dieldrin as for Japanese beetles. DDT is not as satisfactory for white grubs. Avoid larval injury to roots by not planting susceptible crops like corn or strawberries in land recently taken over from sod. Summer or fall plowing or spading kills some larvae and pupae, exposes others to birds.

Khapra Beetle*, *Trogoderma granarium* Everts. Not a garden pest but an imported and important grain problem. A native of India, this small, oval, brownish-black beetle was noted in stored grain in California in 1953 and has spread to New Mexico and Arizona. It is under Federal Quarantine and is being eradicated, but people should still be on the watch for yellow-brown fuzzy larvae and cast skins. It is frequently intercepted by quarantine officials and there have been new flare-ups in supposedly eradicated areas.

Klamath Weed Beetle, *Chrysolina* spp. On July 12, 1958, at Fortuna, California, a monument was unveiled to this Australian beetle. Since it was first released in 1946 it had cleared more than 100,000 acres of the Klamath weed and returned the land to productive grazing. Land values of rangeland have gone up and cattle have gained weight. The beetle is still dispersing and continuing its useful existence.

LADY BEETLES. Ladybird beetles, Ladybugs, members of the large family Coccinellidae, which means scarlet red. With the exception of one genus, containing the Mexican bean beetle and the somewhat less infamous squash beetle, all members of this family are beneficial, preying on aphids or scale insects or mealybugs in both their larval and beetle states. In recent years they have been having a hard time staying alive, because DDT and some other new insecticides are as harmful to them as to injurious insects.

Lady beetles are small, ⅙ to ¼ inch long, red or sometimes tan with black spots, or black with red spots. They are broadly oval and can be distinguished from destructive leaf beetles by having only 3 segments in the tarsus (foot). The larvae have flat, carrot-shaped bodies, broad at the head end, tapering at the other, with a rather warty back spotted with blue or orange on a grayish black background. The eggs are usually orange and

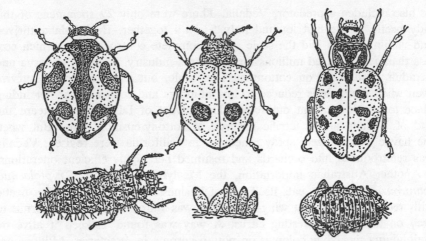

26. *Lady beetles: left to right, Vedalia, two-spotted, and convergent, with detail of larva, eggs, pupa.*

stand on end in a cluster of a dozen or so. The pupae, exposed on the leaf, are cemented to it by one end.

The progeny and potential usefulness of a single female lady beetle are enormous. Depending on her species, she may lay up to 1500 eggs over a period of 2 months, although the normal period is 1 month. The life cycle may take 12 days in warm weather, 20 to 35 days in cool weather. As full-grown larvae, lady beetles consume about 25 aphids a day, and when they change to beetles the daily quota goes up to 50. In an average season the aphid population may be reduced enough so that spraying is unnecessary, but in a cool wet season the beetles reproduce less rapidly and the gardener has to spray a bit.

The aphid-eating species of lady beetles require a lot of plant lice around to maintain themselves. When the aphids are reduced too far, most of the beetles starve to death, so the species practically disappears until a large aphid colony is built up again. Some lady beetles feeding on scales and mealybugs can, however, survive when they have reduced harmful insects to a minimum.

Vedalia*, the Australian Lady Beetle, *Rodolia cardinalis* (Mulsant), is one of these. This small beetle, ⅛ inch long, red with black markings, represents the first successful use of an imported predator to control an injurious insect, the classic example of biological control. The cottony-cushion scale arrived in California from Australia about 1868 on acacia. By the early eighties it had overrun citrus orchards, killing hundreds of thousands of orange trees, threatening the entire citrus industry. So the United States Government and the State of California sent Albert Koebele to Australia to look up some native parasites. In the shipment home of collected parasites he also included a predator, Vedalia. There were only 29 specimens of this lady beetle in the first lot and only 514 all together. But Vedalia thrived and within 2 years had the scale under complete control. A trip which cost less than $5000 saved millions for the citrus industry. Vedalia, as larva and as adult, feeds only on cottony-cushion scale, but she manages to survive even when the scale is reduced to low numbers and comes out of her hiding place to check incipient outbreaks. The advent of DDT almost meant the end of Vedalia and a terrific upsurge of cottony-cushion scale. But when the havoc was realized, spray schedules in California were revised, Vedalia was reintroduced into orchards and resumed her highly efficient operations.

Another Australian importation, the **Mealybug Destroyer,** *Cryptolaemus montrouzieri* Mulsant, eats itself out of business. This blackish, hairy beetle with reddish thorax and wing-cover tips was introduced into California to prey on mealybugs infesting citrus. A way was found to keep it alive by maintaining mealybug colonies on potato sprouts in insectaries. Millions are still being produced and released in citrus areas but the beetle is being some-what replaced by internal parasites.

The **Convergent Lady Beetle,** *Hippodamia convergens* (Guérin-Méne-ville) is the most common species and is the one sold by the gallon to farmers and home gardeners for aphid control. The adult has 12 small black spots on reddish wing covers and 2 convergent white lines on the thorax. The larvae are flat, velvety black or grayish with orange spots. This species hibernates in huge masses in the western mountains and is collected there for distribution. Unfortunately, the beetles have an urge to migrate when released so that importing them by mail may benefit some garden other than your own.

The **Two-spotted Lady Beetle*,** *Adalia bipunctata* (Linnaeus) is very common in eastern gardens and sometimes winters in houses. It has red elytra with 2 round black spots. I find it hunting for aphids on rose canes as early as spring pruning.

The **Twice-stabbed Lady Beetle*,** *Chilocorus stigma* (Say) is black with 2 red spots and dines on scale insects, the female hiding her eggs under the scale shell or in bark crevices. The larvae are grayish with black spines. The adults hibernate under bark or in other protected places in trees.

Some very small lady beetles, *Stethorus* spp., feed on spider mites. They lay small, oval, cream-colored eggs among the mite colonies on undersides of leaves. The larvae are hairy, brownish with black markings; the adults are black.

There are many other species of helpful lady beetles, but space does not permit detailed descriptions.

Larger Elm Leaf Beetle*, *Monocesta coryli* (Say). A large, yellowish beetle with 9 blue-black patches. It appears occasionally in large numbers on slippery or red elm, sometimes on American elm, and it is known to feed on dogwood, hazel, and hawthorn. First described from Illinois, in 1824, it has since been a pest in Arkansas, Florida, Kansas, Maryland, Mississippi, Missouri, North Carolina, Pennsylvania, Virginia, and West Virginia. It appears suddenly in a locality, does a great deal of damage in a small area, completely defoliating trees for a year or so, and then disappears for an indefinite period. The yellow to orange larvae feed in groups. They hibernate in soil, pupate in spring, with adults appearing in late May. Owing to the sporadic nature of outbreaks, control measures are not often attempted.

Larger Mexican Pine Beetle*. See Colorado Pine Beetle.

Lined Click Beetle, *Agriotes lineatus* (Linnaeus). See Click Beetles.

Lion Beetle*, *Ulochaetes leoninus* LeConte. Large, black, tipped with yellow and resembling a bumblebee; breeding in pines, fir, hemlock, in mountains in the West.

Lodgepole Cone Beetle*, *Conophthorus contortae* Hopkins. Adults and larvae bore in small, immature pines, causing them to wither and die, with masses of resin on the stem. Almost all pines are attacked by various species of Conophthorus.

Lodgepole-pine Beetle*, *Dendroctonus murrayanae* Hopkins. A black bark beetle, with reddish wing covers, infesting healthy trees, entering near the base and excavating long egg galleries with pitch tubes at the entrance holes. Mostly on lodgepole pine but recorded on Engelmann spruce.

Margined Blister Beetle, *Epicauta pestifera* Werner. Black with a narrow gray or yellow margin around the wing covers; may be abundant on various ornamentals. See Black Blister Beetle for life history and control.

May Beetles. See June Beetles.

Mexican Bean Beetle, *Epilachna varivestis* Mulsant. Doubtless the worst enemy of eastern home vegetable gardens (Plate IX). Like the Colorado potato beetle, this is an example of an insect long present suddenly assuming great importance. Probably originally from Mexico, the beetle has been known in the Southwest since 1850, but it did not become really dangerous until it reached Alabama about 1920. Since then it has spread to all of the states east of the Mississippi. This gangster member of the ordinarily beneficial lady-beetle family has the typical convex shape but is somewhat larger, up to ⅓ inch, and is coppery yellow with 16 black dots, 8 on each wing cover. It infests all kinds of garden beans and cowpeas. It likes lima beans particularly but does not care much for soybeans, although it will attack them. Larvae and adults feed on pods and stems as well as foliage.

Mexican bean beetles winter as adults in rubbish or weeds, appearing in bean fields late in March in the South, June in New York. After feeding for a week or two, the females lay groups of orange-yellow eggs on underside of leaves. These hatch in 5 to 14 days. Soft yellow larvae, ⅓ inch long and half as wide, with black-tipped spines on the back, skeletonize the leaves, always working from underneath and eating out very regular areas in a lacy pattern. When full grown, the larvae cement their hind ends to an uninjured leaf and the pupae push out of crushed larval skins, adults emerging in 10 days or less. A complete cycle takes about a month. Near New York City there are usually 2 generations, farther north 1 and a partial 2nd, farther south, 3 or 4.

Control. In home gardens spray or dust with rotenone, methoxychlor, or malathion. Commercial growers also use less safe diazinon, Dibrom, or Trithion. Be sure to cover underside of foliage and treat at the first sign of injury; repeat 10 days later. Time of planting is one means of control. Near New York City snap beans planted in early June will mature in July between beetle broods. Discourage hibernating beetles by cleaning up and burning all plant debris after harvest.

Mint Flea Beetle, *Longitarsus waterhousei* (Kutsch). Reported as active in untreated mint fields in Oregon. Mint roots may also be damaged.

Monterey-pine Cone Beetle*, *Conophthorus radiatae* Hopkins. Small, infesting cones of Monterey pine.

Monterey-pine Engraver, *Ips radiatae* Hopkins. Small bark beetle attacking weakened Monterey pine in California, working from the crown downward.

Mottled Tortoise Beetle*, *Deloyala guttata* (Olivier). Golden around the margins of the elytra, the rest mottled black and yellow. The larvae are dull green, bluish along the back, covered with broad, branching masses of excrement. On sweetpotato and morning-glory.

Mountain Pine Beetle*, *Dendroctonus monticolae* Hopkins. Very destructive to pines in mountains of the Northwest. It has practically wiped out thousands of acres of lodgepole and western white pine, is damaging to sugar, ponderosa and other pines; and may attack fir, spruce, and hemlock near pines. The stout black bark beetles, pale brown to black, ¼ inch long, excavate very long perpendicular egg galleries. This species prefers young trees or the tops of old trees.

Native Elm Bark Beetle*, *Hylurgopinus rufipes* (Eichoff). Widely distributed throughout eastern states on elms and basswood. It is chiefly important because, along with the small European elm bark beetle, it may spread the Dutch elm disease. It is a small, brownish black beetle 1/10 inch long, not so shiny as its European cousin. It works under the bark, making its egg gallery transversely across the wood with larval tunnels coming out at right angles. There are 1 or more generations a year, and they pass the winter as either larvae or adults. Often adults of this species emerge in the fall and burrow into the bark of living elm trees. A dormant DDT or methoxychlor spray, 12 per cent by mist blower or 2 per cent in a hydraulic sprayer, is the best way to protect elms. Dying limbs and logs should be immediately removed and burned. See also Smaller European Elm Bark Beetle.

Northeastern Sawyer*, *Monochamus notatus* (Drury). Also called Pine Sawyer, common in northeastern states, attacking white spruce and various pines. The larvae usually burrow extensively in dead or dying trees but may injure apparently healthy trees. The large beetles, ½ to 1½ inches long, blackish with a white or gray pubescence, have very long legs and antennae, a prolonged and flattened head, and a spiny projection from each side of the thorax.

Northern Cedar Bark Beetle, *Phloeosinus canadensis* Swaine. Occurring in the Northeast, breeding mostly in northern white cedar and arborvitae. Twigs in ornamental hedges may break or wilt. The injury is unsightly but not serious.

Northern Masked Chafer*, *Cyclocephala borealis* Arrow. Another lawn pest, similar to other white grubs. Damage to turf is frequently reported, from Maryland particularly, and the injury is often compounded by skunks going after the grubs. The **Southern Masked Chafer*,** *C. immaculata* (Olivier) is its counterpart in South Carolina, Kansas, and other states.

Nuttall Blister Beetle*, *Lytta nuttallii* Say. A large (1 inch long or more) metallic green or purplish beetle, prevalent in the Rocky Mountains. It feeds on legumes and grasshopper eggs.

Obtuse Sawyer, *Monochamus obtusus* Casey. Brown beetle with gray markings, ½ to ¾ inches, larvae 1 to 1½ inches, injuring pine, Douglas-fir, and fir in Pacific Coast States and Idaho.

Olive Bark Beetle, *Leperisinus californicus* Swaine. A very small, robust beetle, black with whitish scales, with exit holes giving a "shot-hole" appearance to bark of olive trees. It prefers sickly trees but may work over into healthy trees. Prune off and burn infested twigs and branches; promote general vigor.

Oregon Fir Sawyer*, *Monochamus oregonensis* (LeConte). A stout black beetle, ½ to 1½ inches long, with gray markings, antennae twice as long as body, and a toothlike projection on each side of the thorax. The larvae, 1 to 1¾ inches, are destructive to scorched, injured, dying or felled Douglas-fir, true firs, and pines in the West.

Oriental Beetle*, *Anomala orientalis* Waterhouse. Also called Asiatic Beetle and a close relative of Asiatic garden and Japanese beetles. It was first discovered at New Haven, Connecticut, in 1920, is now present in New York, New Jersey, Rhode Island, Pennsylvania and North Carolina, and has been intercepted in Florida in airplanes arriving from New England. Presumably a native of Japan, this beetle nearly destroyed sugarcane in Hawaii before a parasitic wasp was introduced from the Philippines.

Here on the mainland grasses are preferred hosts, but this species is also reported on ageratum, cyclamen, iris, hollyhock, phlox, rose and bean, beet, onion, rhubarb and strawberry.

Adults are straw-colored with varying dark markings. They emerge from the soil throughout July and August, are active day and night, but eat much less than Japanese and Asiatic garden beetles. Females deposit eggs singly 1 to 9 inches below soil surface and these hatch in 17 to 27 days. Larval feeding on grass roots continues to mid-October when the grubs move down a foot or more for winter. Root injury starts again in late April with pupation in an earthen cell in early June. The grubs cannot be distinguished from Japanese-beetle grubs except by the arrangement of spines in 2 parallel lines on the underside of the abdomen. Grubproof turf as for Japanese beetles.

Pacific Willow Leaf Beetle*, *Galerucella carbo* (LeConte). A relative of the elm leaf beetle.

Pale-striped Flea Beetle*, *Systena blanda* Melsheimer. Generally distributed, probably a native. The adult is ⅙ inch long, with a broad white stripe down the center of each pale to dark-brown wing cover. It perforates leaves of many different plants—alfalfa, bean, beet, carrot, clovers, corn, cotton, eggplant, grasses, lettuce, melon, parsnip, pea, peanut, pear, pumpkin, radish, sunflower, strawberry, turnip—and many weeds. The larvae, just over ¼ inch long, are slender, white, with light-brown heads. They feed on roots of many plants and on corn seed, causing failure to sprout or a sickly plant. Spray for adults with DDT, malathion, methoxychlor, or rotenone. Keep down weeds; starve out larvae by early and late spading or plowing.

Peach Bark Beetle*, *Phloeotribus liminaris* (Harris). A native pest found in eastern states, attacking mainly peach, sometimes cherry. The small brownish beetle, similar to the shot-hole borer, only 1/10 inch long, winters as an adult in dead or dying wood or in special cells cut in the bark of a healthy cane. The egg gallery runs across the wood rather than lengthwise, as with most bark beetles. Keep trees vigorous by proper cultural methods. Destroy peach prunings and dying trees.

Pine Chafer*, *Anomala oblivia* Horn. Relative of the Oriental Beetle. Adults may defoliate Scotch, loblolly and other pines. Reported as quite damaging in Pennsylvania and North Carolina.

Pine Colaspis, *Maecolaspis pini* (Barber). Feeding on pines, sometimes spruce, cypress, deodar, in the South, being particularly abundant in Louisiana. It is a small beetle, 1/16 to ⅛ inch long, gregarious, feeding on green needles, often leaving them hanging by one edge with tips turning brown. Young pines may die. Spray or dust ornamental conifers with DDT or lead arsenate.

Another species, *Maecolaspis favosa,* is reported damaging to many ornamentals in Florida—crapemyrtle, cuphea, ixora, waxmyrtle, punek tree, with severe injury to ixora.

Pine Engraver*, *Ips pini* (Say). Common through northern United States, attacking all kinds of pines, though favoring white pine, and sometimes killing spruce (Plate X). This bark beetle often infests small white pines that have been transplanted, its presence told by small circular holes on branches or trunk. It has also been a frequent visitor to pitch pine after New England hurricanes. The beetle varies from brown to black, is ⅛ inch long, burrows in sapwood. Long galleries radiate from a circular brood chamber.

A closely related beetle, *Ips calligraphus* Germar, called the **Coarse-writing Bark Beetle,** is larger and more of a pest in the South. It is the first to attack pines suffering from drought. There are many other species of engraver beetles not described in this manual.

Piñon Cone Beetle*, *Conophthorus edulis* Hopkins. On piñon pine in Colorado, Arizona, and New Mexico. Cones dry and wither before they are half grown. Beetles are very small, dark, shiny, cylindrical.

Pitted Ambrosia Beetle, *Corthylus punctatissimus* Zimmerman. From Massachusetts to Colorado and southward, on rhododendron, dogwood, blueberry, mountain mahogany, sometimes hazel, ironwood, sassafras, water birch. The beetle, dark brown to black, stout, ⅛ inch long, makes horizontal galleries in the wood at the base of the stem, causing it to wilt and break over. Shrubs that are heavily mulched are more likely to be attacked. Cut out and burn wilted stems below point of entrance of beetles. Remove excess mulch.

Plum Gouger*, *Anthonomus scutellaris* LeConte. A reddish-brown beetle, living on wild plum and occasionally going over to domestic plums, prunes, apricots, sometimes peaches and cherries. It resembles the plum curculio but lacks the characteristic humps. The gouger emerges from hibernation earlier than the curculio, and the larvae bore into the fruit to pupate. Spray before blossems open and then follow the curculio schedule. See Plum Curculio.

Ponderosa-pine Cone Beetle*, *Conophthorus ponderosae* Hopkins. Infesting cones of yellow pine in the West.

Potato Flea Beetle*, *Epitrix cucumeris* (Harris). A common and very destructive small, black, jumping flea beetle (Plate VII). It feeds on potato and related solanaceous plants such as eggplant, groundcherry, pepper, petunia, tomato, and also on apple, arbutus, ash, bean, beet, cabbage, carrot, celery, clover, corn, cucumber, dogbane, elder, forget-me-not, holly, honeysuckle, horsechestnut, lettuce, maple, muskmelon, phlox, primrose, pumpkin, radish, raspberry, rhubarb, spinach, sumac, sunflower, sweetpotato, viburnum, violet, and watermelon. It is present throughout the country. Very tiny, 1/16 inch long, it winters as an adult, in spring going first to weeds, sometimes tree leaves. As soon as potatoes or tomatoes appear in the garden, the beetles descend on young plants in hordes, completely riddling the foliage. Eggs are laid in the soil and the larvae feed on roots and tubers. They may be quite destructive, causing scurfy or pimply potatoes, and they are also dangerous as a vector of potato virus diseases. There are usually two broods.

Control. Spray or dust with DDT, methoxychlor or malathion. Commercial growers may use Thiodan, dieldrin or endrin. Rotenone dust is still good for home gardens.

POWDER POST BEETLES. A group of beetles belonging to the families Ptinidae, Anobiidae, Bostrichidae, and Lyctidae, whose larvae burrow into hard, dry wood and reduce it to fine powder. Some species may also bore in living shade or fruit trees, killing twigs or branches.

Prairie Flea Beetle*, *Altica canadensis* Gentner.

Red-legged Flea Beetle*, *Derocrepis erythropus* (Melsheimer). On fruit trees; reported as damaging peach in Pennsylvania.

Red Milkweed Beetle*, *Tetraopes tetrophthalmus* (Forster). Fairly large, red; larvae boring in stems and roots of milkweed.

Red Turnip Beetle*, *Entomoscelis americana* Brown. More of a pest in the Northwest. The beetles are bright red with black patches on the head and three black lines on the elytra, ¼ inch long. Bright-red eggs, orange to black larvae, and bright-orange pupae complete the colorful cycle. Feeding is at night, on alyssum, cabbage, radish, turnip, wallflower, sometimes beans.

Red Turpentine Beetle*, *Dendroctonus valens* LeConte. Found in pine forests through the country, also injuring ornamental pines in the Atlantic States and Monterey pine in California; sometimes infesting Engelmann spruce. This is a comparatively large bark beetle, ¼ to ⅜ inch long, reddish, sometimes nearly black. Egg galleries are longitudinal, somewhat winding. Trees are attacked near the base with reddish pitch tubes formed; girdled trees may die. When the pitch tubes are noticed, it may be possible to cut out the beetles with a knife or to fumigate them by injecting carbon bisulfide into the galleries.

Red Spider Destroyer, *Somatium oviformis* (Casey). One of the beneficial rove beetles, very small, slender, black, elevating the tip of the abdomen. It deposits orange eggs on the surface of leaves, and the yellow larvae, ⅛ inch long, may daily consume 20 mites apiece. Adults can be numerous on foliage of deciduous fruit and citrus trees infested with various species of mites.

Red-winged Pine Beetle, *Dendroctonus rufipennis* (Kirby). Similar in appearance and habit to the turpentine beetles, infesting pine in the Great Lakes region. Egg galleries are narrow.

Rhabdopterus Beetles. Several species feed on young foliage of camellias and other ornamentals. *Rhabdopterus deceptor* is found in Texas on camellia, Chinese holly, lychee, redbud, pyracantha, guava, mango, photinia, rose, yaupon, and other plants; *R. bowditchi* is known only in subtropical Florida. It infests avocado as well as ornamentals. *R. picipes,* also known as the Cranberry Rootworm, appears in coastal lowland areas from New England to the Mississippi on blueberry, cranberry, and other bog plants. *R. praetexus* is found inland from Canada to the Rio Grande River and is probably the common species in northern Florida. It injures all camellias, redbud, rhododendron, ampelopsis, rose, loblolly, bay, aronia, myrica and other plants. The beetles are small, compact, elongate-oval in outline, shining blackish bronze, ¼ inch long by ⅛ inch wide. They feed only at night, on buds and tender new leaves, leaving long, rather narrow, usually curved holes or slits in the foliage.

Control. Eliminate grubs by plowing new land a year before infestation.

Some ornamentals can be sprayed with DDT but this may injure camellias and possibly azaleas.

Rhinoceros Beetle, *Xyloryctes satyrus* (Fabricius). Member of a group of very large beetles with a projection like a rhinoceros, mostly southern but this species found as far north as Connecticut. The male is very dark brown, practically black, very broad, over an inch long, with horn curving back from its head (Plate XI). The female is similar but has a small flat tubercle instead of a horn. The larvae, looking like large white grubs, attack lilacs and sometimes other shrubs just under the surface of the ground, girdling and often killing them. The beetles come out at dusk. The life history is not well worked out.

Other members of this subfamily Dynastinae, the giant beetles, are the **Unicorn Beetle,** *Dynastes tityrus* (Linnaeus) and the **Elephant Beetle,** *Strategus* spp. The unicorn beetle is very large, 2 to 2½ inches long, greenish gray spotted with black, with a long horn extending forward. The elephant beetles are black, somewhat over an inch long; the male has three horns on the thorax. The larvae are large white grubs.

Chlordane dust or liquid, injected into holes made by the grubs and the entrance then closed, is suggested for control.

Rose Chafer*, *Macrodactylus subspinosus* (Fabricius). Familiar to most gardners as the "Rose Bug," even though it is a beetle. It is probably called a bug because its wing covers are not as hard and horny as are those of most beetles. The adult is tan, with a reddish-brown head, rather slender, ⅓ to ½ inch long, with prominent long spiny legs (Plate XI). The rose chafer is distributed through the Northeast and may be found as far west as Colorado. Particularly injurious to roses, peonies, and grapes, it feeds on many other plants—apple, bean, beet, blackberry, cabbage, corn, cherry, dahlia, elder, elm, foxglove, geranium, hollyhock, hydrangea, New Jersey tea, peach, pear, peony, pepper, poppy, raspberry, strawberry, Virginia-creeper, wisteria, small grains and grasses. It is more troublesome in sandy areas and seems to increase in importance as one goes north from New York City.

The beetles appear in swarms in late May or early June and feed first on flowers, especially roses and peonies, sometimes iris, then go to newly set fruit, being very injurious to grape blossoms, foliage, and young berries. In some areas elm foliage is rather severely damaged. There is only 1 generation, the feeding period lasting 3 to 4 weeks. The eggs, laid in sandy soil, hatch in 1 to 2 weeks. The larvae, resembling white grubs but thinner and smaller, up to ¾ inch long, feed on roots of grasses and sometimes nursery seedlings, moving down into the soil for winter.

Control. DDT (3 level tablespoons of 50 per cent wettable powder to 1 gallon of water) is more effective than earlier insecticides but must be applied promptly. Methoxychlor may be substituted. Handpicking helps to keep chafers off roses, and some gardeners protect their best bushes with a temporary cheesecloth fence, stretching somewhat higher than the plants. Even if it is open on top, the beetles seem not to fly over the barrier. Chickens are poisoned by eating rose chafers.

Rose Leaf Beetle*, *Nodonota puncticollis* (Say). A small, shiny, green to blue beetle, ⅛ inch long, resembling a flea beetle, though not so active. It is distributed from New England south and west to Arizona and Montana. Besides feeding on buds, blossoms, and foliage of rose, peony, and iris, it favors blackberry, raspberry, strawberry, pear, peach, plum, apple (scarring the fruit), and willow. It feeds in spring on clover and other meadow plants before migrating to roses and fruits. Spray or dust with DDT or malathion; clean up wasteland breeding places.

Roundheaded Pine Beetle*, *Dendroctonus convexifrons* Hopkins. Preventing recovery of injured ponderosa and other pines in Arizona, New Mexico, southern Colorado, Utah, Nevada, and California. Shiny reddish brown, ¼ inch long, with long hairs at tip of wing covers.

Seed-corn Beetle*, *Agonoderus lecontei* (Chaudoir). Sometimes the cause of corn's failing to sprout. This species is dark brown, striped, ¼ to ⅓ inch long. Another beetle, *Clivina impressifrons* LeConte, the same size but a uniform chestnut brown, may also feed on corn seed. These are ground beetles and primarily beneficial, dining mostly on other insects. Corn damage is worse in cold, wet springs when germination is slow or seed is of low vitality. Use good seed; plant late to ensure quick germination. Treating seed with 5 per cent chlordane dust before planting has been helpful.

Silver Fir Beetles, *Pseudohylesinus granulatus* (LeConte) and *P. grandis* Swaine on grand and silver firs and Douglas-fir. These are bark beetles, ⅛ to ¼ inch, dull, variegated, covered with scales; antennae have a dense plume of hairs; egg galleries are bored transversely.

Sitka-spruce Beetle, *Dendroctonus obesus* (Mannerheim). Reddish to dark brown or black bark beetles on Sitka spruce from northern California into Alaska.

Sinuate-striped Flea Beetle, *Phyllotreta zimmermanni* (Crotch). Much like the cabbage flea beetle but with a wavy yellowish stripe on each wing cover; 1/12 inch long. The eggs are laid singly on leaves of cabbage, turnip, and radish; the larvae mine inside.

Smaller European Elm Bark Beetle*, *Scolytus multistriatus* (Marsham). Most famous as the vector of the fungus causing a fatal wilt of elms, widely known as the Dutch elm disease. This is a misnomer; the disease did not originate in Holland, although it was first seriously investigated there. This bark beetle (Plate X) was reported in Massachusetts in 1909 and probably arrived from Europe several years before that. By 1960 it was known in 40 states, all except Florida, Georgia, and South Carolina in the Southeast and Washington, Idaho, Montana, Wyoming, and North Dakota in the Northwest. Although the fungus disease is not present in California, the beetle itself has killed many elms.

The adult is shiny, brown to black, 1/10 to ⅛ inch long, the female slightly larger than the male. Both sexes have a toothlike projection from the undersurface of the abdomen, serving to distinguish this species from other bark beetles. The grub is white, legless, ¼ inch long, much larger at the head end, somewhat curved in its natural position. The beetles attack sickly, dying and recently dead elms and logs by boring small holes through the bark to the sapwood, throwing out sawdust. Each female tunnels out a brood gallery running 1 to 2 inches longitudinally in the wood, and lays from 80 to 100 eggs along this. The grubs make tunnels going out at right angles from the egg gallery, so that characteristic engravings are made in the wood and inner surface of the bark. If many beetles enter, the bark may be separated from the wood all around the trunk or limb.

The grubs transform to beetles in the larval galleries, then exit through small holes, looking like shotholes, in the bark. After emergence the beetles fly to healthy trees and feed by gnawing at the crotches of small twigs before making brood chambers in the older wood. The spores of the Dutch elm disease fungus, formed along the galleries, cling to the beetle when it emerges. As the beetles feed, they inoculate healthy elms with the fungus. There are normally two broods, beetles of the first brood appearing in May or June, adults of the 2nd about 2 months later.

The fungus, *Ceratocystis ulmi,* came to this country about 1930 on beetles concealed in elm burls imported for furniture veneer, and has since killed thousands and thousands of trees in most of the states now inhabited by the beetles.

Control of the disease depends on control of its vector. Dead and dying elms should be cut and burned before beetles emerge in spring. If removal is impossible, the bark surfaces of such trees should be thoroughly sprayed with a DDT-oil mixture. A very potent dormant spray, 12 per cent DDT in xylene, applied with a mist blower at the rate of 3 to 4 gallons per tree (or 2 per cent DDT in a hydraulic spray) applied between late autumn and bud break in spring is recommended for preventing beetle feeding and spread of disease. Some communities combining the dormant spray with sanitary measures have been successful in keeping the disease down to 1 or 2 per cent. Others, starting the program too late, have lost the fight.

There has been bitter controversy because of the hazard to wildlife. In some areas robins have been killed by eating earthworms which have accumulated DDT in their bodies. Methoxychlor used at the same rate as DDT is more expensive but less toxic to man and wildlife. It seems to be about as effective.

Smaller Mexican Pine Beetle*, *Dendroctonus mexicanus* Hopkins.

Southern Masked Chafer*. See under Northern Masked Chafer.

Southern Pine Beetle*, *Dendroctonus frontalis* Zimmerman. A small, native bark beetle, the most serious forest pest of pine in its range, Pennsylvania to Florida and west to Texas and Oklahoma, and occasionally attacking spruce. Epidemics develop with great rapidity, with trees of all sizes attacked but those with trunks larger than 6 inches first, and in the middle and upper parts. The beetle is brown to black, to 3/16 inch long, and it makes winding or S-shaped galleries in the inner bark. There may be 3 to 5 generations a year, with hibernation more commonly as larvae. Feeding begins in early spring, about the time plants start growth, and continues to early summer. Epidemics start in groups of trees, which are more often killed after they have been weakened by flooding, windstorms, or drought.

Control. Trees that can be kept growing rapidly are most resistant to beetle attack. Many natural enemies help in control. Dying trees should be salvaged quickly; where this is impossible, beetles can be killed in felled trees by spraying bark with benzene hexachloride in fuel oil.

Southern Pine Sawyer*, *Monochamus titillator* (Fabricius). A secondary beetle, boring in wood killed by bark beetles or other agency in eastern and southern states. Galleries are mostly in the inner bark but sometimes score the wood. The borings contain much coarse material. Legless larvae with rounded tubercles on the back make U-shaped galleries. The adult, ⅝ to 1 inch long, reddish brown marbled with white and brown, has a small spine at the end of each wing cover and has very long antennae. All dying, killed, or felled timber should be promptly utilized.

Southwestern Pine Beetle*, *Dendroctonus barberi* Hopkins. Very small, very dark brown or black, making transversely winding galleries. On yellow and, more rarely, other pines in the Southwest.

Spinach Carrion Beetle, *Silpha bituberosa* LeConte. Black, with three longitudinal ridges on each elytron, which is short. A scavenger beetle of the Northwest and east to Kansas. Eggs are laid in soil and black-and-white larvae feed at night on edges of leaves of beets, spinach, squash, pumpkin, and some other vegetables.

Spinach Flea Beetle*, *Disonycha xanthomelas* (Dalman). The largest of the common flea beetles, ⅕ inch long, with greenish-black wing covers, yellow thorax, and black head. It feeds exposed on leaves of spinach, beet and various weeds, lays eggs in clusters on leaves. The larva is a gray-to-purple, warty, wrinkled grub about ¼ inch long. Pupation is in the soil, and there are usually 2 generations a year. Control with malathion or rotenone and sulfur.

Spotted Asparagus Beetle*, *Crioceris duodecimpunctata* (Linnaeus). Introduced from Europe a few years after the common asparagus beetle, first seen near Baltimore in 1881, now distributed over much of the same territory east of the Mississippi. Confined to this host, the beetles can be quite destructive but the larvae feed only on berries. The adult is reddish orange or tan, with 6 prominent black spots on each wing cover (Plate IV). Greenish eggs are glued singly by their sides to leaves just before the berries form. Orange larvae appear in a week or two, bore into the developing berry and eat pulp and seeds. Each larva destroys 3 or 4 berries before pupating in soil. Beetles of the new brood emerge in July and lay eggs for the overwintering generation appearing in September. Control measures are the same as for the asparagus beetle, but collecting and burning berries may be sufficient.

Spotted Blister Beetle*, *Epicauta maculata* (Say). Black, covered with fine white hairs except in spots where the black shows through. Feeding on many vegetables and field crops in western states.

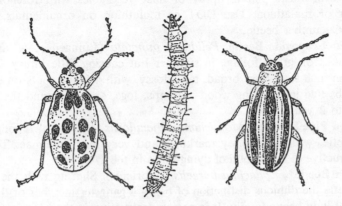

27. Spotted cucumber beetle, left; striped cucumber beetle, right.

Spotted Cucumber Beetle*, *Diabrotica undecimpunctata howardi* Barber. Also known as Southern Corn Rootworm. This species occurs anywhere east of the Rockies but it is more destructive in southern states. West of the Rocky Mountains it is replaced by the Western Spotted Cucumber Beetle. The adult is greenish yellow, rather slender, with 12 black spots, a black head, ¼ inch long. It is prevalent on many flowers and vegetables beside cucumber. Vegetables include snap and lima beans early in the season, later all of the cucurbits—cucumber, melon, squash, gourds—and asparagus, beet, cabbage, eggplant, peas, potato, and tomato.

Although the spotted cucumber beetle eats foliage of many ornamentals, it seems to prefer petals of late summer flowers with light colors, such as aster, calendula, canna, chrysanthemum, coreopsis, cosmos, dahlia, garden balsam, rose, Shasta daisy, sweetpea and zinnia.

The beetle hibernates as an adult at the base of weeds or other overwintering plants and starts flying when the temperature nears 70° F. in spring. Females lay eggs just below soil level, on or near young corn plants, beans, or weeds. The larvae, which feed on such roots, are more wormlike than most beetle grubs, ½ to ¾ inch long, slender with yellowish-white wrinkled bodies and brown heads (Plate XII). They have been called overflow worms, budworms, and drillworms because they bore out the crown of a corn plant and kill the bud. Corn so injured either breaks off or is dwarfed and yellowish. There are at least 3 generations in the South, 1 and a partial 2nd in the North.

The spotted cucumber beetle is especially important as a vector of plant diseases. It carries the bacteria causing cucumber wilt in its intestines and inoculates plants as it feeds. It also disseminates some viruses.

Control. Avert damage to corn by planting late in the season, thoroughly cultivating the soil first. Reduce overwintering beetles by cleaning up weeds, burning over waste places. Spray or dust vegetables with rotenone, methoxychlor or malathion. Use DDT or malathion on ornamentals. See also Striped Cucumber beetle.

Spotted Grapevine Beetle, *Pelidnota punctata* (Linnaeus). A large beetle conspicuous on grape foliage in summer but causing little injury. The adult is over an inch long, very broad, tan, glossy, with 4 black spots on each side. The grubs live in decaying wood—stumps, logs, or roots—and the life cycle takes 2 to 3 years.

Spotted Pine Sawyer*, *Monochamus maculosus* Haldeman. A long, slender dark beetle, with bluish-gray markings and very long antennae. The larvae are destructive to heartwood of dying pines in the West.

Squash Beetle*, *Epilachna borealis* (Fabricius). Sharing with the Mexican bean beetle the dubious distinction of being a gangster member of the usually beneficial lady beetle family. It is not as destructive as the bean beetle, but it is fairly common east of the Rocky Mountains on squash, melon, pumpkin and relatives. It is slightly larger than the Mexican bean beetle, yellow, with 7 black spots on each wing cover. Beetles emerge in June to lay eggs on host plants; these hatch in a week. The spiny larva feeds on foliage for 2 to 4 weeks, then pushes its larval skin down its back while it pupates. The adults hibernate under trash. Control is seldom necessary; malathion or methoxychlor would help.

Steel-blue Flea Beetle, *Altica torquata* LeConte. A small metallic-blue or purple beetle, abundant on grapes in New Mexico, Arizona and southern California. Native hosts are desert and evening primroses.

Steel-blue Lady Beetle*, *Orcus chalybeus* (Boisduval). Metallic steel-blue or emerald green, introduced from Australia to California in 1892 to prey on black, red, and purple scales.

Stink Beetle*, *Nomius pygmaeus* (Dejean). One of the beneficial ground beetles, sometimes called the malodorous carabid. It has a very offensive smell, is present in California and Oregon.

Strawberry Flea Beetle, *Altica ignita* Illiger. Metallic green, golden bronze or purple, 3/16 inch long, on strawberry, kalmia, fuchsia, rose and many other plants; widely distributed. The foliage is riddled with great numbers of small round holes and the leaves often turn brown around the holes. The beetles winter as adults and do most of their damage before strawberries bloom. Spraying with bordeaux mixture, 8–8–100, a week or so before bloom, has been effective.

Striped Ambrosia Beetle*, *Trypodendron lineatum* (Olivier). Infesting conifers; in heartwood of dying trees. Resembling a bark beetle, dark with lighter stripes.

Striped Blister Beetle*, *Epicauta vittata* (Fabricius). Black with a yellow border and median stripe on each wing cover, just over ½ inch long. This very common species, ranging west as far as Montana, is reported occurring in large swarms in Arkansas, both in alfalfa fields and in vegetable gardens. There can be several hundred blister beetles in a square foot of area. Together with the three-striped blister beetle, this species feeds on bean, soybean, beet, corn, melon, peas, potato, radish, tomato, turnip, and other vegetables. DDT is effective where residue is not a problem; rotenone dust can be used near harvest.

Striped Cucumber Beetle*, *Acalymma vittata* (Fabricius). A native insect, the most serious cucumber pest east of the Rocky Mountains, a related species taking over cucurbit destruction in the West. The larvae feed only on roots of cucumber, muskmelon, winter squash, and watermelon, about in the order named, but the adults feed also on beans, corn, peas, and blossoms of other plants.

The beetles are yellowish with 3 black stripes, ⅕ by 1/10 inch (Plate XII). As unmated adults they winter in woodlands near the vegetable garden, under leaves or rotting logs, in lowland hedgerows, or near wild food plants such as goldenrod and aster, but nearly always keeping in direct contact with the ground. They become active in spring when the temperature gets above 55° F. Before cucurbits are up they feed on pollen, petals or leaves of buckeye, willow, wild plum, hawthorn, elm, syringa and other plants. They settle on cucumber and related vines as soon as these appear above ground. Mating takes place as they feed on the vine crops. The female lays orange eggs in or on the soil at the base of such plants.

The very slender white, wormlike larvae, ⅓ inch long, feed on roots and underground parts of stems for 2 to 6 weeks, often destroying the whole root system with subsequent death of vines. From white pupae in the soil, adults appear in midsummer to feed on cucurbits and legumes for another 6 weeks, often eating into the rind of fruits as well as chewing leaves and flowers. There is 1 generation in the North, 2, 3, or possibly 4 in the South.

The beetles are especially dangerous because they transmit bacterial wilt of cucurbits and cucumber mosaic. In my own garden they have frequently been found in spring on Chinese lantern, the leaves of which are often mottled by the mosaic pattern.

Control. Early feeding by beetles can be avoided by starting seeds under Hotkaps or boxes pushed down into the ground, open at the bottom, covered with mosquito netting or fine wire screening over the top. Unprotected vines should be dusted as soon as they appear and weekly thereafter with rotenone or methoxychlor. DDT and lindane may be used on ornamentals but DDT may be injurious to squash and some other cucurbits.

Insecticide mixtures containing sulfur may injure some squash and melon varieties.

Striped Flea Beetle*, *Phyllotreta striolata* (Fabricius). Widely distributed pest of cabbage, 1/12 inch long with a crooked yellow stripe on each wing cover. Eggs are laid in small cavities gnawed in the stem. See also Flea Beetles.

Striped Tortoise Beetle, *Cassida bivittata* Say. Dull yellow, with 5 longitudinal black stripes. The larvae are yellowish white with a median gray line, short marginal spines, and a tail-like projection bearing shed skins but no excrement. White eggs are laid singly on leaf stems or vines, each covered with a daub of black pitch. On sweetpotato, sometimes morning-glory.

Sugar-pine Cone Beetle*, *Conophthorus lambertianae* Hopkins. Hinders seeding of sugar pine in California and Oregon.

Sunflower Beetle*, *Zygospila exclamationis* (Fabricius). Feeding on wild and cultivated sunflower in the West. Another species, *Galerucella notata* (Fabricius), small, dull yellow, is also known as the Sunflower Beetle.

Sweetpotato Flea Beetle*, *Chaetocnema confinis* Crotch. Very small, 1/16 inch long, black with a bronzy reflection. It eats narrow grooves in leaves along the veins. Leaves wilt, plants turn brown. Besides sweetpotato, the beetle infests morning-glory, sugar beet, raspberry, boxelder, corn, cereals, grasses. The larvae feed on roots of bindweed.

Sweetpotato Leaf Beetle*, *Typophorus nigritus viridicyaneus* (Crotch). A metallic blue-green, oblong beetle, a little over ¼ inch. It eats tender leaves at the crown of the plant, devouring them from the margin inward. Pale yellow, plump larvae burrow through the vine underground.

Syneta Leaf Beetle, *Syneta albida* LeConte. Western Fruit Beetle. Common on cherry in the Pacific Northwest, occasional on pear, prune, apple. The beetles, light gray or yellowish, ¼ inch long, emerge from the ground as the trees bloom and stay near the buds for about 2 months. They scar and deform young fruit, also feed on stems, blossoms, leaves. Eggs are dropped to the ground and the grubs feed in fine fibrous roots. Spraying the trees twice with lead arsenate, using an equal amount of lime, greatly reduces injury. Apply just before blossoms open and just after petals have fallen.

Ten-lined June Beetle*, *Polyphylla decemlineata* (Say). Robust, brown, large, covered with yellowish and white scales, arranged to make 2 stripes on the head, 2 on the thorax, and 4 long stripes and 1 short stripe on each wing cover. Larvae are very large white grubs, up to 2 inches long. This species occurs primarily in the Rocky Mountain States and on the Pacific Coast. The larvae may girdle and destroy roots of ornamental shrubs and nursery trees, including California privet, black locust, and wisteria.

Three-lined Potato Beetle*, *Lema trilineata* (Olivier). In some areas damaging to potato and related plants. The adult is reddish yellow with 3 broad black stripes; the larva plasters granular masses of its own excrement over its body.

Three-striped Blister Beetle*, *Epicauta lemniscata* (Fabricius). A western version of the Striped Blister Beetle, which see.

Tobacco Flea Beetle*, *Epitrix hirtipennis* (Melsheimer). Distributed through the United States, including Hawaii. In some years the most important pest of tobacco but also feeding heavily on tomato, potato, ground-cherry, eggplant and pepper and on many nonsolanaceous plants and weeds as an adult. The larvae are restricted to roots of solanaceous plants. The beetles are very small, reddish to dark brown, often with a dark transverse band across the elytra. They hibernate as adults, in soil or under trash, migrating to seedbeds in spring, depositing eggs in crevices in soil. The larva is white, threadlike, with chitinized parts light brown. There may be 3 or 4 generations. Use DDT or methoxychlor for control.

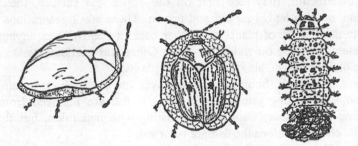

28. Tortoise beetle: adult, two views, and larva carrying its excrement.

Toothed Flea Beetle*, *Chaetocnema denticulata* (Illiger). Small, brassy, with face densely punctured, going to corn and beets from wild grasses.

TORTOISE BEETLES. Sometimes called Sweetpotato Beetles or Gold-bugs. They comprise several species distributed over the United States, feeding on sweetpotato, morning-glory and other members of the Convolvulaceae. They are leaf eaters, relatively small, none over ¼ inch, and nearly as wide as long. The margins of the body are extended to hide the head and most of the legs, making the beetles look like tortoises. They eat holes through the leaves or devour entire leaves, sometimes seriously injuring newly set plants. They winter as beetles in protected places, under bark or trash. The larvae, about ⅜ inch long, have conspicuous horny spines with 2 longer ones at the posterior. On these the larva packs its own excrement and cast skins, and curls this mess over its back like a squirrel's tail (Plate XI). Larvae look like moving pieces of dirt. When full-grown they fasten themselves to leaves to pupate. Spray with malathion or DDT. See also Argus, Black-legged, Golden, and Mottled Tortoise Beetles.

Transverse Lady Beetle*, *Coccinella transversoguttata* Faldermann. Very convex, plain red or with 3 long transverse black spots; common through most of North America.

Tuber Flea Beetle*, *Epitrix tuberis* Gentner. Adults feed on foliage but larvae scar surface of potato tubers and bore into them often causing severe injury. Control with DDT spray or dust.

Twice-stabbed Lady Beetle*. See Lady Beetles.

Two-spotted Lady Beetle*. See Lady Beetles.

Unicorn Beetle. See Rhinoceros Beetle.

Vedalia*. See Lady Beetles.

Watercress Leaf Beetle*, *Phaedon aeruginosus* Suffrian. Small, bronze black, about ⅛ inch long; larvae brownish black with many tubercles of hairs. There seems to be no practical control.

Waterlily Leaf Beetle*, *Galerucella nymphaeae* (Linnaeus). Dark brown beetles, with dull yellow thorax, ¼ inch long, feeding on leaves and flowers of pond lilies and other water plants. The larvae are dark brown above, yellow underneath; they feed first on the upper leaf surface, then on the underside, making leaves ragged and brown. There are 2 generations. Adults winter in dead stems of plants and under bark of nearby trees, laying yellow egg clusters in spring on waterlily leaves. Other leaf beetles (*Donacia* spp.), metallic blue or brown, also feed on water plants.

Control is difficult. Submerging the leaves for a few days, holding down with hoops or netting gets rid of beetles. If fish are removed from pools, leaves and flowers may have a light dusting with malathion, but the water should be changed before the fish are returned.

Western Balsam Bark Beetle*, *Dryocoetes confusus* Swaine. On true firs in the Rocky Mountains, sometimes killing trees. Small, dark, cylindrical beetles, the females with dense, short, yellowish hairs on front of the head. Narrow egg galleries radiate out from a central chamber.

Western Black Flea Beetle*, *Phyllotreta pusilla* Horn. Important in the West. The very small, shiny, olive-green to black beetles often appear in swarms on cabbage, cauliflower, horseradish, mustard, cress, radish, watercress, peppergrass, turnip, sugar beet and corn; also on stock, wallflower, rock cress. The larvae mine in leaves and feed on roots. Spray or dust with rotenone, methoxychlor, or malathion.

Western Cedar Bark Beetle*, *Phloeosinus punctatus* LeConte. Infesting healthy and injured cedar—western, incense, red, Alaska and Port Orford —and giant arborvitae. Small beetles with toothed projections on male wing covers. Egg galleries are short, 1 to 3 inches.

Western Pine Beetle*, *Dendroctonus brevicomis* LeConte. The most important pest of ponderosa and Coulter pines on the Pacific Coast, responsible for tremendous annual damage to timber. The adults are small, ⅛ to ⅕ inch, brown to black bark beetles. They construct a network of winding egg galleries between bark and sapwood. When healthy trees are attacked— seldom those under 6 inches in diameter—resin tubes are formed about the entrance holes. Primarily a forest insect, this beetle may appear in parks and on home grounds. Infested trees should be felled and the bark burned in fall or winter. Woodpeckers and some beetles are natural enemies. Promoting vigorous tree growth is the best preventive measure.

Western Potato Flea Beetle*, *Epitrix subcrinita* (LeConte). Shiny bronze, 1/16 inch long, injuring potatoes and tomatoes but sometimes attacking any of the hosts listed for the potato flea beetle. This western species is serious in Arizona, California, Colorado, Idaho, Montana, Nevada, Oregon, Utah, and Washington.

Western Spotted Cucumber Beetle*, *Diabrotica undecimpunctata undecimpunctata* Mannerheim. Replacing the spotted cucumber beetle west of the Rocky Mountains. It has the same greenish yellow wing covers but is slightly smaller with slightly larger black spots. Soon after native grasses dry up in pastures, the adults swarm into the garden, devastating flowers, lawns, ornamental trees and shrubs, truck crops, fruit trees—in fact nearly every green plant except conifers. The pest is called Diabolical Diabrotica by irate gardeners. The larvae feed on roots of corn and sweetpea as well as grasses. Beetles eat holes in ripening fruit, especially in orchards in uncultivated areas, and spread the fungus causing brown rot of apricots, peaches and other stone fruits.

Control. Spray or dust with DDT, malathion, methoxychlor or Sevin.

Western Striped Cucumber Beetle*, *Acalymma trivittata* (Mannerheim). Most abundant and injurious in southern California but ranging into Arizona and Oregon. The adult is like the eastern species, with a yellowish body and 3 black stripes, but the basal portion of the antenna is yellow instead of black. The larvae attack roots of cucumber, melon, pumpkin, squash and other cucurbits. The adults feed on the tops of these plants and also on bean, beet, corn, pea, sunflower, almond, apple, prune and other fruits.

Western Striped Flea Beetle*, *Phyllotreta ramosa* (Crotch). Shiny black with a brassy reflection and a conspicuous irregular yellow-white band down each wing cover; 1/16 inch long. It may be destructive to cabbage, cauliflower, Brussels sprouts, radish, mustard, stock, turnip, wallflower, watercress and other crucifers in California.

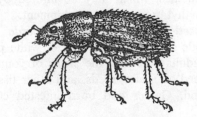

29. White-fringed beetle.

White-fringed Beetles*, *Graphognathus* spp. A complex of species native to South America, first seen in Florida in 1936. Since then the beetles have appeared in Alabama, Arkansas, Georgia, Kentucky, Louisiana, Mississippi,

New Jersey, North Carolina, South Carolina, Tennessee and Virginia but some infestations have been eradicated. The beetles are brownish gray, just under ½ inch long, with a broad, short snout. They are covered with short pale hairs, have margins of wing covers banded with white and two pale lines on head and prothorax. They are gregarious, as many as 200 or 300 beetles being found on one plant eating in from the margins of the leaves or crawling along the ground. The elytra are fused together so they cannot fly. All the adults are parthenogenetic females; no males are known. They feed as adults on about 170 kinds of weeds, vines, trees, shrubs, flowers, and vegetables.

Most damage comes from the larvae, which have been recorded feeding on roots or tubers of nearly 400 plant species. The larvae are yellowish white, curved, legless, up to ½ inch long. Among their numerous host are potato, sweetpotato, cabbage, collards, chufa, turnips, sweet corn, strawberry, blackberry, chrysanthemum, dahlia, daisy, gladiolus, iris, lily, marigold, morning-glory, sunflower, flowering tobacco, violet, and zinnia.

The larvae winter in the soil, usually in the top 9 inches, sometimes lower down, and pupate in a soil cell in spring. The beetles start emerging in May, reaching a peak in June and July. They live for 2 or 3 months, each female averaging 600 to 700 eggs, laid in masses of 11 to 14 at the base of some object—plant, stick, or stone—in contact with the soil. During this time they may crawl ¼ to ¾ mile. The larvae, hatching in 2 weeks to 2 months, eat the soft outer root tissues or may sever the main root. The plants turn yellow, wilt, and die. There is normally 1 generation a year.

Control. Infested areas are under quarantine, and large-scale eradication measures have eliminated the pest in some areas. In home gardens, soil can be treated before planting. Use 2 pounds of 10 per cent DDT dust or 5 per cent chlordane dust to 1000 square feet, working this into the top 3 inches of soil. Or mix ½ pound of 50 per cent DDT wettable powder or ¼ pound chlordane in 2½ gallons of water and apply to 100 square feet of bed space. Spray or dust growing vegetation with DDT every 2 to 3 weeks but avoid this insecticide on camellias, which may be injured by it. Nurseries often fumigate plants with methyl bromide before shipment.

White-pine Cone Beetle*, *Conophthorus coniperda* (Schwartz). A very small, shiny black beetle destructive to cones of white pine from Canada to North Carolina. The adults bore into the stems of young cones to lay their eggs, and the larvae feed on scales, seeds, and other tissues of wilting cones that fall to the ground. Gather and burn infested cones on ornamental plants.

White-spotted Sawyer*, *Monochamus scutellatus* (Say). Large dark beetles mottled with white; important wood pest through the United States except in the South.

Willow Flea Beetle. See Willow Flea Weevil under Weevils.

Yellow-margined Leaf Beetle*, *Microtheca ochroloma* Stål. An introduced pest, from South America, first found in the United States in Alabama in 1947 and since has spread to Louisiana, Mississippi, and Florida. It feeds on crucifers—cabbage, collards, mustard, turnip, radish—and also on potato and members of the primrose family. The adult is small and the brown wing covers have a pale-yellow or white margin and 4 rows of deep pits. It feeds on margins of leaves and makes irregular holes in terminal growth.

BILLBUGS

Billbugs are peculiarly shaped snout beetles present in grasslands and cultivated areas throughout the country but more destructive east of the Great Plains. Adults vary from ⅕ to ¾ inch long, have a cylindrical curved snout (the bill) similar to that of a curculio, and hard body wall and wing covers. They are reddish brown to black, often so covered with mud that their color cannot be told. They gouge out a small hole in a stalk for each white, kidney-shaped egg. When disturbed they "play possum." The grubs are chunky, white, humpbacked, legless, with a hard brown or yellow head. They eat out the pith of stems and then go down to the roots.

Bluegrass Billbug*, *Sphenophorus parvulus* Gyllenhal. Has a body tapered sharply to tip of the abdomen, evenly marked with rounded punctures, ¼ inch long. The grubs excavate stems and eat rootlets of bluegrass and other grasses.

Another species, *S. phoeniciensis* Chittenden, is reported as heavily infesting Arizona lawns.

Maize Billbug*, *Sphenophorus maidis* Chittenden. Broad-bodied, to ⅗ inch long, reddish brown or black, with raised longitudinal lines on wing covers. The billbugs cripple young corn plants, causing excessive suckering, or they kill them outright. The best control is in crop rotation.

Cocklebur Billbug. See Cocklebur Weevil, under Weevils.

Southern Corn Billbug, *Sphenophorus callosus* (Olivier). Known as the Curlew Bug; brown with golden reflections, black elevated bumps, ⅜ inch long. It injures rice and peanuts as well as corn.

BOLLWORMS

Bollworm is the name given to the larva of a moth devouring unripe pods or bolls of cotton. The true bollworm (*Heliothis zea*) is better known to gardeners as the corn earworm or the tomato fruitworm. It is discussed under Earworms.

Pink Bollworm*, *Pectinophora gossypiella* (Saunders). Considered one of the 6 most destructive insects in the world. Probably a native of India, it came to Mexico from Egypt in 1911 and by 1917 had reached Texas. The regulated area now includes Texas, Oklahoma and Arizona, where the pink bollworm is still a problem; Arkansas and Louisiana, where it has been largely eradicated but where occasional specimens are found; and California, still free from this pest and wanting to remain so. Occasionally bollworms are taken from wild cotton or hibiscus blossoms in the Florida Keys or the Everglades. Millions have been spent in containing and eradicating the pink bollworm in this country.

The caterpillars are cylindrical, pinkish, about ½ inch long. They eat holes in the bolls, then drop to the ground to pupate. The moth, dark brown, ¾ inch across the narrow fringed wings, emerges in 9 days and deposits eggs anywhere on the cotton plant, concentrating on terminals. The eggs hatch in 3 to 5 days and the larvae bore into the squares, eat the developing flowers and work in the bolls, consuming lint and seed. Mallow, rose-of-Sharon, abutilon, and hibiscus are sometimes hosts. The bollworm may be spread on okra pods.

Control. Federal and state quarantines regulate the movement of cotton and cotton products and require the treatment of seeds and lint before shipment. Spraying or dusting with DDT or Sevin reduces crop losses.

BORERS

Borers are grubs or caterpillars, larvae of beetles or moths, working in woody tissues or herbaceous stems. There are a great many borers affecting shade and fruit trees, ornamental shrubs, herbaceous annuals and perennials. The proportion selected for inclusion in this manual is small compared to the total number. Borers are particularly destructive to newly set trees and to those weakened from various causes. Some of the factors predisposing trees to bore attack are listed here.

(1.) *Drought* is a primary factor in making trees susceptible to borer attack; the rootlets dry out, the roots are injured, and the whole tree is systemically weakened. Two or three seasons with deficient rainfall are usually followed by large numbers of borers. Newly transplanted trees are subject to attack before they get their root systems established.

(2.) *Sunscald* is important with newly transplanted trees and also on established trees suddenly exposed to the sun by removal of another tree, hedge, or building which had previously kept the trunks shaded.

(3.) *Injuries* from hurricanes, ice storms, frost cracks, bonfires, etc. provide easy entrance for borers.

(4.) *Defoliation by leaf-eating insects* produces a weakened condition highly inviting to borers.

(5.) *Construction activities* with change of grade, lowering or raising of water tables, mechanical injuries from excavations in ditch digging, pipe laying, road building may gravely weaken established trees.

(6.) *Chemical injuries* from leaking illuminating gas in the soil, chlorides applied to roads to lay dust or to melt ice in winter, or fumes from factories are conducive to poor health and borer attack.

The best control measure is the promotion of good health and vigor by proper watering, especially of newly transplanted trees, fertilizing where necessary, spraying to control leaf-eating insects.

Wrapping tree trunks the first year or two after transplanting prevents drying out and sunscald and provides a mechanical barrier to borer attack. The wrapping may be done with strips of burlap or commercial borer wrap (double-thickness paper with a layer of asphaltum in between) or aluminum foil. Start at the first branch and wind spirally downward, overlapping half the width at each spiral. Tie firmly with twine wound spirally in the opposite direction. The trunk should be sprayed with DDT or dieldrin (using wettable powder, not an oil emulsion) before covering. The wrapping should be removed in a year, to make sure no borers have gotten underneath and gone to work, but then it can be replaced for a second year. Spraying transplanted trees and shrubs with an antidessicant such as Wiltpruf helps to prevent borer attack and may replace wrapping.

For borer prevention on established trees and shrubs, spray trunk and branches at the time eggs on the bark are due to hatch. This is spring for many species, late summer for a few. Repeat at monthly intervals to prevent egg laying by the adult. Materials presently recommended are DDT (4 pounds of 50 per cent wettable powder to 100 gallons of water, or 4 tablespoons to 1 gallon), or dieldrin (2 quarts of 18 per cent emulsion to 100 gallons) or lindane (1 quart of 20 per cent emulsion to 100 gallons).

If, despite all precautions, holes and sawdust or pitch tubes on the bark indicate borers already at work, there are still remedies. Hand-worming is first, cutting out borers in the cambium beneath the bark, but a sharp knife should be used with caution lest it injure the wood. Treat exposed wood with a good wound paint. Borers in wood can sometimes be killed by probing with a flexible wire, cleaning out the tunnel, and then injecting nicotine sulfate, malathion, or carbon disulfide into the hole, then sealing the opening with mud, putty, or caulking compound to contain the fumes. Some of the commercial borer preparations now marketed for such injections contain lindane.

It is always important to trim injured trees promptly, making smooth cuts flush with the bark, and to cut out all infested wood before the borers can emerge to attack other trees. Tree-wound dressings are now available as aerosols, making prompt treatment of the cut surface easy.

American Plum Borer*, *Euzophera semifuneralis* (Walker). Larva of a small, inconspicuous moth, family Phycitidae, with long, threadlike antennae. Most members of this family are pests of stored products but this plum borer, widely distributed, bores under the bark and sometimes kills shade trees, including maple, sycamore, linden, mountain-ash, as well as plum, almond, apple, apricot, cherry, pecan. It is also a relatively new pest of stored sweetpotatoes.

Apple Bark Borer*, *Thamnosphecia pyri* (Harris). Also known as Pear Borer, but it more commonly infests apple. It may likewise infest pecan, hawthorn, mountain-ash, and shadbush from Maine to Texas. Larvae of a clearwing moth, family Aegeriidae, the borers are found in crotches and in rough bark of neglected trees.

Apple Twig Borer*, *Amphicerus bicaudatus* (Say). Larva of a false powder beetle, family Bostrichidae, attacking twigs of apple, cherry, pear, grape, Osage-orange, pecan, ash, and other trees in various parts of North America.

Ash Borer*, *Podosesia syringae fraxini* (Lugger). Generally distributed, but apparently limited to ash and mountain-ash, more serious in prairie states. The adult is a clearwing moth, family Aegeriidae. The front wings are opaque blackish brown with a violet reflection and red crossbar; hind wings are transparent with a narrow black border; the abdomen is black with yellow bands. The larvae—white worms 1½ inches long, with brown heads—bore in the tree just below ground level or near the base, making so many burrows that the tree easily breaks over in a wind. Cut and burn infested parts or whole trees. See also Lilac Borer for a species just as common on ash.

Australian-pine Borer*, *Chrysobothris tranquebarica* (Gmelin). Also called Mangrove Borer. This borer attacks living red mangrove and casuarina trees planted as ornamentals and windbreaks in Florida. The adult beetles, family Buprestidae, are greenish bronze, ½ to ¾ inch long, with 3 lighter impressions on each wing cover. They appear in April, laying eggs under the bark. The flatheaded larvae bore through the bark and into the wood to construct pupal cells. DDT sprays may help but the best control is to cut out beetle-infested branches or trees in fall or winter.

Azalea Stem Borer, *Oberea myops* Haldeman. A long-horned beetle, family Cerambycidae, girdling tips of stems of azalea, rhododendron, blueberry, mountain-laurel, and perhaps other plants in spring. The beetle is slender, ½ inch across, with yellow head and thorax, the latter with 3 black spots, and grayish-yellow punctate wing covers. Twigs are girdled in 2 places, ½ inch apart, and a yellow egg is thrust through the bark halfway between. The tip dies and the yellow, legless grub, ½ inch or more long, bores down the twig and into the trunk, pushing out sawdust from holes near the ground. It winters in a cell in the crown of the plant, below ground, pupates in spring, and the adults emerge in June (in New Jersey). Infested bushes have dying tips and readily break over from borings in the lower part of the stems.

Control. Cut out and burn dead and dying tips as soon as noticed. Inject borer paste into holes. Spray with DDT in June or July.

Banana Root Borer*, *Cosmopolites sordidus* (Germar).

Banded Alder Borer*, *Rosalia funebris* Motschulsky. Also known as California-laurel Borer, a long-horned beetle, family Cerambycidae. The larvae mine California-laurel, Oregon ash, willow as well as alder.

Banded Hickory Borer*, *Cerasphorus* (Chion) *cinctus* (Drury). An elongate, cylindrical beetle, family Cerambycidae, up to 1 inch in length, with spines on thorax and elytra and crescent-shaped yellow bands on elytra and spines at the tip. The larva is a slender yellowish borer, with head wider than long. It feeds in dead hickory, oak and other hardwoods.

Black-horned Pine Borer*, *Callidium antennatum* var. *hesperum* Casey. Flattened blackish-blue beetles. The larvae have tough, shiny skins, wide heads, and feed beneath bark and in sapwood of dead pines, spruces, hemlocks, junipers, and cedars.

Boxelder Twig Borer*, *Proteoteras willingana* (Kearfott). A moth, family Olethreutidae. The larvae attack boxelder twigs.

Branch and Twig Borer, *Melalgus* (Polycaon) *confertus* (LeConte). A cylindrical beetle, about ½ inch long, black with brown elytra, burrowing into twig crotches or buds of apricot, olive, avocado, citrus and fig trees, sometimes grapevines. The large, whitish larvae, with fine hairs, work in dead heartwood of many ornamental trees in California and Oregon. Often there is rather extensive killing of twigs and branches. A sporadic but sometimes severe pest of avocado, this borer indicates its presence by the sugary sap, turning white and flaky, exuding from the entrance burrows.

Prune out infested twigs on small fruit trees. Burn dead brush and orchard prunings.

Broad-necked Root Borer*, *Prionus laticollis* (Drury). A brownish black beetle with long, serrated antennae, 1 to 1¾ inches, another member of the Cerambycidae. The large, legless, yellowish grub, 2½ to 3 inches, excavates a burrow in roots of oaks, sometimes poplar, chestnut, apple, pine, and grape. Rhododendrons growing near such roots may also be attacked, infested stems being broken off at ground level. The life cycle may take 3 years. There is no reliable method of control.

Bronze Birch Borer*, *Agrilus anxius* Gory. A native beetle, family Buprestidae, the flatheaded borers. Distributed through northern United States as far west as Colorado and Idaho, this species attacks white, gray, black, and canoe birches, poplar, quaking aspen, cottonwood, and willow. It is more injurious to ornamental trees grown in the open than to forest trees, and flourishes on decadent rather than vigorous trees.

The beetle is slender, olive-bronze, with a blunt head, tapering body, nearly 1 inch long. The grub is white, slender, with the region just back of the head enlarged, and with a horny, forcepslike appendage at the tip of the abdomen. It mines in irregular winding galleries just under the bark, which is loosened. The first sign of injury is the dying back of trees at the top, by which time it is rather late for control measures. This is a serious pest, the entire tree usually dying eventually.

Control. Spray with DDT or dieldrin in June (New York) at time of beetle emergence. Or apply DDT plus malathion in late May and repeat 3 weeks later. Keep white and other ornamental birches well watered in times of drought.

Bronze Poplar Borer*, *Agrilus liragus* Barter & Brown. Similar to the bronze birch borer, olivaceous bronze in color, infesting poplars through northern North America.

Brown Wood Borer, *Parandra brunnea* Fabricius. Also called Pole Borer, a native beetle occurring east of the Rocky Mountains in dead wood and sometimes in cavities in living trees. It may infest almost all hardwood shade trees, some conifers, and apple, pear, and cherry. The beetle is glossy chestnut brown, ¾ inch long, one of the Cerambycidae, the long-horned group, but with antennae no longer than the elytra. Because this borer enters living trees only through wounds, careful pruning, leaving no broken projecting branch stubs, is a preventive.

Burdock Borer*, *Papaipema cataphracta* (Grote). A smooth pale-brown caterpillar, with a white stripe down the back and along each side, sometimes infesting stalks of delphinium, dahlia, hollyhock, goldenglow, and iris. The adult is an owlet or cutworm moth, family Noctuidae.

California Flatheaded Borer*, *Melanophila californica* Van Dyke. Larva of a Buprestid beetle, infesting pines in the far West and the northern Rockies. Small tortuous galleries are formed in slow-growing trees.

California Prionus*, *Prionus californicus* Motschulsky. Also called Giant Apple Borer. This very large, 1½ to 2½ inches, shiny, reddish brown beetle, family Cerambycidae, is common along the Pacific Coast from Alaska through California and eastward into the Rocky Mountain region and the Southwest. The larvae, grubs 2 to 3 inches long, bore in dead of living roots of oak, alder, poplar, and other hardwoods, and in pine, redwood, Douglas-fir, and fir. Fruit trees are sometimes killed. The adults fly at night, midsummer to fall. They are attracted to lights and may hit windows with great force. The females lay their eggs on roots and the resulting larvae bore for 4 or 5 years before they mature. It may be possible to probe for and destroy them with a knife or wire.

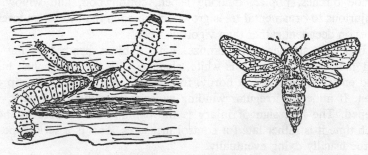

30. Carpenterworm: borer and adult moth.

Carpenterworm*, *Prionoxystus robiniae* (Peck). Widely distributed through the country, attacking many shade trees—ash, elm, locust, maple, oak, poplar, willow and others—sometimes apricot and pear. It is particularly injurious to live oaks and elm on the Pacific Coast. The name comes from the large tunnels—as much as ½ to 1 inch in diameter—which the caterpillar excavates in solid wood of trees. The borer is white, tinted with rose, with small brown tubercles over the body and a dark-brown head; 1 to 2½ inches long. The larvae feed in sapwood when young, later through heart-wood; the trunk may be riddled with burrows. The life cycle may take 3 years or more. The moth (family Cossidae) comes out in June and July, leaving the pupal skin protruding from the burrow. The female is 2½ to 3 inches across the wings, with a stout body, mottled gray fore wings, smaller, smoky hind wings. The male is similar but smaller, with an orange margin on hind wings. Greenish-white sticky eggs are laid in bark crevices, wounds, and old burrows.

Control. Keep all wounds painted. Inject carbon disulfide into openings, about 1 tablespoon to each, and close with putty or grafting wax. Arborists may use calcium cyanide in place of carbon disulfide.

Cedar Tree Borer*, *Semanotis ligneus* (Fabricius). A western beetle, family Cerambycidae, working in bark and wood of cedars, arborvitae, redwood, Douglas-fir, and Monterey pine. The adult is black, ½ inch long, with orange or red markings on elytra. The larvae make winding burrows in inner bark and sapwood, girdling and killing trees.

Chestnut-bark Borer, *Anoplodera nitens* Forster. An elongate, robust beetle, velvety black with golden bands, breeding in moist bark of chestnut and oak trees in eastern states. Adults are found in tree flowers, and they lay eggs in bark at base of tree and in crotches of living branches. Wounds caused by this borer, allowing entrance to disease spores, played a part in the rapid spread of chestnut blight through North America.

Chestnut Timberworm*, *Melittoma sericeum* (Harris). A pest of our old chestnuts and now of oak. The beetle, family Lymexilidae, is chestnut brown, ½ inch long. The larva is slender, white shading to dark brown at the rear. It bores galleries in sapwood and heartwood of dead and living trees. It probably enters through wounds.

Clematis Borer, *Alcathoe caudata* (Harris). The dull-white larva, ⅔ inch long, of a clearwing moth, fore wings black to violet, rear wings transparent with dark margins. The borer works in fleshy roots and crown of clematis and virgin's-bower and may hollow out base of stems. Vines are stunted and branches die. Cut out and burn infested stems; dig out larvae in crowns. Spray or dust with DDT in early spring.

Clover Root Borer*, *Hylastinus obscurus* (Marsham). The small, dark-brown to black beetles, family Scolytidae, and very small white, footless grubs winter in the ground in clover roots. Tunnels made in red and other clovers, sometimes pea roots, cause wilting, browning, and death of plants.

Clover Stem Borer*, *Languria mozardi* Latreille. Yellowish worms, ½ inch long, with 2 hooks at the end of the body, feed on pith in stems of red and sweet clovers. Stems are swollen, cracked or broken off. The adult is a small beetle with blue wing covers and red head and thorax, family Languriidae.

Columbine Borer*, *Papaipema purpurifascia* (Grote & Robinson). Larva of a moth, family Noctuidae, restricted to stems and fleshy roots of wild and cultivated columbine wherever the host is grown. The large reddish-brown moth scatters its eggs on the ground near the plant and the larvae hatch in late April or early May. The salmon caterpillar has a pale stripe down the back, may be up to 1½ inches long. Sawdustlike castings on the ground and dying back of the plant indicate borers at work. Cut off infested stems or destroy plants. Scrape surface of soil in spring to kill eggs. Dust with DDT at weekly intervals in late April and May.

Cottonwood Borer*, *Plectrodera scalator* (Fabricius). A large, long-horned beetle distributed from Maryland to Louisiana and Texas, particularly injurious in the central and southern states to cottonwood, poplar, and willow. The adult is black, mottled, with a white pubescence; 1½ inches, with antennae longer than body. The larva is a large grub, 1¾ to 2 inches, deeply constricted into segments. It tunnels beneath bark and into wood at base of trunks, infested trees readily blowing over. Sawdust and shredded wood mark its presence. The borer feeds as a larva for 2 years before transforming into a beetle to lay eggs at base of trees. Larvae can be killed by injecting carbon disulfide into holes. Spray lower trunks with DDT or dieldrin.

Cranberry Girdler*, *Crambus topiarius* Zeller. One of the sod webworms or grass moths, family Crambidae, injurious to bluegrass as well as cranberry. A DDT-parathion combination, applied by airplane, is recommended for commercial cranberry growers.

Currant Borer*, *Ramosia tipuliformis* (Clerck). A yellowish caterpillar, ½ inch long, larva of a small black-and-yellow clearwing moth that looks like a wasp. It is distributed through North America, attacks red and black currants, being more destructive on the latter, and also gooseberry, black elder, and sumac. The larva hibernates in a tunnel in the wood, pupates in spring; the moths emerge in June and July to lay eggs on bark of canes. Cut out and destroy yellowing unthrifty canes before the moths emerge.

Currant Stem Girdler*, *Janus integer* (Norton). One of the stem sawflies, family Cephidae, with adults looking like delicate wasps. The female lays an egg in spring, girdling it so the tips hang down. Legless larvae bore in currant stems. Cut off and burn infested tips.

Dendrobium Borer, *Xyleborus morigerus* Blandford. Minute brown beetles bore into orchid pseudobulbs and deposit eggs in broad galleries. The larvae make long galleries. Seriously infested bulbs wither and die. Cut out and burn infested portions as soon as noticed. Spray with DDT.

Dogwood Borer*, *Thamnosphecia scitula* (Harris). Sometimes called the

Pecan Borer. A whitish caterpillar with brown head, ½ inch long, working in cambium of flowering dogwood and sometimes pecan. The infested areas may be 2 feet or more long and contain up to 50 borers. Small trees or branches may be girdled and die. Small moths, family Aegeriidae, with blue-black margins to their clear wings, emerge from late spring to midsummer to lay eggs in roughened places on the bark. Spray trunk and branches with DDT or dieldrin in mid-May and repeat a month or so later. Avoid mechanical injuries with lawn mowers by placing a guard around the trunk; protect pruning cuts with tree-wound dressing.

Dogwood Cambium Borer, *Agrilus cephalicus* LeConte. The flatheaded larva of a beetle, working in soft wood; widely distributed but only rarely injurious. Wrap newly transplanted trees; water them properly.

Dogwood Twig Borer*, *Oberea tripunctata* (Swederus). Also known as Elm Twig Girdler, a lemon-yellow grub, larva of a long-horned beetle, boring in center of twigs, making a series of closely placed holes for protrusion of frass. The adult, yellow with blackish wing covers, emerges in early summer and, after girdling the tip, deposits eggs in twigs of dogwood, elm, viburnum, and many fruit trees. Cut out and burn infested twigs.

Elder Borer, *Desmocerus palliatus* (Forster). Cloaked Knotty Horn. A dark-blue beetle with a yellow "cloak" thrown over upper portion of the elytra. The borer is creamy white, an inch long. It riddles base of stems of wild and cultivated elders. The burrows cause dying back of branches, sometimes death of whole shrubs. The beetles sometimes eat notches out of foliage.

Elder Shoot Borer*, *Achatodes zeae* (Harris). The Spindleworm of corn, working in the tassel or spindle, found near golden elder. The larva is yellowish white with a double row of black dots across each segment and a black head. The moth, family Noctuidae, has rusty fore wings mottled with gray, and yellowish-gray hind wings. Cut out dead elder wood in autumn to destroy eggs.

Elm Borer*, *Saperda tridentata* Olivier. Roundheaded larva of a long-horned beetle, family Cerambycidae. The adult is gray with orange-red bands across the elytra; occurring in eastern states. Park and shade trees are often severely injured, particularly those weakened from defoliation by elm leaf beetles. Eggs are laid in cracks in bark, and grubs work in the inner bark and sapwood, cutting off much of the sap flow. Escaping sap and frass appear as moist spots on the bark. The borers are reddish at first, later creamy white, an inch long when grown. Keep trees growing vigorously with plenty of water; watch for signs of injury and dig out borers; protect bark with DDT.

European Corn Borer*, *Ostrinia nubilalis* (Hübner). One of the most destructive corn pests (Plate XIII). It probably arrived in shipments of broomcorn from Italy or Hungary about 1909 but was not recorded until 1917, in Massachusetts. It has since spread throughout the East and west to

Montana, Wyoming, and Colorado, and has edged into Texas. It is chiefly a stalk pest, not only in corn but in aster, cosmos, dahlia, gladiolus, hollyhock, chrysanthemum, zinnia and other flowers as well as in beans, beets, celery, pepper, and potatoes. The corn borer is recorded on about 200 species of plants with stems large enough for the worms to enter.

The larvae, flesh-colored caterpillars with rows of small, round, dark-brown spots, up to 1 inch long, winter in old stalks left around the garden; they pupate in spring. The female moth (family Pyraustidae) is yellow brown with wavy dark bands; the male is somewhat darker. They have a wing-spread of 1 inch, fly mostly at night. Eggs are laid in flat masses on underside of corn leaves over a period of 3 to 4 weeks, each female averaging about 400 eggs. These hatch in early June, young larvae working down into the stalks and into the base of ears. Broken tassels, bent stalks, sawdust castings outside small holes signify borers at work. They are occasionally found in fruit or flowers as well as stalks.

The borers predominating in the eastern and southern portions of the corn-borer area are of a multiple-generation strain, varying with the climate. There is 1 generation in northern states, 2 around New Jersey, perhaps 3 in Virginia. A single-generation strain predominates in the North Central States. Despite control measures this pest costs millions of dollars in crop losses each year.

Control. Sanitation is important—cleaning up and burning all stalks (corn, dahlia, or weed) capable of harboring borers over the winter. In regions where there are 2 generations, corn planted the latter half of May usually matures between broods. Early and late corn should be treated. Spray with DDT, 3 tablespoons to 1 gallon of water, or Sevin, 2 tablespoons of 50 per cent wettable powder to 1 gallon, or dust with Ryania or rotenone. Start when tassels are barely discernible and repeat at 5-day intervals for 3 to 5 applications, directing the chemical down into the whorl of leaves. For ornamentals use DDT spray or dust at weekly intervals in July and August. Of 24 parasites introduced into the United States for corn borer control, 6 have become established. A fungus disease and a protozoan are also helpful.

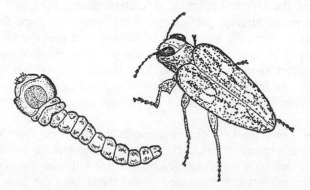

31. Flatheaded apple tree borer and adult beetle.

Flatheaded Apple Tree Borer, *Chrysobothris femorata* (Olivier). A common pest throughout North America (Plate XIV). The larvae mine the inner bark, cambium, sapwood, and heartwood of healthy, injured, or dying deciduous fruit and shade trees, including apple, apricot, ash, mountain-ash, beech, boxelder, cherry, chestnut, cottonwood, currant, dogwood, elm, hickory, horsechestnut, linden, maple, oak, peach, pear, pecan, plum, poplar, prune, sycamore, willow, and also raspberry and rose. In the West, oak is often the preferred host; in the East, maples and fruits are frequently attacked. This borer kills many trees and shrubs in the nursery and many trees the first season after transplanting. Injury is worse in dry seasons and to tree trunks exposed to too much sun through excessive pruning.

The winter is passed as a grub, up to 1¼ inches long, yellowish white, rather slender, with a broad, flat enlargement just behind the head, usually lying with the body curved to one side, appearing rather U-shaped. The grub burrows under the bark until full-sized, then bores deeper in the wood. The tunnels, filled with dry frass, run 6 inches or more down the trunk of a small tree or may go around the trunk to girdle it. Overlying bark is discolored, often slightly sunken, and may die, but the injury is not marked by castings, as with other borers.

The beetles, family Buprestidae, are dark olive gray to brown with a metallic luster, blunt at the head end, tapering at the posterior, ½ inch long. They emerge in May or June and hang around the sunny side of trees or logs. They deposit eggs in bark cracks or some portion of the trunk injured by sunscald or bruising. There is a one-year cycle.

Control. Preventive measures are best. Wrap newly transplanted trees or spray with Wiltpruf. Shade exposed trunks of young fruit trees by placing an upright board about 6 inches wide close to the trunk on the south side. Prune young fruit trees to keep them headed low. Fertilize and water properly. Remove borers already in tree with knife or wire and paint the wounds. Spray with DDT to prevent egg laying.

Flatheaded Cherry Tree Borer, *Dicerca divaricata* (Say). An elongate bronze or grayish beetle, widely distributed, infesting cherry and many dying hardwoods. Another species, *D. horni* Crotch, is commonly destructive in the West. The long larvae mine in weakened trees and shrubs, including ornamentals such as ceanothus, California coffeeberry, madroña, mountain-mahogany, snowberry, elm, sycamore and others.

Flatheaded Cone Borer*, *Chrysophana placida* var. *conicola* Van Dyke. A small metallic-green beetle mining cones and wood of various pines, firs, mountain hemlock, and redcedar in the West. It is destructible to the seed crop.

Flatheaded Fir Borer*, *Melanophila drummondi* (Kirby). Present but not important in the East; infesting normal or injured firs, Douglas-fir, hemlock, larch, yellow pine, and spruce in the West. Adults are metallic black or bronze beetles, ⅜ to ½ inch long, some with golden spots in wing covers. Curved, flatheaded larvae excavate shallow, winding burrows.

Gall-making Maple Borer*, *Xylotrechis aceris* Fisher. A small brown beetle attacking red, silver, Norway, and sugar maples. The cream-colored, roundheaded larvae mine in trunks of small trees and branches of larger trees so extensively, the branch is broken off by wind. New wood produced to heal the wound makes a conspicuous gall.

Grape Cane Gall Maker*, *Ampeloglypter sesostris* (LeConte). A snout beetle causing gall formation.

Grape Cane Girdler, *Ampeloglypter ater* LeConte. Small larvae tunnel in canes causing death of terminal portion. Eggs are laid by a small black snout beetle.

Grape Root Borer*, *Vitacea polistiformis* (Harris). Larva of a brown and orange clearwing moth. Eggs are laid on grape foliage and the round, whitish caterpillars, up to 1¾ inches long, drop to the ground and bore into roots, remaining there for 2 years before pupation in soil outside roots. Cultivate soil to destroy pupae.

Grape Trunk Borer*, *Cerasphorus albofasciatus* (LaPorte & Gory).

Hemlock Borer*, *Melanophila fulvoguttata* (Harris). Also called Spotted Hemlock Borer and Eastern Flatheaded Hemlock Borer. It ranges from Maine to North Carolina, attacks hemlock and, more rarely, spruce. The beetle is flat, ½ inch long, dark bronze with wing covers marked with yellow spots. The larva is white, small, with the same type of enlargement behind the head as the flatheaded apple tree borer. The larvae separate the bark from the wood with wide, shallow galleries, often killing trees in parks and on estates as well as those in forests. The beetles emerge in May, June, and July; there is only 1 generation. Drought is most conducive to injury from this borer. Be sure trees have enough water. Prune off and burn infested branches; cut down fatally injured trees; remove and destroy the bark before storing the wood. There are several parasites.

Honeylocust Borer, *Agrilus difficilis* Gory. A flatheaded borer on living honeylocust, more important west of the Mississippi River in trees weakened by drought. First symptoms are wet, gummy spots around the nodes.

Iris Borer*, *Macronoctua onusta* Grote. The most destructive pest of iris—German, Japanese, and native blue flag—recorded also on blackberry lily (Belamcanda). The borer winters in the egg stage on old iris leaves and debris and particularly at the base of old iris stalks. The larvae, hatching in late April or early May, crawl up the iris leaves and make pinpoint holes as they enter. They gnaw out soft leaf tissue between leaf surfaces and work their way slowly down toward the rhizomes, leaving a water-soaked (due to exuding drops of sap) and ragged appearance to the leaf fans. While in the leaves, the larvae are slender and about 1 inch long, but after reaching the rhizomes, usually in early July, they become fat and repulsive, 1½ to 2 inches long, flesh-colored to pink with chestnut-brown heads. After eating out the interior of the rhizome, the borer pupates in a brown pupa case loose in the soil. The moths, family Noctuidae, have dark purplish fore wings and yellow-brown hind wings. They appear from late August into October, flying only at night. The eggs are flattened and elaborately sculptured, first creamy white with a green tinge, later lavender. They are deposited in groups of 100 or more, a single female averaging 1000 eggs. There is only 1 brood a year.

The chief harm done by iris borers is not so much from their own chewing, devastating as that is, but from their introducing into the plants the bacteria causing the vile-smelling soft rot. This disease was extremely common in gardens before DDT provided an adequate control of borers.

Control. Spray with DDT, 3 level tablespoons of 50 per cent wettable powder per gallon of water, or use a 5 per cent DDT dust, starting when foliage is about 5 or 6 inches high and continuing at weekly intervals to flowering. Dimethoate, 1 teaspoon of Cygon per gallon, is a recent recommendation. Clean up all old iris foliage, stalks and other debris in late autumn to eliminate borer eggs. Young borers may sometimes be killed in place by pressing the leaf between thumb and finger. If iris is to be divided, do it as soon as possible after flowering, cutting out all infested portions. If soft rot is present, soak rhizomes for 20 minutes in a 1 to 1000 bichloride of mercury solution (2 tablets to 1 quart of water) or dust the rhizomes with gypsum. Let them lie in the sun for a few days before replanting.

Larger Shot-hole Borer*, *Scolytus mali* (Bechstein). Sometimes a pest of fruit trees growing near woodpiles. Leaf and fruit spurs may wilt and brown if the beetle feeds in the crotch between spur and twig. This species is recorded from Connecticut, New York, New Jersey, and Ohio.

Lesser Cornstalk Borer*, *Elasmopalpus lignosellus* (Zeller). Found almost anywhere but only injurious in the South. Slender, greenish, brown-striped worms bore into lower part of stalk, not more than 2 inches from the soil surface, causing distortion and curling of stalks of young corn, often failure to produce ears. The borer feeds also on bean, soybean, pea, cowpea, turnip, even strawberries, and has caused heavy losses in peanuts. The larvae spin their cocoons on the ground under trash. The moths, family Phycitidae, brownish yellow with gray margins and black spots, appear in 2 or 3 weeks to lay eggs on leaves or stalks. There are 2 generations. Early planting, fall and winter cleanup of land, and rotating corn with a resistant crop are recommended control measures. Aldrin in a band over the seed furrow has given effective control.

Lesser Peach Tree Borer*, *Synanthedon pictipes* (Grote & Robinson). Nearly as important as the peach tree borer, attacking stone fruits, peach, plum, cherry, in all peach-growing sections except the West; most abundant in the South. Masses of gum mixed with brown sawdust exude from upper trunk and branches, especially at forks. Caterpillars ¾ inch long, white with brown heads, work in bark under such gum masses. They pupate inside the burrows but close to the openings, which are covered with silk webs. Metallic, blue-black, yellow-marked moths emerge in May in the South, June in Connecticut, to lay eggs in bark crevices, around crotches or wounds. They are very active on sunny days.

Control. DDT is not as effective for this species as it is for the peach tree borer. Parathion, 15 per cent, at rate of 1½ to 2 pounds per 100 gallons of water, has given good results if applied at time of emergence and repeated once or twice at 2-week intervals. Guthion is also recommended for the commercial orchardist, also Thiodan and endrin. The home gardener can try malathion but should put most faith in digging out borers by hand, keeping trees properly fed and watered, preventing cultivator damage, prompt treating of wounds with asphalt paint, and choosing trees with wide-angle crotches.

Lilac Borer*, *Podosesia syringae syringae* (Harris). Also known as the Ash Borer and more important on that host than the species officially named the Ash Borer. The lilac borer attacks lilacs, mountain-ash, occasionally privet, through the eastern states to Colorado and Texas. Surely every gardener is familiar with old lilac trunks full of holes and protruding sawdust. On ash there are large, scarlike outgrowths where the caterpillars have burrowed in the trunk (Plate XV).

The white borer, ¾ to 1½ inches long, with a brown head, winters in the wood, usually near the ground, feeds again in spring, pushing its burrow nearly through the bark, and then pupates. There are conflicting dates given for emergences, and more than one race may be involved. New England reports late April and May, Illinois, May to July, Virginia, August and September. The adult is a wasplike clearwing moth with brown fore wings, transparent hind wings with a dark border, wing expanse 1½ inches. It is an active flier. The females lay their eggs in masses at the base of lilac stems or in roughened or wounded places on the bark.

Control. Spray trunks with DDT or dieldrin to prevent egg laying. Borers in their burrows can be killed by injecting carbon disulfide or by inserting a flexible wire. Wounds should be trimmed smooth and painted with shellac or a tree-wound dressing.

Lima-bean Pod Borer*, *Etiella zinckenella* (Treitschke). White to greenish or reddish caterpillar, 1 inch long, attacks seeds, in their green pods, of peas, beans, vetch, lupines, and locust trees. The adult is a Phycitid moth, small, gray, with ocher markings and a broad white band. Crop rotation is suggested.

Lima-bean Vine Borer*, *Monoptilota pergratialis* (Hulst). Larva of a Phycitid moth, reported as causing some damage to lima beans in Delaware and North Carolina.

Linden Borer*, *Saperda vestita* Say. Principally a linden pest, although it may attack poplars. The beetles (family Cerambycidae) are up to ¾ inch long, dark reddish brown with olive-yellow pubescence, 3 dark spots on each wing cover. They feed on growing shoots, leaf petioles, and large veins of leaves, often killing tips of branches. Eggs are laid in incisions in trunk and branches. Larvae, white, slender, 1 inch long, mine in bark and wood. Old, unthrifty trees are rather frequently attacked but die slowly, the larger branches first. Worming by hand seems to be the most feasible control.

Little Carpenterworm*, *Prionoxystus macmurtrei* (Guérin-Méneville). Present throughout eastern United States and west to Minnesota; often more injurious to oaks than the carpenterworm but similar to it in habit and character of damage. Red oaks are favored, especially young trees in street plantings. The female is pepper-and-salt gray, with black, veinlike markings on fore wings, which spread to 2 or 2½ inches; hind wings are clear. The larvae, 2½ inches long, are greenish-white with light-brown heads. See carpenterworm for control.

Live-oak Root Borer, *Archodontes melanopsis* Linnaeus. A very large beetle working on eastern live oak, pecan, and hackberry, from Virginia to Florida and along the Gulf Coast. The adult is dark brown, flat, broad, 1¾ to 2¼ inches long with slender antennae. The larva is white, as thick as a finger, nearly 3½ inches long, with prominent body segments. The female lays eggs in a collar on young trees just below ground level, and the larvae bore into roots of young oaks, enlarging the root into a huge gall and preventing formation of new roots. New suckers around old stumps make for shrub-oak barrens rather than stately live-oak forests. Digging out the worms by hand is the best control.

Locust Borer*, *Megacyllene robiniae* (Forster). Common wherever black or yellow locust is grown and especially injurious to locusts used as street trees. It is a black beetle, ½ to ¾ inch long, with bright-yellow crossbands on thorax and wing covers and a conspicuous W-shaped mark at the base of the latter. It feeds on pollen of goldenrod and other composites in autumn. The larvae—white, cylindrical, widest just behind the head—mine in inner bark and sapwood, later burrow into solid wood. Infested trees may be full of longitudinal burrows a half inch in diameter, up to 3 inches long. The trunk may have swollen areas with the bark cracked open. Pupation is in the burrows, beetles emerging in August and September to lay eggs in bark scars and crevices. These hatch within 2 weeks and the larvae bore through the corky layer of bark to fashion a small cell for winter. Trees under 6 inches in diameter are more likely to be attacked. Bark of the trunk and large branches should be sprayed in late August or early September with DDT, dieldrin, or lindane. One treatment every 3 years may be sufficient.

Locust Twig Borer*, *Ecdytolopha insiticiana* Zeller. Causes elongate galls, up to 3 inches long, in twigs of black locust. The caterpillar is reddish to yellow, ½ to ¾ inch long. The adult is a small moth (family Olethreutidae) with brown fore wings, gray hind wings. Cut out and burn infested twigs. An application of DDT in May is sometimes recommended.

Maple Borer, *Xiphydria maculata* Say. One of the wasplike horntails, family Xiphydriidae, with the abdomen ending in a spine or horn. The larvae—cylindrical, whitish, ¾ inch long—make galleries in dead or dying maple wood.

Maple Callus Borer*, *Sylvora acerni* (Clemens). Also known as Maple Sesian. A clearwing moth seriously injuring hard and soft maples in New England and west to Illinois and Nebraska. It is responsible for rough, enlarged scars and deformities on trunks and branches. The trees have difficulty healing wounds because the larvae—white, ½ inch long with brown heads—work in new callus tissue, enlarging small wounds so that young trees are girdled and killed. The moths are amber, with yellow heads and yellow bands on the abdomen, 1-inch wingspread. They appear in late May or June to deposit eggs around old scars and other rough places. Smooth off roughened bark areas; dig out borers under bark in spring; keep wounds painted.

Maple Petiole Borer*, *Caulocampus acericaulis* (MacGillivray). A sawfly fairly common on maple. The larvae, ⅓ inch long, yellow with brown heads, tunnel in leaf petioles in May and June, causing leaf drop. Defoliation seldom exceeds a third of the total foliage so the effect is not too serious. There is only 1 generation a year.

Nautical Borer, *Xylotrechus nauticus* Mannheim. Stout, cylindrical beetles (family Cerambycidae ½ to ⅝ inch long, dark brown with lighter, zigzag markings. The larvae bore in heartwood of dead oak, madroña, and eucalyptus but may attack living trees, including English walnut and peach. Reported from California, Oregon, and Montana.

Oak Sapling Borer*, *Goes tesselatus* (Haldeman). Kills many oaks by cutting them off at the base, weakens others with mines so they break in wind or ice storm. The larva is yellow white, fleshy. The beetle (family Cerambycidae) is long-horned with yellow-brown wing covers mottled with yellow. The life cycle may last 2 to 3 years.

Oak Timberworm*, *Arrhenodes minutus* (Drury). Also known as Northern Brenthian, a slender beetle with a very long snout (family Brentidae). The shiny brown female, marked with yellow spots, bores a hole in the bark with her snout and pushes an egg to the bottom of the tunnel. The long, slender larvae bore in solid wood of elm, beech, chestnut, and oak, usually in felled timber, sometimes entering living trees through wounds.

Orchid Bulb Borer, *Eucactophagus weissi* Barber. Blackish beetles, slightly over ½ inch long, with pale-yellow blotches on wing covers, feed on leaves and other parts of orchids. The larvae feed inside bulbs and open the way for fungus rots. Remove and destroy infested bulbs, detected by pressing between the fingers. Spray plants with DDT.

Pacific Flatheaded Borer*, *Chrysobothris mali* Horn. Distributed throughout the western states. The adult is a dark-brown to reddish-copper beetle, ¼ to ½ inch long. The larva is similar to the flatheaded apple tree borer and mines normal and injured trees, preferring sunny limbs. Ceanothus is preferred host but alder, apricot, ash, mountain-ash, beech, blackberry, boxelder, California coffeeberry, Catalina cherry, currant, elm, eucalyptus, gooseberry, loquat, manzanita, maple, mesquite, mountain-mahogany, oak, peach, pear, plum, poplar, prune, rose, sycamore, and willow may be attacked. Control measures are the same as for the flatheaded apple tree borer.

Painted Hickory Borer*, *Megacyllene caryae* (Gahan). Distributed from New England to Texas wherever hickory is grown, chiefly a pest of cut timber. It is partial to shagbark hickory but may also infest black walnut, butternut, elm, honeylocust, Osage-orange, and hackberry. The adult is similar to the locust borer, with long antennae, yellow transverse bands, and a yellow W on dark-brown elytra.

Peach Tree Borer*, *Sanninoidea exitiosa* (Say). A native moth, the most important enemy of peach trees, also attacking plum, wild and cultivated cherry, prune, nectarine, apricot, and some ornamental shrubs in the genus Prunus (Plate XVI). First sign of injury is usually a mass of gum and brown frass at the base of the trunk, indicating that the white, brown-headed worms are at work in the bark anywhere from 2 to 3 inches below ground to 10 inches above. They winter as larvae of all sizes in the burrows, finish feeding in spring, when they are about 1 inch long, then pupate in brown silk cocoons in soil near the base of the tree. Just before the moth emerges, the pupa is forced out of the cocoon.

In the North, most of the moths (family Acgeriidae) emerge during July and August; in the South, during August and September. The female is blue-black with clear hind wings and narrow yellow bands on the abdomen. Each female lays several hundred eggs near the base of the tree trunk, the young worms hatching in 10 days to bore inside the bark. Peaches seldom survive repeated borer attacks.

Control. The standard remedy has been a ring of paradichlorobenzene crystals placed around the tree trunk in fall after all eggs are hatched but while the temperature is above 55° F. This means late September in the vicinity of New York City or about the middle of October in Georgia. The soil is loosened around the tree, the crystals applied in a ring 1 inch away from the trunk and then mounded with 2 or 3 shovelfuls of earth to hold in the fumes. The dosage, which must be exact, varies with the age of the tree: ½ ounce for 3-year trees, ¾ ounce up to 6 years, 1 to 1½ ounces for older trees.

Treating the trunks with DDT has now somewhat replaced soil fumigation. Backyard fruit trees can have the trunk and the ground around the base sprayed with DDT, up to 4 level tablespoons of 50 per cent wettable powder per gallon of water, in July and August, followed by lindane in

September. Commercial growers often spray 2 to 4 times with parathion or Guthion. At present Thiodan and endrin are considered superior to parathion. The bacterial spray, *Bacillus thuringiensis,* has possibilities. Probing out the borers with a knife or flexible wire is helpful but it is seldom possible to find all the worms.

Peach Twig Borer*, *Anarsia lineatella* Zeller. A small, reddish-brown larva, under ½ inch, boring in and killing tips of twigs, infesting fruit later in the season. The borer, a minor pest in the East but quite injurious on the West Coast, infests plums, prunes, nectarines, almonds, apricots, as well as peaches. The grayish moth (family Gelechiidae) is so small that it is seldom noticed. A dormant lime-sulfur spray, 1 to 15 dilution, is helpful, as is spraying with lead arsenate before the blossoms reach the pink stage and after petal fall.

Pear Fruit Borer*, *Nephopteryx rubrizonella* Ragonet.

Pecan Borer. See Dogwood Borer. This species attacks pecan in the Southeast, being worse on recently top-worked trees. Protect scions from borer injury by covering all graft wounds with grafting wax which will not crack.

Pecan Carpenterworm*, *Cossula magnifica* (Strecker). Also known as Oak or Hickory Cossid. It bores into trunk and larger branches of pecan, oak, and hickory in southern states. Reddish pellets of wood at the base of the tree indicate that the pinkish larva, 1½ inches long with fine short hairs, is boring within. The moth (family Cossidae) is gray, mottled with brown and black.

Persimmon Borer*, *Sannina uroceriformis* Walker. The larva of a clearwing moth bores into solid wood and taproot of persimmon in southern states, often causing severe damage to trees.

Pigeon Tremex*, *Tremex columba* (Linnaeus). A native wasplike insect, one of the horntails (family Siricidae, order Hymenoptera). The cylindrical white larva, up to 3 inches long, with a short horn at the tip of the abdomen, bores tunnels in diseased and dying trees, most commonly elm and sugar maple, sometimes beech, apple, pear, sycamore, and oak. The female adult, with a 2-inch body and wingspread, has a reddish head and thorax, black abdomen with yellow bands, smoky brown wings, and a horned tail at the end of the body which is a sheath for a long ovipositor. For control, squirt carbon disulfide into the burrows. The ichneumon wasp is a helpful parasite; the female lays her eggs right through wood into the horntail larva in its burrow.

Pitch Mass Borer*, *Vespamima pini* (Kellicott). Larva of a clearwing moth, body black and orange, fore wings opaque, blackish, with metallic sheen, found from Georgia to Canada and west to Wisconsin on pitch pine, white pine, and spruce. Eggs are deposited on bark or near a wound and the larvae bore for 2 or 3 years in inner bark and sapwood, causing a great exudation of pitch. Pupation takes place in this pitch mass.

Plum Gouger. See under Beetles.

Ponderosa-pine Bark Borer*, *Acanthocinus spectabilis* (LeConte). A large white grub commonly found in ponderosa pines killed by the western pine beetle, but not injurious to living trees. Adults are large, speckled gray beetles with very long antennae.

Poplar Borer*, *Saperda calcarata* Say. A large native beetle, distributed through the country, attacking Lombardy and other poplars, cottonwood (except for a resistant form in the Mississippi Valley), aspen and willows. It severely injures ornamental shade trees, marring them with blackened swollen scars on the outside of wood honeycombed with irregular galleries. The beetle is reddish brown with gray and yellow pubescence, yellow stripes on thorax and elytra, 1⅛ inches long. Adults, appearing from July to September, feed on bark of young twigs and lay eggs in slits in the bark. The larvae—yellow grubs up to 1½ inches—work in the bark the first year, tunneling into the wood the second year, sending out frass to the openings. This accumulates at the base of trees. Cut and burn seriously infested trees in spring before beetles emerge. Probe borers with a wire or fumigate with carbon disulfide, injected from an oilcan, closing the opening with putty or wax. Painting egg scars with wood-preserving creosote kills young grubs.

Poplar-and-Willow Borer*, *Sternochetus lapathi* (Linnaeus). Also called Mottled Willow Borer. This is a small European weevil which has spread from Maine to Wisconsin and North Dakota since it was first noticed in New York in 1882. It has also been reported in the Northwest. The borer attacks willow, poplar, alder, and birch, with serious injury to poplars and willows over a year old. It winters as partly grown larvae. The grubs—thick, legless, ½ inch long—make burrows around the trunk in the cambium, girdling the tree. As they mature, they enter hardwood and honeycomb it with galleries. Smaller limbs and branches have swollen knotty areas; foliage may wilt. The dark-brown beetles, ⅓ inch long, are covered with light-brown and gray scales in a mottled effect. They are present in July and August feeding on young shoots. They lay eggs in slits cut in the corky bark, often in scar tissue. Spray trunks in August and September with dieldrin or DDT. Cut and burn seriously infested trees.

Potato Stalk Borer*, *Trichobaris trinotata* (Say). Injures potatoes, early varieties in particular, and may attack eggplant, tomato, groundcherry and related weeds. It is present in most sections of the country and, when abundant, may destroy entire fields of potatoes. It hibernates as an adult, a bluish-gray snout beetle ⅕ inch long, with 3 black spots at the base of the wing covers. It eats deep holes in stems of new plants in spring and deposits eggs singly in such cavities in stem or leaf petioles. The very small, yellow-white, wrinkled grubs hollow out the stems for several inches, causing wilting and death of plants. Before pupating, the larva packs its burrow with "excelsior"—scrapings from the stem—and chews an exit passage for the adult to use in spring. There is 1 generation a year. Clean up and burn or bury deeply all potato vines after harvest; destroy nearby weeds with stalks large enough to harbor borers.

Potato Tuberworm*, *Gnorimoschema operculella* (Zeller). Sometimes called Tuber Moth, destructive to potatoes from Florida north to Virginia and west to California. Eggplant, tobacco and related weeds may also be attacked. The small moths (family Gelechiidae), narrow-winged, gray-brown mottled with darker brown, ½ inch across the wings, escape from storehouses in spring and lay eggs, singly, on underside of leaves or in eyes of potato tubers. The ¾-inch-long larvae, pinkish white with brown heads, burrow in stems or petioles or mine in leaves. Maturing in 2 or 3 weeks, they pupate inside dirt-covered silk cocoons in trash on the ground, appearing as adults in 7 to 10 days. The entire life cycle takes only a month and there may be 5 or 6 generations a season, with most injury in hot, dry summers. Adults of late broods work down through cracks in soil to lay eggs in tubers, the larvae making dirty, silk-lined burrows through the flesh. They come out of the tubers to pupate in odd corners around the storage room.

Control. Plant uninfested seed pieces; keep potatoes well cultivated and deeply hilled during growth. Spray foliage with DDT. Cut and burn infested vines a few days before digging; do not leave newly dug potatoes exposed to egg laying by moths during late afternoon or night; destroy culls. Screen storage places in warm weather. Burlap potato bags should be sprayed with DDT in xylene to prevent reinfestation or to kill larvae in already infested tubers.

Raspberry Cane Borer*, *Oberea bimaculata* (Olivier). A long-horned beetle generally distributed from Kansas eastward, a pest of raspberry and blackberry, sometimes rose; reported on azalea. The slender black-and-yellow-striped female, with 2 black dots on a yellow thorax, makes a double row of punctures around the stem near the tip and lays an egg between the girdles. The tip wilts and the grub, when it hatches in summer, bores down the cane 1 or 2 inches before hibernating. The next season it continues to bore down inside the cane and pupates inside this burrow; the cane dies. Cut out and burn wilting tips as soon as noticed, pruning 6 inches below the punctured area. Cut and burn wilted or dead fruiting canes.

Raspberry Crown Borer*, *Bembecia marginata* (Harris). Also called Raspberry Root Borer, causing wilting and dying of fruiting canes of blackberry and raspberry in early summer, often when berries are ripening. The adult is a clearwing moth, with a black body crossed with 4 yellow bands. Eggs—oval, reddish brown, the size of mustard seed—are deposited on the underside of leaves, near the edge, in late summer. Small white caterpillars hibernate the first winter in blisterlike elevations of bark just under soil level or at base of stems. The borers make extensive galleries in spring, and by the second summer the whole crown may be hollowed out. Spray with DDT 2 weeks after the first egg is deposited (about September 10 in New Jersey) applying it to crown of plant and new canes; repeat in 2 weeks.

Red-headed Ash Borer*, *Neoclytus acuminatus* (Fabricius). Attacking felled hardwoods—ash, oak, hickory, persimmon, mesquite. The adults, working in living trees, are elongate beetles, reddish brown marked with yellow crossbands.

Red-necked Cane Borer*, *Agrilus ruficollis* (Fabricius). In eastern United States, causing cigar-shaped swellings in raspberry, blackberry, or dewberry canes, which may die or break off at the swollen joint. Bluish-black beetles (family Buprestidae) with a coppery thorax, ⅓ inch long, lay eggs in bark of canes, usually near a leaf, which may be eaten and appear ragged. The young flatheaded larvae burrow upward in sapwood and several times around the canes, girdling them. The easiest remedy is to cut out and burn swollen canes. Some varieties are rather resistant to attack.

Rhododendron Borer*, *Ramosia rhododendri* (Beutenmüller). A small, native clearwing moth injuring rhododendrons and sometimes adjacent mountain-laurel and azalea in eastern United States, also reported on blueberries in Michigan. The moths, black with 3 yellow transverse bands on the abdomen, only ⅜- to ½-inch wingspread, lay eggs in May and June on twigs. The yellow-white larvae, ½ inch long, bore in sapwood under the bark, causing branches to wilt or break off. Injury in the same shrubs increases year to year, with leaves turning brown, main trunks filled with holes protruding fine sawdust. Cut and burn infested portions whenever noticed. Spray or paint trunk and branches with DDT before moths deposit eggs in May or June.

Root Collar Borer, *Euzophera ostricolorella* Hulst. Reported from New York to Florida and Tennessee, Kentucky and Indiana on yellow-poplar (tuliptree) and magnolia. The larvae, 1 inch long when mature, bore near the root collar and lower part of trunk, mostly in an area 2 inches below the duff to 5 inches above. Trees of all sizes may die. Experiments indicate that an oil emulsion of benzene hexachloride or DDT applied to the basal 6 feet will prevent attacks.

Rose Stem Girdler*, *Agrilus rubicola* Abeille. Similar to the red-necked cane borer, with the same life history, primarily a rose pest but also infesting raspberry. Distribution is mostly east of the Mississippi, but this greenish beetle is now infesting raspberry in Utah. Eggs are laid under bark, and the grubs make 1 or 2 spiral mines around the canes, which swell and sometimes split at such points. This girdler is common on species roses, particularly *Rosa rugosa* and *R. hugonis,* but is rare on garden roses. Cut out swollen canes early in spring.

Roundheaded Apple Tree Borer*, *Saperda candida* Fabricius. A native beetle distributed generally east of the Rocky Mountains (Plate XIV). It is best known as an apple pest but may be injurious to quince, pear, plum, peach, mountain-ash, hawthorn, wild crab, shadbush, and chokecherry. It usually works in tree trunks at ground level, or just above or below, killing young trees, seriously injuring older specimens. The life cycle is normally completed in 3 years in the North, 2 in the South. The young grub, first brownish red, later creamy white, with a rounded thickening just behind the head, starts to work in the bark, producing brown sap stains, then tunnels in the sapwood for a year or two, ejecting conspicuous coils of rusty-brown frass. The next season it bores into the heartwood, tunneling outward in fall to prepare a winter chamber near the bark. The upper end of the chamber, curved out so that it almost touches the bark, is filled with sawdustlike frass; the lower end is packed with coarse wood cuttings. The larva pupates here in May; the beetle emerges from late May to July.

The adults—just under an inch long, yellow or reddish brown above, white underneath—have 2 conspicuous white stripes the length of the body and prominent gray antennae. They crawl over the tree, feeding somewhat on foliage and fruit, and lay eggs in slits in the bark near ground level.

Control. Examine trees carefully, scooping away an inch or two of earth at the base, for brown castings or stained areas in bark. Cut out borers in shallow tunnels with tip of knife; probe for deep-seated borers with a flexible wire or inject a fumigant. A recommended fumigant is made by dissolving 10 grams of paradichlorobenzene in 10 cc of carbon disulfide. The ordinary apple-spray schedule helps to control the beetles on foliage, but a special spray or DDT or lead arsenate, applied 3 weeks after petal fall and repeated 2 to 3 weeks later, may be more effective.

Roundheaded Cone Borer*, *Paratimia conicola* Fisher. A rusty reddish-brown beetle. The larva tunnels in cones of knobcone and shore pine in California.

Roundheaded Fir Borer*, *Tetropium abietis* Fall. A velvety brown, long-horned beetle, ¾ inch long, pest of western conifers. The grubs work under the bark of felled and standing firs.

Rustic Borer*, *Xylotrechus colonus* (Fabricius). A very common eastern beetle, dark brown with irregular white or yellowish markings. The larvae are found under bark of almost all dead hardwoods.

Sapwood Timberworm*, *Hylecoetus lugubris* Say. One of the ship-timber beetles (family Lymexylidae), slender, elongate with serrated antennae, reddish brown or black. The grubs, with a barbed spine on the 9th segment, make round mines in sapwood of poplar, birch, and tuliptree.

Sculptured Pine Borer*, *Chalcophora angulicollis* (LeConte). Largest of the western flatheaded borers. Adults are over 1 inch long, dark brown to black, with an iridescent bronze luster, and the wing covers are marked with irregularly sculptured areas. Larvae feed in dead pines, firs, and Douglas-fir.

Seagrape Borer, *Hexeris enhydris* Grote. Abundant on this host in southern Florida.

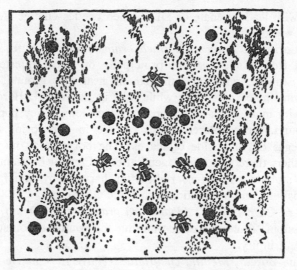

32. Shot-hole borer: section of bark showing emergence holes, small beetles.

Shot-hole Borer*, *Scolytus rugulosus* (Ratzeburg). Equally well-known as the Fruit Tree Bark Beetle, a European insect generally distributed over the country. It makes small holes like shot holes in the bark of healthy tree twigs and in branches and trunks of weakened trees. In addition to fruit trees—almond, apple, apricot, cherry, loquat, peach, nectarine, pear, plum, and prune—it may attack mountain-ash, elm, hawthorn, and June-berry. On stone fruits the shot holes are usually covered with gum. If beetles are abundant the foliage yellows, wilts, and the tree may die. The pinkish-white grub, ⅛ inch long, winters in the inner bark. The larval galleries are winding, sawdust-filled, leading out from a shorter central gallery. The black, blunt beetles, 1/10 inch long, emerge in early summer. The females fly to unhealthy trees to excavate an egg gallery in branch or twig, depositing eggs on each side of this. There may be 1 to 3 generations, depending on climate.

Control. Keep trees in vigorous condition with nitrogenous fertilizers and sufficient water; remove and burn prunings and dying trees. Spray trunks and branches of infested trees with DDT in late spring, repeating in September in the Pacific Northwest. Parathion may be used by commercial growers.

Sinuate Pear Tree Borer*, *Agrilus sinuatus* (Olivier). A European beetle first noticed in New Jersey in 1894, now known in New England, New York, and Ohio. It is primarily a pest of pear but may injure hawthorn, mountain-ash, and cotoneaster. The beetles are slender, very flat, ⅓ inch long, purplish bronze. The grubs are long, slender, flat, and make sinuate galleries in trunk and branches during the winter, with swelling or cracking of bark. Clean up dead or dying trees or branches during the winter. Spray pear foliage with lead arsenate or DDT when beetles emerge (May or June) and repeat 2 weeks later.

Southern Cornstalk Borer*, *Diatraea crambidoides* (Grote). A southern insect, found from Kansas south, principally on corn. Infested stalks are twisted and stunted, with an enlargement near the ground. Leaves are ragged, showing holes eaten out while still in the whorl. Borers are dirty gray-white, with many dark-brown spots, 1 inch long. They pupate in stalks near the ground. Straw-colored moths emerge in late spring to lay many overlapping eggs on underside of leaves. The borers may move from one plant to another; there are 1 to 3 generations. Control by sanitation, cleaning up corn stubble and refuse right after harvest; by late fall or winter plowing or spading; and by rotation with some other crop.

Southwestern Corn Borer*, *Zeadiatraea grandiosella* (Dyar). Found west of the Mississippi. A corn pest resembling the southern cornstalk borer in appearance and injury.

Squash Vine Borer*, *Melittia cucurbitae* (Harris). A native pest, present east of the Rocky Mountains, often spoiling 25 per cent of the commercial squash crop and even more injurious in home gardens. Injuring pumpkin, gourd, cucumber and muskmelon in that order (Plate XVI). The borer winters as larva or pupa inside a silk-lined dark cocoon an inch or two below soil level. The clearwing moth—wasplike with copper-green fore wings, orange-and-black abdomen, 1 to 1½ inches across the wings—appears when vine crops start to run. It glues small, oval, flat brown eggs singly on stems and leaf stalks. Young borers hatch in about a week, tunnel into the stem to feed. The first sign of their presence is a sudden wilting of the vine, then masses of greenish-yellow excrement protruding from holes in the stem. The borer, a wrinkled white caterpillar up to 1 inch long with brown head, can be found by slitting the stem with a knife. Later in the season it is present in fruits as well as stems. After feeding for 4 to 6 weeks it goes into the soil to make its cocoon. There are 2 generations in the Gulf States, normally 1 in the North, sometimes a partial 2nd.

Control is difficult. Dusting with rotenone or methoxychlor at weekly intervals, starting when vines begin to run, kills some larvae before they enter the stem. If the vine starts to wilt, kill the borer with a knife and heap earth over the stem joints to start new roots. Make a second planting of summer squash to mature after the borers are through feeding. Pull up and burn vines immediately after harvest.

Stalk Borer*, *Papaipema nebris* (Guenée). A universal feeder, occurring everywhere east of the Rocky Mountains. The slender, striped caterpillar, ¾ to 1½ inches long, works in the stem of any plant large enough and soft enough for its operations, although it favors giant ragweed and corn in later stages. The stalk borer is a frequent pest of dahlia and iris and is often found on aster, goldenglow, hollyhock, lily, rhubarb, pepper, tomato, potato, and corn. It winters as grayish, ridged eggs on grasses and weeds. These hatch very early in spring with the borers working first in grasses before going over to herbaceous stalks, entering at the side and burrowing up. The young larva has a dark-brown or purple band around the cream-colored body and several brown or purple lengthwise stripes, but these almost disappear and the full-grown caterpillar is grayish or light purple. The borers are very restless, often changing one host for another. They pupate in late summer just under the soil surface or, rarely, inside stalks. The moths (family Noctuidae) are grayish brown with white spots on the fore wings, which spread to 1 inch. They appear in August and September to lay upward of 2000 eggs per female. There is only 1 generation a year.

Control. By the time injury is noted, it is usually too late to save the plant, but sometimes it is possible to slit a stem, kill the borer with a knife, and then bind the stem together. Dust plants with DDT to destroy borers on the move. Clean up weeds in the vicinity.

Strawberry Crown Borer*, *Tyloderma fragariae* (Riley). Rather general east of the Rocky Mountains, especially important in Kentucky, Tennessee, and Arkansas. The adult is a small brown snout beetle less than ⅕ inch long, shaped like a grape seed, each wing cover marked with 3 black bars. The grub is small and yellow, taking on a pinkish tinge as it feeds on strawberry tissues. The adults, which cannot fly, winter under trash in beds and appear about blossomtime to lay eggs—glistening white, elliptical—in shallow holes in crowns and at base of leaf stalks. The grubs hatch in about a week and burrow downward into the center of the crown, killing or stunting the plants. They pupate in the burrow in late summer and the beetles feed on strawberry foliage in early fall, making characteristic small feeding holes. There is 1 generation.

Control. Apply 20 per cent toxaphene dust or 5 per cent chlordane dust to plants and soil just before blooming. Set new strawberry beds with certified plants and, if possible, not less than 350 yards from old fields. Grow only 2 crops before plowing up and destroying the old planting. The borer also lives in wild strawberries and cinquefoil.

Sugarcane Borer*, *Diatraea saccharalis* (Fabricius). Causing an average annual loss of 10 million dollars in sugarcane, also attacking corn, in Florida, Mississippi, Louisiana, and Texas. Related to the southern cornstalk borer, the larva yellowish white, the moth straw-colored with black dots.

Sugar-maple Borer*, *Glycobius speciosus* (Say). A native long-horned beetle, dangerous to sugar maples in the Northeast and apparently confined to them. The striking adult is black with yellow bands and yellow tips to the elytra, the yellow coloration near the base of these forming a W; it is 1 inch long. The roundheaded larva is 2 inches long, somewhat flattened, rose white. It bores a wide channel several feet long in inner bark and sapwood, often going halfway around the tree. The bark over this section cracks, producing an ugly scar to which other insects are attracted. There is a 2-year cycle, adults laying eggs in summer. Remove dead branches before June 1. Cut out grubs where possible. Spray bark in August, wetting it thoroughly with lindane or dieldrin.

Sycamore Borer, *Ramosia resplendens* (Hy. Edwards). A clearwing moth injuring sycamores and live oaks in California.

Tiger Hickory Borer, *Goes tigrinus* De Geer. Also known as White Oak Borer. A long-horned beetle attacking hickory, oak, preferably white oak, and walnut. The adult is a brown beetle with a dark band, covered with fine gray hairs, and with pinkish antennae. The larva is 1 inch long, lemon-yellow, with prominent segments. It excavates large burrows in sapwood and inner bark. The life cycle may last 3 to 5 years.

Tile-horned Prionus*, *Prionus imbricornis* (Linnaeus). Common on oak and chestnut in the Southeast, boring in roots of living trees. The adult is a large, brownish black beetle; the larva is elongate, tapering posteriorly, with a wide head.

Tobacco Stalk Borer*, *Trichobaris mucorea* (LeConte). Similar to the potato stalk borer; attacking potatoes in the Southwest.

Turpentine Borer, *Buprestis apricans* Herbst. On long leaf and slash pines from North Carolina to Texas. The beetles are large, gray bronze with a greenish metallic luster and longitudinal rows of large punctures on each wing cover. They feed on needles in the tops of trees before laying eggs. The larvae—flatheaded, 1½ inches long—mine the sapwood and heartwood for 3 years.

Twig Girdler*, *Oncideres cingulata* (Say). Twigs and small branches up to several feet long are found neatly cut off and lying on the ground under hickory, pecan, persimmon, oak, poplar, sourgum, honeylocust, and other trees in eastern states, also in Oklahoma. Grayish, hard-shelled beetles, with antennae longer than body, girdle the twigs by cutting round and round from the bark inward. In young trees there may be appreciable injury. Pecans may be deformed and the nut crop reduced. In persimmon the beetle wounds afford entrance to the deadly wilt fungus. Gather and burn all severed branches in late fall when eggs and grubs are inside. Three sprays of DDT or a phosphate, at 2-week intervals starting in late August, are sometimes recommended for pecans.

Twig Pruner*, *Elaphidion villosum* (Fabricius). Also called Oak Twig Pruner, found west to Michigan and south to the Gulf States, attacking oak, hickory, pecan, maple, locust, hackberry, elm, walnut, sweetgum, and some fruit trees. Shade trees are often so severely pruned by larvae burrowing in twigs that their shape is ruined. The ground may be thickly strewn with twigs. The adults, brownish elongate beetles about ½ inch long, appear when oak leaves unfold and lay eggs in leaf axils near tips of twigs. Clean up and burn all severed twigs.

Two-lined Chestnut Borer*, *Agrilus bilineatus* (Weber). A native beetle distributed from Maine to Texas. It attacks apparently normal but actually weakened oaks, chestnut, beech, ironwood. The beetle is slender, ⅓ inch long, greenish-black, covered with golden hairs and with a golden stripe down each wing cover. It emerges in May or June, feeds on foliage for some time, then lays eggs under bark scales. The larvae are slender, white, flat, with an enlargement behind the head. They mine in cambium, girdling trunk and branches and working from 40 to 50 feet in the air down to the ground. Weakened trees die rapidly. Foliage sprays of lead arsenate or DDT help protect valuable shade trees. Water and fertilizer will aid in recovery.

Western Cedar Borer*, *Trachykele blondeli* Marsuel. Bright emerald-green sculptured beetles ⅝ inch long, destructive to western redcedar, cypress, California incense cedar, and related species. Flatheaded larvae mine in sapwood and heartwood of living and dying trees.

Western Larch Roundheaded Borer, *Tetropium velutinum* LeConte. On larch, hemlock, sometimes Douglas-fir, spruce, and pine in Rocky Mountain and Pacific Coast regions. Adults are elongated velvety brown beetles. Larvae construct winding mines between bark and wood and may girdle tree.

Western Peach Tree Borer*, *Sanninoidea exitiosa graefi* (Hy. Edwards). A western variety of the peach tree borer, also injuring plum, prune, apricot, sometimes apple and almond. See Peach Tree Borer for control.

White-pine Shoot Borer, *Eucosma gloriola* Heinrich. First reported from Connecticut in 1930 but since then often confused with Nantucket pine moth. Chiefly injuring white and Scotch pine, sometimes on Austrian and red pine, rarely on Douglas-fir, in the Northeast. The dirty-white larvae tunnel in pith of new shoots, laterals or leaders, cutting the wood at base of the tunnel. Shoots break off in wind. Moths, copper red with gray scales, appear at end of April or early May, blending with pine-bud scales, to lay eggs on needles or buds.

BUDWORMS (BUD MOTHS)

Budworms are small caterpillars that feed in or on opening buds. Sometimes the common name is that of the adult state, bud moth.

Black-headed Budworm*, *Acleris variana* (Fernald). An important defoliator of hemlock, true firs, and spruce forests in northern United States and Canada, often reported from Alaska. Small moths (family Tortricidae), gray or dappled, wingspread ¾ inch, lay eggs in August and September on underside of needles. In spring bright-green caterpillars with black heads feed on new foliage or opening buds, webbing the needles together. Outbreaks have occasionally called for aerial spraying by DDT, but there are several natural parasites and a virus that aid in control.

Eye-spotted Bud Moth*, *Spilonota ocellana* (Denis & Schiffermüller). An apple pest through northern apple sections but also infesting blackberry, hawthorn, larch, laurel, oak, pear, plum, cherry, and occasionally some forest trees. It is recorded as serious on cherry in Wisconsin. The larvae, small brown worms with black heads, winter in small silken cases attached to twigs or bud axils. They eat out the buds as they open in spring or tie leaves together with silken threads. They pupate in early summer in their silken nests. Small brown moths, with a light band on each wing, lay eggs on underside of leaves for the summer brood. Control by spraying with malathion or parathion at the delayed dormant stage, or use a dormant dinitro spray, or lead arsenate in the pink-bud stage.

Holly Bud Moth, *Rhopobota naevana ilicifoliana* (Kearfott). An important pest of holly plantings in Oregon and Washington, having spread down from British Columbia. Overwintering in the egg stage, the larvae appear as buds are opening and feed on new leaves inside a web. There is only 1 brood. Malathion and methoxychlor have given good control when applied between opening of leaf buds and time of blossoming.

Jack-pine Budworm*, *Choristoneura pinus* Freeman. Causing serious damage to jack pine and some injury to white and red pine in the Lakes States. Defoliation in Wisconsin, Michigan, and Minnesota is often severe enough to require spraying to reduce epidemic populations. The larvae are similar to those of the spruce budworm. The moths are slightly smaller, wingspread under 1 inch, with reddish tan, mottled fore wings.

Larch Bud Moth, *Zeiraphera griseana* (Hübner). A European species causing heavy defoliation of larch and white fir, sometimes Engelmann spruce and Douglas-fir in Washington, Oregon, Idaho, and Montana. The larvae feed on tender new growth, crawling into opening buds and webbing new needles together. The moths, wingspread ½ to ¾ inch, have grayish-white wings splotched with dark brown and black.

Lesser Bud Moth*, *Recurvaria nanella* (Hübner). Similar in appearance and habit to the eye-spotted bud moth, but mining leaves to some extent.

Pecan Bud Moth*, *Gretchena bolliana* (Slingerland). Primarily a bud feeder; sometimes causes excessive branching or stunting. Young larvae are black, older caterpillars yellow-green with brown heads, just over ½ inch long. Eggs are laid on foliage or, early in the season, on twigs. Spray with calcium or lead arsenate or DDT in spring and summer.

Rose Budworm, *Pyrrhia umbra* Hufnagel. On buds of rose, columbine and other garden flowers. There are 2 kinds of caterpillars. One is green, spotted with black tubercles and with prominent, dark, longitudinal stripes; the other has whitish-orange markings on the back. The adult is the bordered sallow moth. Remove infested buds as soon as noticed. Spray or dust with DDT.

Spruce Bud Moth*, *Zeiraphera ratzeburgiana* Saxesen. An introduced pest established in the Pacific Northwest and Alaska. Very small light-brown moths, with darker diagonal markings, lay eggs on spruce needles. Each young caterpillar crawls into an opening bud, webbing new needles together as it feeds. On Sitka spruce in Washington and Oregon all new tips may be killed; trees are branched excessively.

Spruce Budworm*, *Choristoneura fumiferana* (Clemens). A serious enemy of forest trees, distributed all over northern United States and Canada. It has ranked third in importance of all our insects, next to the cotton

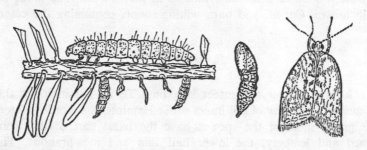

33. Spruce budworm: larva, empty pupa cases hanging from twig, tortricid moth adult.

boll weevil and the corn earworm. It has cycles of enormous abundance in spruce and balsam fir forests and may injure ornamental spruce, fir, Douglas-fir. When attacks are heavy, entire trees are stripped of foliage and killed; whole forests appear as if scorched by fire. When defoliation is not complete, terminals are killed.

The moths (family Tortricidae)—mottled, buff to gray, only ⅞ inch across the wings—appear from late June through July, being most active in the evening. They lay oval, flattened, greenish eggs in 2 overlapping rows along the needles, and the young larvae feed for a while before hibernating in silken cases on branches. When full-grown the caterpillars are up to 1 inch long, brown with a yellow stripe along the side and yellow tubercles. They start activity when buds break in spring, tunneling first in old needles, then in the center of opening buds, feeding also on pollen of staminate flowers. They eat mostly the bases of needles and web the rest together with silk, pupating inside this webbing.

Control. Spray ornamentals with lead arsenate or DDT just as new growth is starting. Large-scale forest spraying by airplane has been quite effective. Adverse weather conditions, birds, insect parasites, and predators combine to reduce outbreaks. Forest management to reduce the proportion of pollen-bearing firs is a possibility.

Tobacco Budworm*, *Heliothis virescens* (Fabricius). Distributed from Missouri, Ohio and Connecticut southward, most injurious in the Gulf States, reported on ornamentals in California. Primarily a pest of tobacco and cotton, this budworm infests groundcherry and other solanaceous plants, ageratum and geranium. Tiny rust-colored or green-striped caterpillars eat holes in buds or unfolded leaves. The moths have light green wings with 4 oblique light bands, a wingspread of 1½ inches. Eggs are laid singly on underside of leaves. Pupation is in the soil and there are 2 generations a year. Dust buds with DDT.

Verbena Bud Moth*, *Endothenia hebesana* (Walker). A pest of verbena and physostegia in eastern United States. The larva, greenish yellow with a black head, about ½ inch long, tunnels in new shoots. The moth is small, purplish brown. Cut off and burn wilting shoots containing the caterpillars.

BUGS

To a layman almost any insect is a bug. To an entomologist the word "bug" means a member of the insect order Hemiptera, suborder Heteroptera. In this group most of the species have the basal part of the front wing thickened and leathery, the lower half thin and membranous. The hind wings are entirely membranous and slightly shorter than the front wings. True bugs have their wings folded flat over the abdomen, instead of being held in a rooflike position like those of leafhoppers and aphids in the suborder Homoptera. Bugs have piercing, sucking mouth parts but the beak arises from the front part of the head instead of the posterior. Bugs have a gradual metamorphosis, nymphs resembling adults except for size and possession of wings. Some adult bugs have short wings and a few are wingless. The antennae have no more than 5 segments.

The water bugs—water boatmen, backswimmers, water scorpions, water striders and giant water bugs—are of little importance to gardeners and hence are omitted, along with bedbugs, household pests. The families of bugs afflicting plants and those preying on plant pests are listed here, followed by descriptions of the more important bugs. Mealybugs and Spittlebugs, not true bugs, are listed under those headings.

Anthocoridae. Flower Bugs or Minute Pirate Bugs, found on flowers or under loose bark or in leaf litter. Most species are black with white markings, very small, less than ⅛ inch. This is a beneficial family, the members feeding on small insects, mites, or insect eggs.

Aradidae. Flat Bugs or Fungus Bugs, found under loose bark or in crevices of dead and decaying trees. They are small, dark brown, very flat. They feed on the sap of fungi or moist, rotting wood and so may be considered scavengers.

Berytidae (Neididae). Stilt Bugs, feeding on plants in dense herbaceous vegetation. They are slender, long-legged, brownish, rather sluggish.

Coreidae. Coreid Bugs. These are squash bugs, leaf-footed bugs and allies, some plant-eating, some predaceous. They are small to large, with rather large compound eyes and 4-segmented antennae. The membranous portion of the fore wings is transversed by numerous parallel longitudinal veins. Some species have conspicuously enlarged legs, some have an offensive odor.

Lygaeidae. Lygaeid Bugs. A large family, with most members plant-eating, chinch bugs being a destructive example, but with some predaceous members. These are very small bugs, with beak and antennae 4-segmented and only a few simple veins in the wing membranes. Ocelli (simple eyes) are present.

Miridae. Plant Bugs, Leaf Bugs. A very large group with almost all members injurious, a few predaceous on other insects. This family includes tarnished plant bug, four-lined plant bug, and apple red bug, also garden fleahoppers. Members possess a cuneus, the apex of the thickened portion of the front wing set apart by a groove. Antennae and beak are 4-segmented.

Nabidae. Damsel Bugs. Wholly predaceous. They are small, brown or black, soft-bodied, with front legs modified for grasping small insects. The beak is long, usually 4-segmented; antennae are 4- or 5-segmented; head and first segment of the thorax are narrow; eyes are large, ocelli are present.

Pentatomidae. Stink Bugs. Small to medium in size, body shield-shaped; antennae 5-segmented; eyes small, 2 ocelli; glands at side of thorax emit strong odor. Some species are plant-eating, some are predaceous on Colorado potato beetles and various caterpillars; some are both.

Phymatidae. Ambush Bugs. Predaceous insects waiting for their prey on flowers, particularly goldenrod. They are small, less than ½ inch long, stout-bodied but with odd shapes, spiny armor, and camouflaging color patterns. The front legs are modified for grasping.

Pyrrhocoridae. Red Bugs and Stainers. Plant-eating and gregarious oval bugs marked with red and black. Some members, like the cotton stainer, stain tissue as they feed. Some are antlike in appearance.

Reduviidae. Assassin Bugs. Predators with large eyes midway or far back on long narrow heads. Ocelli, when present, only 2; antennae with 4 segments, beaks with 3. The abdomen is often widened beyond the margin of the wings. These are beneficial bugs, preying on caterpillars, Japanese beetles and other harmful insects but they are also injurious when they dine on honeybees or bite people. Some are called "kissing bugs."

Tingidae. Lace Bugs. Exclusively plant feeders, sucking sap from underside of leaves, which they cover with brown specks. The family name means "ornamented" and the beautiful small, flat bugs, oval or rectangular in shape, have transparent wings reticulated or netted in a lacelike effect and the head covered with a sort of hood. The nymphs are dark and spiny.

Alder Lace Bug, *Corythucha pergandei* Heidemann. Infesting alder, occasionally birch, crabapple, elm, and hazel.

Alfalfa Plant Bug*, *Adelphocoris lineolatus* (Goeze). A European pest, probably introduced here as eggs in packing materials, first recorded in Iowa in 1929. Very destructive to alfalfa and sweetclover but also feeding on other legumes, chrysanthemum, thistle, beet, castorbean, potato and other plants. Now present from Montana to the East Coast. Yellowish green nymphs and pale-yellow adults, with a tinge of brown, feed on flower buds and newly formed seeds. The feeding injury is apparently phytotoxic.

Andromeda Lace Bug, *Stephanitis globulifera* (Matsumura). A new pest, probably from Japan, seriously damaging *Pieris japonica.* First reported from Connecticut in 1946, it soon spread to Rhode Island, New York, and New Jersey. The upper leaf surface is mottled gray or entirely blanched; the undersurface is stained with dark, molasseslike spots of excrement. Inflorescence is poor and plants may die in a few years from repeated loss of vitality. The adults are ⅛ by 1/16 inch, with intensely black hood and wing veins. Overwintering eggs are imbedded at random over underside of leaves and hatch much earlier than most lace bugs, sometimes late April in New Jersey, mid-May in Connecticut. There may be nearly 60 dark, spiny nymphs on a single leaf, and they go through 5 molts to adult form in 2 or 3 weeks. There may be 4 or 5 generations a season, with some adults still alive in December.

Control. I have had excellent results with lindane, using 1 tablespoon of 25 per cent wettable powder to a gallon of water, spraying in May soon after the first nymphs hatch and repeating if necessary for later broods. Reinfestation may come from untreated gardens within several hundred feet. Malathion and dimethoate are also recommended.

Apple Red Bug*, *Lygidea mendax* Reuter. Distributed east of the Mississippi River, more destructive in New York and New England. Injurious to nearly all varieties of apples, the red bug may also attack pear, hawthorn, and wild crab. The active bright-red bugs, ¼ inch long, fly readily from tree to tree. Leaves are curled and there are numerous small sunken spots, each marking where the insect beak has punctured the surface. The fruit is deformed, pitted in a dimpled effect, sometimes russeted; the texture is woody. The bugs winter in the egg stage, in lenticels on the bark of smaller branches, and the nymphs appear in the early pink stage of apple bloom, puncturing leaves as they unfold, feeding on fruit as soon as it reaches ¼ inch in diameter. Adults appear in June and there is only 1 generation.

Control. Use a dormant spray of 3 to 4 per cent oil. If necessary spray with nicotine sulfate in cluster bud and calyx stages or with DDT or parathion at petal fall.

Another species, the **Dark Apple Red Bug,** *Heterocordylus malinus* Reuter, may be present along with the apple red bug. It is reddish black, covered on the upper surface with white, flattened hairs. It has a similar life history and causes the same injury.

Ash Lace Bug, *Leptophya minor* McAtee. Also called Ash Tingid, serious on Arizona ash and Modesto ash in California, also reported on poplars in Arizona. This species differs from other lace bugs in having a brown, compact body, with darker dorsal markings but no lacy lateral lobes. Adults hibernate in or near trees, lay eggs in April, and generations follow at monthly intervals until October. The leaves are whitened and the undersurface covered with black spots, the injury increasing during the summer.

Lindane used for the ash plant bug will control lace bugs if repeated 2 weeks after the first application.

Ash Plant Bug*, *Tropidostreptes* (Neoborus) *amoenus* (Reuter). This is the eastern species. A western form, **California Ash Mirid,** *T. illitus* (Van Duzee), is more important, being the worst ash pest in California. A third species, *T. pacificus* (Van Duzee) is reported from Oregon. Small, oval adults, black or brown with yellow markings, lay eggs in stems of new growth. There is only 1 generation a year, the eggs hatching the next February or March when leaves are developing. Young leaves wilt and brown; older leaves have large white areas with black spots of excrement. Trees may be defoliated. DDT spray in March controls ash plant bugs but increases woolly aphids. Lindane, 1 pound of 25 per cent wettable powder to 100 gallons of water, controls plant bugs and aphids as well. Also recommended is 1½ per cent light medium oil plus 1 quart of nicotine sulfate to 100 gallons, applied in March or April.

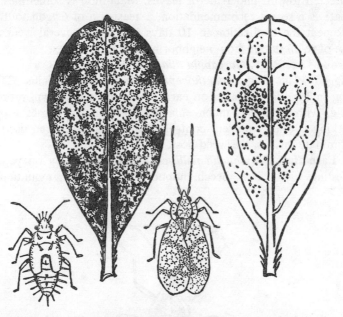

34. Azalea lace bug, showing loss of color from upper leaf surface, excrement and nymphs on lower surface; nymph and adult greatly enlarged.

Azalea Lace Bug*, *Stephanitis pyrioides* Scott. A major pest of azaleas wherever they are grown. Nymphs and adults suck sap from underside of leaves, resulting in a grayish, splotched, stippled or blanched appearance of the upper surface. The injury is most unsightly and the plant vitality greatly reduced. The small adult, ⅛ inch long, has lacy wings with brown-and-black markings, light-brown legs and antennae. The nymphs are nearly colorless at first, later black and spiny. Elongate eggs laid in leaf tissues along the veins hatch in 20 to 25 days, the life cycle being completed in 35 to 45 days. There are 2 or more generations. The rusty color of underside of leaves, due to excrement, is a diagnostic sign of lace bugs.

In Alabama overwintered eggs start hatching in February, building up to a dense population during March, April, and May. Another brood comes along in July, August, and September. In New Jersey eggs start hatching in late May or early June, slightly later than rhododendron lace bugs. The second brood builds up a heavy population in August and September and even later, with evergreen azaleas of the *amoena* or *hinodegiri* type appearing entirely coffee-colored, and foliage of deciduous azaleas stippled grayish.

Control. Former recommendations called for nicotine sulfate and soap sprays in the North, a white-oil emulsion with derris in the South. DDT is effective but increases southern red mite. Lindane is highly satisfactory, 1 tablespoon of a 25 per cent wettable powder to 1 gallon of water, the spray directed toward underside of leaves. Malathion is sometimes used and dimethoate is a recent recommendation, 1 teaspoon of Cygon to 1 gallon of water. Repeat the application in 10 days and again several weeks later, to take care of reinfestation from neighboring bushes.

Basswood Lace Bug*, *Gargaphia tiliae* (Walsh).

Big-legged Plant Bug, *Acanthocephala femorata* Fabricius. The largest plant bug in Florida, common on early potatoes. It is brown, more than an inch long, with hind legs much enlarged. Its sucking causes tops to wilt. Handpicking is often sufficient control. Sunflowers have been used as a trap crop. Eliminate thistles, the weed host.

Birch Lace Bug, *Corythucha pallipes* Parsh. Principally on yellow birch, also infesting white birch, beech, hophornbeam, willow, mountain-ash, and maple.

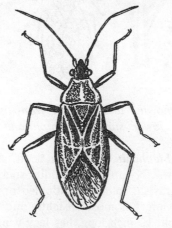

35. Boxelder bug.

Boxelder Bug*, *Leptocoris trivittatus* (Say). A pest wherever boxelder is grown as a shade tree, probably more of a nuisance in the Mississippi Valley. The nymphs are bright red; the adults are brownish black with 3 red stripes on the thorax and red veins on the wings, flat, narrowly oval, ½ inch long. They feed on female pistillate flowers, fruits, foliage, and tender twigs of boxelder, sometimes on ash, maple, and fruit trees. They are as much a household as an outdoor pest because they swarm inside to hibernate in autumn or else congregate in great numbers on porches, walls, and walks. They do not eat food or clothing but they may feed on house plants.

Control. Spray tree trunks and sunny walls where bugs congregate with chlordane or dieldrin. For houses, try one of the bombs containing pyrethrum and rotenone. If bugs continue to be too much of a nuisance, remove pistillate boxelder trees near the house.

Brown Stink Bug*, *Euschistus servus* (Say). Broad, flat, shield-shaped, buff to greenish, ½ inch long, sucking on tobacco stems, petioles, or veins. It is also a serious pest of soybean in southern states and may attack other legumes and peaches.

Caragana Plant Bug*, *Lopidea dakota* Knight.

Ceanothus Lace Bug, *Corythucha obliqua* Osborn & Drake. Common on ceanothus in California, Oregon, and Idaho. The body is black, the hood dark brown, and the wings pale with brown specks and bands.

Chinch Bug*, *Blissus leucopterus* (Say). Distributed throughout the United States, but especially injurious in the Mississippi, Ohio, and Missouri River valleys, and in Texas and Oklahoma. See Hairy Chinch Bug for the species common in eastern lawns. The chinch bug is a grain pest and has caused enormous damage to corn and grain crops for more than a century and a half, losses in a single state in one year running up to 40 million dollars.

This very small bug, 1/16 inch long, black with white wings (which have a triangular black patch in the middle of the outer margins) and red legs, gives off a distinctive vile odor when crushed. It hibernates as an adult in hedgerows, stubble and clumps of prairie grasses. When the days warm up to 70° F., the bugs fly to the grain fields, feed by sucking sap, mate, and lay eggs behind lower leaf sheaths of the plants, on the roots, or on the ground. One female lays several hundred eggs, at the rate of 15 or 20 a day. They hatch in 2 weeks into minute, brick-red nymphs with a white band across the middle. The nymphs darken as they grow older, acquiring wings and the black-and-white color at the last molt. As the grain ripens and plants dry up, the chinch bugs migrate, usually while still wingless, crawling to a field of young corn or sorghum. There they mature, mate, and lay eggs for a second generation on corn or grasses. The adults of this brood fly to winter quarters for hibernation. In the Southwest there may be 3 generations instead of 2.

Control. Farmers can reduce food supply of chinch bugs by not growing small grains in an area where corn is the main crop or by substituting legumes for corn in an area where small grains are of chief importance. Ample fertilizer and early planting reduce chinch-bug injury; some corn strains are resistant. Barriers to prevent crawling bugs from reaching the new crop are used effectively: dieldrin at the rate of ½ pound per acre in strips 4 yards wide between grain and cornfields; or a ridge of earth turned up with a plow and a line of coal-tar creosote applied along the brow of the ridge; or a band of dust using DDT or a dinitro such as DNOC.

Chrysanthemum Lace Bug*, *Corythucha marmorata* (Uhler). Distributed through the United States where chrysanthemums are grown, blanching foliage and stems of chrysanthemum, aster, and scabiosa. The spiny nymphs resemble azalea lace bugs; the adults have lacy wings and hood. They leave dark, resinous spots of excrement on underside of leaves. They breed on weeds, frequently goldenrod. Spray or dust with lindane or malathion.

Consperse Stink Bug, *Euschistus conspersus* Uhler. A Pacific Coast pest of fruit—strawberry, raspberry, blackberry, loganberry—and recorded on pear. The bug is small, pale brown, covered with small black specks, and has red antennae. It gives a disagreeable odor to fruit.

Cotton Stainer*, *Dysdercus suturellus* (Herrich-Schäffer). A southern cotton insect also injurious to hibiscus, sometimes staining eggplant and orange fruit. The bugs are narrow, long-legged, up to ⅗ inch long, with a bright-red thorax and brown wings crossed with yellow. They stain the lint red or yellow when puncturing the seeds in cotton bolls. Control nymphs with strong contact insecticides; handpick adults.

Dusky Stink Bug*, *Euschistus tristigmus* (Say). One of several stink bugs catfacing peaches, frequently reported from Ohio and Indiana.

Eggplant Lace Bug*, *Gargaphia solani* Heidemann. Dark brown and yellow, relatively large. In southern states ranging west to New Mexico and Arizona on eggplant, tomato, potato, and cassia.

Elm Lace Bug*, *Corythucha ulmi* Osborn & Drake. Found only on American elm but wherever this grows. Foliage may lose color as early as mid-June; new leaves sometimes die. Adults winter in leaves on ground. Control with a contact insecticide.

False Chinch Bug*, *Nysius ericae* (Schilling). Similar to, but even smaller than, the chinch bug. A pest of avocado, sometimes killing young trees, of beets, especially sugar beets, cabbage and other crucifers, sometimes corn. It is more important in semiarid areas. The nymphs feed on weeds and grasses, only the adults on cultivated plants. For avocado, 5 per cent chlordane dust is helpful.

Four-lined Plant Bug*, *Poecilocapsus lineatus* (Fabricius). A general plant pest east of the Rocky Mountains, attacking fruits, chiefly currant and gooseberry, mint, and many ornamentals, with chrysanthemums most injured. The sucking causes round, depressed spots, usually tan, sometimes nearly white or almost black on foliage of acanthopanax, aconite, aster,

Chinese lantern, chrysanthemum, coreopsis, dahlia, delphinium, forsythia, gaillardia, globe thistle, goldenglow, heliopsis, heliotrope, honeysuckle, lav-

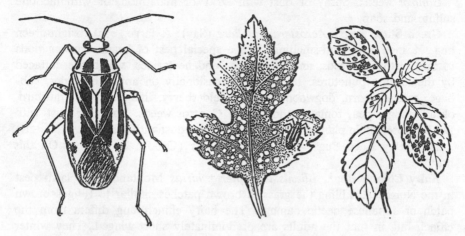

36. Four-lined plant bug, and injury to chrysanthemum and mint.

ender, lupine, morning-glory, peony, phlox, poppy, rose, snapdragon, Shasta daisy, sunflower, sweetpea, weigela, zinnia and other flowers and shrubs. The injury varies somewhat with the plant, aconite showing dark spots and chrysanthemums many round, light-tan areas on new leaves, with sometimes the whole tip wilting. This is one of the few enemies of mint, young leaves often being covered with black, rather angular spots.

Slender white eggs winter in slits in canes of currant and other plants. They hatch in May or June into bright-red nymphs with black dots on the thorax, but when they change to adults they are greenish yellow with 4 wide black stripes down the wings. There is only 1 generation a year, with feeding injury to plants lasting about 6 weeks. Usually these bugs stop feeding about the time Japanese beetles begin.

Control. Ornamentals can be sprayed or dusted with DDT or malathion; use rotenone for mint and other edibles. Start treatment early, as soon as the first nymphs appear.

Garden Fleahopper*, *Halticus bracteatus* (Say). General except in the Far Western states. The small bugs look something like aphids and suck sap from stems and foliage in the same manner, but they jump like flea beetles. The nymphs are greenish, the adults black, 1/10 inch or less, with long legs and antennae longer than body. Fleahoppers appear sporadically on many vegetables—bean, beet, celery, corn, cowpea, cucumber, eggplant, lettuce, pea, pepper, potato, pumpkin, squash, sweetpotato, tomato—and on various ornamentals—chrysanthemum, gladiolus, helianthus, heliopsis, portulaca, marigold, morning-glory, rudbeckia, scabiosa, verbena, zinnia and many others. The foliage has small pale or whitish spots and heavily infested leaves are killed. Plants in shade are preferred. Fleahoppers winter as adults in trash and there may be up to 5 generations a season.

Control weeds. Spray or dust with DDT or malathion, or with nicotine sulfate and soap.

Green Stink Bug*, *Acrosternum hilare* (Say). A large, oval, bright-green bug, ⅝ inch long, bad-smelling. It is a special pest of beans, causing pods to fall, distorting seeds, and of peaches and nectarines, which are catfaced by the feeding punctures. It is found occasionally on apple, boxelder, cabbage, catalpa, corn, dogwood, eggplant, elderberry, linden, maple, mustard, okra, orange, pea, tomato, and turnip. Control weeds. Spray or dust with DDT before edible plant parts are formed; later dust with sabadilla.

Hackberry Lace Bug*, *Corythucha celtidis* (Osborn & Drake). On this host.

Hairy Chinch Bug*, *Blissus leucopterus hirtus* Montandon. A lawn pest in the Northeast, killing the grass in brown patches similar to fungus brown patch or Japanese beetle damage. The hairy chinch bug differs from the chinch bug in that the adults are predominately short-winged. They winter in tall grass and weeds, migrating to the lawn in April or May to lay eggs at the grass roots. When the soil temperature is high enough, usually in June, the bright-red nymphs, with a white crossband, start sucking at the base of grass blades. They darken and grow a little larger as they go through various molts, with a brownish stage before they change to black adults, mostly with short white wings. The females lay eggs for a second and more disastrous brood which appears in August, with nymphs and adults continuing to feed into October. In November the adults either settle down in the lawn or, more often, migrate to tall grasses for the winter.

Injury is most serious in hot dry weather and where grass is in full sun. Chinch bugs show a preference for bent grasses but are not limited to them. Grass blades are punctured close to the roots and are often stained reddish. The brown, more or less circular areas in turf are usually surrounded by a sickly yellow margin where the bugs have just started feeding. When you cannot roll the grass back like a carpet you can suspect chinch bugs rather than beetle grubs as the cause, but you must see them to be sure. This is difficult unless you get nearly flat on the ground, part the grass blades, and gaze intently at one area for a few minutes. Flooding part of the lawn with warm water and covering it with a white cloth is said to bring the bugs onto the underside of the cloth, but I have not tried it.

A southern form of the hairy chinch bug, *Blissus leucopterus insularis* (Barber) is very important on St. Augustine grass and sometimes injures centipede grass in the Gulf States. It is the most serious lawn pest in southern Florida and has been reported as far north as North Carolina but is decreased in severity above Florida.

Control. Diazinon is a current recommendation, using 6 ounces of a 25 per cent emulsion per 1000 square feet, diluting this with 5 to 10 gallons of water and distributing evenly over the measured area. The lawn should be heavily watered prior to application. Where the bugs are not resistant to it, DDT can still be used (6 pounds of a 10 per cent dust per 1000 square feet) or chlordane (5 pounds of a 5 per cent dust). In the North, the first treatment is made in June, when the bugs start action, and the second, if necessary, in August. In southern Florida commercial pest-control operators may service lawns monthly for chinch-bug control and may use the more dangerous phosphate sprays such as parathion, Trithion or ethion, or V-C-13, which is also a nematocide.

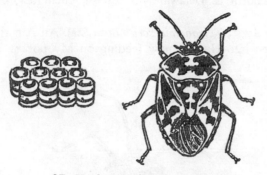

37. Harlequin bug and eggs.

Harlequin Bug*, *Murgantia histrionica* (Hahn). The most important pest of cabbage and related crops in the southern half of the United States. Crucifers—cabbage, cauliflower, collards, cress, mustard, Brussels sprouts, turnip, kohlrabi, radish, horseradish—are favored food plants but the bugs may wander over to asparagus, bean, citrus, cherry, chrysanthemum, corn, eggplant, grape, lettuce, locust, loquat, okra, plum, potato, rose, squash, and sunflower. The bugs are black with bright-red markings, flat, ⅜ inch long. They winter around old cabbage stalks and other garden refuse and lay distinctive eggs on underside of leaves of early garden crops. They look like tiny white barrels with black hoops, and they stand on end in a double row. They hatch in 4 to 7 days, and the nymphs suck so much sap that the cabbages wilt, turn brown, and die. Whole crops may be lost. There are usually 3 generations a season.

Control. Spray or dust with DDT before edible plant parts are formed, then change to rotenone or sabadilla dust.

Hawthorn Lace Bug*, *Corythucha cydoniae* (Fitch). Found on English hawthorn and other thorns, cotoneaster, pyracantha, Japanese quince. I find this small, dark lace bug, with spiny nymphs, very common on English hawthorn in New Jersey, prevalent in midsummer. In the mid-South it is more serious on pyracantha, with the first brood at work by April and a late brood still going strong in October. The upper surface of leaves loses color in a speckled fashion, while the undersurface is colored with dark bits of excrement. This species winters as an adult and the eggs are laid on new leaves in clusters, each standing on end and covered with a black conical mass. Spray with lindane or malathion, or nicotine sulfate and soap, for the nymph stage, treating underside of foliage with sufficient pressure.

Hickory Plant Bug*, *Neolygus caryae* Knight.

Hollyhock Plant Bug*, *Melanotrichus althaeae* (Hussey).

Hop Plant Bug*, *Taedia hawleyi* (Knight).

Horned Squash Bug*, *Anasa armigera* (Say). Southern Squash Bug, similar to the squash bug, breeding also on cabbage, and collards. It is reported as far north as Delaware on squash, cucumber, cantaloupe, and watermelon.

Lantana Lace Bug*, *Teleonemia scrupulosa* Stål. An American insect purposely introduced into Hawaii, now feeding on Myoporum, a native plant.

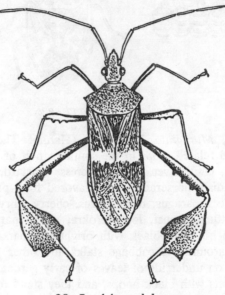

38. Leaf-footed bug.

Leaf-footed Bug*, *Leptoglossus phyllopus* (Linnaeus). Present in the South and as far west as Arizona, a common pest of vegetables and fruits. The bug is dark brown with a yellow band across the body, ¾ inch long, and with hind legs expanded like a leaf. It attacks pecans, potatoes, beans, cowpeas, tomatoes, and many other garden crops. It likes sunflower, may swarm on Satsuma oranges and tangerines, may be abundant on peaches, and breeds on thistle. Quantities of keg-shaped eggs are deposited on leaves; the young nymphs resemble the adult bug. Spray potatoes with malathion or DDT or dust with sabadilla. Handpicking is helpful.

Lygus Bugs, *Lygus hesperis* Knight, *L. elisus* Van Duzee, other species.

Small, flat bugs, greenish to yellowish brown, somewhat mottled, ¼ inch long, relatives of tarnished plant bugs. They are pests of peaches, pears and apples in the Pacific Southwest, infesting leaf buds, puncturing young fruit. Lygus bugs are common on legumes, may injure various ornamentals and trees throughout the Rocky Mountain and Pacific States.

Another lygaeid, *Crophius bohemani,* is recorded as heavily infesting eucalyptus trunks in California.

Masked Hunter*, *Reduvius personatus* (Linnaeus). One of the assassin or "kissing bugs" which can painfully bite people but which mostly suck blood of insects, entering houses in search of bedbugs and other pests. The larval stage acquires a coating of dust which is the mask.

Meadow Plant Bug*, *Leptoterna dolabratus* (Linnaeus). On orchard grasses and bluegrass.

Negro Bug*, *Corimelaena pulicaria* (Germar). Distributed generally east of the Rocky Mountains. The bugs are short, black, oval, 1/10 inch long, with an enlarged hard thoracic shield that makes them look like small beetles. They winter as adults and lay eggs singly on leaves. They hatch in 2 weeks and congregate in great numbers, sporadically, on corn, wheat, celery, and other crops, causing wilting and death. They also feed on lobelia, cardinal-flower and other ornamentals, and some fruits, imparting a bad taste to raspberries and blackberries. Spray with malathion.

Oak Lace Bug, *Corythucha arcuata* (Say). On various species of oak through eastern states north of the Carolinas, feeding in great numbers on underside of leaves and turning them white. Leaves may curl, turn brown, and drop prematurely. The lace bugs winter as adults or eggs, and there are 2 generations, with damage conspicuous in midsummer. Spray with lindane or malathion when nymphs hatch, and repeat in 2 weeks.

One-spot Stink Bug*, *Euschistus variolarius* (Palisot de Beauvois). Also called Spined Stink Bug. It is brown, shield-shaped, about ¾ inch long. It feeds on fruit of eggplant, tomato, on garden beans and other plants, causing depressed blemishes known as catfacing.

Onion Plant Bug*, *Labopidea allii* Knight.

Orchid Plant Bug, *Tenthecoris bicolor.* Causes irregular white stippled spots on underside of orchid leaves. The bug has an orange to black body with black and steel-blue wings, ⅛ inch long. Spray or dust with DDT or malathion.

Pameras, *Pachybrachius bilobata* Say. Very small bugs, related to chinch bugs, often destructive to strawberries in Florida. Nymphs look like yellow ants; adults are black with yellow markings, about ⅕ inch long. They appear in strawberry beds toward the end of the season, turning young berries into hard buttons; plants wither. Destroy wild spurge, the weed host; spray into crown of plant with force, using malathion or nicotine.

Pear Plant Bug*, *Neolygus communis* Knight. Also called Green Apple Bug or False Tarnished Plant Bug. The pear bug resembles the tarnished plant bug but it is smaller and darker except at tips of wings. It winters on bark. Nymphs hatching in early spring injure young fruits by feeding punctures, causing drop or deformities. A DDT dust or nicotine spray directed at the nymphs should give control.

Phlox Plant Bug*, *Lopidea davisi* Knight. A pest of perennial phlox. The active bugs, dull orange or reddish with a black stripe on the back, feed on the upper surface of the more tender leaves and on buds, causing white or pale-green spots. The plant may be stunted, occasionally killed; the blossom head loses its symmetry. There are 2 or more generations. Eggs are laid in fall on phylox stems behind leaf petioles and begin to hatch early in May. Cut and burn old stalks after first frost; rake up all debris in bed. Spray or dust when nymphs appear with DDT or malathion.

Rapid Plant Bug*, *Adelphocoris rapidus* (Say). One of the small plant bugs, similar to lygus bugs and tarnished plant bug, common on alfalfa and other forage crops, sometimes on potato, beans, soybeans, carrot, even asparagus fern.

Red-and-Black Stink Bug, *Cosmopepla bimaculata* (Thomas). A small, shiny black-and-red bug, ⅓ inch long, with a disagreeable odor. It sucks on snapdragon, beard-tongue, columbine, verbascum, and other flowering plants, wintering as an adult in protected places.

Rhododendron Lace Bug*, *Stephanitis rhododendri* Horvath. A European insect important from New England to Ohio and south to the Carolinas; also present, though not so injurious, in the Pacific Northwest. The injury is prominent when plants are growing in full sun, the whole shrub having a yellow cast. The individual leaves are mottled with a fine stippling of creamy-white or grayish dots, each indicating where the bug has inserted its beak on the underside. The small, ⅛-inch, spined nymphs, with light and dark areas on their flat bodies, hatch in late spring—mid-May near Philadelphia, late May or early June near New York City. They start as a group of dark specks, and the undersurface of leaves is covered with bits of excrement looking like dots of dark molasses when fresh, later giving the leaf a mottled, rusty appearance on the underside. This is an excellent sign of lace-bug injury even when the bugs themselves cannot be seen.

The nymphs move about very little, and then with a peculiar, sidewise motion. They turn into adults during June, acquiring beautiful wings, twice as long as the body, rounded at the apex, with veins in a lacy pattern (Plate XVII). They insert eggs, covered with brownish scabs, in irregular rows along the midrib. There are 2 generations a year, the second brood appearing in July, maturing in August, and depositing overwintering eggs in the leaves. Rhododendrons are rarely killed by lace bugs, but infestations unchecked from year to year result in yellowed, sickly bushes and a gradual decline in vigor.

Control. Almost any good contact insecticide applied with pressure to the undersurface of leaves soon after nymphs hatch should be effective. I prefer lindane, 1 tablespoon of 25 per cent wettable powder to 1 gallon of water, but malathion, DDT, and chlordane are sometimes recommended. An older remedy, quite effective if thoroughly applied, is nicotine sulfate, 1½ teaspoons, plus 1 ounce of soap to 1 gallon of water. A second spray 2 weeks after the first is often advisable to take care of late hatching nymphs, and possibly a third for the second brood in July.

Royal Palm Bug, *Xylastodoris luteolus* Barber. On royal palm in Florida; small, flattened, oblong-oval bugs.

Say Stink Bug*, *Chlorochroa sayi* Stål. A western plant bug distributed east to Kansas. Flat, bright green with 3 orange spots and minute white specks, ½ inch long. It destroys wheat, wilts potato shoots, feeds on asparagus, bean, pea, sunflower, grains, grasses, and weeds.

Small Milkweed Bug*, *Lygaeus kalmii* Stål. In western North America on Asclepias, various species of milkweed. The nymphs are red and black, the wings of adults black with white margins. Another species, known as Common Milkweed Bug (*L. reclivatus*) is similar but has 2 white spots on the wings.

Southern Green Stink Bug*, *Nezara viridula* (Linnaeus). One of the more important southern pests; found in Virginia, North and South Carolina, Georgia, Florida, Alabama, Mississippi, Louisiana, Texas, Arkansas, and Tennessee. The host range includes cucurbits, crucifers, legumes, citrus fruits, pecan, peach, potato, sweetpotato, pepper, corn, sunflower, hackberry and mulberry. All plant parts are attacked, but particularly young, tender growth and fruit. The latter is severely distorted, with hard calluses formed around the feeding punctures. The adult is large, light green, shield-shaped. The female deposits eggs on underside of leaves about mid-April, and the nymphs, bluish with red markings, hatch in about 6 days. There are usually 4 generations, adults from the last generation hibernating in any secluded place.

Control. To protect orchards, avoid a legume crop in summer and clean up weeds. Spray or dust with DDT, changing to sabadilla when edible plant parts are present.

Spined Soldier Bug*, *Podisus maculiventris* (Say). One of the stink bugs, but this one is predatory on Colorado potato beetles and other pests and so beneficial to man. This species is broad and flat like other stink bugs, but the pronotum is extended into a sharp spine on each side.

Squash Bug*, *Anasa tristis* (De Geer). Distributed throughout the country, attacking all vine crops, with preference for squash and pumpkin, gourds and melons next in favor (Plate XII). During the feeding process the squash bug apparently injects a toxic substance into the vines, causing a wilting known as Anasa wilt of cucurbits, closely resembling bacterial wilt, a true disease. After wilting, the vines turn black and crisp; small plants are killed entirely; larger vines have several runners affected. The bugs may be so numerous, no squashes are formed, or they may congregate in dense clusters on unripe fruits.

The adult is dark brown, sometimes mottled with gray or light brown; hard-shelled, ⅝ inch long. It gives off such a disagreeable odor when crushed, it is commonly called a stink bug, but it belongs in the family Coreidae while true stink bugs are in the Pentatomidae. Unmated adults hibernate in shelter of dead leaves, vines, boards or buildings and fly to cucurbits when vines start to run. Mating takes place at that time. Clusters of brick-red eggs are laid in angles between veins on underside of leaves and hatch in 7 to 14 days into nymphs with green abdomen, crimson head, thorax and legs. Older nymphs are a somber grayish white, with dark legs. There are 5 molts before the winged adult. There is usually but 1 generation.

Control. Sanitation is the primary control measure. Remove all rubbish offering winter protection; stimulate plant growth with fertilizer; handpick adults and leaves bearing eggs. Dusting the vines with Sevin or sabadilla will kill the nymphs. Do not use DDT or any dust containing sulfur; both are injurious to most squashes although some squash varieties are rather resistant. Winter squashes, hubbard and marrows, are very susceptible. A tachinid fly is an effective parasite.

Superb Plant Bug, *Adelphocoris superbus* (Uhler). Another of the small plant bugs infesting alfalfa and forage crops. The adult is blackish with orange or yellow sides; the nymph is green with brown markings.

Sycamore Lace Bug*, *Corythucha ciliata* (Say). Widely distributed and common on sycamore, recorded occasionally on ash, hickory, and mulberry. The adults are small, ⅛ inch long, but with wide, flat, white, lacelike wings and prominent lacy projections from the thorax. They winter under bark, and in spring glue black eggs along ribs on underside of leaves. The nymphs are light-colored, spiny; the foliage turns white from their sucking. There are 2 generations and injury resulting in defoliation may be severe on street and shade trees. Spray with malathion or lindane when nymphs appear. Repeat in 2 weeks.

Sycamore Plant Bug, *Plagiognathus albatus* Van Duzee. Recorded from Connecticut, New Jersey, New York, Delaware, Pennsylvania and District of Columbia. Nymphs are tan or brown with dark eyes and brown spots on wings, ⅛ inch long. Their feeding produces small, irregular yellowish or reddish spots over the leaves, and sometimes holes where dead tissue drops out. Nicotine sulfate, 1 to 600 dilution, has given control, the first spray applied in early May, the second 10 days later. DDT should be effective but a miticide should be added.

Tarnished Plant Bug*, *Lygus lineolaris* (Palisot de Beauvois). Found throughout the country (Plate V), injurious to more than 50 economic plants. Vegetables include bean, beet, cauliflower, cabbage, chard, celery, cucumber, potato, turnip; fruits include apple, peach, pear, strawberry, occasionally citrus. Among flowers, dahlias and asters are frequent victims and the bug sometimes injures calendula, chrysanthemum, cosmos, gladiolus, garden balsam, marigold, poppy, salvia, Shasta daisy, sunflower, verbena, zinnia and others. The toxin liberated in the plant by the feeding process of the bug causes deformed beet and chard leaves, black joints of celery, blackened terminal shoots and dwarfed pitted fruit of peach, buds dying or opening to imperfect flowers on dahlia.

The adult is small, ¼ inch long, flattened, oval, irregularly mottled with white, yellow, and black blotches. These give it a generally tarnished appearance, but there is a clear yellow triangle, marked with a black dot, on the lower third of each side. Adults hibernate among weeds, under leaves, stones, or bark, flying early in spring to feed on fruit-tree buds, then migrating to other plants to lay eggs in leaves or flowers. Nymphs are very small, greenish yellow, marked with 4 black dots on the thorax and 1 on the abdomen. The cycle takes 3 to 4 weeks and there are 3 to 5 generations a season. In the South, feeding and breeding continue through the winter.

Control. The tarnished plant bug has been hard to control, most efforts being put on removing weeds and trash to prevent overwintering. DDT is reasonably effective; apply dust or spray to flower buds as they start to form and repeat just before they open. Sabadilla dust is useful for edible plant parts near harvest.

Toyon Lace Bug, *Corythucha incurvata* Uhler. A most disfiguring pest of the lovely red-berried photinia or toyon, the California Christmasberry, in California and Arizona. The nymphs are dirty brown with spines; adults are yellowish brown. Eggs are inserted in underside of leaves and covered with a brown, sticky, cone-shaped mass. Nymphs and adults secrete quantities of honeydew, a medium for black sooty mold. There are several broods a year, with adults hibernating under bark and leaves. Spray with lindane, malathion, or nicotine sulfate.

Two-spotted Stink Bug*, *Perillus bioculatus* (Fabricius). A useful insect, predaceous on armyworms, cutworms, other caterpillar and larvae of various beetles. The bug is small, black with reddish markings.

Walnut Lace Bug, *Corythucha juglandis* (Fitch). Occasionally abundant on walnut, butternut, basswood and linden. It is yellow or pale brown with brown bands.

Western Chinch Bug*, *Blissus occiduus* Barber. Black, with short wings; even smaller than the chinch bug. Found in some western states.

Western Leaf-footed Bug, *Leptoglossus zonatus* (Dallas). Large, nearly flat, brown, with yellow markings and leaflike enlargements of the hind legs. The nymphs are bright red and black. Ranging through Arizona and California, this species breeds on pomegranate where it is thought to spread heart-rot disease. It may also damage orange trees, limes, cotton, dates, or watermelon.

Wheel Bug*, *Agrilus cristatus* (Linnaeus). One of the predaceous assassin bugs, living in trees and preying on caterpillars and other insects. This species is common in eastern states north to New York, overwintering as bottle-shaped eggs cemented together. The adult has a semicircular crest on the pronotum, resembling half of a wheel, and is unusually large.

Willow Lace Bug, *Corythucha mollicula* Osborn & Drake. Found through the East on willow, its only host; causing serious injury when present in large numbers.

Yucca Plant Bug*, *Halticotoma valida* Reuter. Present wherever yucca is grown, more prevalent in southwestern and southeastern states. The leaves are stippled, covered with black specks of excrement, and turn yellowish. The adult, ⅛ inch long, rather stout, is blue-black with reddish head and thorax. It does not fly readily but runs fast. The nymphs are bright scarlet and may be numerous on leaves. Spray or dust with malathion or DDT.

BUTTERFLIES

Butterflies, along with moths, belong to the order Lepidoptera. Their wings, usually large and beautiful, are covered with tiny overlapping scales that rub off like dust on the fingers. Their brilliant iridescent coloring comes from light refracted by many fine ridges on these scales and not from actual pigmentation. Antennae of butterflies usually end in knobs, while those of moths are feathery. Butterflies are day fliers, moths mostly nocturnal. Their mouth parts, adapted for getting nectar out of the throats of flowers, are formed into a long tube, proboscis or tongue, which is coiled beneath the head like a watch spring when not in use. Eggs are laid in exposed places singly or in small groups. Larvae are caterpillars, sometimes called worms. The pupae—chrysalids—of butterflies are not enclosed in cocoons but are attached to the surface of a leaf or stem by a silken pad, sometimes also by a silken band around the middle. Only the larval stage is destructive to living plant tissue. The adults do no harm, as they sip nectar and many are beneficial pollinators. Some of the caterpillars, too, are beneficial, acting as scavengers or eating other insects and serving as food for birds.

Only those families of interest to gardeners are given here, followed by descriptions of a few species named for their adult stage. Those named for the larval stage are discussed under Caterpillars.

Danaidae. Milkweed Butterflies and Monarchs. These are large and brightly colored; the larvae feed on members of the milkweed family.

Hesperiidae. Skippers. These form a connecting link between true butterflies and moths. They are mostly small, wingspread seldom more than 1½ inches, and they are named for their erratic close-to-the-ground flight habit, a kind of skipping. The antennae are not knobbed but have a short hook pointed backward. At rest, the fore wings are held vertically, the hind wings partially spread. The bodies are more robust than those of most butterflies. The larva has a large bulbous head, separated from the rest of the body by a narrowly constricted neck. Larvae tie leaves together with silk for their nests.

Lycaenidae. Blues, Coppers, Hair-streaks, and Harvesters. Small, delicate, often brightly colored, very common; antennae usually ringed with white. The caterpillars are sluglike, with short legs and head bent down beneath the thorax; many species have honeydew glands.

Nymphalidae. Four-footed or Brush-footed Butterflies. The fore legs are much reduced and not fitted for walking; antennae are very distinctly knobbed; coloring, patterns, and wing outlines vary greatly. The caterpillars are often quite spiny, with horns on the head. This is the largest family of butterflies and includes some of the best-known species, such as Painted Lady, Mourning-cloak, Red Admiral, Viceroy.

Papilionidae. Swallowtails. Our largest butterflies, brightly colored, most with tail-like extensions of their hind wings. The caterpillars are large, smooth-skinned, with a forked, malodorous retractile organ that can be thrust out from an opening in the first thoracic segment just back of the head.

Pieridae. Pierids; Whites, Sulfurs, and Orange-tips. These are of average size and frequent open fields and roadsides. Fore and hind wings are nearly the same size, but the latter are rounded. Color differences between the sexes and seasonal color variations may be striking. The common cabbage butterfly belongs in this group. The larvae are slender, greenish.

Satyridae. Wood Nymphs and Satyrs. Usually of medium size, dull color, flying low, with bases of main veins in the wings swollen and hollow. The caterpillars are inconspicuous brown or green, almost hairless. Many feed on grasses; many are mountain forms.

Black Swallowtail. See Celeryworm under Caterpillars.

Cabbage Butterfly. See Imported Cabbageworm under Caterpillars.

California Tortoise-shell*, *Nymphalis californica* (Boisduval). A western species feeding on ceanothus, manzanita, amelanchier, sometimes other native shrubs and fruit trees. The caterpillars are black with branched spines and yellow dots. The butterflies are brown and orange, marked with black.

Checker Spot Butterfly, *Euphydryas chalcedona* (Doubleday). Chalcedon. Adults have black wings covered with many yellow spots. Caterpillars are large, bluish black with small orange markings and numerous black compound spines. They feed on aster, buddleia, chrysanthemum, Shasta daisy, monkeyflower, penstemon, veronica, and other plants. They often web foliage as they feed and are quite a garden pest in the Rocky Mountain and Pacific States.

Columbine Skipper, *Erynnis lucilius* (Scudder & Burgess). The caterpillar, ¾ inch long, velvety green, rather stout with small black head, chews holes in columbine leaves and hides in a rolled-up leaf. The adult is a typical skipper with purplish wings. Spray or dust with DDT.

Clouded Sulfur*, *Colias philodice* Latreille. A roadside butterfly, yellow with black wing margins. The larvae feed on clovers.

Hackberry Empress, *Asterocampa celtis* Boisduval & LeConte. The larva of this nymphalid butterfly is bright green with yellow spots and lines, 2 prominent branched horns on a broad head; just over an inch long.

Harvester, *Feniseca tarquinius* (Fabricius). Small brownish butterfly with a larval stage predaceous on aphids; not very common.

Monarch Butterfly*, *Danaus plexippus* (Linnaeus). This milkweed butterfly is common throughout America. It is orange-brown with wings bordered and tipped with black, with small white spots in the black border. This species migrates south in large numbers each fall, roosting in trees at night like a flock of birds, reappearing in the North each spring. The caterpillar is yellowish green banded with black, with 2 threadlike appendages at either end of the body. The jade-green chrysalid is held by a belt spotted with gold.

Mourning-cloak Butterfly*, *Nymphalis antiopa* (Linnaeus). Spiny Elm

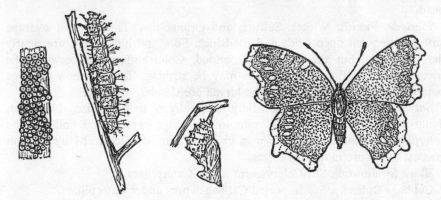

39. Mourning-cloak butterfly: eggs, larva (spiny elm caterpillar), pupa, and adult.

Caterpillar. This common species occurs all over America on elm, especially Chinese elm, also on poplar and willow. The adults have purplish brown wings bordered with a wide yellow stripe, inside of which is a row of blue or purple spots; wingspread is 2½ to 3½ inches. They hide in autumn in nooks and crannies, including tree cavities, fly on sunny March days, but wait until May to deposit sculptured eggs in masses of 300 to 450 around a small branch. The larvae feed in groups on elm, poplar, willow, often defoliating branches. They are black, covered with small white dots and a row of orange or red spots along the back, and lengthwise rows of black, branched spines. They transform to chrysalids in late June or early July, with butterflies emerging in a few days to lay eggs for a second brood in August.

Control. Spray with lead arsenate or DDT when larvae are young; cut and burn infested twigs and small branches. Several wasps are parasites. Yellow-billed cuckoos and some bugs are predators.

Orange Sulfur Butterfly, *Colias philodoce eurytheme* Boisduval. Alfalfa Butterfly. Mostly orange with black wing margins but some females white. The larvae feed on clovers.

Painted Beauty*, *Vanessa virginiensis* (Drury). Hunter's Butterfly. Ranging throughout North America. The caterpillars are banded dark purple, yellow, and green, with a short row of silver-white spots on each side of the back. They feed on everlasting, thistles, hollyhock, mallow, forget-me-not, peony, senecio, sunflowers. The adults are orange brown and black with white spots on the front wings and 2 large eye spots on the underside of each hind wing.

Painted Lady*, *Vanessa cardui* (Linnaeus). Thistle Butterfly, said to be the most widely distributed butterfly in the world; often abundant in the West, sometimes in great migratory flights. The adult is large, 2½ inches across the wings, orange-red with black and white markings. The caterpillar varies from green to brown mottled with black, has a light dorsal stripe and a light yellow stripe along each side, grayish spines, 1¼ to 1½ inches long. It feeds on calendula, hollyhock, lupine, sunflower as well as thistles, mallows and weeds, often tying together terminal portions. The iridescent chrysalids seem to have been dipped in gold. There are at least 2 broods a year, with butterflies in evidence from early spring to late fall. Spray ornamentals with lead arsenate or DDT or malathion. Remove infested tips.

Pine Butterfly*, *Neophasia menapia* (Felder & Felder). Chiefly a pest of coniferous forests in the West, where great areas of yellow pine and Douglas-fir are defoliated, followed by death of trees, but present also in the East. Adults are white, marked with black; larvae are green with white stripes. A wasplike parasite is effective in bringing outbreaks under control in about 3 years. Meanwhile forests can be sprayed by airplane.

Pipevine Swallowtail*, *Battus philenor* (Linnaeus). Feeding on and defoliating Dutchmans-pipe. Caterpillars are dark brown with 4 rows of orange to coral spots and soft hornlike projections; 2 inches long. Adults are blue-green butterflies with white spots on under margin of fore wings and yellow and orange spots on hind wings. Spray with DDT, lead arsenate or malathion.

Red-admiral*, *Vanessa atalanta* (Linnaeus). Adults are velvety deep brown or black with a red or orange oblique stripe on the fore wings and a margin of the same color on the hind wings. The caterpillars are purplish brown or black, covered with minute whitish specks, with a continuous row of yellow spots along each side and branching spines. They feed in groups in webs. The chrysalids are brown with golden tubercles and a grayish bloom. The caterpillars are not important as garden pests, feeding mostly on hops and nettles.

Silver-spotted Skipper*, *Epargyreus clarus* (Cramer). One of the largest of the skipper butterflies, feeding on locust and wisteria, sometimes causing serious defoliation. The caterpillar is leaf-green with a dull-red head. It fastens together several leaflets, feeding inside this case. The butterfly is brown and yellow with triangular white spots on the fore wings.

Spice-bush Swallowtail*, *Papilio troilus* Linnaeus. Feeding on spicebush and sassafras, not too serious. The larva is 1½ inches long, largest at the third thoracic segment, pea-green on top with yellow sides, pink head and under surface, 4 large and 10 small orange spots.

Tiger Swallowtail*, *Papilio glaucus* Linnaeus. Not very important but feeding on apple, ash, birch, cherry, lilac, poplar and other trees. The larva is dark green, 1½ inches long, the 3rd thoracic segment enlarged and marked with a large yellow spot enclosing a purple spot on each side.

Viceroy*, *Limentis archippus* (Cramer). Like the monarch butterfly, feeding on poplar and willow. The head of the larva is green, bilobed, and grooved vertically. The body segments are pink, brown, and green, with tubercles.

Western Parsley Swallowtail, *Papilio zelicaon* Lucas. On members of the parsley family, including carrot, celery, parsnip, and also a problem of young citrus in Pacific Coast states. The butterfly is yellow or orange and black. The caterpillar, sometimes called California Orange Dog, is bright yellow-green with black bands, orange spots, and an orange scent horn. They have been controlled on citrus by a DDT spray or cryolite dust.

Western Swallowtail, *Papilio rutulus* Boisduval. Yellow with black markings common in the West. The larvae—pale green with purple-brown head, orange tubercles—feed on alder, willow, apricot, apple, avocado, cherry, and prune.

Zebra Butterfly, *Heliconius charithonius* (Linnaeus). Black, striped with yellow, occurring in the Gulf States, most common in Florida. The larvae feed on passion-flower. The chrysalid wriggles when disturbed and makes a creaking sound.

Zebra Swallowtail, *Papilio marcellus* Cramer. Striped black and greenish white, with relatively long tails. Feeding on pawpaw.

CANKERWORMS

Cankerworms, often called inchworms or measuring worms, are larvae of small moths, family Geometridae. Some species in this group are obnoxious pests of fruit and shade trees and known as cankerworms; the others are called loopers or spanworms. They all move by a series of looping movements, drawing up the abdomen to the thorax in a loop, grasping the support by their prolegs (false legs at the end of the body), loosening the thoracic legs, stretching the body forward, and so on in rapid succession. They also have a habit of letting themselves down on a thread of silk.

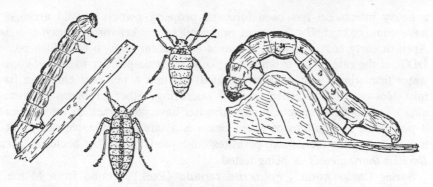

40. *Cankerworms: spring, left; fall, right.*

Fall Cankerworm*, *Alsophila pometaria* (Harris). Distributed generally across the United States from North Carolina northward, a threat to fruit trees, apple preferred, but also feeding on apricot, cherry, plum, prune and other fruits, and to shade trees, especially oak and elm, sometimes basswood or linden, birch, and maple. They even feed on rosebushes near apple trees.

The moths emerge from pupae in the ground in late fall, after there have been freezing temperatures. The males are brownish gray with a 1¼-inch wingspread; the females have wingless gray bodies, ½ inch long (Plate XVIII). They crawl up tree trunks to deposit eggs—grayish, shaped like a flowerpot—in a compact, single-layered mass on main trunk or branches or around smaller twigs. The eggs hatch in spring about the time leaves unfold, and the larvae feed on foliage until June. The caterpillars are brownish above, green below, with 3 narrow white stripes along the body above the spiracles and a yellow stripe below, about an inch long. They often drop down from trees on a silken thread, climbing up again to resume feeding. There is only 1 generation a year and toward the end of their season they may eat conspicuous holes in leaves of rhododendron and other shrubs growing under or near favored food plants. When full-grown they drop to the ground and pupate in a silken cocoon, 1 to 4 inches deep in the soil.

Control. Banding trees with a sticky material such as Tanglefoot, to prevent the wingless female from crawling up the tree to lay eggs, is a practice less popular now than some years ago, for it has been determined that young cankerworms balloon over, via their silken threads, from unbanded trees nearby. Actual foliage injury is only slightly reduced. Also, unless properly applied to a band of paper or Balsam Wool around the trunk so that the Tanglefoot does not come in direct contact with the bark, there may be serious injury to the bark. The band should be in place by late September and the sticky surface scraped or renewed through the fall to prevent late arrivals from crawling up on the backs of their fallen comrades.

Spraying is far more effective as a control measure, and in a season when a heavy infestation has been forecast, property owners should arrange to have elms, oaks, and other trees preferred by cankerworms sprayed in late April or early May—as soon as leaves are out far enough to hold a poison. DDT, at the rate of 2 pounds 50 per cent wettable powder to 100 gallons of water (sometimes with malathion added), or in a 6 per cent emulsion for a mist blower, gives excellent control but brings other problems because it also kills beneficial insects. Many arborists have gone back to lead arsenate, 3 pounds to 100 gallons of water. Sevin is a safe and effective spray but it, too, may reduce beneficial parasites and predators. The bacterial spray, *Bacillus thuringiensis,* is being tested.

Spring Cankerworm*, *Paleacrita vernata* (Peck). Found from Maine to North Carolina, west to Texas and Colorado, and in California. Apple and elm are preferred hosts, then oak, hickory, cherry, maple, sometimes other fruit and shade trees. One of our oldest pests, a native known in New England for more than 200 years. Along with the fall cankerworm, it appears in cycles, being very abundant for 2 or 3 years, nearly defoliating trees in an area, feeding in such numbers you can actually hear the leaves being crunched, and dropping down on unwary pedestrians. Then they almost disappear for a few years and gradually recruit their armies for another peak of abundance. Trees defoliated for 2 or 3 years in succession may die.

The moths appear in early spring, sometimes on a warm day in February, more often in March. The females are wingless, about the same nondescript gray as the fall cankerworm, but they have a dark stripe down the back and transverse rows of stiff reddish spines on the first 7 joints of the abdomen. The male moths are silky gray with 3 transverse dark lines on the fore wings. They often appear around trees (and even in attics) about the time females are crawling up trunks to lay clusters of oval, brownish-purple eggs under bark scales on main trunk or branches. These hatch in about a month. The caterpillars vary from green to brown to nearly black, usually with a yellowish stripe under the spiracles, up to an inch long. They differ from fall cankerworms in having only 2 pairs of prolegs instead of 3.

Control. Measures are the same as for the fall cankerworm, except that if banding is practiced, Tanglefoot is applied or renewed in February. In apple orchards the codling moth spray schedule will also control cankerworms.

CASEBEARERS

Casebearers (family Coleophoridae) are moths whose larvae live in portable cases and feed or mine in leaves, fruits, flowers, or seeds. This is a small family and most of the American species belong to the genus Coleophora. Casebearers of the genus Acrobasis (family Phycitidae) secrete their cases between leaves webbed together.

Birch Casebearer*, *Coleophora salmani* Heinrich. First found in Maine in 1927 and spreading in that state, attacking all varieties of birch and speckled alder. The moth is very small, grayish brown with a fringe on narrow hind wings. The caterpillar is light yellow to green, with a black head, ⅕ inch long. It lives in a small brown cylindrical case, mining and cutting holes in leaves. Badly mined foliage dries and trees appear scorched; buds may be eaten; twigs and limbs die back. There is 1 generation. Larvae hibernate in cases on twigs. Control with a dormant lime-sulfur spray, 1 to 8 dilution, in early spring.

Birch Tube Maker*, *Acrobasis betulella* Hulst. Feeding on black, gray, and paper birch from Maine to New York, also recorded in Colorado and California. Each larva lives in a frass tube spun between the leaves.

California Casebearer, *Coleophora sacramenta* Heinrich. Willow is the normal host, but the larvae commonly feed on almond, apricot, apple, cherry, peach, plum, prune in the San Francisco Bay region of California. The moth is bluish white with gray scales, ⅝ inch wingspread; the larva is orange, making a black case widened at the bottom with a winglike projection. There is 1 generation. Spraying with lead arsenate gives control.

Cherry Casebearer*, *Coleophora pruniella* Clemens. Normally feeding on wild cherry but reported injuring cultivated cherries and sometimes apple in the Middle West and Oregon. It winters in its case attached to twigs, moving to young foliage in spring, producing skeletonized and dead areas as it grows and enlarges the case with leaf tissue. Pupation is in late spring. Moths lay eggs on underside of leaves, and new caterpillars are making overwintering cases by late summer. There are several natural parasites. A dormant dinitro spray is effective.

Cigar Casebearer*, *Coleophora occidentis* Zeller. General in apple-growing regions, attacking apple, except Jonathan variety, pear, plum, cherry, hawthorn, quince. The light-brown partly grown larva hibernates inside a cigar-shaped, brownish-gray silken case, about ¼ inch long, attached to twigs or branches, and starts feeding as buds unfold in spring. It feeds until July, making blotch mines between the leaf surfaces, then pupates and produces mottled gray moths with narrow, fringed wings, ½-inch wingspread. Eggs are laid on underside of leaves with larvae appearing in late summer to make new cases. The ordinary apple spray schedule should take care of casebearers. Spraying at the cluster-bud stage with lead arsenate, DDT, or nicotine sulfate, 1 to 800, is effective.

Elm Casebearer*, *Coleophora limosipennella* (Duponchel). A European insect established in the Northeast, favoring English, Scotch and American elms in local outbreaks. The moth, buff-colored with gray markings, appears in July. The larvae and their cases are dark brown and the mines are between the principal veins in the leaves. Elms sprayed for cankerworms and leaf beetles will not suffer from this pest.

Larch Casebearer*, *Coleophora laricella* (Hübner). Another European pest, first noticed in Massachusetts in 1886 and now found throughout the range of American and European larch in the eastern half of the country. The moth is silver-gray, appears from late May to July. The dark, reddish-brown larva feeds as a miner until September, when it constructs its case for winter hibernation. When larvae are abundant the needles turn white and die, growth is checked, and the tree weakened. Spray with lime-sulfur, dormant strength, in spring before growth starts. There are many natural parasites but they do not give sufficient control.

Pecan Cigar Casebearer*, *Coleophora caryaefoliella* Clemens. Found from New Hampshire to Florida and Texas on pecan, hickory, and black walnut. The moth is brownish, the larva reddish with a black head, and the base is brown, cigar-shaped, ¼ inch long. Mined areas turn brown and sometimes drop out, leaving holes in foliage. There may also be some defoliation. Spray hickories with lead arsenate at 3 pounds per 100 gallons of water and pecans at 2 pounds per 100, with the addition of 6 pounds of hydrated lime; or use DDT.

Pecan Leaf Casebearer*, *Acrobasis juglandis* (LeBaron). Present in the southern part of the pecan belt, from southern Georgia and northern Florida to Texas. The moths are variable, white, gray, brown or black. The very small larvae feed on young buds and leaves and are damaging chiefly to weakened plants which cannot grow faster than the larvae can eat. Control for the pecan nut casebearer takes care of this species.

Pecan Nut Casebearer*, *Acrobasis caryae* Grote. A most serious pecan pest, especially in Texas, often damaging in the other Gulf states, destroying a large percentage of the crop. The larva is olive-green, ½ inch long; the moth is dark gray with ¾ inch wingspread. The larva winters in a hibernaculum, small cocoon, at the base of a bud. In spring larvae feed on buds and bore into tender shoots, pupating in tunnels. The moths, emerging in May, deposit eggs on the nuts. The young larvae spin a web around several nuts, then enter to feed. This brood pupates inside the nut; moths come out in late June and July. There are 3, possibly 4, generations but the first does the most damage.

Control. If not over 3 per cent of shoots of the previous year are infested with overwintering larvae, control is considered unnecessary. Otherwise spray with DDT, 2 to 3 pounds of 50 per cent wettable powder to 100 gallons of water. This is the most effective spray but leads to trouble with mites and aphids. Parathion controls all but must be used with great caution. Lead arsenate, 6 pounds to 100 gallons, is safe in semiarid Texas, may injure in more humid sections. Nicotine sulfate, ¾ pint plus 2 quarts summer oil to 100 gallons, is a safe and fairly effective spray. One application before 1st generation larvae enter nuts—between April 20 and May 25—may be sufficient, but a second spray a week later is advised for heavy infestations.

Pistol Casebearer*, *Coleophora malivorella* Riley. Found from the Mississippi Valley eastward, a minor pest of apple and other fruits. Similar to the

41. Pistol casebearer.

cigar casebearer but the case is bent over like a pistol. The larva winters in
the case; buds are injured in spring and leaves mined. Eggs are laid on
leaves in June. Control with the regular orchard spray schedule, or a special
cluster-bud spray of DDT or lead arsenate, or a summer oil to kill eggs.

CATERPILLARS

Caterpillars are the wormlike larvae of moths and butterflies. Some are
commonly known by the adult form and so are discussed under Butterflies
or under Moths. Some have special names—budworm, cankerworm, casebearer, cutworm, earworm, fruitworm, hornworm, leaf miner, leaf tier, spanworm, webworm—and are treated under such headings. A few of the other
thousands of caterpillars are here in this section.

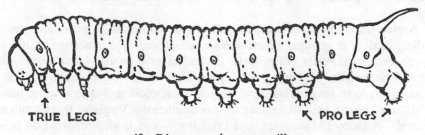

↑
TRUE LEGS   ↖ **PRO LEGS** ↗

42. Diagram of a caterpillar.

Caterpillars are of various shapes but the majority have cylindrical soft
bodies which are naked, hairy, or adorned with spines. They are composed
of 13 segments behind the head with its chewing mouth parts. The first 3
segments each bear a pair of jointed legs terminating in a single claw. In
addition to these true legs, abdominal segments 3, 4, 5, and 6 typically have
a pair of prolegs, false legs, which are unjointed sucker feet provided with

tiny hooks, crotchets, for holding onto a leaf or twig. There is another pair of prolegs on the last abdominal segment. There is also, in many caterpillars, a spinneret near the mouth for making silk.

Control is usually by means of protective spraying, which means a stomach poison on the foliage before the larvae start eating. Sometimes contact sprays are used and sometimes eradication measures are taken against the egg stage.

Alfalfa Caterpillar*, *Colias eurytheme* Boisduval. A southwestern alfalfa pest occasionally present elsewhere and also on garden peas, beans, and other legumes. The caterpillar is dark green with a pale-yellow or white line down the side. The butterflies are sulfur yellow, less frequently white, with wings tipped with wide black bands. Cutting alfalfa low and removing it from the field helps in control, as do some braconid wasps. Microbial insecticides have been successfully used—the polyhedrosis virus and *Bacillus thuringiensis.*

Alfalfa Looper*, *Autographa californica* (Speyer). Causes sporadic damage on the Pacific Coast. This caterpillar is a general feeder, injuring, in addition to alfalfa, many cereal and truck crops, fruits, flowers, ornamental trees and shrubs. The looper is about an inch long, dark olive-green with a paler head and 3 dark lines along the back; only 3 pairs of prolegs. The gray moth, with a silver mark on each fore wing, appears at dusk to visit flowers. Control with rotenone or pyrethrum dust on vegetables, lead arsenate or DDT on ornamentals.

Avocado Caterpillar, *Amorbia essigana* (Busck). Limited to California and mostly to avocado. This is a tortricid or leaf-roller moth, with reddish-brown fore wings an inch across, first noticed in 1922. The yellowish-green larvae skeletonize the leaves or web them together and scar young fruits. There may be 4 or 5 generations. It may be controlled with DDT, adding a miticide to prevent build-up of mites. A tachinid parasite destroys many larvae.

Azalea Caterpillar, *Datana major* Grote & Robinson. A gregarious caterpillar, feeding in groups, all members raising head and posterior in unison when disturbed. Partly grown larva is reddish to brownish black with white or yellow stripes. The full-grown caterpillar has a red pronotal shield, a black body with longitudinal rows of yellowish spots and sparse white hairs. This is a serious pest of azaleas in the Southeast—Virginia, the Carolinas, Florida, Alabama, Mississippi, and Louisiana—and is also reported on blueberry in Delaware, on red oak in Maryland, and occasionally on andromeda and apple in Atlantic states.

Banded Woollybear*, *Isia isabella* (J. E. Smith). Generally distributed, our familiar densely hairy "hedgehog" caterpillar, which rolls into a ball when disturbed or for hibernating. It is about 1¼ inches long, black at both ends with a reddish-brown band around the middle. The width of this band is said to forecast the winter; the narrower the band, the colder and longer will be the winter. The adult is the tiger moth, yellow, wing expanse 1½ to

2 inches, a few dusky spots on the wings and black spots on the abdomen (Plate XX). The caterpillars feed on leaves of many garden plants but are readily killed with lead arsenate, cryolite, or DDT.

Black-headed Fireworm*, *Rhopobota naevana* (Hübner). Cranberry Worm, a destructive cranberry pest. Eggs, overwintered on leaves, hatch when growth starts in spring, producing green larvae, first pale, then dark with black heads, which web leaves together and feed inside. They pupate on the ground. The first brood of moths, ash-gray with irregular brownish bands across the fore wings, spreading to ⅜ inch, emerge in June and those of the second brood in July or August. Dust when new growth is ¼ to ½ inch long with 2 per cent parathion or a mixture of 1 per cent parathion with 1 per cent DDT, or with 10 per cent DDT, or with Sevin.

Bougainvillea Caterpillar, *Asciodes gordialis* (Guenée). The most persistent and damaging pest of this host. The caterpillar, 1 inch long, green, eats and rolls the leaves, but usually drops to the ground unnoticed when the plant is touched. The moth is brown. During the warmer portions of the year spray every 2 weeks with chlordane or DDT.

Cabbage Looper*, *Trichoplusia ni* (Hübner). A native caterpillar common throughout the country. It attacks all members of the cabbage family—broccoli, Brussels sprouts, cabbage, cauliflower, collards, horseradish, kale, kohlrabi, mustard, radish, turnip—and also feeds on beet, celery, lettuce, parsley, pea, potato, spinach, tomato, and on flowers—carnation, chrysanthemum, mignonette, geranium and others. The looper is said to be a serious lettuce pest. It winters as a green to brown pupa wrapped in a cocoon attached by one side to a plant leaf, and transforms in spring into a moth with mottled brownish fore wings, with a small silvery spot in the middle, and paler brown hind wings; wing expanse is just under 1½ inches.

The females lay many small, round, greenish-white eggs, singly, on upper surface of leaves. The larva has a body tapering to the head, greenish, with a thin white line above the spiracles and 2 others down the back; there are 3 pairs of prolegs. After feeding for 2 to 4 weeks, the looper spins a cocoon. There may be 3 or more generations a season.

Control. Microbial insecticides have been effective, either a spray of *Bacillus thuringiensis* or a polyhedrosis virus causing a wilt. DDT, toxaphene, or cryolite have been used on young plants, changing to rotenone as heads form. Endrin controls DDT-resistant loopers.

California Oakworm*, *Phryganidia californica* Packard. On live and other oaks, sometimes on chestnut and eucalyptus in California. It is particularly destructive to live oaks in the San Francisco Bay region, defoliating them periodically in much the same fashion as cankerworms injure eastern oaks. Immature caterpillars feed on live-oak foliage during the winter, but on deciduous trees the oakworm winters in the egg stage. Mature caterpillars are olive-brown with black and yellow longitudinal stripes on back and sides; 1 inch long. After feeding in spring, first by skeletonizing leaves, then by

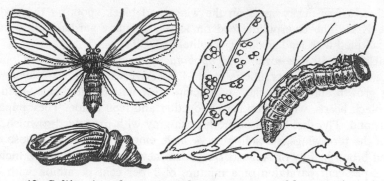

43. California oakworm: moth, pupa, eggs, and larva eating.

eating holes in foliage, they pupate in May and June in smooth white or yellow chrysalids attached by the rear end to leaves, limbs, or tree trunks. The moths emerge in June and July, lay flattened white eggs for the summer brood on any kind of oak, and the adults appear in October and November. They are uniformly pale brown, with slightly darker antennae and wing veins, 1- to 1¼-inch wing expanse. Although they are abundant enough to cause defoliation only at long and irregular intervals, protective measures should be taken each season.

Control. Spray in March and April, when worms are small, with lead arsenate, 3 to 4 pounds per 100 gallons plus ½ pint fish oil, or with DDT emulsion, prepared to give 1 pound actual DDT per 100 gallons. DDT is more effective than lead arsenate, but it kills parasites and predators that normally hold the oakworm in check. Lindane and dieldrin are possibilities. A virus wilt disease markedly reduces oakworm populations.

California Tent Caterpillar*, *Malacosoma californicum* (Packard). Common in California. This species constructs large tents like the eastern tent caterpillar. It infests oak in particular but also almond, apple, apricot, ash, toyon, California coffeeberry, ceanothus, cherry, cottonwood, currant, hazel, madroña, plum, prune, redbud, willow, and other fruit and forest trees. The caterpillars are reddish brown or tawny above, paler underneath, with a blue line on each side. A similar species, known as the **Blue-sided Tent Caterpillar**, *M. constrictum* Stretch, has an orange-brown body with distinctly blue sides and blue dots. It feeds on oaks, shrubs, and fruit in California, Arizona, and Oregon. There is an egg band like that of the eastern tent caterpillar around the twig over winter.

Control. Cut off twigs bearing egg masses or apply a winter oil spray to kill eggs; wipe out nests and remove infested branches; dust young caterpillars with sulfur; spray or dust trees with lead arsenate or DDT. There are many natural enemies, including an efficient wilt disease.

Celery Looper*, *Anagrapha falcifera* (Kirby). General throughout the country and much like the cabbage looper. The moth is large with purple-brown fore wings; the larvae are pale green, with light and dark stripes, up to 1 inch long. They feed on celery, beets, lettuce, and other succulent plants and weeds. Young celery plants can be dusted with DDT. Change to rotenone or pyrethrum near harvest.

Celeryworm*, Black Swallowtail*, Parsleyworm*, *Papilio polyxenes asterius* Stoll. The most important of the swallowtail butterflies, occurring all over the United States east of the Rocky Mountains, feeding on celery, carrot, caraway, dill, parsnip, parsley, but not considered a major pest. The caterpillar is a striking creature, 2 inches long, with a black crossband in each segment and just back of the head an opening for 2 soft, forked orange horns (Plate XIX). When disturbed, the larva protrudes these horns and gives out a sickeningly sweet odor. The butterfly has a spread of 3 to 4 inches, black wings with 2 rows of yellow spots, hind wings with blue shadings between the rows, a black spot bordered with orange on the inner margin, and a projecting lobe—the "swallowtail."

In the North it passes the winter as a tan chrysalid suspended from host plants; in the South the butterflies live over winter. Eggs are laid singly on leaves of food plants, hatching in 10 days. The larvae feed for 10 days to several weeks, occasionally stripping plants of foliage. There are 2 generations in the North, more in the South. Another, but similar, species occurs in the West.

Control. Handpicking may be sufficient. Young plants can be dusted with lead or calcium arsenate, changing to rotenone as they approach edible stage.

Chain-spotted Geometer*, *Cingilia catenaria* (Drury). A looper caterpillar, yellowish with spots along the sides resembling a chain; very slender, about 2 inches long. Present in northeastern America to the Plains, feeding on many shrubs and trees, including bayberry, blueberry, sweetfern, alder, balsam, birch, wild cherry, oak, poplar, and willow. The moths, smoky white faintly marked with black, appear from August to September. Eggs hatch late in spring, larvae feeding from June to August.

Clover Head Caterpillar*, *Grapholitha interstinctana* (Clemens). Feeding mainly in heads of red clover, sometimes other clovers, in eastern states. The caterpillars are very small, ¼ inch, somewhat hairy. The moths, also small, dark brown marked with white, lay eggs on leaves, stems, and heads. The young larvae work their way into the head, destroying half the florets, giving a one-sided appearance.

Clover Looper*, *Caenurgina crassiuscula* (Haworth). Reported on clover and other legumes.

Convict Caterpillar, *Xanthopastis timais*. Also called Spanish Moth, usually found in southeastern states, although the recorded range goes to Maine. Spider lily is the natural host but the larvae devour leaves of amaryllis, narcissus, lilies, and tuberose, often eating foliage down to the ground. The caterpillars are brownish or grayish or black, smooth, about 2 inches long, and they have cream-colored bands around the body like convict stripes. The dark-brown pupa is found in the soil near plants. The moth is pinkish cream to white, with wings spreading almost 2 inches. Control by dusting with lead or calcium arsenate or DDT.

Cross-striped Cabbageworm*, *Evergestis rimosalis* (Guenée). The larva has numerous transverse black bands across the green body. The moth is small, mottled yellow-brown. See Imported Cabbageworm for control.

Eastern Tent Caterpillar*, *Malacosoma americanum* (Fabricius). Also called Apple-tree Tent Caterpillar, present throughout eastern United States and west to the Rocky Mountains. Black cherry, chokecherry, and apple are favored food plants, but when these are scarce it makes ugly nests on hawthorn, pear, plum, birch, elm, maple, oak, poplar, willow, and other fruit and ornamental trees. The winter is spent in the egg stage—a dark-brown varnished collar or belt encircling the twigs (Plate XVIII). The young larvae, hatching very early in March, gather in a fork of the limbs to spin their large, webby nest. They leave it during the day to feed on foliage but return at night or in rainy weather. They are hairy caterpillars, black with a white stripe down the back, brown and yellow lines along the sides, and a row of oval blue spots. They are full-grown, 2 to 2½ inches long, in 4 to 6 weeks, and are often seen in groups crawling down the sides of houses or feeding on roses and other shrubs before spinning their dirty-white cocoons on tree trunks or buildings.

The moths, light reddish brown with 2 diagonal stripes across each fore wing, emerge in about 3 weeks. Each female lays a single egg collar around a twig, containing 150 to 350 eggs, and covers this with a sticky substance which hardens and glistens like varnish. There is only 1 generation a year. The periods of greatest abundance appear at about 10-year intervals.

Control. Apples are protected by the regular spray schedule used for codling moths. Wild cherries growing near apple orchards should be removed. Young caterpillars can be killed by dusting with sulfur or any contact spray. Spraying or dusting ornamentals with lead arsenate or DDT will protect foliage from older caterpillars, but if egg masses are systematically pruned out during the winter and nests wiped out with a crumpled newspaper when first started, spraying should not be necessary. The nests themselves can be sprayed in the evening, when the caterpillars are at home, with DDT in water or kerosene. Burning out nests with a flaming torch is almost always harmful to the tree and often starts brush fires.

There are many natural enemies—ground beetles and other predators, egg parasites, a wilt disease—all of which account for the periodic rise and fall in abundance. It sometimes helps to work along with natural enemies. If egg masses are cut off, encased in fine wire mesh, and left in the open instead of being burned it gives the beneficial parasites a chance to emerge.

False Hemlock Looper*, *Nepytia canosaria* (Walker). In northern United

States and Canada on hemlock, spruce, fir, and larch. The larvae—1 inch long, pale with a yellowish or reddish tinge marked with black dots, a yellowish lateral stripe and 4 dark, wavy hairlines—feed from June to August. The moths emerge in August and September.

Filbertworm*, *Melissopus latiferreanus* (Walsingham). Catalina Cherry Moth, a serious pest of filberts and walnuts in the Pacific Northwest but distributed through much of the United States. The small, pinkish caterpillar, ¾ inch long, bores through oak acorns and galls, hazelnuts, filberts, walnuts, chestnuts, chinquapin, Catalina cherry, and various other fruits and nuts. The moth is pale to dusky with 2 coppery bands near the tip of fore wings. Eggs are laid near nuts or on husks, and worms enter the nuts at the base. They feed for 3 or 4 weeks, then winter in cocoons on the ground.

There is no satisfactory chemical control for nuts. Harvesting at the earliest possible date and drying promptly reduces injury.

Fir Cone Looper*, *Eupithecia spermaphaga* (Dyar). Small, measuring-worm caterpillars bore through seeds and cones of Douglas-fir, true firs, and mountain hemlock. The moth is gray with black and red-brown markings, wing expanse 1 inch.

Florida Fern Caterpillar*, *Callopistria floridensis* (Guenée). Native to tropical America and introduced into northern greenhouses on infested plants from Florida. It seems to breed only on ferns, chiefly nephrolepis and adiantum. The caterpillars work at night or on cloudy days, stripping leaflets from old growth, devouring new growth entirely. They are at first pale green, later velvety black, 1½ inches long. During the day they are concealed in the crown of the fern, along the midrib of a frond or in soil. They pupate underground in an oval cocoon. The moth, with brown, patterned wings, emerges in about 2 weeks. There may be a new generation every 7 or 8 weeks. Control by handpicking caterpillars at night or with a pyrethrum dust or spray.

Forest Tent Caterpillar*, *Malacosoma disstria* Hübner. A native pest of forest, ornamental, and fruit trees, widely distributed from the Atlantic to the Pacific, similar to the eastern tent caterpillar but without a tent. Favorite food plants include maple, oak, poplar, ash, birch, but it may feed on apple, boxelder, cherry, hawthorn, peach, pear, plum, prune, quince, rose, willow and other trees. The caterpillars are gregarious, armyworm style, living in large colonies on a silken mat on larger limbs and tree trunks but not making a nest. The winter egg collars around twigs are cut squarely off at the ends and not rounded down to the twig like those of the eastern tent caterpillar. The larvae, 1½ to 2 inches long, are bluish spattered with black dots and points, with a row of diamond-shaped spots alternating with small white spots down the back. They have pale, longitudinal yellow stripes and are sparsely clothed with soft hair. They eat ravenously in early spring for about 6 weeks. In June or July white cocoons are spun within a leaf or attached to fences or ground objects. The moths emerge in 10 to 14 days to lay about

200 eggs in a band around a twig. They are brownish buff with 2 oblique lines across the fore wings, which expand to 1 or 1½ inches. There is only 1 brood a year.

Control. There are many natural enemies to keep this pest in check, including birds. Inspect ornamental trees for egg bands and cut them off. Shade trees can have a 6 per cent DDT emulsion applied with a mist blower as soon as foliage opens, or can be sprayed with lead arsenate.

Genista Caterpillar*, *Tholeria reversalis* (Guenée). Genista Moth. The caterpillars are orange-green with black-and-white markings and are covered with tubercles. They web foliage of broom (Genista) and may completely defoliate plants. Adults are snout moths, brown with orange hind wings. Spray or dust with lead arsenate or DDT.

Grapevine Looper*, *Lygris diversilineata* (Hübner). Found in northeastern United States to Wisconsin and Missouri, feeding on grape and Virginia-creeper. The slender caterpillar is pale green, often with pink or reddish markings, 1½ inches long. It pupates in loose webs on the foliage. The moth is ochreous yellow, marked with rust and purplish brown, wing expanse to 2 inches.

Great Basin Tent Caterpillar*, *Malacosoma fragile* (Stretch). Common in the West, especially at high altitudes. The caterpillars have tawny hairs on a black body with blue-and-orange markings. They are omnivorous feeders, webbing orchard trees and ash, aspen, ceanothus, cottonwood and others. They defoliate bitterbrush, an important browse plant for sheep.

Green Cloverworm*, *Plathypena scabra* (Fabricius). Found in eastern United States to the Plains, on clover, alfalfa, garden beans, soybeans, cowpeas, strawberry, raspberry, and some other plants. The moths are dark brown, black-spotted, wingspread 1¼ inches. They lay eggs on underside of leaves, and the green larvae feed on them for about a month. There may be 2 to 4 generations but normally they are not abundant enough to justify control measures.

Green-striped Mapleworm*, *Anisota rubicunda* (Fabricius). A native eastern caterpillar found west to Kansas and Nebraska, attacking various maples, boxelder, and oak. The larvae are pale yellowish green, striped above with 8 light and 7 dark-green lines, with red head, 1½ inches long. They have 2 horns on the thorax, 2 rows of spines on each side of the body, and 4 large spines near the end of the abdomen. They are said to feed more ravenously in the western part of their range, often defoliating maples twice in a season and every tree on an avenue.

The moths are pale yellow banded with rose, wing expanse 1½ to 2 inches. They lay pale-green eggs in large masses on leaves. The larvae appear in 10 days, feed for a month, pupate in the soil. Moths appear in 2 weeks and the caterpillars of the second brood pupate in the soil for winter. There may be 3 generations in the South.

Control. Spray with lead arsenate, 3 to 4 pounds per 100 gallons, or with

DDT in time for young larvae of first brood. Several insect parasites and birds aid in control.

Gulf White Cabbageworm, *Ascia monuste* (Linnaeus). The adult looks like the white butterfly of the imported cabbageworm and the larva causes similar injury to crucifers. The caterpillar is yellow with 4 purplish stripes, 1½ inches.

Hemlock Looper, *Lambdina fiscellaria* (Guenée). Also called a Spanworm, enemy of forest and home plantings from New England to Wisconsin and south to Georgia and a destructive defoliator along the northwestern coast. Hemlock and balsam fir are preferred, but the looper may also feed on arborvitae, beech, birch, blueberry, wild cherry, elm, soft maple, oak, pine, spruce, and willow. The larvae are greenish yellow to gray with a double row of small black dots on the back. Trees may be defoliated and killed or have their symmetry spoiled. Eggs winter on twigs, needles, or in bark crevices and hatch in early June. The larvae feed on needles from the top of the tree downward, dropping on a thread of silk when disturbed. Pupation is under bark or in protected places. Tan to grayish-brown moths with purple markings appear at the end of August and fly for several weeks.

Control. For ornamental plantings 6 per cent DDT emulsion applied by mist blower has been recommended. For woodland areas DDT is applied by airplane.

Another **Hemlock Looper,** *Lambdina athasaria athasaria* Walker, kills hemlocks, including ornamentals. The moth is smaller than that of the pine looper but similar. The larva is yellowish with dark markings, 1½ inches long. Outbreaks have been reported in Massachusetts, Connecticut, Pennsylvania, and Ohio.

See also Western Hemlock Looper.

Hickory Horned Devil*, *Citheronia regalis* (Fabricius). Our largest native caterpillar, larva of the regal moth. It is found from Massachusetts to Louisiana and Texas, feeding on hickory, black walnut, butternut, sycamore, sweetgum, ash, persimmon, lilac, sassafras, sumac, and cotton. It is seldom abundant enough to do much damage. The caterpillar, 4 to 5 inches long, has a green body with black spines. Just back of the head are the devil's horns, very long reddish spines bending backward and tipped with black. The moth has a wing expanse of 4½ to 6 inches. Fore wings are dusky olive spotted with yellow, the veins bordered with red scales; hind wings are orange-red spotted with yellow. Control measures are usually unnecessary.

Hickory Shuckworm*, *Laspeyresia caryana* (Fitch). Pecan Shuckworm, usually the most destructive pest of pecans, present also on native hickories, with 50 per cent of the crop sometimes destroyed. Inconspicuous dark, small moths deposit eggs on young nuts or leaves; on hatching the larvae gnaw into the green nuts, causing them to drop. There are several generations and the last finds the shells too hard to penetrate and so stays in the shucks. Full-grown larvae winter in shucks on the ground or in trees. Moths of the first generation emerge in Florida from February to April. There is no very satisfactory control. Keep dropped nuts cleaned up or covered with soil, using a disk tiller.

Imported Cabbageworm*, *Pieris rapae* (Linnaeus). A pest in North America since 1860. Within 20 years of its arrival at Quebec it had spread over the country east of the Mississippi River and now is present practically everywhere. It attacks all of the cabbage family—cabbage, cauliflower, kale, collards, kohlrabi, Brussels sprouts, mustard, radish, turnip, horseradish, and related weeds; also nasturtium, sweet alyssum, mignonette, and lettuce.

The adult is the familiar white cabbage butterfly which has 3 or 4 black spots on wings spreading 1¼ to nearly 2 inches (Plate XXVI). The butterflies are around on sunny days very early in spring, the females alighting frequently to glue an egg on the underside of a leaf until each has deposited several hundred. The eggs are yellow, bullet-shaped, ridged. Velvety smooth green caterpillars, with alternating light and dark longitudinal stripes, start feeding in about a week, depositing repulsive pellets of excrement as they eat huge holes in leaves. When full-grown, about an inch long, they pupate in a naked gray, green, or tan chrysalid, with angular projections, suspended by a belt of silk from some part of the plant or from a nearby object, even a building. Adults emerge in a week or so and there may be 5 or 6 generations. Hibernation is in the pupal stage.

Control. Recommendations for commercial growers include Dibrom, malathion, parathion or Phosdrin, sometimes DDT before edible parts are formed. *Bacillus thuringiensis* as a spray or dust is a safe and effective control. Home gardeners will probably use rotenone or methoxychlor. Clean up old plant parts after harvest; destroy weeds.

Large Aspen Tortrix*, *Choristoneura conflictana* (Walker). A leaf roller present from New York and Utah north to Alaska, serious defoliator of poplar forests. The larva, an inch long, is olive-green with black head and shield. It rolls a leaf more or less funnel-shaped, ties it with silk and feeds inside this protection. The moth is light gray, wing expanse 1¼ inches.

Lesser Appleworm. See Fruitworms.

Linden Looper*, *Erannis tiliaria* (Harris). Also known as Lime-tree or Basswood Looper, fairly common through eastern states and west to the Rocky Mountains. The larvae feed on forest and shade trees—oaks, apple, birch, elm, hickory, basswood, maple—and may cause rather serious defoliation. The loopers are bright yellow with 10 longitudinal wavy black lines down the back, 1½ inches long. The moth is buff, marked with brown, with 1¾ inch wingspread. Eggs are laid from October to November.

Melonworm*, *Diaphania hyalinata* (Linnaeus). Rarely injurious north of the Gulf States, although it may be seen elsewhere. The day-flying moth has pearly white wings margined with a narrow dark band, spreading to 1¾ inches (Plate XXXVI). The body is brown in front of the wings; the abdomen is silver-white tipped with a bushy tuft of slender, hairlike scales.

The caterpillar is slender, greenish, with 2 white stripes along the body in most stages. It feeds chiefly on foliage of muskmelon, cucumber, squash, pumpkin, rarely on watermelon. Commercial growers use parathion, malathion, or lindane for control. Rotenone dusts are effective for home gardens, but do not use mixtures with sulfur, which may prevent fruit formation of some melon varieties.

Navel Orangeworm*, *Paramyelois transitella* (Walder). Reported burrowing into the navel end of oranges in Arizona in 1921, this insect was first thought to be of little importance. Since that time it has become one of the most important fruit and nut problems in California, infesting crops on the tree and in storage, being serious on almond, walnut, and fig particularly but also present in citrus, pomegranate, and macadamia nuts. The larva is yellow or dark gray with a dark head and thoracic shield and it pupates in a cocoon within the fruit. The moth is pale gray with darker markings on the fore wings and a row of crescent-shaped dots on the outer margin. Control measures include plant and orchard sanitation, early harvest of crops, and fumigation of nuts before storage with methyl bromide. Where walnuts are treated with DDT for codling moths, there is little trouble with the orangeworm.

Monterey-pine Looper, *Nepytia umbrosaria* (Packard). A light-green, smooth caterpillar tying needles of young Monterey pines together at tips of branches; in central California. The moth is mottled gray, wing expanse 1½ inches.

Oleander Caterpillar, *Syntomedia epilais jucundissima* (Dyar). The worst pest of oleanders in Florida. The larva is orange with tufts of long black hairs scattered over the body; 1½ inches long. The adult is called Polka Dot Moth because of the white spots scattered over the blue-black body and wings. Its shape resembles that of a wasp. Spray with a strong solution of chlordane, repeating if necessary.

Omnivorous Looper, *Sabulodes caberata* Guenée. A native of, and apparently confined to, California. Most serious as an avocado pest, often numerous enough to strip trees of all foliage, it also feeds on acacia, alder, aralia, boxelder, buckeye, California-laurel, California Christmasberry (toyon), cherry, chestnut, clematis, daisy, elm, English ivy, eucalyptus, geranium, ginkgo, grevillea, groundsel, honeysuckle, lemon verbena, magnolia, maple, olive, orange, passion-flower, pecan, peppertree, privet, rose, sumac, sycamore, tecoma, violet, black walnut, willow. Truly it is well named omnivorous.

The moth is dull brown or yellow, with 2 darker transverse bands, wingspread up to 2 inches. It is nocturnal but may be found during the day on underside of leaves, where it lays clusters of eggs. The larva varies from yellow to pale pink or green, with yellow, brown, or green stripes on sides and back, and black markings as well. It is 1½ to 2 inches long in the last instar and can eat an entire avocado leaf in a day. The pupa is usually webbed between 2 leaves or inside a leaf folded over. There may be 5 or 6 generations a year. Spraying with DDT, at the rate of 1 pound 50 per cent wettable powder to 100 gallons, seems to be effective.

Orange-dog*, *Papilio cresphontes* Cramer. A common and destructive butterfly attacking citrus in Florida. It is called "dog" because one end of the caterpillar looks like the nose of a dog, 2 black spots on the thorax serving as eyes. It is 2½ inches long, dark brown with blotches of light yellow. When disturbed, orange-red hornlike processes are protruded and a strong odor given off. The dogs feed voraciously on foliage, often defoliating a young tree in 2 or 3 days. The adult is a large yellow-and-black butterfly very common in Florida. Eggs, white with a reddish tinge, are laid singly on new shoots about February, hatching in 10 days. The best control is to remove caterpillars by hand from young nursery stock.

Orange-humped Mapleworm*, *Symmerista leucitys* Franclemont. Similar to the red-humped oakworm.

Orange-striped Oakworm*, *Anisota senatoria* (J. E. Smith). A native eastern moth, sometimes found in other states, preferring white and scrub oaks, occasionally feeding on other trees. The adult, appearing in early June, is bright tan, with black dots and a white center spot on the fore wings, which expand to 2½ inches. Females lay white to coral-red eggs in clusters on underside of leaves. The male is smaller and darker. The caterpillar is coal-black with orange-yellow longitudinal stripes and black, hornlike appendages at the end of the body, which is covered with short spines. Local infestations may strip foliage from trees in midsummer. Pupation is in soil. There is usually 1 generation; sometimes 2 in the South. Spraying with lead arsenate, 3 pounds to 100 gallons, or with DDT, is effective.

Orange Tortrix*, *Argyrotaenia citrana* (Fernald). An important lemon and orange pest in California and other warm climates, also feeding on avocado, oak, pine, black walnut, willow, acacia, apricot, asparagus, begonia, cineraria, Jobs-tears, eucalyptus, ferns, geranium, Jerusalem-cherry, lantana, lavender, penstemon, rose and wandering-Jew. It has become a raspberry pest in western Washington. The dirty-white, brown-headed caterpillar webs and rolls the leaves on which it feeds and bores into orange rind, causing premature drop and leaving avenues of infection for decay organisms. Young oranges are scarred around the button. Grapefruit may also be infested, but it is not grown so much where the tortrix is injurious. Moths are fawn or gray with darker mottlings. Eggs are cream-colored, sculptured disks, laid in overlapping masses on both leaf surfaces. There are 2 to 4 generations. Spray or dust with cryolite or, for emergencies, use DDD or parathion. Natural enemies are often able to control the orange tortrix, at least 12 parasites being known.

Another orangeworm, the **Garden Tortrix**, *Clepsis peritana* (Clemens), is recently recognized as important on citrus in California. It is similar to the orange tortrix but somewhat smaller. It is not easily controlled by cryolite but is susceptible to parathion.

Palmerworm*, *Dichomeris ligulella* Hübner. A pest so ancient it is mentioned in the Bible. It occurs from Maine to Texas and is occasionally serious on apple in northeastern states, the peak coming only once in 60 years. It may also feed on cherry, hazel, oak, pear, and plum. The caterpillars, ½ inch long, are olive-green with 2 white stripes along the side and 2 narrow white lines on the back. They skeletonize the leaves, partially protected by a light web, and sometimes eat into young fruit. The small moths, only ½ inch across the wings, appear in July and later hibernate, laying eggs the next spring. The regular spray schedule for codling moth will control palmerworms.

Parsleyworm. See Celeryworm.

Phantom Hemlock Looper*, *Nepytia phantasmaria* (Strecker). Feeding on western hemlock in the Pacific Northwest, also on spruce and Douglas-fir. The moths are white with numerous black markings.

Phigalia Looper, *Phigalia titea* (Cramer). A geometrid caterpillar sometimes causing complete defoliation of trees in Atlantic States, including maple, oak, cherry, sassafras, and dogwood. The larva is flesh-colored, with many fine longitudinal black lines, 1½ inches long. It feeds from May to July. The male moth is pale ash color, with blackish brown markings, 1½-inch wingspread; the female has only partly developed wings.

Pickleworm*, *Diaphania nitidalis* (Stoll). Especially destructive in the Gulf States, but found as far north as New York and Michigan. Muskmelon, cucumber, and squash may be seriously injured, watermelon rarely, pumpkin not at all. Ripening fruits are bored into by white to green caterpillars up to ¾ inch long, with brown heads. They have black spots across each segment in younger stages, are a uniform green or copper when grown (Plate XXXVI). Masses of green, sawdustlike excrement are pushed out from holes in the fruit, which rots and turns sour. Early in the season the caterpillars work on stems, terminal buds, and in squash blossoms. Late crops may be almost totally destroyed. Hibernation is as a pupa inside a rolled leaf, the moth not coming out until late spring, sometimes early June. The adult has a long slender body with a prominent brush of long hairlike scales at the end of the abdomen. The wings, yellowish white with a wide yellow-brown margin, spread to just over an inch. The moths fly at night, lay clusters of 2 to 7 eggs on underside of fruits, or on stems, tender buds, or new leaves. The first generation is not large, but moths emerging from pupation in July lay many eggs, and the 3rd and 4th broods in August really get down to their devastating business. Each worm may enter several fruits before it growth is completed.

Control. As soon as a crop is harvested, burn vines, unused fruits, adjoining weeds and trash. Bury pupae by spading or plowing in early fall. Plan for an early crop; use squash for a trap crop to keep worms away from melons, but destroy vines before larvae are full-grown in squash blossoms. Commercial growers dust or spray foliage with parathion, malathion or lindane when worms appear in the blossoms; home gardeners can use rotenone.

Pine Looper, *Lambdina athasaria pelluscidaria* (Grote & Robinson). Defoliating pitch pine on Cape Cod, red pine in Connecticut, abundant on shortleaf pine in North Carolina. The moth is smoky to ash-gray with fore wings crossed by two dusky lines; 1¼-inch wingspread. The larva is 1 to 1½ inches long, pale straw- to greenish-yellow with black markings.

Pink Scavenger Caterpillar*, *Pyroderces rileyi* Walsingham. Scavenger bollworm, often associated with pink bollworm of cotton and a scavenger on a wide range of food plants, from oranges to corn. The larva is about ⅓ inch long, deep wine-red with brown head and thoracic shield. The moth has chestnut-brown wings with straw-colored streaks, edged by irregular black scales. TDE or parathion in the oil spray used for scales will control this caterpillar if it becomes necessary.

Pink-striped Oakworm*, *Anisota virginiensis* (Drury). From Maine to Georgia and west to Missouri and Minnesota on various species of oak but not an important pest. The caterpillars are 2 inches long, greenish or grayish granulated with white, and with pink stripes, 2 slender horns, and short spines. The moths are dark with a lilac tinge; the wings of the male are triangular.

Poplar Tent Maker*, *Ichthyura inclusa* Hübner. Distributed from New England to Colorado, feeding mostly on poplar, sometimes on willow. The caterpillars are black, mottled with gray, striped with yellow and brown. They have a pair of black tubercles on abdominal segments 1 and 8, are about 1¼ inches long. They are gregarious and make silken nests by webbing several leaves together or folding over a leaf. As they feed on the surface, they gradually add other leaves. Pupae winter under leaves; moths appear in early spring. They are brownish gray with 3 irregular white lines bordered with red on the outer edge; wingspread just over an inch. It is usually possible to cut out and burn whole colonies. Spraying with lead arsenate or DDT when larvae are small will check infestations, as will natural enemies in many cases.

Prairie Tent Caterpillar*, *Malacosoma lutescens* (Neumoegen & Dyar). Similar to the Forest Tent Caterpillar.

Pumpkin Caterpillar, *Diaphania indica* (Saunders). A pest of cucurbits and other plants in India and Australia, reported from Florida in 1959 but apparently present there for some years. Appearance and habits are similar to those of the melonworm and pickleworm.

Purple-backed Cabbageworm*, *Evergestis pallidata* (Hufnagel). Feeding inside a silken web on cabbage and other crucifers.

Puss Caterpillar*, *Megalopyge opercularis* (J. E. Smith). One of the stinging caterpillars, found from Virginia to Texas and southward on oak, citrus, hackberry, elm, plum, maple, rose, sycamore and other deciduous trees and shrubs and even on English ivy. Gardeners should beware of this inch-long larva, covered with long, soft, reddish-yellow hairs interspersed with stinging spines. If a caterpillar falls on the neck there may be severe irritation; if on the wrist, the whole arm may swell. Children are more seriously injured than adults. Lead arsenate sprays will control. Handpicking is possible if you wear thick gloves. A formula to control the nettling caused by stinging is: 10 grains menthol, 2 drams zinc oxide, 8 ounces aq. calcis, 15 drops acid carbolici.

Range Caterpillar*, *Hemileuca oliviae* (Cockerell). A range pest on wild grasses in New Mexico and Colorado but sometimes infesting corn and other cultivated crops. Larvae are yellow, gray, or black, densely covered with coarse, poisonous spines, and with white spiracles encircled with a black line.

Red-humped Caterpillar*, *Schizura concinna* (J. E. Smith). Also called Red-humped Appleworm, distributed over most of the country. The larvae are yellow brown with a bright-red head, a red hump on the 4th segment, dark tubercles on each segment, striped longitudinally with white, brown, red and black, 1 inch long (Plate XX). They rest with the rear end of the abdomen elevated. They feed on both fruit and ornamental trees, stripping foliage of apple, apricot, aspen, bayberry, birch, blackberry, cottonwood, cherry, dogwood, hawthorn, hickory, huckleberry, locust, pear, persimmon, plum, poplar, prune, rose, sweetgum, willow, and walnut. The larva winters in a cocoon in the soil, pupates in late spring or early summer. The moths are grayish brown, wingspread about 1¼ inches; they lay eggs in masses on underside of leaves. The larvae are gregarious, first skeletonizing foliage, then eating everything but midribs. When disturbed they raise both ends of their bodies. They defoliate one branch before moving to another.

The simplest control is to collect and burn young colonies. A regular orchard spray schedule should keep them in bounds. Other plants can be sprayed with lead arsenate, DDT, or cryolite.

Red-humped Oakworm*, *Symmerista albifrons* (J. E. Smith) and *S. albicosta* (Hübner). Both species go under this common name but the first is "official." They are found in eastern North America from Canada to Florida and west to Kansas and Minnesota; quite common on oaks, reported also on basswood, beech, elm, and maple. The caterpillars, 1½ to 1¾ inches long, have an orange head, wider than the thorax, a smooth, yellowish body with dark lines on the back, and the back of the 8th abdominal segment enlarged to form an orange-red hump. The moths have mottled dark-brown to gray fore wings with an area of white along the forward edge; wingspread 1½ inches. They appear from May to July, the females laying pale-green eggs in groups on underside of leaves. The larvae are green at first, with black heads, and in that stage they are gregarious, scattering as they mature to the orange-head, red-humped form. The winter is passed as pupae inside thin white cocoons in the ground litter.

Red-necked Peanutworm*, *Stegasta bosqueella* (Chambers). Frequently reported from Georgia to Oklahoma, infesting peanut buds and terminals. There may be four or five generations with nearly 100 per cent infestation in some fields. The adult is a small moth, family Gelechiidae.

Saddleback Caterpillar*, *Sibine stimulea* (Clemens). A stinging caterpillar widely distributed through the Atlantic States. It feeds on oak, cherry, sometimes other trees; may attack canna, dahlia, holly, lily, magnolia, palm, rose and other plants. Its appearance is most distinctive: flat underneath, rounded above, reddish but with a pea-green patch (the saddle blanket) in the middle of the back and on that a broad purple-brown patch edged with white (the saddle). There are fascicles of spines along the sides and 2 large tufts of spines at both ends. The irritation is severe; see Puss Caterpillar for soothing formula.

Saddled Prominent*, *Heterocampa guttivitta* (Walker). Also called Antlered Maple Caterpillar, common in Atlantic States, ranging also to Texas. It prefers beech, with sugar maple and apple next, but it also feeds on other maples, oak, occasionally blackberry, cherry, poplar, spirea, and witch-hazel. The young larva bears 9 pairs of horns, starting at the head with a large, branched pair like antlers; the mature caterpillar has no horns. It is green to brown or yellow, with a reddish brown saddle spot in the middle of the back. The moth is olive-gray with darker wavy areas and dark dots. Occasionally New England woodlands may be defoliated by this pest and at such times it also feeds on shade trees, but it is not considered a serious pest of ornamentals. Parasites usually take care of the saddled prominent; shade trees can be sprayed with lead arsenate or DDT if the abundance warrants the expense.

Sagebrush Defoliator*, *Aroga websteri* Clarke. Defoliating and killing sagebrush in Oregon, Idaho, Utah and Nevada.

Salt-marsh Caterpillar*, *Estigmene acrea* (Drury). Generally distributed, one of the woollybears. The caterpillars are very hardy, gray when young, then black with yellow broken lines and cinnamon-red hairs, up to 2 inches long. At times, usually in late summer, they may be as bad as armyworms, eating everything in sight—sugar beets, beans, other vegetables, grapes, carnations and other flowers. Moths have white wings with black spots and an orange, black-spotted abdomen. Dusting with toxaphene or DDT is effective in control.

Schizura Caterpillars. Related to the Unicorn Caterpillar. *Schizura ipomoeae* Doubleday feeds on rose, apple, wild cherry, willow and other deciduous shrubs; *S. letonoides* (Grote) on about the same hosts; *S. badia* (Packard) on viburnum.

Southern Cabbageworm*, *Pieris protodice* Boisduval & LeConte. A southern species resembling the imported cabbageworm, with similar control measures. The butterfly has more black markings on the wings and the caterpillar has four longitudinal yellow bands.

Spiny Oakworm*, *Anisota stigma* (Fabricius). A southern species much like the orange-striped oakworm. The caterpillar is bright, tawny orange with a dusky stripe along the back and prominent spines on thoracic segments.

Stinging Rose Caterpillar*, *Parasa indetermina* (Boisduval). A sluglike creature feeding on rose leaves from the underside, also on dogwood, chestnut, oak, wild cherry, hickory, pawpaw, bayberry, plum, apple, and pear. The caterpillar is marked with red, white and violet stripes and 7 pairs of large, spine-bearing processes, ¾ inch long. It winters in a dark cocoon in refuse. The pale, cinnamon-brown moth, wings marked with green and brown, lays eggs in July. Contact with the spines results in a painful burning sensation for several hours.

Striped Garden Caterpillar*, *Polia legitima* (Grote). Generally distributed, more abundant in late summer, a dark, yellow-striped cutworm, similar to the zebra caterpillar, with some preference for crucifers. The moth is grayish with an irregular pattern. Spray if necessary with DDT or malathion; clean up refuse in fall.

Tomato Pinworm*, *Keiferia lycopersicella* (Busck). Found outdoors in the far South and in southern California, where it is one of the worst tomato pests, and in greenhouses. The larvae, yellow, gray or green with purple spots, only ¼ inch long, make serpentine or blotch mines in leaves which are folded and held together with light webs. Developing buds and ripening fruits have pinholes bored in them with entrance usually at the stem end. Injury to vines is not serious but the fruit can be a total loss. The pinworm may also injure eggplant and potato. Dusting with cryolite and sulfur, starting when fruits are about the size of marbles, is said to be effective. DDT or parathion is recommended for commercial growers.

Ugly-nest Caterpillar*, *Archips cerasivoranus* (Fitch). Cherry-tree Tortrix. This leaf roller is a northern pest, abundant only at long intervals, mostly on wild cherry, sometimes on cultivated cherry, rarely on apple, sometimes on nursery oaks. The larvae—yellow with black heads, ¾ inch long—tie twigs and leaves together, making a large nest. The moths are yellow with brown spots and blue band, 1-inch wingspread.

Unicorn Caterpillar*, *Schizura unicornis* (J. E. Smith). On apple, wild cherry, willow, and other deciduous broad-leaved trees, defoliating pin oaks in Ohio. The caterpillar is 1⅓ inches long, variegated brown, orange, and green, with a prominent pointed projection on the first abdominal segment. The moth is brownish gray, wingspread to 1⅓ inches. Newly hatched larvae are gregarious, skeletonizing leaves from the undersurface; other larvae consume all but the midrib. They usually defoliate one branch before moving to the next. Full-grown larvae winter in papery cocoons in the ground litter.

Variable Oak Leaf Caterpillar*, *Heterocampa manteo* (Doubleday). Distributed from Maine to Alabama, more destructive in the South. The greenish-yellow caterpillar, with variable markings, 1½ inches long, devours leaves of oak, especially white oak, basswood, walnut, birch, elm, hawthorn, and persimmon. The moth is pale ash-gray with 3 wavy dark lines crossing the fore wings; wingspread 1⅔ inches.

Velvetbean Caterpillar*, *Anticarsia gemmatilis* Hübner. Found only in the Gulf States on soybeans, velvetbeans, cowpeas, peanuts, kudzu-vine, and young tips of black locust. Soybeans are usually defoliated first. The caterpillars vary from dull green to olive-brown or black with white lines running the length of the body. Nocturnal moths are buff to dark brown or black, with a white diagonal line across the wings. Larvae can be controlled with 3 to 5 per cent DDT dust, 5 per cent methoxychlor, or 10 per cent toxaphene. There is a rather efficient egg parasite and a fungus which attacks the worms.

Walnut Caterpillar*, *Datana integerrima* Grote & Robinson. A native moth found from Maine to Florida and west to Kansas, feeding on walnut, butternut, hickory and pecan, occasionally on peach, apple, beech, honey-locust, sumac, and willow. The caterpillars are 2 inches long, dull black, reddish when young, covered with long, white hairs. The moths are dark buff with 4 brown transverse lines on the fore wings. Eggs are laid in masses on underside of leaves. The larvae feed in colonies, crawling to the tree trunk to molt, then going back to feed again. Pupation is in the soil. There are 2 generations in the South, 1 in the North. Caterpillar masses can be destroyed or the trees sprayed.

Western Hemlock Looper*, *Lambdina fiscellaria lugubrosa* (Hübner). Destroying spruce-hemlock forests, along the coast of Oregon and Washington, appearing in countless thousands in outbreaks. Western hemlock is the preferred host but the looper may attack Douglas-fir, Sitka spruce, western redcedar, huckleberry, salal, and other broad-leaved shrubs and trees. The moths are light buff, fore wings marked with 2 wavy lines, hind wings with 1 line, 1½-inch wingspread. Eggs are laid in September and October, on bark or moss on trunk. Young larvae crawl up tree trunks in spring and feed on young needles. By midsummer a heavily infested forest appears scorched by fire. Full-grown larvae are green to brown with diamond-shaped markings on the back, 1½ inches long. In late summer they clip off small twigs and drop by silken threads to the ground. Outbreaks of this species last about 3 years, then are brought under control by parasites, predators, and a virus disease. Airplane spraying with DDT, 1 pound in fuel oil per acre, is very efficient in destroying young caterpillars.

Western Oak Looper, *Lambdina fiscellaria somniaria* Hulst. Closely related to and resembling the western hemlock looper, periodically destructive to oak in Oregon and Washington. The caterpillars are pale brown mottled with black spots, up to 1¼ inches long. Every few years they get so numerous it is impossible to walk under trees without being covered with them; the trees look as if they had been burned. The moths are yellow to dark brown, dotted with darker scales. In October they cover limbs and branches of trees.

Western Tent Caterpillar*, *Malacosoma pluviale* (Dyar). A common species in the Pacific Northwest. The larvae, tawny with blue and orange spots, live in small, compact nests. They feed on alder, apple, hawthorn, cherry, currant, and rose.

Yellow-headed Fireworm*, *Acleris minuta* (Robinson). Cranberry Worm, sometimes injurious on the drier cranberry bogs. The moth, slate-gray, ¾ inch wingspread, lays eggs on leaves in May. Yellow-headed caterpillars web leaves together and feed inside, pupating in their nest in June, producing a second brood to feed in July, and a third in September. Keeping bogs flooded until about May 20 helps in control. Spray drier bogs with lead arsenate as eggs hatch, 1 pound to 10 gallons of water, or dust with 10 per cent DDT, or use Sevin.

Yellow-necked Caterpillar*, *Datana ministra* (Drury). General, primarily on fruit trees—apple, apricot, blackberry, blueberry, cherry, peach, pear, plum, quince—also on beech, birch, hazel, hickory, linden, oak, walnut, and other ornamental trees and shrubs. The caterpillar is black with a yellow thorax (the neck), 4 yellow stripes along each side; covered with long white hairs. The larvae work in groups and when disturbed elevate both ends. Young larvae skeletonize leaves, older caterpillars eat all but stem and midrib. The moths have brown fore wings, 1½ inch wingspread. Pupation is in the soil. There is 1 generation a year with chief injury in July and August. Shake caterpillars off small trees and crush them. Spray larger trees with lead arsenate when larvae are young.

Yellow Woollybear*, *Diacrisia virginica* (Fabricius). Virginia Tiger Moth. The caterpillars are very hairy, yellow or straw-colored with black lines. They are general feeders, injuring many vegetables and flowers—asparagus, bean, beet, blackberry, cabbage, calendula, calla, canna, carrot, cauliflower, celery, cherry, chrysanthemum, coleus, corn, currant, dahlia, eggplant, fuchsia, gooseberry, grape, hollyhock, lily, melon, morning-glory, parsnip, peanut, pea, petunia, potato, pumpkin, radish, raspberry, rhubarb, rose, Spanish needles, squash, sunflower, sweetpotato, turnip, verbena, and violet. The moths have white wings with black spots and a yellow-brown, black-spotted abdomen. There are 2 broods. Pupae winter inside hairy cocoons. Spray or dust with lead arsenate, cryolite, DDT or toxaphene.

Zebra Caterpillar*, *Ceramica picta* (Harris). General, feeding on truck, cereal, and fruit crops, trees and flowers, including sweetpeas, lilies, and gladiolus, most injurious in late summer. The larvae are velvety black with 2 bright-yellow stripes on each side and many fine yellow transverse lines. The moth is rusty brown. Arsenical or DDT sprays and dusts will give control when larvae are young.

CENTIPEDES AND SYMPHYLANS

Centipedes, "hundred-legged worms" are members of the class Chilopoda, close relatives of true insects. They differ in having only 2 main body parts (they lack a thorax), no wings, and instead of 3 pairs of legs they have 1 pair on each of their many body segments. There are at least 15 pairs of legs but not the hundred that the name implies. Centipedes are like insects in having a single pair of antennae (with 14 or more segments), breathing by tracheae, and with reproductive organs at the posterior end of the body. They look something like worms but are flatter, have a distinct head and jointed legs. They have a pair of poison claws on the first segment behind the head that they use to paralyze their prey. Centipedes usually rest under logs or stones and are swift runners, predaceous on earthworms, snails, and some insects. Their bite is painful to man but not often serious. There are many species and some of the tropical forms go up to 18 inches in length, but as a class they can be considered more beneficial than harmful. True centipedes are not garden pests.

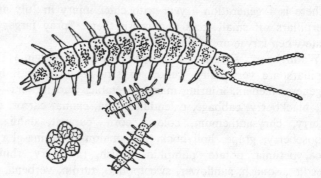

44. Garden centipede or symphylan, showing adult, young, and eggs.

Garden Symphylan*, Garden Centipede, *Scutigerella immaculata* (Newport). Commonly called a centipede because it looks like one, but actually belonging to the class Symphyla. A symphylan is distinguished from a true centipede by having only 12 pairs of legs in the adult form, fewer when young, no poison claws, no eyes, and the genital opening near the anterior end of the body. Symphylans live in damp places rich in organic matter, in leaf mold, manure piles, or peaty soils.

The garden symphylan or centipede is small, ¼ inch long, pure white, very active. It keeps its long antennae constantly moving as it travels through the soil in cracks and tunnels left by decaying plant roots. It is an outdoor soil pest in warm climates, particularly injurious to asparagus in

California, and is a greenhouse pest nearly everywhere. The symphylans eat off fine roots and root hairs and scar underground parts of stems so that plants die or are stunted. Besides asparagus, which has its roots riddled with tunnels while they are below ground, the garden centipede seriously injures lettuce, radishes, tomatoes, cucumbers, and many ornamentals, including sweetpea, snapdragon, aster, and other flowers.

Small white eggs are laid in clusters of 5 to 20 about a foot deep in soil, any time between April and September; the minute young hatch 7 to 10 days later. At first they have only 6 pairs of legs, 10 body segments, and very short antennae, but they add another pair of legs and lengthen antennae at each molt. When greenhouse soil is wet down and crops are started in fall, symphylans start feeding on roots; in outdoor gardens they are active in spring. They are rarely seen on the surface of soil, being strongly repelled by light.

Control. Asparagus fields in California have been flooded with water to a depth of 1 to 3 feet for 3 weeks during late December and early January. Fumigating soil with ethylene dibromide or D-D mixture is recommended, and steam-sterilizing soil brought into greenhouses. Lindane can be applied to the beds, 3 pounds of 25 per cent wettable powder in 100 gallons of water to 2000 square feet of bench space. In rose houses this can be forcefully sprayed on the beds through the mulch.

CICADAS

The cicadas, order Hemiptera, suborder Homoptera, family Cicadidae, are sometimes erroneously called locusts. They are members of a large family—1500 species in the world, although only 75 in North America—but we commonly distinguish only 2 kinds, the periodical cicada ("17-year locust") and the annual, or dogday, cicada. They are large, sucking insects, have front wings of the same texture throughout, and hold their wings in a rooflike position. They are noted chiefly for their shrill noises—"singing"—produced by special vibratory organs under the base of the abdomen of the male.

Dogday Cicada, *Tibicen linnei* (Smith & Grossbeck). Also called Harvestman and Annual Cicada, but it is not literally annual. It has a 2- to 5-year cycle but the broods overlap, so that some appear every summer. This is larger than the periodical cicada, has a black body with whitish bloom, green margins on the wings, and numerous light markings on thorax and abdomen. The cicadas are around on summer dog days, July and August, but do not cause injury enough to worry about. The cicada-killer, a digger wasp, gets some.

Periodical Cicada*, *Magicicada septendecim* (Linnaeus). A native of North America, named for its regular occurrence at long intervals. There

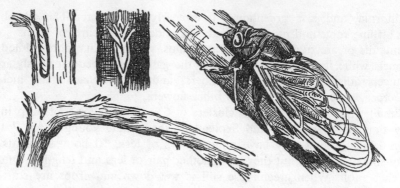

45. Periodical cicada, "seventeen-year locust," laying eggs, and twigs showing bark torn in process.

are 2 races. The southern race, with its northern boundary Virginia to Oklahoma, has a 13-year cycle; the northern race appears every 17 years and is the one called Seventeen-year Locust. Both are more abundant east of the Mississippi and both have a number of broods, which appear in different years, so that it may not be 13 or 17 years between cicada swarms in any given locality. The broods are numbered, and it is possible to predict accurately when each will appear. Brood II was widespread over the eastern seaboard in 1945, its first appearance since 1928; it came again in 1962. Brood VI was present in some areas in 1949, Brood X was serious in Maryland and Pennsylvania in 1953, Brood XIV, in 1957.

The adult periodical cicada has a stout black body about 1 inch long with wings extending well behind the body when at rest. It has reddish-orange eyes, legs, and wing veins. It appears from mid-May to early June and is around for 5 or 6 weeks. A town may have cicadas in such abundance that life is made hideous with their shrill, unending song, and people driving through sometimes stop their cars to see what is the matter with the engines. In some gardens tree trunks will be covered with cast shells of the nymphs and the ground under trees literally perforated with holes ½ inch across. The next town, only a mile or so away, may be lucky and have almost no cicadas.

The female has a tough, horny ovipositor and the chief damage is the tearing of twigs as eggs are deposited in rows, the bark being pushed away and the wood raised into bundles of splinters. About 75 trees, shrubs, and herbaceous plants are used for egg laying, but oak is preferred, with hickory and apple close seconds. Dogwood twigs are frequently injured. Leaves on twigs and branches so punctured usually turn brown but hang on as an eyesore for weeks before the branch breaks and falls to the ground. Eggs hatch in 6 or 7 weeks; the antlike young drop and enter the soil through cracks. They burrow down to the roots and stay 6 to 18 inches below ground level until the seventeenth spring. Then they burrow upward and crawl out when ready for the final molt. Sometimes, in moist places, they construct earthen cones or chimneys before coming out. They crawl to a tree trunk, stick, or other object, the thorax is split, and the winged cicada emerges, leaving the hard, empty shell in lifelike position behind. From 20,000 to 40,000 cicadas may come out of the soil underneath a single large tree.

Control. The periodical cicada was almost impossible to control sufficiently to prevent egg-laying injury until the advent of carbaryl (Sevin). Now we have something really effective. Use 2 pounds of 50 per cent wettable Sevin to 100 gallons of water (2 tablespoons to 1 gallon) and repeat in 6 or 7 days. TEPP and Phosdrin are also effective but much more hazardous. Young trees can be protected with mosquito netting. It may be well to avoid setting out a new orchard a year or two before a large cicada brood is expected. Avoid pruning young trees heavily the year before a brood is due. Cut off injured twigs as soon as possible.

Other **Cicadas.** Several other species of Tibicen and also species of Okanagana appear in western states, some on grass and in rangeland, one on fruit trees. They are somewhat smaller than the eastern annual cicadas but injure plants by their egg laying in the same way. Adults of *Diceroprocta apache* are reported injuring grapevines in California.

CRICKETS

Crickets are relatives of grasshoppers, order Orthoptera, family Gryllidae, for tree and field crickets, Gryllacrididae for cave and camel crickets, Gryllotalpidae for mole crickets, Tridactylidae for pygmy mole crickets, and family Tettigoniidae for the Mormon cricket, which is really a long-horned grasshopper. Crickets have chewing mouth parts but incomplete metamorphosis. They are noted for the chirping notes produced by the males when they rub together specially modified parts of their front wings. They have long, filiform antennae, a spear-shaped ovipositor, and 2- to 4-segmented tarsi. The hardened horny fore wings are called tegmina; they are flat on the back but bend down abruptly along the sides. Most feed on plants; some are predaceous; some are both.

Black-horned Tree Cricket*, *Oecanthus nigricornis nigricornis* Walker. Widely distributed, greenish yellow with head black or with 3 black stripes, destructive in berry-growing regions. It lays eggs in rows in pithy stems of raspberry, blackberry, loganberry, grape, elder, sometimes in woody twigs of maple, elm, peach, apple and other trees. Canes die above the punctures or split and break off. Early spraying with lead arsenate is helpful.

Camel Cricket, *Daihinia brevipes* Haldeman. Found in the Great Plains states from North Dakota to northern Texas, reported as injurious in Oklahoma to tomatoes, watermelon, cotton, cowpeas, and other plants in the seedling stage. It feeds at night, is found mostly in sandy areas. Poison bran-mash bait gives satisfactory control.

Changa*, *Scapteriscus vicinus* Scudder. Puerto Rican or West Indian Mole Cricket, an introduced species similar to the southern mole cricket. It is injurious to truck crops, pastures, lawns in the coastal plain of the Southeast. It is 1½ inches long, brown above, light brown underneath. See Northern Mole Cricket for control.

Coulee Cricket*, *Peranbrus scabricollis* (Thomas). More nearly related to the katydids than crickets, very destructive in Montana and Washington. Feeding on sagebrush, dung, living and dead animals, it also eats nearly all field and garden crops, fruits, and shrubs. Adults are fat, soft-bodied, 1½ inches long, dark reddish brown. Females are wingless; males have short, winged stubs. They are active in the daytime and move in migratory hordes, devastating everything in their path. Ditches can be dug to stop migrating swarms, or poison bait used as for the Mormon cricket. Western meadowlarks are credited with stopping outbreaks.

Field Cricket*, *Acheta assimilis* Fabricius. Present everywhere in small numbers, sometimes seriously abundant. Often black or brown, but they vary in color. Antennae and ovipositor of females longer than the body, ⅗ to 1 inch long. They are indiscriminate feeders, eating plants in the garden, or paper, food, or clothing in the house. They injure seedling cotton and cereals, cucurbits, legumes, tomato fruits, strawberries. They hibernate in the egg stage in the North, where there is but 1 generation; in warm climates they winter as nymphs and there may be 3 generations. During the day they remain under trash, coming out in late afternoon to chirp, feed, mate, and lay banana-shaped eggs in damp soil. Use poison-brain baits or spray or dust with chlordane or dieldrin as for grasshoppers. Maintain a fine dust mulch; spade deeply in fall to bury eggs.

Four-spotted Tree Cricket*, *Oecanthus nigricornis quadripunctatus* Beutenmüller. Like the black-horned tree cricket except for 2 dark spots in each of the 2 basal antennal segments.

Jerusalem Cricket*, *Stenopelmatus fuscus* Haldeman. Sand Cricket, a western species with legs adapted for tunneling in sandy soil. It is large, wingless, amber brown, does not have hearing organs on front tibiae. It is a useful predator, injurious to little except potato tubers in newly broken soil.

Mormon Cricket*, *Anabrus simplex* Haldeman. Western Great Plains, Idaho, or Black Cricket, found in most states west of the Rocky Mountains and in some of the Great Plains states. It is very destructive, migrating periodically from native breeding grounds in the hills to devastate garden crops, fruit, and grain. It is of great economic importance as a scourge of range grasses. Eggs are laid in late summer and fall in light, sandy-loam soil, inserted singly just under the surface in bare spots between clumps of grass or sagebrush. Young crickets start hatching early in April and reach maturity in 6 to 8 weeks. There is 1 generation. Adults are 1 inch long, heavy-bodied, with small, useless wings, antennae and ovipositor as long as the body, tarsi 4-segmented. They are active during the day and may travel ⅛ to 1 mile a day when they start migration.

Control. Metal barriers or ditches to stop migratory hordes have been used in the past. Now poison bait is used, often applied by airplane. There are several formulae. In one, 2 ounces aldrin, 100 pounds steam-rolled wheat, ½ gallon of diesel oil are mixed and applied by plane at the rate of 5 pounds per acre. Another dry formula calls for 100 pounds standard bran (no shorts or middlings), 1 pound toxaphene or ½ pound of chlordane, ½ gallon of fuel oil or kerosene, applied at the rate of 10 pounds per acre.

For broadcasting by hand, a wet bait is made of 100 pounds of standard wheat bran, 4 pounds sodium fluosilicate, 12 to 15 gallons of water. This can be reduced proportionately for gardens.

In 1848 flocks of California gulls terminated a terrific outbreak of Mormon crickets in Utah so successfully a monument was erected to them. The gulls still come to feed on the crickets.

Northern Mole Cricket*, *Gryllotalpa hexadactyla* Perty. A native pest, known in damp muddy places from Canada through Florida but a problem only in the South. A European species, *Gryllotalpa gryllotalpa*, has become established in a few places along the eastern coast and threatens nurseries. These crickets are large, 1½ inches long, brownish above, paler underneath, covered with velvety hairs. Their front legs are greatly enlarged, adapted for burrowing, and they terminate in 4 strong, bladelike teeth called dactyls (Plate XXI). They live deep in the ground during the day, coming out at night to pulverize a garden bed and the plants growing in it. Most injury comes from their tunnels in the upper inch or two of soil, which cut off roots of seedlings, injure lawns. Mole crickets also eat pits in underground roots and stems, cut stems off above ground and eat seeds.

Control. Treating soil with chlordane is standard procedure, or the use of a commercially prepared bait including chlordane. A poison bait sometimes used consists of 5 pounds dry bran or cornmeal, 5 pounds cottonseed meal, ½ pound calcium arsenate, and 2 quarts of a solution of 1 part molasses mixed with 9 parts of water.

Snowy Tree Cricket*, *Oecanthus niveus* (De Geer). Widely distributed throughout North America. Tree crickets are generally beneficial, eating aphids, tree hoppers, and scales, but they do feed somewhat on flowers, fruit, and leaves; twigs may be broken by their egg punctures. This cricket is pale green, with slender body, ⅝ inch long, with a black spot on the first 2 antennal segments (Plate XXI). It lays eggs singly in a line down one side of a twig or cane of apple, ash, blackberry, cherry, loganberry, pear, plum, prune, peach, and other fruits and ornamentals. There is only 1 generation; and egg laying is in autumn. The songs of the males are short, clear, whistling notes. Control by pruning out and burning infested twigs or cane and spraying with lead arsenate in early spring.

Southern Mole Cricket*, *Scapteriscus acletus* Rehn & Hebard. Recorded from Georgia, Texas and other southern states. It is much like the northern mole cricket but it has 2 dactyls instead of 4 and is pinkish buff in color.

CURCULIOS

Curculios, along with weevils, belong in the order Coleoptera, family Curculionidae. They are beetles with a pronounced snout, the head being prolonged forward with biting mouth parts at the end and elbowed antennae arising midway. Curculios usually have a longer snout with a more pronounced downward curve than weevils. The Curculionidae is the largest family of insects in any order, with more than 2000 species in North America. All members eat plants both as larvae and as adults. They are mostly small and dull-colored, with a habit of dropping from bushes and playing dead when disturbed.

Apple Curculio*, *Tachypterellus quadrigibbus* (Say). A native insect found east of the Mississippi River. Preferred hosts are apple, cherry, haw, wild crab, quince, pear, and shadbush. Feeding and egg punctures result in knotty, misshapen, undersized fruit and premature drop. This curculio does not make crescent-shaped marks like the plum curculio but produces a large number of punctures close together. It is brown with 4 humps on the back, a long, slender snout. It winters in leaves and rubbish on the ground, feeding on buds, fruit spurs, and terminal shoots in spring and attacks fruit as soon as it is set. The larvae develop in June drops and in mummied apples left on trees, pupating inside. Adults emerge from the middle of June to early October.

There are three other curculios on apple: the larger apple curculio, *T. quadrigibbus magnus* List, from Illinois to Texas; *T. consors* Dietz, from the Rocky Mountains to the Pacific Coast; and the cherry curculio. Control measures are the same as for the plum curculio.

Black Walnut Curculio, *Conotrachelus retentus* (Say). A common pest of young walnuts in eastern United States. The curculios, pale reddish covered with gray pubescence, hibernate as adults, feeding on young shoots in spring and making crescent-shaped cuts for their eggs in very young walnuts, which drop to the ground half-grown. They pupate in the soil; beetles emerge in August and September to feed on leaf petioles before hibernating. Larvae in dropped nuts can be destroyed by burying deeply or putting nuts in water. Several parasitic wasps and flies aid in control.

Butternut Curculio, *Conotrachelus juglandis* LeConte. Also known as

Walnut Weevil, attacking native and Japanese butternuts and young English walnuts. The adult resembles the plum curculio but with white markings; it is ¼ inch long. It punctures nuts, tender tips, and leaf petioles, lays eggs in new growth and, in young nuts, through crescent-shaped slits. The grubs, dirty-white with brown heads, burrow through the nut or down the twig for 4 or 5 weeks, then go below the soil surface to pupate. DDT applied to new shoots in early June should be effective; lead arsenate has been used in the past.

Cabbage Curculio*, *Ceutorhynchus rapae* Gyllenhal. An ashy-gray weevil, ⅛ inch long, with a short snout. Adults and grubs gouge out stems and adults also work on leaves. They infest seedling cabbage, cauliflower, horseradish, mustard, radish, and turnip. Dust young plants with DDT.

Cabbage Seedstalk Curculio*, *Ceutorhynchus quadridens* (Panzer).

Cambium Curculio, *Conotrachelus anaglypticus* (Say). Common from Massachusetts to Florida and west to Iowa. The larvae feed on cambium and inner bark of many fruit, shade, and forest trees, working around the edges of wounds, retarding healing. They also work in the crowns and roots of columbine, causing wilting and dying, and produce wilting and dieback of young camellia shoots. The snout beetle is small—less than ¼ inch long—reddish brown; the grubs are small, fleshy, legless. Remove and burn infested plant parts.

Cherry Curculio, *Tachypterellus consors cerasi* List. A variety of an apple curculio.

Clover Root Curculio*, *Sitona hispidula* (Fabricius). A common pest of clover and alfalfa, sometimes feeding on soybeans, cowpeas and other legumes. Tiny grayish grubs score and furrow roots, nearly girdling them. Small gray or brown beetles with short blunt snouts feed on foliage, sometimes eating off tops of young soybeans entirely. Crop rotation seems the most practical control.

Cowpea Curculio*, *Chalcodermus aeneus* Boheman. Also known as Cowpea Pod-weevil, injuring cowpeas, seedling cotton, beans and strawberries. Most important in the cotton states, it occurs as far north as Iowa. Black, humpbacked adults lay eggs in cowpeas or beans in the field and larvae destroy developing seeds.

Grape Curculio*, *Craponius inaequalis* (Say). A native pest of wild grape, injuring berries of cultivated grape in some areas. It is reported as injurious in New England, Florida, Kentucky, Missouri, Ohio, and West Virginia. The small, black beetles, just over 1/10 inch long, winter in sheltered locations and feed for a month or two in spring before laying eggs in cavities under skin of grape berries. Footless larvae feed on berry flesh and seeds, drop to the ground, and pupate by midsummer. Adults emerge and feed again before hibernation. Control measures are usually unnecessary.

Hickory-nut Curculio, *Conotrachelus affinis* Boheman. Confined to hickories, pignut preferred, then shagbark, whiteheart, and butternut. The beetles, reddish brown with a broad band of lighter gray across the back, appear when nuts are half formed to lay eggs in circular cavities in nuts and shells. Nuts drop in midsummer; larvae stay inside for about a month, then enter the soil to pupate. Spraying in early spring with DDT or lead arsenate helps to keep the beetles from feeding on foliage. Bury dropped nuts deeply or put in water to kill larvae. There are several parasites.

Plum Curculio*, *Conotrachelus nenuphar* (Herbst). A native snout beetle, found east of the Rocky Mountains, a major pest of stone fruits—plum, peach, cherry, apricot, prune, nectarine—and next to codling moth in importance on apple, sometimes injuring pear and quince. The adult is dark brown with a grayish patch on the back, 4 definite humps on the wing covers, and a long, curved snout which projects forward and downward in an arc ⅓ the length of the body, which is ¼ inch long (Plate XXII). It winters in stone walls, hedgerows, or other protected places, appearing on the trees at blossomtime. The beetles feed on leaves and petals. They injure young fruits by feeding and laying eggs in small circular excavations marked by a crescent-shaped slot underneath. Feeding punctures may result in warts or scars, sometimes misshapen, knotty apples. Grubs in stone fruits render them unmarketable. Also, the punctures on peaches and plums afford entrance to brown-rot spores. Economic losses for the country as a whole run between 8 and 17 million dollars a year.

Eggs hatch, about a week after being inserted in the fruit, into gray-white legless grubs with brown heads and curved bodies. They feed in the flesh for 2 weeks or more, by which time the fruit has probably fallen to the ground, although most cherries and some peaches remain on the tree until ripe. The larvae leave the fruit and enter the soil to pupate, adults emerging in about a month. There are 2 generations in Virginia, sometimes a partial 2nd in Delaware but only 1 farther north. Temperatures affect activity. Above 70° F. brings beetles out of hibernation, promotes egg laying and usually results in severe damage.

Control. Spray apples with lead arsenate, at the rate of 3 pounds to 100 gallons, at petal fall, 7 to 10 days later, and again in 2 weeks. Schedules and poisons for peaches and other stone fruits vary widely. DDT and TDE are ineffective but methoxychlor, 3 pounds per 100 gallons, has given good results. Other possibilities are malathion or Sevin. Commercial growers may use phosphates—EPN, Guthion, parathion or endrin—or dieldrin, at ½ pound per 100 gallons of spray. Treating orchard soils with aldrin, dieldrin, or heptachlor is useful.

It is always advantageous to pick up dropped fruits and to destroy them by deep burial or soaking in waste oil, and to clean up possible winter shelters. It is also helpful to collect curculios during the season by placing a sheet under a tree and jarring off adults with a stick. There are several parasites and a useful fungus disease.

Quince Curculio*, *Conotrachelus crataegi* Walsh. The most serious pest, confined to this host. It resembles the plum curculio but winters in the soil as a grub. The adult—broad, grayish brown without humps on its back—eats irregular cavities in the fruit, which may be knotty and misshapen. The white legless grubs feed in the fruit during summer but seldom cause it to drop. They leave the fruit before it falls naturally, so that picking up fallen quinces is no help in control. Spraying with lead arsenate and lime, 4 pounds of each to 100 gallons, is recommended at petal fall and 10 days later.

Rhubarb Curculio*, *Lixus concavus* Say. Rhubarb Weevil, common from New England south to Florida and west to Idaho. This is one of the largest of the snout beetles, ½ inch long, blackish but covered with a rusty yellow dust. It punctures rhubarb stalks and lays eggs in them, but the larvae develop and feed on common curled dock. Handpick the beetles; destroy all dock plants growing near rhubarb.

Rose Curculio*, *Rhynchites bicolor* (Fabricius). Rose Snout Beetle, bright red with a black undersurface and black curved beak, ¼ inch long. Adults drill holes in buds of both wild and cultivated roses, the buds wither not opening or producing petals riddled with holes. Small white larvae develop from eggs laid in hips but drop to the ground for pupation and hibernation. The rose curculio is particularly destructive in North Dakota and other cold regions, breeding in wild roses but swarming to cultivated roses in such numbers as to prevent almost all bloom. Western forms vary in color from black and red to black with a greenish luster. Spraying or dusting with DDT is recommended for control. See Plate XI.

CUTWORMS

High in the ranks of gardening headaches are the cutworms—smooth, fat, soft, repulsive caterpillars, larvae of night-flying moths, family Noctuidae (Phalaenidae). Different species occur all over the world and injure almost all crops. The solitary or surface cutworms, including black, bronzed, and dingy, are most likely to harass the home gardener. They feed on plants near the surface of the ground, cutting off succulent stems of tomato, bean, cabbage, some other vegetables, and flowers soon after they are set out (Plate XXIII). Climbing cutworms go up the stems of herbaceous plants, shrubs, and vines, sometimes even climbing trees to eat buds, leaves, and fruit. Army cutworms work in large groups and are more prevalent in western gardens. Subterranean cutworms, including pale western and glassy, remain continuously in the soil, feeding on roots and underground stems.

Most surface cutworms have similar habits. They winter as partly grown larvae in cells in the soil, under trash, or in clumps of grass. They start feeding in the spring, working only at night, remaining coiled up in a ball just under the earth surface during the day. When full-grown they dig down several inches in the soil to make a cell where they pupate from 1 to 8 weeks, or over winter. Southern species have several generations a year; most northern species have but 1, with moths appearing in summer.

Control. In the annual garden, treat the soil before planting with 10 per cent toxaphene or DDT dust at the rate of ½ pound per 1000 square feet, leaving the soil undisturbed for several days before planting. If the cutworms are the type that feed below ground level, work the dust an inch into the soil.

Baits have long been used for cutworms. There are many on the market under different brand names or you can mix your own. Add to 1 cup of molasses enough water to make 3 quarts; stir into this 2 tablespoons of chlordane (40 to 45 per cent emulsion) *or* 3 tablespoons of toxaphene (45 per cent emulsion) *or* 7 tablespoons DDT (25 per cent emulsion); sprinkle this liquid slowly over 5 pounds of wheat bran, stirring until every particle is coated and you have a crumbly mass. Spread the bait by hand in late afternoon, ½ pound per 1000 square feet. If the garden is already planted, scatter the bait along rows or around plants but don't let it hit them. Commercial growers may use a mixture starting with 50 pounds of wheat bran to which is added 4 ounces of aldrin or dieldrin or 1 pound of chlordane with sufficient water to moisten the bran.

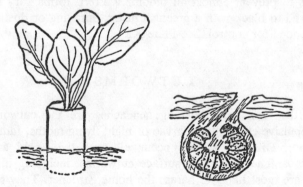

46. *Paper collar around a cabbage seedling to foil cutworms; and cutworm in typical position in earth cell.*

An old method of circumventing cutworms without chemicals is to place a collar of stiff paper or thin cardboard around each plant as it is set out. This should go down an inch or two into the soil to stay in place and to foil worms working just under the surface.

Army Cutworm*, *Chorizagrotis auxiliaris* (Grote). A western species, appearing in armies, attacking all kinds of vegetation in Washington, Oregon, Wyoming, and Utah. Dieldrin has been used in control.

Black Army Cutworm*, *Actebia fennica* (Tauscher). A northern pest, injuring blueberries in Maine, garden vegetables in Alaska.

Black Cutworm*, *Agrotis ipsilon* (Hufnagel). A surface cutworm, known also as the Greasy Cutworm. It is gray to brown to nearly black with a broken yellow line on the back and a pale line on each side, the whole appearance being greasy and shiny. The skin has convex granules, large and small. This species is widely distributed, is very fond of truck crops, and often cuts off tomatoes in home gardens. It is a restless feeder, cutting off many plants to satisfy its appetite. It lays eggs singly or few together on leaves and stems, often on plants in new land. It winters as a pupa. Moths are reddish to brownish gray with silvery patches at bases and tips of fore wings. There are 2 generations in the North, often 4 in the South.

Bristly Cutworm*, *Lacinipolia renigera* (Stephens). On forage crops, alfalfa and clovers, in the Middle West.

Bronzed Cutworm*, *Nephelodes emmedonia* (Cramer). A northern species injurious to corn, grains, and grasses. The larva is dark bronzy brown, striped from head to tail with 5 clear pale lines about half as large as the brown area in between, with a granulate skin. There is 1 generation, the winter being spent as a partly grown larva.

Clay-back Cutworm, *Agrotis gladiaria* (Morrison). On cotton, corn, and alfalfa. Greenish to dark brown with a broad pale stripe down the back.

Clover Cutworm*, *Scotogramma trifolii* (Rottenburg).

Dark-sided Cutworm*, *Euxoa messoria* (Harris). A common species that may climb to feed on tree foliage in the spring. The dull, pale green larvae also attack cultivated crops, wild grasses, and weeds. The moth is silver-gray with dark mottled fore wings. DDT can be used as a spray for trees and some crops.

Dingy Cutworm*, *Feltia subgothica* (Haworth). A northern species sometimes assuming climbing habit. Larvae are dull dingy brown with a broad buff-gray stripe down the back (divided into triangular areas on each segment), a narrow dark stripe on each side, and coarse skin granules.

Glassy Cutworm*, *Crymodes devastator* (Brace). Widespread, except in the more southern states. It is a subterranean species preferring sod and injurious to crops following sod. The larva is greenish white and rather translucent or glassy with a red head; the skin is not granulated.

Granulate Cutworm*, *Feltia subterranea* (Fabricius). Dusty brown with a rough, granulated skin, on many crops in southern states. It defoliates peanuts in Georgia, infests sweetpotato tubers and dichondra lawns in California, tomatoes and peppers in Louisiana, shade tobacco in Florida and so on.

Pale-sided Cutworm*, *Agrotis malefida* Guenée. On cotton, sometimes tomato, pepper, and corn.

Pale Western Cutworm*, *Agrotis orthogonia* Morrison. A subterranean form of great economic importance in the West, where it has destroyed millions of dollars worth of small grains, beets, and alfalfa. The body is greenish gray, unmarked by lines or stripes, with a broad band and flat granules on the skin. The moth is mottled gray, nocturnal and diurnal; it appears in late August and September to lay whitish eggs in small batches just under the surface in soft soil. The larvae feed day and night, on cabbage, carrots, and onions as well as grains. Poison baits have no effect; the chemicals have to be washed into the soil.

Red-backed Cutworm*, *Euxoa ochrogaster* (Guenée). Regularly destructive in many northern sections. Larvae are reddish on the back, feed on succulent plants, may be destructive to cereal, forage, and truck crops. They feed both above and below ground, hibernate in the egg stage. They succumb readily to poison bran bait.

Spotted Cutworm*, *Amathes c-nigrum* (Linnaeus). Generally distributed but rather scarce in the South, a surface feeder preferring garden crops. Larvae have wedge-shaped black dashes on each segment, a dark line through the spiracles, and a smooth skin. Eggs are laid singly, or in patches of 100 or more, on leaves. There may be 2 or 3 generations.

Striped Cutworm*, *Euxoa tessellata* (Harris).

Variegated Cutworm*, *Peridroma saucia* (Hübner). A climbing cutworm, perhaps the most widely known and important species, present in many countries, damaging crops in the United States to the tune of several million dollars a year. The larva is ashy or light brown mottled with dark brown, a distinct yellow dot in the middle of each segment, often a dark W on the 8th segment, a smooth skin. The moth is grayish brown with dark, mottled fore wings and a brassy luster. In early spring it lays small, white, ribbed eggs in large irregular masses on foliage and stems of plants or limbs of trees, or fences or buildings. The larvae eat foliage, buds, and fruits of garden crops, fruit trees, or vines. They injure flowers outdoors and in the greenhouse. There are 2 generations outdoors, more inside. Handpicking, trapping under boards, poison sprays or dusts are all used in control.

Western Bean Cutworm*, *Loxagrotis albicosta* (Smith). One of the climbing cutworms, probably a native, first described from Arizona, now important in Colorado, Idaho, Iowa, Kansas, Nebraska, New Mexico, Texas, and Utah. It feeds on foliage, stems, buds, seeds of beans, leaves, stalks, and ears of corn, and is reported on fruits of groundcherry and deadly nightshade. Controls applied to cornfields by airplane include Thiodan, endrin, DDT granules, Sevin, and diazinon, effective in that order.

Western W-marked Cutworm*, *Spaelotis havilae* (Grote). On cereals and corn in western states, also reported on poplar in California.

W-marked Cutworm*, *Spaelotis clandestina* (Harris). Reported on tobacco and hay in the West.

Yellow-headed Cutworm*, *Apamea amputatrix* (Fitch). Reported on Merion bluegrass in Washington.

EARTHWORMS

Earthworms are friends of man! They are not insects but belong to the animal phylum Annelida, meaning rings, and are made up of many round segments. They are usually 2 to 10 inches long with slender, cylindrical soft bodies, bearing 8 bristlelike projections, setae, on each ring. They are hermaphrodites in that each worm produces ova and sperm cells, but they are not self-fertilized. They mate and the eggs are laid in a round case or capsule which eventually passes off over the head.

Earthworms have been considered by some people the most important of all animals. Charles Darwin estimated that earthworms bring up 7 tons of new soil for every acre of land, that good garden soil normally has about 53,000 worms per acre and poor field soil only half that many. There are earthworm farms raising worms to sell to gardeners with claims made for the wonders worked by so-called "hybrid" worms. However, if your soil is good enough to support earthworms you'll probably have plenty without having to buy them.

Earthworms live in moist soil containing decaying organic matter and crawl out at night to feed, or come out when their burrows are filled with water. They eat the soil and their digestive juices dissolve leafmold and other organic matter; then this digested earth is discharged in the form of castings, soil of the finest quality. Earthworms also drag leaves into their burrows, increasing the organic content of the soil in that way. Strong healthy worms work from 3 to 8 feet underground, making the trip to the surface nightly to deposit castings. Their beneficial action may go much deeper than spade, plow, or rototiller.

Despite the fact that some gardeners want earthworms badly enough to support earthworm farms, others object to lumpy piles of castings on their fine front lawns. They can be a nuisance on golf courses, and the rather recent oriental earthworm (*Peretima hupeiensis*) is definitely a menace. It is known at scattered points from Connecticut to Miami but is concentrated in the Metropolitan New York area. It is light grass-green, has a bad odor when crushed.

Older recommendations called for treating lawns with lead arsenate or Mowrah Meal and lead arsenate is still good for common earthworms, at 5 to 10 pounds per 1000 square feet, but not for the oriental earthworm. Chlordane is better for the latter, 1 quart of 48 per cent chlordane emulsion applied to 1000 square feet. For the common earthworm, spray lawns with 50 per cent wettable chlordane at the rate of 1 pound to 1000 square feet. Toxaphene is also effective for earthworms but DDT has little effect on most species. In fact, earthworms accumulate DDT in their bodies, feeding in leaf litter under sprayed trees, and so become a hazard for birds.

Earthworms in flowerpots are not welcome; they clog up the drainage hole. Limewater is the time-honored remedy, either purchased at the drugstore or made at home by stirring 1 pint of freshly slaked lime into 2½ gallons of water and using it as soon as it clarifies. Use chlordane instead of lime on potted azalea and other plants requiring an acid soil.

EARWIGS

Earwigs are beetlelike insects of the order Dermaptera, readily recognized by tail appendages which look like forceps. They have gradual metamorphosis but biting mouth parts, feeding on decayed or living plant material and on other insects. They are nocturnal, living under bark or stones or debris on the ground during the day. They were named from the mistaken notion that they crawl into the ears of sleeping persons. The European earwig is the species of most consequence to gardeners.

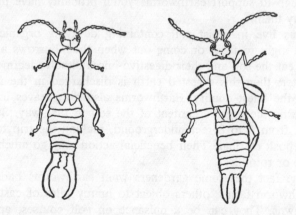

47. European earwig: male, left; female, right.

European Earwig, *Forficula auricularia* Linnaeus. An introduced species, first discovered at Newport, Rhode Island, in 1911, with another colony appearing at Seattle, Washington, in 1915. Since then it has been reported as a garden pest from California, Colorado, Delaware, Idaho, Maine, Massachusetts, New York, New Jersey, Oregon, Pennsylvania, and Utah. The insect is hard, dark reddish brown, up to ⅘ inch long, with a pair of sharp pincers or forceps at the tip of the abdomen, protruding ¼ the length of the body. These structures are larger and more curved in the male than in the female. The front wings are very short and the hind wings are folded up under them, aided by the forceps. Earwigs seldom fly; they run.

The female lays a batch of smooth white eggs in early spring in the soil in any protected place and broods over them until they hatch. She watches over her young until the first molt, then leaves, often to lay another batch of eggs. Young nymphs feed on green plant shoots, eating holes in leaves of many different vegetables and flowers. Older earwigs work on blossoms, eating stamens and bases of petals, and often climb into fruit trees, especially apricot and peach, to dine on ripening fruit. They are quite a pest in houses, crawling over everything at night, into crevices of various sorts, hiding under cushions, dishes, or clothing.

Earwigs are more important in coastal areas. In California eggs are laid from December through February, and the pest is most destructive from April through July. They are also, however, beneficial as scavengers on decaying matter and in feeding on insect larvae, snails and other slow-moving animals.

Control. A poison bait was standard control for many years and may still be used. It consisted of 6 pounds of wheat bran mixed with ½ pound sodium fluosilicate and moistened with 1 pint of fish oil. This is scattered toward evening, thinly, over areas frequented by earwigs. It should not touch plants and is poisonous to pets and birds. Chlordane is now more commonly used, sometimes lindane or DDT, applied as a dust around hiding places and especially along fences and foundations of houses. To keep earwigs out of fruit trees, dust the soil at the base of the trees and the tree trunks with 10 per cent DDT about a month before fruit ripens.

Ring-legged Earwig*, *Euborellia annulipes* (Lucas). In southern states but more of an indoor than an outdoor pest.

Southern Earwig, *Labidura riparia* Pallas. Common in southern gardens and homes, from Georgia to Florida to southern California. Brown, 1 inch long, mainly a scavenger but eating flowers to some extent.

EARWORMS

Corn Earworm*, *Heliothis zea* (Boddie). Present practically everywhere that corn is grown, the worst corn pest in the United States, though more damaging to sweet corn than to field corn. The claim has been made that American farmers grow 2 million acres of corn a year just to feed the earworm. It is damaging to other crops under different names: Tomato Fruitworm, Tobacco Budworm, Cotton Bollworm.

The caterpillars, larvae of moths, family Noctuidae, are nearly 2 inches long when full-grown, yellowish or green or brown with lengthwise light and dark stripes (Plate XIII). In early plantings they attack buds and feed on unfolding leaves, giving a ragged appearance and possibly some stunting. They feed somewhat on tassels but most of the damage is to the ear. The larvae feed from the tip, starting on fresh silk, then working down to the kernels, piling up masses of moist castings. Feeding on the silk prevents pollination, resulting in nubbins; feeding on the kernels introduces various mold fungi. Late season corn may be nearly 100 per cent infested.

As the tomato fruitworm, the larva begins feeding on foliage but soon works into green fruit, usually burrowing in at the stem end and sometimes destroying as much as 25 per cent of the tomatoes. They are restless caterpillars, moving from one fruit to another and over to beans, cabbage, broccoli, and lettuce. As the cotton bollworm, the larva injures green bolls of cotton, and as the tobacco budworm it works in tobacco buds. Other food plants include alfalfa and clovers, globe artichoke, chickpea, geranium, gladiolus, grape, mignonette, okra, peach, pea, peanut, pear, pepper, pumpkin, rose, squash, strawberry, sunflower, and vetch.

The earworm works as a pupa 2 to 6 inches below ground; the moths crawl out through exit holes prepared by the larvae. Adults vary in color; the front wings are grayish brown marked with dark lines shading to olive-green; the hind wings are white with dark spots or markings; wingspread 1½ inches. The moths fly at dusk or on warm, cloudy days, feed on nectar of flowers, and lay 500 to 3000 eggs, yellowish, hemispherical, ridged, singly on host plants. There are 2 or 3 generations a season, and moths of later generations often lay their eggs on corn silk. The newly hatched larva is very small, white with a black head, but grows rapidly, molting every 2 to 5 days. The pupae are seldom able to survive the winter north of Virginia, unless the weather is unusually warm and dry. Most northern infestations come from adults migrating from the South.

Control. There are some corn hybrids on the market partially resistant to corn earworm and there are many natural factors aiding in control, including the fact that one earworm will consume another. There are egg parasites; birds feed on earworms, often damaging ears in the process; moles destroy pupae; cold, moist weather reduces infestations. There is no practical chemical control for field corn but sweet corn has been treated with an oil solution of DDT, using ¼ pint emulsifiable DDT with ¾ pint white mineral oil, water added to make 1 gallon and the mixture shaken until it is uniformly white. This is applied to the silks soon after they appear, using a fine atomizer sprayer and only enough spray to wet the silks. Sevin is presently recommended, also applied as a fine spray.

The worms can also be killed with a special corn earworm oil applied with a medicine dropper 3 to 7 days after silks first appear, putting the end of the dropper a quarter inch into the mass of silk at the tip of the husk and squirting in about 20 drops. Oils on the market may contain dichloro-ethyl ether, DDT, or pyrethrins. Treated ears should be marked with crayon or string to make sure they do not get a second dose.

On tomatoes, fruitworms can be controlled by spraying or dusting with TDE or toxaphene, or by applying pinches of bait, 1 part cryolite to 9 parts cornmeal or cottonseed meal, to the fruit clusters. DDT is sometimes used but may be injurious to tomatoes. Treatments should cease when fruits are half grown.

FLIES

Flies belong to the order Diptera, meaning 2-winged, the order including practically all insects with only 1 pair of wings—mosquitoes, gnats, and midges as well as flies. The second pair of wings is presented, if at all, by threadlike knobbed organs called halteres. There are some wingless flies and some with reduced wings but in these, halteres are usually present. Fly mouth parts are adapted for piercing-sucking or for lapping. The compound eyes are very large and usually there are 3 simple eyes, ocelli. The larvae, called maggots, are footless, grublike creatures, usually soft, white or yellowish, with the head reduced. There is complete metamorphosis, with the pupal stage ordinarily passed inside the last larval skin, called a puparium.

There are a great many species of flies. Some are dangerous to man as carriers of human diseases and some are destructive to crops. But some flies are useful scavengers, cleaning up dead animals and plant wastes, and others are insect destroyers, with predators like the syrphid flies or parasites, living in or on harmful insects.

The families listed here contain members of interest to gardeners.

Agromyzidae. Leaf Miner Flies. Small, yellow or black, the larvae making mines in leaves. See under Leaf Miners.

Asilidae. Robber Flies. A beneficial group, adults being predaceous on a variety of insects. Body usually hairy, head hollowed out between the eyes.

Cecidomyiidae (Itonididae). Gall Midges. Minute delicate flies or gnats with relatively long antennae and legs, reduced wing venation, many living in plants and causing galls, some not gall-forming, a few predaceous.

Chloropidae. Frit Flies. Small, rather bare, flies, some brightly colored with yellow and black, common in meadows and other grassy areas; some are cereal pests, some scavengers; a few are parasitic or predaceous.

Dolichopodidae. Long-legged Flies. Small to minute, with metallic coloring; abundant in swamps, woodlands, meadows; some members are predaceous on bark beetles and other insects.

Drosophilidae. Vinegar Flies, Pomace Flies, Fruit Flies. Found mostly on decaying fruit and vegetation, very small, usually yellow; very useful in studies of heredity.

Mycetophilidae (Fungivoridae). Fungus Gnats. Slender, delicate, mosquitolike, found in damp places with decaying vegetation or fungi.

Psilidae. Rust Flies. Slender with long antennae, small to medium, with a ridge across the basal third of the wing; living in roots or galls of plants.

Stratiomyidae. Soldier Flies. Medium or large, dark or brightly colored, wasplike adults; found on flowers. Some larvae are aquatic, some live in decaying matter, some under bark.

Syrphidae. Flower Flies, Syrphid Flies. Adults often hover around flowers.

Many are brightly colored and resemble bees. Many are highly beneficial, predaceous on aphids and other insects.

Tachinidae. Tachinid Flies. The most beneficial family of Diptera, all species parasitic on other insects. They resemble bristly houseflies, the abdomen usually with large bristles in addition to smaller ones all over the body.

Tephritidae (Trypetidae). Fruit Flies. Small to medium, usually with spotted or banded wings; adults on flowers or vegetation; larvae are maggots in fruit, a few are leaf miners.

Australian Sod Fly, *Metoponia rubriceps* Macq. Introduced into California some years ago. The maggots have become a serious pest of lawns and golf courses in the San Francisco area.

Black Cherry Fruit Fly*, *Rhagoletis fausta* (Osten Sacken). Distributed through northern United States on cherry, wild cherry, pear, and plum. Except that the abdomen is entirely black and that it prefers sour cherries, this species is like the cherry fruit fly.

Bumelia Fruit Fly*, *Pseudodacus pallens* (Coquillett).

Carrot Rust Fly*, *Psila rosae* (Fabricius). A European pest first noticed in Ottawa in 1885, now rather generally present in northern states and quite injurious in gardens in the Pacific Northwest. Carrot is the most important host with serious injury also to celery, parsnip, celeriac, and parsley, and some feeding on coriander, caraway, fennel, and dill. The damage is caused by maggots feeding on the roots, producing stunting, dwarfing, or complete destruction of plants. Larval excrement looks like iron rust in the root tunnels, whence the name rust fly. Soft-rot bacteria follow the maggots so that carrots decompose in a soft, vile-smelling mess.

The fly is small, ⅕ inch, shiny green with yellow hairs, legs, and head, black eyes. It lays eggs about the crowns of host plants. The yellowish maggots, ⅓ inch when grown, work down into the soil to the roots. They feed there for a month, then pupate in the soil to produce a second brood of flies in August. Sometimes a partial third brood damages late carrots and celery, and injury may continue in storage. Brown puparia or maggots winter in soil.

Control. Growers can treat the soil before planting with aldrin or chlordane (2 pounds per acre) worked into the top 6 inches. Treating seed with calomel, as for the cabbage maggot, is helpful. Carrots planted after June 1 (in the New York area) and harvested early may escape injury.

Cherry Fruit Fly*, *Rhagoletis cingulata* (Loew). A native, common in northern United States on cherry, wild cherry, pear, and plum; responsible for most of our wormy cherries. Adults are smaller than houseflies, black with yellow margins on the thorax, 2 white crossbands on the abdomen and dark band across the wings, typical of fruit flies in the family Tephritidae. They emerge from brown puparia in the soil for a period of 5 or 6 weeks, starting in early June (about a week after the black-cherry fruit fly). They fly to trees, feed 7 to 10 days by scraping surface of leaves and fruit, sucking up sap, and lay eggs in young fruit through small slits cut in the flesh. The maggots, developing and eating inside the fruit, produce misshapen, undersized cherries, often with one side shrunken or decayed and turning red before maturity. When full-grown, the worms eat their way out of the fruit, fall to the ground, and spend the next 6 months as puparia 2 or 3 inches below the surface.

Control. The only feasible method is spraying to kill the flies before they lay eggs, which means using a special trap to determine when the first adults appear. Commercial growers use 2 or 3 applications of malathion (½ pound to 100 gallons); or parathion (up to ⅓ pound); Diazinon (¼ pound); methoxychlor or Perthane (1 pound); or rotenone (1¼ to 2 pounds), repeating at 10-day intervals and starting just before blossoms open. Several parasites attack the cherry fruit fly with a braconid wasp (*Opius ferrugineus*) most important.

Currant Fruit Fly*, *Epochra canadensis* (Loew). A native pest in many sections, common on currants and gooseberries in the West. The adult, yellow-bodied with dark-banded wings, about the size of a housefly, emerges from its puparium in the soil in April or May. It lays 100 to 200 eggs singly in fruit. Whitish maggots cause fruit to turn red and drop prematurely. Feeding continues for a few days in fruit on the ground before the maggots enter soil to pupate. There is 1 generation. Early maturing varieties escape most of the damage. A spray consisting of 1 quart of syrup and 2 ounces of lead arsenate to 3 gallons of water, applied as soon as the flies emerge, has been recommended for control. A rotenone spray or dust might be wiser in home gardens.

Eupatorium Gall Fly*, *Procecidochares utilis* Stone.

Frit Fly*, *Oscinella frit* (Linnaeus). Small, short-winged, bare flies abounding in rank vegetations and on grasses. The larvae may seriously damage lawns and golf courses.

Hessian Fly*, *Phytophaga destructor* (Say). One of the most important world pests, causing great losses in wheat and some in barley and rye. The original home of the Hessian fly was probably Russia. It apparently came to this country in straw bedding used by Hessian troops during the Revolutionary War, being noted on Long Island in 1779. The flies are small, frail, black, the maggots greenish white, shiny. They draw sap from stems, causing them to break over, resulting in great reduction in yield.

Although the Hessian fly is not a problem in backyard gardens, the method of control should interest all gardeners, for it uses forethought instead of toil and sweat. Entomologists in all wheat states have worked out the life history of the fly so as to give a safe planting date in each location.

Lantana Gall Fly*, *Eutreta xanthochaeta* Aldrich.

Lesser Bulb Fly*, *Eumerus tuberculatus* Rondani. Several small grayish or yellowish wrinkled maggots, up to ½ inch long, may be found in decaying bulbs of narcissus, hyacinth, amaryllis, onion, iris, shallot. The flies are blackish green with white markings on the abdomen, ⅓ inch long. They appear on flowers in late April or May and lay eggs at base of plants. The maggots can injure healthy bulbs but are more often found in sickly or injured stock. They pupate in the bulbs or in soil nearby; there are 2 generations a year. See Narcissus Bulb Fly for control.

Lupine Fly, *Hylemya lupini* (Coquillett). The most important pest of blue lupine used as a green manure crop in the Southeast; also reported from the West and on various lupine species. The adult resembles the seed-corn maggot; the larva is whitish, somewhat slimy, ¼ inch long. It feeds on the tender bud, then tunnels into the stem, the entry hole being covered with hardened brown frass. There are 3 or 4 generations.

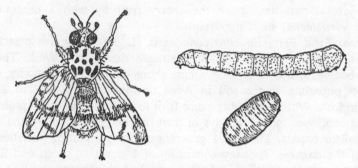

48. Mediterranean fruit fly: larva, pupa, and adult.

Mediterranean Fruit Fly*, *Ceratitis capitata* (Wiedemann). The most destructive member of the fruit-fly family, a potential pest of many deciduous and citrus fruits, including apricot, peach, nectarine, plum, grapefruit, orange, tangerine, kumquat, calamondin, papaya, coffee, Surinam cherry, loquat, figs, guava, mango, prickly pear, sapote, fig, grapes, dates, avocado, apple, pear, quince, and nearly 100 other wild and cultivated fruits.

The Mediterranean fruit fly was discovered in Florida in 1929, scattered over an area covering 10 million acres. By a remarkable eradication campaign, providing for a host-free period from May 1 to October 1, prior to which time all ripe fruits had to be shipped or destroyed and during which time no vegetables could be grown which would reach a susceptible stage before October 1, the pest was completely exterminated. Aided doubtless by travelers, it returned in 1956 and spread over 28 counties before it was again eradicated at a cost of 10 million dollars. It came back again in 1962 but was discovered promptly and the proper measures taken. It may enter again at any time, in coffeeberries brought in as souvenirs from South America, in an orange carelessly tossed from a ship, or in some other fashion. It is frequently intercepted at quarantine.

The fly became esablished at Bermuda in 1865, Brazil in 1901, Argentina in 1905, and Hawaii in 1910. It is somewhat smaller than a housefly, has a glistening black thorax with yellowish white lines in a mosaic pattern, yellow abdomen with silver crossbands, and wings banded with yellow, brown, and black. It has sponging mouth parts and takes only liquid food. The female deposits her eggs through a pinprick hole in the rind of fruit, 2 to 10 at a time but totaling up to 800. The eggs hatch in 2 to 20 days and the legless maggots, about ¼ inch long, burrow in the pulp for 10 days to 2 weeks. The life cycle takes 17 days to 3 months, and there may be up to 12 generations a year.

Control. Traps baited with medlure, a special attractant, give notice of incipient outbreaks. Bait sprays, of malathion and a yeast protein, are applied by airplane or ground equipment. The sprays are effective and relatively safe; there may be some damage to finish of automobiles and some slight effect on fish. Fruit may be fumigated to kill the maggots. Quarantines prohibit movement of fruit from infested areas.

Melon Fly*, *Daucus cucurbitae* Coquillett. Found in 1956 in a bait trap in California, a pest in Hawaii and frequently intercepted at quarantine, this fly is not, at this writing, known to be established in continental United States. It is considered the most important cucurbit pest of the Indo-Malayan region, where it originated. Introduced into Hawaii in 1895, it has seriously curtailed the production there of melons, cucumbers, and tomatoes and has made it almost impossible to grow cantaloupes in the Honolulu area. More than 80 other species of plants may be hosts, including chayote, Chinese cucumber, Chinese melon, cowpea, gourds, squash, beans, and pumpkin as preferred hosts and bellapple, eggplant, fig, mango, orange, papaya, and peach as occasional hosts. The fly is ¼ inch long with wingspread of ½ inch, yellow-brown body with canary-yellow and dark-brown markings between the wings. Malathion bait sprays are largely used for control.

Mexican Fruit Fly*, *Anastrepha ludens* (Loew). A Mexican pest, operating over the border into Texas. This citrus insect is as serious in Mexico as the Mediterranean fruit fly is in Mediterranean countries, but there are fewer host plants and not such wide distribution. It is primarily a pest of citrus fruits and mangoes, but sapotas, peaches, guavas, apples, pears, quinces, plums, apricots and other fruits are included in quarantine regulations against the Mexican fruit fly. It is larger than a housefly, conspicuously marked in yellow or brown, and lays many white eggs under the skin of fruits. Larvae take about 6 weeks for development, first in the rind, later in the pulp. Pupation is in the ground and there are 4 generations a year. By a cooperative agreement the United States conducts eradication measures in adjacent portions of Mexico to keep the flies from crossing the border. Fruit from the regulated area in Texas is treated to kill any possible larvae before being shipped.

Mushroom Flies, *Sciara* spp. Fungus gnats, often troublesome in potted plants in homes and greenhouses. The plants may lack vigor and lose color without visible injury to aboveground parts, although there may be small scars on the roots or fine roots may be eaten off. Small, active, threadlike white maggots are either in the root tissue or in the soil around plants. They may be followed by root rots. Adults—very small, sooty gray to black, long-legged, ⅛ to 1/10 inch long—deposit eggs in clusters which hatch in 4 to 6 days. Maggots feed for 5 to 14 days, pupate, and the adults live about a week. Generations follow rapidly. Because they breed in manure and decaying vegetable matter, potting soil rich in humus is very likely to have these flies.

Control. Spray the soil with malathion or chlordane. Dust plants with DDT, lindane, chlordane or pyrethrum.

Narcissus Bulb Fly*, *Lampetia equestris* (Fabricius). A European species introduced here in bulbs. This large, hairy, yellow-and-black fly, about the size and appearance of a small bumblebee, lays eggs on or near crowns of narcissus (preferred host) and, amaryllis (much favored). Although hyacinths, lilies, scilla, tulips, and iris are often listed, they are merely accidental hosts with larvae failing to mature. The list of true hosts, according to observation in bulb fields, includes cooperia, eurycles, galanthus, galtonia, habranthus, hymenocallis, leucojum, pancratium, sprekelia, vallota, zephyranthes, and cipollini. Ordinarily but one maggot develops in each bulb. It is fat, white to yellow, wrinkled, ½ to ¾ inch long. It soon reduces the bulb contents to a soft brown mass. Puparia are formed in either bulbs or soil; there is usually 1 generation. Plants with infested bulbs have yellow, stunted foliage or almost no growth. The bulbs feel spongy when squeezed.

Control. In home gardens discard all bulbs that feel soft to the touch. Protect amaryllis put out of doors for the summer with a covering of cheesecloth in early summer to keep the flies from laying eggs. Commercial growers have used hot-water treatment, fumigation with methyl bromide and other means to kill larvae in the bulbs, but bulbs already infested may be of poor quality. Preplanting treatments give almost complete protection from attacks by the bulb fly in the field. Soak bulbs in heptachlor (1 pint to 25 gallons of water or 4 teaspoons to 1 gallon); or aldrin (2 pints to 25 gallons or 8 teaspoons to 1 gallon; dieldrin (½ pint of 18 per cent emulsion to 25 gallons or 2 teaspoons to 1 gallon; or chlordane (1 pint of 75 per cent emulsion to 25 gallons, or 4 teaspoons to 1 gallon. It is also possible to treat the soil, applying dust to the furrow before planting and then shaking dust over the bulbs after placing. Use 5 per cent chlordane, 2½ per cent heptachlor, or 1½ per cent dieldrin. Put the dust in a jar with holes punched in the lid.

Olive Fruit Fly*, *Dacus oleae* (Gmelin). Present in Hawaii but not yet in continental United States; often intercepted at quarantine.

Onion Bulb Fly*, *Eumerus strigatus* (Fallén). Similar to the lesser bulb fly and apparently confused with it. Reported on onions, sweetpotatoes, and carrots.

Orchidfly*, *Eurytoma orchidearum* (Westwood). Cattleya Fly, a serious orchid pest in greenhouses. The small, black, wasplike fly, ⅛ inch long, lays eggs in new growth and sometimes in pseudobulbs, causing swollen places; larvae feed in bulbs, stems, leaves, and buds of many kinds of orchids. Cut out the swollen areas; spray or dust with DDT to kill flies.

Oriental Fruit Fly*, *Dacus dorsalis* Hendel. Not established in continental United States, but a few specimens were found in traps in California in 1960. It is frequently intercepted in baggage from Hawaii, where it was established in 1946 to become a very serious pest. It attacks more than 150 kinds of fruits and vegetables, including citrus, guava, mango, papaya, banana, loquat, avocado, tomato, Surinam cherry, rose-apple, passion fruit, peach, pear, apricot, fig, and coffee. The female adult, larger than a house-fly, mostly yellow with dark markings, inserts eggs under the fruit skin.

Papaya Fruit Fly*, *Toxotrypana curvicauda* Gerstaecker. Common on papayas and also on mangoes in southern Florida dooryards. The female has a very long ovipositor which penetrates through the fruit. The larvae feed on seeds, then eat their way out of the fruit. Remove from the tree all fruits that yellow prematurely; pick up and destroy all dropped fruit. Bait sprays, used as for the Mediterranean fruit fly, can be used in control.

Potato Scab Gnat*, *Pnyxia scabiei* (Hopkins). A slender, black-headed maggot, only ⅙ inch long, occasionally infesting tubers in low ground or those stored in damp places. The superficial wounds resemble potato scab.

Syrphid Flies. These are the bright-colored flower flies or hover flies, family Syrphidae. They resemble bees hovering over flowers to feed on nectar and are important in pollination. They are also attracted to tree sap and fermenting fruit. The larvae of a few species, including the narcissus bulb fly, feed on plants and some feed on decaying animals and vegetable matter, but the majority are predaceous on aphids, mealybugs, and other insects and are decidedly friends in the garden. Adults lay white, elongate eggs, singly, among groups of aphids. The larvae are footless, sluglike, tan or greenish; if you see some of these on your rosebuds, withhold sprays for a few days and give the maggots a chance to clean up. They have pointed jaws with which they grasp an aphid, raise it into the air, and suck out all the body contents, leaving the empty skin. A single larva is credited with destroying an aphid a minute over long periods of time and there may be many larvae in a garden.

Tachinid Flies. A most beneficial group, Tachinidae, with all species parasitic on other insects. Most resemble overgrown houseflies; bristly, gray, brown, or black, mottled, without bright colors; usually found resting on foliage or flowers. Eggs are more often glued to the skin of the host insect, sometimes laid on foliage where the insect will eat them along with the leaf. The larvae feed internally on their hosts, which almost always die. Many species have been imported for our benefit. One, brought in to help control gypsy and brown-tail moths, parasitizes over 100 species of caterpillars. Many are parasitic on cutworms and armyworms.

Walnut Husk Fly*, *Rhagoletis completa* Cresson. Native in the central states on wild black walnuts, injurious to English, black, and other walnuts in California, also a pest in Utah and sometimes attacking peaches as well as walnuts. The adult, a little smaller than a housefly, has transparent wings with dark transverse crossbars. The females deposit eggs in cavities below the surface of the husk; the maggots tunnel through the husks for several weeks, then drop to the ground or fall with the nuts, to pupate in the soil. Some emerge as flies the next season, others remain in the ground for another year. The decaying husk stains the shell indelibly, making walnuts unsalable even though the kernels are sound. Recommendations for California growers call for spraying with malathion or parathion, the first treatment applied when adult flight is regular in late July or early August, and the second 25 days later. A few predators aid slightly in control.

Another walnut husk fly, *Rhagoletis suavis* (Osten Sacken), is present in eastern states, staining hulls of black walnuts. They become slimy and stick to the nuts. This species is reported in Ohio, Delaware, Maryland and other states.

West Indian Fruit Fly*, *Anastrepha mombinpraeoptans* Sein. Sometimes reported caught in traps in Texas; found lightly infesting mango in Florida in 1962.

FRUITWORMS

Fruitworms are caterpillars or grubs infesting fruit.

Cherry Fruitworm*, *Grapholitha packardi* Zeller. Larva of a native moth found from Colorado north and west. The worms hibernate in bark cells or stubs of pruned branches. Small gray moths deposit eggs singly on cherries in May or early June. Hatching in 10 days, the pinkish larvae, ⅜ inch long when grown, bore into the fruit, often causing huge losses. There is 1 generation. Sprays for cherry fruit fly control the fruitworm in the Pacific Northwest. Parathion and methoxychlor sprays have been effective in Colorado.

Cranberry Fruitworm*, *Acrobasis vaccinii* Riley. Present in nearly every cranberry bog, also infesting blueberries. The moth is ash-gray mottled with black, has a ¾-inch wingspread. It lays eggs on berries in July; pale-green larvae eat into berries near the stem, closing the hole with silk. One larva eats out the pulp of 2 or 3 berries before attaining full size, ⅞ inch. There is 1 generation. Infested berries shrivel, and on Cape Cod nearly half the crop may be lost. Spray or dust with ryania or rotenone. Control recommendations include flooding bogs for 10 to 14 days after harvesting and early in May.

All infested berries removed by screening should be destroyed. Methoxychlor has controlled this fruitworm in blueberries.

Eastern Raspberry Fruitworm*, *Byturus rubi* Barber. Most destructive to raspberry and loganberry in northern states. Light-brown beetles, ⅛ to 1/16 inch long, feed on buds, blossoms, and tender leaves, and lay eggs on blossoms and young fruits. Slender grubs, white with brown patches, bore into fruits, making them unfit for eating. As the fruit ripens, larvae drop to the ground and pupate in soil. They winter as adults, still in the soil, emerging just about mid-April. Dusting with 1 per cent rotenone or 5 per cent DDT just after blossom buds show and again just before blooms open is helpful. Cultivate the soil thoroughly in late summer.

Gooseberry Fruitworm*, *Zophodia convolutella* (Hübner). Present in northern states on currants and gooseberries. The moth has ashy wings with dark markings; the larva is yellow green with a pinkish cast, darker lines along the sides. Pupae winter in the ground; moths lay eggs in flowers. Larvae completely hollow out fruit, one worm destroying several berries. Spray with rotenone when webbing is noticed; repeat in 7 to 10 days. Destroy infested berries.

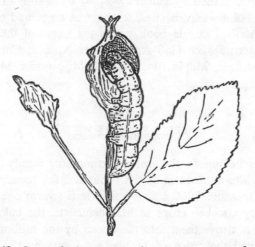

49. Green fruitworm feeding on young apple.

Green Fruitworm*, *Lithophane antennata* (Walker). Generally distributed over eastern states. The larvae feed on foliage of apple, ash, maple, and other deciduous trees and in green fruits of apple, pear, and cherry. The moths emerge in fall, hibernate in woodlands or sheltered nooks in the orchard. They lay eggs in early spring on twigs and branches. The larvae are apple-green with white stripes and slightly raised tubercles, up to 1½ inches long. They eat out the side or one end of young apples, destroying them entirely or making them worthless. Spray with DDT or lead arsenate at the cluster bud stage, when fruit buds have separated but before they open. Later sprays for codling moth have little effect on fruitworms.

Sparganothis Fruitworm, *Sparganothis sulphuriana* Fabricius. Cranberry Sparganothis, Blueberry Leaf Roller. One of the tortricid leaf-rolling moths. Usually controlled in cranberry bogs with parathion plus DDT.

Tomato Fruitworm. See Corn Earworm under Earworms.

Western Raspberry Fruitworm*, *Byturus bakeri* Barber. Similar to the eastern raspberry fruitworm.

GALLS

Insect galls are swellings or deformities of plant tissues resulting from the irritation caused by the feeding of the insect or by a toxin injected during the feeding process. Such plant abnormalities may be blisters or projections on the leaves, swellings on stem or twig, bud galls, flower galls, or root galls. The late Dr. E. P. Felt stated in his book *Plant Galls and Gall Makers* that there were more than 2000 American insect galls—805 the work of gall wasps, nearly 700 caused by gall midges, 80 by aphids or psyllids, and the rest by sawflies, jointworms, beetles, moths, true bugs, and mites.

Galls are described in this book under the name of the insect producing them: e.g., Eastern Spruce Gall Aphid under Aphids; Chrysanthemum Gall Midge under Midges; Maple Bladder Gall Mite under Mites; Mossy Rose Gall under Wasps.

GRASSHOPPERS

Grasshoppers belong to the order Orthoptera, family Acrididae (=Locustidae). They are the locusts of the Bible and the locusts that even in our own time may measure 2000 square miles in a swarm over the Red Sea. In 1740, when they attacked crops in Massachusetts, the colonists, armed with bundles of brush, drove them into the ocean by the millions. In 1818 grasshoppers destroyed the crops of Montana settlers; in 1877 they halted the covered wagons rolling west. Yearly damages still run into many millions, but much better control measures have been developed in the last few years.

Grasshoppers are moderately long insects, slightly deeper than wide, usually dark, mottled, with prominent jaws and eyes, antennae always much shorter than the body, and an "ear," hearing organ, or tympanum, on each side of the first abdominal segment. Their hind legs are enlarged for jumping, and the abdomen of the female ends in 4 hard, movable prongs which function like a miniature posthole digger when she is inserting her eggs an inch or so into the ground. The eggs are laid in masses of 15 to 50, according to species, and surrounded by a gummy substance which hardens to form a case, the whole being called an egg pod. Grasshoppers feed in the daytime in the sun. They are most numerous in states where the average rainfall is between 10 and 30 inches, attacking cultivated crops and range vegetation, destroying clothing and fabrics in houses, polluting water in wells and reservoirs, presenting a hazard to motorists.

There are about 600 species in the United States, 5 of them doing 90 per cent of the damage to crop plants.

American Grasshopper*, *Schistocerca americana* (Drury). Sometimes damaging field crops and fruits, including citrus, in Alabama, Georgia, Florida, Louisiana, and Mississippi. It is large—2½ inches long, with wingspread of 4 inches; colored tan, white, and pink.

Carolina Grasshopper*, *Dissosteira carolina* (Linnaeus). Not very destructive but common through the country, numerous along roadsides in late summer. It is brown, mottled with gray and red, hind wings black with yellow margins, nearly 2 inches long, flies readily when disturbed.

Clear-winged Grasshopper*, *Camnula pellucida* (Scudder). Variable in color, yellow to dark brown with black spots, 1 inch long, migratory habits. Generally distributed but most damaging in Utah, Wyoming, Montana, and Idaho on grains, grasses, garden crops, vineyards, orchards. Egg pods may be numerous in breeding areas. Plowing up such areas is quite effective in controlling this particular grasshopper.

Devastating Grasshopper*, *Melanoplus devastator* Scudder. Found west of the Rocky Mountains, migrating periodically from the mountains to the valleys. This species is small, yellow-brown with a row of elongated black spots, with hind tarsi blue at the base, yellow at the tips.

Differential Grasshopper*, *Melanoplus differentialis* (Thomas). Usually yellow with contrasting black markings, clear, glossy outer wings, 1½ inches long; hind thighs with black bars like chevrons. Fairly rare in the East, it feeds on succulent field and garden crops; in other sections on deciduous fruit trees. In dry years this species persists only in irrigated areas or along streams.

Eastern Lubber Grasshopper*, *Romalea microptera* (Beauvois). Sometimes called Florida Lubber, a large, stout, short-winged, clumsy locust attacking grass, flowers, and ornamental trees and shrubs in Florida and other southern states.

Green-striped Grasshopper*, *Chortophaga viridifasciata* (De Geer). In Nebraska and Wisconsin on forage crops.

High Plains Grasshopper*, *Dissosteira longipennis* (Thomas). Gregarious and migratory, on high ranges and prairies, destroying grasses but not often feeding on cultivated crops. Front wings (tegmina) are long, spotted brown; rear wings are blue at the base, black toward the disk.

Lubber Grasshopper*, *Brachystola magna* (Girard). Ranging east of the Rocky Mountains and in the Great Basin, common and injurious from Montana to New Mexico. It is long, to 2½ inches, with rear wings pinkish and reduced in size.

Migratory Grasshopper*, *Melanoplus sanguinipes* (Fabricius). Found throughout the United States, sometimes migrating in swarms hundreds of miles, destroying crops and range plants wherever it stops. This species is reddish brown, with an irregular black patch on the neck; about 1 inch long.

Packard Grasshopper*, *Melanoplus packardii* Scudder. Occurring throughout the West, often injurious to pasture grasses. It is yellowish-brown with red or blue hind legs; about 1 inch long.

Red-legged Grasshopper*, *Melanoplus femurrubrum* (De Geer). Reddish-brown above, sulfur-yellow underneath, wings colorless, hind legs red, ¾ inch long. It is common along roadsides and is injurious to legumes, particularly to soybeans in the Middle West, where it cuts through pods, causing seeds to mold. It also feeds on other truck crops, vines, and fruit trees.

Rocky Mountain Grasshopper*, *Melanoplus spretus* (Walsh). Formerly migrating in huge swarms from the Plains east of the Rocky Mountains to the Mississippi Valley and Texas, but its place is now taken by the migratory grasshopper. This species is brown with dark markings, bright-red hind legs; 1¼ inches long.

Two-striped Grasshopper*, *Melanoplus bivittatus* (Say). Common, widely distributed pest of grains, vegetables, fruit trees, all cultivated crops. It is stout, 1¼ inches long, greenish yellow with two light stripes down its back.

Control. Until the advent of chlordane, poison-bran baits were the chief means of fighting grasshoppers, but now dusting or spraying with chemicals is considered more effective and economical. Insecticides in use, with recommended dosages of the actual chemical per acre are: aldrin, 1½ to 2 ounces; chlordane, ½ to 1 pound; dieldrin, ¾ to 1 ounce; heptachlor, 3 to 4 ounces; toxaphene, 1 to 1½ pounds. These can be applied as sprays or dusts, with ground equipment or by airplane. If used as dusts, increase dosage per acre by 50 per cent. In home gardens, dust ornamentals with chlordane, lindane, or DDT; use methoxychlor for fruits and vegetables near the edible stage.

Grasshoppers have many natural enemies, including flies, blister beetles, ground beetles, spiders, hairworms, rodents, birds, and fungus and bacterial diseases.

GROUND PEARLS
(See under Scale Insects)

HORNTAILS

Horntails are related to wasps, in the order Hymenoptera. Most are in the family Siricidae and are also called wood wasps. A few are stem sawflies, family Cephidae.

True horntails, family Siricidae, are fairly large, an inch or more long, with a horny, spearlike plate on the 1st abdominal segment. The females are thick-waisted, cylindrical, with a long hornlike ovipositor that resembles a stinger. They alight on freshly felled injured or dying trees and insert the ovipositor deeply into the wood to deposit eggs. The larvae are cylindrical, yellowish-white, with a small spine at the rear of the body which is often held in the shape of the letter S. They work in solid wood without any opening to the outside. They make circular holes in the wood and pack their boring dust in the tunnels behind them. Pupal cells are constructed near the surface of the wood, and when the adults mature, they cut round emergence holes to the surface.

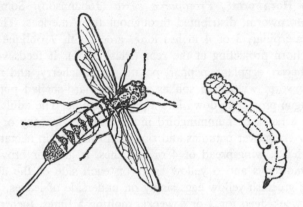

50. A typical horntail with larva.

Horntails are more common in the West, being partial to western conifers. An eastern species called Pigeon Tremex is discussed under borers.

Blue Horntail*, *Sirex cyaneus* Fabricius.

California Horntail, *Sirex californicus* (Ashmcad). Uniformly dark blue with hyaline wings, infesting pines in Pacific Coast states. Another horntail, *Urocerus californicus* (Norton) infests true firs, Douglas-fir, sometimes pine. It is the largest of western species, the females 1¼ to 2 inches long, black with yellow markings and an ovipositer only slightly shorter than the body.

Raspberry Horntail, *Hartigia cressoni* (Kirby). One of the stem sawflies, a western species, injuring young shoots of blackberry, loganberry, raspberry, and rose. Bright yellow-and-black females appear in April and May to insert eggs with a curved point under epidermis of tender tips of host plants. The larvae spirally girdle the tips, causing wilting and death. An eastern species, *H. trimaculata,* is known as the Rose Stem Sawfly. See under Sawflies.

Western Horntail, *Sirex areolatus* (Cresson). Attacking redwood, cypress, cedars, sometimes pines. It is metallic blue with black legs and smoky wings.

HORNWORMS

Hornworms are large caterpillars, larvae of sphinx moths (family Sphingidae) bearing a pointed projection at the end of the body that looks like a horn. The tobacco and tomato hornworms, commonly found in gardens, feed rather interchangeably on tobacco, tomato and other solanaceous hosts. Hornworms named for their adult stage are discussed under Moths. See Achemon Sphinx, Catalpa Sphinx and White-lined Sphinx in that section.

Sweetpotato Hornworm*, *Agrius cingulatus* (Fabricius). A southern species, common in Louisiana, reported from Delaware.

Tobacco Hornworm*, *Protoparce sexta* (Johannson). Sometimes called Southern Hornworm, distributed throughout the Americas. This is an awe-inspiring caterpillar, 3 or 4 inches long, green with 7 oblique white stripes and a red horn projecting at the rear (Plate XIX). It feeds voraciously on tomato, tobacco, eggplant, pepper, potato, groundcherry, and related weeds.

The hornworm winters in soil as a brown, hard-shelled pupa that has a slender tongue projecting down like a pitcher handle. The adult sphinx moth, also called a hawk or hummingbird moth, emerges in May or June to feed at dusk, hovering over petunias and similar flowers to sip nectar with its long tongue. It has a wingspread of 4 or 5 inches, is gray or brown with white and dark mottlings and 6 yellow spots on each side of the abdomen. The female lays greenish-yellow eggs singly on underside of leaves. Young larvae hatch in a week, feed for 3 or 4 weeks, molting 5 times, then pupate 3 or 4 inches deep in the soil. There is 1 generation in the North, 2 or more in the South.

Control. Picking off caterpillars by hand is often sufficient control in the small garden. If hornworms are too numerous, keep plants dusted with 5 per cent TDE. Peppers can be sprayed or dusted with DDT but this may be injurious to tomatoes. Treatment should cease before fruit is half grown to prevent toxic residues. The bacterial *Bacillus thuringiensis* preparations are effective against hornworms and leave no undesirable residue.

Do not destroy caterpillars covered with oval white objects attached to the skin by one end. These are cocoons of a parasitic braconid wasp. The female thrusts her eggs inside the hornworm body; when the larvae hatch they feed for a while inside the caterpillar, then eat their way outside to spin cocoons. If left undisturbed more wasps will emerge to parasitize other hornworms. See Figure 89.

Tomato Hornworm*, *Protoparce quinquemaculata* (Haworth). Almost identical with the tobacco species, feeding on the same plants, controlled in the same way. There are 5 instead of 6 yellow spots on each side of the abdomen of the moth, and 2 narrow stripes extending diagonally across each hind wing. The larva has 8 instead of 7 diagonal white stripes and they join a horizontal white stripe, forming a series of V's. The horn is green with black sides.

KATYDIDS

Katydids, order Orthoptera, family Tettigoniidae, are long-horned grasshoppers, characterized by long, hairlike antennae; 4-segmented tarsi; auditory organs, when present, at the base of front tibiae (in true grasshoppers the "ear" is on the abdomen); and a swordlike ovipositor in the female. The males sing by rubbing front wings together, each species having a characteristic song. They are mostly plant feeders but cannot always be called garden pests. Control measures are unnecessary in many areas.

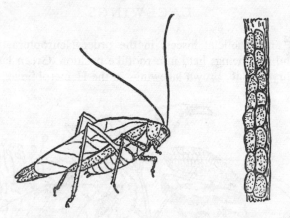

51. Angular-winged katydid and eggs.

Angular-winged Katydid*, *Microcentrum retinerve* (Burmeister). Like the broad-winged katydid but smaller, found chiefly in the southern part of the United States. It is reported feeding on orange leaves.

Broad-winged Katydid*, *Microcentrum rhombifolium* (Saussure). Widely distributed in the East; leaf-green, about 1½ inches long. This species is best-known for its eggs, grayish brown, oval, very flat, ¼ inch long, laid on twigs in double rows, each egg overlapping the next. Gardeners, astonished at the sight of such a prominent display of large eggs, often fear they have a new garden menace.

Fork-tailed Bush Katydid*, *Scudderia furcata* Brunner von Wattenwyl. Widely distributed, taking its name from forked appendages at the tip of the male abdomen. Arboreal in habit, pale green, medium size, with long narrow tegmina (wing covers). Eggs are laid in the edges of leaves between upper and lower leaf surfaces.

Japanese Broad-winged Katydid*, *Holochlora japonica* (Brunner von Wattenwyl).

Northern Katydid, *Pterophylla camellifolia* (Fabricius). True Katydid, also called Eastern Katydid, heard after dusk in late summer saying, "Katy did, Katy didn't." The song is made by special stridulating organs on the wings of the males, though the females can make faint sounds. The tegmina are dark green, very broad, longer than the hind wings and entirely enclose the abdomen. This species lives in small colonies in dense foliage of forest and shade trees and is more often heard than seen. Dark, slate-colored eggs are thrust by the female ovipositor into crevices or loose bark or into soft stems of woody plants. The eggs are large, ¼ inch long, pointed at each end. The northern katydid ranges from New England to Georgia and west to Illinois.

LACEWINGS

Lacewings are beneficial insects in the order Neuroptera, with membranous front and hind wings held in a rooflike position. Green lacewings are in the family Chrysopidae, brown lacewings in the Hemerobiidae.

52. Golden-eye lacewing: stalked eggs, aphid-lion larva, pupa case, adult.

Golden-eye Lacewing*, *Chrysopa oculata* Say. The adult has beautiful gauzy green wings, long hairlike antennae, and iridescent red-gold eyes. She lays her oval eggs singly at the end of hairlike stalks so that her cannibalistic offspring cannot eat each other as they hatch. The larvae, called Aphid-lions, are ugly creatures with double sickle-shaped jaws for capturing prey. The body is flat, tapering at both ends, yellow or gray mottled with red or brown, with projecting hairs or bristles; up to ⅓ inch long. The larvae puncture and suck the juice from aphids, mealybugs, cottony-cushion scales, sometimes thrips and mites. They have a habit of carrying the remains of their victims piled up on the back. The larva pupates in a globular white cocoon, often on the underside of a leaf, and the adult cuts out a small lid that swings back as on a hinge as she emerges.

The golden-eye lacewing is the one common in eastern gardens, but its place is taken in the West by the **California Green Lacewing,** *Chrysopa californica* Coquillett, which is similar.

Pacific Brown Lacewing, *Hemerobius pacificus* Banks. Important predators on red spiders and other mites, sometimes feeding on aphids. Brown lacewings are smaller than the green lacewings and less conspicuous. The adult varies from pale to dark brown and the body is covered with short fine hairs. The larva is spindle-shaped, known as an Aphid-wolf.

Slender Brown Lacewing, *Sympherobius angustus* (Banks). The adult is very small, slender, brown throughout. The larvae feed on many species of mealybugs, so that this species is perhaps the most beneficial of western lacewings.

There are many other species of green and brown lacewings, all useful, particularly on forage crops where chemicals may not be used because of residues. There are, however, hymenopterus parasites that attack the lacewings and reduce this potential help.

LEAF CRUMPLER

Leaf Crumpler*, *Acrobasis indigenella* (Zeller). Abundant in Upper Mississippi Valley and some other northern states on apple, plum, prune, crabapple, quince, cherry, wild cherry, wild plum and pear. The caterpillar is dark brown, somewhat hairy, ⅓ to ½ inch long. It winters in cocoons ¾ to 1½ inches long, made by crumpling dead leaves and tightly fastening them to an apple twig. In spring, as apple buds open, the worms loosen their cases and feed on buds, fastening new leaves together with silken threads. They pupate in May and June. The moths, with brown, white-mottled wings, expanding only ¾ inch, lay eggs on new leaves. Young caterpillars, hatching in 2 or 3 weeks, make curved, cornucopia-shaped cases in which they feed for the rest of the season, then use for winter quarters.

In addition to its regular habitats the leaf crumpler has been reported on pyracantha in North Carolina and on cotoneaster in South Dakota.

Control. If trees are sprayed regularly for codling moth and other pests, leaf crumplers will not be much of a nuisance. If present, lead arsenate can be applied at cluster-bud, calyx, and 3 weeks after calyx stages. Young trees may be sprayed in August.

LEAF CUTTERS

Caterpillars that neatly cut out portions of leaves are called leaf cutters.

Maple Leaf Cutter*, *Paraclemensia acerifoliella* (Fitch). Also called Maple Casebearer, a native pest of sugar maple, sometimes beech, rarely on red maple and birch. The small caterpillar, not over ¼ inch long, dull white with rusty head and thorax, eats as a leaf miner for 10 to 14 days, then cuts out oval sections up to ½ inch in size, to make a case for overwintering in leaf litter. Foliage may be nearly destroyed. The moth, with iridescent blue fore wings, fringed, smoky brown hind wings, emerges in May. Control by raking and burning fallen leaves in autumn, spraying with lead arsenate and fish oil in June.

Morning-glory Leaf Cutter, *Loxostege obliteralis* (Walker). A greenish caterpillar with dark spots, ¾ inch long, resembling the garden webworm. It cuts off stalks as leaves wilt and eats large holes in leaves, hiding during the day in shelters made by rolling and folding wilted leaves. The adult is a yellowish moth with faint brown markings. Other hosts include dahlia, mint, sunflower, violet, wandering-Jew, and zinnia. Spray or dust with lead arsenate to kill young caterpillars; hand-pick others.

Waterlily Leaf Cutter*, *Synclita obliteralis* (Walker). The larvae of this moth are aquatic, breathing by means of gills, feeding on waterlily and other plants, often in greenhouses, in boatlike cases made by cutting oval pieces out of leaves and fastening them together with silk. Wind, blowing the cases around a pool, helps to spread the infestation. Foliage is reduced to a ragged, rotten mass. Gather and destroy cases. If infestation is severe, lower water in pool and spray or dust with malathion. Fish must be removed before treatment and not returned until the water has been changed.

LEAF FOLDER

Grape Leaf Folder*, *Desmia funeralis* (Hübner). Generally distributed east of the Rocky Mountains, also found in California, on wild and cultivated grapes, Virginia-creeper, and redbud. The caterpillar is glossy, translucent yellow-green on the sides, darker above, with brown head; 1 inch long. It feeds inside folded leaves. In the East, injury is little more than ragged foliage, but in California there may be extensive damage to late maturing grape varieties. Larval attacks are followed by decay of fruit; leaves are rolled tightly instead of being folded over. The moths—black with white markings, wing expanse ¾ to 1 inch—emerge from inside rolled or folded leaves for a summer brood. There are two or three generations in warm climates but only one in New England, where pupation is in the soil. In California the 3rd brood larvae may feed in the grape bunches, breaking the berry skins and allowing entrance to spoilage organisms.

Control. An arsenical spray is effective if applied before the leaves are folded (using 4 pounds lead arsenate to 100 gallons of water). Growers sometimes use parathion dust, 2 per cent, for the 2nd and 3rd broods. DDT is sometimes recommended for the early spray. There are a number of parasites.

LEAFHOPPERS

Leafhoppers belong to the insect order Hemiptera, suborder Homoptera, family Cicadellidae. There are around 175 genera and 2000 species in our country. Most of them are small, not over ½ inch long, and they feed on foliage of almost all types of plants, usually sucking from the under-surface and hopping away quickly when disturbed. They have piercing-sucking mouth parts and gradual metamorphosis, nymphs resembling adults except for wings. The two pairs of wings are of uniform texture and are held in a rooflike position when at rest. Leafhoppers have a long, wedge-shaped appearance, and the front margin of the head, as seen from above, is either triangular or broadly curved. The large eyes are at the side of the head and small, hairlike antennae arise in front of the eyes. There are 2 ocelli between the eyes and a double row of spines on the underside of the hind tibiae. They expel honeydew.

Withdrawal of plant sap from the host causes loss of color—often in a stippled pattern—sometimes stunting and general decline in vigor. Some leafhoppers cause a diseased condition in the plant known as hopperburn, which may be due to a toxin injected during the feeding process. Leafhoppers act as vectors of many important virus diseases: aster yellows, elm phloem necrosis, curly top of sugar beet and other plants, Pierce's disease of grapes, yellow dwarf of potatoes, peach yellows, cranberry false blossom and many others.

Leafhoppers are controlled largely by contact insecticides, formerly nicotine sulfate or pyrethrum, now largely by DDT, which is very efficient because of its long residual action.

Apple Leafhopper*, *Empoasca maligna* (Walsh). Common east of the Rocky Mountains except in the lower Mississippi Valley, also present in the Northwest. During late summer and fall apple foliage turns pale, the green upper surface flecked with many small white spots, the underside covered with dark bits of excrement, often white cast skins. Nymphs and adults are greenish white. There is 1 generation a year and no migration to another type of host, as with the potato leafhopper, but this species may infest roses as well as apples. Hibernation is in the egg stage under loose bark.

Beet Leafhopper*, *Circulifer tenellus* (Baker). A western species, found eastward to Illinois and Missouri, dangerous as a vector of curly top, a virus disease (Plate XXIV). The pale greenish or yellowish leafhoppers, ⅛ inch long, are darker toward winter, which they spend as adults on salt bush, Russian thistle, greasewood, filaree, and other wild hosts in arid foothills or desert. Egg laying takes place in March, and the first generation matures on these wild plants. From early May to June adults of this generation fly in swarms, often hundreds of miles, to sugar-beet fields. As they feed, they introduce the curly-top virus. They are the only known vectors of this disease, which makes the leaf veins warty, petioles kinked, leaves rolled and brittle on the edges, plants stunted and finally killed.

The leafhoppers insert their eggs in veins, leaf petioles, or stems. Nymphs hatch in 2 weeks, become adult in 3 to 8 weeks more. There may be 3 or more generations. When the sugar beets are plowed out, the leafhoppers, carrying the virus, swarm to neighboring gardens, infecting tomato, table beet, cantaloupe, celery, cucumber, pepper, spinach, squash, and other vegetables, and many flowers—geranium, nasturtium, pansy, zinnia among others. Symptoms in all plants are the same—curled leaves, stunting—often resulting in death.

Control. Although the leafhoppers can be killed by dusting or spraying with DDT, they may already have spread the disease. Rogue out plants with curly top as soon as noticed; eliminate Russian thistle and other winter weed hosts so far as possible. The fog belt along the coast of California is fairly free from leafhopper attack and there are a number of natural enemies.

Blunt-nosed Cranberry Leafhopper*, *Scleroracus vaccinii* (Van Duzee). Famous as the vector of cranberry false-blossom disease, found from Wisconsin east. The hopper is light brown, short, with a rounded, blunt nose. It winters in the egg stage and hatches in May; there is 1 brood a year. Flooding the bogs in late June when young nymphs are present, spraying or dusting with DDT or Sevin, and use of resistant varieties give fair control of the disease and its vector.

Bramble Leafhopper*, *Ribautiana tenerrima* (Herrich-Schäffer).

Clover Leafhopper*, *Aceratagallia sanguinolenta* (Provancher). Prevalent when potatoes are grown next to clover and vector of potato yellow dwarf. The virus winters in the adult leafhopper.

Grape Leafhopper, *Erythroneura elegantula* Osburn in the West, especially California, and *E. comes* (Say) in Ohio, Michigan, and elsewhere. Adults are slender, less than ⅛ inch long, yellow with red markings, active on grape, Virginia-creeper, apple and other plants. They winter among fallen grape leaves or grasses, feed on developing leaves in spring, inserting eggs in leaf tissue. The nymphs feed almost entirely from underside of leaves. There are 2 or more generations.

A third grape form, the **Variegated Leafhopper,** *Erythroneura variabilis* Beamer, is common in southern California. It is similar but somewhat darker in color.

Control. Home growers should spray or dust with DDT, malathion, or Sevin. Commercial growers sometimes use demeton, Trithion, or diazinon.

Japanese Leafhopper, *Orientus ishidae* (Matsumura). An introduced pest reported in 1919, now well distributed in northern fruit districts, known on apple, aralia, and hazel. It is larger than the apple leafhopper, ⅕ inch long, dark gray, wings milky with brown veins, legs black; nymphs brown with white spots. Leaves turn yellow where nymphs first congregate, often near water sprouts; later, triangular sections of leaves all over tree are killed. Damage may be extensive with weakening of tree. Eggs winter near base of trunk, being hatched in late May or early June. Spraying with DDT or parathion is effective.

Japanese Maple Leafhopper, *Japanus hyalinus* (Osborne). On Japanese and Norway maples.

Mountain Leafhopper*, *Colladonus montanus* (Van Duzee). A western species—small, brown with a yellow band—common on grasses, carrot, larkspur, goldenrod, apple, prune and many other plants, being abundant in mint fields. It is a vector of peach yellow leaf roll virus.

Norway-maple Leafhopper, *Alebra albostriella* (Fallén). Causing some injury near New York City. Swollen twigs on Norway maple, looking as if diseased, are produced by eggs laid under bark. Foliage is infested with numerous small, yellowish hoppers. They may also infest alder, birch, elm, and oak.

Painted Leafhopper*, *Endria inimica* (Say). On forage crops, legumes, lawn grasses, wild grapes and brambles, vector of wheat mosaic. Widespread, reported as abundant in Rhode Island and also Nebraska.

Plum Leafhopper*, *Macropsis trimaculata* (Fitch). An eastern pest important as the vector of peach yellows and little peach, virus diseases affecting peaches, nectarines, plums, almonds, apricots. The leafhoppers, blunt, short, with 3 dark spots, are strong fliers and may travel long distances, although usually staying near the tree where they were hatched. There is 1 generation, eggs laid on peach twigs in July and August not hatching until the next May.

Poplar Leafhopper, *Idiocerus scurra* (Germar) is occasionally abundant on Lombardy poplar. *I. pallidus* Fitch occurs on poplar and willow.

Potato Leafhopper*, *Empoasca fabae* (Harris). The most injurious potato pest in eastern United States, found in some western states, although there its place is usually taken by other species (intermountain, arid, and western potato leafhoppers). This small, ⅛ inch long, wedge-shaped green leafhopper, with white spots on head and thorax, plays many roles (Plate XIV). Down South, where it shines as a bean pest, it is called the "bean jassid." It is responsible for dahlia stunt, potato tipburn or hopperburn, peanut pouts, and other "diseases" as well as normal leafhopper injury.

Instead of hibernating in the North, the potato leafhopper winters in the Gulf States, breeding on alfalfa and other legumes and weeds. Coming north in spring, it feeds first on apple foliage, moving to beans as soon as the plants are up, often migrating suddenly in swarms. When potatoes are several inches high the hoppers move over to them, laying eggs in main veins and in petioles, each female laying 2 or 3 eggs a day for 3 or 4 weeks. The eggs hatch in 10 days with nymphs full-grown in about 2 weeks, at the fifth molt. There are 2 generations in the Middle Atlantic States, so that both early and late potatoes are infested.

On potato, eggplant, rhubarb, horsebean, dahlia and sometimes rose the condition known as hopperburn is prevalent. First a triangular brown spot appears at the tip of the leaf, then similar triangles at the end of each lateral leaflet, then the entire margin rolls inward and turns brown, often appearing scorched, with only a small part of each leaf along the midrib staying green. The yield of potatoes is cut enormously; dahlias may be so stunted they do not flower. I often find the tipburn effect on rose foliage in August but seldom any rolling. Authorities are not too clear on how this effect is produced. Some state that the potato leafhopper mechanically plugs the phloem and xylem vessels in the leaves so that transport of food materials is impaired.

On bean and apple, leafhopper feeding produces whitening of foliage and sometimes stunting, crinkling, and curling but not the brown, burned effect. In California the potato leafhopper punctures and blemishes the rind of citrus fruit.

Control. Spraying or dusting with DDT has become standard control, with applications started when plants are 4 to 8 inches high and repeated at 10- to 14-day intervals as long as the vines can be kept green. More recent work indicates that Sevin, Thiodan, and a DDT-Dibrom combination may be more effective than straight DDT. Parathion, for commercial growers, malathion, or methoxychlor are other possibilities.

For dahlias in home gardens DDT is still satisfactory—2 tablespoons of 50 per cent wettable powder to 1 gallon of water.

Privet Leafhopper, *Fieberiella florii* (Stål). A large species, widely distributed, recorded from many plants—privet, quince, peach, plum, cherry, currant, cotoneaster, myrtle, spirea, sometimes on legumes. It is a vector of peach yellow leaf curl virus, western X-disease, and western aster yellows.

A somewhat smaller leafhopper, *Osborniellus borealis* (DeLong & Wolcott), is also found on privet and myrtle.

Prune Leafhopper*, *Edwardsiana prunicola* (Edwards).

Red-banded Leafhopper, *Graphocephala coccinea* Foerst. Probably our most conspicuous leafhopper, with its wings gaudily decorated with alternate bands of magenta and green or blue. It is common on garden flowers, including aster, calendula, gladiolus, hollyhock, marigold, rose, and zinnia but the injury is not serious.

Rose Leafhopper*, *Edwardsiana rosae* (Linnaeus). Imported from Europe, attacking most plants of the rose family but primarily apple and rose,

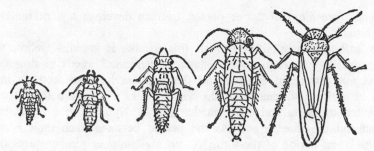

53. Stages in development of the rose leafhopper.

being especially serious on apple in the Northwest and reported also on dogwood and spirea. It hibernates in the egg stage, usually on rose canes or apple bark. The adults, creamy white to light yellow, ⅛ inch long, produce characteristic light stippling and sometimes a yellowing and slight curling of foliage but no hopperburn. Eggs for the 2nd generation, which defaces rose foliage late into the fall, are laid in July in leaf veins and petioles. DDT is very effective in controlling this leafhopper but it so enhances the mite problem on roses, I personally do not use it for the spring generation, getting along with pyrethrum and rotenone in my combination spray. But for the late fall brood, which is so much more serious in my section, I add DDT, 1 to 2 tablespoons of 50 per cent wettable powder, to each gallon of my combination spray. Malathion and Sevin are also recommended but they also may increase mites. Dimethoate, 1 teaspoon of Cygon per gallon, is another possibility.

Saddled Leafhopper*, *Colladonus clitellarius* (Say). An important vector of peach X-disease.

Sharp-nosed Leafhopper, *Scaphytopius magdalensis* (Provancher). Vector of blueberry stunt, a virus disease.

Six-spotted Leafhopper*, *Macrosteles fascifrons* (Stål). Aster Leafhopper. This species is tremendously important to gardeners because it transmits the virus disease known as aster yellows, not only to asters but to many other ornamentals, among them alyssum, anchusa, browallia, cape-marigold, cornflower, calendula, chrysanthemum, cineraria, clarkia, coreopsis, cosmos, gaillardia, gypsophila, lobelia, mignonette, petunia, phlox, poppy, rudbeckia, scabiosa, schizanthus, strawflower, sweet-william, vinca, and zinnia. Lettuce and celery are particularly subject to yellows, and the virus may also cause disease symptoms on carrot, parsnip, parsley, and other vegetables as well as grain crops. Symptoms vary with the different plants but there is usually a general yellowing of foliage rather than a mottling or mosaic. There is a clearing of affected veins, plants are always stunted and usually distorted, with excessive branching and shortening of internodes along with virescence (greening) of flower petals. Lettuce develops a condition known as rabbit ear.

The leafhopper responsible for all this trouble is greenish yellow with 6 black spots. It winters in the egg stage on perennial weeds or flowers. The virus is not carried in the egg and the hoppers have to feed on infected plants in spring and then hold the virus 10 to 18 days before it can be transmitted to asters and other garden plants. Nymphs in early instars do not transmit the disease because the period between each molt is shorter than the latent period of the virus. At normal summer temperatures the life cycle is about 40 days, so there may be several generations a season.

Control. DDT or other sprays or dusts will reduce leafhopper populations but not entirely eliminate aster yellows. Commercial growers protect their asters with cheesecloth or muslin, not coarser than 20 threads to the inch, on wooden frames. In home gardens all diseased plants should be rogued immediately, before the virus can be spread.

Southern Garden Leafhopper*, *Empoasca solana* DeLong. Similar to the potato leafhopper but with a more southern distribution, although occurring in New York. It infests flowers and other ornamentals, aster, dahlia, willow, amaranthus, tamarix, and potato, peanut, grape, cantaloupe, sweetpotatoes, and other fruits and vegetables.

Three-banded Leafhopper*, *Erythroneura tricincta* Fitch. On grape, Virginia-creeper, apple, and other plants. Much like the grape leafhopper and more injurious in some states. It makes a very coarse stippling.

Virginia-creeper Leafhopper*, *Erythroneura ziczac* (Walsh). Another species similar to the grape leafhopper, feeding on grape, elm, Boston ivy and Virginia-creeper, which may have foliage almost completely whitened.

Western Potato Leafhopper, *Empoasca abrupta* DeLong. Similar to the potato leafhopper.

White-banded Elm Leafhopper*, *Scaphoideus luteolus* Van Duzee. Vector of elm phloem necrosis, which has killed so many elms in Ohio and neighboring states. Eggs wintered on elm bark hatch about May 1; nymphs crawl to leaves and feed on veins; adults move from diseased to healthy trees. DDT-xylene sprays are used as for elm bark beetles.

White Apple Leafhopper, *Typlocyba pomaria* McAtee. On apple, rose, sometimes currant, gooseberry, raspberry. Winter is passed in the egg stage underneath bark of small apple branches, and the small greenish nymphs hatch when apple blossoms are at the pink stage. Adults lay eggs in July and second-generation nymphs feed in August and early September, adults being most numerous in late September and October. Apple foliage is blanched white and after that the hoppers move in great numbers to nearby rose gardens. The foliage shows a rather coarse stippling and the underside is covered with shiny black dots of fecal deposits. DDT and parathion are both effective on apple. Home gardeners should use DDT, Sevin or other safe material on roses.

Willow Leafhoppers, *Keonolla* spp. Often abundant on willows and poplars along watercourses in western states, sometimes entering houses.

Yellow-headed Leafhopper*, *Carnocephala flaviceps* (Riley). A western species, small, pale green with yellow head, feeding on grass and grains.

LEAF MINERS

Leaf miners are insects which feed between the two leaf surfaces. They may be larvae of flies, moths, sawflies, or beetles. They make blisters or blotch mines or serpentine tunnels and, because they are protected by the host plant most of their lives, control has been difficult, depending on an exact knowledge of the life history of each individual miner. New chemicals have provided more effective control methods, but detailed knowledge is still necessary as to chemical required and best time of application. DDT has been satisfactory for some leaf miners, less effective for others. Lindane is satisfactory in many instances.

Apple Leaf Blotch Miner, *Phyllonorycter crataegella* (Clemens). Widespread, mining leaves of apple, crabapple, hawthorn, and wild cherry. Another species, *P. malifoliella,* may also injure apple leaves, sometimes enough to reduce fruit size.

Apple Leaf Trumpet Miner*, *Tischeria malifoliella* Clemens. On apple (preferred), blackberry, raspberry, and hawthorn. Numerous trumpet-shaped mines are made in leaves, pupation taking place there. Very small moths, dark with narrow, fringed wings, emerge through slits in the leaves. There are 2 or more broods. Special control measures are not always needed. DDT or parathion is effective.

Arborvitae Leaf Miner*, *Argyresthia thuiella* (Packard). Distributed from Maine to Missouri, common in home plantings. Very small larvae—⅕ inch long, green with a reddish tinge and black head, short bristles across the back of each segment—mine in the terminal leaves, eating out the inside. The mined tips turn yellow or whitish, finally brown, and stand out prominently against normal green foliage. In the most severe cases all the foliage is mined and the shrubs turn brown all over. Small gray moths, wingspread only ⅓ inch, emerge from mined leaves in May and June to lay eggs which hatch in late June. For a few plants the easiest control is to cut off and burn discolored tips. DDT sprays are effective but are followed by serious mite infestations. Spraying with nicotine sulfate—2½ teaspoons per gallon of slightly soapy water—in July, helps to kill newly hatched larvae.

Two other leaf miners also infest arborvitae.

Asparagus Miner*, *Melanagromyza simplex* (Loew). Present through the Northeast and in California on asparagus but rather a minor pest. Maggots of a small fly mine in the stalks just below the soil surface. Foliage may turn yellow and die prematurely. Puparia winter in the larval tunnels and the flies appear in late May to lay eggs, with adults of a second generation abroad in July. Pull up and burn old stalks to destroy puparia. Plant rust-resistant strains which are also more resistant to the miner.

Aspen Blotch Miner*, *Lithocolletis tremuloidiella* (Braun). Present in California, Idaho, Utah, abundant in Wisconsin, making irregular mines in leaves of aspen and other poplars, resulting in premature defoliation. The adult is a small, drab moth.

Aspen Leaf Miner, *Phyllocnistis populiella* Chambers. Leaving a labyrinthian trail of frass on underside of aspen and poplar leaves. It has caused epidemics in Wyoming and Idaho forests, with trees stunted and many killed.

Azalea Leaf Miner*, *Gracilaria azaleella* Brants. Azalea Leaf Roller, found in most states where azaleas are grown but more of a greenhouse than a garden pest in the North; often injurious in Southern nurseries and gardens. Eggs are laid in leaves by a small moth, marked with purple and yellow, wing expanse ½ inch. Small yellow caterpillars hatch in 4 days, enter the leaves, and feed between surfaces, causing blisters. When partly grown, the larvae emerge and start to roll leaves at the tip, feeding inside the protection of the roll. A cocoon is made inside a leaf rolled in from the margin. Spray with lindane or malathion. DDT is effective but may injure some varieties.

Basswood Leaf Miner*, *Baliosus ruber* (Weber). A pest of basswood throughout its range, known also on oak, linden, and apple. The adult is a reddish-yellow, wedge-shaped beetle which winters under leaves and trash, becomes active in May, skeletonizing the foliage. Eggs are laid singly in feeding areas and covered with excrement. The larvae start feeding into the leaves in single mines, then several join together in a common mine. Spiny pupae appear in the mines in August; beetles emerge to do more feeding before hibernation. Spray spring or fall, when beetles are feeding, with lindane or lead arsenate.

Beet Leaf Miner*, *Pegomya betae* (Curtis). Maggot of a fly.

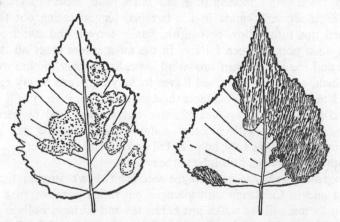

54. Birch leaf miner: initial blotch mines and final blighted leaf.

Birch Leaf Miner*, *Fenusa pusilla* (Lepeletier). An imported sawfly, first discovered in Connecticut in 1923 and now a major scourge in New England, New York, New Jersey, Pennsylvania, and a recent pest in Oregon. Infested trees look as if they had been blighted by a disease. Gray, paper, and European white birches are most favored, in woods and in home plantings. The mature larva—½ inch long, rather flat, whitish with black spots on underside of thorax and first abdominal segments—winters in a cell in the soil. The black sawfly, 1/16 inch long, emerges in early May, about the time leaves are half open, and lays eggs in these new leaves. The larvae first make small gray, kidney-shaped blotches in a leaf, but gradually half the leaf turns brown. There are several generations, with flies laying eggs always in newly developing leaves. Hence the first brood is the worst, when all the leaves are new; later broods mostly infest ends of branches or water sprouts.

Control. Nicotine sulfate was recommended for many years but it was difficult to time the spray properly; DDT proved only partially successful. Lindane gives excellent control, using 1 tablespoon of 25 per cent wettable powder or 1½ teaspoons of a 20 per cent emulsion to a gallon of water. Spray in May as soon as the small blotches can be seen, and repeat in about 6 weeks. Sevin is also good; malathion can be used. The birch leaf miner is fairly readily controlled by treating the soil with a systemic such as phorate, but that is too poisonous for an amateur to handle; it must be left to a professional. Zectran is safer as a systemic and offers promise for this miner.

Blackberry Leaf Miner, *Metallus rubi* Forbes. Sometimes important in the Northeast. Whitish sawfly larvae, with brown heads, make blotch mines between leaf surfaces; plants appear scorched by fire. The adult is blackish, ⅙ inch long. There are 2 broods.

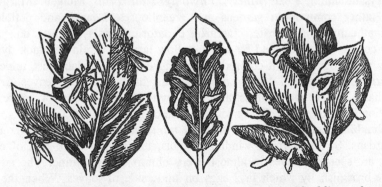

55. *Boxwood leaf miner: flies laying eggs, maggots inside blistered surface, pupa cases protruding from mines.*

Boxwood Leaf Miner*, *Monarthropalpus buxi* (Laboulbène). The most commonly destructive boxwood insect. It is a European fly, established in the East in 1910, not as much of a problem in Virginia and the Carolinas as in more northern states. The mines are small blotches or blisters in which yellow to orange maggots feed, 2 or 3, sometimes more, to a blister. In spring, some days before emergence, a small opaque window is formed on the underside of the leaf in the middle of the blotch, and, if the leaf is torn open, the maggots are found to have pupated and acquired dark heads. Shortly after that the windows are broken, the pupae push part way through the leaf, and when the small orange midges or flies emerge they leave white pupal skins protruding from the leaves. Appearing in swarms, usually early in the morning, the flies continue to emerge over a period of 10 days to 2 weeks. Each particular female, however, emerges, mates, inserts her eggs through upper epidermis of a new leaf, and dies in about 24 hours.

Time of emergence varies with the location and the season. In Maryland and Cincinnati, Ohio, it is late April. In New Jersey my earliest record was May 8, my latest May 20, with May 14 an average date. New blisters show up in leaves by midsummer, the tiny maggots having started to feed about 2 weeks after egg laying. Infested plants are not killed, at least for several years, but they have a most unthrifty appearance. They are yellow with sparse foliage, an eyesore in a lovely garden.

Control. The old molasses-and-nicotine concoction was replaced by DDT, which proved highly satisfactory, using 2 tablespoons of 50 per cent wettable powder to a gallon of water. It is essential, since the fly lays its eggs immediately, that the spray be on the plant in advance of emergence. With proper timing, 1 spray is sufficient. If there is a long interval after application before emergence, a second treatment may be desirable. If emergence occurs before you get around to spray, it is still possible to kill the young miners inside foliage by spraying in July with lindane emulsion or dimethoate.

Chrysanthemum Leaf Miner*, *Phytomyza atricornis* Meigen. Marguerite Fly. Rather common in gardens and greenhouses. Leaves and petioles of chrysanthemum, marguerite, cineraria, eupatorium, daisy, Shasta daisy, and other composites are mined by a pale-yellow larva of a minute black fly. The mines are irregular, light-colored, extending over the surface just under the epidermis. Larvae feed on parenchyma cells; badly infested leaves dry up and hang on plants; tunnels are filled with black specks of excrement; pupation is inside mines. Spray with lindane or malathion.

Columbine Leaf Miner*, *Phytomyza minuscula* Goureau. Very common in gardens. Striking white, winding tunnels, filled with black bits of excrement, are seen on leaves in almost every clump of columbine. The adult is a pale-brownish fly which lays eggs on underside of leaves. When the pale maggots are grown, they emerge through crescent-shaped slits and attach to the leaf brown puparia from which flies emerge in about 2 weeks. There are several generations, with pupation of the last brood in the soil. Another species causes a blotch instead of a serpentine mine on columbine. Spray with lindane, 2 teaspoons of a 25 per cent emulsion to 1 gallon of water.

56. Columbine leaf miner injury.

Corn Blotch Leaf Miner*, *Agromyza parvicornis* Loew. Wheat Leaf Miner, an eastern species ranging west to Utah. The adult is a small black fly whose maggots make irregular blotch mines in corn and grains, injury being worse in young corn. There are several generations in Florida, with breeding through the winter. Pull up and destroy seriously infested plants. Plant an excess of corn, to have a good stand left after the miners get their share.

Eggplant Leaf Miner*, *Keiferia glochinella* (Zeller). Attacking eggplant and other solanaceous plants in the South. Larvae and moths are like those of the potato tuberworm (see Borers) but a little smaller. There are several parasites which make this a relatively unimportant pest.

Elm Leaf Miner*, *Fenusa ulmi* Sundevall. An imported species attacking English, Scotch and Camperdown elms, sometimes American. Small, shiny black sawflies lay eggs through slits in upper leaf surfaces. In late May white legless larvae, ⅓ inch long, make blotch mines in leaves, often 15 to 20 larvae working in one leaf, which turns brown and shrivels. Leaves may drop prematurely. There is only 1 generation; after about 3 weeks the larvae remain in papery brown cocoons in the soil until pupation the next May. Spray with lindane, malathion, or Sevin.

European Alder Leaf Miner*, *Fenusa dohrnii* (Tischbein). Distributed through the Northeast on alder. Whitish larvae, ⅓ inch long, winter in papery cocoons in the soil and pupate in spring. Small black sawflies emerge in May to lay eggs in slits in upper leaf surfaces. Ten or more yellow blister mines may be present in a single leaf. There is a 2nd generation in July and sometimes a 3rd in September. See Birch Leaf Miner for control.

Grape Leaf Miner, *Phyllocnistis vitigenella*. Newly reported on cultivated grapes in Arizona.

57. Work of holly leaf miner, left, and native holly miner, right.

Gregarious Oak Leaf Miner*, *Cameraria cincinnatiella* (Chambers). Making blotch mines on oak, mostly white oak. The larvae are gregarious, 10 or more in a single mine and sometimes several mines in a leaf. There are 2 generations a year with the winter passed in the pupal state. Rake and burn infested leaves during the winter. Spray with lindane, Sevin, or malathion. See also Solitary Oak Leaf Miner.

Holly Leaf Miner*, *Phytomyza ilicis* (Curtis). A European species very common on our native holly, sometimes on English holly, causing conspicuous blotch mines on the upper surface, often several on a leaf. A native species, the American or serpentine **Native Holly Leaf Miner**, *Phytomyza ilicicola* Loew produces very slender, sinuous mines packed with frass. It is not so common, but sometimes the two types of mines are seen in the same leaf. The European miner winters in the mines, a yellow-green larva ⅛ inch long, and pupates there in spring. Small black flies, 1/16 inch long, emerge about the time holly twigs have 3 or 4 new leaves. This may be late April in Maryland, early May in New Jersey, and mid-May in Connecticut. They feed for about 10 days before egg laying. The female makes feeding punctures in foliage with her ovipositor, but both males and females lap the exuding sap. These feeding punctures look like pinpricks, but may be so numerous—up to 50 on a leaf—that the leaf is distorted. Eggs are laid singly in lower surface of new leaves, small larvae starting to feed in about a week, but the mines are not noticeable until late summer.

Control. DDT applied at the beginning of emergence, with usually a second spray 10 days later, gives satisfactory control. Use 2 level tablespoons 50 per cent wettable powder and spray as soon as you see black flies around new growth. Nurseries and holly plantations may use a DDT emulsion applied with a mist blower. If spraying for adults is neglected, young larvae can be killed in the mines by spraying with lindane or dieldrin in late July.

Larkspur Leaf Miner*, *Phytomyza delphiniae* Frost. A fly common on delphinium, larkspur, aconite. Several larvae feed together to form tan to brown blotch mines filled with dark flecks of excrement. The flies puncture the leaves from the underside, making them turn brown. Foliage often appears blighted by disease. There are several generations, with pupation in summer on the outside of a leaf near a mine. Spray with lindane, DDT, or malathion. Remove infested leaves.

Lilac Leaf Miner*, *Gracilaria syringella* (Fabricius). Lilac Leaf Roller. A European moth first known in America in 1925, now widespread, frequently reported injurious to lilac and privet in Rhode Island and in the West—Washington, Oregon, Montana, and Colorado. It has also been reported from ash, deutzia, and euonymus. The brownish moths, with 6 yellow lines on their fore wings, lay eggs in vein axils on underside of leaves. The pale-yellow translucent larvae, ⅓ inch long, first mine and then roll and skeletonize the leaves. There are 2 generations, larvae of the 2nd hibernating in cocoons in the soil. Moths emerge in May and July. When the miner is abundant, the beauty of lilac and privet is spoiled and there may be injurious defoliation. Spray in May with lindane or malathion; repeat in July.

Locust Leaf Miner*, *Xenochalepus dorsalis* (Thunberg). Locust Leaf Beetle, distributed through eastern states south to Mississippi and west to Missouri, feeding principally on black locust. The beetle, ¼ inch long, is orange-yellow with a broad black stripe down the back, black head and appendages. It is active in spring when locusts are coming into leaf; it lays eggs on underside of leaves, 3 to 5 in a pile covered with excrement. The larvae, yellow-white with black heads, burrow from the bottom of this mass into the leaf, making a common circular mine. As it grows older, each larva makes a separate new mine. After feeding for a month, the larvae pupate inside the mines; the leaves turn brown and drop. There may be a second generation of the beetles and it is not uncommon for locusts to lose all their foliage twice in a single season. In most seasons the trees make a brown eyesore on hillsides or along roads unless they are sprayed.

Control. Spray with DDT, lindane, or lead arsenate in May when leaves are expanded and in early July.

Lodgepole Needle Miner*, *Recurvaria milleri* Busck. An important pest of lodgepole pine in California, Idaho, Montana, also mining needles of western white and Jeffrey pine in epidemic areas. In Yosemite National Park and other recreational areas it has killed up to 80 per cent of mature trees in epidemic years. Moths, very small, white or gray, appear every other year to lay eggs behind twig and needle scales and around buds. The greenish larva mines one needle the first year, moves to another for the second year. Lindane-emulsion sprays are helpful, but outbreaks of needle miners are eventually brought under control by parasites and climatic conditions. Use of a malathion-oil spray has reduced the number of parasites.

Morning-glory Leaf Miner*, *Bedellia somnulentella* (Zeller). Convolulus

Leaf Miner. Small pale caterpillars, larvae of gray moths, make irregular blotch mines in leaves—first serpentine, then widening into blistered blotch mines. Pupation is in cocoons attached to leaves. This species may be abundant on sweetpotato as well as morning-glory. A parasitic wasp, *Apanteles bedelliae,* is helpful.

Native Holly Leaf Miner*. See Holly Leaf Miner.

Pea Leaf Miner*, *Liriomyza langei* Frick. Causing large losses in various truck crops in California; injurious to onions in Oregon; also reported on chrysanthemums.

Pine Needle Miner*, *Exoteleia pinifoliella* (Chambers). Common in eastern states, sometimes abundant on ornamental pines. Brown larvae, ⅕ inch long, mine tips of needles, entering at some distance from the tip, and then excavate the whole leaf. Injured tips turn yellow, dry up. There is usually 1 generation in the Northeast, with yellow-brown moths, marked with white or gray, laying eggs in June and July. There may be more broods in the South. Spray with DDT in June or July.

Pine Needle-sheath Miner, *Zelleria haimbachi* Busck. Jack-pine Needle Miner. On jack, lodgepole, ponderosa, and Virginia pines. Small caterpillars mine in the sheath, severing the needles near the base, sometimes webbing them in clusters. The adult is a small gray moth.

Privet Leaf Miner*, *Gracilaria cuculipennella* (Hübner). A European moth sometimes destructive here. Whitish caterpillars, ⅞ inch long when mature, make blotch mines in leaves, then feed externally in rolled leaves. Spray with lindane or malathion.

Serpentine Leaf Miner*, *Liriomyza brassicae* (Riley). Common throughout the country, more devastating in the South and California. The yellow maggots, larvae of minute black-and-yellow flies, make long, slender, winding white mines under epidermis of bean, beet, cabbage, cowpea, cress, nasturtium, sweetpea, pepper, potato, radish, spinach, turnip, watermelon, and field crops. Pupation is in the mines or in brown puparia in the soil. There are several generations. In addition to decreasing the attractiveness of green vegetables for food, the mines afford entrance to disease and decay organisms. Chlordane or lindane has been helpful, diazinon has been recommended. Removal of infested leaves by hand is suggested for the home garden. There are natural parasites working on this miner.

Solitary Oak Leaf Miner*, *Cameraria hamadryadella* (Clemens). Disfiguring many species of oak. The pale blotch mines, several on a leaf, contain a single larva each. There may be 5 or 6 generations in the vicinity of Washington, D.C. The larvae winter in mines in dried leaves so that raking up old leaves is helpful. Spray in spring with lindane, Sevin, or malathion.

Spinach Leaf Miner*, *Pegomya hyoscyami* (Panzer). Generally distributed on spinach, beet, sugar beet, chard, and many weeds, especially lambsquarters. Slender gray, black-haired flies, ¼ inch long, lay oval white, sculptured eggs, singly or in small groups, on underside of leaves. These hatch in

3 or 4 days into pale-green or whitish maggots which first eat slender, winding mines but then widen these and join them together to make large, light-colored blotches filled with dark excrement. Maggots may migrate from leaf to leaf; they are full-grown in 1 to 3 weeks and pupate usually in the soil. Adults appear in 2 to 4 weeks and there may be 3 or 4 generations a season. Leaf vegetables are unfit for greens; seed and root development are checked.

Control. In home gardens remove infested leaves; keep weed hosts destroyed; spray with pyrethrum or malathion. Commercial growers may use parathion or diazinon.

Spotted Tentiform Leaf Miner, *Phyllonorycter crataegella* Clemens. Rather common in the East, known in the Northwest, damaging in California. Leaves of apple, quince, plum, cherry, wild haw, sweet-scented crab may have up to 15 blotch mines apiece and may be buckled like a tent. The adult is a very small moth with spotted wings. There may be three generations, with leaves sometimes losing most of their function, but outbreaks are very irregular, probably due to parasites. Parathion and DDT have been effective.

Spruce Needle Miner*, *Taniva albolineana* (Kearfott). On blue, Norway, Engelmann, and Sitka spruce from Maine to North Carolina and in Colorado, Idaho, Oregon and Washington. Dark-brown moths, wingspread ½ inch, lay eggs on needles from mid-May to mid-June. Larvae bore into needles at base and make webs from entrance holes in needles to twigs. Each larva destroys an average of 10 needles. The entire crown of small ornamental spruces can be webbed; on larger trees heaviest infestation is on lower branches. A simple control is to wash off all loose needles and webs with a hose in March and early autumn, cleaning up and burning the trash flushed to the ground.

Two other species mine spruce needles. *Epinotia nanana* Treitman webs dried mined needles together, giving the trees an unsightly, unhealthy appearance. This species, from Europe, occurs from Maine to Ohio and Michigan. A single larva may mine 10 or more needles. The adult is dark smoky brown with 7/16-inch wingspread. *Recurvaria piceaella* (Kearfott) has a similar life cycle, occurs from Maine to Colorado on blue, Norway, red, and white spruce. The moths—grayish with pale yellow head and thorax—are active in June and July, lay eggs on needles; the larvae mine the needles, then spin them together with silk.

Strawberry Crown Miner*, *Aristotelia fragariae* Busck. Reddish larvae, ¼ inch long, burrow in crowns of plants, causing stunting and poor foliage and offering entrance to disease organisms. In the Northwest moths emerge in June and July and lay eggs about the crown. Larvae are full-grown by October. Crop rotation is recommended as well as cleaning up plants.

Sweetpotato Leaf Miner*, *Bedellia orchilella* Walsingham. Related to the morning-glory leaf miner.

Sycamore Leaf Miner, *Phyllonorycter felinella* Heinrich. The moth lays eggs beneath leaf hairs on the lower leaf surface and larvae—yellowish, ¼ inch long when grown—enter leaf directly. The mines are brownish with black fecal pellets. Raking and burning fallen leaves is helpful.

Tupelo Leaf Miner*, *Antispila nysaefoliella* Clemens. Sourgum Casecutter. The larvae of this tiny moth mine in the leaves of tupelo, sourgum, and, when mature, cut oval cases out of the leaves, falling with them to the ground. The larva attaches its case to some object by a silken thread and pupates inside. Although it is reported abundant in some years, causing browning of leaves by late summer, my only experience with it was on an estate in Pennsylvania a few years ago, when all the gardeners stopped working to wonder at the bits of leaves walking around on the ground. In that instance, every leaf on the tree seemed to have been infested. A lead arsenate-nicotine spray in May when moths emerge has been recommended.

Unspotted Tentiform Leaf Miner, *Callisto geminatella* Packard. On apple, pear, crabapple, haw, plum, wild cherry. Greenish-gray larvae mine leaves and buckle them, as do those of the spotted tentiform miner. Moths are gray without spots. Hibernation is as a pupa inside folded edges of the leaf. Destroy fallen leaves in autumn.

Verbena Leaf Miner. *Agromyza artemisiae* (Kaltenbach). Practically inevitable in any garden growing verbenas. Each maggot feeds singly, making a blister or blotch mine, but several mines can run together to make the foliage most unsightly. The adult is a tiny midge. Try spraying or dusting with lindane. Rake and burn all plant trash in autumn.

White-fir Needle Miner*, *Epinotia meritana* Heinrich. On white fir, reported particularly damaging in Utah. Moths are small, grayish, mottled with black; minute green larvae winter in fir needles, then mine and web them the following spring. DDT in oil has given control.

Wild Parsnip Leaf Miner, *Phytomyza albiceps* (Meigen). A European species generally distributed, making serpentine mines in aster and columbine. The larvae are white, puparia black, flies small, black or metallic blue. Pupation is in the soil.

LEAF ROLLERS

Leaf rollers are caterpillars which feed protected by the rolled-up leaf of the host plant, but not between the two leaf surfaces as do leaf miners.

Avocado Leaf Roller, *Gracilaria perseae* Busck. Serious in Florida. The adult is a small grayish moth, ¼ inch long. The larva feeds on the lower surface of the avocado leaf and rolls it back from the tip, pupating in the rolled portion. Lead arsenate provides effective control.

Basswood Leaf Roller*, *Pantographa limata* Grote & Robinson. General through eastern states. The moths—straw-colored with intricate olive-purple markings, 1½-inch wingspread—emerge in June and July. The larva—1 inch long, bright green with a black head—lives inside the apical half of a leaf rolled into a tube, and feeds from July to September. When full-grown it leaves this nest and makes a small one lined with silk in a fold from one edge of the leaf, spending the winter in fallen leaves inside this protection. Raking and burning leaves in autumn may be sufficient control.

Bean Leaf Roller*, *Urbanus proteus* (Linnaeus). A southern pest troublesome to early fall crops of beans, and found as far north as Delaware. The 1-inch-long caterpillar is greenish yellow, velvety, with a broad head and constricted neck. It rolls up edges of leaves after cutting slits in them. The adult, a blue skipper butterfly 2 inches across, with long tails on hind wings, lays eggs on beans in summer. In warm weather larvae take 14 days to mature, a month when it is cooler. Pupation is on plants. By September beans in Florida may be so heavily infested no pods can be formed.

Boxelder Leaf Roller*, *Gracilaria negundella* Chambers. Boxelder leaves are mined from the underside, whitened and rolled; severe injury is reported in Utah and Nevada.

European Honeysuckle Leaf Roller*, *Harpipteryx xylostella* (Linnaeus). On Tartarian honeysuckle. Leaves are rolled and ragged. Larvae are leaf-green with 2 brown median stripes outlined with blue-green stripes; ¾ inch long, tapering to a narrow head and tail. The white cocoon, pointed at both ends, is fastened to a leaf. The moth is chestnut-brown with cream-colored lower markings on fore wings, which expand to ¾ inch. Spray with lead arsenate to prevent defoliation.

Fruit-tree Leaf Roller*, *Archips argyrospila* (Walker). Present from coast to coast, capable, in occasional years of abundance, of ruining 90 per cent of an apple crop. This is a general feeder on most deciduous fruits—apricot, blackberry, cherry, currant, gooseberry, loganberry, pear, plum, quince, raspberry—and has been damaging to citrus in California. It may also infest ash, boxelder, elm, horsechestnut, hickory, locust, oak, Osage-orange, poplar, rose, sassafras, English walnut, and willow. It winters in the egg stage, in masses of 30 to 100 plastered on twigs, branches, and tree trunks, covered with a brown or gray varnish. About the time apple buds separate in spring the young worms—pale green with brown heads—crawl to feed on leaves, buds, and small fruits for about a month. They spin a light web around several leaves, roll these together, often enclosing a small cluster of young apples. Cavities eaten in fruit show as deep russeted scars at harvest. When the caterpillars are full-grown, ¾ inch long, they pupate inside rolled leaves or make a flimsy cocoon on trunk or branches. Moths emerge in late June or July. They are brown with gold markings, wing expanse ¾ inch. There is only 1 generation.

Control. A heavy application of a dormant oil spray put on before buds break and applied so as to cover every egg mass has been effective. Spraying with lead arsenate to kill very young larvae is fairly successful. Parathion and TDE are sometimes recommended. There are many parasites, accounting for the fluctuating abundance of this pest.

Gray-banded Leaf Roller*, *Argyrotaenia mariana* (Fernald).

Hickory Leaf Roller*, *Argyrotaenia juglandana* (Fernald). Found in the Northeast and west to Wisconsin. The larvae—pale green, semitranslucent, ¾ inch long—roll hickory leaves and feed inside the rolls in May and June. The moths, appearing in June and July, have dark-brown fore wings marked with black, gray hind wings.

Larger Canna Leaf Roller*, *Calpodes ethlius* (Stoll). Ranging through the South and north to Washington, D.C. The caterpillar, which is up to 1¾ inches long, green, semitransparent with a dark-orange head set off by a narrow neck, cuts off a strip from the margin of a canna leaf and folds it over, feeding above and below from within this protection, eating larger irregular holes as it grows. Damage can be extensive. The adult is a skipper butterfly, brown with white spots. Spray or dust with lead arsenate or DDT before leaves are rolled. The caterpillars can also be killed by pressing the leaf between thumb and finger.

Lesser Canna Leaf Roller*, *Geshna cannalis* (Quaintance). Also serious on canna in the South. The caterpillar—yellow white but with a green tinge after feeding on foliage, 1 inch long when grown—fastens young leaves together before they have unrolled. They are ragged, often turn brown and die. The moths, uniform light brown, appear in February and March in Florida. It may be possible to kill larvae inside rolled leaves by pressing with your fingers. Clean off and burn dead trash from beds and remove infested plant parts.

Locust Leaf Roller*, *Nephopteryx subcaesiella* (Clemens). Found from Maine to West Virginia and Colorado on locust, honeylocust, and wisteria. The larvae, up to 1 inch long, green with faint stripes, black head, feed inside 2 or 3 leaves spun together with silk. They winter as pupae in silken cocoons among leaves on ground. Gray moths, shaded with red, emerge from May to July. In some states there is a second generation with moths again in August and September. The injury is rather common but probably not serious enough to call for control measures.

Oak Leaf Roller, *Argyrotoxa semipurpurana* Kearfott. Larva of a tortricid moth, seriously defoliating red, pin, scarlet and shrub oaks in Massachusetts, Connecticut, New York and Pennsylvania. Several other species occasionally infest oaks.

Oblique-banded Leaf Roller*, *Archips rosaceanus* (Harris). Rose Leaf Tier. The omnivorous larvae of this moth feed on flowers in greenhouse and garden, chewing holes in rosebuds, rolling up leaves and tying them together, feeding on aster, carnation, geranium, sunflower, verbena. They also feed on vegetables, fruits, ornamental trees and shrubs including apple, apricot, ash, basswood, bean, birch, blackberry, boxelder, celery, cherry, currant, dewberry, dogwood, gooseberry, hawthorn, hazelnut, honeysuckle, horsechestnut, lilac, loganberry, maple, oak, peach, pear, plum, poplar, prune, raspberry, rose, spirea, strawberry, sumac, thistle.

The pale-green, black-headed larvae mine the leaves first, then work inside rolled areas, often tying several leaves together. They may also infest fruit. Eggs are laid in overlapping green masses on branches of host plants or on rose leaves in greenhouses.

Control. Parathion or DDT aerosols will control in greenhouses. Fruit trees can be sprayed with lead arsenate or Sevin or TDE. There are a number of natural parasites.

Omnivorous Leaf Roller, *Platynotus stultana* Walsingham. Known for many years on citrus, a more recent pest of cotton in California and Arizona; truly omnivorous, feeding on alfalfa, celery, lettuce, sugar beet, melon, strawberry, boysenberry, begonia, oleander, and carnation and rose in greenhouses, to mention only a few hosts. This is a tortricid moth, similar to the orange tortrix. The full-grown larva is yellowish or greenish brown with a ragged stripe down the back. It is controlled with TDE or parathion, sometimes DDT.

Raspberry Leaf Roller*, *Exartema permundanum* Clemens.

Red-banded Leaf Roller*, *Argyrotaenia velutinana* (Walker). A native insect widely distributed in the Northeast, and ranging to North Carolina and Texas, that has increased in importance since DDT has been used in orchards. It feeds on apple, cherry, plum, some small fruits, vegetables, ornamental trees and flowers—chrysanthemum, geranium, hollyhock, honeysuckle, lobelia, rose, violet, zinnia. The moth, brownish with red bands across the wings, which spread only ¾ inch, appears in spring soon after apple buds break. The larva is slender, greenish, just over ½ inch long, and pupates in fall inside a half cocoon on trees and other objects. There may be 3 generations. Eggs of the 1st are placed on bark, those of the 2nd on foliage or fruits. Early season larvae feed on leaves, spinning light webs, but late season larvae feed on fruits, eating patches off the surface. They roll and tie leaves and terminal growth of ornamentals.

Control. DDT is not satisfactory for this leaf roller; it kills the parasites and increases the rollers. TDE or Sevin may be used in orchards or lead arsenate applied at petal fall and first cover.

Redbud Leaf Roller, *Fascista cercerisella* (Chambers). From Maryland to Illinois and Kansas and through the South. The moth is velvety black, with white head and collar, slightly bronzed fore wings, wingspread ⅗ inch. The larva, white with black markings, webs leaves together. There are 2 generations with moths emerging from May to September.

Strawberry Leaf Roller*, *Ancylis comptana fragariae* (Walsh & Riley). On strawberry, dewberry, blackberry, and raspberry in northern United States, Louisiana, and Arkansas. The caterpillars, greenish or bronze, up to ½ inch long, fold or roll and tie the leaves into tubes, feeding from within. Plants are weakened, leaves turn brown and die. Fruits are withered and deformed; infested beds appear white or gray from a distance. Small gray moths with light waxy markings across the fore wings, ½ inch wingspread, appear in large numbers near the strawberry patch in May to lay eggs on underside of leaves. The larvae feed for 25 to 50 days, first on underside of leaf, then on upper, then pupate inside folded leaves. There are two or more generations.

Control. Spray or dust with malathion, Sevin, TDE, or parathion before leaves are folded; repeat if necessary for the 2nd generation. It is sometimes advisable to mow strawberry beds close to the ground and burn over right after harvest.

Sweetpotato Leaf Roller*, *Pilocrocis tripunctata* (Fabricius). Bluish-green caterpillars, up to 1 inch long, feed inside folded leaves, eating holes through leaves and skeletonizing them.

Three-lined Leaf Roller*, *Pandemis limitata* (Robinson).

Western Strawberry Leaf Roller, *Anacampsis fragariella* Busck. Occurring in Washington and Oregon along with the strawberry leaf roller. The caterpillars are creamy pink, ½ inch long. Leaves are rolled in May and June, moths emerge in July; hibernation is in the egg stage on old strawberry leaves. There is only 1 generation. A nicotine and oil spray applied when eggs are on foliage is effective. Top plants after harvest.

LEAF SKELETONIZERS

Leaf skeletonizers are caterpillars like leaf rollers, but they feed more openly, eating out everything except epidermis and veins, without the protection of conspicuously rolled leaves.

Apple Leaf Skeletonizer*, *Psorosina hammondi* (Riley). On apple, sometimes plum and quince, most abundant in central states, where it is of fluctuating importance. The green upper surface of the leaf is eaten off entirely or in part, making the foliage look brown and dead; trees appear to have been struck by fire. Leaves at end of branches may be lightly folded with 2 or 3 lightly webbed together. Brown pupae winter in fallen leaves; dark-brown moths, wings mottled with silver, lay eggs on leaves in late spring. Brownish-green caterpillars, ½ inch long, with 4 black tubercles on the back, feed in June and July, then pupate on leaves; 2nd generation feeds in late August and September. The ordinary spray schedule, if it includes summer sprays for codling moth, will control leaf skeletonizers.

Apple-and-thorn Skeletonizer*, *Anthophila pariana* (Clerck). A European pest, first found in New York in 1917, now present from Maine to New Jersey and in the Pacific Northwest, feeding on apple, pear, cherry, and hawthorn. It hibernates as a small dark-brown moth, lays eggs in spring. The caterpillars—yellow-green with black tubercles, brown heads—feed on underside of leaves first, then make shelters by drawing upper surfaces together with silk, leaves becoming a mass of webbing and frass. There are several generations. Spraying with lead arsenate or DDT is effective.

Bean Leaf Skeletonizer*, *Autoplusia egena* (Guenée).

Birch Skeletonizer*, *Bucculatrix canadensisella* Chambers. General in the Northeast, found as far west as Wisconsin and south to higher altitudes in North Carolina, on gray, paper, yellow, and European white birches. The moths, ⅜ inch across the wings, which are brown crossed with silver, appear in July to lay eggs singly on leaves. The young larva, yellow-green, bores directly from the bottom of the egg into the leaf, mines it in 2 to 5 weeks, then cuts a crescent-shaped opening through the lower side of the leaf and spins a molting cocoon. After molting, the larva skeletonizes the leaf from the underside, molts again, feeds for another week, then drops to the ground and makes a brown, ribbed pupal cocoon for the winter. There is 1 generation. Spraying with lead arsenate (3 pounds to 100 gallons of water) about the middle of August will prevent defoliation but the injury comes so late in the season, the expense of spraying may not be justified. The pest is serious for 2 or 3 years out of every 10. There are many parasites.

Cotton Leaf Perforator*, *Bucculatrix thurberiella* Busck. Hollyhock Leaf Skeletonizer. A cotton pest, larva of a small gray-and-tan moth. It mines in and completely skeletonizes foliage of hollyhocks in California. Spray or dust with lead arsenate.

Grape Leaf Skeletonizer*, *Harrisina americana* (Guérin-Méneville). Common on wild grapes, sometimes injuring cultivated varieties. The larvae feed in groups, side by side across a leaf, eating the upper surface only. Adults are small, smoky black, narrow-fringed moths. The insect is so heavily parasitized no other control is required.

Maple Trumpet Skeletonizer*, *Epinotia aceriella* (Clemens). The leaves of red maple, sometimes sugar maple, are folded loosely in July and August. The small green larva lives inside a long, trumpetlike tube near the skeletonized areas. The injury is more spectacular than serious.

Oak Skeletonizer*, *Bucculatrix ainsliella* Murtfeldt. In the Northeast, on red, black, and white oaks, also reported as causing severe injury in Wisconsin. The yellowish-green larva is ¼ inch long. The moth is creamy white with brown markings, active in May and late July and August, there being 2 generations. The winter is passed as pupae in cocoons on fallen leaves or debris.

Palm Leaf Skeletonizer*, *Homaledra sabalella* (Chambers). Palm Leaf Miner, the major pest of palms in Florida, feeding on saw, cabbage, dwarf, and sabal palmettos, on coconut palm and various date palms. The caterpillars are gregarious, living in colonies of 35 to 100, feeding under a protective web of silk and depositing their excrement in the upper surface of this web. Continued feeding causes dark-brown blotches on leaves, followed by shriveling and death. In heavily infested areas every frond and leaflet may be attacked. The moths, which are rarely seen in the day, are attracted to lights at night. They lay eggs on the brown, papery husk which encloses young leaflets. Larvae start to feed directly from the bottom of the eggs on leaf tissue, keeping the eggshells as protection until the silken web is formed. There are often 5 broods, with the winter passed in egg, larval, or pupal stages.

Control. Spray repeatedly, perhaps every 2 months, with DDT, chlordane, or lindane. Cut out and burn infested fronds; remove interleaf husks that may bear eggs.

Western Grape Leaf Skeletonizer*, *Harrisina brillians* Barnes & McDunnough. Occurring in Arizona, California, New Mexico, and Texas. Black-and-yellow larvae feed on leaves of wild and cultivated grapes in late summer. They move in compact colonies as they completely skeletonize leaves. Moths are metallic-black or -green. Dusting with 50 per cent cryolite, 5 per cent DDT, or with methoxychlor is effective.

LEAF TIERS

Leaf tiers are much like leaf rollers, tying leaves together with strands of silk and feeding inside that protection.

Beech Leaf Tier, *Psilocorsis faginella* (Chambers). Common in the Northeast on beech. The larvae, whitish with pink tint, brown heads, feed in August and September. They winter as pupae with moths appearing in late May and June. The fore wings are light brown with transverse darker streaks. Leaves are tied together, skeletonized, and browned, but the injury is seldom serious enough for control measures.

Celery Leaf Tier*, *Udea rubigalis* (Guenée). Greenhouse Leaf Tier. Present throughout North America, a special pest of celery, feeding on a great many garden and greenhouse vegetables and ornamentals—ageratum, anemone, aster, bean, beet, cabbage, carnation, cauliflower, cineraria, chrysanthemum, cucumber, dahlia, daisies, geranium, heliotrope, kale, ivy, lantana, lettuce, lobelia, nasturtium, parsley, passion-flower, pea, sweetpea, rose, spinach, snapdragon, strawberry, thistle, wandering-Jew, to give a partial list.

The moths are brown, fore wings crossed by wavy dark lines, spreading ¾ inch. They are quiet during the day, fly at night. The female lays flattened, scalelike translucent eggs singly or in overlapping groups on underside of leaves, usually close to the soil. They hatch in 5 to 12 days into pale-green caterpillars, turning yellow when grown, ¾ inch long with a white stripe down the back and a dark-green line in the center of the white stripe. As they feed, they web foliage together in large masses, filling it with frass, and they mine into soft stems and hearts of plants, especially celery. When disturbed they wiggle violently in their webs or drop to the ground. They pupate in silken cocoons inside the webs. The life cycle takes about 40 days; there may be 7 or 8 generations in greenhouses and 5 or 6 outdoors in warm climates.

Control. Spray or dust young plants with DDT, changing to pyrethrum for older plants and repeating in a half hour. Parathion or DDT aerosols can be used in greenhouses, or nicotine fumigation. Harvest infested outdoor crops early and spade under all crop refuse.

Holly Leaf Tier, *Norma dietsiana* Kf. Larvae tie leaves of American holly. Reported in 1961 as a new record for Delaware.

58. *Hydrangea leaves fastened together by leaf tier, which is eating the enclosed flower bud.*

Hydrangea Leaf Tier, *Exartema ferriferanum* (Walker). A small green caterpillar with a dark head sews terminal leaves of hydrangeas tightly around the bud, the effect being that of little pocketbooks. It is often possible to tear open these tied leaves and kill the worm before it destroys the flower bud. DDT or lead arsenate applied early enough should give control but the leaves are usually tied together before one gets around to spraying.

Oak Leaf Tiers, *Psilocorsis quercicella* Clements and *P. reflexella* Clements. Similar to the beech leaf tier but on oak.

Omnivorous Leaf Tier*, *Cnephasia longana* (Haworth). Strawberry Fruitworm. A European pest destructive in California and the Northwest, first found in Oregon in 1929 on strawberries and Dutch iris. The larvae feed also on flax, peas and other legumes, and many cultivated flowers including calla lily, bachelors-button, gladiolus, heather, marguerites. Both flowers and foliage are webbed and eaten, and fruit of strawberries. The moth lays its eggs on rough bark of trees, many kinds, or rough wooden objects; the larvae are carried to food plants by the wind.

Control. In strawberries a dust of 5 per cent DDT mixed with 10 per cent sulfur applied to the early bloom stage has given commercial control. DDT should be satisfactory for most ornamentals if a miticide is included.

Sweetgum Leaf Tier, *Nephopteryx uvinella* (Ragonet). Reported tying and feeding on leaves of sweetgum in Maryland.

MAGGOTS

Maggots are the larvae of flies. Those that are commonly known by their adult name have been treated under Flies; those that normally go under the name of maggot are considered here.

Apple Maggot*, *Rhagoletis pomonella* (Walsh). Also known as Railroad Worm, Apple Fruit Fly, a native pest injurious to apples from the Dakotas east and Arkansas north (Plate XXV). It probably fed originally on wild haws and wild crabs; now it eats apples, blueberries, plums, cherries. A smaller variety of this species breeds on snowberry in the West, but there it is not an apple pest. In Connecticut the maggot is considered the primary apple pest, wormy fruit in unsprayed orchards often reaching 100 per cent.

Hibernation takes place inside a small brown puparium buried 1 to 6 inches deep in the soil, but flies do not emerge until summer—late June in some sections, early July in most. They are slightly smaller than houseflies, black, with white bands on the abdomen and conspicuous zigzag black bands on the wings. The females lay their eggs singly through punctures in the apple skin. In 5 to 10 days these hatch into legless white maggots which tunnel through the fruit by rasping and tearing the pulp into brown, winding galleries. Early varieties soon become a soft mass of rotten pulp; later varieties have corky streaks through the flesh and a distorted, pitted surface. Completing their growth about a week after apples have fallen to the ground, larvae leave the fruit and burrow in the soil to pupate. Ordinarily pupation continues until the next summer, but in its southern range the apple maggot may have a partial 2nd generation.

Control. Apply a special lead arsenate spray, 3 pounds plus 3 pounds of hydrated lime to 100 gallons, when flies appear, but not within 1 month of harvest. DDT in cover sprays is fairly effective as is methoxychlor. Very important in control is cleaning up and disposing of dropped fruit, twice a week for summer varieties, before maggots leave the apples to pupate.

Cabbage Maggot*, *Hylemya brassicae* (Bouché). Introduced from Europe more than a century ago; a serious pest in northern states, of little consequence south of Pennsylvania. Early cabbage and broccoli after transplanting, late cabbage in the seedbed, early turnips, late spring radishes are most severely injured by maggots, but other crucifers—including Brussels sprouts, cauliflower, cress, mustard, and sometimes beet, celery, and a few other vegetables—may be attacked (Plate XXVI).

The winter is spent in puparia, 1 to 5 inches deep in the soil. About the time sweet cherries bloom and young cabbage plants are set out, a small fly, ¼ inch long, dark gray with black stripes on thorax and black bristles, crawls out of the soil to lay white, finely ridged eggs at the base of the stems and on adjacent soil. These hatch in 3 to 7 days into small, white, legless maggots, blunt at the rear end, which enter the soil to feast on roots and stems just under the surface, riddling them with brown tunnels. Seedlings wilt, turn yellow, and die. Maggot abundance fluctuates from year to year but often 40 to 80 per cent of young plants are lost. After 3 weeks the maggot forms a puparium from its larval skin, producing another fly in 12 to 18 days. The number of generations is indefinite; ordinarily the first is important on cabbage and its relatives, while late broods menace fall turnips and radishes. In addition to its own feeding injury the maggot is credited with introducing the fungus causing blackleg.

Control. Protect seedbeds with a cheesecloth cover to prevent egg laying. Place a 3- to 4-inch square of tar paper around the stem of each seedling when it is transplanted, and don't let it get covered with soil in cultivating. Dusting stems before setting with calomel, 1 pound mixed with 6 ounces of cornstarch, is still recommended in some states. Commercial growers may dust or spray bases of plants in the row with chlordane or dieldrin.

Carnation Maggot*, *Hylemya brunnescens* (Zetterstedt).

Carnation Tip Maggot*, *Hylemya echinata* Séguy.

Cherry Maggot. See Cherry Fruit Fly under Flies.

Onion Maggot*, *Hylemya antiqua* (Meigen). A northern onion pest, rarely injurious in the South. In dry years the onion maggot is of little importance, but in a series of wet springs 80 per cent or more of the crop may be destroyed, larvae tunneling in bulb and crown so thoroughly that the onion dies or is worthless. One small maggot can kill a seedling onion; early plantings are most injured.

The winter is spent in chestnut-brown puparia, resembling grains of wheat, several inches deep in soil or piles of cull onions or trash. The flies—gray or brown, bristly, ¼ inch long, with large wings and a rather humpbacked appearance—emerge in May or June and lay sausage-shaped white eggs at the base of plants or in cracks in soil. They hatch in 2 to 7 days. Dirty-white, cylindrical maggots, ¼ inch long, feed for 2 or 3 weeks behind leaf sheaths and in bulbs, then pupate in soil. There are 2 or more generations. The 3rd brood often attacks onions just before harvest and causes storage rot.

Control. Destroying all cull onions immediately after harvest is most important. Foliage can be sprayed, when flies appear, with diazinon or malathion. Commercial growers may use granular ethion, Trithion, or V-C-13 at planting time.

Pepper Maggot*, *Zonosemata electa* (Say). First noticed in New Jersey in 1921, now present from Massachusetts to Indiana and south to Florida and Texas. It is serious on pepper, also reported on eggplant, tomato, groundcherry, and weeds of the nightshade family. There is 1 generation a year. Pupae winter in the soil with flies emerging from late June to August. They are yellow with brown bands on clear wings; they deposit large white eggs, the shape of a crookneck squash, in young peppers. The maggots resemble sharp-pointed pegs, translucent white but turning yellow on maturity. The fruits drop or decay. Dust with malathion, chlordane, or rotenone, starting when first flies appear. Keeping the fruits thoroughly dusted with talc during the summer prevents the females from getting a foothold on the skins for ovipositing.

Raspberry Cane Maggot*, *Pegomya rubivora* (Coquillett). A northern insect found from coast to coast on blackberry, dewberry, loganberry, raspberry, rose. The tips of new shoots wilt, sometimes with a purplish discoloration at the base of the wilted part, or are broken off clean as though cut by a knife. Sometimes galls are formed in the canes. The white maggots, ⅓ inch long, tunnel down in the pith after they have girdled the cane and caused the break. Pupation is in canes. The flies, half the size of houseflies, emerge in spring to lay eggs in leaf axils of tender shoots. Cut off infested tips several inches below wilted portions.

Seed-corn Maggot, *Hylemya cilicrura* (Rondani). A European insect that arrived in New York more than 100 years ago and is now general over the country. Chief injury is to germinating seed, with peas and beans often more seriously injured than corn. Melon, cucumber and potato sprouts are often killed; young plants of cabbage, beet, bean, pea, onion, turnip, spinach, radish, sweetpotato are frequent victims, sometimes gladiolus and coniferous seedlings.

Yellowish-white maggots, ¼ inch long, sharply pointed at the head end, burrow in seed so that it fails to sprout or produces a weak, sickly plant. Injury is worse in cold, wet seasons on land rich in organic matter. The winter is spent in puparia in soil or as free maggots in manure. Grayish-brown flies, ⅓ inch long, emerge in early July to deposit eggs in rich soil or on seeds or seedlings. There may be 3 to 5 generations.

Control. One method is to wait to plant, or to replant, until the ground is warm enough to allow quick germination and rapid growth. Shallow planting also speeds up germination. Seed can be treated with lindane, aldrin, dieldrin, or heptachlor before planting. Chlordane or lindane dust can be worked into the soil before planting. Gladiolus corms can be sprayed in the trench at planting time, before covering, with lindane or chlordane.

Sunflower Maggot*, *Strauzia longipennis* (Wiedemann). Sunflower Peacock Fly, present in many parts of the country, infesting stems of wild and cultivated sunflowers. The flies are a gay yellow. The female has an orange ovipositor and the male a tuft of black spines on the head.

Turnip Maggot*, *Hylemya floralis* (Fallén). Similar to the cabbage maggot, a very serious pest of crucifers in Alaska. Aldrin and heptachlor provide effective control.

MANTIDS

The praying, or preying, mantis and its relatives are very definitely friends in the garden. They belong to the grasshopper order, Orthoptera, and the family Mantidae. They are all predaceous on other insects, capturing their prey with marvelous front legs, long and muscular, fitted with grooves and spines for grasping and holding. While waiting for some unwary insect, they sit in an attitude of prayer. Baby mantids, looking ridiculously like their elders except for wings, are cannibals from the day they are born. They start with aphids, or perhaps one another, going on to larger insects as they grow. A full-grown praying mantis is not afraid to strike at a frog, a lizard, or a hornet. Of course they are just as likely to eat a harmless or beneficial insect as one that is a pest. There are about 20 species known in North America; four are common in the East.

Carolina Mantis*, *Stagomantis carolina* (Johannson). A southern native, found as far north as southern New Jersey, Pennsylvania, and Ohio. It has uniformly green wings, is about 2½ inches long.

Chinese Mantis*, *Tenodera aridifolia sinensis* Saussure. The common form in the Middle Atlantic States. It was introduced accidentally from Asia about 1895, in nursery stock sent to Philadelphia, and was not imported later to fight Japanese beetles as some believe. In fact, praying mantises don't like Japanese beetles particularly, though they sometimes eat them. The Chinese mantis has spread to Ohio and southern New England and is often seen in gardens in late summer. It is large, 4 or 5 inches long, and the broad green front margin of the wings is sharply separated from the larger, brown portion. Its triangular head is highly movable, and it has very large eyes that appear highly intelligent. In egg laying the female hangs head-down and produces a gummy fluid which she beats into a froth the color of ripe grain to make her egg mass. This is made up of a series of plates providing chambers for 100 or more eggs and is attached to any shrub or tall grass around the garden or in a field. It looks like a short, broad cornucopia of brown-and-tan dried foam.

If you accidentally cut off egg masses during the fall cleanup or spring pruning, simply tie them onto other shrubs and the babies will hatch later. Don't try to keep egg masses in the house; they will hatch too soon and you cannot provide them with their necessary prey. Egg cases can be purchased but this is more for fun than for the expected pest control.

European Mantis*, *Mantis religiosa* Linnaeus. Another accidental importation, found near Rochester, New York, in 1899 and established since in most eastern states. It is a little larger than the Carolina mantis, 2 to 4 inches long, but resembles it.

Narrow-winged Mantis*, *Tenodera angustipennis* Saussure. Another Oriental mantid, discovered in Delaware in 1930 and now well established. It is like the Chinese mantis but somewhat smaller and more slender.

MEALYBUGS

Mealybugs are relatives of scale insects, members of the family Pseudococcidae in the order Hemiptera, suborder Homoptera. They are really soft scales, with small, oval, soft, segmented bodies covered with a white powdery wax extending in filaments beyond the body. Most mealybugs have these filaments of equal length all around the body, but long-tailed mealybugs have longer threads at the posterior end of the body (Plate XXVII). Most species are house or greenhouse pests in the North, garden pests only in subtropical regions, but Comstock and Taxus mealybugs winter out of doors as far north as New York and Connecticut. Mealybugs injure plants by sucking sap and producing copious honeydew, which attracts ants and forms a medium for growth of sooty-mold fungi. Some species disseminate plant-disease organisms.

The life history of most mealybugs is about the same. The adult female deposits her eggs, 300 to 600, in a compact, waxy sac beneath the rear end of her body. Egg laying continues for a week or two, then the female dies. These conspicuous egg sacs, well-known to anyone who has grown house plants, are chiefly at axils of branching stems or leaves but sometimes on other plant parts. Indoors, eggs hatch in about 10 days; the young nymphs remain in the case for a short period, then crawl over the plants. As crawlers, they are oval, light yellow, 6-legged insects with smooth bodies, feeding like aphids by inserting their beaks into plant tissue and sucking out the sap. Soon after feeding begins, waxy filaments start forming, covering the bodies and radiating out on 36 leglike projections. The bugs get more sluggish but do not entirely stop moving. The mature female is much like the nymph, up to ¼ inch long, but the male forms a white case within which it changes to a minute, active 2-winged insect like a fly. It mates with the female and dies soon after, being unable to feed in the winged state. The long-tailed mealy-bug differs by giving birth to living young instead of forming an egg sac.

Mealybugs outdoors were formerly controlled by oil sprays, but now para-thion and other phosphate aerosols are widely used in greenhouses, and malathion sprays in homes. Outdoors, much reliance is placed on biological control.

Apple Mealybug*, *Phenacoccus aceris* (Signoret). On apple in New England, a problem on filberts in Oregon. Sooty mold growing in honeydew smuts the apple fruit. On filberts, cottony masses are in bark crevices, with winged males abundant.

Azalea Mealybug. See Azalea Bark Scale.

Citrophilus Mealybug*, *Pseudococcus gahani* Green. First observed in California in 1913. It attacks apple, azalea, blackberry, citrus, climbing fig, cherry, columbine, cyclamen, English ivy, eugenia, foxglove, heliotrope, mallow, Mexican-orange (Choisya), mustard, nightshade, peach, pear, pit-tosporum, plum, prune, potato, pepper-tree, privet, raspberry, rhubarb, rose, grevillea, sunflower, walnut. It differs from the citrus mealybug in having 2 tapering filaments at the end of the body and ⅓ the length of the body. The body fluid is darker than in other species and the waxy coating is scarce in 4 areas which look like 4 longitudinal lines. For many years it was kept under control by an Australian beetle, Crytolaemus, reared on potato sprouts and

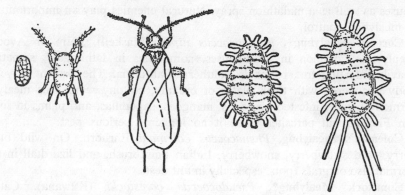

59. Mealybugs: citrus, egg, larva, male and female adults; long-tailed (at right).

distributed to growers but since 1929 a couple of internal parasites from Australia have had this species under commercial control.

Citrus Mealybug*, *Pseudococcus citri* (Risso). Distributed throughout the world in greenhouses and outdoors in subtropical climates; an omnivorous feeder. As a greenhouse and house-plant pest it is especially troublesome on soft-stemmed foliage plants such as African-violet, coleus, begonia, fern, fuchsia; it is almost always present on gardenia, readily infests amaryllis, avocado, bignonia, camellia, crassula, cineraria, cycas, cactus, chrysanthemum, croton, daphne, dracaena, heliotrope, ivy, lantana, oleander, orchids, poinsettia, rubber plant, umbrella plant, yucca. It is an outdoor pest of citrus trees in California and Florida and in the latter state is troublesome on sprouts of spring-grown potatoes kept through the summer for planting the fall crop. In southern California the citrus mealybug is found in the open on most of the plants mentioned above and also on bottle-brush, bouvardia, palms, moonflower, passion-flower, plumbago, strelitzia, and wandering-Jew. It can also live outdoors in Alabama and parts of New Mexico but is not so much of a pest there.

The white powder over the back of the citrus mealybug is very dense, and the filaments are about equal length around the body.

Control. A few mealybugs on house plants can be picked off with a toothpick or killed with a small cotton swab dipped in alcohol. Keeping foliage washed or syringed off frequently will prevent mealybug infestations. An aerosal bomb containing rotenone and pyrethrum will keep down light infestations, but spraying with malathion is more effective. Spraying with a white-oil emulsion such as Volck, using 3 to 5 tablespoons per gallon, has long been recommended. Plants should be kept out of direct sun during and after treatment and syringed off with water several hours later. DDVP, parathion, or Sulfotepp aerosols or sprays are often used in commercial greenhouses as well as a malathion spray. Natural enemies play an important part in mealybug control.

Coconut Mealybug*, *Pseudococcus nipae* (Maskell). Palm or Avocado Mealybug. Common in greenhouses, sometimes in lathhouses, sometimes heavily infesting tree palms in southern California. The brown or yellow body is covered with thick plates of creamy, cottony wax. This mealybug formerly heavily infested avocados, mangoes, sapodillas, and palms in southern Florida, but parasites make it no longer a serious pest.

Coleman's Mealybug, *Phenacoccus colemani* Ehrhorn. On wild blackberry, wild strawberry, snowberry, Indian paintbrush, and lizardtail in California; also on grass roots, especially in ant nests.

Comstock Mealybug*, *Pseudococcus comstocki* (Kuwana). Catalpa Mealybug. A Japanese pest distributed from Massachusetts to Florida, known in Ohio, Indiana, Louisiana, and also in California. One of the few mealybugs to winter outdoors in temperate climates, it feeds on apple, boxwood, catalpa, holly, grape, horsechestnut, Japanese honeysuckle, magnolia, maple, mulberry, Osage-orange, peach, pear, Monterey pine, poplar, and weigela. It has long been known as a serious pest of umbrella catalpa but has been actively injurious to apple more recently. In addition to injury from sapsucking, the fruit is greatly disfigured with sooty mold growing in honeydew, often coincident with soft rot. When the mealybugs congregate at a split in the tree or at a pruning scar, knotty galls are formed.

The Comstock mealybug winters in the egg stage in bark crevices, hatching when leaves are about an inch long. There is a second generation maturing in late summer in Connecticut, with 3 broods in Virginia. This is one of the species with 2 longer filaments at the end of the body.

Control. Chief dependence is on parasites. Parathion kills some parasites without reducing the mealybugs. DDT has been more effective on apple in Connecticut. On catalpa and other ornamentals some control is obtained by cleaning all old leaves from the trees and brushing out mealybugs from crotches and crevices with a stiff brush. Thorough washing of trunk and branches with the hose is helpful, as is spraying with nicotine sulfate and soap. Sometimes a dormant spray of oil or lime-sulfur is used.

Cypress Mealybug, *Pseudococcus ryani* Coquillett. Present throughout California, most common on Monterey cypress but feeding also on other cypress, arborvitae, araucaria, Norfolk Island pine, incense cedar, redwood. This species has short lateral filaments and a pair of tail filaments ⅓ to ½ the length of the body.

Fruit Mealybug, *Pseudococcus malacearum* Ferris. On citrus, fig, grapes in California.

Golden Mealybug, *Pseudococcus aurilanatus* (Maskell). Introduced into California from Australia and New Zealand on Norfolk Island pine and the monkeypuzzle tree. It is common in southern California and is found up to San Francisco. The body is reddish purple, covered with yellow wax; eggs are purple in a yellow sac.

Grape Mealybug*, *Pseudococcus maritimus* (Ehrhorn). Baker's Mealybug. Another omnivorous feeder. It was originally found on roots of buckwheat in California; it also occurs on roots or tops of clover, elder, buckeye, willow. From these it has gone over to cultivated plants, including apple, century plant, California poppy, coleus, columbine, Canary date palm, carnation, grevillea, lima bean, grape, English ivy, ginkgo, laburnum, lemon, orange, Mexican orange, passion-flower, pear, potato, Japanese quince, strawberry, English walnut, and Japanese yew.

The grape mealybug is present generally in California, where it is most important on grapes and pears in the Santa Clara Valley, on citrus and English walnut in the coastal section, and in Florida where it injures avocado, sweetpotato, and tomato. It has been recorded from scattered localities in Oregon, Michigan, Missouri, and New York. It may be present in quantity on stored gladiolus bulbs, is carried over in calla-lily corms to infect foliage later, and spreads a fungus disease of Texas bluebell.

On grape, the mealybug winters as eggs under loose bark, the spring generation developing on buds, leaves, young fruits. The 2nd generation congregates on grape clusters, where excessive honeydew encourages black sooty mold, making grapes entirely unappetizing. Ants help the mealybugs to get about.

Control. Parathion applied in February as a dormant spray is effective. It can be used only by commercial growers; malathion is better suited to gardeners. Chlordane to control ants will indirectly reduce mealybugs. Spraying grapes and pears with a dormant oil emulsion has been recommended. There are efficient natural parasites.

Ground Mealybug*, *Rhizoecus falcifer* Kunckel d'Herculais. Root Mealybug. A European species living on terminal or outer roots of potted plants, especially cacti. It also feeds outdoors in California on roots of grasses, acacia, boxwood, chrysanthemum, currant, Shasta daisy, gooseberry, grape, larkspur, marguerite, orange, peach, pepper, petunia, plum, California privet, thyme, among others. There is no entirely satisfactory control around growing plants. Chemical control in vineyards appears to be unnecessary. This mealybug differs in being smaller than average and lacking the wax rods and filaments. It is uniformly covered with white waxy powder. It may be a problem on African-violet.

Another ground mealybug, *Rhizoecus kondonis* Kuwana, may be a problem in California. It is reported heavy on laurel and on lawn grass roots, around roots of prune trees.

Japanese Mealybug, *Pseudococcus krauhniae* (Kuwana). Closely related to the citrus mealybug but with an elongated or serpentine egg sac. It infests orange, wisteria, and Japanese persimmon in the Ojai Valley, California.

Juniper Mealybug, *Pseudococcus juniperi* Ehrhorn. A dark-red mealybug on juniper in the Middle West.

Loblolly Mealybug, *Dysmicoccus obesus* Lobdell. Originally described from Mississippi and in 1956 found heavily infesting an ornamental planting of loblolly pines in Delaware. Trees were spindly, with sparse foliage, shorter height, with a white, powdery deposit indicating mealybugs under bark scales. Ants were numerous. A single thorough application of malathion cleaned up this infestation.

Long-tailed Mealybug*, *Pseudococcus adonidum* (Linnaeus). Widely distributed in greenhouses and outdoors in warm climates. This species has 2 pencil-like filaments at the tail which are as long as, or longer than, the body. Living young are produced instead of eggs. This is the most important mealybug on avocado, killing the scions after grafting, and infests a long list of other plants. It occurs on citrus—orange, grapefruit, lemon—and on banana, begonia, cactus, calla, cineraria, coleus, croton, dracaena, eucalyptus, ferns, fig, fuchsia, gardenia, guava, pandanus, plum, poinsettia, primrose, rubber plant, sago palm, strelitzia, umbrella plant, carob, zinnia.

Control. On avocado, after grafting, dust top 6 inches with 5 per cent chlordane, or paint the area with a slurry made of 2 pounds 50 per cent wettable powder to 1 gallon of water. This controls ants that bring mealybugs. Spray other plants with malathion or parathion. Biological control is fairly efficient, with brown and green lacewings particularly useful. Natural enemies, however, can be upset by ants, insecticides, or heavy road dusts.

Mexican Mealybug*, *Phenacoccus gossypii* Townsend & Cockerell. Introduced from Mexico on cotton and now a general greenhouse pest and an outdoor problem in warm climates. It is often serious on chrysanthemum. Hollyhock, geranium, English ivy, lantana, and stock are other favored food plants. It is not much of a pest on citrus but may infest guava and poinsettia. This is a short-tailed mealybug, blue gray, covered with a thin powder, with posterior filaments ¼ the length of the body. It attacks leaves, stems, flowers in all stages of growth; it causes stunting of chrysanthemums with distortion of foliage.

Control. Fumigation of greenhouses with hydrogen cyanide is quite effective for this Mexican mealybug, and it has been controlled by low-dosage soil treatment with sodium selenate. Parathion, TEPP, or sulfotepp aerosols are also used commercially.

Pineapple Mealybug*, *Pseudococcus brevipes* (Cockerell). Chiefly a tropical species, sometimes occurring on pineapple, banana, and sugar cane in Louisiana and Florida. This is a toxicogenic insect which causes, by its feeding on plants, a condition known as pineapple wilt.

Redwood Mealybug, *Pseudococcus sequoiae* (Coleman). Common on cypress and redwood, distinguished from the cypress mealybug by anal filaments being very short or lacking.

Solanum Mealybug, *Pseudococcus solani* Ferris. On paper-white narcissus bulbs in storage, especially in Florida, migrating to roots of these bulbs in the field from ambrosia, aster, malva, pansy, peanut, potato, tomato and other plants. The body is pale yellow, sparsely covered with fine white powder. Growers can fumigate bulbs with calcium cyanide after harvesting and curing.

Striped Mealybug, *Ferrisia virgata* (Cockerell). A tropical species, recorded in Texas in 1895 and in Maryland in 1953, also known in Virginia. It infests azaleas and many other flowering plants. The nymphs are light yellow; the adults are covered with glassy threads several times as long as the body. They do not secrete honeydew. There are at least 2 generations, with nymphs wintering on seed tassels. Spraying with malathion gives satisfactory control.

Taxus Mealybug, *Pseudococcus wistariae* Green (=*P. cuspidatae* Rau). First reported in a New Jersey nursery in 1915, now common in New Jersey, New York, Connecticut, Massachusetts and probably present on yew over much of the Northeast. All species of Taxus are infested, those with dense foliage, like *Taxus cuspidatae nana* and *T. wardi* being preferred. This species has been collected from apple, basswood, cedar, maple, and rhododendron but probably does not breed on these plants. It is very abundant on yew in home gardens. I have treated a hedge 100 feet long with trunks and axils of every bush completely covered with the mealybugs. But because the insects are on the interior, infestations usually go unnoticed until general poor health causes a close examination.

The female is about ⅜ inch long and half as wide, covered with white wax so distributed that the reddish body fluid shows through in 4 longitudinal lines. There are 15 filaments on each side of the body and tail filaments about ⅓ body length. This species gives birth to living young. Nymphs winter in bark crevices and are mature by June. There are 2 or 3 broods; adults disappear in early fall.

Control. I have had excellent luck with nicotine sulfate, 1 to 400 dilution (2 teaspoons per gallon), spraying with sufficient pressure into the interior of the bushes. Malathion may be even more effective.

Yucca Mealybug, *Puto yuccae* (Coquillett). Found in California, Arizona, and New Mexico. This large species has a pale body entirely covered with thick plates of white, cottony wax. Besides yucca, food plants include artemisia, aster, banana, black sage, ceanothus, eriophyllum, evening primrose, ice-plant, lantana, lemon, lime, monkeyflower. Roots, crowns, or tops may be infested.

MIDGES

Midges are very small flies, 2-winged insects of the order Diptera. The biting midges, punkies and nosee-ums, make the gardener miserable when he takes to the woods for a vacation. The gall midges or gall gnats, family Cecidomyiidae (=Itonididae) make the gardener miserable when he stays home and worries about his rosebuds or galls on the chrysanthemums. Many of the galls on trees are caused by midges. DDT is effective for control of some midges of economic importance.

Apple Leaf-curling Midge, *Dasyneura mali* Kieffer. An apple pest in

New England and New York. Small orange maggots live inside curled edges of leaves on new shoots. The fly is red with iridescent wings. Spraying with DDT or nicotine sulfate near petal fall gives control.

Artemisia Gall Midges, *Diarthronomyia artemisiae* Felt and other species. In Utah and Colorado, globose bud, rosette, or bladder galls are formed on artemisia. In California, brown or reddish subconical galls form on underside of leaves, or white confluent galls on stems, or small, oval, thin-walled, hairy galls on leaf surfaces.

Balsam Gall Midge*, *Cecidomyia balsamicola* Lintner. Making small, subglobular swellings at base of needles. Rather widespread but not too serious on balsam and Fraser firs, also on Douglas-fir.

Cactus Fruit Gall Midge, *Asphondylia opuntiae* Felt. A small gray midge with white larvae, often present in great numbers on green and ripening fruit of opuntia cactus, leaving brown pupal skins protruding from exit holes. Common in California, Colorado, New Mexico, Texas.

Catalpa Midge*, *Cecidomyia catalpae* (Comstock). A yellow fly, 1/16 inch long, appearing in late May or early June, lays eggs on unfolding catalpa leaves. Whitish to orange maggots occur in great numbers close to midrib and large veins on underside of leaves. There are several generations. Maggot injury looks like a fungus disease, with circular dead spots on the leaves and later wilting, browning, crumpling, defoliation. Late in the season maggots enter pods and destroy seeds. Persistent killing of terminal buds stunts and dwarfs trees. The midge winters as pupae in the soil. Cultivate the soil beneath trees to destroy pupae; spray in late May with malathion, or malathion plus DDT.

Cattleya Midge, *Parallelodiplosis cattleyae* (Moll). Yellowish maggots, ⅛ inch long, feed in tips of roots of many kinds of orchids, causing nutlike galls. Cut off and destroy galls. Repot plants and spray with DDT or lindane when midges come out.

Chrysanthemum Gall Midge*, *Diarthronomyia chrysanthemi* Ahlberg. Limited to chrysanthemums, all varieties in greenhouse or garden. The frail, long-legged orange gnat, ¼ inch long, lays about 100 minute orange eggs on new shoots (Plate XXVIII). Hatching in 3 to 16 days, white, yellow, or orange maggots bore into tissues. The irritation of their feeding causes many cone-shaped galls on upper surface of leaves and on stems, where a number together often form knots. Developing buds are distorted and ruined; stems are twisted. When flies emerge from the galls, usually between midnight and 4 A.M., they leave protruding empty pupal cases. The life cycle is about 35 days with 5 or 6 generations a year on greenhouse chrysanthemums. I usually find 2 in gardens.

Control. Pick off and burn infested foliage. Spray with 25 per cent lindane emulsion, 1 teaspoon per gallon, or with 1 tablespoon of wettable powder per gallon, 2 or 3 times at 5-day intervals. Make the application toward evening to kill flies coming out at night. DDT is effective against adults but repeated applications are needed. Parathion aerosols may be used in commercial greenhouses.

Cranberry Tipworm Midge, *Dasyneura raccinii* Smith. Runners are cupped together, with 1 to 5 maggots in each tip.

Dogwood Club-gall Midge*, *Mycodiplosis alternata* Felt. Common on flowering dogwood, a club-shaped gall, ½ to 1 inch long, in twigs. The reddish-brown midge attacks young shoots in late May; development of small orange larvae in galls is completed by September, when they drop to the ground. Cut off and burn swollen twigs while larvae are present.

Douglas-fir Cone Midge, *Contarinia oregonensis* Foote. Causes loss of seed in local areas. Guthion has been effective in control.

False Leaf Mining Midge, *Cricotopus ornatus.* Sometimes present on waterlily. Leaves of a small fly mine in serpentine tunnels, followed by bacteria; new leaves turn brown and rot.

Gouty Pitch Gall Midge, *Retinodiplosis inopsis* Osten Sacken. Small orange maggots feeding on tender bark of pine twigs, mostly in the Northeast and Northwest, causing globular masses of resin.

Grape Blossom Midge*, *Contarinia johnsoni* (Slingerland & Johnson). Sometimes attacking blossoms and buds and preventing fruit development. Eggs are laid in buds, reddish maggots develop, feed, drop to the ground to pupate in a little more than 2 weeks, remaining there until the next spring.

Grape Gall Midge, *Cecidomyia viticola* Osten Sacken. Small conical reddish or greenish leaf galls, ¼ inch long; also on flowers, vines, and tendrils. Reported from Ohio and Virginia.

Grapevine Tomato Gall Midge, *Lasioptera vitis* Osten Sacken. A green or reddish swelling in new growth, leaf, or tendril, ¼ to ¾ inch long, with pinkish maggots inside.

Honeylocust Pod Gall Midge, *Dasyneura gleditschiae* Osten Sacken. Widely distributed, important in Indiana, Ohio, Connecticut, and other states, especially in nurseries and on Moraine locust. In severe infestations all leaflets may become podlike galls, dry up and drop prematurely. Adult midges appear in April as new growth starts. Males are black, females have a red abdomen; they are ⅛ inch long. Minute kidney-shaped eggs are inserted in young leaflets; the larvae hatch in a day or two and feed on the inner surface, stopping its development. The outer surface grows normally, thus producing the pod. There may be 5 to 7 broods. Lindane, 1 pint emulsion in 100 gallons of water, is recommended for control.

Juniper Midge, *Contarinia juniperina* Felt. Yellow maggots cause blisters at base of needles which may drop; tips die. Larvae winter in the soil and flies lay eggs on needles in April. Control by pruning dead tips and cultivating soil or treating it with lindane.

Monterey Pine Midge, *Thecodiplosis pini-radiatae* Snow & Mills. A common and serious pest of Monterey pine in California, also present on other pines and Monterey cypress. Minute dark flies lay orange eggs in masses on terminal buds from January to March; orange maggots feed at base of needles until November or December, then pupate in soil. Needles are shortened, yellow, swollen at base. Trees are weakened, look as if swept by fire, and drop needles; some trees die. Cultivate around trees in early winter to destroy pupae.

Monterey-pine Resin Midge*, *Cecidomyia resinicoloides* Williams. A pitch midge living in the resin exudations of Monterey pine but not particularly injurious.

Pear Midge*, *Contarinia pyrivora* (Riley). The fly deposits eggs in pear-blossom buds in late April or May. When full-grown the maggots drop to the ground or remain in fruit, which becomes bloated, lopsided with dark blotches, and drops early.

Pear Leaf Midge, *Dasyneura pyri* Kieffer. Rolls or folds pear leaves.

Rhododendron Tip Midge, *Giardomyia rhododendri* Felt. Young leaves are rolled, swollen, with margin browned by small, whitish maggots. New growth does not develop properly. Spray tips with lindane or DDT.

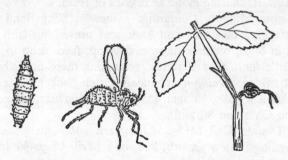

60. Rose midge: maggot, adult, and dead bud.

Rose Midge*, *Dasyneura rhodophaga* (Coquillett). Confined to roses, a greenhouse pest since 1886, first reported in gardens in 1916 and now found in scattered localities in many states. It arrives in a garden with unbelievable suddenness and works with devastating thoroughness, more often in mid- or late summer. A rose flower garden is changed almost overnight into a green garden with every potential bud in a leaf axil black and crisp, every tiny new shoot dead, buds on pedicels twisted, deformed, blackened.

The adult—minute, 1/20 inch long, reddish or yellow-brown—lays small yellowish eggs on succulent growth, under sepals of flower buds, in unfolding leaves. In warm weather they hatch in 2 days and young whitish maggots feed at base of flowers, often 20 or 30 in a bud, or on upper side of leaves and leaf petioles, causing them to become distorted, turn brown and die (XXVIII). They reach maturity, orange, 1/12 inch long, in about a week. They fall to the ground to pupate in small white cocoons, and new adults appear in 5 to 7 days. The life cycle takes 12 to 16 days in greenhouses, longer out of doors.

Control. DDT, which is very effective, has replaced ineffective tobacco sprays, mulches etc. At first indication of infestation spray with 50 per cent wettable DDT, 2 tablespoons per gallon. Cover bush and ground underneath thoroughly. Repeat twice at 7- to 10-day intervals. Prune off into a paper bag and burn all infested buds.

Spruce Gall Midge, *Phytophaga piceae* Felt. Eggs are laid at base of needles of new shoots or under bud scales. Larvae, up to 100 in a shoot, live in galls similar to those caused by aphids on spruce.

Sunflower Seed Midge*, *Lasioptera murtfeldtiana* Felt. Infesting sunflower seeds but the exterior appears normal.

Violet Gall Midge, *Phytophaga violicola* Coquillett. The small fly lays white eggs in curled margins of unfolding new violet leaves. The maggots cause curling, distortion, twisting of leaves, followed by a wet rot. Infested plants are dwarfed; blossoming is rather limited. Gather and burn fallen leaves frequently.

Willow Beaked-gall Midge*, *Phytophaga rigidae* (Osten Sacken). A fusiform gall, with a beak 1 inch long near tip of stem. Often found on pussy willow.

MILLIPEDES

Millipedes, "thousand-legged worms," class Diplopoda, are long, hard-shelled, cylindrical, with 2 pairs of legs on each of their many segments. They are brown or pinkish brown, occasionally grayish, about an inch long, rarely up to 2 inches, and are usually found coiled up like a watch spring. Most gardeners confuse them with wireworms, which are also hard-shelled but are flat, not round in cross section, have only the 6 legs of a true insect, and do not coil up like a spring (compare Plates XXIII and XXIX). Millipedes have 60 to 400 legs, not 1000. They are useful as scavengers, feeding on decaying vegetable matter and manure, but they do sometimes eat small roots or seedlings and bean, corn, or pea seed. They slide into cabbage heads to horrify the cook, tunnel into potato tubers or into carrots, beets, parsnips, or turnips. Fruits that touch damp ground, especially muskmelon, tomatoes, or strawberries, are often entered by these wiry worms. They are frequently found in decaying bulbs but are seldom the original cause of decay. Chief injury is in greenhouses in soil rich in organic matter. They are found in camellia grafts, injuring young leaves.

Each female deposits about 300 eggs, in clusters of 20 to 100, in soil or on the surface. The eggs are nearly translucent and are covered with a sticky material. They hatch in about 3 weeks. Young millipedes have at first only 3 pairs of legs and fewer segments than the adults. They grow slowly and there is probably only 1 generation a year.

To control millipedes spray soil with malathion, Sevin or diazinon or

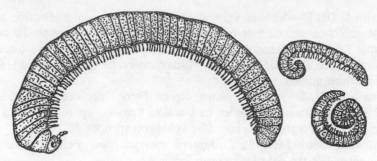

61. Millipede, much enlarged, and in typical positions.

spray or dust with lindane, chlordane, or DDT. Cover all hiding places in greenhouses. In gardens, protect ripening fruits with salt hay or other mulch. Destroy refuse.

Millipedes are seldom differentiated by gardeners, but species sometimes mentioned in reports include:

Blaniulus guttulatus Bosc. Introduced from Europe many years ago and now widespread, being the most common millipede pest of potatoes in the Northwest. It may also infest many other vegetables and some flowers. It is just over ½ inch long, light brown with white legs—55 to 75 pairs—with prominent reddish-brown ovate spots on each side of the body. Tunnels are bored in potato seed pieces or tubers and several hundred worms may be present in a roiling mass.

Orthomorpha gracilis (Koch). Dark brown to black, a common pest in greenhouses and outdoors in the South and on the West Coast, recorded as severely infesting philodendron. In experiments with greenhouse roses dimethoate and endrin proved effective for millipedes resistant to DDT, malathion, and lindane.

Orthomorpha coearctata (Sauss). Often numerous in lawns in Florida but apparently not very harmful. They may be controlled by spraying the area with chlordane.

Spirobolus marginatus (Say). One of the largest millipedes, up to 4 inches, dark brown, narrowly ringed with red.

Some millipede species, such as *Callipus lactarius* Risso and *Cambala annulata* (Say), are carnivorous, eating insects, and so to be classed as beneficial.

MITES

Mites are not true insects. They belong to the animal class Arachnida, which includes spiders, scorpions, harvestmen (daddy longlegs) and ticks, all grouped together by having 4 pairs of legs instead of the 3 pairs characterizing members of the insect class Insecta. Arachnids also differ from insects in lacking antennae, true jaws, and compound eyes, and in having only 2 body regions, head and thorax being joined together into a cephalothorax. Mites, members of the order Acarina, differ further in having the body seemingly all one piece, without segments. Young mites have only 3 pairs of legs; the 4th pair is added at maturity. Ticks are large members of the order Acarina; mites are the very small, almost microscopic forms.

Many mites are injurious to human beings or to animals. The families listed here include only those having members that are injurious to plants or are beneficial predators on plant pests.

Acaridae (Tyroglyphidae). Acarid mites. A large family with members living on all kinds of organic substances, including cheese, dried meats, flour, and seeds. The bulb mite belongs here.

Carpoglyphidae. Dried-fruit mites.

Eriophyidae. Gall or blister mites. Very minute, elongate, with only 2 pairs of legs, causing pouch or blister galls on leaves or a rusty appearance to foliage, or bud injury. The pear leaf blister mite and citrus rust mite are prominent examples.

Tarsonemidae. Soft-bodied mites, with the cyclamen mite common and injurious. They are very small, flat, pale, with short legs.

Tenuipalpidae (Phytoptipalpidae). False spider mites.

Tetranychidae. Red spiders, Spider mites. Small, oval, varying from yellow, green, red or brown, moderately long legs; a few hairs arranged in longitudinal rows on the back; web-spinning.

Trombidiidae. Harvest mites. Resembling red spiders but larger. This bright-red species commonly found in moist leaf litter is a scavenger and not a pest. This family includes chiggers, which attack man.

Since the advent of DDT and some other chlorinated hydrocarbons mites have increased enormously in importance. This has been due to the killing off of beneficial predators and parasites and apparently, in some cases, to a direct effect of DDT on plant tissues—predisposing them in some way to mite injury—and to an effect on the mites themselves—making them more active. Many excellent new acaricides, miticides, have been developed— some very toxic to humans and to be used with caution, others relatively safe. Among the latter are Aramite, Kelthane, Tedion, and Dimite.

Apple Rust Mite*, *Aculus schlechtendali* (Nalepa). A western pest, prevalent in Washington. Controlled by Thiodan at prebloom; Zectran is effective in tests.

Ash Flower-gall Mite, *Aceria fraxinivorus* (Nalepa). Stamens and flowers of white ash are transformed into galls, ¼ to ¾ inch in diameter, drying and remaining on trees. A dormant oil spray has been recommended.

Avocado Brown Mite, *Oligonychus punicae* (Hirst). On avocado in California, sometimes causing defoliation but not as serious as other mites. It is dark brown, makes light, delicate webbing, has amber eggs.

Avocado Red Mite*, *Oligonychus yothersi* (McGregor). The most common pest of avocado in Florida, also attacking mango, camphor, Australian silk oak, and camellias. It has been reported from elm, oak, and pecan in South Carolina. The mites are reddish purple, oval, with immature states greenish. Eggs are laid singly on both leaf surfaces. Leaves are speckled or russeted along the midrib and may drop off. Dusting with sulfur has been quite satisfactory. On avocado, parathion has given a good initial kill but is followed by an increase in mites. Dimethoate may be used on camellias to control mites as well as scale.

Azalea Mite, *Aculus atlantazaleae* Keifer. On terminal buds.

Balsam Root Mite, *Rhizogloephus sagittatae* Faust. Pale-yellow mite on tender leaves of balsam root (Balsamorhiza).

Bamboo Mite, *Schizotetranychus celarius* (Banks). A spider mite known only on bamboo, in Florida, Georgia, California; forming restricted colonies on underside of leaves and living under dense webbing.

Banks Grass Mite*, *Oligonychus pratensis* (Banks). Also known as Date Mite. Common on grasses and grains in western states, occasional on grasses elsewhere. An important pest of date palms in California, also on Washingtonia and Canariensis palms near date gardens, occasional on maple, cypress and other ornamental trees. The small, pale-yellow mite webs leaves and fruits together; the fruit is scurfy, shriveled, cracked, yellow. The mites winter on grasses and small palm seedlings. Dusting with sulfur is effective.

Beech Mite, *Aceria fagerinea* Keifer.

Beet Mite, *Rhizogloephus tarsalis* Banks. On sugar beets and dried figs.

Bermuda Grass Mite, *Aceria neocynodonis* Keifer. First found on Bermuda grass in an Arizona lawn in 1959, now known in California, Texas, New Mexico, Nevada, Florida, and Georgia. Mites are most numerous in well-fertilized lawns. The internodes are shortened resulting in rosetting and tufting of growth; plants are killed; lawns are thinned out. Diazinon has been satisfactory in tests.

Blackberry Bud Mite, *Eriophyes gracilis* (Nalepa). White, on developing drupelets of Himalaya blackberry.

Blueberry Bud Mite*, *Aceria vaccinii* (Keifer). Blossom buds may be so deformed they do not set fruit, or the berries have rough, blistered skin. The mites live all year under leaf or fruit-bud scales but can be controlled with a post-harvest spray of a summer oil, 3 per cent dilution.

Boreal Mite. See Yellow Spider Mite.

Boxwood Mite, *Eurytetranychus buxi* (Garman). Rather general on boxwood, especially where DDT has been used to control leaf miners. Injury shows as a light mottling of leaves early in the season, followed by a general grayish, dingy, unhealthy appearance. What appear to be minute hen scratches on foliage are an early indication of mites at work. The mites are yellow-green or reddish, 1/64 inch long. Yellow eggs winter on leaves, hatch in April. The mites breed rapidly with 5 or 6 generations in a summer. Dusting with sulfur has been recommended in the past, or a dormant oil spray before growth starts. Aramite is effective, 1 tablespoon wettable powder to 1 gallon of water.

Broad Mite*, *Hemitarsonemus latus* (Banks). Often associated with cyclamen mite and causing similar injury in greenhouses and sometimes in gardens. The broad mite is pale, almost translucent, slightly smaller and wider than the cyclamen mite. It moves more rapidly and feeds exposed on undersurface of leaves, completing its life cycle in 7 or 8 days. The injury is a blistered and glassy or silvery appearance to the leaf, which may become rather brittle, and sometimes a puckering downward. The broad mite attacks many ornamentals—cyclamen, delphinium, snapdragon, African-violet, begonia, china aster, marguerite, chrysanthemum, fuchsia, lantana, gerbera, geranium, marigold, verbena, zinnia—also avocado, mango, guava, and citrus seedlings in greenhouses.

Control. Sulfur dust is effective for this species.

Bugle Bud Mite, *Aceria ajugae* (Nalepa). Recently reported from ajuga (bugleweed) in California.

Bulb Mite*, *Rhizoglyphus echinopus* (Fumouze & Robin). Injuring bulbs or corms of amaryllis, crocus, freesia, gladiolus, hyacinth, lily, narcissus, onion, tulip, and underground stems of asparagus, peony, and a few other plants. The mite is whitish, often with 2 brown spots on the body, 1/50 to 1/25 inch long, slow-moving, found in colonies. It is abundant on rotting bulbs and decaying plant material, but it can also burrow into healthy bulbs and carry bacteria and fungi that produce rots. The mites spread infection from diseased to healthy bulbs in field, greenhouse, and storage.

The egg develops into a 6-legged larva, lasting 3 to 8 days, ending in a quiescent state. It molts into a protonymph with 8 legs, feeds for 2 to 4 days, has a second resting period, and molts into a tritonymph, then finally into the adult form. If conditions are unfavorable after the second molt, the mite goes into a heavily chitinized, non-feeding but active stage, the hypopus, in which it attaches itself to any moving object, perhaps a mouse or a fly, and so is transported to a new breeding place.

Control. Burn all infested (soft, mushy) bulbs. Treat others for 10 minutes in a 1 to 400 dilution of nicotine sulfate at 122° F. or in 2 to 4 per cent lime-sulfur held at 125° for 1 minute; or in hot water held at 110° to 111.5° for 3 hours; or store in tight containers with 2 per cent nicotine dust. Predaceous mites attack the bulb mite.

Bulb Scale Mite*, *Steneotarsonemus laticeps* (Halbert). Related to the cyclamen mite and not associated with rots, as is the bulb mite. The mites feed between leaves and flowers in neck region of the bulb, which becomes soft and spongy. Bulbs have yellow-brown, scarlike streaks; flowers and foliage are severely injured. Store bulbs in a cool place. If necessary, treat as for the bulb mite.

Citrus Bud Mite*, *Aceria sheldoni* (Ewing). Found on lemon in California in 1937, causing blasted or multiple buds, deformed twigs or leaves, blossoms, or fruits, bunched growth, blackening of rind beneath fruit buttons. Also present, but less important, on other citrus varieties in southern California. An oil spray every 6 to 8 months gives good conrtol; chlorobenzilate is also used.

Citrus Flat Mite*, *Brevipalpus lewisi* McGregor. False spider mite, reported also on privet. It can be controlled with sulfur dust or Kelthane.

Another flat mite (*B. phoenicis*) is reported severe on Murcott orange in Florida.

Camellia Bud Mite, *Aceria camelliae* Keifer. Reported heavy on certain varieties of camellias in California.

Carnation Mite, *Aceria paradianthi* Keifer. On carnations in California.

Citrus Red Mite*, *Panonychus citri* (McGregor). Purple Mite in Florida, Red Spider to many citrus growers, more serious in arid California than in moist Gulf States. This mite prefers lemons in California, satsuma oranges along the Gulf, but infcsts other oranges and grapefruit. Foliage is speckled silver, may turn brown and drop; fruit is gray or yellow and the crop light. Eggs are red, with a vertical stalk, laid on fruit, twigs, leaves. Larvae are at first orange, later dark red; adult females are almost black; males are lighter red but with a dark band around the body. They have red tubercles with white bristles.

Control. Oil sprays applied for scale insects keep down citrus red mites. Kelthane and Aramite are specific miticides. Three sprays per year of malathion are successful in Florida, often replacing the former parathion-Ovotran recommendation.

Citrus Rust Mite*, *Phyllocoptruta oleivora* (Ashmead). More serious in the Gulf States than in California on oranges, grapefruit, lemons, limes and other citrus fruit. A severe attack starts as faint black areas on green oranges, increasing until the whole fruit looks rusty, dry, rough. Outer cells are killed, size is reduced, rind thickened, quality impaired. The mite is long, wedge-shaped, orange as an adult, only 1/150 inch long. Yellow eggs are laid in depressions on fruit or on leaves. Cycles are completed in 10 days or less and mites are present through the year in Florida but least numerous in January and February. Sulfur is a specific for rust mite. It may be applied as lime-sulfur, 1 to 50 or 1 to 100 dilution, or as a wettable sulfur spray, or as sulfur dust with 3 to 6 applications a year.

Clover Mite*, *Bryobia praetiosa* Koch. Almond Mite, Brown Mite, distributed throughout the United States. Hosts include fruits—apple, apricot, almond, cherry, peach, pear, prune, raspberry—many shade trees and herbaceous plants and, of most consequence, lawns and shrubbery around houses. This mite has become an annoyance indoors, entering houses in large numbers in autumn but not actively injuring furnishings. In southern states the mite winters on various clovers and malva, but in the North it winters as small red eggs, looking like brick dust, on bark and around buds.

These hatch in early spring. Young mites are red, adults rusty brown, larger than other mites, with front legs longer than the others. Their feeding causes foliage to turn yellow and drop.

Control. The luxuriant well-fertilized grass around new dwellings is a factor in the increase of clover mites. Keeping an 18-inch grass-free band around houses and trees will markedly reduce infestations in houses, for the mites migrate between the grass, where they feed, and dwellings or trees where they oviposit and molt. Outside walls of houses and a 10-foot band of grass can be sprayed with Kelthane, or Aramite, chlorobenzilate, Ovotran, or malathion. Chlordane in aerosol form helps to clean up mites indoors.

Currant Bud Mite*, *Cecidophyes ribis* (Nalepa). Injurious to black, native, and flowering currants. The buds swell and die before opening, after which mites emerge to infest buds on normally developing canes. Cut and burn infested shoots; dust with sulfur in early spring.

Cyclamen Mite*, *Steneotarsonemus pallidus* (Banks). Pallid Mite, Strawberry Crown Mite. First noted in New York in 1898 and now present throughout the country as a greenhouse and garden pest. It is particularly injurious to cyclamen, snapdragon, and African-violet indoors, but the greenhouse list includes ageratum, azalea, begonia, gerbera, marguerite, lantana, marigold, verbena, zinnia. Outdoors this mite is probably the worst enemy of delphinium, deforms aconite and snapdragon, is often the limiting factor in strawberry production, may infest peppers and tomatoes.

The mite is too small to see with the naked eye but it can be readily identified by the characteristic reaction of the plants on which it feeds. Cyclamen infested early does not flower; later infestation produces distorted, streaked, or blotched blooms that fall early, with wrinkled, purplish foliage curled into cups (Plate XXX). African-violets are stunted, have twisted stems. Delphinium leaves are thickened, puckered without normal indentations; flower stalks are gnarled, twisted, darkened; buds turn black and seldom open; the whole plant may be stunted to less than ¼th normal height. Mite injury on delphinium is often known as "blacks" and thought to be a disease caused by a fungus or bacterium. Mites feeding in young, unfolding leaves of strawberries cause stunting, distortion, chlorosis, browning, and shriveling of flowers and no fruit.

The young cyclamen mite is glassy white or transparent pale green, 1/100 inch long, slow-moving; the adult is pale brown. The female lays 5 or 6 eggs a day for 2 or 3 weeks at the base of the plant or in crevices about leaves and buds. They hatch in a week into 6-legged larvae which are active for 7 days, then quiescent for 3 days before changing to the 8-legged adults. This is a cool-weather mite, injuring delphinium from early spring to June and in late summer but seldom active in the heat of midsummer.

Control. Keep this pest out if you can. Purchase only perfect, healthy specimens, whether delphinium for the garden or African-violets for the house. Buy certified strawberries. Space plants indoors so they do not touch; avoid handling clean plants after touching those possibly infested. Discard heavily infested plants. Valuable plants lightly infested can be immersed in hot water at 110° F. for 15 minutes. For African violets a capsule of sodium selenate can be laid on the surface of the pot, which is then filled to the brim with water.

Endrin is particularly effective as a spray for cyclamen mite but is too poisonous for amateurs. Commercial growers also use Thiodan. Kelthane is safe for home gardeners and quite effective if sprays are started early in the season. Dimite, 1 teaspoon per gallon, is also useful.

Cypress Mites, *Oligonychus coniferarum* (McGregor) and *Eotetranychus libocedri* (McGregor). In western and southwestern states on cypress, Italian cypress, and incense cedar.

Date Mite. See Banks Grass Mite.

Desert Spider Mite*, *Tetranychus desertorum* Banks. Widespread through southern United States on a variety of plants—cactus, carrot, celery, corn, cotton, cucumber, melon, strawberry, and monkeyflower, sweetpea, sunflower, gladiolus, and zinnia.

Dried-fruit Mite*, *Carpoglyphus lactis* (Linnaeus). Light colored, on dried figs, raisins, prunes.

Dryberry Mite*, *Phyllocoptes gracilis* (Nalepa). Blackberry Bud Mite. White, on developing drupelets of Himalaya blackberry.

European Red Mite*, *Panonychus ulmi* (Koch). An imported species first noted in 1911, now serious in the Northeast and Northwest, particularly damaging following use of DDT in orchards. It is most injurious to apple, pear, plum, prune but may infest almond, walnut, citrus, and ornamental trees and shrubs, including mountain-ash, elm, black locust, and rose. Bright-red to orange eggs, each with a stalk, winter on twigs and branches, often in crevices of fruit spurs. They hatch in spring just before blooming. The first nymphal stage is bright red, the 2nd and 3rd dull green or brown. The adult female is velvety red with 4 rows of curved spines arising from white tubercles; 1/50 inch long. Foliage is speckled and turns a sickly bronze, looking as if covered with dust, but there is not much webbing. Fruit buds are weakened; many leaves drop. Fruit is undersized, of poor quality. Pear-leaf scorch is associated with this mite.

Control. Thorough spraying with a dormant oil emulsion will kill over-wintering eggs and reduce summer population of mites. Choice of summer acaricide depends on what resistance has been built up; possibilities include chlorbenside, chlorbenzilate, EPN, Guthion, TEPP for commercial growers, and Kelthane or Tedion for home gardeners as well as orchardists.

Fig Mite*, *Aceria ficus* (Cotte). Fig Rust Mite. First reported in California in 1922, now present in Oregon and Florida, probably elsewhere. Eggs are laid in the bud, on leaves or on branches. The mites are very small, invisible to the naked eye, and are present on terminal buds and young leaves. From 10 to several hundred mites may infest a single bud, causing defoliation. The fig mite also transmits the virus of fig mosaic and scars the inner surface of fig fruit, causing dead areas for development of smut and mold. Oil sprays are helpful.

Filbert Bud Mite*, *Phytoptus avellanae* (Nalepa). Filbert Big-bud. Buds are swollen to 2 or 3 times normal size, with no further development into foliage. In May, when mites leave swollen buds and start crawling to normal buds, some can be killed with an acaricide.

Four-spotted Spider Mite*, *Tetranychus canadensis* (McGregor). Widespread on trees in eastern and southwestern states. Hosts include apple, plum, elm, linden, horsechestnut, Osage-orange, poplar, rose, and umbrella-tree.

Fruit-tree Mite, *Bryobia rubrioculus* (Sheuten). Prevalent in western states—New Mexico, California, Oregon, Washington, Utah—on fruit trees, damaging young foliage of apple, pear, peach, apricot, and cherry; also found on alder.

Garman Spider Mite, *Eotetranychus uncatus* Garman. A fruit-tree pest in New England, damaging foliage by feeding on the undersurface of leaves, causing a crinkled effect. Leaves may be bronzed and, in severe infestations, trees may be completely defoliated and the fruit small. The adult, flesh-colored to lemon-yellow, more elongate than most mites, winters on the tree.

Germander Leaf Crinkle Mite, *Aculus teucrii.* First U. S. Report from Ohio in 1960; moderate damage on germander.

Grape Erineum Mite*, *Eriophyes vitis* (Pagenstecher). A very small mite, overwintering in grape buds and feeding on underside of leaves in spring, causing a superfluous growth of leaf hairs called an erineum, first white, later turning brown.

A strain of the erineum mite called the **Grape Bud Mite** does not produce erinea. It spends the entire year in buds and leaf axils.

The **Grape Rust Mite,** another Eriophyid, *Calopitrimerus vitis* (Nalepa), causes leaves of white grapes to turn yellow, those of dark grapes to turn red. Sulfur dust controls this mite.

Grevillea Mite, *Tuckerella pavoniformis* (Ewing). Tuckerellid Mite. On silk-oak in Florida. Also reported on redbud and ligustrum.

Hackberry Witches-broom Mite, *Eriphyes* sp. Associated with a powdery mildew fungus in the witches-broom formation so common on hackberry in eastern states.

Honeylocust Spider Mite, *Eotetranychus multidigituli* (Ewing). Only on honeylocust, *Gleditsia triacanthos,* but widespread, a serious pest in Indiana, Ohio, Illinois, found also in Connecticut, Pennsylvania, North Carolina, Washington, D.C., and Louisiana. The color of the larva changes from pale yellow to dark green as it feeds. The adult is green in summer, orange-red in winter. Aramite, chlorobenzilate, and malathion have given effective control.

Litchi Mite, *Aceria litchii* Keifer.

Lewis Spider Mite, *Eotetranychus lewisi* (McGregor). A citrus pest along the Pacific Coast, causing silvering of lemons and russeting of oranges, recorded also on ceanothus, castor-bean, and olive; a recent pest of poinsettias in greenhouses in the Northwest and in Florida. The foliage is speckled or peppered, turns pale and there may be webbing near the flower. Miticides reported effective by grower include Aramite, Kelthane, demeton, parathion, and Sulfo-tepp.

Mango Bud Mite, *Aceria mangiferae* (Hassan). A serious pest of mango in Hawaii, reported in Florida in 1960. Terminal buds are dark brown, terminal leaves drop off from some branches; new leaves are deformed.

Maple Bladder-gall Mite*, *Vasates quadripedes* (Shimer). Bladderlike galls—first red, then green, then black, single or in clusters—appear on upper surface of leaves. They may be thick enough to deform the leaves, injury being more serious on young silver or soft maples. White or pinkish mites winter in bark crevices or bud scales and migrate in late April when the buds break. A dormant lime-sulfur spray will control this but cannot be used near houses. Try Kelthane in May.

McDaniel Spider Mite, *Tetranychus mcdanieli* McGregor. Reported from Michigan on raspberry in 1931 but only recently a serious pest of deciduous fruit trees in the Northwest. It has been collected from apple, plum, prune, cherry, and currant, besides raspberry, from Washington, Oregon, Utah, California, New Mexico, Montana, North Dakota, Michigan, and New York. It is similar to the European red mite but a distinct species.

Oak Mite, *Oligonychus bicolor* (Banks). Severe in eastern United States, important on oak and elm, especially where heavy dosages of DDT have been used for bark beetles, sometimes on beech, birch, hickory, maple and other shade trees. The mite is dark green to black with forward part of the body lighter and brownish; dorsal spines are slender with no spots at the base; eggs are brown, flat on top. The foliage looks very dusty. To prevent trouble, add Aramite or Kelthane or Tedion if DDT must be used on shade trees.

Olive Leaf Mite, *Oxypleurites maxwelli* Keifer. Sometimes causing serious flower drop in California.

Omnivorous Mite, *Brevipalpus californicus* (Banks). False spider mite, a citrus pest and serious on orchids under glass. Intensely red adults are less than 1/100 inch long, ovate, flat; eggs are elliptical and bright red. The mites do not spin webs but feed on upper or lower leaf surfaces, producing a speckled white appearance. Dimite is effective in control.

Oncidium Mite, *Brevipalpus orchidii* Baker. Another false spider mite important on Oncidium and Odontoglossum orchids in California.

Pacific Spider Mite*, *Tetranychus pacificus* McGregor. Important along the Pacific Coast from California to Washington on apple, pear, cherry, grape, plum, prune, almond, walnut, beans, and various ornamentals. Since 1954 it has been considered an economic pest of citrus. Foliage is heavily webbed, turns bronze, and there may be extensive defoliation; fruit fails to color properly, often with heavy drop before harvest. This species resembles the two-spotted mite and makes similar webs. Adults winter in trash on ground, migrating to trees in spring and feeding on lower foliage first. Eggs are laid in webbing. There are several generations with peak of abundance in late summer, when mites spin webs at calyx end of fruit. Grapes turn prematurely red or brown; bean leaves are webbed.

Control. Dimite, Ovotran, and the highly poisonous phosphates have been recommended for sprays.

Pallid Mite, *Tydeus californicus* (Banks). Sometimes abundant on avocado. It is white, a little larger than the six-spotted mite, without spots.

Peach Silver Mite*, *Aculus cornutus* (Banks). Peach Rust Mite. Very small, pinkish, feeding more often on upper surface of leaves, causing silvering. It hibernates under bud scales. It is more of a problem on the Pacific Coast but can be controlled with a dormant lime-sulfur spray.

Pear Leaf Blister Mite*, *Eriophyes pyri* (Pagenstecher). Present wherever pears are grown, sometimes on apple, mountain-ash, shadbush, and cotoneaster. Brownish blisters appear on underside of leaves, each about ⅛ inch across but often massed together to nearly cover the leaf. When blisters are opened, small, elongated pinkish or white mites, 1/125 inch long, can be seen with a hand lens. Adults winter under scales of fruit and leaf buds, often hundreds in a single bud. They lay eggs in the buds as they swell in spring, and the young burrow in unfolding leaves, feeding entirely inside the blisters. Successive generations develop in the leaves, but they migrate to buds at the approach of cold weather.

Control. Apply a dormant lime-sulfur spray, 1 to 15 dilution, before buds open, or an oil emulsion just as buds begin to swell. The weather has to be warm enough for the oil to penetrate.

Pear Rust Mite*, *Epitrimerus pyri* (Nalepa). Bronzing foliage and russeting fruit of pears, sometimes infesting apple, prune, and cherry. A pest on the Pacific Coast and also in New York.

Pecan Leafroll Mite*, *Aceria caryae* (Keifer). Feeds on margin of leaflets, causing them to roll into a thickened gall-like growth parallel to the midvein. Another mite, *Eotetranychus hicoriae* McGregor, seems to be even more important on pecan, causing a scorching of leaves and defoliation. Parathion has given effective control.

Phaelenopsis Mite, *Tenuipalpus pacificus* Baker. A false spider mite, serious pest of Phaelenopsis and other orchids.

Pine Bud Mite*, *Phytoptus pini* Nalepa. Very minute, yellow blister or gall mite, injuring needles of pine in California and Oregon. Seriously infested pines may have to be removed. A dormant oil spray is helpful.

Platanus Mite, *Oligonychus platani* (McGregor). A serious pest of sycamore in hot interior valleys of California, also of loquat; present on avocado but under satisfactory natural control. Other hosts include live oak, cork oak, camphor, cotoneaster, cypress, eucalyptus, pyracantha, toyon, walnut, and willow. The mites feed on upper surface of leaves, causing a brownish discoloration.

Plum Rust Mite, *Aculus fockeui* (Nalepa & Trouessart). Plum Nursery Mite. Causing silvering and longitudinal curling of leaves and, in myrobalan plums, a disease known as chlorotic fleck. Present on the Pacific Coast and also in New York.

Pomegranate Leafroll Mite, *Aceria granati* (Canestrini & Massalongo). On pomegranate in California.

Privet Mite*, *Brevipalpus obovatus* Donnadieu. Widely distributed false spider mite, injuring privet, azalea, and other flowering shrubs, palms, ivy, ash, ceropegia, chrysanthemum, coleus, fuchsia. The mite was first described from goldenrod. The egg is elliptical, bright orange-red at first, then darker. The mites are bright orange to dark red with various dark pigmentations. They feed on underside of leaves, on stems and petioles. Leaves turn bronze underneath and deep red on upper surface of some plants, yellow on others. Privet turns yellow, azalea leaves brown or bronze and drop off. Undersides of fuchsia leaves are badly pitted with heavy leaf drop. Chlorobenzilate, Dimite, and Aramite have been effective in control.

Redberry Mite*, *Aceria essigi* Hassan. Blackberry Mite. A western species on blackberry, microscopic in size. Mites feed near the base of drupelets, preventing fruit from ripening in whole or in part, causing "redberry disease." Affected fruit stays bright-colored, hard, clings to bushes. Mites winter in buds. Use a dormant lime-sulfur spray, 1 to 15 dilution, in March as buds are opening, and a second spray, 1 to 40 dilution, when fruiting arms are about 1 foot long.

Schoene Spider Mite*, *Tetranychus schoeni* McGregor. Widely distributed in eastern and southwestern states on a wide variety of hosts, including apple, elm, black locust, bean, raspberry and other brambles.

Six-spotted Mite*, *Eotetranychus sexmaculatus* (Riley). A yellow mite, long a pest of citrus in Florida and southern California, more recently a very important pest of avocado in California. Mites occur in colonies on underside of foliage. Such areas, often near veins, are depressed and covered with webs. The upper surface of the leaf has yellowish blisters with a smooth, shiny surface. Oil sprays, DN or sulfur dusts, parathion, and Ovotran have been used for control.

Southern Red Mite*, *Oligonychus ilicis* (McGregor). Holly Mite, the Red Spider of the South, also injurious to many shrubs in the North. This mite is most important on holly and azalea but may also damage camellia, camphor, cypress, eucalyptus, loquat, live oak, plane, pyracantha, English walnut, and rose, sometimes other ornamentals. The mites feed on both leaf surfaces, rasping the epidermis. Leaves turn gray or brown as feeding continues. Adult females are nearly black, males and nymphs light red. Both have spiny hairs curving backward. Red eggs are laid on both leaf surfaces, and heavily infested leaves look as if they had been dusted with red pepper. There may be extensive defoliation. There are many generations but in the South most damage is in the fall or spring with low populations in midsummer. In the North mites start feeding on holly at the end of April, and populations increase rapidly in summer.

Control. Parathion has been very effective but can perhaps be replaced by safer dimethoate. Aramite and Kelthane are safe for home-garden use.

Southern Two-spotted Mite, *Tetranychus cinnabarinus* (Boisduval). Very similar to the two-spotted spider mite but carmine in color; most important in southern states but present elsewhere. This mite is frequently reported as a pest of melons, is common on cotton, and recorded on philodendron, mulberry, sugar beet and other, widely varying types of plants.

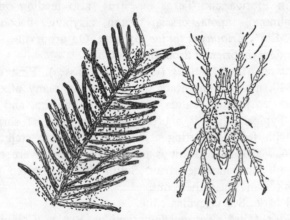

62. Spruce twig webbed by spruce spider mite and mite as seen under a microscope.

Spruce Spider Mite*, *Oligonychus ununguis* (Jacot). A most important evergreen pest. Arborvitae turns brown, spruce grayish, juniper yellow, hemlock nearly white from the sucking of these very small mites. They are dark green to nearly black, with spines on the back and salmon-pink legs. Spherical eggs, wintering at the base of needles, hatch in April or May, complete a generation in 4 or 5 weeks, and go on building up populations until winter eggs are laid in October. The mites spin a quantity of webbing between the needles. Injury is worse in hot, dry seasons and following use of DDT. Young spruces may die the first season; older trees die progressively, from lower branches upward, over a period of years.

Control. Syringing with a hose to break webs is helpful, and sulfur dust has been much used in the past. Aramite, 1 tablespoon of 15 per cent wettable powder to 1 gallon of water, gives good control; Kelthane may be substituted. Ovotran is effective against the egg stage.

Strawberry Spider Mite*, *Tetranychus atlanticus* McGregor. Widely distributed, New York to Florida and California, mostly on low-growing plants but occasional on pear, peach, apple, walnut, and lemon. This is a serious pest of strawberries, also of beans, soybeans, melon, parsley, eggplant, cotton, clover, alfalfa, and is found on many weeds. The females are straw-colored or greenish with a pair of black spots. They feed in definite colonies on underside of leaves. Plants are stunted with loss of vigor, reduced yield, and sometimes die. Spray with Kelthane or Tedion or use Aramite on non-bearing strawberry beds.

Taxus Bud Mite, *Cecidophyes psilaspis* (Nalepa). Foliage of yew is distorted; 1000 mites may be present in a single bud.

Texas Citrus Mite, *Eutetranychus banksii* (McGregor). A species complex known in Florida and Texas on citrus, also feeding on castor-bean, velvetbean, almond, sapota, cassia, croton, zizyphus, flacourtia, and fig.

Tip-dwarf Mite*, *Eriophyes thujae* Garman. On arborvitae, dwarfing tips, reported abundant on oriental arborvitae in Ohio.

Tomato Russet Mite*, *Aculus lycopersici* (Massee). First found in California in 1940, now an important tomato pest in many other states. The mite also feeds on potato, petunia, groundcherry, datura, and other solanaceous hosts. Typical injury is a bronzing or russeting of surface of stems and leaves, with feeding starting at base of the main stalk. Leaves turn brown 3 or 4 weeks later. Fruit is attacked only in severe cases but loss of foliage results in sunburned fruit. Sulfur dust has given good control. Predaceous mites and thrips help out.

Tuckerellid Mite. See Grevillea Mite.

Tumid Spider Mite*, *Tetranychus tumidus* Banks. Common in southeastern states, in California, and in greenhouses. Destructive to potted ornamentals such as palms, maranta, to pittosporum, and to low-growing vegetable crops, including celery, beans, beet, okra, peas, and sweetpotato.

Two-spotted Spider Mite*, *Tetranychus telarius* (Linnaeus). A pest in every garden, probably the most common of the mites we call Red Spider. The mites turn rose leaves gray or reddish or yellow or brown, with defoliation by midsummer. Leaves of phlox, hollyhock, primrose, violet, and many other flowers turn yellow, as does the foliage of beans and other vegetables and that of many fruits. Ivy in the house is a sickly gray from red spiders. Nearly all greenhouse plants are subject to infestation.

Red spiders are very small. The female is less than 1/50 inch, the male even smaller. The body is oval, yellow or greenish with 2 dark spots on the back, sparsely covered with spines. In some strains the adults are red.

E.MELADY.

I   MELON APHID: (a,1) winged female; (a,2) last nymphal stage; (a,3) eggs and young nymph; (a,4) wingless female or stem mother; (b) cantaloupe leaves starting to curl; (c) aphid-transmitted cucumber mosaic on fruit; (d) cucumber leaf mottled by mosaic. BEAN APHID: (a,1) winged female; (a,2) wingless female; (b) aphids on bean; (c) aphids clustering under nasturtium leaves.

II ROSY APPLE APHID: (a,1) first generation; (a,2) summer aphid; (a,3) eggs, much enlarged, and eggs hatching on apple bud; (a,4) fall aphid, winged female; (a,5) fall aphid, winged male; (a,6) egg-laying female; (a,7) apples distorted, leaves curled. POTATO APHID: (b) injured potato leaves. WOOLLY APPLE APHID: (c) woolly masses on twig, galls on roots. MELON APHID: (d) wingless form and curled leaves. EASTERN SPRUCE GALL APHID: (e) galls on Norway spruce. COOLEY SPRUCE GALL APHID: (f) terminal gall on blue spruce. SNOWBALL APHID: (g) viburnum foliage curled, distorted.

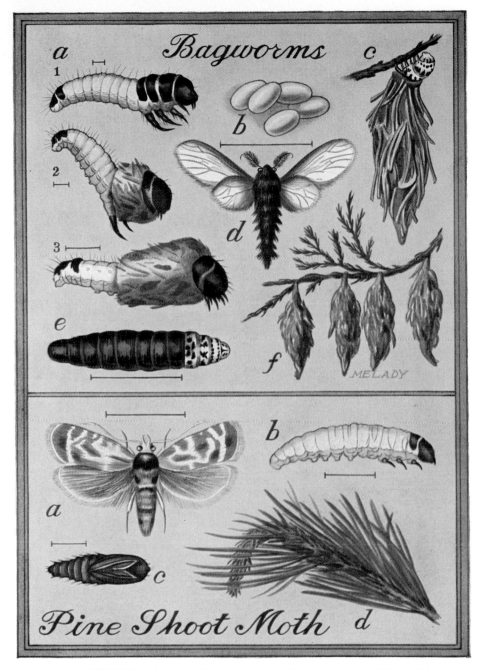

III BAGWORMS: (a,1,2,3) larva and stages in construction of bag; (b) eggs, highly magnified; (c) female in bag, actual size; (d) winged male moth; (e) wingless female removed from bag; (f) bags in winter. EUROPEAN PINE SHOOT MOTH: (a) moth; (b) larva removed from infested tip; (c) pupa; (d) pine shoot with typical crooking and discoloration.

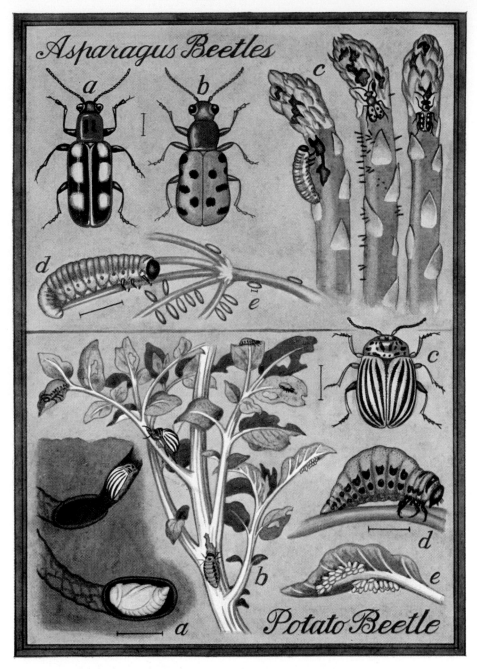

IV ASPARAGUS BEETLE: (a) adult; (c) typical injury to asparagus shoots
by grubs and beetles; (d) grub and eggs. SPOTTED ASPARAGUS BEETLE: (b)
adult. COLORADO POTATO BEETLE: (a) pupa in soil and adult emerging from
soil; (b) portion of potato vine showing larvae, eggs, and beetles; (c) adult beetle;
(d) humpbacked grub; (e) egg clusters on underside of potato leaf.

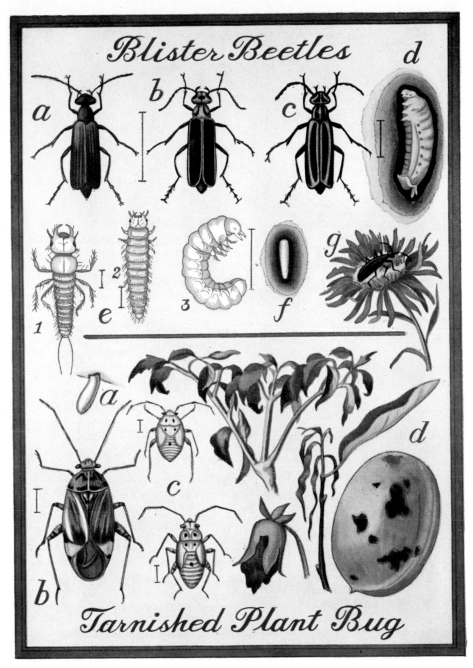

V CLEMATIS BLISTER BEETLE: (a) adult. MARGINED BLISTER
BEETLE: (b) adult. STRIPED BLISTER BEETLE: (c) adult; (d) pseudopupa
in soil; (e,1) triungulin or first larval stage; (e,2) second larval stage; (e,3) third
larval stage; (f) egg in soil, much enlarged; (g) adult feeding on aster. TARNISHED
PLANT BUG: (a) egg, enlarged, inserted in stem; (b) adult bug; (c) nymph in two
instars; (d) injury to fruit, bug, terminal shoot, leaves.

Gypsy Moth

Elm Leaf Beetle

VI GYPSY MOTH: (a) large female moth; (b) small dark male moth; (c) pupa inside scanty thread cocoon; (d) pupa enlarged; (e) full-grown hairy caterpillar; (f) egg mass. ELM LEAF BEETLE: (a) adult; (b) pupa; (c) grub; (d) egg cluster on underside of leaf and single egg, much magnified; (e) elm leaves skeletonized by larvae and with holes eaten by adults.

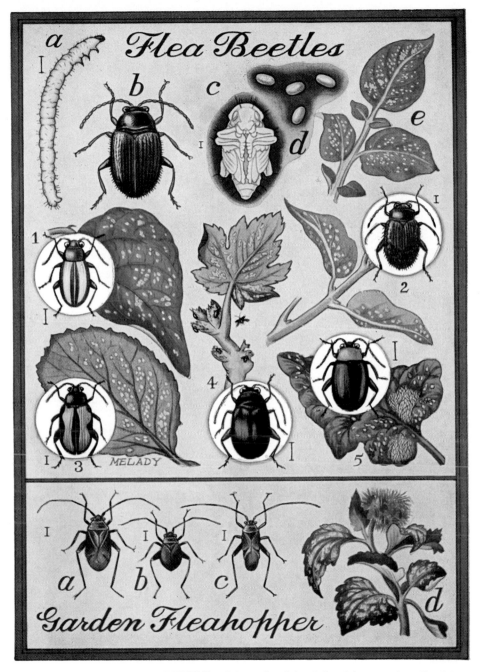

VII POTATO FLEA BEETLE: (a) grub; (b) adult; (c) pupa in soil; (d) eggs in soil; (e) "shot-hole" injury to potato leaf. PALE-STRIPED FLEA BEETLE: (1) adult and injury on bean. EGGPLANT FLEA BEETLE: (2) adult and riddled foliage. STRIPED FLEA BEETLE: (3) adult and injured cabbage leaf. GRAPE FLEA BEETLE: (4) adult and injury to grape leaf. SPINACH FLEA BEETLE: (5) adult, and spinach leaf skeletonized by grubs, riddled by beetles. GARDEN FLEAHOPPER: (a) long-winged female; (b) short-winged female; (c) male; (d) ageratum with foliage yellowed by loss of sap.

VIII JAPANESE BEETLE: (a) adult, with injury on peach, rose, corn; (b) egg in soil, much enlarged; (c) pupa in soil; (d) grub; (e) turf damage from grubs. JUNE BEETLE: (a) white grub actual size; (b) egg, enlarged, and young larva; (c) pupa; (d) adult.

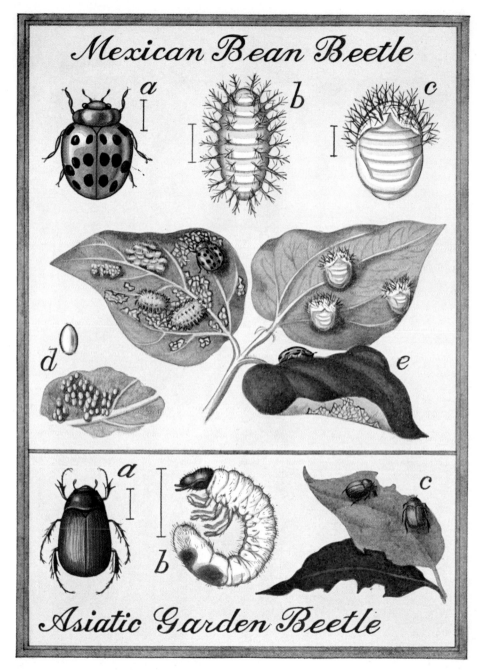

Mexican Bean Beetle

Asiatic Garden Beetle

IX   MEXICAN BEAN BEETLE: (a) adult; (b) grub; (c) pupa with larval skin pushed back at one end; (d) egg cluster on back of leaf and single egg enlarged; (e) bean leaf showing beetle in all stages and feeding pattern. ASIATIC GARDEN BEETLE: (a) adult; (b) grub; (c) beetles, natural size, feeding on foliage.

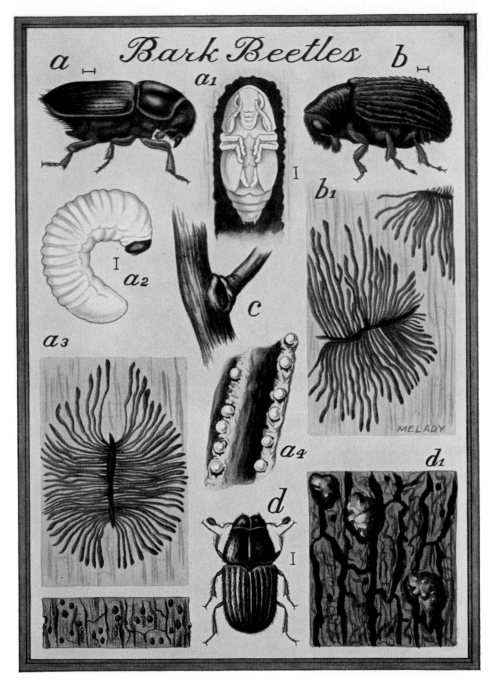

Bark Beetles

X SMALLER EUROPEAN ELM BARK BEETLE: (a) adult; (a,1) pupa; (a,2) grub; (a,3) characteristic pattern of galleries under bark and exit holes in bark; (a,4) eggs lining gallery, much enlarged; (c) feeding injury at crotch. NATIVE ELM BARK BEETLE: (b) adult; (b,1) galleries in transverse position. WESTERN PINE BEETLE: (d) adult; (d,1) pine bark with resin tubes around entrance holes and small exit holes.

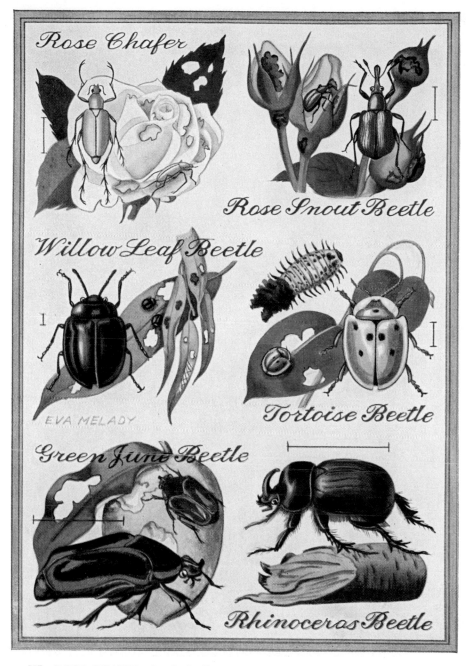

XI ROSE CHAFER: beetle feeding on rose. ROSE CURCULIO: (Rose Snout Beetle) on rosebuds. IMPORTED WILLOW LEAF BEETLE: willow leaves showing skeletonization by larvae, holes eaten by adults, and single beetle much enlarged. BLACK-LEGGED TORTOISE BEETLE: black-spined larva with excrement on back, adult feeding on leaf, natural size and enlarged. GREEN JUNE BEETLE: feeding on fruit and foliage. RHINOCEROS BEETLE.

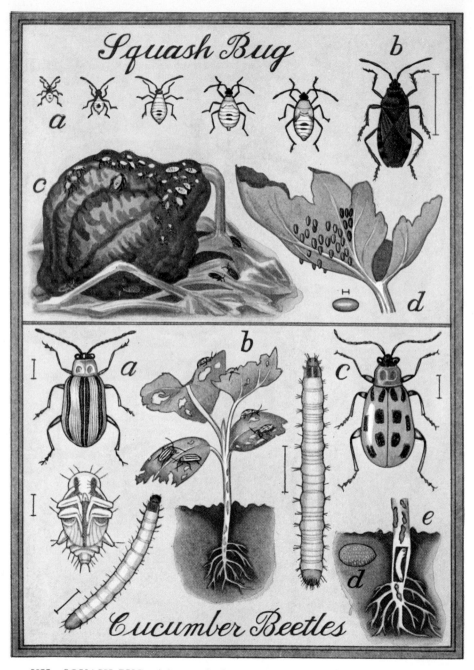

XII SQUASH BUG: (a) nymphs in successive instars; (b) adult; (c) nymphs feeding on squash; (d) eggs grouped on underside of leaf, and single egg, enlarged. **STRIPED CUCUMBER BEETLE:** (a) adult, pupa, and grub; (b) adults feeding on seedling. **SPOTTED CUCUMBER BEETLE:** (c) adult and rootworm larva; (d) egg in soil, enlarged; (e) larva in underground corn stem.

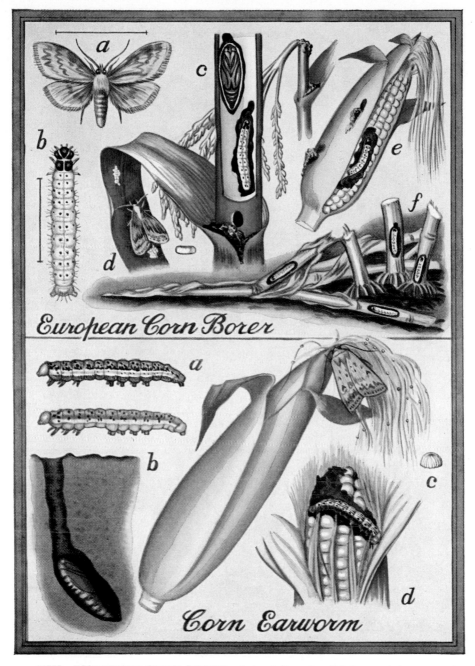

XIII EUROPEAN CORN BORER: (a) adult moth; (b) larva; (c) pupa and larva inside corn stem, frass protruding from hole; (d) moth laying eggs on corn leaf; (e) borer working in ear; (f) larvae overwintering in old corn stalks. CORN EARWORM: (a) larvae, brown or green striped caterpillars; (b) pupa in soil; (c) moth laying eggs on corn silk and single egg, much enlarged; (d) worm feeding in mass of frass at tip of ear.

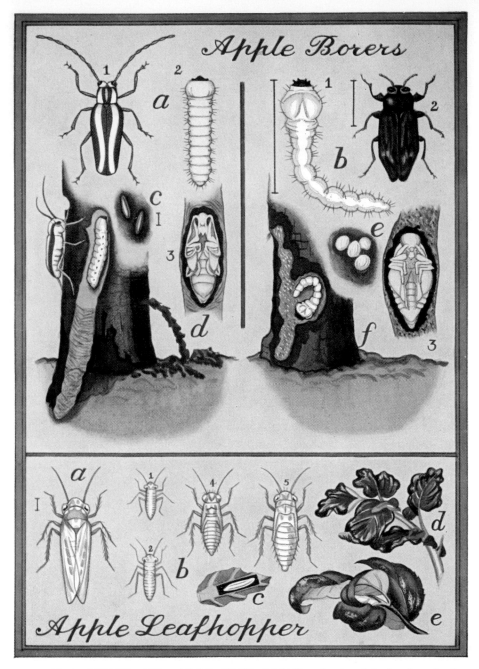

Apple Borers

Apple Leafhopper

XIV ROUNDHEADED APPLE TREE BORER: (a,1) adult beetle; (a,2) roundheaded grub; (a,3) pupa in wood cell; (c) eggs; (d) section of tree trunk, showing borer at work, frass protruding. FLATHEADED APPLE TREE BORER: (b,1) larva with flat enlargement behind head, characteristic curved position; (b,2) beetle; (b,3) pupa in cell; (e) eggs; (f) larva in winter chamber in tree trunk. POTATO LEAFHOPPER (Apple Leafhopper): (a) adult; (b,1,2,4,5) nymphs in different instars; (c) egg in leaf vein.

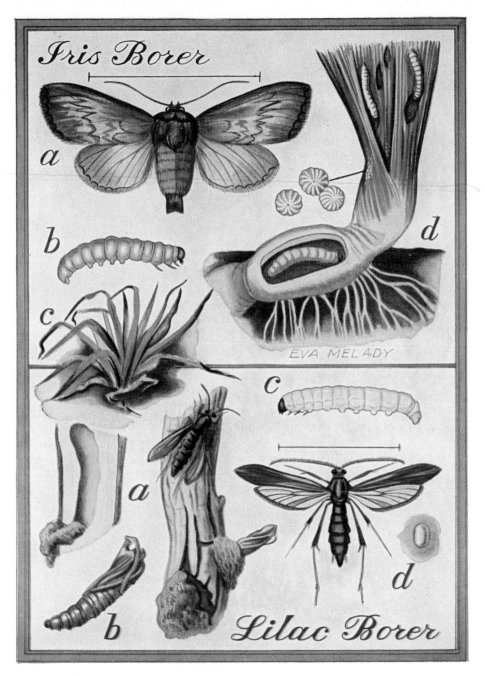

XV IRIS BORER: (a) moth, somewhat enlarged; (b) borer, not quite full grown; (c) infested iris; (d) young borers on outside of leaves (usual position is inside fold), older borer in hollow rhizome, and eggs, enlarged. LILAC BORER: (a) lilac stems showing tunnel and protruding sawdust, moth and pupa case; (b) pupa; (c) borer; (d) adult moth and egg (enlarged).

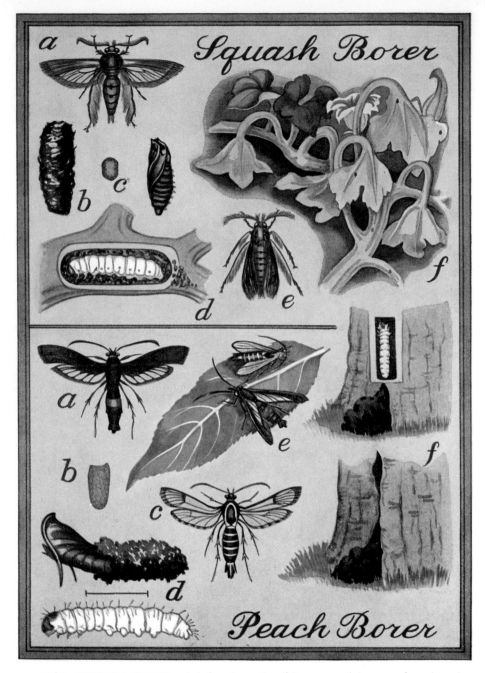

XVI SQUASH BORER: (a) female moth; (b) cocoon; (c) egg, enlarged, and pupa; (d) borer in stem; (e) male moth; (f) vine wilting from borer injury. PEACH TREE BORER: (a) female moth; (b) egg, enlarged; (c) male moth; (d) pupa protruding from cocoon, and borer; (e) adults on peach leaf; (f) section cut in tree trunk to show borer in position, jellylike frass at base.

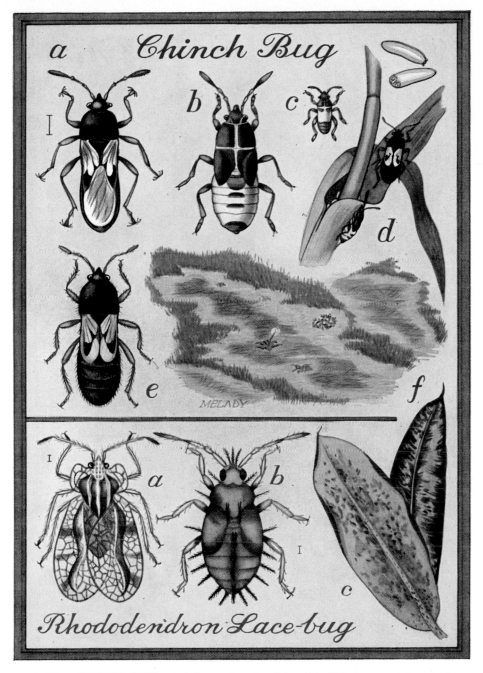

XVII CHINCH BUG: (a) long-winged adult; (b) fifth instar; (c) nymph, first instar. HAIRY CHINCH BUG: (d) eggs, much enlarged, and bugs in typical position behind boot of lower grass blade; (e) short-winged adult; (f) turf with brown areas killed by bugs and yellow margins where bugs are working. RHODO-DENDRON LACE BUG: (a) adult; (b) nymph in last stage of development; (c) rhododendron leaves showing browning of lower surface and loss of color on upper surface.

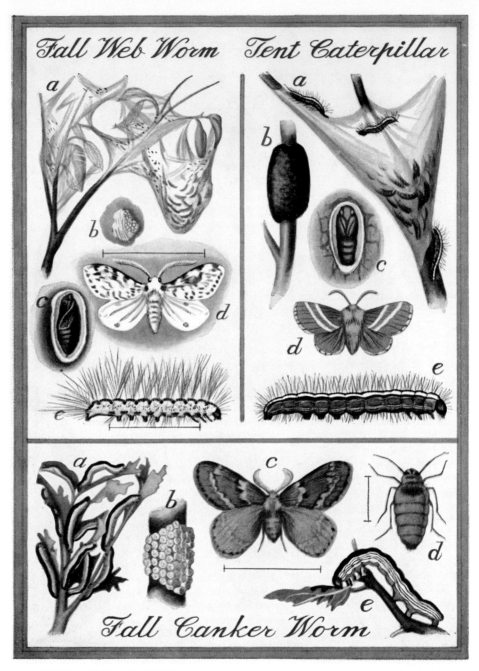

Fall Web Worm   Tent Caterpillar

Fall Canker Worm

XVIII FALL WEBWORM: (a) web or nest over end of branches; (b) egg mass covered with hairs on underside of leaf; (c) pupa in cocoon in soil; (d) adult moth; (e) full-grown hairy caterpillar. EASTERN TENT CATERPILLAR: (a) nest of caterpillars in tree crotch; (b) egg collar around twig; (c) pupa inside cocoon on bark; (d) adult moth; (e) full-grown caterpillar. FALL CANKER-WORM: (a) larvae ravaging foliage; (b) egg mass on twig; (c) male moth; (d) wingless female moth; (e) full-grown caterpillar with 3 prolegs.

The young, 6-legged mite feeds for a day or two after hatching, then enters a resting stage; it molts into a second active stage and again rests. The female goes through a 3rd such period before becoming adult, the male only 2 periods. Mating takes place a few minutes after the female reaches adult form, and she lays 100 to 200 eggs on underside of leaves in 3 or 4 weeks. Eggs from unmated females develop into males only. The mites make mealy cobwebs on the underside of leaves and from one leaf to another, sometimes entirely covering a new shoot, flower buds and all.

The number of generations increases with the temperature. At 75° F. the adult stage is reached in 5 days; it takes 40 days at 55°. In greenhouses there is a new generation every 20 to 30 days. Outdoors, mites hibernate as adults in soil, on tree bark, on leaves of plants retaining foliage, starting activity quite early in spring but often reaching peak of abundance in July. In situations of high humidity where air is stagnant, mites are always serious. Plants under overhanging eaves, in walled gardens, in dense clumps or thick hedges are most susceptible. Where DDT is used in mist blowers for mosquito control, red spiders build up enormous populations in gardens.

Control. There are many excellent acaricides. Aramite is still recommended for ornamentals, Kelthane and Tedion may be used on both ornamentals and food crops. Phosphates such as parathion and TEPP have been used by commercial growers, but some mites have become resistant. Pentac and dimethoate are possibilities for commercial growers. Syringing plants with the hose is still a good idea; use force enough to break the webs.

Walnut Blister Mite*, *Aceria erinea* (Nalepa). Yellow or brown feltlike galls are formed on underside of leaves but are not very injurious. The mite can be controlled with a dormant lime-sulfur spray, 1 to 10 dilution, when buds swell in spring.

Willamette Mite, *Eotetranychus willamettei* (McGregor). Known from southern California to Washington. A serious pest of grape, also present on apple, pear, cherry, raspberry, boxelder, serviceberry, oak, and sycamore. This species is similar to the Pacific mite but there is less webbing. Summer sprays of parathion, rotenone and oil, TEPP are used by growers. In some sections sulfur applied for control of powdery mildew on grapes controls the mite but in other areas it has become resistant to sulfur.

Yellow Spider Mite*, *Eutetranychus carpini borealis* Pritchard & Baker. Boreal Mite. Present from British Columbia to central California, a frequent pest of apple, pear, sometimes cherry, raspberry, blueberry, spirea, alder, and willow. This species is similar to the common red spider (two-spotted mite) but is smaller and greenish yellow.

Yuma Spider Mite*, *Eotetranychus yumensis* (McGregor). In California and Arizona on citrus fruits, especially lemon and tangerine.

MOTHS

Moths belong to the insect order Lepidoptera, having wings covered with scales. They differ from butterflies in being mostly night fliers, not holding wings vertical when at rest, in having a heavy, hairy body, antennae that may be feathery but not knobbed, in laying eggs in large clusters often coated with hairs, and with pupa usually inside a cocoon. There are many families, with different workers not always in agreement. The list below, in alphabetical order, includes only families with members injurious to cultivated plants. Species commonly known by their adult state are treated in this section. Those best known for their caterpillar stage will be found under Borers, Budworms, Cankerworms, Casebearers, Caterpillars, Cutworms, Earworms, Fruitworms, Hornworms, Leaf Folders, Leaf Rollers, Leaf Skeletonizers, Leaf Tiers, Spanworms, or Webworms.

Aegeriidae. Clearwing moths. Mostly day fliers, wasplike, having wings mostly without scales, the rear edge of fore wings locking over front edge of hind wings. The larvae are borers in woody and herbaceous plants— e.g., peach tree borer, squash borer.

Arctiidae. Tiger moths. Nocturnal, with wings held rooflike over the body when at rest; brightly spotted or banded. The larvae are very hairy—e.g., woollybears, fall webworm.

Citheroniidae. Royal moths. Stout-bodied with large wings. The larvae have horns or spines, feed on trees, pupate in the ground without a cocoon. The hickory horned devil belongs here.

Coleophoridae. Casebearers. Small brown or gray moths, with pointed wings fringed along hind margins. The larvae first mine leaves, then make cases.

Cosmopterygidae. Small moths with long, narrow wings sharply pointed at the apex. The larvae are leaf miners or skeletonizers—e.g., palm leaf skeletonizer.

Cossidae. Carpenterworm moths. Large, heavy-bodied, with spotted or mottled wings. The larvae are wood borers.

Crambidae. Grass moths. Common in meadows and lawns, whitish or pale yellowish brown, holding wings close to the body. The larvae are sod webworms.

Dioptidae. Only 1 species in the United States, the California oakworm.

Gelechiidae. Gelechiid moths. Small, dull-colored with narrow fore wings, hind wings often with a curved outer margin, and long, upcurving labial palps. Pink bollworm, potato tuberworm.

Geometridae. Measuring worms, geometrid moths. Small, slender-bodied, some species with wingless females. The larvae have 2 or 3 prolegs at the end of the body and move with a looping motion. Cankerworms, spanworms.

Gracilariidae. Leaf blotch miners. Very small moths with tapering wings, the larvae making blotch mines.

Heliozelidae. Shield bearers. Small moths with lanceolate wings, the hind wings having no discal cell. The larva of the resplendent shield bearer is a leaf miner and casebearer.

Hepialidae. Ghost moths or swifts. Medium to large moths, wingspread 1 to 3 inches, mostly brown or gray with silvery spots. The larvae feed on roots and woody tissues.

Hyponomeutidae. Plutellid moths. Small with narrow fore wings, fringed hind wings. When resting, the wings are tight against the sides of the body, the antennae directed straight forward. Example, diamondback moth.

Incurvariidae. Small moths with minute spines on wing membranes; female with piercing ovipositor; e.g., maple leaf cutter, yucca moth.

Lasiocampidae. Tent caterpillars. Robust, very hairy moths with feathery antennae. The hairy larvae live in webs.

Lymacodidae. Slug caterpillars. The larvae are short, fleshy, sluglike, without prolegs.

Lymantriidae. Tussock moths. Medium size, hairy, males with plumose antennae, females wingless in some species. The larvae are hairy, some with tussocks of hairs; e.g., gypsy moth, brown-tail moth, white-marked tussock moth.

Megalopygidae. Flannel moths. Medium-sized with a dense coat of scales mixed with fine, curly hairs. The larvae are hairy, sometimes stinging; e.g., puss caterpillar.

Nepticulidae. Minute moths. Spinelike hairs on surface of wings. The larvae are leaf miners in trees and shrubs.

Noctuidae (=Phalaenidae). Owlet or Noctuid moths. Largest family in the Lepidoptera, with 2700 species. Nocturnal, mostly medium size, dull color, heavy-bodied, front wings narrow, hind wings broad. Smooth, dull larvae—armyworms, cutworms, loopers—are very destructive.

Notodontidae. Prominents. Brown or yellow with prominently projecting tufts on hind margins of wings. The yellow-necked or red-humped larvae have conspicuous tubercles.

Oecophoridae. Webworms. Small, flattened moths, brownish with broad wings rounded apically.

Olethreutidae. Small brown or gray moths, banded or mottled, fore wings rather square-tipped, fringe of long hairs on basal part of hind wings. Smooth-skinned pale larvae feed on foliage, fruits, or nuts; e.g., codling moth, Oriental fruit moth.

Phaloniidae. Web spinners and borers. Moths similar to Tortricids.

Phycitidae. Inconspicuous moths with long, threadlike antennae. The larvae tunnel in fruit, stems, or seeds.

Prodoxidae. Yucca moths. Wing surface with minute spines; females have a piercing ovipositor and pollinate yucca.

Psychidae. Bagworm moths. Females are wingless, larvae live in baglike cases.

Pterophoridae. Plume moths. Small, slender, gray or brown with wings split into 2 or 3 featherlike divisions; long legs. Larvae are leaf rollers and stem borers.

Pyralidae. Pyralid moths. Snout moths. Small, delicate, with front wings elongate or triangular, hind wings broad, labial palpi projecting into a snout. Larvae are various, including European corn borer, grape leaf folder, melonworm.

Saturniidae. Giant silkworm moths. Very large, brightly colored, wings with transparent eyespots.

Sphingidae. Sphinx or hawk moths. Medium to large, with heavy, spindle-shaped body. Feed at dusk; look like hummingbirds. Larvae are hornworms.

Tortricidae. Leaf roller moths. Small, with front wings square-cut; wings at rest, bell-shaped.

Zygaenidae. Leaf skeletonizer moths. Smoky gray or black moths, small. The larvae have tufted hairs.

Abbott's Sphinx, *Sphecodina abbotti* (Swaine). In eastern states and west to Kansas, not abundant but sometimes injuring grape and Virginia-creeper. The caterpillar is 2 inches long, of variable color but basically chocolate or reddish brown. It has a polished eyelike tubercle instead of a caudal horn.

Abutilon Moth, *Anomis erosa* Hübner. Okra caterpillar. Feeding on abutilon, okra, hollyhock, hibiscus, and mallow. It is a light-green semi-looper, similar to the cabbage looper, growing to 1⅜ inches, pupating in a folded leaf. It can be controlled with lead arsenate or DDT if its parasitic wasp does not do a good enough job.

Achemon Sphinx*, *Pholus achemon* (Drury). A large moth, wings expanding to 3 or 4 inches, fore wings gray with brown marks, hind wings pink; a high flier. The female lays pale eggs on upper surface of leaves; pupation is in mahogany-brown chrysalids in soil. The caterpillars are large, 2 to 3½ inches, green or pinkish, with oblique white bars on the sides; the young larva has a black horn but this disappears with the first molt. Cultivated grapes, wild grapes, and Virginia-creeper may be defoliated. There are 2 generations. This is controlled on grapes by DDT used for leafhoppers; lead arsenate may also be used.

American Dagger Moth*, *Acronicta americana* (Harris). Common in the Northeast on apple, basswood, elder, elm, maple, oak, willow, recently reported on boxelder in Nevada, on birch in Idaho. The larva is 2 inches long, covered with yellowish hairs and 3 long black pencils of hairs. The body under the hairs is greenish white above, black underneath. It feeds from June to October.

Apple Fruit Moth*, *Argyresthia conjugella* Zeller. A small, dark-gray night-flying moth, serious in Canadian apple orchards, now a problem in

Maine, New Hampshire, New York, California, and Alaska. Hosts include cherry, plum, *Vaccinium* spp., serviceberry, pear, and mountain-ash. The larva—at first white, then pink or flesh-colored with brown spots—feeds in fruit, then pupates in soil.

Artichoke Plume Moth*, *Platyptilia carduidactyla* Riley. The adult has big, brown, divided (plumed) wings, 1 inch across. Caterpillars feed on new foliage and inside stems, leaf stalks, buds, with noticeable damage to the head. There are 3 overlapping generations in California, with worst injury in spring. Pick and destroy all wormy artichokes; bury all old plant tops under 10 inches of soil; remove nearby thistles. Use a pyrethrum-oil spray.

Banded Sunflower Moth*, *Phalonia hospes* (Walsingham). Of economic importance on sunflowers in North Dakota.

Bella Moth*, *Utetheisa bella* (Linnaeus). A tiger moth on peanuts, reported a pest in Alabama.

Brown-tail Moth*, *Nygmia phaeorrhoea* (Donovan). Introduced into Massachusetts on nursery stock prior to 1897 and present in all New England States but of less importance in recent years. It may infest apple, cherry, oak, pear, plum, hawthorn, rose, willow, occasionally elm and maple. The caterpillars, 1½ inches long, are reddish brown to nearly black, with a broken stripe along each side, a red tubercle on segments 11 and 12, and are covered with tufts of brown hairs. These are barbed and poisonous, causing a severe rash when they touch the skin, even death if large numbers of small hairs are breathed into the lungs. They winter as young larvae, several hundred webbed together in a nest, feed during the spring and in June pupate in a cocoon among webbed leaves.

The moths are pure white except for brown scales at the tip of the abdomen, have a 1½-inch wingspread, are active fliers. They appear in July to lay eggs in globular yellow clusters, covered with light-brown hairs, on underside of leaves. There is 1 generation a year.

Control. Cut off and burn winter webs; spray trees with DDT or lead arsenate or methoxychlor in early spring when leaves come out or in August when young caterpillars appear. A fungus disease kills many caterpillars. Brown-tail moths are included in quarantine regulations for gypsy moths. See Puss Caterpillar for a recipe to soothe the rash.

Buck Moth*, *Hemileuca maia* (Drury). Ranging from southern New Hampshire to Georgia, Oklahoma, and Texas, named because it appears in autumn when deer run. The caterpillars feed gregariously on oak, sometimes on willow. They are brownish black, covered with pale-yellow papillae. Each segment bears 6, 7, or 8 tufts of spines, except segment 11, which has only 5. These irritate the flesh. Moths are brown or blackish except for a wide white band across the wings which encloses ring spots. Eggs, laid in autumn around a branch, hatch in May. Larvae eat enormously until July, when they pupate in the ground. Spray with lead arsenate or DDT.

Buddleia Moth, *Pyramidobela angelarum* Keifer. In leaf folds of buddleia plants; heavy infestation in some California gardens.

Catalpa Sphinx*, *Ceratomia catalpae* (Boisduval). On native species of catalpa from New Jersey to Florida and west to Illinois and Texas, causing almost annual defoliation in the Middle West. Early fishermen in Georgia and Florida cultivated catalpas to get the sphinx caterpillars for bait. They are about 3 inches long, with a black horn, variable in color from nearly black on top to pale yellow. The hawk moths are gray with irregular light and dark markings, 3 inches across the wings. Naked brown pupae winter in the soil under or near catalpa trees, and moths fly as soon as trees come into leaf, laying up to 1000 eggs in white masses on underside of foliage. Young caterpillars start feeding in 2 weeks, first in groups, then separately. There are 2 generations in the North, 3 or 4 in the South. Outbreaks are periodic, with defoliation and sometimes death for a period of about 3 years before parasites get the pest under control again. If necessary, spray with arsenate of lead.

Ceanothus Clearwing, *Ramosia mellinipennis* (Boisduval). Abundant on ceanothus in California.

Cecropia Moth*, *Hyalophora cecropia* (Linnaeus). More conspicuous than destructive, this huge silkworm moth, wing expanse 5 or 6 inches, is dusky brown with a white crossband bordered with red and a red spot near the apex of each fore wing, a white crescent-shaped spot in the center, and coral-red, blue, and yellow tubercles on the body. The caterpillars are pale green, ornamented with blue, red, and yellow tubercles 4 inches long. They feed on oak, linden, maple, boxelder, elm, birch, willow, poplar, and other trees. Large gray-brown silk cocoons are conspicuous on bare trees in winter. Control by removing and destroying cocoons.

Codling Moth*, *Carpocapsa pomonella* (Linnaeus). Apple Worm, a European species distributed throughout apple-growing sections of the world (Plate XXV). It came to this country prior to 1819 and is the most serious pest on apple and pear fruit that we have. Crabapples, apricots, cherries, loquats, peaches, plums, haws, and similar fruits are occasionally attacked. Green nuts of English walnut are commonly infested on the Pacific Coast. Unsprayed apples are sure to be 20 to 95 per cent infested. Crop reductions come from wormy fruit, from early drop of immature apples, and from "stings"—small holes surrounded by dead tissue which lower fruit value even though the worms are poisoned before doing further damage.

The insect winters as a full-grown larva, a pinkish-white 1-inch-long caterpillar with a brown head, inside a silken cocoon under loose scales on apple bark or in other sheltered places. In spring the worms change to brown pupae and the moths emerge in two to four weeks. They are grayish brown, with irregular golden-brown lines on the fore wings and paler, fringed hind wings, spreading ½ to ¾ inch. They lay flat white eggs, singly, on upper surface of leaves, on twigs, and on fruit spurs. They work at dusk, when the weather is dry and the temperature fairly high, above 55° F. A cold, wet spring at time of egg laying means less trouble later with wormy apples.

Hatching in 6 to 20 days, small worms crawl to young apples, entering by way of the calyx cup at the blossom end. They tunnel to the core, often eating the seeds, then burrow out through the side of the apple, leaving a mass of brown excrement behind, and crawl to the tree trunk to pupate in cocoons for the next generation. Some infested fruits drop, the worms completing development in apples on the ground. There are usually 2 generations, with the 2nd working from late July to September. Second-brood larvae enter the fruit at any point without preference for the blossom end.

Control. Lead arsenate has been the standard spray, with the calyx or petal-fall application very important. DDT for a time was far superior to lead arsenate, but now many codling moths are resistant to it. Ryania is good but may build up leafhoppers. Sevin is effective, is as safe for humans as Ryania but builds up mites. Guthion is rather widely used by commercial orchardists. To control codling moths and other apple pests, get a spray schedule from your county agricultural agent that is tailored to your particular locality. The recommendations may change from year to year.

Cottonwood Dagger Moth*, *Acronicta lepusculina* Guenée. Through northern states on poplar, sometimes on willow. The larva is 1½ inches long, densely clothed with long yellow hairs and with 5 single black hair pencils. It feeds from July to October.

Crinkled Flannel Moth*, *Megalopyge crispata* (Packard). Cream-colored with black and brown markings on wings. The poisonous caterpillar is thick, fleshy, up to 1 inch long, covered with long silky brown hairs which project upward to form a crest along the middle of the back. It feeds on apple, bayberry, birch, cherry, locust, oak, raspberry, and sweetfern in northern states. It is also reported as defoliating many acres of shin-oak in Texas.

Cynthia Moth*, *Samia cynthia* (Drury). Ranging from southern Connecticut to Virginia, one of the few pests known to feed on ailanthus and often completely defoliating it. The caterpillars—3½ inches long, green with black dots and blue tubercles—may also feed on wild cherry and plum, have been reported on linden, sycamore, and lilac; they are found mostly near cities. The moth is a beautiful brown with white markings, wing expanse 6 to 8 inches. It was introduced here in the hope of making silk from its cocoons.

Cypress Cone Moth, *Laspeyresia cupressana* (Kearfott). Small grayish white larvae bore in green-cone clusters and bark of Monterey and other cypress in California. The adult is small, coppery brown with wing expanse of ⅝ inch. It is also reported on arborvitae.

Cypress Moth, *Recurvaria apictripunctella* (Clemens). Found in the Northeast on bald cypress and hemlock. The moth is yellow with black markings, very small, with fringed wings. The larvae mine leaves and web them together in late summer and early fall, hibernate, resume feeding in spring. Lead arsenate with fish oil has been recommended.

Cypress Tip Moth, *Argyresthia cupressella* Walsingham. Common on Monterey and other cypress from California north into Washington. The adult is small, golden with brown markings, only ⅓ inch across. The larva, ¼ inch long, is yellow-green with a brown head. It winters in mined twigs, then makes papery white cocoons on foliage. Spray with DDT or nicotine-oil in early spring.

Cypress Webber, *Epinotia subviridis* Heinrich. Often found with the cypress tip moth. Brownish-green larvae with light tubercles, ⅖ inch long, eat leaves and tie them up with twigs into a nest. Foliage may turn brown; chief injury is in February and May.

Diamondback Moth*, *Plutella maculipennis* (Curtis). Considered a minor cabbage pest, although sometimes damaging to any crucifer. It may also attack sweet alyssum, candytuft, stock, and wallflower in gardens and greenhouses. The moths, which winter in cabbage debris, are small, ¾ inch across, with gray or brown wings and white marks making a diamond when the wings are folded; hind wings are fringed. Young larvae, greenish yellow with black hairs, ⅓ inch long, at first mine the leaves, later feed externally. Pupation is inside a lacy cocoon on a leaf; moths emerge in a week. There may be 2 to 6 generations.

Control is the same as for the imported cabbageworm, commercial growers using parathion, endrin and other poisons or the bacterial *Bacillus thuringiensis,* home gardeners the safer malathion, methoxychlor or rotenone.

Douglas-fir Cone Moth, *Barbara colfaxiana* Kearfott. On Douglas-fir along the Pacific Coast. Small yellow-white caterpillars mine through scales and seeds. Adults are very small gray moths.

Douglas-fir Pitch Moth*, *Vespamima novarroensis* (Hy. Edwards). Attacking wounds on Douglas-fir, weakened larch, and Sitka spruce. Larvae are slender, white, 1 to 1½ inches; adults are clearwing moths with orange-red markings on body.

Douglas-fir Tussock Moth*, *Hemerocampa pseudotsugata* McDunnough. Defoliating and killing Douglas-fir and true fir in the Northwest, reported also as defoliating willow, ceanothus, and other shrubs. The caterpillars, up to 1 inch long, have bright-colored tufts of hairs and 2 black pencils of hairs at the head and 1 pencil at the posterior. Moths are dull brownish gray; females are wingless. Young larvae are carried by wind and defoliate tops of trees first. Spray with DDT.

Eight-spotted Forester*, *Alypia octomaculata* (Fabricius). Ranging from New England to Colorado and Texas, feeding on grape, Virginia-creeper, and Boston ivy, sometimes defoliating. The moth is black, wingspread 1½ inches, with 2 yellow spots on each fore wing, 2 white spots on each hind wing. The caterpillar is bluish white, banded with orange, with black lines and dots, orange head with black spots, orange prolegs, black legs, 1½ inches long. Spray with DDT or lead arsenate or pick off caterpillars by hand.

Elm Sphinx*, *Ceratomia amyntor* (Hübner). Feeding on elm, basswood, and birch through Atlantic states to the Mississippi Valley. The larva, 3 inches long, varies from pale green to reddish brown, with seven oblique whitish stripes on each side. Adults are sphinx or hawk moths.

Ermine Moth*, *Hyponomeuta padella* (Linnaeus). Small moths, with black dots on white front wings. The larvae feed in a web on apple and cherry.

European Pine Shoot Moth*, *Rhyacionia buoliana* (Schiffermüller). First discovered on Long Island in 1914, now present from Massachusetts to Virginia and west to Illinois and Wisconsin, a serious problem in home gardens, nurseries, pine plantations. It has become so important in southern Wisconsin that pine plantations are discouraged. It was found in Oregon in 1961, but eradication measures were started immediately. Red, mugho, Scotch, and Austrian pines are favored, others may be attacked (Plate III). Hibernation is as a partly grown larva, brown with a black head, in a bud or mass of pitch on a bud. Becoming active in warm weather in spring, the caterpillar leaves its winter bud and bores into an uninfested bud on a new shoot. The shoot grows 1 or 2 inches, becomes crooked, straw-colored, dead, usually with a mass of pitch at the point of larval entrance. Infested shoots are very easy to detect by the color, the crook, or the pitch. Pupation is in the shoot in May and June, with moths starting to emerge in early or mid-June and continuing to mid-July.

The moths have reddish-brown fore wings marked with silver cross lines, dark-brown hind wings. They are about ¾ inch across. Eggs are laid near tips of twigs, on bark, or in needle sheaths. In 10 days the larva starts boring through needle bases, with needles on terminal shoots turning yellow. At the end of summer the larva moves over to a bud and bores in for the winter.

Control. Infestations in small pines around the house are easily taken care of by breaking off infested shoots in May before moths emerge, making sure the brown caterpillar is inside the part broken off and dropping everything into a paper bag for burning. When pines are too large for this, in nurseries or in plantations, spray with DDT, malathion, or methoxychlor in spring or with Sevin in summer. Systemics such as dimethoate are promising. Granular phorate and Di-Syston applied to the soil around small red pines have been effective. There are many parasites, 17 being recorded in West Virginia.

Fan Palm Moth, *Litoprosopus coachella* Hill. A problem in residences where fan palms grow in California.

Fir Seed Moth*, *Laspeyresia bracteatana* (Fernald). Small pink larvae bore in seeds of white, red, and other firs in Oregon, California, and Colorado. Moths are small, dull.

Geranium Plume Moth, *Platyptilia pica* Walsingham. A California pest that has come east, apparently with cuttings, and is now present on geranium in greenhouses in Ohio, New Jersey, New York, and Pennsylvania. The larva bores in flower buds, feeds on flowers and leaves. The small tan moth, 1-inch wingspan, lays 100 to 200 eggs on flower bracts and sepals of buds and these hatch in 1 to 2 weeks. Zectran, parathion, lindane, or Thiodan may be used for control.

Grape Berry Moth*, *Paralobesia viteana* (Clemens). Generally distributed east of the Rocky Mountains on wild and cultivated grapes, most injurious in the Northeast, common in home gardens. Grape berries are webbed together, turn dark purple, drop when about half size. A nearly ripe berry will have a hole and be attached by webbing to a leaf. The moth winters in cocoons, usually in fallen grape leaves, sometimes attached to loose bark scales. About flowering time the grayish purple adult, ½ inch across the wings, emerges to lay flat, circular, cream-colored eggs on stems, flower clusters, newly forming berries. The larvae, ⅓ to ½ inch long, greenish with brown heads, web parts together as they feed, each worm destroying several berries. When full-grown, the larva cuts out a bit of leaf, folds it over, and constructs a cocoon within the fold. These remain on the leaves or fall to the ground. Moths of the 2nd generation emerge in July; there may be 3 generations in the South. Cocoons of the 2nd generation are formed on bits of leaves under the trellis.

Control. Standard recommendation is a DDT spray (1½ pounds of 50 per cent wettable to 100 gallons or 1½ tablespoons to 1 gallon) applied just before blossoming and repeated 2 or 3 times at 10- to 20-day intervals. Parathion, Sevin, methoxychlor, Guthion, and diazinon are about as effective as DDT and may replace it or alternate with it to reduce residue at harvest. Rake and burn fallen leaves and debris around grapevines in fall and winter.

Grape Plume Moth*, *Pterophorus periscelidactylus* (Fitch). Common on grapevines. Eggs winter in branch crotches on old canes; pale yellow-green larvae enter buds, then web together unfolding leaves. After the first molt, caterpillars are fuzzy, covered with long hairs. Pupation is in the webbed leaf. The moth is brown with divided wings. Use a dormant oil or lime-sulfur spray when buds start to swell.

Great Ash Sphinx*, *Sphinx chersis* (Hübner). On ash and lilac, Canada to Florida and to the West Coast. The larva is light green with 7 oblique yellowish stripes and a pale-blue horn at the rear, 3 inches long. The adult is a typical hawk moth.

Gypsy Moth*, *Porthetria dispar* (Linnaeus). An expensive pest of shade, forest, and fruit trees in New England and a threat elsewhere. In 1869 a scientist at Medford, Massachusetts, lost, due to a windstorm which broke open screened cages, some caterpillars he had imported for improving the breed of silkworms. About 10 years later these caterpillars were numerous on trees in that vicinity and in 20 years trees in eastern Massachusetts were being defoliated. An appropriation was made for control, but in a year or two the legislature decided to "economize" and stopped the work. By 1905, when control measures were resumed, the gypsy moth covered 4000 square miles. In 1953 it defoliated a million and a half acres of trees in New England. An infestation that started in New Jersey in 1920 was eradicated within a few years, a small infestation in Ohio was promptly wiped out, and a larger one in Pennsylvania was almost subdued. Discovery in the spring of 1954 of a 10,000-acre infestation near Lansing, Michigan, brought prompt action by state and federal authorities.

There has been reinfestation of some areas outside New England and an all-out eradication campaign was started in 1957. It has bogged down due to widespread (largely unjustified) public criticism.

Gypsy moths are devastating to ornamental trees around the house and may defoliate many hardwood forest trees. Two successive defoliations may kill deciduous trees and only 1 year of complete defoliation may mean death of an evergreen. Gypsy moths are partial to apple, alder, basswood, gray and river birch, hawthorn, oak, poplar, and willow but also feed on other birches, cherry, elm, black gum, hickory, hornbeam, larch, maple, sassafras. Older larvae eat beech and hemlock, cedar, pine, and spruce. The caterpillars are brown, hairy, 2 inches long, with 5 pairs of blue tubercles along the back followed by 6 pairs of red tubercles (Plate VI). They feed at night in June and July, stripping the trees, pupate inside a few threads spun on limb or trunk and produce moths in 17 or 18 days. The brown, yellow-marked male flies freely; the heavy female does not use her wings with their wavy dark markings. She lays large oval egg clusters, covered with tan hairs, near the place of pupation on a tree, stone, or any hard surface. There is 1 generation; the eggs hatch about the first of May. Distribution is by wind dispersal of young larvae, crawling of caterpillars, or moving of an automobile, railroad car, plant, or other object with attached egg cluster.

Control. The Federal Government enacted quarantine regulations in 1906 which are still in effect. These provide for inspection and certification of all products—forest, quarry stone, nursery stock, Christmas trees—to which egg clusters may adhere, before shipment out of infested areas. A barrier zone 25 to 30 miles wide has been maintained from Canada to Long Island along the Hudson Valley to keep the gypsy moth east of the Hudson River. For many years continuous scouting and clean-up spraying in this zone kept the moth from invading the rest of the country. Eventually this proved insufficient and in 1957 a joint Federal-State program was launched to eradicate the moth infestations in New York, New Jersey, and Pennsylvania and to work gradually toward the center in New England. The project was completed satisfactorily in New Jersey and Pennsylvania but in New York there was, perhaps, inadequate supervision, and outraged citizens brought suit in Federal Court charging invasion of private rights and damage to wildlife, crops, and human health. The judge ruled against the plaintiffs, stating that the injury was minor in view of the results obtained and that the states did have police power for the public good. The atmosphere was such, however, that large-scale control measures have not been resumed and lands that were completely eradicated and might have been kept so are being reinfested. Long Island, for instance, is receiving gypsy-moth larvae wind-blown across the Sound from Connecticut.

Traps baited with Gyp-lure, a synthetic form of the female sex attractant, are used to determine infestations of moths and reduce the necessary spraying to keep the moth in bounds. DDT in fuel oil, at the rate of 1 pound actual toxicant per acre applied to forests by airplane, gives complete control of gypsy moth larvae with no apparent harm to most wildlife and bees but may kill some fish. For ground treatment in residential areas DDT is used in hydraulic sprayers at the rate of ¼ to ½ pound actual DDT to 100 gallons. Lead arsenate may be used, at rate of 5 to 10 pounds per 100 gallons, but is more expensive and less effective. Experiments with Sevin, relatively harmless to mammals and birds, are promising but this material is far more toxic to bees than DDT and the results against the gypsy moth are less certain. *Bacillus thuringiensis* preparations are being tested for this pest.

Some reduction of moths on ornamentals can be obtained by a burlap band around tree trunks. This is folded down at the middle and the larvae, seeking shelter inside this fold during the day, can be killed by hand. Egg masses can be killed in winter by touching them with a brush wet with coal-tar creosote. For nearly sixty years parasites and predators have been hopefully imported for help in subduing the gypsy moth. Of more than 40 species of beneficial insects brought in, 9 parasites and 2 predators have become successfully established. But they are far from adequate to the task of keeping gypsy moths under practical control.

Hag Moth*, *Phobetron pithecium* (J. E. Smith). One of the slug caterpillars, more interesting than destructive. The larva is brown, with 10 tapering, curved, plumelike processes extending from either side of the back like hanks of hair. It feeds on foliage of various trees and shrubs during the summer but not extensively. It has stinging hairs.

Hickory Tussock Moth*, *Halisodota caryae* (Harris). Hickory Tiger Moth, ranging from New England through North Carolina and west to Missouri; a general feeder on deciduous trees and shrubs but preferring walnut, butternut, apple, pear, and hickory. It may be abundant locally but seldom causes widespread defoliation. The moth has light-brown fore wings with 3 irregular rows of transparent light spots and thin, pale-yellow hind wings, expanse 2 inches. It appears in June to lay white eggs in patches of 100 or more on underside of leaves. The larvae pass through 8 or 9 instars and feed for 2 or 3 months before spinning cocoons among leaves on the ground. The full-grown caterpillar is 1½ inches long, covered with dense tufts of gray-white hairs and with a row of black tufts along the back; it has a pair of black pencils of hairs on the 1st and 7th abdominal segments. Some parasites, an ichneumon wasp in particular, attack the caterpillars.

Hornet Moth*, *Aegeria apiformis* (Clerck). Rather widely distributed in northern states, also in California. The moth resembles the giant hornet, with brown abdomen banded with yellow; transparent wings with brown borders. The larvae are borers in roots, trunks, and large limbs of poplar and willow, causing swellings and sometimes death of young trees. They are stout, smooth, white with brown heads and rims around the spiracles; they make extensive burrows. They winter in cocoons in wood borings at the base of trees and pupate in spring. It takes two years to complete the life cycle. Spraying trunks with DDT or dieldrin may help.

Imperial Moth*, *Eacles imperialis* (Drury). A large moth, wing expanse 4 to 6 inches, sulfur-yellow, banded and speckled with purple-brown. The caterpillar is 3 to 4 inches long, green with a brown head and 6-spined yellow horns behind the head. It feeds on many forest and shade trees in eastern United States but is not an important defoliator. Control is seldom necessary.

Io Moth*, *Automeris io* (Fabricius). In eastern states and west to New Mexico, sometimes abundant locally on birch, blackberry, wild cherry, currant, black locust, poplars, willow and other deciduous trees and shrubs. It is common in Florida on rose, ixora, other plants. The female moth is purplish red with a large black eyespot on each hind wing; wing expanse 3 inches. The male is smaller, deep yellow. The caterpillar is pale green with a broad brown or reddish stripe, underscored with white along each side of the body, which bears 6 rows of branching green spines tipped with black. The spines are irritating; some people may be poisoned by them.

Juniper Moth, *Periploca nigra*. A new species, first noticed in California in 1959 and now infesting ornamental junipers over the state.

Lantana Plume Moth*, *Platyptilia pusilodactyla* (Walker).

Lappet Moth*, *Epicnaptera americana* (Harris). In eastern United States on aspen, wild cherry, hickory, oak and other deciduous trees. The moth is reddish brown with deeply notched wings, expanse 1¼ to 2 inches. The larva is 2½ inches long, flattened, bluish gray with a small lobe or lappet on each side of each segment. Another lappet moth, *Tolype velleda* Stoll, is reported on holly in Florida.

63. Leopard moth.

Leopard Moth*, *Zeuzera pyrina* (Linnaeus). A European species first noted in 1879 in a spider's web at Hoboken, New Jersey, now present from southern Massachusetts to Philadelphia. It is recorded on nearly 100 plants. Favored are elm, maple, ash, beech, walnut, oak, chestnut, poplar, willow, lilac, and apple, plum, pear, and other fruits. The moths are white with blue and black spots, the female 3 inches across the wings, the male 2 inches. Adults emerge from May to September. The female has a heavy body, is a feeble flier, but lays up to 800 salmon-colored eggs, singly or in small groups, in bark crevices. The young larvae hatch in 10 days and bore into heartwood or enter twigs at base of buds, causing wilting. They make irregular galleries in large limbs and the main trunk, feeding for about 2 years before pupation. The borers are pale yellow or pinkish, spotted with brown or black tubercles of hairs. Small nursery trees and branches of larger trees die; small branches break and hang down; the bark is full of holes with protruding sawdust. Prune off and destroy infested branches; cut down heavily infested trees. Kill borers in valuable trees with a wire or carbon disulfide or other fumigant.

Luna Moth*, *Actias luna* (Linnaeus). The lovely adult has delicate green wings expanding to 4 inches, a purple band on front edge of fore wings and around eyespots, hind wings extending into long, narrow swallowtails. The caterpillar is 3 inches long, green, with 6 pink or green tubercles bearing yellow bristles on each segment. It has a blue-green head and a yellow crossline at the joining of each segment. It feeds on hickory and walnut, sometimes on beech, birch, persimmon, sweetgum, willow, and other trees. Control measures are unnecessary.

Madroña Shield Bearer, *Coptodisca arbutiella* Busck. The larva mines leaves of madroña and cuts out elliptical sections for its pupa case.

Monterey-pine Tip Moth, *Rhyacionia pasadena* (Kearfott). The moth is reddish and silvery gray. The larvae infest terminals of branches of Monterey and other pines along the coast of California.

Nantucket Pine Tip Moth*, *Rhyacionia frustrana* (Comstock). Found from Massachusetts to Florida and west to Texas, injurious to almost all 2- and 3-needle pines. A variety of this species occurs in Minnesota, the Dakotas, Nebraska. There hibernation is in a cocoon in litter on the ground, but usually this moth winters inside the tip of the injured twig. There is 1 generation in Massachusetts, 2 in Delaware and Pennsylvania, 4 in Louisiana and Texas. In Delaware spring-brood moths start emerging the first of April and continue to early June; 2nd-brood moths work from early July to August. They are small, ½ inch across the wings, reddish brown with silver-gray markings; they lay yellow, flattened, circular eggs on needles, buds, or shoots. The larvae—yellow to pale brown, ⅜ inch long—mine in needles, then in buds, spinning a web around the needles, often covered with pitch, and then burrow in twigs of new growth to pupate. Young pines are seriously deformed and occasionally die. Loblolly pine is often injured.

Control. Cut off infested tips in late fall or winter (except in central states where larvae are not in tips at that time). Spray with DDT or Sevin, starting at the end of April (in Delaware), repeating twice at 14-day intervals.

Nevada Buck Moth, *Hemileuca nevadensis* Stretch. In the Southwest on willow, poplar, and shin-oak. The spiny yellow-and-black larvae feed gregariously.

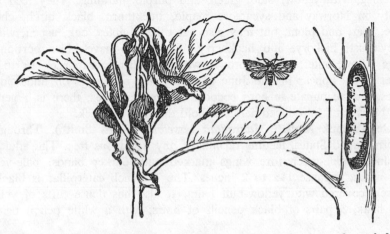

64. Oriental fruit moth injury to peach, and detail of moth and larva.

Oriental Fruit Moth*, *Grapholitha molesta* (Busck). Introduced from the Orient prior to 1915 on nursery stock; established wherever peaches are grown in eastern states and now important in the West. Most serious on peaches, the fruit moth also attacks quince, apple, pear, apricot, plum, cherry, and Chinese hawthorn. First indication in spring is a blackening and dying back of new growth. Fruit injury is similar to that of codling moth in apple but, because the worm enters through the stem, there may be no external sign of injury until breakdown after picking reveals numerous feeding burrows.

Full-grown larvae, pinkish white with brown heads, ½ inch long, winter in cocoons on bark or in rubbish, weeds, or mummified fruit on ground; they pupate in late spring. Moths, gray with chocolate-brown markings, ½ inch across, lay flat white eggs on leaves or twigs shortly after peaches bloom. First-brood larvae attack growing tips, which die, and spin cocoons on bark. Larvae of later broods attack both shoots and fruit. There are 3 or 4 broods in New York, up to 7 farther south.

Control. Until the advent of DDT not much could be done for the Oriental fruit moth except the release of parasites, but now spraying is the rule, using DDT, Guthion, parathion or Sevin, the latter safest for home gardens. The exact spray schedule must be obtained from your own County

Agent, several applications usually being required, beginning at husk-split. Cultivation of soil to a depth of 4 inches in infested orchards 1 to 3 weeks before blooming kills many overwintered pupae. Cull fruits should be promptly destroyed.

Oriental Moth*, *Cnidocampa flavescens* (Walker). A Japanese insect found around Boston in 1906 and confined to eastern Massachusetts. The larvae are sluglike, shaped like a dumbbell, with long spiny tubercles, ⅞ inch long, with yellow, blue, green, and purple markings. They feed preferably on Norway and sycamore maple, buckthorn, black birch, cherry, apple, pear, and plum, but may also eat other maples, oak, aspen, willow, honeylocust, hickory, and hackberry. The moths have inner portions of wings yellow, outer, reddish brown, with dark fringe; expanse 1¼ to 1½ inches. They appear in late June and July, lay oval eggs on underside of leaves. Larvae pupate in hard cocoons in limb crotches; there is 1 generation. Native and introduced parasites hold this pest in check.

Pale Tussock Moth*, *Halisodota tesselaris* (J. E. Smith). Throughout eastern United States, feeding on almost any deciduous tree. The adult has translucent pale-green fore wings marked with darker bands, pale-yellow hind wings, expanse 1½ to 2 inches. The 1¼-inch caterpillar is blackish, sparsely covered with yellow-buff hairs. It also has dense tufts of yellow-gray hairs, 3 pairs of black pencils of hairs, with a white pencil beneath each.

Pandora Moth*, *Coloradia pandora* Blake. Important in western pine belts. Moths have brownish-gray fore wings with a spattering of white scales, black lines and a black spot, hind wings with pinkish hairs; expanse 3 to 4 inches. They lay flattened green eggs in clusters on bark of pine trees in spring. Caterpillars, appearing in August, are dark when young, brown to green with short spines when mature; 2½ to 3 inches long. The life cycle takes 2 years. Large areas of Jeffrey and yellow pines may be defoliated. There are many natural enemies, including a wilt disease, ground squirrels, and chipmunks. Indians have used the caterpillars for food, drying them, then making them into a stew. Some tribes roast the pupae.

Pea Moth*, *Laspeyresia nigricana* (Stephens). A serious pest in northern pea-canning areas, sometimes a garden problem. Present since 1900, the pea moth attacks all field and garden peas, sweetpea, and vetch. Growing pods have irregular cavities eaten out of the side; seeds are spoiled and pods are partly filled with pellets of excrement and caterpillar silk; they turn yellow, ripen prematurely. Inactive larvae winter in silk cocoons covered with soil particles just below the soil surface or in cracks and crevices around barns. They change to brownish pupae in late spring when peas bloom. Small brown moths, marked with black and white lines on fore wings, are active about pea plants in late afternoon, laying minute, flattened white eggs singly on pods, leaves, flowers or stems or on other nearby plants. Young larvae drill into pods. They are yellow-white with dark spots, pale short hairs over the body, dark areas at each end; ½ inch long. They eat their way out of pods and make cocoons in soil. Some transform to moths for a 2nd generation, others remain in soil until the next spring. Control with cultural measures, sanitation, early planting.

Pine Cone Moth, *Dioryctria abietella* Dyar & Shannon. An iridescent greenish-red caterpillar ¾ inch long. Bores through scales and seed of Douglas-fir, true fir, pine and spruce cones. The moths are gray, mottled with black, 1 inch across the wings.

Pine Tortrix, *Tortrix pallorana* Robinson. On pines, including those in Christmas-tree plantings, also injuring alfalfa and clover.

Pine Tube Moth, *Argyrotaenia pinatubana* (Kearfott). On white pine through eastern states, lodgepole and whitebark pine in the Rocky Mountain region. Moths have rust-red fore wings, with 2 oblique lines across each, silky gray hind wings, ½ inch wingspread. They emerge in late April and May, and the 2nd brood comes in July. Larvae, ⅓ inch long, are greenish yellow with a faint dark line down the back. They make tubes by tying needles together side by side, squarely eating off the free end. The tubes stand erect and may be quite conspicuous; pupation is in the tubes. Control by removing and burning tubes in winter. Parasites are effective.

Pine Tussock Moth*, *Dasychira plagiata* (Walker). On various pines in the Middle West, causing heavy defoliation of jack pine.

Pitch Blister Moth, *Petrova albicapitana* (Busck). Reddish larvae ½ inch long, bore into twigs, producing pitch, on jack, lodgepole, and ponderosa pines in northern states.

Pitch Twig Moth*, *Petrova comstockiana* (Fernald). On hard pine from Massachusetts to Virginia, west to Minnesota. The moth is reddish brown mottled with gray, ⅝ inch wingspread; the larva is pale brown with dark-brown head; ½ inch long. It infests small branches and twigs, leaving a thick mass of pitch at the entrance. Cut out such twigs.

Polyphemus Moth*, *Antheraea polyphemus* (Cramer). One of the giant silkworms, feeding on oak, elm, sassafras, wild cherry, ash, sweetgum, maple, poplar, lilac, birch and other trees but rarely injurious. The moth has brownish yellow wings crossed with a dusky band edged with pink, and a large eyespot on each hind wing. The caterpillar is 3 inches long, light green with an oblique yellow line on sides of each abdominal segment except first and last, 6 small golden tubercles on each segment, with 1 to 3 bristles.

Promethea Moth*, *Callosamia promethea* (Drury). The most common of the giant silkworms, feeding on lilac, wild cherry, tulip tree, ash, sassafras and other plants. The female has light reddish-brown wings, crossed near the middle with a white, waxy line and an angular discal spot; wingspread to 3 inches. The male has dark-brown to nearly black wings with light-brown borders and zigzag line. The caterpillars are 2 inches long, pale bluish green with rows of black, polished, warty tubercles, 2 larger coral-red pairs of tubercles on 2nd and 3rd thoracic segments and a yellow pair on the 8th abdominal segment. The cocoon is long, spindle-shaped, enclosed in a leaf.

Red-cedar Tortrix, *Tortrix cockerellana* Kearfott. Webbing and defoliating redcedar. Newly reported from Nevada.

Regal Moth. See Hickory Horned Devil under Caterpillars.

Resplendent Shield Bearer*, *Coptodisca splendoriferella* (Clemens). Small moth with lanceolate wings, gray and yellow marked with brown and silver. The larva make a linear mine in a leaf of apple, wild cherry or related tree, and when full-grown makes a case from this mine, lining it with silk and attaching it to limb or trunk.

Rusty Tussock Moth*, *Orgyria antiqua* (Linnaeus). A European species in northern states, a pest of apple, quince and other fruits, feeding also on beech, mountain-ash, birch, poplar, willow, and other trees. The male moth has rust-brown wings marked with gray lines, a white spot near the hind border of each wing; the female is gray and wingless. The caterpillar is dark gray, 1⅛ inches long, with a pair of black hair pencils from orange tubercles on the 2nd abdominal segment, tufts of white or yellowish hairs on other segments, and a black head.

Satin Moth*, *Stilpnotia salicis* (Linnaeus). First discovered in Massachusetts in 1920, now present in New England, New York, and Oregon, Washington, California, and Idaho, defoliating poplars, feeding also on willow, sometimes on oak. Partly grown larvae winter in small webs in bark crevices, start feeding in late April or May. They are black with conspicuous irregular white blotches down the back and a transverse row of reddish-brown tubercles with tan hairs on each segment. They pupate in a cocoon in leaves or on twigs, and the satin-white moths, wing expanse 1½ to 2 inches, emerge in July. They lay eggs in white, glistening clusters on trunk, branches, and leaves. The larvae appear in 2 weeks but grow slowly, finishing their development the next spring. Then they feed ravenously, defoliating trees and often killing them, sometimes migrating to fences, walks, and buildings, annoying people.

Control. Several natural enemies are at work. Spray trees in spring with lead arsenate; if egg masses are abundant, paint them with creosote.

Sequoia Pitch Moth*, *Vespamima sequoiae* (Hy. Edwards). Opaque, dirty-white larvae infest branches and trunks, mine the cambium layer of knobcone, lodgepole, Monterey and yellow pine, Douglas-fir, redwood and other conifers in Montana, Washington, Oregon, and California. The moth looks like a yellow-jacket wasp, black with the last segment of the abdomen bordered with bright yellow. The larvae start working from wounds, and a large mass of gummy pitch covers the point of entrance. They pupate in this mass and the pupa case is protruded so the moth does not touch the pitch on emergence. The species is common but not serious enough to call for control measures.

Silver-spotted Tiger Moth*, *Halisodota argentata* Packard. Found from the Atlantic to the Pacific, principally on Douglas-fir but also on true firs, Sitka spruce, shore pine and other conifers. The moth has reddish-brown fore wings 1½ to 2 inches across with silvery white dots. The larvae hibernate in webs during the winter, then feed gregariously in spring. They are about 1½ inches long densely covered with long, brushlike, poisonous brown to black hairs. They spin brown cocoons in June, attaching these to needles, bark, or debris on forest floor.

Smeared Dagger Moth*, *Acronicta oblinita* (J. E. Smith). From Maine to Florida and west to the Rocky Mountains, feeding on alder, boxelder, wild cherry, poplar, and willow. The caterpillar is velvety black, dotted and banded with yellow, bearing short reddish hairs.

Snapdragon Plume Moth, *Platyptilia antirrhina* Lange. Small greenish larvae at first mine leaves, then feed openly on terminal leaves, bore inside developing flowers, seeds, and inside main stems. Mature caterpillars are green or purplish red. Naked pupae are suspended from any part of plants, giving rise to grayish brown moths, ½ inch wingspread. Netted ovate eggs are laid singly anywhere on plants. There are 3 generations a year outdoors in California, more in greenhouses.

Snowberry Clearwing, *Hemaris diffinis* (Boisduval). From New England to Georgia and the Great Plains on snowberry and bush honeysuckle. The hornworm larvae, 1½ to 2 inches long, are green to brown or purplish, with dark spiracles. The sphinx moths have clear, transparent wings with dark-brown margins, expanding 1½ to 2 inches, black bodies marked with gold. There are 2 generations; hibernation is as pupae in soil. Handpicking is usually sufficient control.

Spotted Tussock Moth*, *Halisidota maculata* (Harris). Common in the Northeast, ranging through northern states to California, feeding on alder, apple, birch, boxelder, wild cherry, maple, oak, and willow but not a serious defoliator. The moths are about 2 inches across, with dark-yellow fore wings marked by bands and spots, plain, nearly transparent hind wings. Larvae are 1¼ inches long with tufts of yellow hairs in the middle of the body, black hairs at both ends, a line of black spots along the back, and a few long, whitish pencils of hairs.

Spruce Epizeuxis, *Epizeuxis aemula* (Hübner). Common on ornamental spruce in the Northeast. Small brown larvae, with black tubercles and spiracles, web needles together in large masses and fill them with excrement. They feed on older needles. Moths, brownish gray with wings crossed by narrow bands, emerge in June and July. Eggs hatch in late summer; partly grown larvae winter in webbed masses of dry needles.

Spruce Seed Moth*, *Laspeyresia youngana* Kearfott. Distributed through northern states. The larvae bore into spruce cones, feeding on seeds. The moth is brown, only ⅜ inch across the wings.

Strawberry Crown Moth*, *Ramosia bibionipennis* (Boisduval). In various sections, most common in the Northwest. White to yellowish larvae, ½ to

¾ inch long, bore in the crown, as many as 50 borers sometimes working in a single plant. The foliage turns yellow, recent transplants die; older plants are much weakened. Raspberries and blackberries may be infested. The clearwing moth resembles a yellow-jacket wasp. Nearly mature larvae winter in strawberry crowns, pupate in May. Moths emerge in June and July, laying eggs on lower leaves; there is 1 generation. Control by sanitary measures; pull and burn infested plants in spring before moths emerge; top plants after harvest; cover beds with straw after topping to prevent egg laying.

Sunflower Moth*, *Homoeosoma electellum* (Hulst). Destructive to cultivated sunflowers. The moth is gray, lays eggs in florets; the larva is greenish yellow with 5 brown stripes down the back. The larvae feed on the head, in a mass of webbing and frass, destroying the seeds. They pupate in the head. Dusting with DDT and sulfur or toxaphene and sulfur, when flowers first appear, reduces injury.

Sycamore Tussock Moth*, *Halisodota harrisii* Walsh. Abundant on sycamore in the Northeast but rarely calling for control measures. The yellow larva has white to yellow hairs and long orange hair pencils. The adult is like the pale tussock moth.

Virginia-creeper Sphinx*, *Ampeloeca myron* (Cramer). Feeding on grape and Virginia-creeper like the Abbott's Sphinx.

Walnut Sphinx*, *Cressonia juglandis* (J. E. Smith). From Canada to Florida and west to the Great Plains on butternut, black walnut, hickories, pecan, and hornbeam. The caterpillar is 2 inches long, from light green to reddish, granulated with white, and with 7 oblique yellowish stripes, a brownish caudal horn.

Western Tussock Moth*, *Hemerocampa vetusta* (Boisduval). California Tussock Moth, on Pacific Coast from southern California to British Columbia. The female is gray, wingless; the male has brown wings with gray markings. Eggs are laid in felty gray masses on old cocoons or bark of host plants—apple, almond, apricot, blackberry, California Christmasberry, California coffeeberry, cherry, hawthorn, manzanita, oak, pear, plum, prune, walnut, willows. The caterpillars are gray with red, blue, and yellow spots, 4 tufts of hairs in the middle of the body, 1 white and 1 black tuft at the end, and 2 long black tufts, looking like horns, at the head; ¾ to 1 inch long. They feed on leaves and young fruit. There is only 1 brood. Eggs are laid on trees in late summer and fall, hatch when leaves unfold in spring.

Control. Remove egg masses in winter; jar caterpillars from trees and prevent return by banding as for cankerworms. DDT is very effective as a spray but parathion or malathion have a shorter residual effect and so are less harmful to beneficial parasites and predators.

White-lined Sphinx*, *Celerio lineata* (Fabricius). Striped Morning Sphinx. Common in the West, occurring throughout the country on apple, azalea, beet, collards, currant, elm, fuchsia, gooseberry, grape, melon, pear, plum, portulaca, prune, tomato, turnip and other crops. The hornworm larva is serious on beets and tomatoes in Florida. It is 2½ to 3 inches long, usually green, with yellow head and horn and pale spots bordered with black. Some larvae, however, are black with orange head and horn, 3 yellow spots on the back.

The moths resemble hummingbirds, with brown bodies marked with white and darker brown; fore wings with white-lined veins and a broad buff stripe; dark hind wings with a rosy band across the middle. They visit flowers at dusk. Pupation is in soil, in shiny dark brown chrysalids. There are 2 broods.

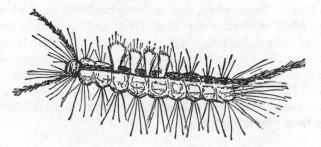

65. Larva of white-marked tussock moth.

White-marked Tussock Moth*, *Hemerocampa leucostigma* (J. E. Smith). A native, common in the East, ranging west to Colorado. This is primarily a city pest, feeding on many deciduous shade trees—elm, linden, maple, horse-chestnut, poplar, sycamore, buckeye, willow, and others, and on fruits—apple, pear, quince, plum—but not on evergreens. Foliage is skeletonized and fruits scarred by conspicuous hairy caterpillars, 1½ inches long. These have red heads, 2 pencil-like tufts of long black hairs projecting like horns, with a third tuft at the rear, a black stripe down the middle of the back, bordered with a wide yellow line, 4 white brushes or tussocks of hairs on the first segments of the abdomen.

The female moth is nearly wingless, gray, hairy; the male has brownish wings marked with gray, spreading to 1¼ inches, feathery antennae, legs tufted with white hairs. Eggs are laid in fall in conspicuous masses, about 1 inch long, of 50 to 100, covered with a white lathery substance, on trunk, branches, dead leaves, or on top of the cocoon from which the female emerged. Caterpillars feed from April to June, depending on location, pupate in cocoons on trunk and branches, and the moths emerge to lay eggs for a 2nd generation which feeds in August and September. There are 3 generations in Washington, D.C., and farther south.

Control. A great many parasites work on this insect, but unfortunately there are also a great number of hyperparasites living on the parasites. Birds eat young larvae. Tree experts climb trees to scrape off egg masses or daub them with creosote containing a little lampblack to mark those treated.

Lead arsenate or DDT sprays for cankerworms or elm leaf beetles will also control tussock moths.

White-pine Shoot Moth. See White-pine Shoot Borer under Borers.

Yucca Moth*, *Tegeticula yuccasella* (Riley). A southwestern species responsible for the pollination of yucca plants. The female has specially modified mouth parts with which she scrapes together pollen from the stamens and carries it with her to another flower, where she lays eggs through the wall of the ovary into the seed cavity.

Zimmerman Pine Moth*, *Dioryctria zimmermani* (Grote). On Austrian, pitch, red, Scotch, Swiss, white, and yellow pines over most of their range, reported on other conifers in the West. The moth is reddish gray marked with dark and light lines, 1 to 1½ inches across the wings. It lays eggs on bark, often near wounds, and the larvae, white to reddish yellow or green, ¾ inch long, bore into trunks and branches. Entire tops of trees may break off, or branch tips turn brown. Pitch tubes are formed at the base of injured parts. Prune out infested portions where possible. A DDT spray in mid-August has been recommended.

NEMATODES

Nematodes are wormlike or threadlike animals in the group Nematoda, recently classified as a separate phylum. Some nematodes are parasites of vertebrate animals, some are free-living in soil or water, a few are predaceous on other nematodes or fungi, and a very large number are currently being recognized as plant parasites.

Although we have known for 200 years that certain nematodes, such as the wheat eelworm, could cause plant disease, nematology as a separate science is very new. Work in this field in institutions has been relegated sometimes to the plant-pathology department because the end result is a disease, sometimes to the department of zoology or entomology because nematodes are animals. For a long time root knot was thought to be the major disease caused by nematodes, and it was considered mostly a southern problem. Now, with more specialists working in the field, more students being trained, more surveys made, we know that nematodes are a problem in every state and account for a large share of plant ill-health on farms and in home gardens. Indeed, it is now estimated that nematodes cost one dollar out of every ten expended by the farmer and may be equally injurious in home plantings.

Nematodes injure plants directly by their feeding, causing general stunting and lack of vigor, and indirectly by making wounds that facilitate entrance of rot and wilt fungi and bacteria.

Plant parasitic nematodes are seldom over a millimeter long and are rarely visible to the naked eye. They are long and cylindrical in shape, usually tapering at both ends (fusiform) and round in cross section. A few nematodes are filiform (threadlike) with a uniform body diameter throughout. In some genera the female is pear-shaped or saclike, the male fusiform.

Nematodes in general lack coloration, being transparent or with a whitish or yellowish tint. They are unsegmented, not divided into definite regions. They lack a true head but there is a mouth, usually at the anterior end, that is surrounded by lips bearing the sensory organs. Basically there are 6 lips but these may be fused in pairs. The sense organs, amphids, are important diagnostic characters, one class of nematodes having amphids with conspicuous openings, the other having amphids with minute pores. Most plant parasitic nematodes belong to the latter group.

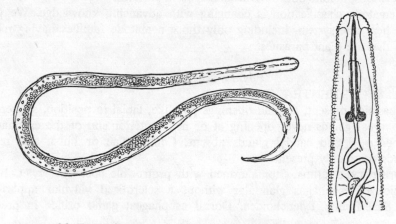

66. Typical nematode with detail of stylet and bulbs.

Behind the mouth there is a cavity, (stoma), then the esophagus, the intestine, and the rectum. The latter terminates in a ventral terminal or subterminal anus in females, in a cloacal opening in males, the sexes being usually separate. There are no specialized organs of circulation or respiration. The body region behind the anus or cloacal opening is called the tail.

Near the posterior end of many nematodes there is a pair of cuticular pouches called phasmids. They may be sense organs like the amphids and are also used in dividing nematodes into two main classes, one with phasmids present, the other with phasmids absent.

The mouth leads into the buccal capsule, varying in shape and differentiation. In some orders the buccal capsule is armed with a conspicuous protrusible spear or stylet, used to puncture plants and animal prey. In some families there is a stomatostylet, a hollow spear derived from the sclerotized walls of the buccal cavity. Commonly in such families, the nematode punctures plant tissue with its stylet, then injects a secretion from its salivary gland that predigests the food before it is sucked in through the stylet. In the family Dorylaimidae the spear is an enlarged tooth (odontostylet) originating in the esophagus wall.

The structure of the esophagus varies in different groups and is also an important diagnostic character. The esophagus commonly has one or more muscular swellings known as bulbs. Those provided with a glandular apparatus are called true bulbs; those lacking such apparatus are pseudobulbs. True bulbs are the chief pumping and sucking structures and may be situated near midlength, *median,* or at the end of the esophagus, *posterior.*

The body wall of nematodes consists of cuticle, hypodermis (epidermis), and a single layer of muscles. The body surface may be smooth but it is often marked by a regular series of transverse striations (rings) or by punctations, minute dots or ovals arranged in patterns.

Nematode classification is changing with advancing knowledge. We present here one system, including only those nematode families having members that are plant parasites.

Phylum NEMATODA
Class SECERNENTEA (Phasmidia).

Phasmids present, amphid openings porelike, labial in position, subventral esophageal glands never opening at or near anterior end of the esophagus. Hypodermal and caudal glands absent. Caudal alae or bursa and rectal glands commonly present.

Order TYLENCHIDA. Stoma armed with protrusible spear or stylet, basal portion of esophagus glandular without a sclerotized valvular apparatus.

Superfamily Tylenchoidea. Dorsal esophageal gland orifice in precorpus.

Family *Criconematidae.* Esophagus distinct, esophageal musculature present; cuticle usually heavily annulated or squamous, often bearing spines; spear greatly elongated.

Genus *Hemicriconemoides.* Cuticular striations interrupted by 8 or more lateral incisures; mature female retaining last molt; body annules not retrose; knobs of stylet with anteriorly directed processes.

Hemicycliophora, as above but with knobs of stylet with posteriorly directed processes.

Criconema. Mature female not retaining last molt; body annules retrose; cuticular spines or scale present in adults.

Criconemoides. Like Criconema but cuticular spines or scales not present in adults.

Cacopaurus. Cuticle finely annulate; female minute with obese, swollen body; male with adanal bursa.

Paratylenchus. Cuticle finely annulate; female minute but body not swollen; bursa absent in male.

Belonolaimus. Cuticle coarsely annulated; both sexes of moderate size; very elongate, eel-shaped; esophageal glands lying free in body cavity, overlapping intestine; male with adanal caudal alae.

Tomato Hornworm

a

b

c

d

Celery Caterpillar

a

b

c

d

XIX TOBACCO HORNWORM, on Tomato: (a) adult moth, natural size; (b) egg on leaflet and egg enlarged; (c) larva with "horn"; (d) pupa in soil. CELERY-WORM: (a) chrysalid; (b) male butterfly, black swallowtail; (c) caterpillar on celery; (d) front view showing forked horn.

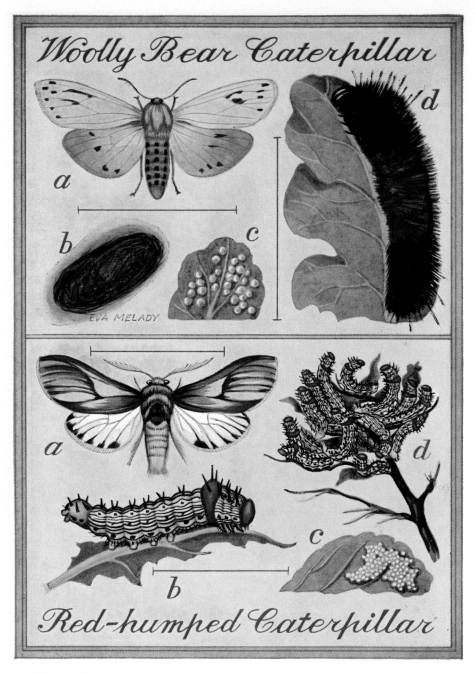

XX   BANDED WOOLLYBEAR CATERPILLAR: (a) moth; (b) pupa in hairy cocoon; (c) eggs; (d) hairy caterpillar. RED-HUMPED CATERPILLAR: (a) moth; (b) larva with red head and hump; (c) eggs; (d) caterpillars in typical position.

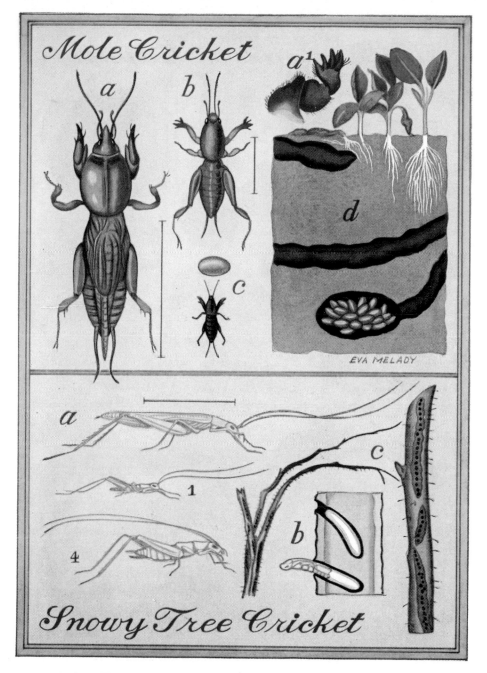

XXI NORTHERN MOLE CRICKET: (a) adult, slightly enlarged; (a,1) detail of front leg showing adaptation for digging; (b) nymph; (c) egg, magnified, and first nymphal stage; (d) injury to seedlings from burrows, and eggs in soil pocket. SNOWY TREE CRICKET: (a) adult; (a,1) first instar; (a,4) fourth instar, nymphs with wing pads; (b) egg in position in wood and hatching nymph, much enlarged; (c) egg punctures in a row along stem.

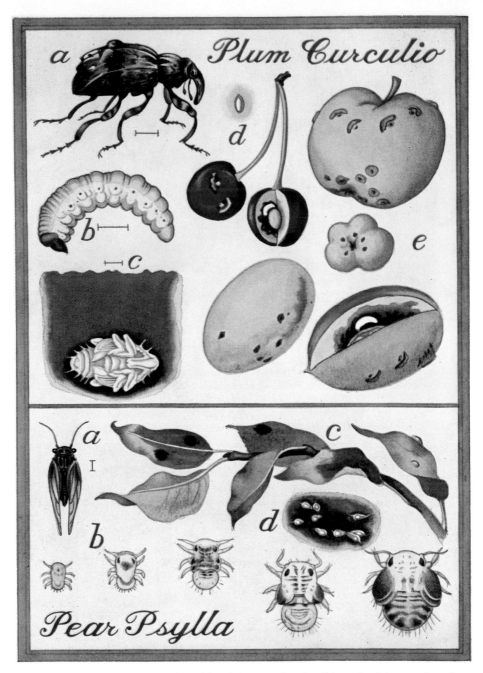

XXII PLUM CURCULIO: (a) adult snout beetle; (b) grub; (c) pupa in soil;
(d) egg; (e) typical injury, crescent-shaped scar, on cherry, plum, and apple.
PEAR PSYLLA: (a) adult; (b) nymph in different instars; (c) injury to pear
leaves; (d) eggs attached to bark by one end.

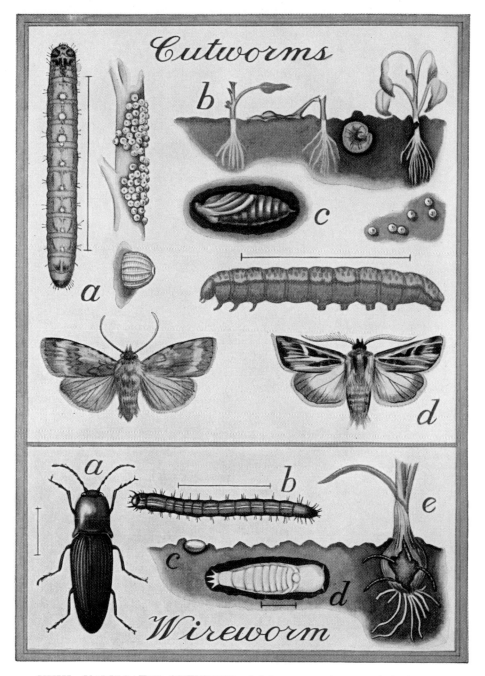

XXIII   VARIEGATED CUTWORM: (a) larva, egg cluster, and single egg enlarged, and moth. DINGY CUTWORM: (b) seedlings cut off and cutworm in
typical coiled position; (c) pupa in soil, eggs and larva. WIREWORM: (a) click
beetle adult; (b) larva; (c) egg; (d) pupa in soil; (e) larvae feeding in bulb.

Beet Leafhopper

Six-spotted Leafhopper

EVA MELADY

XXIV BEET LEAFHOPPER: (a) curly-top disease of beet, the virus transmitted by leafhopper, showing clearing of veins, wartlike protuberances, leaf rolling;
(b) nymph in fifth instar; (c) adult; (d) eggs on leaf and young nymph; (e) diseased
tomato leaf. SIX-SPOTTED LEAFHOPPER: (a) adult, showing 6 black spots; (b)
yellows disease of lettuce, transmitted by leafhopper; (c) aster yellows.

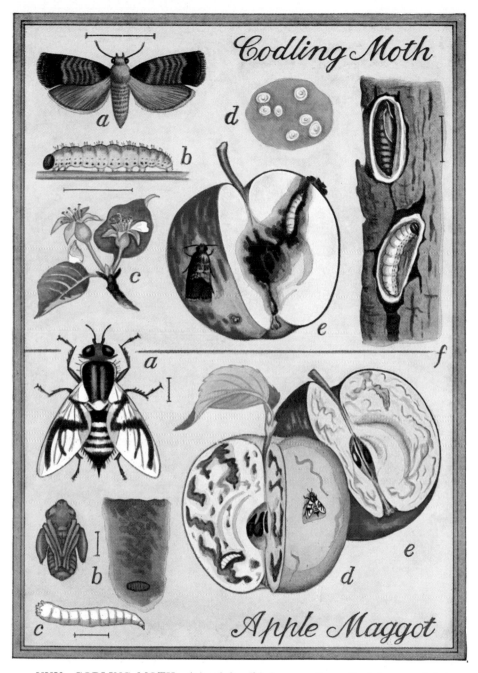

Codling Moth

Apple Maggot

XXV CODLING MOTH: (a) adult; (b) larva or "worm"; (c) stage of fruit when first worms enter; (d) eggs, enlarged; (e) larva tunneling out, moth on surface of apple, and sting from second-brood larva entering fruit; (f) larva in winter position under bark scales and pupa formed in spring. APPLE MAGGOT: (a) adult fly; (b) pupa, enlarged, and puparium (containing pupa), natural size in soil; (c) maggot; (d,e) injury to fruit with maggot inside and fly puncturing skin to lay eggs.

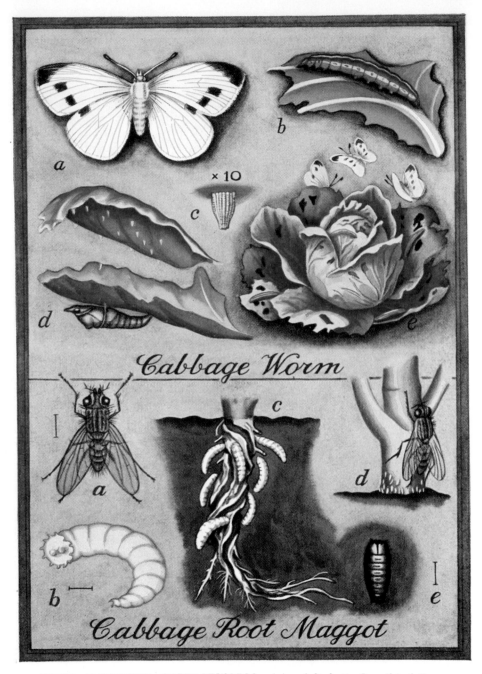

XXVI IMPORTED CABBAGEWORM: (a) adult butterfly; (b) full-grown
caterpillar; (c) egg, magnified 10 times; (d) chrysalid attached to leaf; (e) injury
to cabbage head by larvae, adults laying eggs. CABBAGE MAGGOT: (a) adult
fly; (b) legless maggot (much enlarged); (c) maggots working on roots; (d) fly
laying eggs at base of stem; (e) puparium in soil.

XXVII TWO-SPOTTED MITE (Red Spider): (a) adult 8-legged mite, magnified 50 times; (b) young 6-legged larva or nymph; (c) egg enlarged and mites in web on underside of bean leaf; (d) typical mite injury to phlox, juniper, rose, bean, and violet. LONG-TAILED MEALYBUG (a). CITRUS MEALYBUG (b). COCONUT MEALYBUG (c). MEALYBUGS: (d) on begonia; (e) on fuchsia; (f) on coleus; (g) on palm.

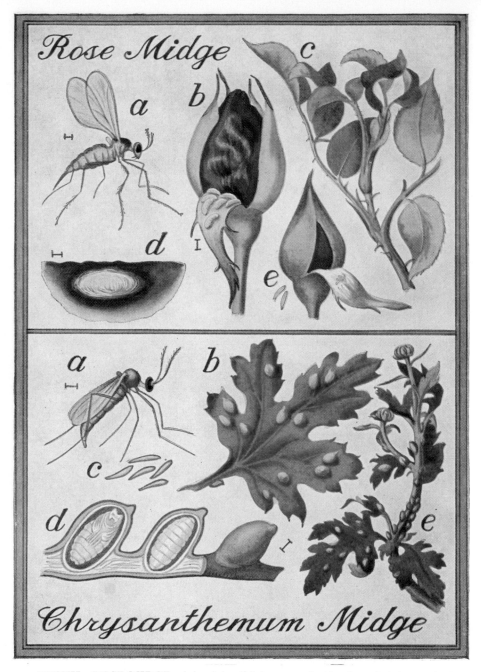

XXVIII ROSE MIDGE: (a) adult; (b) larvae on inside of sepal, injury to bud;
(c) distortion of young shoot; (d) pupa in cocoon in soil, much enlarged; (e) egg
mass on sepal and egg magnified. CHRYSANTHEMUM GALL MIDGE: (a) adult,
much enlarged; (b) conical galls on leaf; (c) eggs; (d) stem cut to show pupa and
maggot inside galls; (e) shoot with galls on stem and leaves.

XXIX MILLIPEDES: (a) millipede enlarged to show 2 pairs of legs on each segment, typical coiled position; (b) seeds injured by millipedes; (c) injury to young seedling; (d) tomato attacked when resting on ground. SPOTTED GARDEN SLUG: (a) slimy trail on cineraria; (b) seedlings eaten; (c) egg cluster; (d) month-old slug; (e) mature slug with spots. SOWBUGS: (a) adult; (b) young sowbug; (c) form known as pillbug, which rolls into a ball; (d) infested seedlings; (e) sowbugs working at roots; (f) favorite hiding place under moist flowerpot.

XXX GLADIOLUS THRIPS: (a) adult, showing fringed wings; (b) eggs, much enlarged; (c) typical injury to flowering spike and foliage; (d,1) first-stage larva; (d,2) second-stage larva; (d,3) third-stage (prepupa); (d,4) pupa with wing pads; (e) injured corms at left, healthy corm at right. CYCLAMEN MITE: (a) delphinium spike, with typical distortion; (b) injured cyclamen; (c) adult male, highly magnified; (d) young 6-legged larva; (e) eggs; (f) adult female.

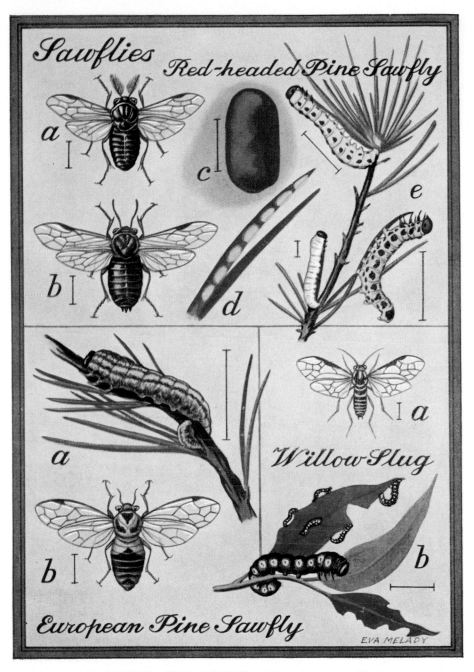

Sawflies

Red-headed Pine Sawfly

Willow Slug

European Pine Sawfly

EVA MELADY

XXXI RED-HEADED PINE SAWFLY: (a) male adult; (b) female sawfly; (c) pupa in papery cocoon on ground; (d) eggs in slits along needle; (e) young and mature larvae feeding on pine. INTRODUCED PINE SAWFLY (labeled European Pine Sawfly): (a) larva in typical position on twig; (b) adult. WILLOW SAWFLY (Willow Slug): (a) adult; (b) larvae feeding on willow leaves.

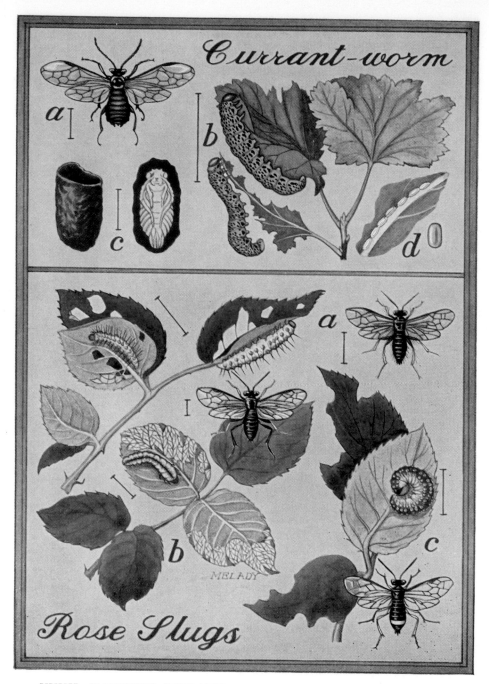

XXXII IMPORTED CURRANTWORM: (a) adult female sawfly; (b) larvae and feeding injury; (c) cocoon and pupa inside cocoon; (d) eggs along vein and single egg, enlarged. BRISTLY ROSE-SLUG: (a) adult sawfly and larvae feeding on leaf. ROSE-SLUG: (b) leaf showing typical skeletonizing but larva and adult enlarged. CURLED ROSE SAWFLY: (c) larva in coiled position, injured leaf, adult.

XXXIII JUNIPER SCALE: (a) round, white, female scale, much enlarged;
(b) male scale, same enlargement; (c,d) scale on juniper twigs. PINE NEEDLE
SCALE: (a) two forms of the female scale; (b) ridged male scale; (c) infested
pine needles. EUONYMUS SCALE: (a) dark, oyster-shaped female; (b) narrow,
white, ridged male; (c) infested euonymus; (d) on bittersweet.

XXXIV SAN JOSE SCALE: (a) round female scale; (b) oblong male scales; (c) young crawler; (d) adult winged male; (f) infested apple twig and fruit. SCURFY SCALE: (a) single female, much enlarged, and branch with male scales; (b) single male and branch with male scales; (e) female scale removed, showing eggs. OYSTERSHELL SCALE: (a) single female and branch with female scales; (c) young crawler; (d) adult male; (e) female turned over to show eggs under the shell. COTTONY MAPLE SCALE: (a) female with cottony egg mass and infested maple twig; (c) young crawler; (e) eggs.

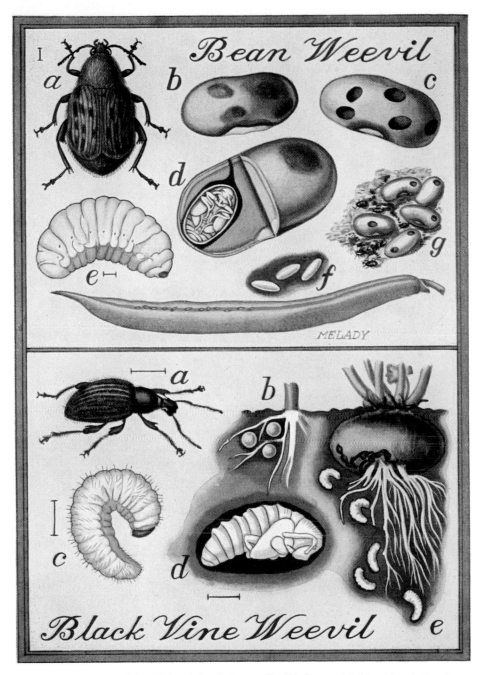

XXXV BEAN WEEVIL: (a) adult weevil; (b) bean with blemishes indicating weevils inside; (c) exit holes in seed; (d) pupa in position inside seed; (e) grub, much enlarged; (f) eggs, magnified and in position on bean pod; (g) remains of a weevil-infested bag of seeds. BLACK VINE WEEVIL: (a) adult; (b) eggs among roots in soil; (c) grub, enlarged; (d) pupa in earthen cell below soil surface; (e) grubs in soil, natural size, and injury to cyclamen corm.

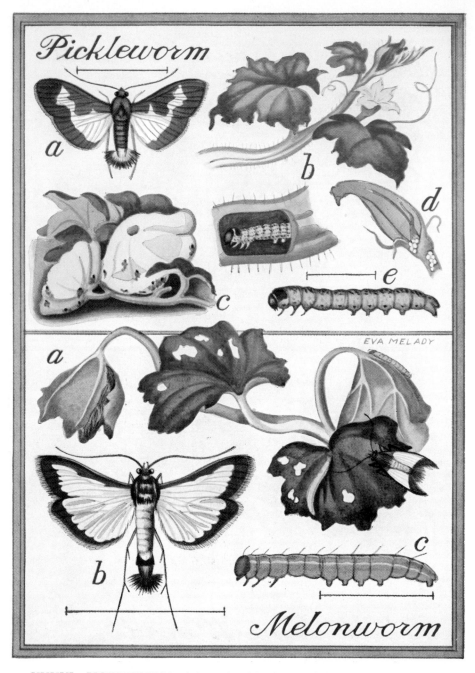

XXXVI PICKLEWORM: (a) moth with characteristic scaly brush at end of abdomen; (b) melon shoot showing feeding injury, and stem cut to show young larva; (c) squash with entrance holes; (d) eggs at base of bud; (e) full-grown larva. MELONWORM: (a) squash vine with feeding holes, pupa in folded leaf, moth; (b) adult moth; (c) full-grown larva.

Dolichodorus. Esophageal glands enclosed in terminal bulb, not overlapping the intestine; male with terminal caudal alae.

Family *Hoplolaimidae.* Esophagus distinct, esophageal musculature present; cuticle finely to moderately annulated, plain; spear short; head with internal cephalic sclerotization.

Genus *Meloidera.* Female swollen, pear to lemon-shaped; male with short, bluntly rounded tail; anus subterminal; vulva equatorial.

Heterodera. As above but vulva terminal; female body forming a cyst, packed with eggs.

Meloidogyne. Female body not forming a cyst, not packed with eggs; vulva terminal.

Naccobus. Female swollen, saccate to reniform, with 1 ovary; male tail conoid; anus not subterminal.

Rotylenchulus. Like Naccobus but female has 2 ovaries.

Pratylenchus. Female not swollen; 1 ovary.

Hoplolaimus. Female not swollen; 2 ovaries; phasmids very large, transverse striae continuing across lateral fields; spear knobs anteriorly furcate and pointed.

Scutellonema. Phasmids large; lateral field smooth without transverse striae; spear knobs rounded.

Tylenchorhynchus. Phasmids small, porelike; esophageal glands forming a distinct bulb.

Helicotylenchus. Phasmids small, esophageal glands free in body cavity, overlapping the intestine; tail length equal to anal body diameter; dorsal gland orifice ⅓ or more of stylet length.

Rotylenchus. Dorsal gland orifice less than ⅓ stylet length; lip region longitudinally striated; tail length equal to body diameter; esophageal glands free in body cavity; phasmids small.

Radopholus. Tail length twice as long as anal body diameter; esophageal glands extending far back over intestine, free in body cavity; phasmids small.

Pratylenchoides. Esophageal glands only slightly overlapping intestine; tail length twice as long as body diameter. Phasmids small.

Family *Tylenchulidae.* Female swollen to saccate, head without internal cephalic sclerotization; cuticle finely to moderately annulated, plain; spear short.

Genus *Trophotylenchulus.* Excretory pore located posterior to normal position near nerve ring; male stylet degenerate; lip region with circumoral elevation; excretory pore not closely approximated to vulva.

Tylenchulus. Lip region without circumoral elevation, excretory pore closely approximated to vulva.

Trophonema. Female spiral, thickened; excretory pore normal, near nerve ring; male stylet lacking.

Sphaeronema. Female spherical, otherwise like Trophonema.

Family *Tylenchidae*. Female vermiform; head without internal cephalic sclerotization; cuticle finely to moderately annulated, plain; spear short.

Genus *Neotylenchus*. Intestine not joining esophagus near nerve ring; glands within a basal bulb, overlapping intestine; head framework octagonal.

Paurodontus. Basal esophageal bulb bearing a stemlike extension; spear knobs symmetrical.

Nothotylenchus. Head framework hexagonal; esophageal glands not overlapping intestine; spear with tylenchoid basal knobs.

Beleodorus. As above but spear with flangelike basal projections.

Atylenchus. Head armed with setae; cuticle with transverse and longitudinal striae.

Tylenchus. Median bulb in first half of esophagus; female tail attenuated; 1 ovary; head not armed with setae.

Psilenchus. Median bulb in latter half of esophagus; female tail attenuated; 1 or 2 ovaries.

Anguina. Female body obese, tail conoid, subacute; esophageal glands in form of basal bulb, not overlapping intestine; 1 ovary.

Ditylenchus. Female body slender; tail conoid, subacute; lateral lips not enlarged; 1 ovary.

Tetylenchus. Female tail short, pointed or subacute; 2 ovaries.

Superfamily Aphelenchoidea. Dorsal esophageal gland in metacarpus.

Family *Aphelenchidae*. Male with a bursa with 4 pairs of ribs or papillae.

Single genus, *Aphelenchus*.

Family *Aphelenchoididae*. Male without a bursa.

Genus *Aphelenchoides*. Posterior portion of esophagus not a distinct glandular bulb; esophageal glands considerably overlap the beginning of the intestine; head without sclerotized frontal disc; tail tip without a bursalike membrane.

Class ADENOPHOREA

Phasmids absent, amphid openings spiral, circular, vesiculate, tuboid or, rarely, porelike, sublabial (not on lips); bursa and rectal glands usually absent. Hypodermal and caudal glands usually present.

Order DORYLAIMIDA. Setae on head absent; stylet present or absent; esophageal gland orifices at anterior end of esophagus or posterior to nerve ring; caudal glands absent; excretory system absent or poorly developed.

Family *Dorylaimidae*. Amphids with obscure slitlike apertures; enlarged portion of esophagus not surrounded by muscular sheath.

Genus *Xiphinema*. Spear greatly attenuated; spear extension flanged; labial region not prominently set off and not clearly subdivided into anterior and posterior labial lobes.

Longidorus. Body elongated, slender; spear attenuated but extension not flanged; labial region not set off into lobes.

Dorylaimus. Spear with simple basal extensions, anterior portion not curved; spear with a guiding ring; anterior portion of esophagus normal, not set off; lip region about as wide as the adjacent neck without cuticularized pieces.

Trichodorus. Spear a modified mural tooth, not hollow; slender, elongate, curved, without basal knobs.

Plant-parasitic nematodes may be sedentary or migratory. The latter move through moist soil with a threshing motion but only for very short distances. Major dispersal is by shipment of infested nursery stock and soil. Locally nematodes may be spread on tools, feet, in irrigation water, in plant parts or as dry cysts by wind. Plant nematodes may be facultative or obligate parasites. They may be *endoparasites,* living inside roots or other tissues, or *ectoparasites,* inserting only the head for feeding. Some forms are intermediate between the two types. Many other nematodes live saprophytically around plant roots and are not parasites of living plant tissue.

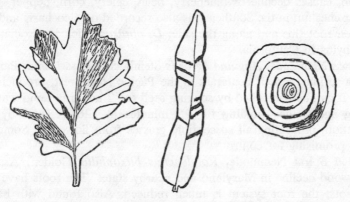

67. *Nematode injury to chrysanthemum, fern, and hyacinth* (*cut surface*).

Most plant-parasitic nematodes infest roots but some live in stems, bulbs, leaves, or buds. Although some nematodes cause galls or other distinctive symptoms, many produce merely a general yellowing, stunting, or dieback that could be due to any number of causes. Only an expert nematologist can determine nematode species and decide which, if any, are responsible for a plant's ill-health. In submitting samples to an experiment station for diagnosis, dig up roots and some surrounding soil, place immediately in a plastic bag to prevent drying out, and mail as soon as possible.

Control measures for nematodes include crop rotation and other cultural practices and soil treatment with chemicals. Most chemical fumigants are designed for treatment of fallow soil; a few, such as Nemagon or V-C-13 are relatively safe around living plants. Details of nematocides and their application are given at the end of this section, on page 331. Greenhouse soils are often steam-sterilized and plants are sometimes dipped in hot water, the duration of the soak and the temperature depending on the tolerance of the plant and the kind of nematode to be eradicated.

American Dagger Nematode, *Xiphinema americanum* Cobb. A native, first described in 1913 from specimens taken around roots of corn, grass, and citrus trees. Found all over the United States, associated with many kinds of plants—azalea, bean, boxwood, clover, camellia, citrus, dogwood, elm, geranium, melon, palm, pea, pecan, peach, pepper, pine, rose, soybean, strawberry, sweetpotato, viburnum, and walnut. In addition to causing decline and sometimes winterkill by its feeding on roots, this species is believed to transmit yellow bud mosaic to strawberries and to increase the incidence of Cytospora canker of spruce.

AWL NEMATODES. Family Criconematidae. Members are long (at least 2 mm) slender, with very long stylet, tail pointed but not very long. These are ectoparasites, sometimes penetrating seed and feeding in embryos, reducing germination. The common awl nematode, *Dolichodorus heterocephalus* Cobb, causes decline of blueberry, bean, celery, corn, pepper, tomato, and water chestnut in the Southeast, is also recorded on eleocharis and pecan. It feeds on root tips and along the side. *D. obtusus* Allen is associated with arctostaphylus in California.

Bentgrass Nematode, *Anguina agrostis* Steinbuch. Grass Nema. Parasite of grasses, a serious pest of bentgrass in the Pacific Northwest, producing galls in seeds. It can be controlled by soaking seed for 2 hours in tepid water with a wetting agent, then holding for 15 minutes at 126° F., and by 1-year crop rotation, preventing all susceptible grasses from flowering. Some herbicides are promising for control.

Boxwood Spiral Nematode, *Rotylenchus buxophilus* Golden. Associated with boxwood decline in Maryland and nearby states. The roots have minute brown spots; the root system is much reduced. Also found with barberry, privet, and peony.

Bud and Leaf Nematode. See Chrysanthemum Foliar Nematode.

Bulb and Stem Nematode. See Stem and Bulb Nematode.

Burrowing Nematode, *Radophilus similis* Cobb. A subtropical species first reported in 1893 from banana roots in the Fiji Islands, now associated with spreading decline of citrus. This disease, the most important on citrus in Florida, has been known for many years but the nematode connection was not established until 1958. The burrowing nematode is also responsible for avocado decline and may infest, but is not always important on, plants in 38 families. Possible hosts include acanthus, allamanda, aluminum plant, calathea, Barbados cherry, banana, castor-bean, cocculus, hibiscus, Japanese boxwood, Japanese persimmon, ixora, jacobinia, ginger-lily, loquat, pandanus, peperomia, philodendron, periwinkle, pothos, podocarpus, pepper, palms, guava, ruellia, corn and tomato. In addition to serious infestations of citrus in central Florida this species has been found in Louisiana in roots of ornamental banana, pothos, philodendron, and sugarcane.

The burrowing nematode, family Hoplolaimidae, is an endoparasite spending its entire life cycle inside roots. Both sexes are wormlike, about 0.6 mm long. They enter the cortical parenchyma of young succulent roots slightly back of the tip and form burrows, leaving behind avenues of infection for soil fungi and bacteria. Infected trees seldom die outright but have poor growth and cease to produce a profitable crop. The disease spreads in all directions from an infected specimen but somewhat unevenly, the distance ranging from 25 to 200 feet in a year, averaging about 50 feet. Long-distance spread is by transplants from nurseries.

Control. Living trees, once infected, cannot be restored to vigor. Diseased trees in quarantine areas are pulled and burned, including 2 trees beyond those known to be infested in an orchard, and the soil is treated with D-D Mixture. Bare-rooted nursery stock is treated with hot water, 10 minutes at 122° F. Crotalaria has been recommended as a cover crop for the 2-year period before it is safe to replant citrus, but crotalaria is not entirely immune to the burrowing nematode. Resistant citrus varieties are a possibility.

Cabbage Cyst Nematode, *Heterodera cruciferae* Franklin. Cabbage-root or Brassica-root Nematode. On cabbage and other crucifers in California, closely related to the sugar-beet nematode. Hosts include broccoli, Brussels sprouts, cauliflower, kale, kohlrabi, mustard, radish, rutabaga, seakale, lobularia, sweet alyssum, candytuft, wallflower, and garden cress. See also Cyst Nematodes.

Cactus Cyst Nematode, *Heterodera cacti* Filipjev & Stekhoven. Obtained from various localities in Mexico, where it is probably indigenous, and likely to occur on cacti wherever grown as ornamentals. The cyst is lemon-shaped.

California Dagger Nematode, *Xiphinema index* Thorne & Allen. Feeding in root tips, causing terminal swelling and angling of main roots, death of lateral roots of grape, fig, and rose.

California Meadow Nematode, *Pratylenchus minyus* Sher & Allen. On pear, grape in California, on bean, corn, grape in the Northeast.

California Sessile Nematode, *Cacopaurus epacris* Allen & Jensen. A small, sedentary ectoparasite of roots, the female somewhat saucer-shaped. It punctures cells with a long, slender stylet and injects a salivary secretion which kills roots. This species is associated with a decline of black-walnut trees in California. Another species, *C. pestis* Thorne, is connected with dieback of Persian walnut, causing reduction in leaves, twigs, nuts, sometimes defoliation and death.

Carnation Pin Nematode, *Paratylenchus dianthus* Jenkins & Taylor. First reported on carnation in 1955 in Maryland, now well distributed through the Northeast. See Pin Nematodes.

Carolina Spiral Nematode, *Rotylenchus brachyurus* Steiner=*Scutellonema* *brachyurum.* Working at crown and roots of African-violet, destroying root cells, depositing eggs in cortical tissues.

Cereal Root Nematode. See Oat Cyst Nematode.

Chamber's Dagger Nematode, *Xiphinema chambersi* Thorne. Stunting strawberries, reported from Wisconsin, Maryland, West Virginia.

Christie's Stubby Root Nematode, *Trichodorus christiei* Allen. On many plants, including beet, corn, celery, cabbage, chayote, fig, various grasses, onion, azalea, blueberry, cranberry, peach, and strawberry.

Christie's Spiral Nematode, *Scutellonema christiei* Golden & Taylor=*Rotylenchus christiei.* Common on lawn grasses in Florida, also on apple and grasses in Maryland and West Virginia.

Chrysanthemum Foliar (Leaf) **Nematode,** *Aphelenchoides ritzema-bosi* Schwartz. Bud and Leaf Nematode. Present wherever garden or greenhouse chrysanthemums are grown, first reported in New Jersey in 1890. This species may also infest aster, calceolaria, dahlia, delphinium, phlox, verbena, zinnia, and a morphologically similar species produces a yellow bud blight of Vanda orchids. In spring the nematode is a bud parasite, causing retarded growth, small crinkled foliage; then it becomes a leaf parasite. First symptoms are dark spots on underside of leaves, but by the 5th day after infestation discolored veins stand out sharply on upper leaf surfaces. Diseased leaves turn brown or black, the discoloration showing first in distinctive wedge-shaped areas between veins. Later the leaves dry, wither, and hang down along the stems. In northern climates the nematodes winter in buds and growing points at base of old stems, migrating up new stems the next year when the plant is wet with rain or dew and entering lower leaves through their stomata. The nematodes feed on and destroy leaf parenchyma but not the epidermal cells. The life cycle, from egg to egg, takes only 2 weeks, and the nematodes may survive in dry foliage for a year or more, reviving when this is moistened.

Control. Keeping foliage dry is a great deterrent. Avoid syringing in the greenhouse, overhead watering in gardens; provide a mulch to prevent splashing. Commercial growers may spray with parathion (¼ pound active to 100 gallons of water) but this is too dangerous for home gardeners. Making tip cuttings, avoiding all crown divisions may provide new plants nearly free of nematodes. Dormant plants can be treated with hot water, 5 minutes at 122° F. or 30 minutes at 112° F.

Citrus Nematode, *Tylenchulus semipenetrans* Cobb. First noted in California in 1912, now widespread in citrus regions, more important in California than in Florida, present also in Texas and Arizona. Olive, persimmon, grape, and lilac may also be infested. This is a sedentary ectoparasite, family Tylenchulidae, with the females saccate and only the anterior portion of the nemas entering roots. Infected roots are abnormally dark, branch rootlets are shortened, swollen, rough. Aboveground symptoms are those of drought and malnutrition, with reduction in size and amount of fruit. Particles of soil adhere to roots in the gelatinous material in which eggs are deposited. Control measures include soil fumigation, selection of resistant understock, and treatment with hot water, 25 minutes at 113° F. or 10 minutes at 116° F.

Citrus Ring Nematode, *Criconemoides citri* Steiner. On citrus in Florida, an ectoparasite with broadly annulated head often buried deep in roots, the tissue dying in that area.

Citrus Spine Nematode, *Criconema civellae* Steiner. A ring nematode reported on citrus roots in a Maryland greenhouse.

Clover Cyst Nematode, *Heterodera trifolii* Coffart. On clover and other legumes except peas. Spinach, beet, soybean and carnation are minor hosts. The cysts are brown, lemon-shaped.

Cobb's Awl Nematode. *Dolichodorus heterocephalus* Cobb. See under Awl Nematodes.

Cobb's Lance Nematode. See Crown-headed Lance Nematode.

Cobb's Meadow Nematode, *Pratylenchus penetrans* Cobb. A root-lesion nematode associated with decline in alfalfa, amaranth, apple, arborvitae, azalea, bean, blackberry, blueberry, boxelder, cabbage, carrot, cedar, celeriac, celery, cherry, chrysanthemum, clover, corn, cucumber, eggplant, fern, gayfeather, gladiolus, grass, hemlock, holly, horseradish, lettuce, maple, mock-orange, onion, parsnip, peach, pear, peony, pepper, Japanese pieris, pine, mountain pinks, phlox, plum, potato, raspberry, rose, safflower, soybean, spinach, spirea, strawberry, sweetpotato, tobacco, tomato, turnip, and yarrow.

Apples have necrotic black or amber spots on white rootlets; roots may be stunted and distorted; tree vigor is reduced; leaves are small. The disease has been called "little leaf" and "rosette." The nematodes invade cortex only; secondary fungi may play a part in the symptoms. See Lesion Nematodes for control.

Cobb's Ring Nematode, *Criconemoides similis* Cobb. An important factor in decline of peach trees in Maryland and North Carolina, also present with pine in Florida.

Cobb's Spiral Nematode, *Helicotylenchus multicinctus* Cobb. Associated with azalea, cherry, cranberry, marsh grass, hibiscus, peach, pine, spruce, yew. See Spiral Nematodes.

Cobb's Stubby Root Nematode, *Trichodorus obtusus* Cobb. On Bermuda grass.

Coffee Meadow Nematode, *Pratylenchus coffeae* Zimmerman. Associated with strawberry black root and decline in Arkansas.

Corn Meadow Nematode, *Pratylenchus zeae* Graham. Associated with corn, also alfalfa, bean, chrysanthemum, cucumber, grasses, pea, phlox, potato, soybean, tobacco, tomato.

Cotton Root-knot Nematode, *Meloidogyne incognita acrita* Chitwood. Confused Root-knot Nematode. A southern native, associated with many plants —forage crops, bean, cabbage, cantaloupe, carrot, celery, chard, rhubarb, corn, cucumber, grape, hollyhock, iris, India love grass, lettuce, pepper, petunia, potato, radish, soybean, spinach (New Zealand), squash, tobacco, tomato, turnip, watermelon, willow; also on azalea, camellia, calathea, coleus, collinsia, gardenia, daylily, hibiscus, nephthytis, roystonea, schefflera, scindapsus. There are some resistant soybean varieties and asparagus; strawberry, and peanut can be used in a rotation. See also Root-knot Nematodes.

Crown-headed Lance Nematode, *Hoplolaimus tylenchiformis* Daday=*H. coronatus.* Widespread in turf, especially in the South, on zoysia, nursery crops, corn, sugarcane, citrus, tomato, sweetpotato, pine seedlings, carnation. This species may feed from the outside, burying head only, but seldom, at the root tips, or it may enter the root completely, destroying the cortex, which is sloughed off, and feeding on the phloem. Nemagon and V-C-13 are somewhat effective as turf drenches.

CYST NEMATODES. Members of the genus Heterodera, family Hoplolaimidae. Partially endoparasitic, rather sedentary, attached to the root by neck only. The female is lemon-shaped to globoid, white, yellow, or brown, 0.5 to 0.75 mm. Eggs are deposited or retained in body of the mother, whose leathery wall forms a true cyst. Eggs may remain alive for years inside the cysts, which are spread by wind, or in soil with non-host plants. Males are slender worms. Control is by quarantines, hot-water treatment of plants, and soil fumigation. See Golden and Sugar-beet Nematodes; see Cactus, Carrot, Cabbage, Clover, Grass, Soybean, and Tobacco Cyst Nematodes.

DAGGER NEMATODES. Migratory ectoparasites, family Dorylaimidae, with very long stylets. They are very common in garden and greenhouse soils and may be introduced with virgin soil from the woods. Feeder roots are destroyed. See American and European Dagger Nematodes.

De Man's Meadow Nematode, *Pratylenchus pratensis* de Man. Important on grasses, strawberry, lily, narcissus. Associated with many other hosts, including forage plants, grains, amaranth, apple, arborvitae, asparagus, azalea, bean, blueberry, boxwood, broccoli, cantaloupe, carrot, cherry, chrysanthemum, corn, delphinium, dogwood, Douglas-fir, gladiolus, holly, horseradish, larkspur, lettuce, maple, lilac, oak, onion, parsnip, pea, peach, peony, pieris, pine, potato, raspberry, rose, soybean, spinach, spruce, Japanese spurge, strawberry, sweetpotato, tobacco, tomato, viburnum, yew. See also Lesion Nematodes.

European Dagger Nematode, *Xiphinema diversicaudatum* Micoletzky. A proven pathogen of rose, strawberry, and peanut, also associated with corn and pine. Very common in commercial rose greenhouses, reducing vigor, causing chlorosis. This species produces galls on rose roots, similar to root-knot galls but more elongate and near the tip, causing curly-tip. This is one of the largest of the plant nematodes, about twice as long as the root-knot species. Cleaning up a greenhouse infestation means disposal of all plants in a bed, careful sterilization of soil, and replanting with clean stock.

False Root-knot Nematode of Sugar Beets, *Naccobus batatiformis* Thorne. A gall-forming, sedentary endoparasite, family Hoplolaimidae. The female is saccate but the posterior part is somewhat tapering. Galls are formed on sugar beet, garden beets, cacti, crucifers, carrot, gaillardia, lettuce, and salsify.

Fern Nematode. See Spring Crimp Nematode.

Fig Cyst Nematode, *Heterodera fici* Kirianova. First reported in Russia in 1954, found since in Florida and California on fig, *Ficus carica* and *F. elastica*.

Fig Pin Nematode, *Paratylenchus hamatus* Thorne & Allen. Celery Pin Nematode. On azalea, bean, boxwood, celery, chrysanthemum, clover, corn, geranium, gladiolus, turf grasses, hemlock, holly, horseradish, iris, oak, onion, parsley, peach, pieris, pine, mountain pink, prune, rose, soybean, strawberry, tomato. This species is responsible for celery losses in New England, plants being severely stunted and chlorotic, and with decline of fig in California. The nematodes can be starved out of celery fields by 2-year rotation with lettuce and spinach.

Fig Spine Nematode, *Criconema decalineatum* Chitwood. This species on fig has rings, 10 rows of spines, and a long stylet.

Godfrey's Meadow Nematode, *Pratylenchus brachyurus* Godfrey=*P. leiocephalus*. Smooth-headed Meadow Nematode. Associated with alfalfa, clover, cereals, asparagus, citrus, dogwood, grass, pieris, pine, soybean, strawberry, tomato, peanut, potato, pineapple, avocado. This vagrant lesion nematode forms unsightly lesions in peanut shells and lives through curing.

Golden Nematode, *Heterodera rostochiensis* Wollenweber. Potato Root Eelworm. On white potatoes, also tomato, eggplant and other members of the Solanaceae but not on tobacco. This cyst nematode was first discovered on Long Island, New York, in 1941 and has been kept there by a rigorous quarantine. Known as "potato sickness," the disease has been serious in the British Isles for many years. Crops do not show much damage until heavy populations have been built up in the soil, then there is midday wilting, stunting, poor root development, early death, and up to 85 per cent reduction in potato yield. The eggs survive in the soil inside cysts which may contain up to 500 eggs each, and may remain viable up to 17 years. In spring, when the soil temperature is around 60° F., a chemical given off by potato or tomato roots stimulates hatching, and the larvae, which have had a first molt inside the eggs, leave the cysts and migrate to host plants, entering the roots. The females become stationary, swell to pear shape, and break through the roots, though remaining attached by a thin neck. Cylindrical males break out of the roots and cluster around to mate with the females. After the eggs are formed, the female dies and becomes the cyst—first white, then gold, orange, finally brown. Cysts are spread in bits of soil clinging to roots, in potato bags, crates, machinery, even in trouser cuffs of farm workers. Lily-of-the-valley pips, cacti, and other non-host plants intercepted at quarantine have had golden-nematode cysts in fragments of soil around the roots.

Control. Withholding potatoes from infested land is the best means of preventing spread, plus soil treatment with D-D mixture or other fumigant. Healthy potatoes are sold in paper bags to prevent reinfestation from second-hand burlap bags.

Grass Cyst Nematode, *Heterodera punctata* Thorne. Found on wheat and associated with bentgrasses in North Dakota and Minnesota.

Grass Sheath Nematode, *Hemicycliophora similis* Thorne.

Javanese Root-knot Nematode, *Meloidogyne javanica* Traub. Common in southern peach orchards and nurseries, widespread in Georgia on peaches such as Yunnan and Shali that are otherwise resistant to root knot. Found elsewhere in greenhouses. May be associated with azalea, carrot, *Cocos plumosa,* impatiens, potato, bean, beet, cabbage, calendula, carnation, corn, cucurbits, eggplant, snapdragon, tomato. Resistant peanut, strawberry, cotton, and pepper can be used in rotation.

Northern Root-knot Nematode, *Meloidogyne hapla* Chitwood. Northern Peanut Nematode. Common on many outdoor crops in the North and in florist and nursery stock. Hosts include abelia, barberry, bean, blueberry, boxwood, California-laurel, cantaloupe, carrot, cherry, clovers, cress, cucumber, eggplant, escarole, forsythia, geranium, germander, grass, gladiolus, grape hyacinth, goldenchain, kale, lettuce, marigold, mock-orange, morning-glory, mulberry, myrtle, mustard, parsnip, pachysandra, pansy, peanut, peony, pepper, periwinkle, potato, privet, rose, soybean, spirea, strawberry, tomato, viburnum, weigela.

This is the only root-knot species really injurious to strawberries, causing galls, reducing growth of main roots, with excessive production of branch roots, stunting, sometimes death. Injury is more serious in sandy than in heavy soils. Yields have been increased by using granular Nemagon, mixed with fertilizer, as a side-dressing. Rotation with corn and some grains may be practical.

Oak Sheathoid Nematode, *Hemicriconemoides biformis* Chitwood & Birchfield. On roots of oak, Florida.

Pacific Dagger Nematode, *Xiphinema radicicola* Goodey. Reported on oak in Florida.

Pea Cyst Nematode, *Heterodera göttingiana* Liebscher. On pea, soybean, lupine in Europe. Cyst is lemon-shaped.

Peanut Root-knot Nematode, *Meloidogyne arenaria* Neal. Common in greenhouses and nursery stock all over the United States and on peanuts wherever grown, especially serious in Alabama, Georgia, and Virginia. This species has been recorded from abelia, African-violet, carnation (often followed by bacterial wilt) calendula, garden balsam, gardenia, oleander, wandering-Jew, viburnum, and bean, beet, cabbage, carrot, corn, escarole, melon, pea, pepper, radish, potato, tomato. This species may injure peach roots but does not reproduce in them. Strawberries and sweetpotato Maryland Golden are resistant and can be used in a rotation.

Persian Sessile Nematode, *Cacopaurus pestis* Thorne. This is a small, sedentary ectoparasite occurring in California on roots of Persian walnut. The sausage-shaped female punctures epidermal cells with a long, slender stylet and injects a salivary secretion. The roots die, trees die back, may be completely defoliated, and may also die.

PIN NEMATODES. Species of the genus Paratylenchus, family Criconematidae. They are common ectoparasites related to ring nematodes but thinner. Males are vestigial or rare, with weak stylets. Females have a long stylet and ventrally curved body. See Carnation Pin and Fig Pin Nematodes.

Pine Cystoid Nematode, *Meloidodera floridensis* Chitwood, Hannon & Essex. On pine in Florida, a genus intermediate between root-knot and cyst nematodes. Eggs are retained in the female but there are neither distinct cysts nor galls on the plants.

Pine Sheathoid Nematode, *Hemicriconemoides floridensis.* Chitwood & Birchfield.

Pine Sting Nematode, *Belonolaimus gracilis* Steiner. On a wide variety of hosts. A large ectoparasite with very long stylet, first reported from pine, also injuring corn and listed on many other hosts, but on these it may have been confused with *B. longidorus.* See Sting Nematode.

Potato Rot Nematode, *Ditylenchus destructor* Thorne. Related to the stem nematode and a problem in Idaho and Wisconsin. It attacks potatoes below ground, discolored spots on tubers progressing to a gray or brown decay. The tissues have a granular appearance and dry and shrink; the skin may crack. Invasions continue in storage, sometimes with complete destruction of tubers. Ethylene dibromide has given good results in soil fumigation.

Reniform Nematode, *Rotylenchulus reniformis* Linford & Oliveira. Kidney-shaped, in family Hoplolaimidae, similar to the citrus nematode in habit. First described from pineapple roots in Hawaii, now found in Florida and other warm states on turf, cotton, peanut, tomato, gardenia, jacquemontia, and other ornamentals. This nema is partially endoparasitic, head and neck going into the rootlet, the swollen body projecting outside, covered with a gelatinous material so that soil particles cling to it.

Rice White-tip Nematode. See Summer Dwarf Nematode.

Rice-root Nematode. *Radopholus oryzae* von Breda de Haan. Related to the burrowing nematode, reported on rice in Texas and Louisiana.

RING NEMATODES. Members of the genera Criconema and Criconemoides, family Criconematidae. They are short, stout, and heavily annulated (with rings). Most have long stylets and they feed at root tips or along sides of roots with only the anterior end of the body embedded. See Citrus Ring and Cobb's Ring nematodes.

ROOT-KNOT NEMATODES. Members of the genus Meloidogyne, family Hoplolaimidae, formerly considered only one species, *Heterodera marioni*

68. *Root-knot nematode: knots in roots, male, and female with eggs.*

and linked with the cyst nematodes. They are endoparasites causing root galls, round or irregular swellings. Root knot is the best-known nematode disease, with over 1800 host plants susceptible to one or more species of Meloidogyne. Reported first from England, the disease was recorded in the United States in 1876, on violet. Infected plants are stunted, often wilt, turn yellow and die. Grains and grasses are about the only plants resistant to all forms of root knot.

The long, thin larva takes form inside the egg, breaks out and migrates through the soil to a root tip, moving into the axial cylinder. Through its short stylet it injects a secretion into the tissue that stimulates the formation of 3 to 5 giant cells around the injection cell. As it feeds, the female, which remains in this spot the rest of its life, becomes whitish and pear-shaped, barely visible to the naked eye. The male becomes long and cylindrical.

The female deposits its eggs in an extruded brown jelly and the larvae develop inside the eggs, becoming free in the soil when the root cracks or decays. The larvae may attack a new root or the same root in another place. In warm weather, around 80° F., the life cycle takes only 25 days; at 67° F. it averages 87 days, and below 55° F. activity ceases. Root-knot nematodes are injurious through their feeding punctures even when galls are not formed, and the wounds frequently afford entrance to bacteria and fungi causing crown gall, wilt, and other diseases.

Soil fumigation kills larvae free in the soil, but those inside the knots usually remain viable. Not all species of Meloidogyne attack the same crop plants, so that choice of crop affords some control. See also Cotton, Northern, Southern, Peanut, Thames, and Javanese Root-knot Nematodes.

Scribner's Meadow Nematode, *Pratylenchus scribneri* Steiner. First recorded on potatoes in 1889 in Tennessee. Associated with amaryllis, hibiscus, strawberry in Florida, roses in California, and in New Jersey clover, corn, dahlia, orchids, parsnip, peach, potato, raspberry, rose, soybean, and tomato. See also Lesion Nematodes.

Seinhorst Stubby Root Nematode, *Trichodorus pachydermis* Seinhorst. Reported on turf. See Stubby Root Nematodes.

SHEATH NEMATODES. Members of the genus Hemicycliophora, family Criconematidae, relatives of ring nematodes. They are ectoparasites with pronounced sedentary habits. Molting skins are retained on the bodies remaining attached to the root. There is a long and slender stylet.

Smooth-headed Meadow Nematode. See Godfrey's Meadow Nematode.

Southern Root-knot Nematode, *Meloidogyne incognita incognita* Kofoid & White. Native to the South and common there but overwintering as far north as New Jersey. This is the most important root-knot species on peach; it is also recorded on abelia, banana, bean, carrot, coleus, corn, cucumber, daylily, eggplant, gardenia, geranium, hibiscus, onion, okra, sweetpotato, pepper, tomato, watermelon, willow. It causes stunting and chlorosis on gardenia. It does not occur on peanuts or strawberries, and these may be used for rotation. Some peach understocks are highly resistant, and resistant crotalaria and oats can be used as cover crops in peach orchards. Nemagon injected into soil around living peach trees has given good control.

Soybean Cyst Nematode, *Heterodera glycines* Ichinohe. Causing yellow dwarf disease of soybeans. An immigrant from Japan or Korea, first noted in North Carolina in 1954, thence spread to Arkansas, Kentucky, Mississippi, Missouri, Tennessee, Virginia. Plants are yellow, stunted, roots are small and dark with few or no bacterial nodules but with lemon-shaped brown cysts clearly visible. The nematode reproduces only in roots of lespedeza, vetch, and bean, besides soybean, but the cysts occur as contaminants of narcissus bulbs and gladiolus corms grown in infested soil and may be so disseminated.

All infested areas are under federal and state quarantines. Soil fumigation temporarily reduces nematode populations and increases plant growth and yield.

SPIRAL NEMATODES. Species in 3 genera—Helicotylenchus, Rotylenchus and Scutellonema—in the family Hoplolaimidae. The body is long, cylindrical but is held in the shape of a spiral. Species are mostly ectoparasites, sometimes partially end parasitic. See Boxwood, Carolina, Christie's Spiral Nematodes.

Spring Crimp Nematode, *Aphelenchoides fragariae* Ritzema Bos=*A. olesistus.* Spring Dwarf, Strawberry Dwarf Nematode, Fern Nematode. A bud parasite of the cultivated strawberry from Cape Cod to Maryland and found in scattered localities along the Pacific Coast. This is a cold-weather species, persisting through the winter and with several thousand individuals present in a single bud as the leaves unfold in spring. The foliage is small, twisted, thickened, glossy, with swollen petioles; blossom buds are killed or poor and no fruit is set. Some plants are killed, others recover.

Dieback of Easter lilies in the Northwest and greenhouse trouble with ferns and begonias is probably due to this same nematode, although formerly reported as *A. olesistus* on these hosts. Lilies from infested bulbs develop "bunchy-top" and dieback with thick, twisted foliage. Fern leaves have a blotched appearance with dark-brown to black areas on the fronds. Dark blotches appear on begonia leaves and the plants are stunted. The fern nematode is also associated with anemone, bouvardia, calceolaria, chrysanthemum, clematis, coleus, crassula, dianthus, doronicum, geranium, hydrangea, peony, primrose, saintpaulia, scabiosa, zinnia and other ornamentals.

Control. A parathion spray is suggested for lilies. Bulbs are treated with hot water, with formalin added to prevent basal rot, for 1 hour at 111° F. Potted begonias can be submerged, pot and all, for 1 minute at 120° F. or for 3 minutes at 116°. African-violets may be treated for 30 minutes at 110° F. Strawberry plants in nurseries should be inspected and certified in spring. Mother plants, near the end of the dormant period, can be treated with hot water, 2 minutes at 127° F. Crop rotation helps. Nemagon can be used as a side-dressing.

Steiner's Spiral Nematode, *Helicotylenchus nannus* Steiner. A small species common in the Southeast. Found damaging roots of apple, azalea, boxwood, asparagus fern, blueberry, calathea, camellia, clovers, corn, cranberry, delphinium, gardenia, grasses, peach, peperomia, philodendron, privet, rose, royal palm, rubber plant, laurel-oak, soybean, peanut, tobacco, tomato, weigela, and yew.

Stem and Bulb Nematode, *Ditylenchus dipsaci* Kühn. Bulb and Stem Nematode, Teasel Nematode. An internal parasite of bulbs, stems, leaves, rarely roots, causing Eelworm Disease of Narcissus, Ring Disease of Hyacinth, Onion Bloat, Stem Disease of Phlox. The name *dipsaci* covers many strains and probably more than one species. The type was found in 1857 in Fuller's teasel. The strains on hyacinth and narcissus are not reciprocally infective, although the hyacinth strain does not infect onions. This nematode is also reported on grape hyacinth, scilla, tulip, galtonia, garlic, shallot, and other bulbs, on some vegetables and, as a stem nematode, on many flowers besides phlox.

Hyacinths have yellow flecks on foliage which is often twisted, short and split. There are pustules (spikkels) on narcissus leaves which can be felt with the fingers; serious diseased bulbs may produce no foliage.

The strain on phlox attacks campanula, sweet-william, evening primrose, goldenrod, schizanthus, anemone, foxglove, orchids. The leaves are narrow, crinkled, with a tendency to lengthened petioles. Stems may be swollen near the top or bent sidewise; plants are stunted, may not bloom; they die prematurely. The nematodes enter through stomata of young shoots and work upward as stems develop. They infest seed of phlox and other composites and may be so disseminated.

In onions, the inner bulb scales are enlarged, causing a split onion that seldom flowers and sometimes rots at the base. Seedlings are twisted, stunted, covered with yellow spots. On plants grown from sets a slight stunting and flaccid condition of outer leaves is followed by leaf-tip necrosis and continued stunting. The larvae may live long in infested soil.

Control. Take up and burn infested phlox and similar plants. Put new plants in a new location or fumigate soil. For onions, fumigate soil or plan a very long rotation; fumigate seed with methyl bromide. Commercial growers routinely treat narcissus bulbs in hot water, 4 hours at 110° F. after a presoak of 2 hours. The hot water should contain formalin, 1 pint to 25 gallons, to prevent basal rot. The poisonous organic phosphate Systox applied as a drench has controlled nematodes in leaves but with some phytotoxicity. Avoid spreading the nematodes in infested soil on tools or in irrigation water.

The nematode on bulbous iris is sometimes considered a part of the *Ditylenchus dipsaci* complex, and is sometimes listed as *D. iridis.*

STING NEMATODES. Belonging to the genus Belonolaimus, family Criconematidae. They are migratory obligate ectoparasites, usually found free in the soil near growing tips. They are long, slender, with blunt ends, strongly annulated body, elongated spear; about 2 mm in length. A recently reported species, *Belonolaimus longicaudatus* Rau, is probably responsible for much of the root damage formerly attributed to *B. gracilis* (see Pine Sting Nematode). It injures celery, cabbage, bean, potato, soybean, turnip, peanut, corn, turf grasses, azalea and other plants and is a major pest of strawberries. Roots develop short stubby branches with necrotic lesions; plants are stunted.

Soil treatment with Nemagon or ethylene dibromide has increased peanut yields.

STUBBY ROOT NEMATODES. Members of the genus Trichodorus, family Dorylaimidae. Migratory ectoparasites, cylindrical, tapering at the anterior end, with short tail, long, needlelike stylet. Its feeding causes numerous short stubby branches on roots.

STUNT NEMATODES. Stylet Nematodes. Members of the genus Tylenchorhynchus, family Hoplolaimidae. Somewhat migratory, internal or external root parasites, stunting plants.

Sugar-beet Nematode, *Heterodera schactii* Schmidt. A cyst nematode occurring in sugar-beet areas from California to Michigan, also infesting table beets and crucifers—cabbage, broccoli, rape, turnip, rutabaga, radish. The females, numerous white specks clinging to roots, contain 100 to 600 eggs. Slender larvae puncture root cells with their strong stylets and pass through 3 molts inside the roots. The wormlike males then leave the roots to search for the flask-shaped females, which are attached to the roots only by their heads. Eggs are deposited in a gelatinous mass. These soon hatch to start other generations but the females die with more eggs inside their bodies, which turn brown and become cysts. Eggs inside cysts may remain viable 5 or 6 years. Control depends on a very long crop rotation or soil fumigation.

Sugar-cane Stylet Nematode, *Tylenchorhynchus martini* Fielding. On sugar cane and rice.

Summer Dwarf Nematode, *Aphelenchoides besseyi* Christie, including *A. oryzae*. Crimp, Strawberry Bud or Dwarf Nematode, Rice White Top. A bud nematode, ectoparasite, building up serious populations on strawberries in hot weather. Unfolding leaves are small, narrow, crinkled, abnormally dark; plants have a spread-out, spidery appearance. The nematode occurs along the Atlantic seaboard from Maryland to Florida and west to Louisiana and in scattered locations in California. It causes a serious disease of rice in Arkansas and Louisiana. In spring the nematode population is low, allowing nearly normal formation of strawberry leaves, but in summer a single bud may harbor up to 1300 nemas. Buy certified plants. Rogue and burn diseased plants. Treat dormant infested plants with hot water, 2 minutes at 127° F.

Tarjan's Sheath Nematode, *Hemicycliophora parvana* Tarjan. An ectoparasite damaging celery in Florida, also recorded on dracaena, corn, and beans.

Teasel Nematode. See Stem Nematode.

Tesselate Stylet Nematode, *Tylenchorhynchus claytoni* Steiner. Common in the Northeast on many plants, associated with andromeda, apple, arborvitae, azalea, bean, blueberry, boxwood, broccoli, cherry, cereals, clovers, corn, cranberry, dogwood, forsythia, grape, grasses, hemlock, holly, lettuce, lilac, maple, peach, pepper, pine, potato, raspberry, rhododendron, soybean, strawberry, tomato, tuliptree, veronica, willow, yew.

Thames' Root-knot Nematode, *Meloidogyne arenaria thamesii* Chitwood. Occurring naturally in southern Florida on Boehmeria (Chinese silk plant), also reported on tomato and scindapsus; present elsewhere in greenhouses.

Thorne's Lance Nematode, *Rotylenchus robustus* de Man=*Hoplolaimus uniformis* Thorne. Reported on azaleas and many other ornamentals.

Thorne's Meadow Nematode, *Pratylenchus thornei* Sher & Allen. On wheat, other grains and grasses.

Thorne's Needle Nematode, *Longidorus sylphus* Thorne. In the family Dorylaimidae, having a long, slender spear. Fairly common in the Pacific Northwest, causing severe stunting of peppermint. Soil treatment with ethylene dibromide or Nemagon has greatly increased yields.

Tobacco Cyst Nematode, *Heterodera tabacum* Lownsbery & Lownsbery. Reported from Connecticut on tobacco, tomato and other solanaceous plants but not potato.

Walnut Meadow Nematode, *Pratylenchus vulnus* Allen & Jensen. A lesion nematode, described in 1951 from California as an important parasite of walnut and rose on the West Coast, also present elsewhere. It may infest avocado, boxwood, almond, fig, forsythia, gayfeather, apricot, citrus, peach, plum, raspberry, loganberry, rose, strawberry. Soil fumigation has increased growth of infested roses by 400 per cent.

Wesson's Sheathoid Nematode, *Hemicriconemoides wessoni* Chitwood & Birchfield, reported on myrica in Florida.

West African Spiral Nematode, *Scutellonema blaberum* Steiner=*Rotylenchus blaberus.* On banana yams, red spider-lily and African-violet.

Wheat Nematode, *Anguina tritici* Steinbuch. Known as the Wheat Eelworm or Wheat Gall Nematode, this was the first nematode species recognized as causing plant disease. Wheat and rye may be stunted with leaves wrinkled, twisted, kernels modified into galls. The nemas are spread by infested seed grain. Plant clean seed in uninfested soil.

Zimmerman's Spiral Nematode, *Helicotylenchus erythrinae* Zimmerman. Rather common in Florida around roots of grasses and other plants. Also present in other states on blueberry, boxwood, cauliflower, cedar, clovers, corn, cranberry, turf grasses, oak, oat, pachysandra, pepper, pieris, pine, rhubarb, soybean, strawberry, wheat, yew.

Zoysia Spine Nematode, *Criconema spinalineatum* Chitwood. One of the ring nematodes, reported on zoysia.

NEMATOCIDES FOR SOIL TREATMENT

Chloropicrin. LARVACIDE; PICFUME. Tear gas, extremely irritating; use mask. Soil should be moist, temperature above 60° F. Use special applicator, injecting ½ cc 6 inches deep at 10-inch intervals; dosage 300 to 400 pounds per acre. Apply a water seal immediately; wait 2 to 4 weeks before planting. Do not treat soil in the vicinity of living plants.

D-D MIXTURE. Use normal precautions; wash off if spilled on the skin. Soil temperature should be between 40° and 80° F. Inject 4 to 5 cc 6 inches deep at 12-inch intervals; dosage 20 to 40 gallons per acre. A water seal is unnecessary but helpful. Wait 2 to 4 weeks before planting; do not use around living plants.

Ethylene dibromide. DOWFUME W-85. Relatively safe to handle. Use at 50° F. or above. Inject 5 to 6 cc at 12-inch intervals; dosage 5 to 10 gallons per acre. No seal is required. Wait 2 to 3 weeks before planting.

Methyl bromide. DOWFUME MC-2. Extremely poisonous, to be used only by professionals. Use above 50° F.; apply according to directions with special applicator under plastic cover; dosage 1 pound per 100 square feet. Wait 4 to 5 days before planting.

MYLONE. Safe to handle. Apply to moist soil with temperature above 50° F. Use as a spray or powder; disc into the soil 6 inches deep; dosage 300 pounds per acre or ¾ pound per 100 square feet. Apply a water seal. Wait 2 to 3 weeks before planting.

NEMAGON. DBCP. Relatively safe, widely available under various trade names, useful for home gardens for either pre- or post-planting treatment.

For Fallow Soil. Soil temperature should be 50° to 80° F. Drench soil, using ½ gallon per acre for row treatment to 1½ gallons total area (or 86.5

pounds of 10 per cent granules). Work 6 inches deep. No cover is necessary. Wait 2 to 3 weeks before planting.

For Living Plants. Drench turf, some perennials, or trees, using 1 pint of 75 per cent concentrate with 100 gallons of water for 1000 square feet.

For row plants: Make a narrow trench, 6 inches deep on each side of the plants, and apply 1½ teaspoons of concentrate, diluted with sufficient water, per 1000 feet of row. Tamp soil back into the trench.

When planting shrubs: After the hole is three quarters full of soil, inject 1 drop (2.2 ml) from a machine-oil can, using a mixture of 9 parts water and 1 part concentrate, at 1-foot intervals.

For established roses in beds: Place 1 teaspoon of 10 per cent granules in the bottom of each 6-inch hole, spacing the holes 12 inches apart around the bush. Fill the holes with soil and firm it down.

TELONE. Very irritating to the skin, very harmful to the eyes; use all precautions. Use on fallow soil only, injecting at the rate of 20 to 40 gallons per acre when temperature is between 40° and 80° F. Wait 2 to 4 weeks before planting.

VAPAM. Safe for the operator but very toxic to plants, used as a weed killer as well as a nematocide; do not apply near living plants. Dilute 1 quart with 20 to 25 parts of water and use to drench 1000 square feet of fallow soil, when temperature is above 50° F. Wait 1 to 3 weeks before planting.

V-C-13 NEMACIDE. Safe to use around living plants, fairly safe for the operator; avoid skin contact or inhaling.

For Fallow Soil. Use 15 to 25 gallons per acre to drench soil; work into the top 6 inches. Temperature should be above 50° F. Wait 2 weeks before planting.

For Living Plants. Drench turf with 1 gallon of 75 per cent emulsifiable concentrate with 25 to 50 gallons of water and apply to 1600 square feet; water well.

For shrubs: Add 2 to 3 teaspoons to 1 gallon of water and apply to 4 square feet, in holes 9 inches deep, 12 inches apart.

For potting soil: Use 1 teaspoon to 1 quart of water for 1 cubic foot of soil.

ORTHEZIA

Greenhouse Orthezia, *Orthezia insignis* Browne. A close relative of scales and mealybugs, in the family Coccidae. It infests 125 or more varieties of greenhouse plants and is a garden pest in warm climates. Favored hosts are lantana, coleus, chrysanthemum, cacti, heliotrope, periwinkle, petunia, salvia, silver lace-vine, verbena. It is called lantana bug for its predilection

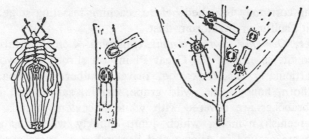

69. Greenhouse orthezia.

for that plant and has even been introduced in Hawaii as a beneficial insect to cope with *Lantana camea,* which has become a weed there.

The dark-green wingless nymphs are about the size of pinheads and are covered with rows of minute waxy plates. The mature female is pale brown or dark green with a conspicuous waxy fringe around the body and a long, white, fluted egg sac. The total length of adult and sac is only ⅓ inch. Plants become sickly and sometimes die from the constant sucking on leaves, stems, and roots.

Control measures are the same as for mealybugs: malathion or parathion or diazinon or Trithion or sulfatepp aerosol.

PLANTHOPPERS

Planthoppers are sucking insects of the family Fulgoridae. They have been called fulgorids, lightning leafhoppers, lanternflies, mealy flata. The tropical species have many grotesque forms but ours are similar to leafhoppers, with the same jumping habit. They are larger, however, with the antennae arising below the eyes and with few spurs on the hind tibiae.

Citrus Flatid Planthopper, *Metcalfa pruinosa* (Say)=*Ormenis pruinosa.* Widespread on various shrubs, including viburnum, azalea, camellia, and occurring on citrus (first noticed in Texas in 1947, but not very important). It sometimes destroys small buds or causes fruit drop. The nymphs are found on succulent terminal growth surrounded by masses of white, flocculent, waxy material. The adults are ⅓ inch long, light brownish gray, with very broad wings giving the insect a wedge-shaped appearance. On citrus, sprays or dusts of parathion or TEPP have given control.

Corn Planthopper*, *Peregrinus maidis* (Ashmead). Also called Corn Leafhopper, serious in Florida, reported from South Carolina, Texas, and other states. The adult is yellowish green, ⅙ inch long; it has clear wings longer than the body with dark markings near the tip, antennae with greatly thickened basal portion. Abundant in late August in Florida, the lanternflies collect in large numbers near buds or in axils of leaves; nearly every stalk of young corn may be killed before reaching tasseling stage. It can be controlled with sulfur or pyrethrum dust.

Planthopper, *Ormenis septentrionalis* (Spinola). Common through most of the United States east of the Great Plains on shrubs and woody vines, viburnum particularly, also boxwood, privet, mulberry, catalpa, Japanese cherry, hawthorn, honeysuckle, wild grape, dahlia, salvia, and lilies. Tree trunks and branches are covered with white flocculent strands concealing the young greenish nymphs, which jump quickly when disturbed. The adults, which are around in August and September in home gardens, are a little larger than the citrus planthopper and have wide bluish-green wings. Eggs are laid in slits in bark of twigs and covered with a white, waxy secretion. There is only 1 generation. This species is more conspicuous than injurious, and control measures are seldom necessary.

PSYLLIDS

Psyllids belong to the family Psyllidae, order Hemiptera. They are related to aphids and are often known as jumping plant lice. They are small sucking insects, usually under ¼ inch, with hind legs enlarged for jumping. Adults are very active, moving quickly when disturbed. Some species are serious pests; some are a nuisance because of copious honeydew and subsequent growth of disfiguring sooty mold.

Acacia Psyllid, *Psylla uncatoides* (Ferris and Klyver). Recently serious on acacia in California, also reported on albizzia.

Alder Psyllid, *Psylla floccosa* Patch. Common in the Northeast. The nymphs produce large quantities of wax, and groups of the psyllids look like masses of cotton on stems.

Apple Sucker*, *Psylla mali* (Schmidberger). An introduced species established in Canada. Eggs laid on apple twigs in fall hatch as buds open. Becoming adult in June, psyllids may leave apples for vegetables, returning in autumn for egg laying. Feeding by nymphs injures opening buds, destroys flower clusters, prevents fruit from setting. There is a great amount of honeydew.

Blackberry Psyllid, *Trioza tripunctata* Fitch. A native on wild blackberry in the Northeast, infesting cultivated blackberries and other brambles. The adult is ⅙ inch long, yellow-brown, each wing marked with 3 yellow-brown bands. It winters in protected places, and soon after growth starts in spring lays eggs in hairs of leaf stems and tender shoots. Nymphs and adults puncture stems, curl leaves, produce stunting and almost gall-like distortion. There is 1 generation. Spray with malathion or nicotine sulfate.

Boxelder Psyllid*, *Psylla negundinis* Mally. On boxelder, similar to the alder psyllid. Spray with DDT or methoxychlor or malathion in mid-May or early June.

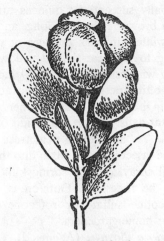

70. Boxwood leaves cupped by boxwood psyllid.

Boxwood Psyllid*, *Psylla buxi* (Linnaeus). Confined to boxwood. Terminal leaves are cupped and young twig growth checked by a small, gray-green nymph covered with a white cottony or waxy material. The adult, a small green "fly" with transparent wings, appears in late May or June and lays eggs in the base of buds. First-instar nymphs winter there and infest terminal leaves as they unfold in spring. Their feeding punctures cause the leaves to curl and form a cup concealing and protecting the nymphs. Spray with DDT or methoxyclor in mid-April (New Jersey) and/or with malathion for adults in May or June.

Hackberry Nipple-gall Psyllid*, *Pachypsylla celtidismamma* (Riley). Pale to dark reddish brown, forming globular hairy galls on underside of leaves and craterlike depressions on the upper surface. Three other species also form galls on hackberry. Spray with malathion plus DDT or with Sevin.

Laurel Psyllid, *Trioza alacris* Flor. A pest of laurel or sweetbay in California, New Jersey and other Atlantic states, also on cherry-laurel. Leaves curl and thicken, redden at margins, form galls; plants are unsightly, lose much of their foliage. Nymphs are pale yellow and orange, hidden by long, white wax; adults are very small, 1/12 inch long, greenish yellow to pale brown with light and dark spots. Eggs are white to yellow, covered with fine powdery wax, laid in March or April in New Jersey, adults having wintered in or on hosts. Spray with lindane, malathion, or nicotine sulfate.

Pear Psylla*, *Psylla pyricola* (Förster). An important pest of pear in eastern states since it was first found in Connecticut in 1832 and serious in the Pacific Northwest since 1939. The copious honeydew secreted by pear psyllids covers foliage and fruit; sooty mold growing in this makes brown spots on the leaves, scars and blackens the fruit. There may be partial defoliation, loss of vigor; buds may not develop normally. Bartlett and d'Anjou pears are especially susceptible; quinces are occasionally infested. The adult is dark reddish brown, 1/10 inch long, and looks like a miniature cicada (Plate XXII). It winters in bark crevices or under leaves on ground and starts in early spring to lay pear-shaped yellow eggs around buds. In 2 weeks these hatch into wingless nymphs, 1/80 inch long, which broaden and darken through 5 molting periods, becoming adult in a month. There are 3 to 5 generations in a season, with summer eggs laid on leaves or petioles. Nymphs cluster at axils and on underside of leaves, secreting their abundant sticky honeydew. A "decline" in pear trees on the Pacific Coast is laid to the pear psylla. The insect injects a toxin into the tree.

Control. A dormant oil spray in early spring kills many adults and eggs, but summer sprays may be necessary. Guthion is now recommended for commercial growers. Nicotine sulfate or rotenone with a summer oil is fairly effective and safe for home gardeners.

Persimmon Psylla*, *Trioza diospyri* (Ashmead). On persimmon in Florida.

Potato Psyllid*, *Paratrioza cockerelli* (Sulc). Tomato Psyllid.* Present from the Great Plains to the Pacific Coast, causing a disease known as psyllid yellows. Adults are first green, then black with white margins, 1/10 inch long. The females lay bright-yellow oval eggs, each attached by a stalk to edges of underside of leaves, usually when the temperature is around 80° F. They hatch in 4 to 15 days into flat, scalelike nymphs, first yellow or orange, then green with a fringe of hairs all around the body. During feeding they inject into the potato plant a substance that disturbs the proper relation between foliage and tubers. The effect on the potato or tomato varies somewhat with the number of insects present, 10 to 30 being required for full expression of the disease. Even when psyllid nymphs feed on only a few leaves, symptoms appear over the whole plant. Basal portions of leaflets turn yellow at margin and roll upward; terminal leaves have a reddish or purple cast; older leaves turn brown and die; stems do not elongate; nodes swell; axillary buds on potatoes develop into aerial tubers or short shoots with swollen bases and small distorted leaves. Feeding by adults does not produce such symptoms; the power is confined to nymphs.

The psyllid winters in southern Texas, New Mexico, and Arizona on wild plants, mostly matrimony vine (*Lycium*) and moves northward to potato and tomato fields in late spring, returning to the southern range in October or November. Other plants of the nightshade family, especially Chinese lantern and groundcherry, may be infested.

Control. Spray potato foliage with DDT (1 to 1¾ pounds active per acre) or parathion (4 to 8 ounces active per acre), starting when first adult is found and repeating every 2 weeks for 4 or 5 times. Eliminate weed hosts, so far as possible, and potatoes sprouting in cull piles. There are several useful parasites and predators.

Sumac Psyllids, *Calophya californica* Schwartz. Black to brown on California sumac in southern California. *C. triozomima* Schwartz, reddish or black with yellow abdomen, occurs in Arizona, Colorado, and California. In the East *C. flavida* infests smooth sumac. The immature nymphs are dark gray or black with a narrow white fringe; they are found on bark of terminal twigs in winter. *C. nigripennis* infests shining sumac; the adult has black, opaque wings.

Willow Psyllid, *Trioza maura* Förster. Infesting a large variety of willows throughout North America. It varies in color from bright orange to reddish brown or dark red.

ROOTWORMS

Rootworms arc larvae of beetles. They work on the roots of plants, and sometimes these are quite different from the plants injured by the adults. For instance, the clover rootworm is the grape colaspis; the southern corn rootworm is the spotted cucumber beetle. Both have been discussed under beetles.

Cranberry Rootworm*, *Rhabdopterus picipes* (Olivier). Important in the beetle stage on rhododendron, camellias, and other ornamentals, not too serious as a root pest of cranberry. It is found along the coast from New England to Florida and along the Gulf to the Mississippi River. The beetles are oval, ¼ × ⅛ inch, brown to black with a metallic luster. They hide in leaves or rubbish during the day, feed at night or on cloudy days on young foliage as it is opening, making characteristic right-angled holes or crescents. Dusting ornamentals with 5 per cent DDT, 5 per cent chlordane, 10 per cent toxaphene or lead arsenate at time new growth starts, repeating in 10 to 14 days, has given fairly good control but DDT injures many camellia varieties. See also Rhabdopterus Beetles under Beetles.

Grape Rootworm*, *Fidia viticida* Walsh. Present in eastern states, except extreme North and far South, on grape and related wild plants. Small, curved, white, brown-headed grubs winter deep in soil, migrating near the surface in spring, changing to soft white pupae in small cells. About 2 weeks after grapes bloom, hairy, chunky brown beetles, ¼ inch long, feed on upper side of leaves, making conspicuous chains of small holes. They lay eggs in clusters on grape canes, often under loose bark. Young grubs drop to the ground, burrow in soil until they reach the roots; they cut off small feeding roots and gouge channels in larger roots until cold weather. Infested vines lack vigor, have little new growth, and yellow foliage.

Control. Spray with DDT for the beetle stage as soon as first leaf punctures are noticed, using 1½ tablespoons of 50 per cent wettable powder to a gallon of water, repeating in 10 days if necessary. The spray schedule for grape berry moth usually controls the rootworm.

Northern Corn Rootworm*, *Diabrotica longicornis* (Say). Present from New York to Kansas on corn, causing most injury in the Upper Mississippi Valley. The larvae feed only on corn, the adults on many summer-flowering plants, including sunflower heads in South Dakota. Eggs are laid in the ground in fall, around corn roots, and hatch rather late in spring. The larvae, threadlike, wrinkled white worms with brown heads, ½ inch long when grown, burrow through corn roots, making brown tunnels. They leave the roots in July and pupate in soil. Beetles, uniform yellow-green, ⅙ to ¼ inch long, appear in late July and August, feed on corn silk and pollen of other plants, lay eggs in cornfields, and die at first frost.

Control. Rotate corn with another crop. Treat soil with aldrin, heptachlor, or chlordane; dust silks with DDT.

Southern Corn Rootworm*. See Spotted Cucumber Beetle.

Strawberry Rootworm*, *Paria fragariae* Wilcox. This and other species are found over much of the United States on strawberry, raspberry, blackberry, grape, rose, peach, apple, walnut, butternut, wild crab, mountain-ash, and several other hosts. Rose leaves, in greenhouses or outdoors, may be riddled with small shot holes, bark of new shoots may be gnawed off, buds eaten out. Leaves of strawberries and other fruits may be destroyed. The beetles—very small, ⅛ inch long, shiny dark brown—winter as adults and lay eggs on ground near plants in spring. The small, white, brown-spotted grubs feed on strawberry roots all spring, then pupate, with beetles feeding until frost. In greenhouses and warm climates there may be 2 or more generations.

Control. Spray or dust strawberries with DDT as beetles leave hibernation (about time blossoms appear). Treating soil with chlordane before setting out plants is helpful for the first year. In greenhouses a phosphate aerosol has been effective for roses.

Western Corn Rootworm*, *Diabrotica virgifera* LeConte. Active in the Middle West on corn, sorghum, alfalfa, and soybeans; similar to the northern corn rootworm.

Western Grape Rootworm*, *Adoxus obscurus* (Linnaeus). Present on grape, serious in California many years ago, now of minor importance. Fireweed is the native host. The beetle is fat, nearly black, covered with short hairs. It eats chainlike strips in leaves and gouges into young berries. The C-shaped, white grubs eat smaller roots entirely, the bark of larger roots. They winter in the soil at a depth of 2 feet or more but in spring burrow up near the soil surface to pupate. Disking the soil at this time crushes many of the pupae. Spray foliage with DDT just before or just after bloom.

SAWFLIES

Sawflies belong to the order Hymenoptera, along with bees and wasps. Like other members of that order, the adults have 2 pairs of transparent wings, hooked together. As members of the suborder Symphyta (Chalastogastra), the females have an ovipositor (egg-laying apparatus) adapted for sawing or boring but not for stinging. It consists of 2 short outer plates and 2 saw-toothed blades which move in opposite directions when the female is slitting a leaf before laying her egg. Almost all sawflies feed on plants in the larval stage. Larvae look like caterpillars, but they have more than 5 pairs of prolegs and they do not have crotchets. Most live exposed on foliage, singly or in groups; a few spin webs, some are leaf miners. The families given here include those of importance to gardeners.

Cephidae. Stem sawflies. Adults slender, compressed; larvae boring in stems of grasses and berries.

Cimbicidae. Cimbicid sawflies. Resembling bumblebees; large, robust, with clubbed antennae. The elm sawfly is the most common species.

Diprionidae. Conifer sawflies. Medium-sized sawflies with 13 or more antennal segments, serrate in the female, comblike in the male. The larvae are very injurious to pine, spruce, and other conifers.

Pamphiliidae. Web-spinning sawflies. Small, stout-bodied, spinning webs, rolling or tying leaves.

Tenthredinidae. Typical sawflies. Medium-sized to small, brightly colored, usually found on foliage or flowers, the larvae highly destructive to trees and shrubs. The family includes birch and elm leaf-miners, rose-slugs, pear-slug, imported currantworm, larch sawfly.

Arborvitae Sawfly, *Monoctenus melliceps* Cresson. In northeastern states, also in Kansas, on arborvitae and juniper. The larvae are ⅝ to ¾ inch, dull green with 3 dark stripes, black legs, light-brown head.

Balsam-fir Sawfly*, *Neodiprion abietis* (Harris). From New England west to Minnesota and Missouri, defoliating balsam fir, feeding some on spruce. Larvae are green, striped with dark green and brown, with black head; ¾ inch long when grown. Adults emerge from late June to early September, cut slits singly in needles for eggs, which hatch in late May or June. Larvae feed gregariously, then spin reddish-brown cocoons on twigs or in litter on ground. Spray for young larvae with DDT or lead arsenate.

Birch Sawfly*, *Arge pectoralis* (Leach). On various birches in the Northeast. The larva is fat, yellowish, with rows of black spots, reddish-yellow head; ¾ inch long.

Blackberry Sawfly, *Pamphilius dentatus* MacGillivray. Occasionally blackberry leaves are rolled and webbed by bluish-green larvae, ¾ inch long, which feed inside the roll. Adults appear in May, lay oval, white eggs end to end on larger veins; larvae feed until July, then enter the soil to remain until the next May.

Black-headed Ash Sawfly*, *Tethida cordigera* (Palisot de Beauvois). Distribution and habits like the brown-headed ash sawfly. The larva is whitish with a yellow tinge, with shiny black head; ¾ inch when grown.

Bristly Rose-slug*, *Cladius isomerus* Norton. Found east of the Mississippi north of Virginia and in California, a very serious defoliator of wild and cultivated roses. Larvae are sluglike, greenish white, with long, rather stout bristles, ⅝ inch long. They first skeletonize the leaves by feeding from the undersurface, later eat holes clear through. Eggs are laid in slits in upper side of the midrib. There may be as many as 5 or 6 generations. Pupation for summer broods is in cocoons on leaves or twigs; overwintering cocoons are in the soil. Almost any stomach poison on the foliage *before* larvae start feeding and repeated at frequent intervals will control rose-slugs: DDT, methoxychlor, lead arsenate, and rotenone are all effective.

Brown-headed Ash Sawfly*, *Tomostethus multicinctus* (Rohwer). A serious defoliator of red and white ash used as shade trees in eastern and central states. Adults emerge when leaf buds show green, and lay eggs in developing leaflets. Yellow-white or greenish-white larvae with brown heads eat ravenously until late May or June, then construct cocoonlike cells in the soil where they stay until spring.

Butternut Woolyworm, *Blennocampa caryae* North. Found on butternut, hickory, and English walnut. The false caterpillars are covered with long white filaments, standing straight up, and when several of them feed side by side on the undersurface of leaves, they seem to be covered with masses of white wool. Underneath the filaments the larvae are pea-green, about an inch long, with 8 pairs of prolegs. They eat from the side of the leaf inward, often leaving nothing but the midrib. They pupate near the surface of the ground. The adult is black with reddish thorax. The injury is ordinarily not enough to call for spraying.

California Pear-slug*, *Pristiphora californica* (Marlatt). Attacking blossoms and foliage, also reported from Colorado.

Cedar Cone Sawfly, *Augomonoctenus libocedri* Rohwer. Cones are injured by slugs. The adults are blue-black with 5 segments of the abdomen brick-red.

Cherry Fruit Sawfly*, *Hoplocampa cookei* (Clarke). A Pacific-Coast pest of cherry, plum, prune, sometimes peach and apricot. Adults have black bodies, yellow appendages, are ⅛ inch long. Larvae, white with brown heads, ¼ inch long, work in partly developed fruits and feed on seeds, then leave through a hole in the side to pupate in a silken cocoon for winter. Fruits whither and drop. Spray with lead arsenate just before blossoms open.

Curled Rose Sawfly*, *Allantus cinctus* (Linnaeus). Coiled Rose Worm, found from Maine to Virginia and west to Minnesota on wild and cultivated roses. It curls up like a cutworm, starts in by skeletonizing but ends by devouring entire leaflets except the largest veins. The larva is metallic green above, marked with white dots, grayish white underneath, with yellow-brown head; ¾ inch long when grown. The larvae form cells in the pith of pruned ends of rose shoots and pupate there. There are 2 generations in the southern part of the range, 1 in New England. Eggs are laid in upper surface of leaflets. Spray or dust with any stomach poison.

Cypress Sawfly, *Susana cupressi* Rohwer & Middleton. Feeding on foliage of Monterey cypress in California.

Dock Sawfly*, *Ametastegia glabrata* (Fallén). In northern United States on dock, sorrel, and knotweed but burrowing into apple fruit for the winter. The larvae are olive or bluish green with conspicuous white tubercles.

Dogwood Sawflies, *Macremphytus tarsatus* (Say) and *M. varianus* (Norton). Common defoliators of species of Cornus in the Northeast and the Lakes States. The larvae have a shiny black head and body covered with white powder. Spray with DDT or lead arsenate.

Dusky Birch Sawfly*, *Croesus latitarsus* Norton. Common in New England and the Great Lakes area on gray birch, sometimes other birches. The larvae —yellow green with black markings, black heads, up to 1 inch long—feed in gangs all around the margins of leaves. Saplings may be defoliated. There are 2 overlapping generations, with larvae feeding from early June to late fall. Adults, blue-black with white leg markings, appear in May and June. Spray young trees with DDT or lead arsenate.

71. Elm sawfly larvae (note how the rear end is secured to stem).

Elm Sawfly*, *Cimbex americana* Leach. Giant American Sawfly. Distributed through northern states to Colorado on elm, including Chinese elm. Adults are large, nearly an inch long, steel-blue and black, with 3 or 4 yellow spots on each side, long, buff antennae with knobbed ends, smoky-brown transparent wings. The larva is pale yellow-green with a black stripe down the back, black spiracles, 8 pairs of prolegs; 1¾ inches when grown. It rests in a coiled position, feeds with its rear end curled around a twig. Eggs are laid in leaf tissue in May, each egg showing as a blister on the underside of the leaf. Young larvae crawl out through a slit in the epidermis, feed for 6 to 8 weeks (from June to October) then spin brown, papery cocoons in soil litter, transforming to true pupae in spring or early summer. Although elm and willow are the principal food plants, alder, basswood, birch, maple, and poplar are sometimes eaten. Adults may injure by gnawing bark of twigs.

Control. Spraying with lead arsenate or DDT for elm leaf beetles should also control sawflies. Several parasitic wasps and flies are on the job.

European Apple Sawfly*, *Hoplocampa testudinea* (Klug). First discovered on Long Island about 1940, now destructive to apple, crabapple, plum, pear in Connecticut, Massachusetts, New Jersey, New York and Rhode Island. Adults, brown-and-yellow "flies," emerge from puparia in the ground when trees bloom; eggs are inserted in calyx cups. Larvae, white with 7 prolegs, bore into the fruit, leaving a chocolate sawdust on the surface. One larva may damage several fruits. There is 1 generation. Two sprays of rotenone, one at petal fall and the second a week later, are suggested for home gardens. Chlordane and methoxychlor are possibilities.

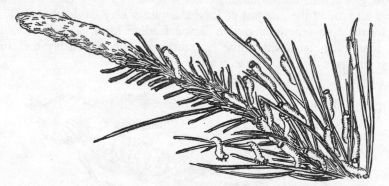

72. Young larvae of European pine sawfly chewing off needles.

European Pine Sawfly*, *Neodiprion sertifer* (Geoffroy). An introduced species first noted in New Jersey in 1925. Exceedingly troublesome in home gardens, nurseries, watersheds etc. Now present in all of New England, in New York, New Jersey, Pennsylvania, Indiana, Illinois, Michigan, and South Dakota. Favored food plants are red, jack, Swiss mountain, mugho pines, which are seriously defoliated. Eggs are laid in rows in slits in pine needles; just before hatching in late April or early May they look like pine leaf scales. The tiny young larvae, green with shiny black heads, join together in gangs but they match the needles so well they are scarcely ever noticed until far too much damage has been done. They feed at first on the side of needles, causing a few tip needles to turn straw-colored and curl slightly, an excellent diagnostic sign. After the first molt, larvae eat entire needles, right down to the base. Several hundred may work together, and after demolishing one twig move on to the next. When disturbed, they move in uncanny unison, elevating their rear ends. Feeding is confined to old needles; infested ornamental pines about the house will show, by the end of May, new green plumes waving at the end of long, naked branches. After 4 or 5 weeks of feeding the full-grown larva is grayish green with a light stripe down the back, 2 white lines bordering a broken stripe of intense green; ⅞ inch long.

Mature larvae drop or crawl to the ground to spin golden-brown cocoons in litter on top of the soil or in protected places on the trunk, sometimes in frass left by pine webworms. Pupae are formed in the cocoons in late summer, adults emerging in September and October to lay their eggs in the current year's growth of needles. They look like small bees or large, fuzzy flies; males are blackish with feathery antennae, females are yellow-brown.

Control. One thorough spraying at the time larvae are hatching—with DDT, 2 tablespoons 50 per cent wettable powder to 1 gallon of water, or with lead arsenate—will give control for the season. In most seasons this should be the end of April or first of May. A delay of a week or two may mean conspicuous defoliation, naked branches that the pine can never replace. A reminder of the time to spray comes when two or three terminal needles turn yellow, indicating that the young larvae are starting to feed. Sometimes a single infestation on one branch of an ornamental pine can be cleaned up with an aerosol bomb. Parasitic wasps have been liberated for pines on watersheds, and a virus, disseminated both by airplane and ground equipment, is quite effective in killing off the larvae.

European Spruce Sawfly*, *Diprion hercyniae* (Hartig). This European species was first found on the American continent in 1922 near Ottawa but did not attract attention until 1930 when there was great damage on the Gaspé Peninsula. Since then it has spread at an alarming rate, and by 1937 was rated the worst enemy of northeastern spruce forests. In Maine it reached its high peak of population in 1939; since then it has declined in numbers due to rodents eating cocoons on the ground, insect predators and parasites, and a wilt disease. This sawfly is now present in all of New England, in New York, New Jersey, feeding on white, red, black and Norway spruces, occasionally others. Trees that are entirely defoliated usually die.

Eggs are laid singly on the needles, with young larvae beginning to feed at the tip. They are light green at first, later dark green with 5 narrow white stripes. They pupate in small brown cocoons beneath trees. The female sawfly is stout-bodied, black with yellow markings; males are rare; reproduction is usually without fertilization. There are 2 or 3 broods. Ornamentals can be sprayed with DDT or lead arsenate. In forest areas most reliance is on natural controls.

Goldenglow Sawfly, *Macrophya intermedia* (Norton)=M. simillima (Rohwer). Light-gray larvae, with a darker-gray median stripe and a row of black spots, occasionally defoliate plants. They rest on leaves in a typical coiled position. There is 1 generation; adults appear in June. Spray with lead arsenate or DDT.

Grape Sawfly*, *Erythraspides vitis* (Harris). Sometimes heavy enough on grape to require control.

Green-headed Spruce Sawfly*, *Pikonema dimmockii* (Cresson). On various spruces in northern states, but seldom causing serious defoliation.

Hemlock Sawfly*, *Neodiprion tsugae* Middleton. A western species defoliating hemlock from Oregon northward. Larvae are green, striped when young, 1 inch long when grown. Cocoons are attached to needles or laid in debris on ground. There is 1 generation, with larvae feeding in July and August. A number of parasites keep this sawfly in check.

Honeysuckle Sawfly*, *Zaraea inflata* Norton. Climbing and bush honeysuckles may be stripped of leaves by dull-gray, yellow-striped, black-dotted larvae about an inch long. They spin cocoons in the soil. Adults, emerging in spring, are large, with a black abdomen, yellow ring at the base, a line of silver hairs on each segment. Lead arsenate or DDT will protect the foliage.

Imported Currantworm*, *Nematus ribesii* (Scopoli). Arrived from Europe about 1857, now general over the United States. It is rare to find a garden with currants or gooseberries without this problem. Larvae or pupae winter in cocoons on the ground; black, yellow-marked adults appear in spring to lay white, flattened, shiny eggs on veins and midribs on underside of leaves. Larvae hatch about the time currants are in full leaf. They feed in from leaf margins in groups, eventually devouring entire leaves. The worms are green with black heads and body spots (Plate XXXII). When disturbed they elevate front and rear ends of their bodies. After feeding for 2 or 3 weeks they pupate in the ground. Eggs for the second generation, which is less injurious, are laid in late June and July. Spray or dust with malathion or rotenone.

Introduced Pine Sawfly*, *Diprion similis* (Hartig). Commonly defoliating ornamental pines in the Northeast, first discovered in Connecticut in 1914. White pines and other 5-needled pines are preferred, but others may be eaten. Larvae are yellow green with a double black stripe the entire length of the back, a broken yellow stripe on each side, and the sides mottled yellow and black; 1 inch long. Adults are black and yellow, wings spreading ¾ inch (Plate XXXI). Adults emerge from pupae on ground in April and May, lay eggs in slits in the edge of needles. There are 1 or 2 generations annually, with most of the larval feeding in May and June and August and September, on new growth as well as older needles. There may be complete defoliation and death of small pines.

Control. Rake up and burn debris under trees in autumn. Watch for 1st-brood larvae and spray with DDT or lead arsenate. Nicotine sulfate added at the rate of 1 teaspoon per gallon will kill all young larvae hit with the spray.

Jack-pine Sawfly*, *Neodiprion pratti banksianae* Rohwer. On ponderosa and lodgepole pines in Idaho, Montana, and the Great Lakes region.

Larch Sawfly*, *Pristiphora erichsonii* (Hartig). A serious defoliator of larch, first recorded in Maine and Massachusetts in 1882, in Minnesota in 1909, though apparently present long before that. Outbreaks have been periodic, sometimes defoliating and killing large stands of forest trees or larches in home plantings for 2 or more years in succession. The wasplike yellow-and-black adults, wings expanding ⅘ inch, lay eggs from late May to early July in slits cut in young twigs, causing a twisting. The eggs hatch in about a week, and the larvae feed ravenously in groups of 40 to 50, working the lower branches first. They are dull gray-green above, paler underneath, with black head and legs. There is 1 generation, sometimes a partial 2nd. The larvae winter in tough brown cocoons in duff on the ground.

Control. Birds and mice destroy cocoons; parasitic wasps and flies and a fungus attack larvae. Rake up debris from under ornamental larches in autumn. Spray with lead arsenate in June or July if necessary.

Loblolly Pine Sawfly, *Neodiprion americanum* Leach. In Atlantic states, defoliating loblolly pine in Virginia, sometimes feeding on shortleaf pine. The larvae—greenish white with a green line down the back, black spots along the side, reddish-brown head; ⅞ inch long—feed from late April to June on old needles. There is 1 generation.

Lodgepole Sawfly*, *Neodiprion burkei* Middleton. Distributed through Oregon, Idaho, Montana, Wyoming, defoliating and killing lodgepole pine. Larvae are green or grayish with lighter stripes, brown heads, 1 inch long. Street trees have been successfully protected with lead arsenate.

Monterey-pine Sawfly, *Itycorsia* sp. Attacking and killing only Monterey pine in its native habitat in California. Larvae—dark green or brown with black heads—web needles and excrement into a mass.

Mountain-ash Sawfly*, *Pristiphora geniculata* (Hartig). More or less abundant in New England, New Jersey, and New York on mountain-ash. Winter is passed in cocoons on soil; adults, yellow with black spots, deposit eggs in slits near edges of leaves in late May. Larvae, green with black dots, work from early June to the middle of July. Often feeding shortly before Japanese beetles appear in New Jersey, their chewing is wrongly attributed to the beetles. They work mostly on the upper foliage, leaving nothing but larger veins and midribs. Occasionally there is a partial 2nd generation. One thorough spraying with lead arsenate after the leaves are fully open will control these sawflies. If young larvae are already present when spraying is done, add 1 teaspoon of nicotine sulfate per gallon.

Peach Sawfly, *Pamphilius persicus* MacGillivray. One of the leaf-rolling species. Pale blue-green larvae sometimes eat foliage in June and July. They winter in cocoons in the soil, pupate in spring. Adults, black with yellow markings, emerge in late spring. They are usually controlled by sprays for other peach insects.

Pear-slug*, *Caliroa cerasi* (Linnaeus). Cherry Slug. On pear, cherry, plum throughout the country, occasionally on hawthorn, Juneberry, mountain-ash, quince. Larvae are dark-green to orange, tadpole-shaped, covered with slime, ½ inch long, looking like small slugs. They skeletonize the leaves, eating everything but a network of veins. Black-and-yellow sawflies, slightly larger than houseflies, emerge from cocoons in the earth just after cherries or pears come into full leaf and lay their eggs in leaves. Larvae feed for 2 or 3 weeks from the upper leaf surface, drop to the ground to pupate, with adults coming out in July or August for a 2nd brood, which may completely defoliate young trees.

Control. The standard spray program should control slugs. If necessary, spray with DDT, parathion or lead arsenate 2 to 3 weeks after bloom. The slugs can be washed off backyard trees with a strong stream of water from the hose.

Pine Sawflies. In addition to those treated separately, various other species may infest pine. *Diprion rohweri* Middleton is reported defoliating pinyon pine. *Neodiprion excitans* Rohwer feeds from the Carolinas to Texas on loblolly, shortleaf, and other pines. *Neodiprion nanulus contortae* Ross feed on lodgepole and ponderosa pine. *N. taedae linearis* Ross is reported heavy on pines in Arkansas. This by no means exhausts the list of pine sawflies.

Pin-oak Sawfly, *Caliroa lineata* (Linnaeus). Noted seriously damaging pin oaks in New Jersey in 1946, with widespread infestation in the state the next 2 years, of less importance since then; reported also from North Carolina and New York. The larvae are similar to pear-slugs, up to ½ inch long, yellowish green with black heads, skeletonizing leaves from the upper surface. Infestation starts at top of trees, with the foliage in upper third of trees turning golden brown by late summer, most disfiguring to street trees and those in public parks.

Plum Web-spinning Sawfly*, *Neurotoma inconspicua* (Norton). Serious in the Dakotas, present also in northeastern states, on plums and sand cherries. Webs, like those of the fall webworm, enclose ends of branches soon after plums come into full leaf. Smooth, grayish-yellow larvae, up to ¾ inch long, feed inside webs, sometimes defoliating branches. Black adults, with red legs, insert eggs in leaf midribs in early spring. Cut off webbed ends of branches. There are several predators attacking larvae.

Poplar Leaf-folding Sawfly*, *Nematus bozemani* (Cooley). From the prairies of Canada south into the United States. Adults lay eggs May to July, injuring leaves so they fold over; injured portions turn black, making foliage unsightly. Larvae eat holes through leaves. When grown, they drop to the ground with the leaves and pupate inside the folds.

Poplar Sawfly, *Trichiocampus viminalis* (Fall). A European species long present in northeastern and northern states, often destructive to ornamental Carolina or Lombardy poplars. The larvae are bright yellow with 2 rows of black spots on the back, 2 rows of small black spots near the spiracles, tufts of short white hairs over the body, black heads; ¾ inch long. They arrange themselves side by side on a leaf and eat ravenously; trees may be entirely defoliated. When grown, in 35 to 40 days, they make cocoons in bark crevices or under clods of earth. There may be 2 generations. Spray with lead arsenate when larvae are very young.

Raspberry Sawfly*, *Monophadnoides geniculatus* (Hartig). Ranging through northern states but more common on the Pacific Coast, on raspberry, loganberry, dewberry, and blackberry. Adults are black with yellow and reddish markings; larvae are pale green with white spiny tubercles. They feed on underside and on edges of leaves, sometimes stripping the plants. Spray with lead arsenate just before blossoming; use rotenone dust or spray after fruit is set.

73. *Older larvae of red-headed pine sawfly, which have eaten off needles down to the base of the fascicles.*

Red-headed Pine Sawfly*, *Neodiprion lecontei* (Fitch). Leconte's Sawfly, injurious to ornamental pines from Maine to Florida and west to Minnesota and Louisiana on Virginia, jack, red, eastern white, Scotch, loblolly, lodgepole, mugho, longleaf, pitch, ponderosa, and Austrian pines, also American larch and deodar. This is the most widespread and destructive of our native pine sawflies. The larvae live in groups and devour the needles, often defoliating young pines, which either die or are spoiled for ornamental purposes. Young larvae are whitish with brown heads, later yellow with 6 rows of conspicuous black spots and a red head; 1 inch long. In many sections there are 2 overlapping broods, with larvae feeding from May until late fall. Prepupal larvae winter in tough, papery, capsule-shaped cocoons in duff or topsoil under trees. Eggs are laid in slits in needles. The larvae prefer old needles but will eat new growth toward the end of the season, including tender bark of young twigs.

Control. Spray thoroughly with lead arsenate or DDT when larvae are young.

Red-pine Sawfly, *Neodiprion nanulus nanulus* Schedl. On red, pitch, and Japanese pine, reported from Maine, Wisconsin, other states.

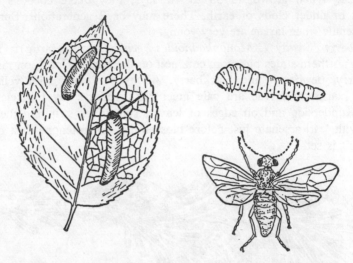

74. Rose-slug; larvae skeletonizing leaf, and sawfly adult.

Rose-slug*, *Endelomyia aethiops* (Fabricius). European Rose Slug, common on rose east of the Rocky Mountains. This is a yellow-green, rather velvety slug, up to ½ inch long, appearing dark green from the food ingested. It eats the soft part of leaves, which, with nothing left but a network of veins and 1 epidermis, turn brown and crisp, making rose growers think they have "rust." When the leaves are only partly eaten, they appear to have windows in them. When full-grown, the larva enters the soil, constructs a capsule-shaped cell, and stays quiet in this cavity until early spring when the adult lays eggs in pockets in leaf tissue (Plate XXXII). There is only 1 generation of this species; feeding in late summer is due to the bristly rose-slug. Control measures are the same and it is important to have lead arsenate or other stomach poison on the foliage almost as soon as roses come into full leaf to prevent unsightly disfiguration.

Rose Stem Sawfly, *Hartigia trimaculata* Say. One of the horntails, a wasp-like insect appearing in early summer and laying eggs in punctures made in rose canes. Whitish larvae bore through the canes, 1 to a cane, causing shoots to wilt, stunt, or die back.

Striped Alder Sawfly*, *Hemichroa crocea* (Fourcroy). May defoliate various species of alder in northeastern and Great Lakes states, occasionally feeding on birch. Young larvae are pure white, later yellow with brown stripes, ⅘ inch long. They eat everything except midrib and larger veins. There are 2 generations.

Swaine Jack-pine Sawfly*, *Neodiprion swainei* Middleton. Feeding on Jack pine in Canada.

Violet Sawfly*, *Ametastegia pallipes* (Spinola). Often a serious pest of violets and pansies in eastern states, outdoors and in greenhouses. Larvae are blue-black or olive green, smooth, about ½ inch long, marked with white spots on back and sides. They work at night, first skeletonizing lower surface of leaves, later eating holes or feeding from leaf margins to entirely defoliate plants, most often in May and June. Pupation is in stalks of pithy plants; adults, black-and-yellow, emerge in 2 weeks to blister leaves with eggs inserted in lower side; foliage may wither. There may be several broods. Spray or dust with lead arsenate or rotenone.

Willow Red-gall Sawfly*, *Nematus proximus* (Lepeletier).

Willow Sawfly*, *Nematus ventralis* Say. Yellow-spotted Willow Slug, widely distributed in eastern states on willow and poplar, often defoliating willows in ornamental plantings, very injurious to basket willows in the South. The small, dark-brown to black sawfly, marked with yellow spots, lays eggs in leaves, producing blisters. The slugs are black with a greenish tinge and heart-shaped yellow spots along each side of the body. They feed close together in characteristic curved positions for about 3 weeks, then pupate on the ground for a second generation. There may be several overlapping generations in the South. Spray with lead arsenate or DDT.

Willow Shoot Sawfly*, *Janus abbreviatus* (Say). The larva is white, without abdominal prolegs but with a prong at the tip of the abdomen. It bores down in the pith. The female adult punctures shoots of poplar and willow for egg laying, causing dieback above the puncture. Cut and burn infested shoots.

Yellow-headed Spruce Sawfly*, *Pikonema alaskensis* (Rohwer). In the most northern states and New England, on white, red, black, Norway, Colorado blue, and Engelmann spruces. Larvae are yellow-green, striped with gray-green, and have chestnut-brown heads. They prefer new foliage until they are half grown. Eggs are laid in new needles in May or early June, hatching in 6 to 8 days. Larvae feed 30 to 40 days. There is 1 generation, with pupation in spring in cocoons in the soil.

SCALE INSECTS

Scale insects constitute a very large group of plant feeders. Along with mealybugs, which are really soft scales, they belong to the family Coccidae, order Hemiptera, suborder Homoptera. Armored scales are covered with a protective shell or scale of wax, usually hard and separate from the body, though made of wax secreted by the insect together with cast skins (exuviae) of the early stages. Females are wingless and are mostly responsible for plant injury. After a very brief 6-legged crawling stage they insert their threadlike mouth parts through the epidermis of a leaf, or bark of a stem, and start sucking sap. They molt twice, lose legs and antennae, and remain in the same spot the rest of their lives, laying eggs, in some cases giving birth to living young, under the shell. The males have an elongated body after the 2nd molt and after a 4th molt have 1 pair of wings, legs, and antennae but no mouth parts. They look like small gnats but have a style-like process at the end of the abdomen.

Soft scales or tortoise scales are not covered by a separate shell, but their chitinous bodies may be as hard as the shell on an armored scale. They also keep their small and poorly developed legs and can move, though so sluggishly they appear stationary.

Heavy scale infestations kill branches or entire trees or shrubs. Standard control for armored scales has been a dormant spray, oil or lime-sulfur, before growth starts in spring, but many scales may now be controlled in the crawling stage with malathion or, in a few cases, with DDT. White oil or summer-oil sprays have been advised for unarmored scales prevalent in greenhouses and warm climates but in recent years parathion has been rather extensively used by commercial growers, with malathion recommended to home gardeners.

Acuminate Scale, *Coccus acuminatus* (Signoret). Serious in Florida on ornamentals, also reported from Georgia, Massachusetts, and New York. It is found on albizzia, apple, banana, bay, bottle-brush, Brazilian pepper-tree, cajeput, cashew, ceriman, cocculus, cotoneaster, duranta, yellow elder, eugenia, eurya, feijoa, fern, *Ficus* spp., firethorn, flacourtia, frangipani, gall-berry, gardenia, gum-tree, holly, ixora, jasmine, Java bishopwood, lancewood, loquat, magnolia, mango, marlberry, mountain ebony, myrsine, sweetolive, persimmon, photinia, osmanthus, sapodilla, sciadophyllus, tabernaemontana, and tevetia. The scale is pale green or yellow, thin, flat. In warm rainy seasons it is controlled by a fungus, *Cephalosporium lecanii*. Oil sprays can be used on mango.

Araucaria Scale, *Eriococcus araucariae* Maskell. Imported into California on Norfolk Island pine; found also in Florida on this host. Oval, white, with wax; this is a soft scale or mealybug.

Artemisia Scale, *Eriococcus artemisiae* Kuwanna. With conspicuous globular white sacs, crowded on twigs of artemisia in California and other western states.

Asiatic Red Scale, *Aonidiella taxus* Leonard. On podocarpus in Florida; quarantined to prevent dissemination in nursery stock.

Azalea Bark Scale, *Eriococcus azaleae* Comstock. Azalea Mealybug, a native of Japan. Common on outdoor azaleas in the South, also blueberry, fetter-bush, and stagger-bush, rather frequent on rhododendrons in the North. White cottony sacs, enclosing dark red females and their eggs, are present in forks of branches and over twigs, sometimes on main stems down to the ground. The males have a similar white covering but are small and more elongate. Foliage and twigs are often covered with black sooty mold growing in secreted honeydew. Azaleas appear yellow and unthrifty.

The winter is spent in the nymph stage, on the plant. There are 2 generations in the South, 1 in the North. In Alabama females mature very early in spring and start to lay eggs in March, with reddish-brown crawlers hatching in 3 weeks and maturing in about 100 days. The second brood appears in September. In Connecticut eggs start hatching about June 20, with the young migrants not maturing until the next spring.

Control. Spray with malathion, mid-July in Connecticut, May and late September in the Deep South. Commercial growers may use parathion.

Bamboo Scale, *Asterolecanium bambusae* Boisduval. Generally distributed where bamboos are grown. Oval, somewhat convex, glassy in appearance, transparent with a yellow or green tinge, marginal fringe of pairs of short, pinkish filaments. On stems and leaves.

Another species, *Kuanaspis hikosani,* was first reported on bamboo in this country in 1960 from South Carolina.

Barberry Scale, *Lecaniodiaspis* sp. Convex, reddish brown, soft scale, sometimes numerous. Spray with miscible oil when plants are dormant or with malathion for crawling stage.

Barnacle Scale*, *Ceroplastes cirripediformis* Comstock. Found in California, Florida, Georgia, Louisiana, Mississippi, and North Carolina on bark or leaves of many plants: ampelopsis, sugar-apple, prickly-ash, California athel, avocado, blueberry, Brazilian pepper-tree, buckthorn, carissa, cherry, citrus, crossandra, golden dewdrop, euonymus, firethorn, flame vine, fuchsia, gardenia, gaura, guava, holly, inkberry, ixora, jasmine, garbia lily, Spanish lime, litchi, myrtle, parkinsonia, passion-flower, pear, Australian-pine, poinsettia, pomegranate, rockrose, sanchezia, sapodilla, schinus, snowberry, strobilanthes, sycamore, tabernaemontana, tea tree, tecoma, thornapple, viburnum, and weigela. The female is reddish brown covered with white wax shading to gray or light brown, and with a spinelike process extending through the waxy covering at the anal end of the body.

Beech Scale*, *Cryptococcus fagi* (Baerensprung). A European species first present in Nova Scotia, found in Massachusetts in 1929 and now present in most of New England and New York, infesting American and European beech. In Massachusetts eggs are laid from mid-June to late July, with hatching starting about August 1 and continuing into September. Young crawlers are abundant during this period. When the pale-yellow nymph settles into a bark crevice, it secretes cottony material which spreads out to cover several individuals. It becomes adult the next spring, nearly circular, 1/50 to 1/30 inch across, covered with white wax.

The feeding of the scale kills inner tissue of outer bark, but the most important injury comes from a fungus (*Nectria coccinea* var. *faginata*), which enters the tree through scale wounds. Foliage and twigs die, bark cracks, wood is infected. Apparently the fungus cannot enter until the scale has fed for a year, nor can it reproduce the disease without the scale.

Control. A thorough dormant spray with 5 gallons of liquid lime-sulfur to 50 gallons of water, or 20 pounds dry lime-sulfur to 100 gallons, is very effective. Miscible oils would kill the scale but are often injurious to beech. Late summer spraying for crawlers with malathion can supplement the dormant spray.

Bermuda-Grass Scale, *Odonaspis ruthae* Kotinsky. On grass in Florida, California, Louisiana, Texas, usually found in leaf axils in loose soil at surface of the ground. Oval or nearly circular, moderately convex, pure white, exuviae, near end of body, straw-colored and covered with whitish secretion.

Black Araucaria Scale, *Chrysomphalus rossi* (Maskell). Almost black, much like the Florida red scale. This is a tropical species with a limited distribution on ornamentals in southern California—araucaria, rarely on redwood, sometimes on abutilon, artemisia, banksia, euonymus, hyssop, oleander, olive, orchids, palm, cycad, also on macadamia.

Black Pine Leaf Scale*, *Aspidiotus californicus* Coleman. Distributed over most of North America, often associated with pine needle scale on pine, reported also on Douglas-fir, hemlock, and other crucifers. It may kill young pines. Mature scales are nearly circular, 1/16 inch across, yellow-brown to black. There are 1 to 3 generations with hibernation as half-grown scales. They can be controlled with lime-sulfur. Seedlings sometimes have to be dipped in 1 to 12 lime-sulfur before shipping.

Black Scale*, *Saissetia oleae* (Bernard). An unarmored species, possibly the most important economically, present in all citrus-growing regions but not as important in the Gulf States as in California, where it has caused an annual 2-million-dollar loss. The black scale may be a greenhouse pest in the North. Besides orange, grapefruit and lemon, important food plants include almond, apple, apricot, avocado, beech, fig, grape, oleander, olive, plum, rose, and English walnut. Injury comes not only from the extraction of sap but from the black sooty mold which, growing in honeydew, covers all surfaces of foliage, cutting off light and reducing photosynthesis, coating fruit so it has to be washed.

Overwintering females become adult in spring. They are almost hemispherical, ⅕ inch across, dark brown to black, with a longitudinal ridge and 2 transverse elevations on the back forming the letter H; they deposit an average of 2000 eggs. These, white at first, later orange, hatch in about 20 days. The young remain under the parent briefly but start crawling and feeding within 3 days, settling on leaves or new growth. They migrate to twigs and branches when partly grown and take 8 to 10 months to mature. There is usually 1 generation, sometimes 2 or a partial 2nd. Males—thin, narrow, flat, semitransparent—are rare; most reproduction is parthenogenetic.

In addition to the favored food plants listed, there are many ornamental hosts—acalypha, allamanda, aralia, prickly-ash, artemisia, assonia, banyan, asparagus fern, California mountain-holly, California nutmeg, Brazilian pepper-tree, carissa, cassava, camellia, deodar, ceriman, chinaberry, clerodendron, coral-vine, croton, cypress vine, elder, eugenia, euonymus, feijoa, fuchsia, fern, guava, frangipani, gardenia, golden dewdrop, golden-shower, holly, hibiscus, ixora, jasmine, jacaranda, mountain ebony, mountain-ash, myrtle, orchids, palms, pittosporum, poinciana, poinsettia, pomegranate, Japanese quince, rubber plant, sumac, sapodilla, sapota, sausage-tree, soapberry, strawberry-tree, silk-oak, willow, yucca, and many others.

Control. Originally the black scale was controlled on citrus trees in California by fumigation with hydrogen cyanide under fumigation tents, but the scale in many cases developed a resistance to cyanide. Malathion can be used on ornamentals. The scale is not so important as formerly because of the highly effective work of *Aphycus helvolus* Compère, a parasite shipped to California from South Africa in 1937. There are other parasites and some predators, but the latter are less efficient.

Black Thread Scale*, *Ischnaspis longirostris* (Signoret). Nearly cosmopolitan, a greenhouse pest in the North, serious on palms, sometimes found on ornamentals including: acacia, agave, andira, bignonia, bottle-brush, Brazilian pepper, camellia, ceriman, coffee, fern, fig, cape-honeysuckle, iris, ixora, jasmine, justicia, lancewood, Indian laurel, Spanish laurel, privet, lily, mahogany, mango, mountain ebony, nolina, sweetolive, palmetto, philodendron, screwpine, randia, strobilanthes. The female is very narrow, thread-like, 1/16 inch long, dark brown to black. Its habit of attaching itself parallel to the ribs keeps it from being observed before palms are abundantly infested.

Boisduval's Scale, *Diaspis boisduvalli* Signoret. Circular or somewhat ovate, thin, flat, semitransparent, white to light yellow, exuviae central; male white, narrow, with 3 ridges on the back. Cosmopolitan on palms and orchids; also on palmetto, achemea, anthurium, billbergia, cactus, caladium, dracaena, pineapple, spider-lily, strelitzia, travelers-tree, yucca. The scales are present on leaf, bark, and fruit. DDT is effective on palms and orchids.

Brown Soft Scale*, *Coccus hesperidum* Linnaeus. Soft Scale, Soft Brown Scale, widely distributed in greenhouses and outdoors in warm climates on ornamentals and fruits. It is rather flat, soft, oval, yellowish green or greenish brown, often with a marbled or ridged effect, ⅛ inch long. It usually resembles the host plant in color and is unnoticed until the infestation is very large. Young are born alive, 1 or 2 daily for a month or two. They are sluggish, settling down near the parent, maturing in about 2 months. A large amount of honeydew is produced, resulting in much smutting of foliage. Plants are weakened, stunted.

This is a rather common pest of gardenia, infesting foliage and tender branches; it is also frequent on fern, camellia, oleander. Other host plants, indoors and out, include acalypha, abutilon, agave, aloe, apple, apricot, anthurium, aralia, ardisia, araucaria, prickly-ash, assonia, avocado, banana, bay, begonia, bottle-brush, bougainvillea, boxelder, Brazilian pepper-tree, cajeput, cassia, clematis, clerodendron, caladium, calla, camellia, camphor, carnation, century plant, citrus, ceriman, coral-vine, croton, date palm, dracaena, elaeagnus, elder, euonymus, feijoa, fig, grape, seagrape, guava, hawthorn, hibiscus, holly, hollyhock, English ivy, jasmine, ixora, Jupiter tree, lantana, laurel, locust, madroña, magnolia, mango, manzanita, maple, mountain ebony, morning-glory, mulberry, myrtle, peach, pear, phlox, orchids, palms, papaya, parkinsonia, persimmon, Australian, Italian, and Norfolk Island pine, pittosporum, poinsettia, plum, poplar, pothos, quisqualis, redbud, rosary pea, rose-of-Sharon, rose, sage, sapota, snow-on-the-mountain, stephanotis, strobilanthes, sweet-william, strawberry-tree, sycamore, tabernaemontana, viburnum, willow, wisteria, yucca, zephyranthes and others.

Control. There are a large number of parasites which do an excellent job of controlling this soft scale, but many of these are killed when parathion is used in orchards and greenhouses while the scale flourishes. Malathion gives effective control; summer oils are also satisfactory.

Cactus Scale*, *Diaspis echinocacti* (Bouché). On cacti and orchids, common in Florida and the Southwest and on house cacti in the North. This is an armored scale. Female gray, circular; male white, slender. The surface of many cacti may be completely encrusted. A white summer oil with nicotine sulfate is effective but must be used with caution on cacti. Some scales can be rubbed off with a stiff brush or a piece of wood. Use malathion for crawlers.

Calico Scale*, *Lecanium cerasorum* Cockerell. Found in California, on cherry, elm, maple, pear, prune, Boston ivy, Virginia-creeper, English walnut. The female—hemispherical, shiny, marked with yellowish areas on a brown background—winters on lower surfaces of larger branches, and the young move to smaller twigs and branches in spring. Control measures are seldom necessary.

California Red Scale*, *Aonidiella aurantii* (Maskell). The most important citrus pest in California, also serious in Arizona and Texas, less damaging in more humid Gulf States. It probably came from Australia to southern California prior to 1875 on citrus nursery stock. Found in greenhouses in many parts of the country, it occurs outdoors only in the South. Ordinarily a pest of citrus—citron, grapefruit, lemon, orange, tangerine—it also infests acacia, aloe, apple, aspidistra, avocado, breadfruit, banana, boxelder, boxwood, chinaberry, coconut, eucalyptus, euonymus, fig, fuchsia, grape, hibiscus, holly, Japanese yew, jasmine, mango, mulberry, oak, olive, palms, passion-flower, pistachio, privet, quince, rose, sago palm, sweetbay, English walnut, willow, yucca. The scales attack leaves, twigs or fruit, injecting a toxic substance into the tree. Leaves and fruit are spotted with yellow; sometimes the entire foliage turns yellow.

The mature female is pinhead size, 1/12 inch across, armored, reddish brown, circular. Young scales are born alive; they stay under the parent shell for a few hours, crawl about for a day or two, then settle down and insert their sucking beaks at the places where they will spend the rest of their lives. Cottony secretions are molded into a caplike covering with a small nipple in the center. After the first molt, in 10 to 15 days, the cast skins (exuviae) are incorporated into the center of the cap, which is enlarged at the side. After a second molt and the enlargement, there is a gray margin extending beyond the body. The gray adult is fertilized by the small, yellow-winged male. She continues to give birth to 2 or 3 scales a day for 2 or 3 months. There may be 4 generations a year.

Control. Parathion with oil is used by many orchardists. Deciduous ornamentals can have a dormant oil spray from December to February and evergreens a summer oil emulsion; or malathion or nicotine sulfate can be used for crawlers. There are a number of parasites and some effective predators.

Camellia Mining Scale, *Pseudaonidia clavigera* (Cockerell). Reported in Florida in 1962 infesting camellia, azalea, boxwood, holly, crapemyrtle, cestrum, and viburnum.

Camellia Parlatoria, *Parlatoria camelliae* (Comstock). The most common scale on camellia on the Pacific Coast, especially on plants under lath. It is present in Florida, also in Georgia, Louisiana, Mississippi, Oregon, South Carolina, Texas, and Virginia but not very important. It attacks sweetolive as well as camellias. The scale is very small, flat, oval, brownish, found on both leaf surfaces. The female body under the shell is light purple. Parathion has been used effectively by commercial growers.

Camellia Scale*, *Lepidosaphes camelliae* Hoke. Not so important as the tea scale on camellia, present most often on cuttings and on young plants in greenhouses. The female shell is light to dark brown, oyster-shaped, 1/10 inch long, covering a white to purplish body. The male shell is smaller and narrower. The female starts laying eggs 40 to 50 days after birth, with the life cycle completed in 60 to 70 days. Few crawlers are present during the winter months outdoors because the females do not reproduce them. Foliage is devitalized, drops prematurely, but is not discolored. The camellia scale can be controlled with oil or other sprays applied as for tea scale. A parasitic wasp and lady beetles are helpful.

Another armored scale on camellia in California is *Aspidiotus degeneratus.*

Camphor Scale*, *Pseudaonidia duplex* (Cockerell). First noted in New Orleans in 1920, now present in Alabama, Mississippi, Louisiana, Florida. This scale is circular, moderately convex, dark blackish brown with orange exuviae, about 1/10 inch across. It feeds on nearly 200 plants, with preference for the camphor-tree, Japanese persimmon, sweetolive, camellia, azalea, Satsuma orange and other citrus, Japanese honeysuckle, fig, Confederate jasmine, glossy privet, rose. It is sometimes injurious to avocado, elm, grape, hackberry, and pecan. It is so injurious to camphor-trees that just a few scales on a twig can cause defoliation, and a tree can be killed within 6 months of attack. Ants help to disseminate the scale. Spraying with a 2 per cent oil emulsion is effective.

Chaff Scale*, *Parlatoria pergandii* Comstock. A greenhouse pest, infesting some outdoor plants in California, many more in Florida. Food plants include acacia, agave, asparagus fern, assonia, araucaria, aucuba, bay, bignonia, box, cajeput, camellia, camphor, carissa, cinnamon, citrus, cocculus, croton, camphor, cycad, currant, eugenia, euonymus, feijoa, fig, guava, holly, honeysuckle, jasmine, mango, magnolia, maple, orchids, lantana, laurel, mountain-laurel, privet, mimosa, silk-oak, oleander, palms, sweet-olive, orchid, parkinsonia, pepper-tree, persimmon, photinia, screwpine, pittosporum, Confederate rose, smilax, Spanish bayonet, tea, tung-oil, viburnum, wandering-Jew. The female is circular to elongate, smooth, semitransparent, brownish gray with marginal yellow exuviae; found on bark or leaves.

Cassava Scale, *Lepidosaphes alba* (Cockerell). On cassava, tea weed, and *Tunrera ulmifolia* in Florida, also reported from New Mexico. Oystershell-shaped, straight or curved, rather convex, pale grayish or brownish white; terminal exuviae, slightly darker than shell.

Chinese Obscure Scale, *Parlatoria chinensis* Marlett. Found in Florida, reported also from Missouri, on trunk and branches of *Ficus* spp. but not commercial fig. The shape is variable—short, elliptical to oval, flat or slightly convex. Very thin, whitish; exuviae large, light brown to greenish, marginal or submarginal. The scale is covered with bits of bark and is hard to see.

Citricola Scale*, *Coccus pseudomagnoliarum* (Kuwana). A serious citrus pest in parts of California; found also on hackberry, pomegranate, English walnut and elm. It resembles soft scale but is grayer, lays eggs instead of producing living young, has only 1 generation. It feeds on underside of leaves and on smaller twigs during the summer, migrating to branches in late winter or early spring. Oil, oil plus DDT, parathion, and sulfur dust or spray have been recommended for control. Most of the parasites of brown soft scale also attack this species.

Citrus Snow Scale*, *Unaspis citri* (Comstock). Present in southern states and California, limited to citrus. It is somewhat oyster-shaped, moderately convex, brown to blackish brown with brownish yellow exuviae. The numerous males are snow-white, elongate.

Coconut Scale*, *Aspidiotus destructor* Signoret. On palms in southern Florida and other tropical climates, also found on almond, annona, Jamaica apple, sugar-apple, asparagus fern, avocado, banana, bottle-brush, box, cajeput, calophyllum, croton, gerbera, eugenia, frangipani, geiger-tree, umbrella grass, gumbo-limbo, honeysuckle, lawsonia, ligustrum, mahogany, mango, silk-oak, palmetto, papaya, pandanus, screwpine, poinciana, pondapple, wax privet, satinleaf, shore bay, soursop. The scale is very small, circular, thin, faint yellow but transparent, with deeper-yellow exuviae. It may be abundant on foliage, may also occur on bark and fruit. It is under control by parasites.

Cottony Bamboo Scale, *Antonina crawi* Cockerell. On bamboo in greenhouses, outdoors in southern California. Oval, dark reddish-purple bodies are enclosed in thick, white, cottony sacs, often crowded at leaf axils. They may be quite injurious. Spray with malathion or other phosphate or a summer oil.

Cottony Cochineal Scale, *Dactylopius confusus* (Cockerell). A mealybug, on cactus in Florida, Arizona, Colorado, California, New Mexico. Oval, dark red, filled with red fluid, enclosed in a white, cottony mass.

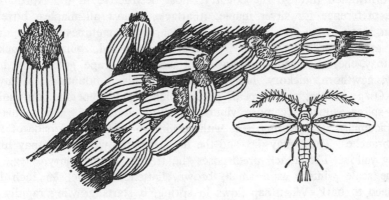

75. Cottony-cushion scale; females with fluted egg masses, and winged male.

Cottony-cushion Scale*, *Icerya purchasi* Maskell. An Australian scale introduced into California on acacia about 1868, soon threatening the entire citrus industry and now present throughout the South, and in greenhouses, on a long list of hosts. Food plants include acacia, acalypha, almond, amaranthus, apple, apricot, Australian-pine, boxwood, buckeye, California sage, castor-bean, cedar-of-Lebanon, chrysanthemum, citron, croton, cypress, fig, geranium, grape, grapefruit, sweetgum, Guadalupe palm, hackberry, ironwood, Boston ivy, laurel, lemon, lime, locust, magnolia, maple, mistletoe, oak, orange, peach, pear, pepper, pithecellobium, pine, pittosporum (very commonly infested), poinsettia, pomegranate, potato, quince, rose, sunflower, verbena, veronica, English walnut, willow. Trees may be completely covered with white cushions and sooty mold growing in the honeydew.

The insect itself is reddish brown, but the female attaches a large, compact, white, fluted mass, holding from 600 to 800 bright-red eggs. This white egg mass sticks out at an angle from the twig and is very conspicuous. Hatching of eggs in the fluted ovisac occurs in a few days in summer, up to 2 months in winter. Young larvae are red with dark legs, dark antennae, long hairs at the end of the body. Even after molting, the scale keeps its legs and can move about until the egg sac is formed. The males are very tiny, with long white filaments. There are 3 or more generations.

Control. The spectacular control of cottony-cushion scale by Vedalia, the Australian lady beetle, marked the first successful subjugation of a pest by the introduction of a natural enemy. Vedalia still keeps this scale from obtaining economic importance on citrus, except where the biological balance has been disturbed by chemicals such as DDT, which has more effect on the predators than on the scale. Where Vedalia is not present or unable to act, spraying with parathion has been very effective. Malathion should be substituted for use on ornamentals in home gardens.

Cottony Maple Scale*, *Pulvinaria innumerabilis* (Rathvon). A native species distributed through the country, most destructive in the North. With some preference for silver maple, it attacks almost all maples, boxelder, linden, black locust, red mulberry, white ash, and sometimes alder, andromeda, apple, beech, blackberry, blueberry, boxwood, bumelia, buckeye, sweetbay, cherry, currant, dogwood, elm, euonymus, grape, gooseberry, hackberry, hawthorn, hickory, holly, honeylocust, lilac, mountain-ash, myrtle, oak, Osage-orange, peach, pear, pecan, plum, poplar, persimmon, quince, rose, spirea, sumac, sycamore, viburnum, Virginia-creeper, willow. This is a conspicuous scale, covering trees with cottony masses on underside of twigs and branches. These may die, and the foliage of the whole tree may turn a sickly yellow. The attack predisposes the tree to borer injury.

The scale winters as a small, brown, flattened female, ⅛ inch long, attached to bark. When sap flows in spring, it starts growing rapidly, depositing 1500 to 3000 eggs in a cottony mass several times the size of the original scale (Plate XXXIV). Around New York the young hatch in late June or July, crawling from twigs to leaves, where they suck sap along the midrib and veins and secrete honeydew. They mature in August and September and mate; the males die, the females crawl back to twigs for winter. There is only 1 generation.

Control. Former recommendation was to spray before growth starts with a miscible oil, but this may be injurious to soft maples. A current recommendation is to spray with malathion or Sevin in late June or early July.

Cottony Peach Scale*, *Pulvinaria amygdali* Cockerell. Fruit Tree Pulvinaria. The scale is flat, oval, yellow or reddish, usually covered with white, cottony wax and with a compact white, cottony egg sac. It feeds on leaves, bark, fruit of peach, prune, plum, apple in California and New Mexico.

Cottony Pine Scale, *Pseudophilippia quaintancii* Cockerell. Reported from Florida, Virginia, and North Carolina on pines, usually at base of needles. The female is oval or hemispherical, yellowish or light brown, covered with fluffy snow-white secretions.

Cottony Taxus Scale, *Pulvinaria floccifera* (Westwood). A tropical insect reported in Florida and in greenhouses on angel's trumpet, ardisia, guava, English ivy and mulberry, camellia, abutilon, and acalypha. It is also becoming a northern pest, being found out of doors on yew (Taxus) in Rhode Island in 1950 and in Connecticut in 1953 and reported on various ornamentals in Oregon. It winters as a small, light-brown, flattened hemispherical scale, ⅛ inch long, and in spring produces a long, narrow, fluted cottony egg mass. Eggs hatch in June and infest underside of needles and sometimes twigs of previous year's growth. One or two egg masses may cover the underside of a needle and the scale may be abundant enough to coat branches, with serious injury to plants. DDT in April and malathion in August have given control.

Cranberry Scale, *Aspidiotus oxycoccus* Woglum. Metacide is reported effective in control.

Cyanophyllum Scale, *Aspidiotus cyanophylli* Signoret. Of cosmopolitan distribution on orchids, rubber plant and many other hosts. The very long list includes acacia, acalypha, allamanda, annona, anthericum, Jamaica apple, sugar-apple, ardisia, avocado, azalea, banana, bay, begonia, billbergia, bottle-brush, bougainvillea, calathea, callistemon, camellia, camphor, carissa, cestrum, coconut, coffee, cycas, gerbera, dogwood, dracaena, elaeagnus, euonymus, euphorbia, fig, flame vine, grape, seagrape, guava, sweetgum, hackberry, hibiscus, holly, honeysuckle, ivy, jasmine, cherry-laurel, privet, lily, liriope, loquat, magnolia, maple, maranta, morinda, mountain ebony, crapemyrtle, silk-oak, ophiopogon, palms, screwpine, pittosporum, plumeria, pomegranate, quisqualis, smilax, yucca, stephanotis, tabernaemontana, tung-oil, viburnum, Virginia-creeper, zamia.

The female is elongate ovate or triangular; scales are very thin, flat, semitransparent with the yellow body showing through; exuviae are central, yellow. Parasites keep this under control.

Cypress Bark Scale, *Ehrhornia cupressi* (Ehrhorn). Cottony Cypress Scale. Common on Monterey cypress, also attacking Guadalupe and Arizona cypress and incense cedar in California. Limbs turn yellow, then red or brown. Trees look scraggy; some die, especially those in hedges. The scale has a pink body covered with loose white wax, and is usually found in pits or cracks in bark. Spray with a miscible oil in August and again in late September or with malathion.

Dictyospermum Scale*, *Chrysomphalus dictyospermi* (Morgan). Spanish Red Scale, widely distributed in subtropics, reported as serious in Connecticut greenhouses on palms in 1905, found outdoors in California, Florida, and other warm states. It is a rather important pest of avocado, a potential threat to citrus, fairly common on acacia, palms, latania, rose, sometimes orchids. In Florida it is also recorded on acacia, agave, albizzia, allamanda, anthurium, aralia, arborvitae, ardisia, asparagus, aspidistra, bamboo, banana, bauhinia, bay, billbergia, bird-of-paradise, bottle-brush, boxwood, cactus, camellia, camphor, canna, carissa, century plant, Barbados and Surinam cherry, cinnamon, citrus, cocculus, cotoneaster, croton, cypress, gerbera, daphne, dracaena, elaeagnus, eucalyptus, euonymus, euphorbia, feijoa, fern, fig, firethorn, gardenia, gold-dust tree, golden dewdrop, golden-shower, guava, India-hawthorn, holly, honeysuckle, ivy, jasmine, jatropha, juniper, laurel, laurestinus, ligustrum, lily, Spanish lime, liriope, litchi, macadamia, magnolia, mango, mountain ebony, muehlenbeckia, mulberry, myrtle, nolina, silk-oak, oleander, olive, ophiopogon, orchids, osmanthus, palms, palmetto, pandanus, parkinsonia, pecan, philodendron, Australian-pine, screwpine, photinia, plum-yew, podocarpus, poinsettia, rose, sapo-dilla, sparkleberry, tea plant, viburnum, walnut, willow, woodbine, and yew.

Scales infest bark, leaf and fruit. The female is circular, ⅙ to 1/12 inch with dark-brown armor. It deposits eggs and there are 3 or 4 generations in California, 5 or 6 in Florida. Malathion will control this species. Palms in greenhouses should be syringed forcefully and repeatedly with water. Elimi-nate ants, which carry around young scales.

Dogwood Scale*, *Chionaspis corni* Cooley. A northern species present from Massachusetts to Indiana and Kansas, looking much like scurfy scale on apple. It is occasionally so abundant on pagoda, silky, and red-osier dog-wood, it turns the stems white. A dormant lime-sulfur spray is effective or a miscible oil may be applied just before growth starts in spring. The scales are heavily parasitized.

Elm Scurfy Scale*, *Chionaspis americana* Johnson. Distributed from New England south to Florida and west to Oklahoma and Texas, more serious in the Middle West than in the East. Found most often on American elm, it may attack Camperdown and other elms, killing branches or young trees outright. It also attacks hackberry. The female—pear-shaped, convex, rather thick, 1/12 to ⅛ inch long, naturally white but grayish from bark frag-ments—is found only on bark. The male, white, very small and narrow, is found on both bark and leaves. Purple eggs winter under the female shell. There are 2 generations in the North, more in the South. It can be con-trolled with a dormant oil spray.

Euonymus Scale*, *Unaspis euonymi* (Comstock). Doubtless known to everyone growing euonymus, though my own observations lead me to believe it is not as prevalent in the Deep South and in California as in cooler climates. It is also common on bittersweet and pachysandra, is sometimes present on ivy and other ground covers growing near euonymus, and has been reported on camellia in Florida. Female scales look like dark-brown oyster shells, 1/16 inch long; males are almost needle-thin, pure white (Plate XXXIII). Stems and leaves are often entirely covered with white males, with a scattering of brown females. Leaves turn yellow, drop; vines die back. Climbing euonymus covering walls is more often infested than some of the upright forms; winged euonymus is usually free from scale. The scale overwinters as an immature or mature fertilized female. Orange-yellow eggs, laid under the female shell, hatch in late spring to crawlers of the same color and are visible in late May and June. A 2nd brood appears in late August and September, and, in warm climates, a partial 3rd may be present.

Control. Use a dormant spray, same strength as for lilacs and other deciduous shrubs, before growth starts in spring. This may be oil but preferably Elgetol. Spray for crawlers in June with malathion, diazinon, or DDT. Repeat as necessary for the summer brood. Cut off and burn vines that are completely encrusted with scales.

Another scale, *Lepidosaphes yanagicola* (Kuwalt) has been found recently on *Euonymus alatus*. It is reported from Indiana, Ohio, and Rhode Island and also from Maryland on pachysandra.

European Elm Scale*, *Gossyparia spuria* (Modeer). A soft scale, first found at Rye, New York, in 1884, now spread across the country wherever elms are found, being particularly destructive to ornamental and street elms. Infested trees have yellowed foliage, usually shed prematurely; small branches die, then the larger branches, sometimes the whole tree. Copius honeydew drops to sidewalks and cars and keeps branches black with sooty mold growing in it.

Nymphs winter in bark crevices, and in very early spring the males form conspicuous white cocoons in which they transform to minute, reddish, winged or wingless "gnats." Females become adult early in May; ⅙ to ⅜ inch long, they are oval, reddish brown, surrounded with a white fringe. They deposit eggs under their bodies from late May through June, and these hatch within an hour into yellow crawlers which migrate to the leaves, feeding there until fall. Most migrate back to trunk or branches before leaves drop in autumn.

Control. Foliage sprays of Sevin, diazinon, Guthion, or mixtures of DDT and malathion provide excellent control if applied at the right time (July 1 to 14 in Kansas). A strong stream of water from the hose will wash off some scales. There are few natural enemies.

European Fiorinia Scale, *Fiorinia fioriniae* (Targ). Similar to the Tea Scale, found on asparagus fern, avocado, bay, bottle-brush, cajeput, camphor, English ivy and palms. The female is brownish yellow to orange.

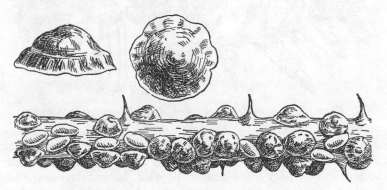

76. *European fruit lecanium on blackberry cane.*

European Fruit Lecanium*, *Lecanium corni* (Bouché). Brown Apricot Scale, Brown Elm Scale, distributed through the country, quite injurious on the Pacific Coast. Besides fruit trees—apricot, plum, prune, peach, cherry, apple, persimmon, quince—it may also infest arborvitae, alder, ash, basswood, beech, blackberry, blueberry, black walnut, boxwood, boxelder, butternut, Catalina cherry, cherry-laurel, chinaberry, currant, elm, gooseberry, greasewood, grape, hawthorn, hackberry, hazelnut, hickory, locust, magnolia, maple, mulberry, oak, Osage-orange, pecan, poplar, redbud, rose, sassafras, willow. The scale has various forms and may represent more than 1 species. Typically the female is large—⅛ to 1/16 inch—hemispherical to oval, and very convex, smooth shiny brown or reddish brown but sometimes covered with a white powder. It winters on twigs and branches, laying eggs under the shell in spring, with hatching from May to July. The males are smaller, flatter, elongated, and almost transparent, with ridges down the back. The nymphs migrate to the leaves and are found mostly among the veins, but they return to bark of twigs and branches for winter. There is 1 generation.

Control. Spray trees when dormant (December to February in California, perhaps March or April elsewhere) with a miscible oil emulsion. The fruit lecanium is heavily parasitized, infected individuals turning black.

European Fruit Scale*, *Aspidiotus ostreaeformis* Curtis. Pear Tree Oyster Scale, on deciduous fruit and ornamental trees.

False Cottony Maple Scale, *Pulvinaria acericola* Walsh & Riley. In eastern United States on soft and sugar maples. Oval, purple, with a medium-brown stripe and a long, cottony egg mass. It may cause early dropping of leaves or death of twigs and branches.

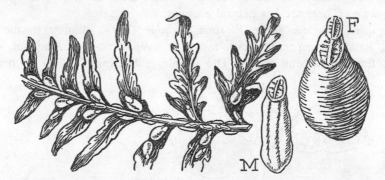

77. *Fern scale, with detail of pear-shaped female, thin male.*

Fern Scale*, *Pinnaspis aspidistrae* Signoret. This may be a severe pest of ferns and African-violet in Florida, of ferns and aspidistra in homes and greenhouses. It may also infest acacia, begonia, banana, cajeput, camellia, century plant, cinnamon, citrus, croton, dracaena, fig, geranium, hibiscus, liriope, mountain ebony, mango, ophiopogon, orchids, palms, pepper-tree, screwpine, spiceberry, spleenwort, and violet. This is an armored scale. The males are thin, white, conspicuous, the females ocher brown, oyster-shaped. Parathion has given good control in greenhouses; malathion should be used in homes. Small potted ferns may be dipped in a solution of nicotine sulfate and soap.

Fig Scale*, *Lepidosaphes ficus* (Signoret). On figs in California, infesting fruit, leaves, wood up to 2 years old. It is similar to the purple scale but smaller. It may be controlled with a dormant oil emulsion, December to March, or a foliage spray of parathion in May. A hymenopterous parasite, *Aphycus,* imported from France, is effective.

Fletcher Scale*, *Lecanium fletcheri* Cockerell. Arborvitae Soft Scale. On arborvitae for many years, now damaging yew and pachysandra. Branches and underside of foliage may be covered with scales, with loss of color, vigor, premature defoliation, sooty mold growing in honeydew. Young scales are amber; mature females are dark brown, hemispherical. Immature scales winter on stems and underside of foliage; eggs are deposited under the female in late spring, with hatching in June. There is little summer development and most of the feeding and injury occur the next spring. Malathion, 2 to 3 teaspoons of 57 per cent emulsion per gallon, is effective if applied in August, or from April to mid-May.

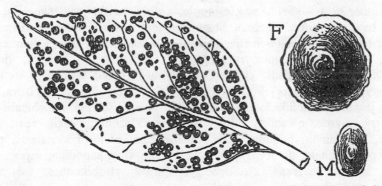

78. *Florida red scale on underside of leaf, with detail of male and female.*

Florida Red Scale*, *Chrysomphalus aonidum* (Linnaeus). An important citrus pest in Florida and the Gulf States, also serious on palms, camphor, and roses; on some nursery plants in California but not on citrus to any extent. The Florida red scale is fairly common on ivy and other house and greenhouse plants. Outdoors in warm climates it may infest acacia, acalypha, agave, allamanda, aloe, anise-tree, annona, apple, aralia, ardisia, aspidistra, araucaria, avocado, azalea, banana, bay, bird-of-paradise, begonia, bottlebrush, bougainvillea, boxwood, cajeput, caladium, calycanthus, camellia, camphor, canna, coconut, carissa, cassia, century plant, cherry, cinnamon, citrus, eucalyptus, eugenia, euonymus, feijoa, fern, fig, firethorn, grape, sea-grape, guava, gardenia, gladiolus, hawthorn, hibiscus, holly, iris, ivy, ixora, jasmine, laurel, lilac, lily, liriope, litchi, loquat, magnolia, mango, maranta, melaleuca, monkeypuzzle tree, monstera, mountain ebony, muehlenbeckia, mulberry, myrtle, silk-oak, oleander, olive, orchids, ophiopogon, palms, palmetto, pecan, persimmon, photinia, screwpine, pittosporum, plum, plumbago, podocarpus, poinsettia, pothos, pyracantha, rose, satinleaf, sapota, schefflera, soursop, spice plant, spiraea, spurge, tabernaemontana, tea plant, ternstroemia, travelers-tree, rubber plant, viburnum, vinca, wisteria, and zamia.

This is an armored scale, small, 1/12 inch, circular, reddish brown to nearly black with a lighter central portion; often very numerous on leaves, either surface, and on fruit, but not infesting twigs. It deposits eggs which hatch in a few hours, and there can be 5 or more generations in greenhouses. This species does not produce noticeable honeydew.

Control. Florida citrus growers spray with oil from mid-June to mid-July or with parathion June through August. TEPP aerosols have been used in greenhouses; malathion in homes. Keeping ivy and other house plants frequently bathed with water will reduce scale infestation. There are several parasites and predators.

Florida Wax Scale*, *Ceroplasters floridensis* Comstock. Found in Alabama, Florida, Louisiana, Mississippi, North Carolina and probably other subtropical areas. This species is very important on camellias and may infest many other hosts—abelia, acacia, apple, ardisia, prickly-ash, avocado, barberry, bay, bear grass, bignonia, blueberry, bottle-brush, boxwood, Brazilian pepper-tree, buckthorn, bumelia, cajeput, carissa, cedar, cherry, cinnamon, citrus, cotoneaster, crapemyrtle, croton, cunninghamia, cuphea, dahlia, duranta, elder, elaeagnus, eugenia, euonymus, feijoa, fern, fig, firethorn, gallberry, gardenia, glory-bush, guava, gumbo-limbo, hawthorn, ixora, jasmine, jessamine, litchi, loquat, magnolia, mango, maple, muehlenbeckia, mulberry, myrtle, oleander, olive, palms, parkinsonia, peach, pear, periwinkle, persimmon, photinia, pine, pittosporum, plum, podocarpus, poinsettia, pomegranate, quince, raphiolepis, rubber vine, sapodilla, sapota, sassafras, serissa, seagrape, sparkleberry, spiraea, strobilanthes, tea plant, tecoma, and viburnum.

The reddish or purple-brown body is covered with a thick, white waxy coating tinted with pink, often with some dark spots. Red eggs are laid under the body of the scale, which shrinks as they accumulate. Crawlers collect on underside of leaves along midribs; adults cling to twigs. There are 3 generations in Florida. This species can be controlled with a summer oil emulsion, 1 to 2 per cent according to host tolerance.

Forbes Scale*, *Aspidiotus forbesi* Johnson. Present east of the Rocky Mountains on cherry (especially sour cherry), apple, apricot, pear, plum, quince, currant, almond, peach, and dogwood. This species has been increased by the use of DDT in orchards. Scales are grayish, thin, flaky, circular, with a tiny raised reddish area in the center; they are massed on trunk and branches. Partly grown scales winter on bark; young appear in May, born alive and also produced from eggs. There are 1 to 3 generations. Dormant oil sprays may not give complete control; a delayed dormant spray is more effective in some areas. Parathion or malathion can be used in cover sprays.

Frosted Scale, *Lecanium pruinosum* Coquillett. In California and Arizona, increasing as a walnut problem with DDT used for codling moth and infesting about the same list of fruit and ornamental hosts as the European fruit lecanium. It is a large, convex brown scale, covered with a frosty wax. A dormant parathion spray is recommended for walnuts, applied in late fall or winter after complete defoliation.

Globose Scale*, *Lecanium prunastri* (Fonscolombe).

Gloomy Scale*, *Chrysomphalus tenebricosus* (Comstock). Present from Washington, D.C., to Florida and Texas, most injurious to soft maples; also on sugar maple, hackberry, elm, boxelder, buckthorn, sweetgum, gallberry, mulberry, soapberry. It is dark gray, circular, very convex, melting into the bark in color. It is mostly controlled by natural enemies.

Glover Scale*, *Lepidosaphes gloverii* (Packard). Found in southern states, often associated with purple scale and with a similar life history; more important in Florida than California. Hosts include arborvitae, boxwood, citrus, cherry, coconut, croton, euonymus, ivy, laurel, ligustrum, mango, magnolia, mulberry, myrtle, cabbage palmetto, and podocarpus. The female is long and narrow, straight or curved, yellow brown to dark brown. It may infest bark, leaf, or fruit.

Golden Oak Scale*, *Asterolecanium variolosum* (Ratzeburg). Pit-making Oak Scale. Found wherever oaks are grown, often injurious to young ornamental trees and sometimes killing mature trees if they suffer from drought. The scale is circular, slightly convex, polished greenish gold, with a marginal fringe and minute glassy spines. It makes small pits in the bark and lies in these depressions, its feeding producing galls or swellings. It winters as a mature female and, because of its waxy case, is rather resistant to oil sprays, although a dormant oil in April is still recommended in the East. A summer oil spray with toxaphene has given control in California.

Grape Scale*, *Aspidiotus uvae* Comstock. Generally distributed on grape, sometimes on peach, hickory, sycamore, resembling San Jose scale in size and habits. Shells are circular to elliptical, gray or yellow brown with a pale yellow spot and white nipple at 1 side of center; they are usually present on old canes under loose bark. There is 1 generation. Severe pruning may be sufficient; if not, apply a dormant spray of oil or lime-sulfur.

Greedy Scale*, *Aspidotus camelliae* Signoret. A common armored scale attacking ornamentals throughout the country, mostly in greenhouses, outdoors in warm climates. The female is quite convex, elliptical to round, small, gray, with yellow or dark-brown exuviae near one edge. The scales are omnivorous feeders on bark, sometimes leaves and fruit, of acacia, almond, apple, avocado, bay, birch, cactus, camphor, chinaberry, camellia, ceanothus, cherry, cissus, cotoneaster, cottonwood, English holly, English ivy, English laurel, eucalyptus, euonymus, fig, fuchsia, genista, guava, grape, heather, mountain-holly, honeysuckle, Japanese quince, California-laurel, lavatera, locust, magnolia, maple, manzanita, mistletoe, myrtle, mulberry, olive, orange, Oregon-grape, oak, palms, passion-flower, pear, pecan, pepper-tree, pittosporum, pomegranate, pyracantha, quince, redbud, rose, sage, sedum, sequoia, strawberry-tree, silver tree, strelitzia, silk-oak, umbrella tree, English walnut, willow.

Control with aerosols in greenhouses and by spraying with malathion or summer white oils in gardens.

Green Scale*, *Coccus viridis* (Green). Found in tropical climates, infesting many types of plants in Florida, including apple, aster, bamboo vine, banana, blue dawn-flower, button-bush, cabbage palmetto, castor-bean, citrus, coffee, eggfruit, elder, ferns, fig, fireweed, frangipani, grape, seagrape, groundsel, guava, iresine, ixora, jasmine, lancewood, lantana, marlberry, sapodilla, sapota, satinleaf, snowberry, soursop, Spanish needle, sumac, tea, thistle, Virginia-creeper, mangrove, willow and yerbe maté. The female is oval, more or less pointed in front, pale green with 2 black spots. The friendly fungus *Cephalosporium lecanii* keeps the green scale under control.

Green Shield Scale*, *Pulvinaria psidii* Maskell. On ornamentals in Florida. A white, cottony egg sac projects from a green shield. Food plants include acalypha, akee, alder, almond, anthurium, apple, aralia, avocado, bay, bignonia, bottle-brush, Brazilian pepper-tree, cajeput, camellia, canna, carissa, ceriman, chalice-vine, chinaberry, citrus, clerodendron, coffee, croton, currant, cypress vine, elder, elm (Chinese), feijoa, fern, fig, frangipani, gardenia, geiger-tree, gerbera, seagrape, groundsel, guava, hackberry, hamelia, holly, honeysuckle, ice-plant, ixora, jasmine, laurel, Spanish lime, litchi, mango, marlberry, muehlenbeckia, mulberry, myrtle, crapemyrtle, silk-oak, palm, passion-vine, California pepper, persimmon, pittosporum, plumeria, plum, sapodilla, sapota, snowberry, soapberry, soursop, Spanish-needles, tabernaemontana, tecoma, and travelers-tree. This species is mostly in southern Florida and may be serious on species of Ficus and on guava.

Ground Pearls. Scales or mealybugs, small, shining bodies with an iridescent luster found loosely scattered in soil or on roots of plants. Those in the tropics have been used for adornment by the natives. Some species are becoming turf problems in the warmer sections of the United States. The only successful treatment seems to be ample water and fertilizer applied through the growing season.

Margarodes meridionalis Morrison. Cream to silvery, elliptical, with a rather brittle, thin-walled, waxlike shell, varying in size from a grain of sand to 4 mm. Found on Centipede grass in Florida and through the Southeast, recorded on St. Augustine grass in California, Bermuda grass in Arizona. It is also present in Florida in soil around grapefruit and other citrus trees.

Margarodes rileyi Giard. Riley's Ground Pearl. On plant roots in the Florida Keys. It is nearly globular, 2 to 4 mm, with a thin wax secretion, color like a pearl.

Eumargarodes laingi Jakubski. A serious pest of Centipede grass in Florida, reported also from North Carolina, also infesting roots of St. Augustine grass. It is globular, very small, brownish yellow to light red when the adult is ready to emerge from under its waxy covering. The 1st pair of legs in the female is adapted for digging.

Hall Scale, *Nilotaspis halli* (Green). An almond pest, formerly established in California but an example of a pest that has been successfully eradicated.

79. *Hemispherical scale on fern (note detail showing cushion shape and height).*

Hemispherical Scale*, *Saissetia hemisphaerica* (Targioni-Tozzetti). A tropical species common in greenhouses and in gardens in mild climates. It is frequently present but not important on citrus and avocado, may be important on cycads, conspicuous on ferns, palms, and other ornamentals, including allamanda, aloe, almond, amaryllis, annona, anthurium, ardisia, asparagus fern, avocado, banana, bamboo, begonia, bignonia, bergamot, bougainvillea, Brazilian pepper-tree, carissa, cherry, citrus, clerodendrum, camellia, chrysanthemum, coffee, coral plant, croton, dracaena, duranta, Dutchmanspipe, elder, eugenia, ferns, fig, frangipani, gardenia, geiger-tree, gerbera, seagrape, guava, holly, honeysuckle, ixora, jacaranda, jasmine, crapemyrtle, ligustrum, lily, myrtle, nephthytis, oleander, olive, orchids, sago palm, periwinkle, mountain-holly, sapodilla, soursop, Spanish-needles, spiceberry, stephanotis, tabernaemontana, Turks-cap, viburnum, willow, and zamia. The female is a smooth glossy brown, hemispherical with flared margins, about ⅛ inch in diameter. It secretes much honeydew, which attracts ants and is a medium for black sooty mold, making fern fronds an eyesore. Parathion kills some stages but not late immature scales. Malathion, or nicotine sulfate and soap, or a summer oil and nicotine may be satisfactory, depending on host and circumstances.

Hemlock Scale*, *Aspidiotus ithacae* (Ferris). A native American species, widely distributed, quite common in the West. Scales are circular, nearly black, in great numbers on underside of needles of hemlock, Douglas-fir, Monterey, yellow, knob-cone and other pines. They sometimes kill young trees.

Another species, *Fiorinia externa* Ferris, has become even more important on hemlock in the East and sometimes infests yew and spruce. It is reported as a problem in New York, Connecticut, Maryland, Massachusetts, New Jersey, Ohio and Pennsylvania. Hemlocks appear whitewashed from the abundance of insects on the needles, usually on the underside. Trees turn yellow, may be defoliated. The female is elongate, pale yellow to pale brown, but it lives inside the cast skin of the last molt so that it appears white. Females continue to reproduce throughout the year in some areas; in Massachusetts there are 2 generations—in late June and in September. Two sprays of malathion, 10 days apart, have been recommended for crawlers. Dimethoate has been reported as giving excellent control.

Hickory Scale, *Chionaspis caryae* Cooley. On pecan in Florida, on bark of hickory in some other states, but not common. The female is pear-shaped, dirty-white, terminal exuviae pale yellow or brown.

Holly Scale*, *Aspidiotus brittanicus* Newstead. On holly in Pacific Coast States. The scales are circular, flat, 1/16 inch across, on leaves, twigs, and berries. When numerous they weaken trees.

Another holly scale, *Asterolecanium puteanum* Russell, feeds on American holly, yaupon, and bumelia from Delaware to Alabama. It makes both shallow and deep pits in twigs. A species of Lecanium is reported injuring new growth of holly, with sooty mold growing in honeydew. It is convex, amber to reddish brown with crawlers appearing in late June and July. There is 1 generation and a delayed dormant or a summer oil has given better control than malathion.

Howard Scale*, *Aspidiotus howardi* Cockerell. A Rocky Mountain species occurring mostly at high altitudes in Colorado and New Mexico. Pear is the preferred host, but it may feed on almond, apple, ash, peach, plum, prune and other deciduous fruits and vegetables. Also identified as this species is a scale on yucca in Florida and other southern states. The scale is circular, flat, pale gray with a reddish tinge; it causes pitting and a reddish stain on fruit. Control is the same as for the San Jose scale.

Italian Pear Scale*, *Epidiaspis piricola* (Del Guercio). A California pest of pear, plum, prune, apple, Persian walnut, and a special pest of California Christmasberry, which may be killed by it. The female is dark red or purple, covered with a circular, dark-gray, shiny shell with dark-brown exuviae. The male is slender, white with yellow exuviae. Infestations of long duration cause deep depressions in limbs and may hasten death. Lichens usually cover the scales. Spray in winter with a heavy oil emulsion, drenching limbs and trunk, adding 1 ounce of caustic soda to each 2 gallons of spray to remove the lichens protecting the scales.

Japanese Scale, *Leucaspis japonica* Cockerell. Originally considered a pest of maple and privet, now infesting also boxwood, holly, Japanese quince, and rose from Rhode Island to Maryland. The scale resembles a narrow oyster shell, 1/16 to 1/12 inch long, dull grayish white, often thickly encrusting trunk and branches. A dormant oil spray gives satisfactory control.

Japanese Wax Scale, *Ceroplastes ceriferus* Anderson. General in Florida and other subtropical climates and found north to Virginia on blueberry, azalea, camellia, Chinese elm, citrus, fig, eugenia, gumbo-limbo, Chinese holly, yaupon, jasmine, mulberry, pear, persimmon, plum, quince, sapodilla, sapota, and Turks-cap. The female is circular, thick, waxy, very convex with surface more or less roughened, white or creamy white, 3 to 8 mm across. Under the shell the body is brown or purplish brown. The scales are found on bark and leaves.

Juniper Scale*, *Diaspis carueli* Targioni-Tozzetti. On juniper, sometimes arborvitae, incense cedar, and cypress used as ornamentals throughout the United States, not important here in forest stands. Also responsible, after having been introduced into Bermuda, for killing off most of the native junipers on that island. Whenever junipers around the house look dingy gray or yellowish or generally unthrifty, examine the needles closely for very small, 1/20-inch, dirty-white, round scales with a yellow center. These are females; the male is even smaller, white, narrow with a ridge down the back. They winter as nearly grown scales, and the young hatch in early June (Plate XXXIII).

Control. Spray with lime-sulfur, 1 to 9 dilution in early April unless the shrubs are too close to painted surfaces. Malathion can be used for the crawling stage in June.

Latania Scale, *Aspidiotus lataniae* Signoret. Widely distributed in greenhouses and warm climates on palms, orchids, canna, gladiolus, raspberry, rose, tamarisk and other ornamentals. Florida hosts also include Australian-pine, loquat and many other plants. This is an armored scale, gray, circular, 1/16 to 1/12 inch. It lays yellow eggs, and sulfur-yellow crawlers appear on branches, twigs, leaves or fruit. Malathion is effective in control but natural enemies may suffice.

Lesser Snow Scale, *Pinnaspis strachani* Cooley. A general pest of ornamentals in Florida, sometimes killing hibiscus. The female is pear-shaped, white, semitransparent, sometimes speckled with brown from incorporation of bark fragments. The male is very small, elongate, very white, and is so numerous it looks like salt over the bark. Hosts include abelia, abutilon, acacia, agave, althea, balsam-apple, prickly-ash, asparagus fern, aspidistra, assonia, avocado, bignonia, bird-of-paradise, camphor, candleberry, carissa, carob, cassia, cassava, castor-bean, chinaberry, cinnamon, cissus, sea-grape, crassula, croton, cuphea, dracaena, echeveria, elaeagnus, elder, eucalyptus, fern, fig, frangipani, geranium, grape, hackberry, hemlock, hibiscus, hollyhock, honeysuckle, ice-plant, inkberry, ivy, jacaranda, jasmine, jessamine, lantana, ligustrum, lily, liriope, Spanish lime, litchi, magnolia, mango, maple, morning-glory, mountain ebony, oak, silk-oak, oleander, orchids, passion-vine, peach, pepper-tree, persimmon, screwpine, pittosporum, poinciana, poinsettia, rubber, sansevieria, sapodilla, Spanish bayonet, spiceberry, sumac, sunflower, thunbergia, tung-oil, umbrella tree, wisteria, woodbine, and zizyphus.

This species may build up a heavy infestation but it is usually heavily parasitized. It may be controlled if necessary with malathion or summer oils.

Long Soft Scale, *Coccus elongatus* (Signoret). Outdoors in Florida, in greenhouses elsewhere. It is elongate-elliptical, moderately convex, smooth, yellowish or brownish gray with darker mottled areas. It is found on acacia, acalypha, albizzia, annona, assonia, bottle-brush, buckthorn, cassia, ceratonia, croton, dracaena, euphorbia, fern, fig, golden dewdrop, hibiscus, jacaranda, jasmine, Japanese pagoda-tree, litchi, maranta, mountain ebony, myrtle, silk-oak, parkinsonia, Australian-pine, pithecolobium, plum, poinsettia, rose, soursop. It is not considered economically important.

Magnolia Scale*, *Neolecanium cornuparvum* (Thro). A soft scale, probably a native, distributed through eastern states and also recorded from Nebraska, on various species of magnolia. This is the largest scale insect in the United States. The female is ½ inch across, notably convex, covered with white wax under which the body is shiny brown with honeycomb pits and large glands. When the scales are numerous, the branches appear to be covered with white cotton and when the scales are removed, a scar is left on the bark. Trees may be severely injured and appear sickly, leaves remaining small. There is much honeydew with resultant sooty mold over leaves and branches. Young nymphs hibernate on new wood, molt early in spring, again in June, and start secreting white wax. By August they are producing living young. There is 1 generation in the North.

Control. A dormant oil spray gives excellent results. Ethion may be used by professional arborists, or a mixture of phorate and malathion. Home gardeners can scrub off many scales with a stiff brush and soap and use malathion for the crawling stage.

Mango Scale, *Leucaspis indica* Marlatt. In Florida and Hawaii on mango, Spanish-needles, and soursop. The female is long, narrow, thin but very convex, white.

Maple Phenacoccus, *Phenacoccus acericola* King. In northeastern states, mostly on sugar maple. It resembles cottony maple scale with its large white, cottony masses, but these are always on the underside of leaves and not on the twigs. It is conspicuous but not very important.

Masked Scale, *Chrysomphalus personatus* (Comstock). In Florida (Key

West) on bauhinia, Barbados cherry, eugenia, fig, rose, sapodilla, seagrape. Very small, circular or thimble-shaped, gray-brown to nearly black, brittle.

Mexican Wax Scale. See Japanese Wax Scale.

Mimosa Scale, *Chrysomphalus mimosae* (Comstock). In Florida (Key West) on acacia, Spanish jasmine, and hog plum, but not serious. The female is circular or elongated, very small, moderately convex, whitish gray and hard to distinguish from the bark of the host. Another mimosa scale, *Aspidiotus diffinis,* is recently reported from the state.

Mining Scale*, *Howardia biclavis* (Comstock). On many ornamental plants in warm climates. The list includes acacia, allamanda, banyan, bignonia, bougainvillea, camellia, Australian-pine, chinquapin, duranta, eggfruit, elder, fig, gardenia, hamelia, heather, honeysuckle, ixora, jacobinia, jasmine, jessamine, lantana, ligustrum, Spanish lime, loquat, mango, mountain ebony, silk-oak, olive, papaya, pepper-tree, pomegranate, quisqualis, sapodilla, sapote, sage, strobilanthes, tabernaemontana, tamarind, tecoma, wisteria, and zizyphus. The scale—circular, moderately convex, white or grayish—mines partly into bark and epidermis of leaves and twigs.

Another mining scale, *Pseudaonidia clavigera,* has recently been reported in Florida on camellia, gardenia, jasmine, ligustrum, macadamia, osmanthus, pyracantha, oak, rhododendron, and viburnum. See also Camellia Mining Scale.

Newstead's Scale, *Lepidosaphes newsteadi* (Sulc). Reported in Florida, California, Mississippi on leaves of arborvitae, Florida cedar, cypress, junipers, pine, and retinospora. It is oystershell-shaped, moderately convex, light brown with terminal exuviae.

Nigra Scale, *Saissetia nigra* (Nietner). First noted as a citrus pest in California in 1900 and since found on 161 species of plants in that state. This is now general in subtropical regions. Florida hosts include andromeda, sweetbay, guava, hibiscus, mango, myrtle, pandanus, papaya, strobilanthes, Turks-cap and willow. It may be abundant on hibiscus but it is usually controlled by parasites—and the parasite introduced for the black scale makes it now unimportant in California. The scale is elongate-oval, slightly curved lengthwise, moderately convex or humpbacked, brown to brownish black, shiny.

Oak Eriococcus, *Eriococcus quercus* (Comstock). A mealybug in southern states, clustering on stems and leaves of blueberry, gallberry, ivy, oak and water oak. It has an oval, fluted sac.

Oak Kermes, *Kermes pubescens* Bogue. Oak Gall Scale. Distributed widely on oak in northern United States but more conspicuous than injurious. The females—globular, mottled light brown, ⅛ inch across—look more like hard galls along the leaf veins and terminal twigs than scales. Leaves are sometimes distorted, puckered, growth checked. The winter is spent on bark but in spring females migrate to leaves. The young are at first covered with a white pubescence.

Oak Lecanium, *Lecanium quercifex* Fitch. On oak in eastern United States. It is elliptical, quite convex, more or less tapering at ends, light to dark brown.

Oak Scale, *Chionaspis quercus* (Comstock). On oak, reported from Florida, California, New Mexico, and Texas. It is long, narrow at the exuvial end, widened at the posterior, convex, very small, light to dark gray, with yellow-brown exuviae.

Obscure Scale, *Chrysomphalus obscurus* (Comstock). On pecan, hickory, elm, hackberry, and oak, from Massachusetts to Florida and Arkansas. It is a special pest of pecans from Alabama to Texas and may occur on chestnut, chinquapin, dogwood, grape, plum, maple, soapberry, viburnum, willow, and wild myrtle. The female is roughly circular, grayish, closely resembling tree bark. The male is half her size. On pecans the infestation starts on lower and inner tree parts and gradually spreads up and out, killing many smaller branches, reducing vigor, making the tree more susceptible to attacks of other insects. There is 1 generation a year, with crawlers moving in June. Spray with a dormant oil emulsion (2 per cent for weak trees, 3 per cent for vigorous) in January or February before buds swell.

Oleander Scale*, *Aspidiotus hederae* (Vallot). Ivy Scale. Present throughout the warmer states and in houses and greenhouses in the North. As the names imply, it is especially serious on oleander and ivy, but it is an omnivorous feeder with a very long list of host plants, including century plant, cycads, palms, olive, lemon, orange, also acacia, aloe, aucuba, avocado, azalea, bay, blueberry, camellia, cactus, chinaberry, cocculus, dogwood, elaeagnus, fern, hibiscus, genista, holly, jasmine, ligustrum, magnolia, orchids, osmanthus, pepper-tree, poinsettia, periwinkle, persimmon, privet, rose, redbud, rubber-tree, yucca, tung-oil, verbena, vinca. The females are circular, somewhat flattened, pale yellow, sometimes with a purple tinge, 1/10 inch across. The males are much smaller, pure white, numerous. Heavily infested plants lose their color and vigor, may die.

Control. Prune out heavily encrusted branches. Spray for crawlers with malathion or summer oil. Parathion is satisfactory for commercial growers.

Olive Scale*, *Parlatoria oleae* (Colvée). Olive Parlatoria. An introduced pest estabished at 3 widely scattered points; near Baltimore, Maryland, on privet, and in California and Arizona. Since it was found in California in 1931 it has become a major agricultural pest, having been reported on 211 plant species, including, besides olive, almond, apricot, apple, peach, pear, plum. For many years the insect stayed on a few plants on the university campus at Tucson, Arizona, but after a series of mild winters it became established on many hosts, affecting twigs, leaves, fruits. Ornamental hosts include ash, Brazilian pepper, cotoneaster, elaeagnus, grape, English ivy, jasmine, Kentucky coffee tree, loquat, Chinese lilac, mulberry, oleander, palms, periwinkle, photinia, pomegranate, privet, pyracantha, rose, sage, trumpet-vine, tung-oil, viburnum, Virginia-creeper. The female shell is dirty-gray, ovate, circular, very small; the insect itself is purplish brown. The scales overwinter as adult females, with egg laying starting in late March. Hatching on deciduous fruit trees is in April, on olives in May. There are 2 generations.

Control. The most effective spray for commercial growers seems to be parathion applied with oil. Malathion injures young olive fruit but may be used on ornamentals. Many natural enemies have been liberated in olive orchards.

Orchid Scale, *Furcaspis biformis* (Cockerell). On orchids in the Miami, Florida area. Resembling the Florida red scale, nearly circular, very small, dark reddish brown, with somewhat lighter margin, exuviae central or subcentral.

Oriental Scale, *Aonidiella orientalis* Newstead. Sometimes a serious pest of coconut palms in Florida, also found on annona, avocado, banana, bay, bird-of-paradise, cactus, canna, carissa, carnation, chinaberry, croton, gerbera, date, elaeagnus, eucalyptus, fig, frangipani, golden-shower, guava, hibiscus, ivy, ixora, jasmine, mango, oleander, olive, orchid, palmetto, palms, persimmon, Natal plum, plumeria, rose, rubber, tabernaemontana, tamarind, tea plant, trumpet plant, and zamia. The scale is circular or oval, rather flat, light yellow-brown with lighter edges, polished, with central exuviae. It is mostly under control by natural enemies.

Osborn's Scale, *Aspidiotus osborni,* Newell & Cockerell. In southern states and as far north as Kansas and Ohio on grape and pecan. The shape is irregular, the color dirty-gray, the subcentral exuviae is orange but covered with secretion.

Oystershell Scale[+], *Lepidosaphes ulmi* (Linnaeus). Generally distributed on deciduous trees and shrubs, known to every gardener and fruit grower. As the name implies, the scales look like miniature oysters encrusted over trunks, limbs, twigs or on soft stems (Plate XXXIV). There are 3 color races of this scale with different life cycles. The gray race occurs on common lilac, beech, maple, willow, and many ornamentals. The scales are small, ⅛ inch long by 1/16 inch wide, broadened at the posterior end, usually curved, with many parallel cross ridges, acquiring a whitish bloom with age. There is only 1 brood, with crawlers appearing in June.

The brown race, the apple oystershell, is common on fruits—apple, apricot, pear, plum, quince, currant, fig, grape, raspberry, almond, and Persian walnut; it is also serious on dogwood, hybrid lilacs, boxwood, mountain-ash, horsechestnut. When old, the scales are very dark, almost black; there are 2 generations. The yellow-brown race has a yellow fringe on the rear portion, is common on birch and poplar, has a second brood in late July. Other plants that may be infested with oystershell scales are peony, ailanthus, alder, aspen, basswood, bittersweet, boxelder, boxwood, butternut, camellia, camphor, clematis, cotoneaster, elm, ginseng, hackberry, heather, holly, honeysuckle, Juneberry, locust, mountain-holly, New Jersey tea, oak, orchid, pachysandra, sassafras, spirea, sycamore, tamarisk, tulip-tree, viburnum, Virginia-creeper, yucca.

The winter is passed as elliptical, nearly white eggs under female shells; they hatch late in spring, late May or June. The young crawlers, whitish with 6 barely visible legs, move about for a few hours, then insert their beaks into the bark and start making the waxy scale covering. The brown and yellow-brown races mature about mid-July, when the tiny yellowish 2-winged males mate with the females. As the female deposits her eggs under the shell, her body gradually shrinks until death. With the brown and yellow-brown races the eggs hatch within 2 weeks; with the gray race, not until the next spring.

Control. Lilacs and other shrubs that almost always have this scale should have a dormant spray, 1 to 15 dilution of miscible oil, in spring before buds break, usually late March. A dinitro spray can be substituted. Malathion may be used later for crawling stages. Remove heavily encrusted and weak branches before spraying. There are many natural enemies—birds, mites, parasitic wasps, and predators.

Palmetto Scale, *Comstockiella sabalis* (Comstock). In Florida on palm and palmetto, also reported from California, Louisiana, Mississippi and Texas. It is circular, irregular when crowded, snow-white, with central exuviae.

Parlatoria Date Scale*, *Parlatoria blanchardi* (Targioni-Tozzetti). Date Palm Scale, a small gray-and-white scale, introduced from Egypt in 1890, a menace to the date industry of California and Arizona. An eradication campaign, started in 1922, was successfully concluded in 1934. This included destroying some infested trees, pruning others and searing them with a gasoline torch.

Parlatorialike Scale, *Pseudoparlatoria parlatorioides* (Comstock). In Florida, California, South Carolina, and Texas, sometimes serious on acalypha, alternanthera, avocado, bay, bignonia, blackberry, blueberry, camellia, camphor, carnation, coleus, fern, fig, flame vine, guava, hamelia, hibiscus, holly, honeysuckle, inkberry, ivy, ixora, jacobinia, jasmine, laurestinus, magnolia, oleander, tea-olive, orchid, palm, palmetto, papaya, pepper-tree, redbud, strawberry bush.

Peach Lecanium, *Lecanium persicae* (Fabricius). Widely distributed; found on peach, pear, plum, nectarine, also English ivy, ginkgo, gooseberry, grape, holly, Japanese quince, mulberry, rose, and silver thorn but not considered an important pest. Oval, moderately convex, 3 to 7 mm long, light to dark brown, sometimes sprinkled with white wax.

Peony Scale, *Pseudaonidia paeoniae* (Cockerell). Killing twigs and branches of azaleas and camellias in the South, sometimes present on ligustrum and other shrubs. The small brown convex shell is very inconspicuous, looking like a slight hump on the bark until the scale is rubbed off, or dies and falls off, leaving a conspicuous white circle on the twig. Crawlers, purple in color, are present in May; there is only 1 brood. Sprays are ineffective unless timed for crawlers, usually late May. Parathion is good and used by some nurserymen. Volck, at a 1 to 60 dilution, or malathion, will be safer for home gardeners.

Pineapple Scale*, *Diaspis bromeliae* Kerner. Tropical pineapple pest, also present in greenhouses; it infests cactus, canna, chalice vine, hibiscus, English ivy, jasmine, olive, orchids, palm, sago palm, and various tropical plants. It has a nearly round, thin, white or light-gray shell over an orange-yellow body with purplish tints.

Pine Needle Scale*, *Phenacaspis pinifoliae* (Fitch). A native, widely distributed, common in home plantings on nearly all species of pine and on various spruces; occasional on hemlock, fir, incense cedar; most prevalent east of the Mississippi River. The female is pure white, 1/10 inch long, widening toward the lower end, varying in shape according to the needle it is on. The male, 1/25 inch long, is white, with 4 parallel ridges. Pine branches infested with scale usually turn yellow. On small Austrian and mugho pines every leaf may be white with scales, the needles yellowing, the whole shrub unhealthy, or a single branch may be heavily infested and the rest free from scale (Plate XXXIII). Reddish eggs winter under the scales and start hatching in May, with a 2nd brood appearing in late July.

Control. Spray with lime-sulfur, 1 to 9 dilution, or with a dormant oil, evergreen strength, before new growth starts, or spray with malathion for crawlers in late May. When a single branch is infested, it can usually be pruned out without spoiling the shape too much. Lady beetles and some hymenopterous wasps share in control measures.

Pine Scales. Various other scales infest pines, including at least 14 species of the genus Matsucoccus. These are small, oval, yellow to brown, and inconspicuous, half buried in bark or needles. Some of these are treated separately. See Pinyon Pine Scale, Prescott Scale, Red-pine Scale. *Matsucoccus gallicolus* (Morrison) occurs in many states east of the Mississippi and on many species of pine, often heavily infesting pitch pine, browning needles near tip of branches, sometimes killing limbs. This species can be controlled by spraying with lime-sulfur or malathion when crawlers appear on new growth.

Matsucoccus paucicatrices Morrison injures and sometimes kills sugar pine in California, may also infest western white and limber pines in Oregon, Montana, and Wyoming.

Pine Tortoise Scale*, *Toumeyella numismaticum* Pettit & McDaniel. On Scotch, Austrian and jack pines in northern states, killing Christmas-tree pines in the Middle West. Females are reddish brown, oval, very convex. Heavily infested pines are coated with black sooty mold; there is heavy foliage drop; needles are shorter than normal; young trees may die. Another species (*T. pini* King), infesting mugho, lodgepole, Scotch and cluster pines is reported in Connecticut, Pennsylvania, Michigan, and Florida.

Pinyon Needle Scale, *Matsucoccus acalyptus* Herbert. Credited with killing hundreds of pinyon pines in Utah and Nevada, also present in other states.

Pit Scales. Small scales producing pits in bark or leaves. *Asterolecanium arabidis* (Signoret) occurs on English ivy, green ash, privet, pittosporum, sage. *A. minus* Lindinger lives in pits in bark of oak and has killed many chestnut oaks in Pennsylvania. It has recently been reported from North Carolina.

Prescott Scale, *Matsucoccus vexillorum* Morrison. Causing extensive killing of branches of ponderosa pine in the Southwest. The females settle on twigs, mainly at nodes, lay eggs, and cover them with fluffy white wax. Larvae feed beneath scales at base of needles and in cracks and crevices in twigs.

A **Privet Scale,** *Parlatoria pyri.* Recently reported from Washington, D.C., first in this country.

80. Purple scale on citrus fruit, with detail of oyster-shaped male and female.

Purple Scale*, *Lepidosaphes beckii* (Newman). The most important citrus pest in Florida and the Gulf States, outranked in California only by California red-and-black scales. It appeared in Florida in 1857 on lemons imported from Bermuda; it reached California in 1889 when 2 carloads of Florida orange trees were planted without previous disinfection. Besides citrus, purple scale infests allamanda, anise, avocado, banksia, bergamot, Barbados cherry, beauty bush, carissa, cassia, croton, dogwood, elaeagnus, eucalyptus, fig, magnolia, jessamine, euonymus, feijoa, eugenia, jasmine, jatropha, laurel, ligustrum, lilac, magnolia, mango, myrtle, pachysandra, oak, olive, orchid, passion-flower, pecan, sago palm, pepper-tree, periwinkle, pittosporum, plum, privet, Spanish bayonet, Spanish dagger, silver thorn, thunbergia, walnut, yucca, and other plants.

This is an armored scale, the female shaped like an oystershell, straight or curved, light to dark brown or purple, ⅛ inch long. The male is similar but smaller and narrower. Foliage turns yellow where scales have been feeding, may turn brown and fall out; fruit is stunted, ripening delayed, color and flavor affected; feeding wounds afford entrance to disease fungi. The female deposits from 40 to 80 pearly eggs under her shell which hatch in 2 weeks to 2 months. The pale nymphs crawl for a short time, seek a shaded location on bark or fruit, insert their beaks, and settle down, secreting 2 long protective threads. The females molt twice at 3- to 4-week intervals, becoming thicker and purplish or reddish brown. The male molts 4 times, emerging in 2 months as a 2-winged insect. There are 3 generations. Some sprays, notably those containing copper and zinc, increase populations of purple scale on citrus.

Control. Oil sprays are used in Florida from June 15 to July 15, or parathion is applied during the period from June through August. In California the nymphs are vulnerable to parathion in late July and August. There are many natural enemies, including the twice-stabbed lady beetle, Australian lady beetle, predaceous mites and hymenopterous parasites.

Pustule Scale, *Asterolecanium pustulans* (Cockerell). Severe in Florida on oleander and fig, in pits and pustules in stems and leaves. The scale is circular to oval, convex, rough, about 2 mm long, yellow-green to pale yellow. Other hosts include acacia, bay, bougainvillea, carissa, cassia, century plant, chinaberry, clerodendrum, clitoria, cork tree, cuphea, dombeya, eugenia, fig, flame vine, gardenia, geranium, grape, sea grape, gumbo-limbo, hackberry, hibiscus, holly, ivy, jacaranda, jacobinia, jasmine, lantana, mango, mountain ebony, mulberry, myrtle, silk-oak, oleander, Russian-olive, orchid, palm, passion-vine, peach, pear, persimmon, pithecolobium, plum, plumbago, poinciana, poinsettia, rose, Confederate rose, rubber-tree, sapodilla, stephanotis, strobilanthes, sumac, symphoricarpos, tabernaemontana, zizyphus.

Putnam Scale*, *Aspidiotus ancylus* (Putnam). Similar to San Jose scale but not so serious, found over most of the United States. It is circular, dark gray to nearly black, with brick-red exuviae, just off center. Basswood and soft maples are quite susceptible to this scale; it is also found on apple, ash, beech, blueberry, bladdernut, cherry, chestnut, currant, cranberry, dogwood, elm, gooseberry, hackberry, hawthorn, hickory, linden, locust, Osage-orange, oak, peach, pecan, persimmon, pear, plum, quince, snowball, tuliptree, willow, walnut.

Pyriform Scale*, *Protopulvinaria pyriformis* Cockerell. Distributed generally in Florida on a wide variety of hosts. The scale is broadly triangular or pear-shaped, greenish to brown with white egg sac appearing like a fringe around the margin. Food plants include acalypha, allamanda, aralia, prickly-ash, aspidistra, avocado, azalea, banana, bay, bignonia, bottle-brush, boxwood, Brazilian pepper-tree, bumelia, button-bush, cajeput, camellia, camphor, carissa, caryophyllus, ceriman, Barbados cherry, chinaberry, cinnamon, cassia, cocculus, coffee, croton, currant, gerbera, dracaena, elm, eucalpytus, eugenia, euonymus, feijoa, fig, frangipani, gardenia, guava, holly, honeysuckle, ivy, ixora, jasmine, jessamine, lantana, laurel, litchi, loquat, mango, mountain ebony, myrtle, silk-oak, oleander, palm, papaya, paradise tree, peach, phlox, privet, ricepaper-plant, rubber, sapodilla, sapota, sassafras, schefflera, serissa, soursop, sparkleberry, sumac, trumpet flower, and viburnum.

Quohog-shaped Scale, *Palinaspis quohogiformis* (Merrill). Shape similar to a quohog, very small, brownish, covered with sandlike material, attached at bud axils. Found in Florida but not economically important on acacia, bleeding-heart, bougainvillea, camellia, cotoneaster, croton, elder, fig, gardenia, grape, grevillea, hibiscus, honeysuckle, jacaranda, jasmine, ligustrum, litchi, mango, mignonette-tree, mountain ebony, mulberry, silk-oak, jessamine, pepper-tree, plum, poinciana, sandalwood, sapota, serissa, soapberry, tamarind, tecoma, thunbergia, trumpet creeper.

Red Bay Scale, *Chrysomphalus perseae* (Comstock). In southern states, also recorded in New Jersey. It is circular, flat, dark reddish or chocolate-brown, with dark gray central exuviae, very small. Plants infested in Florida include avocado, azalea, bay, blueberry, camphor, white cedar, Arizona and Italian cypress, feijoa, gordonia, hemlock, holly, ivy, Jacob's ladder, juniper, ligustrum, lyonia, magnolia, mangrove, oak, olive, orchid, osmanthus, palm, palmetto, pine, screwpine, retinospora, sparkleberry, yucca.

Red Date Scale*, *Phoenicococcus marlatti* (Cockerell). Common on date palm in California and Arizona but apparently not very injurious. The female is reddish purple, resting in, and somewhat enveloped by, cottony filaments. The male is wingless. Feed plants are restricted to 3 species of Phoenix palms.

Red-pine Scale, *Matsucoccus resinosae* Bean & Goodwin. First discovered in Connecticut in 1946, and on Long Island in 1950, this scale has been killing red pine in parts of New York and Connecticut and now has invaded New Jersey. There is first a slight yellowing of needles of current year's growth, then the foliage turns brick-red and the tree dies. Larvae and adults are small, inconspicuous, yellow to brown, hidden in bark or beneath needle fascicles. There are 2 generations, with eggs laid in May and late August. There is no practical control except to cut infested stands.

Red Wax Scale*, *Ceroplastes rubens* Maskell. First collected in Florida in 1955, considered eradicated but it has appeared again. It has infested aralia, philodendron, spindletree and breadfruit in the Miami area.

Rhodes-grass Scale*, *Antonina graminis* (Maskell). Destructive to lawns and golf courses in Florida and Texas. St. Augustine grass loses color and vigor. The scales are small, dark, covered with a white growth. They usually stay around nodes at base of grass blades; mature adults winter on roots. Crawlers are dark, lively, found on any part of grasses, and on any of 74 grass species. Parathion dust, 1 per cent, applied at rate of 50 pounds per acre, has been effective if repeated at 10-day intervals. Apply parathion as a spray at rate of ¼ pound active chemical per acre, in 2000 gallons of water.

Rhododendron Scale, *Aspidiotus pseudospinosus* Woglum. A small, circular, dirty-tan scale on rhododendron, covering stems and underside of leaves, with yellow spots appearing on upper leaf surfaces. This came into prominence in New Jersey following spraying of trees with DDT, although present before DDT came into use. The species is also recorded on ilex in Oklahoma. A dormant oil spray is fairly effective. Use malathion for crawlers in June or July.

Rose Scale*, *Aulacaspis rosae* (Bouché). Widely distributed wherever roses or bramble hosts are grown. The round, flat, white female shells, covering orange or pinkish bodies and red eggs, ⅕ inch across, are very conspicuous on canes, which often appear as if whitewashed. The males are small, narrow, snow-white. Blackberry, loganberry, raspberry, dewberry, thimbleberry, and related plants may be infested. Climbing roses and neglected hybrid perpetuals are more likely to be attacked than hybrid teas pruned low each spring, but now that rosarians prefer more moderate pruning, scale may become a problem here too. In New York, eggs hatch in late May or June with a 2nd generation in August.

Control. If roses are sprayed with lime-sulfur at 1 to 9 dilution directly after pruning in spring (provided buds have not opened more than ¼ inch) rose scale is readily controlled. For climbers near painted surfaces a dormant oil will have to be substituted or else malathion for crawlers, but in my experience neither is as effective as lime-sulfur. Prune out heavily infested canes.

Rose Palaeococcus, *Palaeococcus rosae* R. & H. A kind of mealybug, yellowish with short waxy filaments around the body. Reported from Key West on sugar-apple, Otaheite gooseberry, rose, and sapodilla.

Rufous Scale, *Selenaspidus articulatus* (Morgan). In Florida on acacia, sugar-apple, avocado, banana, bauhinia, citrus, croton, fig, gumbo-limbo, jacaranda, jasmine, ligustrum, Spanish lime, mountain ebony, oleander, palm, pine, hog-plum, pomegranate, rose, rubber, sapodilla, tamarind. The scale is circular, slightly convex, semitransparent, gray to yellow brown with lighter margin, central exuviae, copper-colored.

San Jose Scale*, *Aspidiotus perniciosus* Comstock. Probably from China, first discovered at San Jose, California, in 1880, now present in every state. It is particularly injurious to deciduous fruit trees, often causing death if left unchecked. Fruit hosts include apple, pear, quince, peach, plum, prune, apricot, nectarine, sweet cherry, blackberry, currant, gooseberry. Ash, mountain-ash, poplar, hawthorn, lilac, linden, elm, willow are also subject to injury. Other hosts include acacia, actinidia, akebia, alder, almond, arborvitae, beech, birch, false bittersweet, button-bush, buckthorn, catalpa, ceanothus, chestnut, cotoneaster, dogwood, elder, eucalyptus, euonymus, fig, hackberry, hibiscus, honeysuckle, locust, loquat, maple, mulberry, pecan, orange,

Osage-orange, persimmon, photinia, privet, Japanese quince, rose, sassafras, shadbush, silver thorn, smokebush, snowball, snowberry, spirea, sour-gum, strawberry, sumac, Virginia-creeper, English walnut, willow.

The female is yellowish, covered with a gray, circular, waxy scale, 1/16 inch in diameter, elevated in the center into a nipple surrounded by a yellow ring. Young scales are small and nearly black. The male is oblong-oval, acquires 2 wings. Young scales winter on bark, becoming full-grown when apples bloom. After mating, females give birth to living young, crawlers with 6 legs which move over the bark until they find a suitable place to insert their mouth parts. There are 2 to 6 generations a year, depending on location. The scale is spread by being carried on bodies of birds and larger insects and through shipments of nursery stock. Bark on trees is often reddened around the scales, which may be so numerous they overlap, completely covering a branch. On fruit they form gray patches at blossom and stem ends; there is often a red, inflamed area around each scale.

Control. Lime-sulfur first came into use as a dormant spray for the control of San Jose scale, and it may still be used in some places at a 1 to 9 dilution before buds break in spring. However, as early as 1914 the scale started to show some resistance to lime-sulfur, so oil sprays have been used, sometimes combined with bordeaux mixture. When orchardists started using DDT for codling moth they noted a decrease in San Jose scale, enough so that dormant sprays could be omitted in some cases. A summer program of DDT and parathion is sometimes used commercially. But if DDT is not used in cover sprays, a dormant spray is practically obligatory. Malathion, Guthion, or Sevin may replace parathion for the crawling stage; the latter should not be used on McIntosh and related varieties.

Scurfy Scale*, *Chionaspis furfura* (Fitch). A native pest of deciduous fruit and ornamental trees, widely distributed in the United States. The female is grayish white, rounded at one end so it is rather pear-shaped, ⅛ inch long. The male is smaller, snow-white, narrow, with 3 longitudinal ridges (Plate XXXIV). Food plants include pear, apple, quince, cherry, gooseberry, currant, black raspberry, peach and many shade trees, such as mountain-ash, white and prickly-ash, aspen, black walnut, elm, hawthorn, hickory, horsechestnut, maple, willow. The scales are abundant on bark, giving it a scurfy appearance; they infest foliage and may spot fruit. Scurfy scale is most often present on shaded parts of trees in neglected orchards where foliage is too dense; it is not so important on trees receiving good care.

Reddish-purple eggs winter on bark under female shells, hatching in late spring, May or June, after trees are in full leaf. Purple crawlers move about for a few hours, then settle down on bark. There are 2 generations in the southern range, with eggs of the summer brood laid in July; overwintering eggs are laid in late August and September. There is only 1 brood in the North.

Control. A 3 or 4 per cent dormant oil spray is usually effective. In some spray programs this is supplemented with dinitro compounds to kill the eggs. Spraying with DDT or parathion kills crawlers.

Soft Azalea Scale, *Pulvinaria ericicola* McConnell. On azalea, rhododendron, and huckleberry in District of Columbia, Maryland, New York, and Florida. The elongate, oval, reddish brown body is covered with glassy wax and has a prominent white egg sac.

Soft Scale. See Brown Soft Scale.

Sour-gum Scale, *Phenacaspis nyssae* (Comstock). On gums and hornbeam in Florida, Georgia, Indiana, North Carolina and Texas. The scale is nearly triangular, flat, delicate, snow-white, with light-yellow terminal exuviae.

Spirea Scale, *Ericoccus borealis*. Occasionally infesting spirea. It is a white mealybug in forks of branches; it resembles azalea bark scale.

Spruce Bud Scale*, *Physokermes piceae* (Schrank). A special pest of Norway spruce but present on other species, distributed from New England to Maryland and Minnesota. Mature scales are ⅛ inch across, round, gall-like, reddish brown with flecks of yellow, dusted with powdery wax, situated in clusters of 3 to 5 at base of branchlets, and so closely resembling spruce buds they are difficult to detect. Infestation is at tips of lower branches. Great quantities of honeydew attract bees and form a medium for black mold. Young insects are born in June or July, winter as partly grown scales. There is 1 generation. Use a dormant oil spray in spring before growth starts or nicotine or malathion for crawlers.

Sweetgum Scale, *Cryptophyllaspis liquidambaris* Kotinsky. On sweetgum, recorded from Florida, Georgia, Mississippi, Louisiana, Texas, Ohio, District of Columbia, and New York. The minute, circular to oval female, lemon yellow, lives in a pit on lower side of leaf. The area above becomes a small, rough, conical mound. The pits are usually near intersection of veins and midrib.

Sycamore Scale, *Stomacoccus platani* Ferris. Occurring naturally on native sycamore in California and now a serious pest of introduced Oriental plane. The female is dark yellow, 1/16 inch long. It winters on bark of trunk and branches, protected by loose cottony threads. Nymphs migrate to leaves and mature there, causing brown spots, sometimes distortion and defoliation, but they return to trunk and limbs for egg laying. There are 3 generations, with young scales becoming active in late January which is the best time for a spray. A medium oil is used with toxaphene, DDT or benzene hexachloride. Parathion can be used in nurseries but is too dangerous for street trees.

Tea Scale*, *Fiorinia theae* Green. The most important camellia insect in the Deep South, not so serious in California; sometimes found on greenhouse camellias in the North. Although the scales are on underside of foliage, infested camellias can be told at a distance by yellowish blotches on upper leaf surface, generally unhealthy appearance of the whole plant, premature dropping of leaves. Bloom is decreased, cuttings may die before roots develop. The scale is as serious on Chinese holly as on camellias in some

81. Tea scale on camellia, showing brown females and nymphs covered with white cotton on underside of leaf and yellowing of upper leaf surface.

parts of the South and may at times infest bottle-brush, dogwood, euonymus, ferns, mango, palms (? perhaps misidentified), figs, Satsuma orange, orchids, tea plant, yaupon.

The female is at first thin, light yellow, later hard, brown, elongate-oval or boat-shaped, 1/16 inch long, with the residue from the first molt attached at one end. Yellow eggs, 10 to 16, are held under the shell. The male is soft, white, narrow, with a ridge down the middle. Both scales are held in a conspicuous tangle of white, cottony threads; often the entire undersurface of the leaf is white, dotted with small brown female shells. The eggs hatch in 7 to 21 days, depending on the weather. Flat yellow crawlers move to new growth, attach themselves after 2 or 3 days, secreting first a thin white covering, later the many white threads. The 1st molt is in 18 to 36 days, the 2nd a week later; egg laying starts 41 to 65 days after birth. There are many overlapping broods, so that crawlers and young nymphs are present on foliage at any time between March and November in Alabama.

Control. The standard recommendation for many years was a spray in spring right after blooming, when cold weather was past, with a white oil emulsion such as Florida Volck, using 6 level tablespoons per gallon, hitting the underside of leaves with great force. Parathion was then used effectively by commercial growers but was too dangerous for home gardeners. Now we have a safer phosphate, dimethoate, which seems to be particularly effective for tea scale on camellias, although it may not be quite so safe on Chinese holly. Use 1 teaspoon of Cygon to a gallon of water and apply 2 foliar sprays 6 weeks apart, the first soon after new growth starts in spring. After the first year 1 annual application may be sufficient. Cygon may also be used as a soil drench, 2 tablespoons to 1 gallon of water for plants up to 6 feet tall.

Terrapin Scale*, *Lecanium nigrofasciatum* (Pergand). Black-banded Scale. A native insect widely distributed over eastern states and Canada. It is a branch-and-twig scale, attacking common fruit trees, many shade trees, and shrubs. A partial list of hosts includes maple, sycamore, boxelder, hawthorn as preferred food plants, with occasional infestation on ash, cottonwood, European plane, mulberry, linden, live oak, redbud, willow. Florida hosts include bay, blueberry, buckthorn, bumelia, gum, holly, jasmine, cherry-laurel, lime, maple, saffron-plum, sparkleberry. The soft, unarmored female is nearly hemispherical, ⅛ inch in diameter, dark reddish brown, smooth, shining, with 10 or 12 dark bands radiating from the high center of the back to the fluted edges. Partly grown females winter on twigs, reach full size in June when they give birth to living young. Each nymph leaves the mother for a day or two, migrates to a leaf for 6 weeks, then moves back to a branch, where it is fertilized by a minute winged male. When scales are numerous, twigs are said to give off a putrid odor. The drain on the tree is serious; smaller branches die; foliage is thin; sooty mold grows in quantity in honeydew, covering trunk and branches and dropping to sidewalks.

Control. There are many predaceous and parasitic insect enemies. Lime-sulfur has little effect but a dormant miscible oil, applied as late in spring as possible before buds burst is satisfactory.

Tesselated Scale, *Eucalymnatus tessellatus* (Signoret). Palm Scale. A tropical tortoise species appearing in greenhouses on many kinds of palms, orchids, and other plants, found mostly on leaves, rarely on bark. Plants infested outdoors in Florida include allamanda, avocado, banana, bay, bottlebrush, cactus, cajeput, carissa, Chinese paper-plant, cinnamon, dracaena, eugenia, feijoa, fig, gardenia, gingerlily, guava, holly, yaupon, ivy, ivora, jasmine, jessamine, laurel, litchi, mango, ribbonbush, myrtle, oleander, palms, sapota, soursop, strobilanthes, tabernaemontana, thunbergia, and viburnum. The scale resembles brown soft scale but it is larger, darker brown, and the surface is marked with pale lines to form a mosaic. In Florida the friendly fungus *Cephalosporium lecanii* helps to keep it under control.

Tuliptree Scale*, *Toumeyella liriodendri* (Gmelin). Liriodendron Scale. Probably a native, noted as injurious in Michigan in 1870. It is distributed over the United States east of the Rocky Mountains, on tuliptrees for the most part, sometimes on magnolia and linden. In Florida it may be serious on magnolia and also infests banana shrub, bay, button-bush, fig, cape-jasmine, and walnut. One of the largest of the soft scales, the female is ⅓ inch across, very convex, hemispherical, a dark, rich brown. Scales are usually crowded together and somewhat distorted along the twigs and branches. The winter is spent as small, partly grown nymphs, brown with lighter ridges, clinging tightly to twigs. They grow fast in spring and produce young by August. There is 1 generation. Parasites often keep this scale under control. Spray with a dormant oil emulsion in spring. During the season large scales can be scrubbed off twigs or small trees with a rag or brush and soapy water. Malathion may be used for crawlers.

Utah Cedar Scale, *Aonidia shastae* Coleman. Redwood Scale. Very small, thin, dirty-white, transparent, cone-shaped. Found on redwood leaves in California, on cedar in Kansas and Utah.

Walnut Scale*, *Aspidiotus juglans-regiae* Comstock. A European scale found on a wide variety of trees and shrubs, including English, Persian, and Japanese walnuts, almond, apple, apricot, ash, azalea, bay, boxwood, box-elder, cherry, cherry-laurel, coralberry, cottonwood, currant, dogwood, elder-berry, elm, gallberry, sweetgum, gordonia, haw, holly, honeysuckle, hack-berry, laurel, horsechestnut, linden, locust, maple, oak, peach, pear, plum, prune, pecan, persimmon, tuliptree, pyracantha, redbud, rose, spiraea, sumac and viburnum. The female is mottled orange, covered with a flat, nearly circular, gray to reddish-brown shell, ⅛ inch in diameter. Spraying thoroughly with lime-sulfur, 1 to 8 dilution, just before buds expand in spring has been recommended in the past.

White Peach Scale*, *Pseudaulacaspis pentagona* (Targioni-Tozzetti) West Indian Peach Scale. Present from Florida north to Maryland and occasionally farther up the coast. It is an armored scale attacking privet, walnut, flowering peach, cherry, lilac, catalpa, and various fruits—peach, plum, cherry, pear, apricot, grape, and persimmon. Other Florida hosts include abelia, alla-manda, ash, boxwood, buddleia, chaste-tree, Jersualem-cherry, chinaberry, cotoneaster, deutzia, dogwood, elaeagnus, Chinese elm, fig, fringe tree, ger-anium, gold-dust tree, goldenrain-tree, holly, honeysuckle, hypericum, cherry-laurel, English laurel, laurestinus, ligustrum, magnolia, mountain ebony, mul-berry, sweetolive, orchid, palm, Brazilian pepper, redbud, photinia, Scotch broom, spiraea, sumac, tung-oil, and walnut. The female is 1/10 inch, light gray or dingy white, with yellow exuviae; the male is elongated, pure white. The scales are often clustered at base of branches, which die. There are several generations, on bark, leaf, and fruit. Sometimes serious, it is mostly controlled by parasites. A dormant spray may be advisable.

Woolly Pine Scale. See Cottony Pine Scale.

Willow Scurfy Scale, *Chionaspis salicis-nigrae* (Walsh). A common scale on willow in Middle Atlantic states, also infesting poplar, dogwood, shad-bush, tuliptree, alder, ceanothus. The female is large, white, somewhat pear-shaped but broadest at the middle; the male is long, narrow, snow-white. Purple eggs winter under the female shell; there are 2 generations. Willow twigs and branches may be coated with scales. Both branches and young trees may die. Spray with lime-sulfur at dormant strength or oil just before buds break.

Yellow Scale, *Aonidiella citrina* (Coquillett). Almost identical with Cali-fornia red scale except for yellow color and the fact it is found only on foliage and smaller twigs.

Yew Scale. See Cottony Taxus Scale.

Zamia Scale, *Diaspis zamiae* Morgan. Reddish with a prominent convex shield which is waxy with marked radial stripes.

SLUGS AND SNAILS

Slugs and snails are not insects but mollusks, belonging, along with oysters, clams, and other shellfish, to the large animal phylum Mollusca, characterized by individuals which have soft, unsegmented bodies, usually protected with a hard calcareous shell. They are in the class Gastropoda, containing forms that have a univalve shell or none, and in the order Stylommatophora. A slug is merely a snail without a shell, or with a shell reduced and located internally (Plate XXIX).

Snails have two pairs of tentacles or feelers, a large pair above, bearing eyes at the tips, and a smaller pair below, used for smelling. The mouth is in the center of the head, below the lower pair of tentacles, and below that is the opening of a large mucous or slime gland. The soft visceral hump contains most of the internal organs. Over this is formed the shell, secreted by the mantle which forms a fold where the shell joins the body or "foot" of the snail. On the right side, under the edge of the mantle, is the breathing pore with the anus immediately in back of that. The foot contains mucous glands and muscles by which the animal crawls. When disturbed it may withdraw entirely into the shell. It can even become dormant under unfavorable circumstances, sealing the opening of the shell with a mucous sheet, the operculum, which soon hardens to a leathery texture. Snails have been known to remain dormant as long as 4 years.

Slugs are much like snails in structure but they lack the visceral hump and shell. The mantle is a smooth area in the anterior 4th or 3rd of the back. Slugs range in length from ¼ inch to 8 or 10 inches, in color from whitish yellow to black, usually mottled. Without the protection of a shell they need damp places and are usually found in the daytime under decaying boards and logs or any debris around the garden. They feed at night by rasping holes, their mouths being equipped with a horny file, the radula. Although more than 30 species of slugs and several hundred species of snails have been recorded in this country, only a few are of economic importance.

Metaldehyde baits and sometimes dusts and sprays are standard for slug control. Chlordane is also used and more recently Sevin, either alone or as a bait with metaldehyde. At this writing Zectran is a very promising control.

An introduced slug, *Arion ater* (Linnaeus), that has not been given an official common name is now abundant in the Pacific Northwest. First reported in Oregon in 1942, it has become the dominant species in certain areas in Washington, is important in California and has been recorded from Michigan and Kansas. The slugs interfere with commercial production of narcissus bulbs, are a serious strawberry pest, and are generally a nuisance on flowers and vegetables in home gardens, feeding at night. They are hard to control. Metaldehyde baits are somewhat effective and so is a band of metaldehyde dust around a flower bed, so placed that the slugs must cross it in nocturnal movements.

Banded Wood Snail*, *Cepaea nemoralis* (Linnaeus). In flower gardens in parts of the South, also noted in Utah. The shell is conspicuous, light yellow with longitudinal chocolate-brown striping, 1 inch across.

Brown Garden Snail*, *Helix aspersa* (Müller). European Brown Snail, distributed over the world, known in California since 1850, where it is thought to have been deliberately "planted" for food purposes from stock brought from France. It is now very numerous in citrus orchards, is a pest on avocado. It eats holes in citrus leaves, makes pits or scars on fruit, covers tree trunks with shells. It feeds on avocado foliage, blossoms, and young fruits, scarring the latter. This snail is also important in flower and vegetable gardens, is destructive to grasses, shrubs, and trees. Most serious on the Pacific Coast, it also occurs in many parts of the South.

Full-grown shells have 4½ to 5 whorls, are 1¼ to 1½ inches in diameter. They are grayish yellow with brown applied in 5 bands. The mouth is surrounded by fleshy lips but inside there is a chitinous jaw to cut or scrape off food. White, spherical eggs are laid in a nest in the soil. Young snails have only 1 whorl; they take 2 years to reach maturity.

Control. Hand-pick snails; surround trees with a barrier of lime on the soil which acts as an irritant and keeps snails from walking through it. Broadcast poison baits of arsenic or metaldehyde or both, in pellet form, around the "skirts" of trees, following rains or irrigation, when there is plenty of moisture present. If many small snails are feeding, it may be helpful to spray the tree with tartar emetic.

Citrus Tree Snail, *Drymaeus dormani* (Binney). Manatee Snail, believed by some Florida growers to be helpful in a biological control program. They may reduce enemies of beneficial insects and they clean up plants by feeding on sooty-mold fungi and algae.

Grass Snail, *Vallonia pulchella* (Müller).

Gray Field Slug*, *Deroceras laeve* (Müller). Fern Snail. Dark gray or buff to black, ½ to 1 inch long. It is common in lawns and fields and sometimes in greenhouses. There it hides in soil during the day but at night eats parenchyma tissue from the underside of fern leaves. Spray underside of fronds with nicotine sulfate and soap early in the morning; remove slugs by hand.

Gray Garden Slug*, *Deroceras reticulatum* (Müller). True Garden Slug. Very common, small, averaging ¾ inch, never over 1½ inches, hiding in small cracks and crevices. The color varies from white to pale yellow, lavender, purple or nearly black with brown specks and mottlings. This is one of the worst pests of garden and field crops, especially in humid regions.

Greenhouse Slug*, *Milax gagates* (Linnaeus). Widely distributed, very destructive. It is a uniform black to dark gray with a longitudinal ridge down the body and a diamond-shaped mark in the center, 1½ to 3 inches long. It shows some preference for coleus, cineraria, geranium, marigold, and snapdragon. A 15 per cent metaldehyde dust has been used for floricultural crops.

Greenhouse Snails, *Oxychilus* spp. Four species of snails are common in greenhouses and cellars throughout the United States. The shell is a uniform gray or brown, with a very flat coil, ½ inch in diameter.

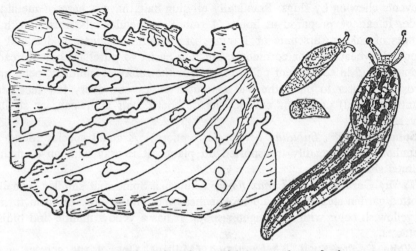

82. Spotted garden slug and injury to hosta leaf.

Spotted Garden Slug*, *Limax maximus* Linnaeus. Giant Slug. Ranging from 1½ to 7 inches, averaging 3 to 5 inches. The smaller slugs are often a uniform dark gray or black, the larger are yellow gray or brown mottled with black, usually with 3 rows of black spots extending from the mantle to the rear end of the body; the mantle is yellowish with black spots. The eggs are oval, translucent light yellow with a tough elastic outer membrane. They are laid in masses of 25 or more, held together with a mucilaginous substance, under boards, trash, or flowerpots, in compost piles, under stones or in other damp places, any time from spring to fall outdoors, also in winter in greenhouses. The eggs hatch in about 28 days at room temperature, sooner at high temperatures. The young slug is dull white, less than ½ inch long, thin; it darkens and develops slowly. In a month it is an inch long, dark brown, with spots beginning to show. It usually takes more than a year to develop full size.

Working mostly at night, these slugs extend their slimy length over leaves, eating large ragged holes, leaving behind a viscous trail of slime. Slugs are among the earliest pests to start chewing in gardens, and they keep on until late in the autumn. Hollyhock leaves almost always show slug holes in early spring, as do primroses, iris, saxifrage, violets, and many other plants with foliage close to the ground. Slugs also like to hide in cabbage and lettuce heads.

Control. Cleaning up the garden to get rid of hiding places is always effective. Removing old iris leaves after first frost not only outwits borers, it makes slugs homeless. Shingles in the garden will trap slugs, ready for mass execution. They hate to crawl through anything dusty or scratchy, so a circle of lime or cinders or even sharp sand around a plant is a deterrent. Chlordane dust helps some. Spraying or dusting plants with lead arsenate prevents chewing by slugs. Practically all slug baits have a base of metaldehyde. It can be prepared at home (1 ounce of metaldehyde mixed with 2 ounces of calcium arsenate or 1 ounce of sodium fluosilicate and added to 2 pounds wheat bran or cornmeal), but it is easier to purchase baits already prepared and in convenient pellet form. For the safety of children, pets, and birds, it is wiser to place the bait (about a tablespoon every few feet near plants attacked) under jar covers, bits of board, half a tin can, or similar cover.

Subulina Snail*, *Subulina octona* (Bruguiere). A small species found in greenhouses and readily transported on plants; it is gray with an elongate, pointed shell.

Tawny Garden Slug*, *Limax flavus* Linnaeus. Somewhat smaller than the spotted garden slug, seldom up to 4 inches, and with a more uniform tawny or yellowish color with faint lighter spots. It has a yellow mantle and bluish tentacles.

White Garden Snail, *Theba pisana* (Müller). One of the species used as food in Europe. It has a white shell with irregular darker mottlings, a little smaller than the brown garden snail. It became established in California in 1914 as an important pest of citrus, but infestations have been eradicated, as they appeared in various counties, by quarantines, inspection, handpicking in residential areas, cutting and burning infested wild vegetation, flaming of rocks and soil, and use of calcium arsenate-bran bait.

SOWBUGS AND PILLBUGS

The words sowbug and pillbug are used rather interchangeably for soil pests related to crayfish. They are in the class Crustacea, which includes arthropods having 2 pairs of antennae and at least 5 pairs of legs. They have flat, oval, brown bodies about ½ inch long, with 7 pairs of legs on the thoracic segments and with the abdominal segments fused and compressed (Plate XXIX). One species, the common **Pillbug** *Armadillidum vulgare* (Latrielle) also called Roly-poly, has a habit of rolling up into a ball like an armadillo, which it resembles in miniature.

The **Dooryard Sowbug,** *Porcellio laevis* Koch, does not roll up when disturbed. The female sowbug has a ventral pouch known as a marsupium.

The eggs are laid in it and held for about 2 months, and then the young, 25 to 75 in a brood, stay in the pouch for some time longer. Young sowbugs are similar to adults; they take a year to mature.

Sowbugs and pillbugs breathe by means of gills and prefer damp, protected places. They are found as scavengers on rotting plant parts, under flowerpots or decayed boards, or in manure, and they may be quite injurious to seedlings—eating roots, girdling the young stems. They are mostly greenhouse problems, although commonly present in garden soil. Occasionally they damage tender growth of field or garden crops.

Control. A poison bait of 1 part Paris green to 9 of sugar was long recommended for greenhouses, and a calcium arsenate dust for the garden. These have been largely replaced by newer chemicals. Spray soil surface and greenhouse benches with malathion or Sevin, or dust with 5 per cent DDT or 2 per cent lindane or chlordane.

SPANWORMS

Spanworms are caterpillars with the looper or measuring-worm habit, and some have already been discussed under Caterpillars.

Bruce Spanworm*, *Operophthera bruceata* (Hulst). In northern states on sugar maple, poplar, birch, with serious outbreaks reported in Vermont and Wisconsin. The larva, ¾ inch long, is bright green with three narrow yellowish-white stripes. The male moth is gray with flecks of brown, 1⅛-inch wing expanse; the female is brownish gray, wingless. She lays eggs in November in bark crevices and these hatch in early spring. There is 1 generation.

Cleft-headed Spanworm, *Amphidasis cognataria* Guenée. Pepper and Salt Moth. The larva is about 2 inches long, with deeply cleft head, greenish to reddish brown, with tubercles, resembling twigs of its food plant. The adult is dull white, sprinkled with brown or black. This species occurs in the Atlantic States, feeding on willow, poplar, wild cherry, sweetfern, apple, locust and other deciduous trees.

Cranberry Spanworm*, *Anavitrinella pampinaria* (Guenée).

Currant Spanworm*, *Itame ribearia* (Fitch). Present in various parts of the East and in Colorado, feeding on currants and gooseberries, sometimes blueberries. The worms are light yellow with many prominent black dots, just over an inch long. Like other loopers, they drop down on a silken thread when disturbed. Sometimes they are numerous enough to defoliate bushes. The moths have slender bodies with broad yellow wings marked with black. Eggs are laid in stems in summer, hatching the next spring when leaves are out. Use rotenone sprays or dusts.

Elm Spanworm*, *Ennomos subsigniarius* (Hübner). Snow-white Linden Moth. Found from New England to Georgia and west to Colorado. Before

1880 this species was very abundant around New York and Philadelphia; about 1910 it was numerous in forest areas in the Catskills; there was a major outbreak in Massachusetts in 1914 and in Connecticut in 1938. It is a particular pest in cities, and in outbreak years it defoliates maple, beech, linden, elm, horsechestnut, yellow birch and other trees, but there are long periods between epidemics. The worm is about 1½ inches long, brownish black, with head and anal segments bright red. The moth is frail, pure white, wings expanding to 1¼ to 1½ inches. Eggs are laid about midsummer, in groups on branches, and do not hatch until the next spring. Larvae begin at once to devour foliage, grow rapidly, and pupate in a loose cocoon in a crumpled leaf. When moths appear in late July they migrate long distances, appearing in cities like a summer snowstorm.

Control. The English sparrow is credited with doing a grand job of ridding cities of this pest, helped along by at least 2 insect parasites. In years of peak infestation trees should be sprayed with lead arsenate or DDT as they come into full leaf.

Walnut Spanworm, *Coniodes plumogeraria* (Hulst). Similar to the spring cankerworm, found in Pacific Coast states. The larvae are pinkish gray varied with darker gray, or black and yellow.

SPITTLEBUGS

Spittlebugs are sucking insects of the order Hemiptera (suborder Homoptera), family Cercopidae. They are not true bugs but rather closely related to leafhoppers and are sometimes called froghoppers. The adults are drab brown, gray or black, sometimes marked with yellow, and they look rather like short, robust leafhoppers. Antennae and 2 ocelli are situated between the eyes. Hind tibiae are smooth with only 1 or 2 heavy spines on their outer sides and clusters of small ones at the extremities. They hop away but do not fly very much. They insert eggs in plant stems or between stem and leaf sheath in grasses.

The remarkable thing about spittlebugs is the frothy mass (children call it frog spit) enveloping the nymphs. This spittle is a combination of a fluid voided from the anus and a mucilaginous substance excreted by glands on the 7th and 8th abdominal segments, mixed with air drawn in between a pair of plates under the abdomen. The mixture is forced out under pressure, as from a bellows, to make uniform bubbles. The tail, going up and down, operates the bellows and keeps the bubbles coming. As soon as the first bubbles are formed, the nymph reaches back with its legs and hooks onto the globules, dragging them forward to its head. The greenish nymph is soon hidden under a mound of snow-white foam, protected from sun and preying insects. Many spittlebugs are relatively harmless but several are economically injurious to plants.

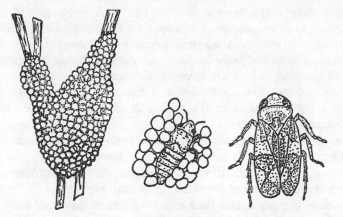

83. Spittlebug on grass blades: frothy "spittle"; nymph in bubbles; adult without protection.

Alder Spittlebug*, *Clastoptera obtusa* (Say). Ceanothus Spittlebug. On alder and ceanothus, other hosts.

Cranberry Spittlebug, *Clastoptera vittata* Ball.

Dogwood Spittlebug*, *Clastoptera proteus* Fitch. Blueberry Spittlebug. Causing frothy masses on twigs.

Lined Spittlebug*, *Philaenus lineatus* (Linnaeus). Related to the meadow spittlebug.

Meadow Spittlebug*, *Philaenus spumarius=P. leucophthalmus* (Linnaeus). The most important species, damaging strawberries especially, alfalfa and other forage crops, but feeding on 400 species of garden and forage plants and very widespread. Chrysanthemums, stock, and other flowers in greenhouses and gardens may be seriously stunted. Strawberry fruit is distorted, small, and the plant greatly weakened. This pest is most serious in regions of high humidity, the Northeast and in Oregon. Adults— ¼ inch long, pale straw to dark brown, with blunt heads, prominent eyes— appear in late May or June and live until fall, with only 1 generation a year. Eggs are deposited in late August and September.

Control. Spray alfalfa and other forage crops with methoxychlor as young nymphs hatch and in late summer to prevent oviposition. Seedling plants, where residue is not a problem, can be sprayed with endrin or heptachlor. Lindane and DDT can be used on ornamentals.

Pecan Spittlebug*, *Clastoptera achatina* Germar. The frothy mass is found on young nuts and on tender shoots in spring and early summer. Pecan trees have been injured in Illinois, although this species is not considered a serious pest in the South. There are 2 broods, May and July. Dieldrin and benzene hexachloride have been effective in Illinois; parathion has been used in Florida.

Pine Spittlebug*, *Aphrophora parallela* (Say). A native pest of pine from New England to Arkansas, most injurious on Scotch pine but also infesting white, pitch, red, jack, and Virginia pines, and Norway spruce. Eggs are laid at base of terminal buds in July and August, hatch in May, and the young feed on twigs, which are covered with spittle. The insects continually eject undigested sap like light rain, and branches are covered with black sooty mold. Scotch pine may die within 2 or 3 years. Spray with DDT in oil, lindane, or chlordane.

Saratoga Spittlebug*, *Aphrophora saratogensis* (Fitch). From New England to Florida and west to the Great Lakes states, seriously damaging jack and red pine. The nymphs live on sweetfern, willow, brambles and other plants, below the surface of the litter in forests and above the root collar. Adults migrate to pine in late June and July, where they feed until October, extracting large quantities of sap. They are tan with lighter markings forming a diamond pattern. The nymphs have a bright-red abdomen during the first 4 instars, in the 5th instar are brown. Control with DDT, lindane, or chlordane.

Sunflower Spittlebug, *Clastoptera xanthocephala* Germar.

There are many other spittlebugs that have as yet no common name. *Clastoptera arizona* has become such a nuisance on acacia trees in California that they are sometimes cut down. *Clastoptera arborina* is abundant on junipers in Colorado, is reported on arborvitae and redcedar in Indiana; *C. elongatus* appears on chokecherry in New Mexico and *C. lawsoni* on grapevines.

Becoming a problem on holly is *Prosapia bicincta* (Say), found from Massachusetts to Florida and west to Kansas and Texas. The adults, a bit larger than most spittlebugs, are dark brown with 2 lighter bands across the wings. The nymphs frequent many grasses, including Centipede, Bermuda, and St. Augustine, and these tend to dry out. The adults feeding on holly distort, stunt, or discolor new foliage and cause light blotches on underside of older leaves.

SPRINGTAILS

Springtails belong to the insect order Collembola, a group of small insects less than ⅕ inch long, without wings and with almost no metamorphosis. They have chewing or piercing mouth parts and short antennae with few segments. They can jump incredible distances by means of a forked appendage, the furcula, which is folded forward under the abdomen when at rest. Under the first abdominal segment there is a short, tubelike structure believed to have a respiratory function. There are more than 2000 species distributed from the Arctic to the Antarctic in damp places. About 70 of these attack seeds and seedlings, mushrooms, sugar cane, and invade houses but only 1 species is usually considered in garden literature. Some species congregate on the surface of snow and are called "snowfleas"; others live on surface of ponds or on sea beaches; others are in leaf mold or decaying material. In fact, springtails are around us most of the time, but they are so small we seldom notice them.

84. Garden springtail.

Garden Springtail*, *Bourletiella hortensis* (Fitch). A dark, active species found most often on young plants in seedbeds and in outdoor gardens. They have a soft, round body, black to dark purple with yellow spots, and a distinct head. They are very small, 1/25 inch long. They jump quickly by means of the tail-like appendage. They chew holes in thin leaves such as spinach, and make pits in cotyledon leaves of beans and cucumbers, and may damage any small plant close to the ground. Malathion dust has given good control. Chlordane dust is effective in some cases, not in others; lindane is used on some ornamentals.

SYMPHILANS. See Centipedes and Symphylans, page 206.

TERMITES

Termites are not ants, although they are often called "white ants." They are not even in the order Hymenoptera where true ants belong. Termites are in the order Isoptera, meaning equal wings. These are long, narrow, membranous, folded flat over the back when at rest. The best way to tell termites from ants is to look at the "waist." Ants are deeply constricted, while termites have a broad joining between thorax and abdomen. Termites have chewing mouth parts but gradual metamorphosis. They live in galleries in wood or in the ground, except when the winged forms are swarming.

Termites are social insects like ants and have a well-developed caste system with: (1) primary reproductive members, kings and queens, sexual forms which escape from an old colony to found a new one, losing their wings after migrating; (2) secondary reproductive members, mature males and females without wings but with wing buds, which take charge in case the king and queen are killed; (3) ergatoid kings and queens, sexually mature but lacking wings entirely; (4) workers, blind, pale, wingless, non-reproductive, constituting the main population for the colony; (5) soldiers, wingless insects with enlarged heads and mouth parts.

85. *Termites: winged sexual form and nymph; and wood tunneled by termites. Note thick "waist" compared to true ant.*

The food of termites is wood or cellulose in some form and they have protozoa in their intestines to enable them to digest this cellulose. Some species live in dry wood above ground, but the species most important to the householder and gardener are the soil-inhabiting forms, particularly the **Eastern Subterranean Termite***, *Reticulitermes flavipes* (Kollar) and the **Western Subterranean Termite***, *R. hesperus* Banks. These work on wood on or in the ground or build covered runways to reach wood above the ground. They are not new pests, as some termite-control operators advertise; they have been found in fossils and probably were on this continent before man. Their periods of abundance seem to be in waves, however, with some years when damage to buildings is abnormally high.

Subterranean termites sometimes injure living trees and shrubs, being more harmful in warm climates. In Florida they eat away the bark around the collar of newly transplanted orange trees, sometimes injure apple, peach, pear, cherry, plum, apricot, lemon, guava, pecan, walnut. The injury is usually worse in recently cleared woodland containing old, decaying stumps, or in land rich in humus. Fruits which drop and lie on the ground may be invaded. In cities, roots and heartwood of shade trees are entered; seedlings are injured in nurseries.

Flowering plants, mostly those with woody stems, can be infested in gardens or greenhouses, the termites starting on decaying wooden stakes or labels or wooden benches in contact with moist earth. Chrysanthemums are rather commonly injured and heliotrope, begonia, geranium, poinsettia, cosmos, jasmine, pansy, oleander, and others have been injured on occasion. Termites reach potted plants through the hole in the bottom of the pot. In southern states field and truck crops may be injured—corn, cotton, sugar cane, rice, grasses, white and sweetpotatoes, artichoke, bean, beet, cabbage, carrot, cranberry, peanut, rhubarb, squash, turnip, cantaloupe and other melons.

In California the western subterranean termite may damage citrus and also grape; infesting heartwood of the vines. The **Desert Dampwood Termite,** *Paraneotermes simplicicornis* (Banks), sometimes injures roots of young citrus trees but the **Drywood Termite,** *Kalotermes minor* Hagen feeds on wood above ground, usually in dead heartwood, sometimes in living tissue, gaining entrance through wounds or crevices and not via the soil.

Control. Use resistant wood for garden stakes and posts—redwood is excellent for grape stakes and fence posts—or use wood treated with creosote, zinc chloride, or mercuric chloride. Tree surgery and cleaning up old grapevines and other woody debris around the garden reduce the termite menace. Paint pruning scars with a mixture of 1 part creosote to 3 parts coal tar after shellac has been applied to protect living tissue at edges of the bark. Avoid use of manure while termites are in soil.

Subterranean termites can be killed in soil around trees by applying carbon disulfide or carbon tetrachloride emulsion. Poke small holes around plants 12 inches apart and pour in about 1 teaspoon in each; more can be used in fallow soil. DDT, chlordane, lindane, or lead arsenate worked into the soil around living trees and shrubs will deter termites. Sap-pine stakes can be used to trap termites; the stakes are then pulled up and drenched with boiling water. When swarming indicates the position of a colony, drench the spot with kerosene. In new greenhouses proper construction keeps termites from entering. Benches in older houses can be cleaned up with kerosene emulsion.

THRIPS

Thrips belong to the insect order Thysanoptera, the name meaning bristle or fringe wings. They are very small, slender insects, about as wide as a fine needle, only just visible to the naked eye. The 2 pairs of long narrow wings, with few or no veins, are edged with long hairs like stiff fringe. The mouth parts are fitted for piercing and rasping; antennae are usually short, 6- to 10-segmented; tarsi (feet) have 1 or 2 segments and end in a bladderlike vesicle instead of claws. Thrips often scar fruit and foliage with their scraping mouth parts and are commonly found on flowers. Some are predaceous on mites and small insects, some eat fungi and decayed vegetable matter but most are very injurious.

There are 2 suborders, with most of the plant pests belonging to Terebrantia, distinguished by having a sawlike ovipositor, and to only a few families in this suborder.

Aeolothripidae. Broad-winged or banded thrips. Adults are dark, have broad wings with 2 longitudinal veins and several cross veins, usually banded or mottled. The antennae are 9-segmented and the ovipositor of the female curves upward. Most forms are predaceous.

Merothripidae. Large-legged thrips. The front and hind tibiae are enlarged, the pronotum has a longitudinal suture on each side, antennae are moniliform, and the ovipositor is much reduced. The common species, *Merothrips morgani* Hood, occurs under bark, in debris, and on fungi.

Phloeothripidae. In the suborder Tubulifera, the female lacking an ovipositor and the last segment tubular. Larger and stouter than most other thrips, usually dark brown or black, often with light-colored or mottled wings. Some are beneficial predators; a few, like the lily-bulb thrips, are plant feeders.

Thripidae. Common thrips. This family contains most of the species of economic importance as plant feeders. Wings are narrow, pointed at the tip; antennae are 6- to 9-segmented.

Banded Greenhouse Thrips*, *Hercinothrips femoralis* (O. M. Reuter). A pest in greenhouses, and of sugar beets, cacti, and date palm outdoors in California and Arizona. The thrips is dark brown or black, with head, prothorax, and end of abdomen reddish yellow, fore wings dusty with white areas. This species may moderately or heavily infest alstroemeria, amaryllis, agapanthus, aralia, buddleia, yellow calla, chrysanthemum, dracaena, rubber plant, gardenia, gerbera, gladiolus, hydrangea, hymenocallis, nerine, philodendron, sprekelia, sweetpea, snapdragon, screwpine and other greenhouse plants including sweetpotatoes and tomatoes. Control is the same as for the greenhouse thrips.

Bean Thrips*, *Hercothrips fasciatus* (Pergande). Widely distributed, a general feeder on legumes, truck, field, and forage crops, grasses, deciduous and citrus trees, a special pest of beans, avocado, olive, pear, and orange. Nymphs are reddish yellow, adults gray-black, with black-and-white wings. They feed in colonies, making foliage of beans, peas, and other crops bleached or silvered, wilted, covered with black bits of excrement. Eliminate weeds around the garden, especially prickly lettuce and sow thistle. Spray or dust with DDT, except on edible plant parts.

Another common species on bean, including soybean, is *Sericothrips variabilis* (Black), which causes yellow spotting or browning of foliage.

Blueberry Thrips*, *Frankliniella vaccinii* Morgan. A pest of blueberries in Maine and part of New York. Adults appear when first blueberry leaves separate in the buds, causing a tight curling, reddening, and malformation of leaves. The female is light brown with gray head, legs, wings, and first antennal segments. Recommended procedure has been a quick burning over of blueberry fields.

Camphor Thrips*, *Liriothrips floridensis* (Watson). Very injurious to camphor-trees in the Gulf States. The adult is black, 1/50 inch long; the young are straw-colored, changing to orange-red at the 2nd molt. The thrips feed on buds and tender tips, causing dieback, and on branches, causing blackening, cracking of bark, deformation of limbs. Breeding is nearly continuous. Injury is worse on nursery trees, or on older trees that have been trimmed and cut back. Apply shellac to pruning cuts. Spray with DDT.

Chrysanthemum Thrips*, *Thrips nigropilosus* Uzel. Often serious on greenhouse chrysanthemums, sometimes outdoors. Young leaves are flecked whitish from loss of sap and often have a gummy residue. The shoots die back if thrips are numerous. DDT or lindane sprays or dusts are effective outdoors. Commercial greenhouses may use malathion, lindane, parathion, dieldrin, or heptachlor.

Citrus Thrips*, *Scirtothrips citri* (Moulton). Important in the Southwest and probably third in importance of all citrus pests in California. It is a native insect, restricted to the Southwest, not occurring in the Gulf States. It is serious on sweet and mandarin oranges, lemon, lime, grapefruit, pomelo, kumquat, tangerine, sometimes infests pomegranate, grape, umbrella tree, apricot, rose, rarely occurs on walnut, olive, willow, almond. Pepper-tree is the only host besides citrus on which it overwinters—in the egg state, the nymphs hatching in March. The injury is a very definite ring scar around the fruit at the blossom end, withering and curling of leaves, blossom-drop before fruit is set. The nymphs are yellow to orange, the adults are orange-yellow with black eyes, 1/50 inch long. There may be 10 to 12 generations a year in the warmer localities.

Control. DDT and DDT-sulfur are applied as dusts; dieldrin, sabadilla, nicotine sulfate, wettable sulfur, lime-sulfur, and tartar emetic have all been tried as sprays, with treatment at petal-fall to prevent fruit scarring and in the summer to protect new growth.

Composite Thrips*, *Microcephalothrips abdominalis* (D. L. Crawford). Frequently found on zinnia, marigold, calendula, and other flowers but of minor importance. The entire life cycle is passed in the flower heads. Adults are very small, dark brown; greatest abundance is in autumn, when there may be injury to flower seeds.

Cuban-laurel Thrips*, *Gynaikothrips ficorum* (Marchal). Recently a problem in California on Indian laurel fig, rubber plant and other species of Ficus, also known in Florida.

Dogwood Thrips, *Rhopalandrothrips corni* Morison. Present in California.

Dracaena Thrips, *Heliothrips dracaenae* (Heeger). Dusky yellow with abdomen shaded with brown; netted head, thorax, and wings. It is present in California on dracaena, rubber tree, Kentia palm, Sago palm, and century plant.

Florida Flower Thrips, *Frankliniella bispinosa* (Morgan). A southern pest of roses, the white-blossomed Spanish needle, and other flowers; of strawberry blossoms, which either drop off or turn into brown, hard berries; of citrus bloom. They are found in tomato blossoms but are only occasionally damaging to these. The adult has an orange head and thorax, lemon-yellow abdomen, which is often curled over the back when disturbed. The larvae are similar but paler in color, lack wings.

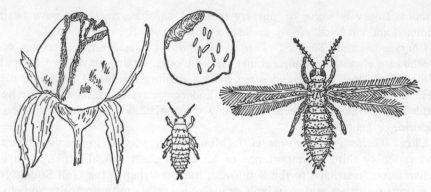

86. *Flower thrips: injury to rose; nymph and adult much enlarged.*

Flower Thrips*, *Frankliniella tritici* (Fitch). Wheat Thrips, present in nearly every state but primarily on eastern species. It is an omnivorous feeder on grasses, weeds, flowers, field, forage, and truck crops, fruit and shade trees, berries, vines, but with preference for grasses, legumes, roses, and peonies. Young thrips are lemon-yellow, adults amber or brownish yellow with an orange thorax; 1/20 inch long. They injure only the flowers, not foliage, and come to roses and other ornamentals daily from flowers on trees, grasses, weeds, etc. nearby.

Rosebuds turn brown and either ball, petals staying stuck together, or open part way to crippled, distorted blossoms with brown edges on the petals. The thrips can be seen inside the petals, usually near the base. They apparently prefer yellow and other light-colored blossoms and are most injurious with the June bloom. The life cycle may be completed in 2 weeks and there can be many generations, but there is comparatively little injury to the fall display of roses. Daylilies and peonies are often markedly injured by flower thrips. They are common on Japanese iris, though seldom so harmful on this host.

Control. This is an exceedingly difficult insect to control because thrips are continuously arriving on rosebuds from weed, tree, and grass flowers. The old tartar-emetic-and-brown-sugar concoction was given up in favor of DDT but this has not been too efficient. Lindane is temporarily effective but frequent applications have to be made. Some prefer malathion or dieldrin. A systemic phosphate, dimethoate, is promising, but recommendations to date call for its use as a spray (1 teaspoon Cygon to 1 gallon of water). Infested buds and all blooms as they start to fade should be promptly removed to reduce the thrips population.

Gladiolus Thrips*, *Taeniothrips simplex* (Morison). All too universally present in gardens. A relatively new insect, noticed first in 1929 in Ohio and Canada and rapidly distributed through the country. Of chief importance on gladiolus, it is also a pest of iris—Spanish, Japanese, German, and bulbous—and is known to feed and breed on amaryllis, aster, carnation, delphinium, freesia, hollyhock, narcissus, and poker plant (Plate XXX).

Although one of the larger species of thrips, the adult is only 1/16 inch or less, black or brownish black with a creamy white band across the base of the wings. Females insert kidney-shaped eggs in growing plant tissues. First-stage larvae, white with red eyes, hatch in about a week, changing soon to pale-yellow 2nd-stage larvae. The next, prepupa, stage is orange; the true pupal stage is light yellow with white antennae, wing pads, and legs; red eyes. The dark adult appears in about 3 days. The complete life cycle takes 2 to 4 weeks, depending on the temperature, the effective range being 50° to 90° F. There are several generations in the garden and breeding may continue on corms in storage. Thrips are killed by low temperatures and do not winter in the ground except in warm climates.

Injury on gladiolus is a silvery appearance of the foliage, due to the many small areas where cell sap has been lost, followed by browning and dying of leaves. Flowers are deformed, with whitish flecks or streaks; spikes may not open. Corms in storage become sticky, corky, russeted, and fail to germinate when planted or produce poor or no flowers.

Control. Until DDT came to the rescue, many gardeners had almost given up growing gladiolus; now this species can be readily controlled. Starting when leaves are about 6 inches high, spray every 7 to 10 days with DDT (2 tablespoons 50 per cent wettable powder to 1 gallon of water) or apply 5 per cent DDT dust until flowering. Other possible chemicals include dieldrin, dimethoate, toxaphene, or lindane. After harvest and curing put corms in a paper bag, add 1 teaspoon DDT dust to each 100 corms, shake well, and store as usual. If corms appear infested at planting time, soak in Lysol solution for 3 hours (1½ teaspoons Lysol to 1 gallon water).

Grape Thrips, *Drepanothrips reuteri* Uzel. A pest of grapes in California. It looks like the flower thrips and causes burning and curling of young leaves, scarring of berries. Spraying or dusting with DDT for leafhoppers controls this thrips.

Grass Thrips*, *Anophothrips obscurus* (Müller). Sometimes abundant on grains and grasses, occasionally on corn, destroying softer parts of foliage, flowers, and developing kernels. Destroy old stems and litter where insects hibernate.

Greenhouse Thrips*, *Heliothrips haemorrhoidalis* (Bouché). Practically world-wide, present outdoors in California, Florida, Georgia and similar warm climates and in greenhouses nearly everywhere. Infested garden plants include avocado, on which this is a major pest, citrus, grape, mango, sapote, cherimoya, guava, and other subtropical fruits and many ornamentals. Among the latter are arbutus, azalea, carissa, croton, cypress, eucalyptus, eugenia, hibbertia, laurestinus, mandevilla, mesembryanthemum, myrtle, rhododendron, rose, statice, toyon, viburnum. In greenhouses there may be serious injury to amaryllis, begonia, chrysanthemum, citrus, croton, cyclamen, dahlia, ferns, fuchsia, gloxinia, nasturtium, orchids, palm, rubber plant and others.

The greenhouse thrips is distinguished by a deep network of lines over head and central portion of the body, which is blackish brown, with the posterior end lighter; 1/24 inch long, legs yellow, wings slightly clouded but without bands, antennae slender and needlelike at the tip. Feeding is almost entirely on foliage and fruits, often in concentrated colonies on inner parts of trees and shrubs with all stages present at the same time. Eggs are inserted just under the epidermis of leaves or fruit, producing blisters. Plants look silvery or bleached, leaves papery, wilting, dying, sometimes dropping off. Foliage and fruit are spotted with reddish-black dots of excrement.

Control. Avocado can be sprayed with DDT or malathion with a miticide added to take care of increase in mites. On citrus, dieldrin added to the regular oil spray for scales gives control. Spray or dust ornamentals with DDT, malathion, or dieldrin.

Hollyhock Thrips. *Liriothrips varicornis* Hood. Apparently limited to a semiarid climate; found in California principally on hollyhock. It resembles the toyon thrips; larvae are brilliant red and black, adults all black. Colonies feed in depressions in leaves, stems, and roots. Water the soil around base of plants heavily; destroy all old stalks and volunteer plants during fall and winter.

Iris Thrips*, *Iridothrips iridis* (Watson). Often abundantly infesting Japanese iris, sometimes other types. Larvae—first white, later yellow—rasp folds of inner leaves, causing russeting, blackening, stunting; tops die and turn brown. Adults are dark brown, usually wingless. Spray or dust with DDT. Destroy thrips in divisions by immersing in hot water, 110° F., for 30 minutes.

Lily Bulb Thrips*, *Liothrips vaneecki* Priesner. Confined to lily and orchids; known in New York, North Carolina, California, Oregon, and Washington. This species, shiny black, 1/16 inch long, with salmon-pink and black larvae and pupae, spends its entire life on bulbs, feeding on epidermis of outer scales near base. Injured areas tend to turn rusty brown and be sunken or flabby, but there is no great damage.

Madroña Thrips, *Thrips madroni* Moulton. In Oregon and California on ceanothus, madroña, azalea, elderberry, rhododendron. It is pale yellow to dark brown.

Mullein Thrips*, *Haplothrips verbasci* (Osborn).

Onion Thrips*, *Thrips tabaci* Lindeman. Probably the most widely distributed thrips in the world, found in all onion-growing sections, attacking nearly all garden plants, many field crops and weeds. Many hosts are incidental with little breeding upon them, but some of the more important vegetable hosts, besides onions, are: bean, beet, carrot, cabbage, cauliflower, celery, cucumber, melons, peas, squash, tomato, and turnip. Injury to onions shows first as whitish blotches, then blasting and distortion of leaf tips, followed by withering, browning, and falling over on the ground. The bulbs are distorted, undersized. Thrips congregate in great numbers between leaf sheaths and stem, and carry over on bulbs in storage. Peas, cucumbers, and melons have crinkled, curled, dwarfed foliage.

Ornamentals infested by the onion thrips include rose and carnation, which have petals spotted and streaked, asparagus fern, calla, campanula, chrysanthemum, dahlia, gaillardia, gloxinia, mignonette, foxglove, Jerusalem-cherry, sweetpea. This species transmits the spotted-wilt virus to tomatoes, dahlias and other flowers.

The onion thrips varies in color, from pale yellow to dark brown, is 1/25 inch long. Wings are a uniform dusky gray without bands; larvae are creamy white; pupation is in soil. Eggs are laid in surface tissue and hatch in about 5 days in summer. The 1st molt of the larva is on plants, the 2nd in soil. A generation is completed in a little over 2 weeks and in mild climates like California reproduction continues through the year. Winter hosts elsewhere are weeds and bulbs in storage.

Control. Onion growers may use diazinon, malathion, parathion or Phosdrin, making 2 or 3 applications at 1- to 2-week intervals, beginning when thrips are numerous enough to scar leaves. For ornamentals use DDT, malathion, or dieldrin.

Orchid Thrips, *Chaetanaphothrips orchidii* (Moulton). A Florida species first noted in grapefruit in 1937. It is light yellow, very active, causing a silvery to dark-brown discoloration of immature fruit.

Pear Thrips*, *Taeniothrips inconsequens* (Uzel). An imported species, first noted in California in 1904, now present in Washington, Oregon, New York, Pennsylvania, and Maryland. Prune is injured even more than pear. Other hosts include apple, apricot, cherry, grape, peach, plum, poplar, maple, California-laurel, madroña, willow, and weeds and grasses around orchards. The adult is uniformly dark brown, slender, bluntly pointed at each end, 1/25 inch long, with grayish wings lighter at the base. It emerges from the ground in spring and feeds in developing buds, causing a bleeding and gumming of pear buds, blackening of prune buds, deformed leaves and blossoms, and crop reduction. After feeding 3 weeks, eggs are laid in stems of fruit and foliage. White larvae appear in 2 weeks and feed under husks of young fruit, causing scarring and distortion. After 3 more weeks they drop to the ground, burrow into the soil, and construct cells several inches to 3 feet below the surface, where they remain until the next spring.

Control. Spray trees thoroughly after buds begin to show green with DDT, at rate of 2 pounds 50 per cent wettable powder to 100 gallons of water.

Privet Thrips*, *Dendrothrips ornatus* (Jablonowski). An eastern species very injurious to privet in some seasons, turning hedges uniformly gray and dusty-looking. The leaves may be somewhat puckered. The larvae are yellow, spindle-shaped, as many as 20 to 25 on underside of a single small leaf. The adults are dark brown to black with a bright-red band. They can be killed with DDT but this encourages privet mites. Two treatments with nicotine sulfate and soap or a pyrethrum-rotenone spray at 10- to 14-day intervals will control this species without increasing mites.

Red-banded Thrips*, *Selenothrips rubrocinctus* (Giard). A pest from the West Indies that has invaded Florida, infesting avocado, guava, and mango. It is dark brown or black with a bright-red band across the body. Injury and life history are similar to that of the greenhouse thrips.

Tobacco Thrips*, *Frankliniella fusca* (Hinds). On tobacco, cotton, and other plants, a vector of the spotted wilt virus. Nymphs are yellow, adults brown.

Toyon Thrips, *Rhyncothrips ilex* (Moulton). On California Christmasberry. The adult—black, glossy, with silvery-white wings—hibernates in curled leaves, mates in early spring, feeds on new, unfolding leaves, and lays yellow, waxy eggs loosely on them. The larvae—pale yellow, later reddish—feed with adults on new growth, causing it to be distorted, curled, sometimes killed. When mature, larvae drop to the ground to pupate, rest while the toyon is in bloom, then the new adults feed on the 2nd rush of new growth. Natural spread is slow; most dissemination is on nursery stock. Pick off and destroy curled leaves in fall and winter. Spray for active stages with DDT, nicotine sulfate and soap, or pyrethrum.

Tubulifera Thrips, *Haplothrips clarisetis* Priesner. An African species, of the suborder Tubulifera, first noticed in this country in 1958 in New Mexico, doing serious damage to young lettuce, also reported from California. It is very dark brown to jet black with silvery wings.

Western Flower Thrips*, *Frankliniella occidentale* (Pergande)$=F.$ *moultoni* (Hood). On practically all types of plants. The thrips vary from lemon-yellow to dusky yellow-brown, winter on weeds, and feed in tree blossoms in spring, causing scarring and distortion of fruits. They are more injurious to apricot, peach, plum, and nectarine blossoms in southern California than farther north, where the blooming season is over before populations build up. They injure grapes in season, beans as they come through the ground. They injure cucurbit vines suffering from lack of water, cause blossom-drop of peas, tomatoes, melons, sometimes strawberries. Blooms of roses, carnations, sweetpeas, and gladiolus are streaked. This species spreads spotted wilt disease that infects tomatoes and many other vegetables and ornamentals on the West Coast.

Eggs are laid in tender stems, buds, flowers, and hatch in 5 to 15 days. Larvae feed on succulent portions for 7 to 12 days, molt once on the host, drop to the ground, pupate, molt once during this resting stage, and, in cool climates, hibernate in protected spots. Peak of infestation is in late spring. Adults can be carried long distances by wind but migrations are usually local. See Flower Thrips for control.

TREEHOPPERS

Treehoppers are sucking insects in the order Hemiptera, suborder Homoptera. They are closely related to leafhoppers but belong to the family Membracidae, which is characterized by having a pronotum (taking the place of the thorax in other insects) greatly enlarged and grotesquely developed into horns, knobs, and other peculiar shapes. Treehoppers have been called the brownies of the insect world. They injure trees and shrubs by their egg laying, and the nymphs feed on weeds, grasses, corn, and legumes.

87. Buffalo treehopper, side view.

Buffalo Treehopper*, *Stictocephala bubalus* (Fabricius). Serious in the Middle West, often damaging in the East to apple, pear, peach, quince, cherry, and other fruits, and to rose, elm, locust, cottonwood, and other ornamentals. The injury comes from the wounds made by the female in oviposition. These are double rows of curved slits inside which 6 to 12 elongated yellowish eggs are embedded in the inner bark. Infested trees look rough, scaly, or cracked and seldom make vigorous growth. The fungi causing rose cankers and other diseases gain entrance through the slits.

Eggs winter in the wood; they hatch in late spring into pale-green spiny nymphs which drop from the tree and feed on sap of various weeds and grasses until mid-July or August, when they become adult. Viewed from above, they are triangles—light green, blunt at the head end with a short horn at each upper corner, pointed at the rear—¼ inch long. The female has a knifelike ovipositor to cut slits in twigs for her August egg laying.

Control. Clean cultivation of an orchard, keeping down all weeds or grassy growth, and avoiding summer cover crops for a season or two help in control. A dormant spray of 4 to 6 per cent oil kills many overwintering eggs. DDT is partially effective as a spray, and parathion applied to trees and ground covers before egg laying in June has been successful.

Oak Treehoppers, *Platycotis vittata* (Fabricius) and *P. quadrivittata* (Say). Both species feed gregariously on deciduous and evergreen oak and are widely distributed. *P. vittata* is green to bronze, ⅜ inch long, with surface punctures and red dots. *P. quadrivittata* is pale blue with 4 red longitudinal stripes and well-developed pronotal horns. The nymphs are black with red and yellow markings, 2 black spines.

Quince Treehopper*, *Glossonotus crataegi* (Fitch).

Thornbug, *Umbonia crassicornis* A & S. Known in Florida for more than 100 years but a common pest only in the last decade—on calliandra, pithecellobium, tamarind, and various flowering legumes. The hoppers are green with tan to red lines, brownish wings, a high horn at the back; ½ inch long. Eggs are laid in grooves in branches.

Three-cornered Alfalfa Hopper*, *Spissistilus festinus* (Say). A western alfalfa pest, also a nuisance in Florida on beans, cowpeas, tomato, watermelon, with adults common on hickory, oak, black locust, viburnum. It is yellow-green with the outline of a triangle when viewed from above. DDT combined with lindane has been helpful in some instances.

Two-marked Treehopper*, *Enchinopa binotata* (Say). Frequently found on butternut, sometimes on locust, bittersweet, sycamore, hickory, willow, wild grape, redbud, hoptree, and viburnum. This small treehopper looks much like a bird in side view, with a high, curved horn projecting forward from the thorax. It is dusky brown with 2 lemon-yellow spots on the back. The female lays eggs in butternut buds and in twigs just below the buds. These are uncovered, but she also lays eggs in bark of locust and other trees and these she covers with a frothy, waxy material in corrugated layers. Eggs are laid in August and September and hatch the following May into small, white, powdery nymphs which mature in late June and July into very active adults. Butternut buds are often destroyed by the egg laying, and leaves are punctured. Grape stems and bittersweet vines may be punctured. There is no very satisfactory control. Some nymphs can be killed with nicotine sulfate in late May.

Wide-footed Treehopper, *Campylenchia latipes* (Say). Through the United States on a wide variety of grasses, shrubs, forage plants. It is cinnamon brown, with a deeply keeled pronotal horn, 2 lateral horns, a densely punctured and hairy pronotum.

WALKINGSTICKS

Walkingsticks belong to the grasshopper order, Orthoptera, and to the family Phasmatidae, a remarkable group of insects that so closely resemble their environment, twig or leaf, they go unnoticed until they move. Many species are tropical. Those in this country, except for one in Florida, are wingless. They are very long and thin, with the thorax about half body length; they have long legs and antennae. The legs are all alike, the forelegs not being modified for grasping as in the mantids, with which they might be confused. They have the power of partially replacing a lost leg at another molt. They have biting mouth parts and feed on foliage.

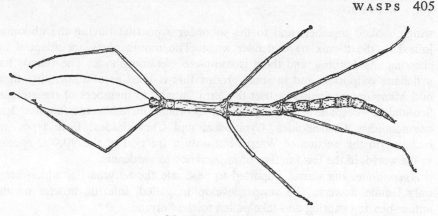

88. Walkingstick.

Giant Walkingstick, *Megaphasma dentricus* (Stoll). Very large, up to 6 inches, similar to the common walkingstick but not numerous enough to be destructive.

Prairie Walkingstick, *Diapheromera velii* Coquillett. On shrubs and grasses in the Great Plains west of the Mississippi but rarely abundant. It is similar to the common walkingstick but has a more elongate head.

Two-striped Walkingstick*, *Anisomorpha buprestoides* (Stoll). Reported defoliating ornamentals in Alabama and Georgia. A related species, *A. ferruginea* Beauvois, feeds on trees and shrubs from Nebraska to the Carolinas and Georgia. It is credited with the widespread outbreak in Kansas in 1961, with black locust and white oak the worst victims.

Walkingstick*, *Diapheromera femorata* (Say). Northern Walkingstick. The common species from New England to the Rocky Mountains, frequently defoliating trees in the Midwest. It prefers black oak and wild cherry but feeds also on hickory, locust, basswood, and other trees, even on roses and various shrubs. Young walkingsticks are pale green, changing to dark green, gray, or brown as they mature. The female is stouter and longer than the male, up to 3 inches. They are adult after 4 or 5 molts, mate in August, and drop bean-shaped black eggs promiscuously on the ground from the trees. They remain in the litter until the next May or even the following May. The nymphs feed on tree foliage rather ravenously.

Occasionally control spraying is advised, using DDT applied by airplane at 1 pound per acre or lead arsenate for individual ornamentals.

WASPS

Most wasps are not garden pests. The few harmful species are far outnumbered by the beneficial forms. Like bees, ants, and sawflies, wasps belong to the order Hymenoptera, characterized by 2 pairs of membranous wings hooked together, and to the suborder Apocrita, having the abdomen joined to the thorax by a slender waist. The mouth parts are adapted for chewing and lapping, and there is complete metamorphosis. The female has a definite ovipositor and in some groups this is used as a stinger, in others not. Many entomologists restrict the term "wasp" to members of the stinging Scolioidea, Vespoidea, and Sphecoidea; others include superfamilies Ichneumonoidea, Chalcidoidea, Cynipodea, and Chrysidoidea. Both types are included in this section of Wasps, but only a fraction of the 90,000 species in the world, in the few families of importance to gardeners.

Agaontidae. Fig wasps, imported to pollinate the Smyrna fig, which bears only female flowers. The wasps develop in galled, infertile flowers on the anther-bearing caprifig and take pollen to the Smyrna.

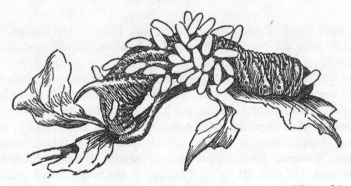

89. *Tomato hornworm parasitized by braconid wasp. The white egglike objects are cocoons.*

Braconidae. Braconids, small insects with a short abdomen; important parasites of aphids (note the many dead aphids with a round hole in the back), of larvae and pupae of moths and butterflies and some beetles. Some species pupate in cocoons on the outside of the host body. Tomato hornworms and catalpa sphinx caterpillars are often covered with white oval objects that look like eggs but are cocoons of braconid wasps.

Chalcididae. Chalcids, minute or very small insects, short-bodied, with head as wide as or wider than the thorax; black or brown; wings almost veinless; legs short with hind femora much enlarged. All forms are parasites, chiefly on larvae of beetles, moths, butterflies, and flies, but some are hyperparasites living on other beneficial insects and in that way become harmful.

Chrysididae. Cuckoo or jewel wasps, brilliant green, blue, red or purple with sculptured body, seldom over ½ inch. They are external parasites of other bees and wasps, lay eggs in other nests.

Cynipidae. Gall wasps, very small, responsible for most of the galls on leaves and twigs of oaks and other plants. There are many species, and the galls may be numerous and unsightly but the hosts are not killed and seldom even weakened.

Eurytomidae. Seed chalcids, jointworms. Some are parasitic, some are injurious. They are usually black, often rather hairy, with thorax coarsely punctate, abdomen rounded or oval and somewhat compressed.

Ichneumonidae. Ichneumons. A large family of slender insects with elongate abdomens (sometimes sickle-shaped), often with an ovipositor longer than the body but not used for stinging man. One species has a body 1½ inches long and a 3-inch hairlike ovipositor which penetrates bark of trees to parasitize horntails. The various members of this famliy are important natural controls of harmful beetles, caterpillars, and sawflies.

Pelicinidae. Pelicinid wasps. The female has a long filiform abdomen. There is only 1 species in the United States, *Pelecinus polyturator* (Drury). This is shiny black, 2 inches long, a parasite on Japanese-beetle larvae.

Perilampidae. Stout-bodied chalcids, with large, coarsely punctate thorax, small, shiny, triangular abdomen, often found on flowers. Many species are hyperparasites, attacking our beneficial parasites.

Pompilidae. Spider wasps, slender with long, spiny legs, mostly dark-colored, usually feeding on spiders.

Pteromalidae. Minute black or metallic insects, triangular in profile, mostly parasites on crop pests.

Scelionidae. Egg parasites, useful in controlling Mormon crickets and grasshoppers, but sometimes killing mantids, lacewings, and other beneficial insects.

Sphecidae. Solitary wasps, tunneling in soil or wood, stocking their larders with spiders, grasshoppers, caterpillars, aphids, bugs, and flies. This group contains the mud-daubers and the giant cicada killer.

Tiphiidae. Tiphiid wasps, mostly fair-sized, black, somewhat hairy, parasites on grubs of scarabaeid beetles. One species was introduced to control Japanese beetles and has been quite a help.

Torymidae. Very small, metallic-green parasites, mostly on insects living inside plant tissues, galls, or seeds.

Trichogrammatidae. Very minute parasites inside eggs of other insects, important in the control of various caterpillars. Cards covered with Trichogramma eggs are sometimes sold to farmers and home gardeners.

Vespidae. Social wasps—the hornets, yellow jackets etc., making nests from wood fiber—and solitary potter wasps. Most are beneficial, feeding their young with injurious caterpillars, acting as pollinators, but the giant hornet is a real garden pest.

Apple Seed Chalcid*, *Torymus druparum* Boheman. The larvae infest seeds of untreated apples.

Blackberry Knot-gall Wasp, *Distrophus nebulosus* Osten Sacken. Causing knotty, rounded or elongate swellings, 2 to 6 inches long, often with deep longitudinal furrows.

Blueberry Stem-gall Wasp, *Hemadas nubilipennis* Ashmead. Causing a kidney-shaped gall, first green then reddish brown. Common on blueberry stems.

California Pepper-tree Chalcid, *Eumegastigmus transvaalensis.* An introduced species, first reported in California in 1960.

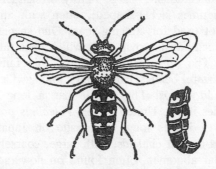

90. Cicada killer, digger wasp, with side view of abdomen showing ovipositor, "stinger."

Cicada Killer*, *Sphecius speciosus* (Drury). Digger Wasp. A very large wasp, up to 1½ inches long, black with the abdomen banded with yellow, and a wickedly long, curved ovipositor or stinger. Appearing in midsummer or later, this wasp makes a mess of lawns, tunneling far underground and marking the openings of its burrows with little mounds of earth. It also damages paths, banks, and terraces. I have seen it abundant enough to lift and crack concrete sidewalks with its tunnels and mounds, to say nothing of scaring to death all the passers-by. After making her burrow, the wasp goes to look for a cicada in a tree. She darts at it and they both fall to the ground. The wasp stings the cicada to paralyze it and then, straddling her bulky prey, she crawls up a tree to a good launching point to take flight toward her burrow. If she does not make it the first time, she tries another tree and another glide. Arrived at the opening, she drags in the cicada, stores it in a cell, and lays an egg between its legs. Each cell is provided with 1 or 2 cicadas, sealed off before the next cell is filled. The egg hatches in two or three days and the larva feeds on the cicada contents for about 2 months, then makes a cocoon of silk and rests in it until the next summer, when it pupates and produces the adult.

Control. I used to whack these creatures with a kind of giant flyswatter made of heavy wire mesh on a stick, and squirt carbon disulfide into the holes. Dusting with 5 per cent chlordane into and around the openings is easier and probably more effective.

Clover Seed Chalcid*, *Bruchophagus gibbus* (Boheman). A general and important pest of clover and alfalfa seed, but it does not destroy the value of these crops as forage.

91. *Giant hornet, natural size and slightly enlarged, tearing bark from lilac stem for nest.*

Giant Hornet*, *Vespa crabro germana* (Christ). European Hornet, Vespa Hornet. This is the largest hornet in this country, 1 inch long, dark reddish brown with orange markings on the abdomen, resembling the cicada killer but stouter and hairier, and without such a terrifying ovipositor. It is a special pest of lilacs near New York City, tearing the bark from twigs and branches and girdling them. The result appears to be the work of a squirrel; it seems impossible that an insect could inflict that much damage. The giant hornet may also injure boxwood, birch, willow, poplar, franklinia, and other trees and shrubs. It is found along the Atlantic seaboard from Massachusetts to Georgia and is also present in Pennsylvania and Ohio. The injury comes in late August and September, when the wasps tear off the bark to use in making their nests in hollow trees or suspended from the roof inside barns and other buildings or from the eaves of houses.

Control. Some recommend trying to find the nest and puffing in calcium cyanide dust but this is difficult. I have had fair success spraying trunks and branches of lilacs with a very heavy dose of rotenone or double strength DDT at the first sign of hornets at work. Dieldrin is also recommended, applied as for borers.

Grape Seed Chalcid*, *Evoxysoma vitis* (Saunders).

Mossy Rose-gall Wasp*, *Diplolepis rosae* (Linnaeus). The galls appear in June and July. Each is a globular mass of mosslike filaments surrounding a cluster of hard cells, each of which contains one larva which remains in the cell until spring. There is no control except the removal of infested canes.

Oak Gall Wasps. Hundreds of wasps cause galls on the many species of oak—on roots, at the crown, in the bark, on branches and twigs, on buds, and on foliage. They are far too numerous to discuss individually. In addition to the many small leaf galls there are the familiar large brown galls known as oak apples, each of which is a leaf deformed by a wasp. An interesting wasp on white, chestnut, and basket oaks, is the wool sower, *Callirhytis seminator* Harris, which produces a globular, white, pink-marked woolly growth, 1½ to 2 inches across, on twigs. There is really nothing the gardener can do about oak galls.

Rose Root-gall Wasp*, *Diplolepis radicum* (Osten Sacken). Causing a large, conspicuous swelling 1 to 2 inches across on roots of cultivated roses. It is not very common.

WEBWORMS

Webworms are caterpillars that feed protected by webs. Some, like the tent caterpillar, have been treated elsewhere; those commonly known as webworms are discussed here.

Ailanthus Webworm*, *Atteva aurea* (Fitch). From New York to Illinois and southward, more common in southern states. Tree-of-heaven is the preferred host. The adult moths have bright-orange fore wings, marked with 4 crossbands of yellow spots on a dark-blue ground; dusky, nearly transparent hind wings; expanse 1 inch. The caterpillars, olive-brown with fine white lines, feed gregariously in fine webs in August and September, with moths appearing in September and October. Control measures are seldom used, but either lead arsenate or DDT would be effective for young larvae.

Alfalfa Webworm*, *Loxostege commixtalis* (Walker). Larvae are greenish-yellow caterpillars with a light stripe down the back; adults are buff-colored moths, irregularly marked with light and dark gray, with a row of spots on underside of hind wings, spreading to 1 or 1¼ inches. Food plants and control are the same as for the beet webworm.

Barberry Webworm, *Omphalocera dentosa* (Grote). Black, white-spotted caterpillars, 1½ inches long, web twigs together and devour leaves of common and Japanese barberry in late summer and fall. The ugly, frass-filled masses remain over ends of shoots during the winter. Spray in summer with lead arsenate or DDT.

Beet Webworm, *Loxostege sticticalis* (Linnaeus). Present from the Mississippi Valley west to the Continental Divide. Along with the alfalfa webworm, this small webbing caterpillar is a general and destructive feeder on cabbage, beet, sugar beet, bean, pea, potato, spinach, cucurbits, and other vegetables, alfalfa and forage crops. The larvae work like armyworms, cleaning up one field, then moving en masse to the next. They are yellow or green to nearly black, with a black stripe down the middle of the back and 3 small black dots bearing bristles at the end of each segment. As they skeletonize and devour leaves, they make a tube, several inches long, to a hiding place under a clod of earth or other protected spot where they retreat when disturbed. They pupate 2 to 3 weeks in a cell an inch or 2 underground. The night-flying moth is smoky brown with straw-colored spots and lines and a continuous dark line near the margin of the hind wings. White to yellow or green oval eggs are laid on underside of leaves. There may be 3 partial generations.

Control. Use pyrethrum, rotenone, methoxychlor or malathion spray or dust in the home garden. Commercial growers may also use Dylox, endrin, parathion, or phosphamidon.

Bluegrass Webworm*, *Crambus teterellus* (Zincken). See Sod Webworms.

Boxwood Webworm, *Galasa nigrinodis.* Larvae of a Chrysaugid Moth forming webs on boxwood, known in Maryland and Pennsylvania.

Cabbage Webworm*, *Hellula rogatalis* (Hulst). An imported species distributed through the states. The caterpillars, grayish yellow with purple stripes, ½ inch long, feed under webbing on inner leaves, hearts, stalks of cabbage, cauliflower, kale, sometimes on beets, collards, horseradish, radish. The moths are grayish, mottled with brown. Use DDT very early, before heads are formed and before worms are protected by their webs.

Corn Root Webworm*, *Crambus caliginosellus* Clemens. One of the sod webworms. The caterpillar is whitish, just over ½ inch long; the snout moth is straw-colored with indistinct markings. Walking over the grass stirs up the moths, which move in jerky flights and rest with their wings so tightly folded around their bodies, they look like tubes. Eggs are laid in summer; young larvae feed a little, then hibernate in nests in grass and sodland, becoming active in spring. They destroy roots and work from the crown into cornstalks, injuring developing leaves like budworms, and often chew stalks at the surface of the ground like cutworms. Full-grown in July and August, they pupate underground in a silken cocoon. Do not plant corn in land recently taken over from sod. If young corn shows injury, dig it up and plant a substitute crop.

Cotoneaster Webworm, *Cremona cotoneaster* (Busck). Yellow larvae, turning dark when grown, make silken webs from a larger silken refuge at the base of branch junctions. They skeletonize leaves and make unsightly webs. They winter in the refuge, pupate there in spring, produce grayish black, night-active moths. Small plants die; others are weakened. Use DDT, lead arsenate, or rotenone.

Fall Webworm*, *Hyphantria cunea* (Drury). Widely distributed, feeding on at least 120 varieties of fruit, shade, and woodland trees. Popular hosts are apple, cherry, peach, pecan, English walnut, black walnut, ash, boxelder, birch, chokecherry, elm, hickory, linden, poplar, sycamore, white oak, willow. Roses and other shrubs are sometimes webbed. The webworm acts much like the tent caterpillar but makes its nest over the ends of branches rather than at tree crotches.

Cocoons enclosing brown pupae winter under trash on the ground or under bark. Satiny white moths, often marked with brown spots, wings spreading 1½ to 1¾ inches, emerge over a long period in spring. They lay greenish eggs in masses of 200 to 500, often covered with a woolly layer of scales. The caterpillars are pale green or yellow with a dark stripe down the back and a yellow stripe along each side. The body is covered with very long silky gray hairs arising from black and yellow tubercles. When full-grown, about an inch long after 4 to 6 weeks of feeding, they crawl down trees to form cocoons. There are 2 broods in Middle Atlantic States, the first feeding in late May and June, the 2nd and more destructive from July through September. The larvae spin a layer of silk over the surface of a leaf as soon as they start feeding, eventually webbing together ends of several branches. The nests are always most unsightly, and one or more branches may be defoliated but seldom the entire tree.

Control. Summer sprays for codling moth will prevent damage by webworms on apples. Ornamentals can be sprayed with DDT or lead arsenate if necessary. It is often possible to cut off webbed ends of branches and to burn the nests without resorting to spraying, if this is done as soon as webs are first seen. There are several natural enemies, egg parasites and others.

Garden Webworm*, *Loxostege similalis* (Guenée). A native, found over most of the country but more of a pest in the Middle West and Southwest. It is much like the alfalfa and beet webworms, attacking alfalfa, clover, and field crops, but also working on garden vegetables such as beans, soybean, cowpeas, beets, and on strawberries, scarlet verbena, and castor-bean. The hairy caterpillars, a little over an inch long, are greenish with dark spots. They spin webs wherever they go and make silken tubes for shelter on the ground. The moth, buff-colored with grayish markings, is 1 inch across the wings. There are up to 5 generations in Texas, 2 or 3 in the North.

Control. Dust vegetables near harvest with pyrethrum or rotenone, others with DDT or toxaphene.

Juniper Webworm*, *Dichomeris marginella* (Fabricius). A European species first recorded in 1910, now present from Maine to North Carolina and west to Missouri, also in California on common and Irish juniper and redcedar. The winter is passed as partly grown larvae in silken cases in webbed foliage. They are light brown with a reddish-brown stripe down the back, 2 wider dark-brown stripes along the side, with short white hairs over the body, ½ inch long. They feed in early spring, then pupate in May. The moths, emerging in June and early July, have brown fore wings with white margins, fringed gray hind wings, wingspread only ⅗ inch. They lay eggs in leaf axils of new terminal growth, and the caterpillars web the needles together with silk. The webs enclose a good bit of frass and the needles turn brown and die. Sometimes the whole top of a small juniper is webbed and massed together.

Control. Spray with lead arsenate or DDT in midsummer to kill young caterpillars. Cut out webbed masses where possible. In spring a nicotine or pyrethrum spray applied with enough force to break the webs is helpful.

Lespedeza Webworm*, *Tetralopha scortealis* (Lederer).

Mimosa Webworm*, *Homadaula albizziae* Clarke. Discovered on mimosa in Washington, D.C., in 1940 and now a serious pest of both mimosa (Albizzia) and honeylocust from New Jersey to Georgia, Alabama, Mississippi, Arkansas, Illinois, and Missouri. The moths—gray with a silver luster, stippled with black spots, ½ inch wingspread—appear in June and lay eggs on mimosa flowers as well as foliage. The larvae—dark brown sometimes diffused with rose or pink, just over ½ inch long—feed first gregariously in a web spun over flowers and leaves, later singly on tender terminal leaves and on green pods of both hosts. The foliage is usually skeletonized, eaten from the underside, with the upper epidermis left intact. Leaves die, turn dull gray on mimosa, brown as if fire-scorched on honeylocust. In midsummer larvae descend to the ground on silken threads and spin cocoons in cracks in bark or in the ground cover. There are 2 generations and a partial 3rd. The webbing is most conspicuous in August from the 2nd brood.

Control. Lead arsenate and DDT are both effective. In Maryland DDT at the rate of 2 pounds 50 per cent wettable powder to 100 gallons of water has given satisfactory control applied about June 15 and August 20.

Oak Webworm*, *Archips fervidanus* (Clemens). On oak in northwestern states and west to Wisconsin. The gray-green larvae with black heads, ¾ inch long, live gregariously in a web. The moth has yellowish-brown fore wings, gray hind wings, is ⅞ inch long. Another species, *Tetralopha asperatella* (Clemens), also occurs on oak in eastern states. The larvae are ¾ inch long, brown with yellow stripes, and live in 2 or 3 leaves webbed together.

Pale Juniper Webworm, *Phalonia rutilana* (Hübner). A European species introduced about 1878, now present from Maine to New Jersey and Indiana on juniper. The larvae are brownish yellow; the moths have yellow fore wings marked with red, gray hind wings; wing expanse ⅜ inch. Foliage is webbed and brown.

Parsnip Webworm*, *Depressaria heracliana* (Linnacus). Present on parsnip, celery and related weeds in northern states east of the Mississippi River. Flower heads are webbed together and eaten by small yellow, green or grayish caterpillars with small black spots and short hairs. They interfere with seed production and may mine in stems. The moth is gray, winters under loose bark, lays eggs in spring on developing flowers. Caterpillars pupate in mines in stems, moths coming out in late summer. Cut and burn infested flower heads. Spray or dust with DDT, pyrethrum, or toxaphene.

Pine False Webworm*, *Acantholyda erythrocephala* (Linnaeus). A sawfly found in Connecticut, New York, New Jersey and Pennsylvania on red and white pines, sometimes other species. The larvae are greenish gray striped with purplish red; up to ⅘ inch long. Adults emerge from earthen cells from mid-April to early May and lay eggs on needles. These hatch the last 3 weeks in May and the young larvae feed gregariously in a loose webbing, cutting off the needles and pulling them into the web. There can be extensive defoliation. Older larvae make silken tubes along the twigs, then drop to the ground in late June. There is only 1 generation. Spray with DDT or lead arsenate in May before needles are webbed.

Pine Webworm*, *Tetralopha robustella* Zeller. Pine Pyralid, a native present from New England to Florida and west to Wisconsin on pitch, red, white, jack, and loblolly pines, injurious to seedlings or small trees, not to larger trees. The moths, with purple-black fore wings with a transverse gray band, smoky black hind wings, spreading to 1 inch, emerge from June to August. The larvae—yellow-brown with 2 dark stripes along each side, ¾ inch long when grown—work near the ends of terminal twigs, producing quantities of brown frass in silken webs. When mature they go into the ground and spin flimsy cocoons for the winter. Either lead arsenate or DDT is effective if applied before webbing starts.

Sod Webworms, *Crambus* spp. Lawn Moths, small millers that fly up as you walk across the grass. There are many species damaging lawns in different parts of the country, but they are more abundant in warm climates. They usually injure blue or bent grass. In California *Crambus bonifatellus* (Hulst) prefers moist lowlands, *C. sperryellus* Klots, drier locations. The former is a slender, gray, black-spotted larva with a brown head; the moth is creamy buff with small white, brown, or black spots. The latter is a light-gray larva with dark spots on head and body; the moth is golden with fore wings streaked with silver.

The **bluegrass webworm***, *C. teterellus* (Zincken) is more at home in Kentucky and other parts of the Southeast. It is often accompanied by the striped and leather-colored sod webworms. The predominant species in the East is the **vagabond crambus***, *C. vulgivagellus* Clemens. This is normally a grass feeder but sometimes attacks corn.

All these moths have snouts, made of labial palps, and they fly slowly over grass at dusk in a zigzag fashion, dropping eggs anywhere. Young larvae skeletonize grass blades; older caterpillars cut them off completely. They make silken tubes between the grass stems, shelters camouflaged with bits of grass and bright-green excrement. Pupation is in silken cocoons just below the surface of the ground; there may be several overlapping generations.

Control. Many chemicals are suggested for control, applied in the evening at monthly intervals: chlordane, 2½ pounds of 5 per cent dust per 1000 square feet; DDT, 2½ pounds 5 per cent dust; dieldrin, granulated, or diazinon or ethion according to manufacturer's directions.

Southern Beet Webworm*, *Pachyzancla bipunctalis* (Fabricius). Sometimes serious on spinach.

Spotted Beet Webworm*, *Hymenia perspectalis* (Hübner). The larva is green with purple dots on its head; the moth is cinnamon-brown with narrow white bands on the fore wings. Eggs are laid on leaves of beet and amaranth.

Use pyrethrum-sulfur dust if the foliage is to be used for greens, otherwise DDT.

Sweetgum Webworms, *Salebria afflictella* Hulst and *Tetralopha melanogramma* Zeller. Reported damaging this host in Delaware.

Vagabond Crambus*, *Crambus vulgivagellus* Clemens. See under Sod Webworms.

WEEVILS

Weevils are really beetles, of the order Coleoptera, with the head more or less prolonged into a beak or snout, with mouth parts at the end. Most species are in the family Curculionidae and are injurious plant feeders. Weevils infesting fruits and nuts are often called curculios and have been treated under that heading.

Adaleres Weevil, *Adaleres humeralis* Casey. Light- to dark-brown beetles with grayish mottling, punctate wing covers, feeding on foliage and terminal buds of avocado. Since they cannot fly they can be kept off trees with a sticky band around the trunk.

Alfalfa Weevil*, *Hypera postica* (Gyllenhal). The most important enemy of alfalfa, also infesting clovers, imported from southern Europe about 1900 and first reported from Utah in 1904, now widely distributed. Grayish brown to black weevils with short gray hairs, ⅛ to ¼ inch long, with medium beak, winter about the crown of alfalfa or in debris, feed in spring, then lay shiny yellow oval eggs in cavities in alfalfa stems. The larvae are white at first, then green, with a prominent middorsal stripe. Plants are stunted or eaten to nothing but woody fibers. Careful timing of cutting the crop helps in control, as well as an imported ichneumonid parasite. Malathion and methoxychlor may be used as sprays for forage alfalfa; seed alfalfa may be protected with DDT or dieldrin.

Apple Flea Weevil*, *Rhynchaenus pallicornis* (Say). Found from Missouri and Illinois east to New York, but more destructive in the western portion of this range, on apple, haw, winged elm, hazelnut, quince, wild crab, and blackberry. The adults, very small black snout beetles 1/10 inch long, winter in trash or grass under apple trees. In spring they puncture newly opening leaves and buds, lay eggs along midribs. The grubs mine between the upper and lower leaf surfaces, pupate in a cell inside the leaf, emerge as beetles in late May and June. They feed for 2 weeks on foliage, riddling the leaves with tiny shot holes, then go into hibernation. A spray of DDT or parathion, applied at the pre-pink or pink stage, is effective if applied to underside of leaves.

Arborvitae Weevil*, *Phyllobius intrusus* Kono. A Japanese species found in Rhode Island in 1947, now present in Connecticut and Massachusetts. The adult, covered with greenish scales and fine short hairs, emerges from the soil in early May and is around until July, laying eggs around roots. The eggs hatch in 13 to 17 days. The larvae, white to light pink with brown heads, feed on roots of arborvitae, retinospora, juniper. They pupate in late spring, 10 inches deep in the soil, and the adults feed in the daytime on the top thirds of plants, eating tiny, cup-shaped areas from new terminal leaves. Adults can be killed by spraying with DDT or lindane. Or spray foliage and soil with chlordane or dieldrin in late May or early June.

Asiatic Oak Weevil*, *Cyrtepistomus castaneus* (Roelofs). A new and serious pest of oak and chestnut, first found in New Jersey in 1933, now known from Connecticut to North Carolina and also present in Kentucky, West Virginia, Ohio, Pennsylvania, Tennessee. There is a 1-year cycle with larvae apparently feeding and wintering on roots. They pupate in June with adults emerging in great numbers about a week later. The weevils, black to dark reddish brown, with metallic-green scales, start feeding on sapling oaks and chestnuts, eating everything but mid-veins of leaves, but by August they move to larger trees and also invade hickory, hazelnut, beech, dogwood, raspberry, and some other trees and shrubs. They enter houses in the fall.

Bean Weevil*, *Acanthoscelides obtectus* (Say). Probably a native American although found around the world. Beans stored for food or seed are almost certain to be devoured by weevils unless precautions are taken. This seed weevil is a small snout beetle, ⅛ inch long, olive-brown mottled with darker brown and gray, with reddish legs and antennae. Escaping from stored beans in the garden, it lays eggs in holes chewed along the seam of the bean pod. Small, hairy white grubs, produced in 3 to 30 days, enter and feed in young seed (Plate XXXV). If the storage room is warm, there may be many generations during the winter, the grubs pupating in cells inside the beans, the weevils eating their way out through the seed coat, leaving conspicuous round holes.

Control. Never plant seed known to be infested. After harvest, dry seeds quickly, fumigate with carbon disulfide in a tight steel bin or heat, dry, at 135° F. for 3 to 4 hours, or suspend seeds in a bag in water, heat to 140° F. and then dry rapidly. Treat seed beans with DDT or lindane before planting.

Bean Stalk Weevil*, *Sternechus paludatus* (Casey).

Black Elm Bark Weevil*, *Magdalis barbita* (Say). A small, jet-black beetle with a prominent snout, found from New York to South Dakota and south to Georgia. The beetles emerge from branches of unhealthy elms in May or June and lay eggs in bark. Grubs burrow to the inner bark and sapwood, making longitudinal galleries 1½ inches long. Maintain tree vigor by fertilizing; water during droughts.

Black Vine Weevil*, *Brachyrhinus sulcatus* (Fabricius). Cyclamen Grub. A European species now widely distributed here. It is a serious pest of yew (Taxus), rhododendron, azalea, retinospora, and some other broad- and narrow-leaved evergreens and is a greenhouse menace. Nearly 80 hosts have been listed, including ampelopsis, begonia, blackberry, cranberry, cyclamen, gloxinia, geranium, gardenia, maidenhair fern, primrose, raspberry, spirea, strawberry (though not as injurious as the strawberry root weevil), wisteria.

The adult is a small weevil, ⅜ inch long, with a short snout. It is black or brownish with fine yellow hairs and a sort of corrugated effect down its hard, wingless body (Plate XXXV). Larvae are small, whitish, curved grubs which remain in soil feeding on small roots, often destroying them completely. Hibernation is usually as partly grown larvae, sometimes as adults in soil. After feeding on roots during April and May, larvae turn into soft white pupae, emerging as weevils in June. They hide in the soil during the day, feed on foliage at night. They feed for a month or more before laying eggs in cracks and crevices in the soil and in trash around plants. The young grubs, hatching in 10 days, feed on fine hair roots and on bark around the crown but their heaviest damage is the next spring.

Specimens of yew newly transplanted from nursery to garden are particularly subject to grub injury. Small roots are eaten off, larger roots girdled. If plants in a yew hedge do not start into new growth at the normal time in spring, if tops turn yellow, then brown, the black vine weevil is probably to blame. Feeding by the adult is from the tip of the needle or along the side. On rhododendrons large irregular holes are eaten in from leaf margins at night. In greenhouses grubs continue to feed during the winter months, causing stunting, death, of cyclamen, primrose, and other plants. Adults appear earlier in spring than out of doors and lay eggs over a longer period.

Control. It is easier to kill adults than grubs in soil. In late June, as adults are emerging, spray soil, base of plants and foliage with dieldrin or chlordane (1 teaspoon of 76 per cent emulsion to 1 gallon of water) or use 1 per cent dieldrin dust or 5 per cent chlordane dust, well watered into soil.

Boll Weevil*, *Anthonomus grandis* Boheman. Cotton Boll Weevil. The most notoriously evil insect in the world, yet with such a beneficial influence on methods of agriculture, that in one section of the country it has had a monument erected to it. As home gardeners, you are not directly concerned with controlling the boll weevil but as citizens, you are profoundly affected by it. It has been estimated that every person in the United States pays ten dollars a year more for cotton goods because of the boll weevil. Its arrival in Texas from Mexico in 1892 closed down cotton gin and oil mills, caused banks to fail, depreciated land values, turned wealthy growers into paupers. It still costs us an enormous amount each year. Cotton farmers spend about $75 million annually just for insecticides to beat the weevil and yet losses average nearly $230 million a year.

If, when the boll weevil was first noted, a barrier zone—an area about 50 miles wide where no cotton was grown—has been instituted, the weevil might have been kept within bounds. But at that time it did not seem possible to live in Texas without growing cotton and, rather than take away the source of livelihood from families in such a barrier zone, the Texas legislature turned thumbs down on that proposal and let the boll weevil go its destructive way.

The weevil is small, ¼ inch long, hard-shelled, yellow, gray or brown, nearly black with age, covered with grayish fuzz, with a long, slender snout. It lays an egg in each of 100 to 400 cotton buds or squares and there may be 8 to 10 generations a year. It also feeds on okra, hollyhock, and hibiscus, plants related to cotton.

When the boll-weevil devastation was at its height, cotton farmers learned to do two things. One was ordinary sanitation, clearing the fields and burning old stalks. The other was diversification of crops. They grew corn, hay, potatoes, sugarcane, and especially peanuts and hogs. One county in Alabama cleared $5 million on its first peanut crop. And so, at Enterprise, Alabama, the citizens of Coffee County erected a fountain in honor of the boll weevil, and put on it this inscription, which I once made a special trip to read:

> IN PROFOUND APPRECIATION
> OF THE BOLL WEEVIL
> AND WHAT IT HAS DONE
> AS THE HERALD OF PROSPERITY
> THIS MONUMENT WAS ERECTED
> BY THE CITIZENS OF
> ENTERPRISE, COFFEE COUNTY, ALABAMA

Broadbean Weevil*, *Bruchus rufimanus* Boheman. Confined to the West Coast, attacking broadbeans first, then peas and vetches. It is slightly smaller than the pea weevil and has several individuals in a seed instead of 1, but resembles it otherwise.

Bronze Apple Tree Weevil*, *Magdalis senescens* LeConte.

Cabbage Seedpod Weevil*, *Ceutorhynchus assimilis* (Paykull). In the Pacific Northwest and California, damaging seeds of crucifers—cabbage, turnip, radish, mustard. Adults are black to gray, ⅛ inch long; they lay eggs in seed pods after making punctures with their snouts. The larvae, small, white, legless, feed on seed embryos for about 3 weeks. Dusting with lindane or parathion has given commercial control.

Carrot Weevil*, *Listronotus oregonensis* (LeConte). A pest of carrot, parsley, celery, feeding also on parsnip, dill, and related wild weeds, from New England to Georgia and west to Colorado. The beetles, dark brown, ¼ inch long, hibernate in grass and debris, lay eggs in May in cavities in leaf stalks. White, legless, curved, brown-headed grubs, up to ⅓ inch long, burrow down into the upper part of the carrot root or into celery hearts. The zigzag feeding destroys much tissue. Mature in about 2 weeks, the grubs leave the roots and pupate in soil. Beetles appear in July to lay eggs for a 2nd brood which is injurious in August. There may be a partial 3rd brood.

Control. Rotation of crops has been standard treatment. Spray with DDT, beginning in late April or early May, repeating at 2-week intervals. For parsley use apple pomace bait, 1 part Paris green or calcium arsenate to 20 parts, by weight, of dried apple pomace moistened with water.

Cattleya Weevil, *Cholus cattleyae* Champney. Adults, just under ½ inch long, with white marks on their backs, feed on pseudobulbs and puncture leaves. Larvae also feed on leaves and stems and afford entrance to decay organisms. Hand-pick and spray with DDT.

Citrus Root Weevil*, *Pachnaeus litus* (Germar). Found in southern Florida on citrus, beans, strawberry, avocado, tobacco. Eggs are laid in leaves; larvae drop to the ground and feed on roots. Parathion reduces populations to some extent.

Clover Head Weevil*, *Hypera meles* (Fabricius). Through the East to the Mississippi River, also in Kansas and Utah. A pest of clover, lowering seed production and skeletonizing bean foliage. The adult is black or reddish black, elongate oval, with punctate back covered with gray or brown, sometimes metallic, scales.

Clover Leaf Weevil*, *Hypera punctata* (Fabricius). Chiefly damaging alfalfa and clovers, but with adults feeding on many flowers. They are dark brown with black flecks on the back, paler underneath, with a robust snout. They can be controlled on ornamentals with DDT.

Clover Seed Weevil*, *Miccotrogus picirostris* (Fabricius).

Cocklebur Weevil*, *Rhodobaenus tredecimpunctatus* (Illiger). Cocklebur Billbug. Common on sunflower, evening primrose and similar plants, sometimes a pest of dahlia and chrysanthemum. The adult is reddish with 13 black spots and a long, curved snout, about ⅓ inch long. It winters in trash, lays eggs on tender stalks in May or June; larvae hollow out the stalk near the base, pupate in August. Hand-pick the weevils; spray with DDT; plant dahlias late to avoid injury; clean up ragweed, thistle, joe-pye-weed and other weed hosts near the garden.

Corn Stem Weevil, *Hyperus humilis* (Gyllenhal). First observed as a pest of sweet corn in Florida in 1959, not previously known to injure cultivated crops. Grubs mine the lower stems, causing stunting. The adults, dark brown with white scales, are active at night. DDT or parathion, applied on the day of seedling emergence and at 4-day intervals for 6 applications, has increased yields.

Cowpea Weevil*, *Callosobruchus maculatus* (Fabricius). Present in southern states and California, where there may be 6 to 9 generations a year. Yellowish grubs, ¼ inch long, feed inside seeds in growing cowpea pods. Adults—bronze-black, hump-backed snout beetles, ⅕ inch long—feed on plants and lay eggs in holes eaten through pods.

Cranberry Weevil*, *Anthonomus musculus* Say. Small, black, with reddish wing covers. On leaves and dormant buds. New shoots are killed, entire crops may be destroyed.

Cribrate Weevil, *Brachyrhinus cribricollis* (Gyllenhal). First reported in California in 1929 as a pest of privet, viburnum and turf, more recently a pest of globe artichoke and other plants, including blackberry, mustard, willow, lilac, pyracantha, ornamental plum, rose, pittosporum, pomegranate, camellia, and olive trees. The larvae feed on roots, the adults on buds and foliage. Aldrin and endrin, or a combination of the two, have given good results in tests. A fungus, *Beauveria bassiana,* kills adults in the field.

Currant Fruit Weevil*, *Pseudanthonomus validus* Dietz. In western states on currant. The adults, very small, pale reddish brown marked with pale yellow or white pubescence, puncture young fruit near stems in which eggs are inserted; larvae feed on developing seeds; fruits dry up and drop.

Deodar Weevil*, *Pissodes nemorensis* Germar. A native snout beetle present from southern New Jersey to Missouri and throughout the South, injurious to deodar, Lebanon and Atlas cedars, also reported on Scotch and white pine in a weakened condition. The adult, brownish with irregular markings of brown-and-white scales, gnaws through the bark with its slender beak and feeds on the cambium, often girdling a leader or side branch. It lays eggs in small holes in the bark; the grubs, white with brown heads, ⅓ inch long, burrow in wood and kill leaders and terminal twigs which start to die in January. Small trees may be killed. The grubs pupate in March and the beetles feed in April, then disappear in the surface litter to rest until fall. Spray with DDT; feed the trees as necessary; water during drought periods.

Douglas-fir Twig Weevil*, *Cylindrocopturus furnissi* Buchanan. Feeding on small branches of Douglas-fir and ponderosa pine in the Pacific Northwest, sometimes killing young trees.

Engelmann Spruce Weevil*, *Pissodes engelmanni* Hopkins. Injuring terminals of Engelmann spruce in the West, similar to the Sitka-spruce weevil.

Filbert Weevil*, *Curculio uniformis* (LeConte). Infesting filbert nuts in New Mexico, Arizona, California, Oregon, Washington, and Utah. Cleaning up and destroying dropped nuts is quite effective in control.

Gorse Weevil, *Apion ulicis* Forster. A seed weevil from France introduced into California and Oregon for the biological control of gorse, a noxious weed. The weevil has been spreading satisfactorily.

Hazelnut Weevil*, *Curculio obtusus* (Blanchard). Occasionally injuring the hazelnut seed crop.

Hibiscus Weevil, *Apion hibisci* Fall.

Hollyhock Weevil*, *Apion longirostre* Olivier. Known since 1907; present from New York to Iowa and Kansas. The adults are black, covered with gray hairs, and have a long snout. They make small round holes in leaves and lay eggs in flower buds. Small white legless larvae eat the seed embryo and pupate in its place, adults emerging in August. Spray or dust hollyhocks before pods are formed with lindane, dieldrin, chlordane or DDT; cut and burn stalks with infested seed pods.

92. Imported long-horned weevil, showing characteristic long antennae and foliage injury.

Imported Long-horned Weevil, *Calomycterus setarius* Roelofs. Another Japanese pest, first noted in New York in 1929, reported from Connecticut in 1932 and since then from Illinois, Iowa, Maryland, New Jersey, Pennsylvania, Rhode Island, and Vermont. It is a general feeder, consuming foliage and blossoms of grasses, legumes, flowering garden plants, vegetables, field crops, ornamental shrubs, house plants, vines. It also wanders into houses, crawls over walls and ceilings, gets into food.

Adults, black but appearing gray from their gray scales, ⅜ inch long, with prominent long antennae (the long horns) emerge in late June and are abundant in July and August. They eat irregular areas in from margins of leaves. Eggs are laid in sod and grubs are in the soil until the next June. Adults are wingless and natural spread is slow, but the weevils readily get around by crawling on people and into vehicles. Among the preferred hosts are ivy, lespedeza, African marigold, rose, strawberry, and Virginia-creeper. Chlordane helps in control.

Iris Weevil*, *Mononychus vulpeculus* (Fabricius). Breeds commonly in seed pods of blue flag iris, sometimes punctures ovaries of Japanese and European iris, causing rough, corky scars. Fat grubs feed on the seeds, pupate within the pods. Adults—black, covered below with yellow-and-white scales, ⅕ inch long—emerge when pods burst open. Unless seeds are being saved for breeding, destroy all flower heads as they fade. If seeds are needed, cover blossoms with cheesecloth bags or dust with DDT.

Japanese Weevil, *Pseudocneorhinus bifasciatus* Roelofs. First collected near Philadelphia in 1914, now found at scattered locations in Connecticut, Delaware, Maryland, New Jersey, New York, Pennsylvania, and Virginia, as well as the District of Columbia. It feeds heavily on California privet, sometimes on azalea, camellia, Japanese barberry, chrysanthemum, clematis, elm, fern, forsythia, geranium, hemlock, lilac, lima beans, mimosa, mountain-laurel, lily-of-the-valley, rhododendron, rose, rose-of-Sharon, oak, strawberry, weigela, and veronica. I met it only once when I doctored gardens, but then the weevils were present on privet by the hundreds, cutting broad, rounded sections from the margin of the leaves, resulting in a crenulated appearance. The adults feed in the daytime. They have fused wing covers so they cannot fly, are dark with a broad abdomen, rather short snout. Aldrin, dieldrin, and heptachlor give a quick kill. Chlordane and malathion work more slowly.

Large Chestnut Weevil*, *Curculio proboscideus* (Fabricius). A limiting factor in growing Asiatic chestnuts to replace our lost American species. DDT sprays are quite effective in control.

Lesser Clover Leaf Weevil*, *Hypera nigrirostris* (Fabricius). One of the more important clover pests, especially of red clover. Adults feed on foliage, lay eggs in stems or bud; plants are stunted, misshapen. They are first brown, then grass-green.

Ligustrum Weevil, *Ochyromera ligustri* Warner. A new species found in North Carolina in 1959, feeding on Japanese privet and lilac, now reported also from South Carolina on most species of privet, lilac and on grape leaves. The adult is small, shiny brownish yellow with golden scales. The female lays eggs in seed capsules or fruit in summer and larvae winter in seed, pupating in May. Adults feed on foliage in late June and early July, cutting round or oblong holes; they also feed on pollen.

Lilac Weevil, *Brachyrhinus meridionalis* (Gyllenhal). Recorded as damaging lilac, arborvitae, and privet in California and Washington, lilac in Nevada.

Lily-of-the-Valley Weevil, *Hormorus undulatus*. Notches leaves in from the margin in curious fashion. The injury is common but appears after blooming, so control measures are seldom attempted.

Lily Weevil*, *Agasphaerops nigra* Horn. Heavy infestations are recorded on lily in California.

Lodgepole Terminal Weevil*, *Pissodes terminalis* Hopping. Mines through pith of terminals and kills them down to the first whorl of branches.

Monterey-pine Weevil*, *Pissodes radiatae* Hopkins. Infesting Monterey and other pines on the Pacific Coast. It mines the stems, tops, and bases of young pines above and below ground.

New York Weevil*, *Ithycerus novaboracensis* (Forster). Sometimes injurious to apple trees and young pears near woodlands, also on oak, hickory, beech in the Northeast. Large snout beetles—¾ inch long, gray, spotted with black—prune off twigs and eat into buds. Control measures are seldom used but the beetles can be jarred from young fruit and shade trees and destroyed.

Orchid Weevil, *Diorymerellus laevimargo* Champney. Dendrobium Weevil. On various species of cattleya and dendrobium. The beetles, ⅛ inch long, shiny black with striated (grooved) wing covers, feed on tender leaves or flower petals and lay eggs in root tips, especially in the cattleyas. Small, legless, curved larvae feed on new roots, hollow out old roots, cause tips to blacken. DDT kills the adults as they emerge.

Pales Weevil*, *Hylobius pales* (Herbst). A native, found from Maine to Florida, west to Minnesota, favoring white pine, often on red, sometimes on Scotch, loblolly, shortleaf pines, American larch, Norway spruce and other conifers. It is important in Christmas-tree plantings. The adult is reddish brown to black, speckled with gray or yellow scales, black head and thorax, ⅓ inch long. The larva is white with a light-brown head, ½ inch long. The weevils feed, mostly at night, on bark of seedlings, girdling young trees near ground level and killing many; they also feed on twigs of older trees. They hibernate as adults, lay eggs in fresh-cut logs or stumps in May. Grubs burrow beneath bark, grow slowly, pupate under the bark in September. Most damage comes from the young adults after emergence, before winter hibernation.

Control. Spray ornamental pines with DDT or lead arsenate, making sure the base of the trunk is thoroughly covered.

Pea Leaf Weevil, *Sitona lineata* (Linnaeus). First noted in British Columbia in 1936, now a menace in Oregon and Washington. The adults —slender, grayish brown with alternating light and dark lines—eat U-shaped notches in from margins of leaves, resulting in a scalloped appearance but they may go on to complete defoliation. The larvae destroy root nodules in pea fields and are restricted to legumes. The adults feed also on apple, blackberry, raspberry, rose, and strawberry.

Pea Weevil*, *Bruchus pisorum* (Linnaeus). A seed weevil, present throughout the country. The beetles are short, chunky, ⅕ inch long, brown, flecked with white, black, and gray patches. The larva is white with a small brown head. The female lays her eggs on the outside of a pea pod; the larva bores through the wall of the pod and into one of the young peas, growing inside for 5 or 6 weeks, consuming the contents. It pupates inside the pea and the adult emerges in 1 to 3 weeks. Several larvae may enter a pea, but only 1 survives. There is no continuous breeding in storage, as with bean weevils. The weevils may remain in stored seed a year or two before emerging, but usually they come out soon after pupation and hibernate in any protected place.

Control. In home gardens dusting with rotenone or DDT weekly from the time peas start to blossom until they go out of bloom will give nearly weevil-free peas. Seed can be treated with pyrethrins. Destroy vines immediately after harvest. Many birds feed on pea weevils.

Pecan Weevil*, *Curculio caryae* (Horn). Hickory Nut Weevil. Found wherever pecans or hickories grow, sometimes causing loss of 80 per cent of the pecan crop. The dark brown adults, ⅜ inch long, attack newly formed pecans, causing them to shrivel and drop. Early maturing varieties, such as Stuart, Schley, Mahan, and Moneymaker, are most commonly infested. The female has a beak longer than its body (that of the male is slightly shorter) and with it she punctures the nuts and places eggs, usually 3 to a nut, in the kernel as soon as the water stage is passed. Larvae emerge from nuts in late fall, go down 3 to 9 inches deep in the soil, stay there 1 to 2 years, then pupate in September or October, transforming to the adult in 3 weeks. They remain in the soil until the next July or August, when they come out to feed on nuts. Thus the life cycle takes 2 or 3 years.

Control. DDT is very effective. Spray susceptible varieties with 6 pounds of 50 per cent DDT to 100 gallons water, making the 1st application in late July or early August and the 2nd 10 to 14 days later. Toxaphene is also effective and does not increase mites as rapidly as DDT. EPN is recommended. With only a few trees, weevils can be reduced by jarring the trees with a pole and collecting the weevils on sheets underneath, then dropping them into kerosene. Clean up all dropped nuts.

Pepper Weevil*, *Anthonomus eugenii* Cano. A Mexican insect now important in California, Arizona, New Mexico, Texas, Georgia, and Florida. Small white grubs feed inside buds of bell, sweet, and chili peppers, causing buds and most of pods to drop off. Adults are reddish brown to black with a brassy luster; they have curved beaks, are ⅛ inch long. There are several generations a year. Dusting with DDT every 7 to 10 days until pods mature has been recommended; Sevin is effective but is followed by build-up of green-peach aphid; Thiodan gives control.

Pine Gall Weevil*, *Podapion gallicola* Riley. Forming galls on twigs of scrub, pitch and red pines.

Pine Reproduction Weevil, *Cylindrocopturus eatoni* Buchanan. Killing small ponderosa and Jeffrey reproduction pines in California. Adults puncture needles and bark.

Pine Root Collar Weevil*, *Hylobius radicis* Buchanan. Important in the Northeast on Scotch pine, also on Austrian, red and jack pines in roadside plantings. The soil around base of trees is blackened and soaked with pitch, larvae being present here or in cambium of root collar. Lindane or dieldrin applied as water emulsion to the ground around trees gives effective control.

Puncturevine Weevil, *Microlarinus* spp. Beneficial insects on puncturevine seed pods in California, being released elsewhere. One species feeds on stems.

Red Elm Bark Weevil*, *Magdalis armicollis* (Say). A reddish snout beetle infesting weakened elms. Keep trees fed and watered; remove dying or injured limbs.

Sand-cherry Weevil*, *Anthonomus hirsutus* Bruner.

Sassafras Weevil, *Odontopus calceatus* (Say). Found east of the Mississippi injuring sassafras, tuliptree, and magnolia. Small black snout beetles feed on leaves as buds break, producing many holes. Eggs are laid in midrib of leaves; larvae produce blotch mines.

Sitka-spruce Weevil*, *Pissodes sitchensis* Hopkins. Important in the Pacific Northwest, killing or injuring terminal shoots of young trees, causing a crook in the trunk and/or a forked, worthless tree. The weevil is so prevalent in much of Washington and Oregon, Sitka spruce is no longer planted. Adults are light to dark brown, oval, 3/10 inch long, with a prominent, curved beak. They lay eggs in cavities in bark of the preceding year's terminals. The larvae work down the stem, pupating in wood or pith. DDT should prevent egg laying on small ornamental trees.

Small Chestnut Weevil*, *Curculio auriger* (Casey). More abundant than the large chestnut weevil, often destroying 90 per cent of nuts in Asiatic chestnut stands. Three properly timed DDT sprays reduce the weevils considerably.

Strawberry Root Weevil*, *Brachyrhinus ovatus* (Linnaeus). Present throughout the northern United States, a special pest of strawberries and conifers—hemlock, arborvitae, Japanese yew, some spruce, junipers—also on raspberry, blackberry, cranberry, grasses, cucurbits, crucifers, deciduous trees and shrubs. It is recorded as severely injuring peppermint in Washington. This species is much like the black vine weevil in looks and habit. The beetles are nearly black, striated, ¼ inch long, with short, blunt snouts; the larvae are white, legless, curved. Strawberries are stunted, leaves bunched together, darkened, with fine roots and crowns eaten. Root feeding by grubs often kills small hemlocks, but needle feeding by adults is negligible. Arborvitae roots are not often seriously injured, but terminal twigs are girdled by adults and tender new foliage is eaten. The weevils start emerging from the soil in early June, feeding for 10 to 14 days before laying eggs through the summer. Eggs hatch in 7 to 10 days. Larvae feed on roots until cold weather, when they move down 6 to 14 inches, working up and feeding again in spring. Some winter as adults in trash.

Control. The same chemicals are used for the strawberry root weevil as for the black vine weevil but applied 2 to 3 weeks earlier. Aldrin, chlordane, or dieldrin can be worked into strawberry beds before planting; malathion and parathion can be sprayed on foliage as required.

Strawberry Weevil*, *Anthonomus signatus* Say. An eastern pest of strawberry, raspberry, dewberry; also found on wild blackberry and cinquefoil. The dark, reddish brown, very small snout beetle winters under trash, is active early in spring when strawberries are coming into bloom. The female punctures buds with her long beak, inserts an egg, then crawls down and girdles the stem of the flower bud, causing it to wilt. The grubs feed in the buds for about 4 weeks, pupate, and adults emerge just before midsummer. Spray or dust with DDT or methoxychlor a few day before blossoms open.

Sweetclover Weevil*, *Sitona cylindricollis* (Fabricius). On clover, alfalfa, soybean and cowpea, burrowing in and girdling roots.

Sweetpotato Weevil*, *Cylas formicarius elegantulus* (Summers). Sweetpotato Root Borer. Formerly confined to the Gulf States, now known in New Jersey, feeding on sweetpotato, morning-glory and other plants of the same family. The beetles are ¼ inch long, slender, with blue head, wing covers, and abdomen, red thorax and legs, a long, straight, black beak. The weevil attacks potatoes in the field, entering near the stem, and breeds in stored roots, which are honeycombed by fat, legless white grubs.

Control. Sort out infested potatoes at harvest and destroy; clean up and burn all old vines; destroy volunteer sweetpotatoes and related weeds. Plants can be dipped before setting in DDT, 4 tablespoons 50 per cent per gallon of water; or soil around base of plants can be treated with dieldrin in strips 6 to 8 inches wide.

Thurberia Weevil*, *Anthonomis grandis thurberiae* Pierce. A variety of the boll weevil.

Vegetable Weevil*, *Listroderes costirostris obliquus* (Klug). A beetle from Brazil, first reported in Mississippi in 1922, now spread through the Gulf States and along the coast in California. The weevils are buff-colored with a lighter, V-shaped marking on the wing covers, ⅜ inch long. They have well-developed wings but seldom fly. They go into a summer resting period in late April or early May under trash or loose bark on trees, remaining inactive until early fall, when the parthenogenetic females crawl to vegetable crops to feed and lay eggs, continuing through the winter, except in coldest weather. One weevil lays from 300 to 1500 eggs. The larvae are greenish, sluglike, ½ inch long. They feed voraciously on plants at night, along with adults. They attack beet, cabbage, carrot, cauliflower, lettuce, mustard, onion, potato, radish, spinach, Swiss chard, tomato, turnip, feeding first in the crown, then defoliating whole plants, leaving only stem and midribs. This is also a pest of dichondra lawns in California.

Control. Apply DDT to the soil, 1 per cent rotenone to edible plant parts. Rotate crops and cultivate thoroughly to destroy pupae in soil; keep down weeds.

Vetch Brucid*, *Bruchus brachialis* (Fåhraeus).

White-pine Weevil*, *Pissodes strobi* (Peck). The most serious pest of white pine in the East, a constant threat in home plantings, plantations, and forests, sometimes injuring Norway spruce. Scotch, pitch, and jack pines, other pine and spruce species. You can tell the injury at a distance for the terminal leader is brown in sharp contrast to the rest of the tree. When the yellow, footless grubs, ⅓ inch long, mine in the bark and sapwood of the terminal shoot, they girdle it. When this dies, a lateral branch grows up and tries to replace the leader. Sometimes 2 laterals grow up and the tree is forked. Sometimes the tree is killed back beyond the leader.

Adults are reddish to dark brown, somewhat mottled with brown-and-white scales, with a white spot on lower third of each wing cover, a long, curved snout, ¼ inch long. Adults hibernate under cover on ground, feed in May, lay 2 or 3 pearly eggs in cavities dug in bark of leaders. Egg laying continues through June. The grubs hatch in 6 to 10 days and feed on the inner bark as they girdle the shoot. They pupate in small, oval chambers in the wood and beetles emerge from late June to early September. There is only 1 generation. Wilting and drooping of terminal twigs in spring is the first sign of larval activity.

Control. Infested shoots must be cut off and burned as soon as noticed, making sure the cut is below all grubs. Tie a lateral to a stake to replace the leader and cut off the others. To protect shoots from infestation spray in early spring, when buds are swelling, with DDT or lindane.

Willow Flea Weevil*, *Rhynchaenus rufipes* (LeConte). A small native snout beetle found from Maine to Iowa and in Oregon and California, Colorado, and New Mexico on willow, Lombardy poplar, aspen, sometimes red birch. The grubs—dirty-white, 1/12 inch long, widest at the thorax—mine in leaves, mostly willow, sometimes poplar. The adult is a tiny, jet-black beetle, elliptical, covered with short gray hairs, with reddish-yellow antennae and legs. Weevils hibernate under loose bark or trash on ground, feed in May on opening buds and new leaves, eating circular holes, sometimes killing back twigs. They lay eggs in June, in pits on underside of leaves; larvae pupate in mined leaves; beetles emerge in August. Spray with DDT, chlordane, or lindane.

Yosemite Bark Weevil*, *Pissodes yosemite* Hopkins. On ponderosa and other pines in California, Oregon, and Washington.

Yucca Weevil, *Scyphophorus yuccae* Horn. The adult, black with deeply grooved wing covers, feeds on sap of living yucca in southern California; the larvae breed in bases of green flower stalks and hearts of the same plants.

WHITEFLIES

Whiteflies are minute, sucking insects belonging to the family Aleyrodidae (meaning like flour) of the order Hemiptera (suborder Homoptera). The adults have 2 pairs of broadly rounded wings covered with snow-white waxy powder; they look like tiny white moths. Whiteflies are often present in great numbers on the underside of leaves but are rarely noticed unless the plant is disturbed, when they fly out in clouds. They are primarily tropical insects, but are abundant in greenhouses and on house plants and are common on some garden plants in summer in the North, most of the year in the South.

The life history is much the same for all species of whiteflies. Oval eggs, 1/100 inch long, are attached to underside of leaves by short stalks. They hatch in 4 to 12 days into active, pale-yellow, 6-legged crawlers. The crawlers, usually called larvae, sometimes nymphs, move about for a short time, avoiding strong light, then insert their beaks and start sucking sap. At the 1st molt they lose their legs and antennae and look like very small, very flat, oval scales, often with a marginal fringe of white waxy filaments, sometimes covered with rods or plates of wax. They secrete copious honey-dew through a special opening on the upper surface of the body. After a second molt, the insect becomes a pupa, larger and more distinctly seg-mented, and then the 4-winged adult leaves the pupal skin by a T-shaped opening in the back.

For many years summer oil sprays were used for the control of white-flies; now more reliance is placed on parathion (for commercial growers) or malathion (for backyard gardeners) and sometimes DDT with oil.

Acacia Whitefly, *Tetraleurodes acaciae* (Quaintance). On acacia and coffeeberry in California. The pupa case is shiny black with a short marginal fringe.

Avocado Whitefly*, *Trialeurodes floridensis* (Quaintance). A pest of avo-cado in Florida, also occurring on papaya, banana, guava, annona, citrus. The adult is very small, less than 1 mm, pale yellow with white wings; the larva has a white marginal fringe and remains affixed to foliage over winter. Adults appear in early March to lay white eggs in circles on leaves. There are 3 generations and a partial 4th. An oil spray is recommended in the fall when foliage begins to harden and in spring after fruit is set. Parathion or EPN will give good control.

Azalea Whitefly*, *Pealius azaleae* (Baker & Moles). In eastern and southern United States and in California wherever *Rhododendron mucrona-tum* (*Azalea ledifolia alba* or *indica alba*) is grown. This type has evergreen leaves covered with fine hairs and sticky bud scales. The eggs are pale yel-low, pupae greenish white, oval, present in great numbers on underside of foliage. The leaves lose color from sucking of plant juices and are often covered with sooty mold growing in the honeydew. The mold interferes with photosynthetic function of leaves, the sapsucking reduces vigor and flowering. Spraying in spring with Volck or a similar summer oil has been recommended, applied in late February in the South, April in New Jersey. Malathion, parathion, or diazinon are current recommendations.

Banded-wing Whitefly, *Trialeurodes abutilonea* (Haldeman). On cotton, tobacco, etc. Vector of cotton leaf crumple and sweetpotato feathery mottle.

Barberry Whitefly, *Aleuroplatus berbericola* (Cockerell). Colorless pupal case, adult yellow with white wings. On barberry and Oregon grape (Maho-nia).

Citrus Blackfly*, *Aleurocanthus woglumi* Ashby. A biological control zone is maintained to keep this serious Mexican pest from invading the United States. Many parasites are released in addition to a chemical con-trol zone where eradicative treatments are applied. It has appeared and been eradicated in Florida and Texas. The nymph has a black body with white fringe, the adult a dark-brown body with dark-bluish wings.

Citrus Whitefly*, *Dialeurodes citri* (Ashmead). The most important eco-nomic species of whitefly, a native of Asia introduced into Florida prior to 1885, when it was found on oranges. It appeared in California in 1907 and at later dates, but infestations have been fairly well eradicated so it remains for the most part a pest in the Gulf States, where it has been the most important citrus enemy, although today it ranks below purple scale and rust mite. It injures through the consumption of sap and by the honeydew which encourages sooty mold all over fruit and foliage. It breeds in large numbers in chinaberry trees. Besides these, and citrus, preferred food plants are umbrella trees, cape-jasmine (gardenia) privets, Japanese and wild persimmons, lilac, coffee, prickly-ash. Occasionally infested shrubs or vines include allamanda, banana, cerasus, camellia, choisya, cherry-laurel, green ash, jessamine, pear, pomegranate, smilax, viburnum, wild olive, ailanthus, water oak, Osage-orange, palmetto.

Small yellow eggs, looking like dust, hatch in 10 to 12 days, those from unfertilized females turning into males. The larvae are thin, translucent, scalelike; they lose legs and antennae after the first molt, about 7 days after hatching. The 2nd molt is in 5 or 6 days, the 3rd after 10 to 12 days, after which the insect assumes the pupa or resting state, taking much less food, becoming thicker, the outline of the adult taking form, and finally the winged whitefly emerging through a T-shaped opening in the pupal skin. There are usually 3 generations in Florida, the spring brood of adults at its maximum in late March, the summer brood in June, and the fall (largest) brood in late August and early September.

Control. Oil or parathion sprays for scale insects control whiteflies fairly well. If special treatments are required, use oil or malathion in summer. Cutting down chinaberry trees reduces infestations. There are a number of parasites and predators but they cannot be depended upon for control. Red-and-yellow fungi (species of Aschersonia) grow on whiteflies but are not considered as useful as formerly; they are dependent on proper weather conditions.

Cloudy-winged Whitefly*, *Dialeurodes citrifolii* Morgan. Similar to the citrus whitefly, chiefly a Florida pest, not found in California. Aside from citrus, special hosts are yam vines and a species of Ficus. The eggs are black, covered with a network of ridges, often laid on water sprouts; the adults have a dusky area in each wing. Maximum spring flight is early April; summer, early July; fall, late October. Remove and destroy water sprouts when most eggs are present—May, August, September, or January. Spray as for citrus whitefly, or, if the cloud-winged is the only species, about 3 weeks later.

Crown Whitefly, *Aleuroplatus coronatus* (Quaintance). Abundant on live, valley, and tan oaks, Christmasberry, manzanita, wild coffeeberry throughout California. The pupa case is dark, surrounded by flat, waxy white plates that give the appearance of a crown. Adults have pale yellow-white wings.

Fern Whitefly, *Aleyrodes nephrolepidis* (Quaintance). Found on various ferns in homes and greenhouses. The pupa case is bright yellow, without covering.

Glacial Whitefly, *Trialeurodes glacialis* (Bemis). On bush fruits, blackberry, boysenberry, loganberry, raspberry, and on bean, columbine, wild clematis, coffeeberry, ninebark, sage, snowberry, tan oak in California. The young are yellow with a crystalline fringe, the adults pure white.

Grape Whitefly*, *Trialeurodes vittatus* (Quaintance). On leaves of European grape in California, but normally breeding on chaparral. The young appear in great numbers on underside of leaves, causing smutting of fruit and foliage with mold fungi. The pupa is dark brown with a marginal fringe. DDT will control.

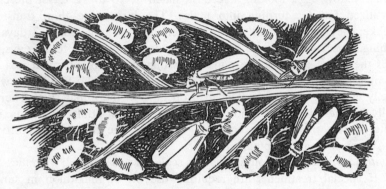

93. Nymph and adults of greenhouse whitefly, much enlarged, on underside of leaf.

Greenhouse Whitefly*, *Trialeurodes vaporariorum* (Westwood). The most common species in greenhouses and gardens. It does not overwinter outdoors in the North but it gets to the garden with greenhouse-grown seedlings of tomatoes and other plants. In my own garden practice I always expect to find whiteflies on ageratum, eggplant, gourds, heliotrope, in dense quantities on underside of squash foliage, on tomatoes. In other sections they are also pests of aster, avocado, barberry, bean, begonia, bignonia, blackberry, calceolaria, calendula, chrysanthemum, cineraria, coleus, coffeeberry, cucumber, fern, fuchsia, geranium, grape, hibiscus, honeylocust, black locust, honeysuckle, Jerusalem-cherry, lantana, lettuce, loganberry, lupine, mallow, morning-glory, muskmelon, pea, pepper, potato, primrose, redbud, rose, sage, soybean, strawberry, watermelon. Infected plants lack vigor, turn yellow, sometimes wilt and die; leaves are sooted with black mold in the South, not so much outdoors in the North.

The eggs are elongated, pale yellowish green; the young are oval, thin, flat, pale green, semitransparent with white waxy threads radiating from their bodies. The larval stages last about a month; under greenhouse conditions there are several overlapping generations. Both male and female adults as well as larvae suck sap from undersurface of leaves.

Control. In greenhouses parathion or Dithione aerosols kill adults with several applications, but sprays are required for the larvae—malathion, parathion, DDT or sulfotepp—or fumigation with hydrogen cyanide. Malathion is usually recommended for garden plants. For house plants try aerosol bombs containing rotenone and pyrethrum.

Inconspicuous Whitefly, *Aleyrodes inconspicua* (Quaintance). Present along the West Coast on California laurel, Christmasberry, clematis, coffeeberry, maple, manzanita, live and tan oaks, Oregon grape (Mahonia). It is also reported from Florida. The pupa is pale or dark yellow with only a narrow fringe. The wings are dusky brown.

A **Jasmine Whitefly,** *Dialeurodes kirkaldyi* (Kotinsky). Known in Hawaii on citrus; reported in 1963 from Florida on several species of jasmine and on morinda. It is similar to the citrus whitefly.

Kellogg's Whitefly, *Aleyrodes kelloggi* (Bemis). Often present in numbers on leaves of Catalina cherry, growing wild or used as an ornamental. The pupa is pale yellow, resting on dense white rods and covered with wide white wax ribbons so it looks like a minute flower.

Madroña Whitefly, *Trialeurodes madroni* (Bemis). Shiny black pupa case with wide white fringe. On madroña in California.

Manzanita Whitefly, *Trialeurodes merlini* (Bemis). Brown pupa case densely covered with white cottony wax. Often so numerous on manzanita, the bush appears covered with snow. Also infesting madroña.

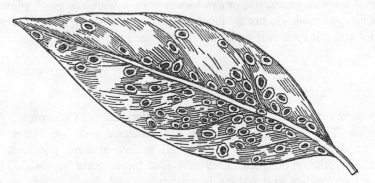

94. Nymphs of mulberry whitefly, black with white fringe.

Mulberry Whitefly*, *Tetraleurodes mori* (Quaintance). An eastern species that survives outdoors. Popular host plants include mulberry, dogwood, azalea, hackberry, holly, mountain-laurel, linden, maple, sycamore. The larvae are elliptical, very small, jet-black, edged with a white fringe of waxy filaments. Adults are around from June to September, increasing in numbers late in the season. Apparently there is no great injury to host plants.

Pruinose Whitefly, *Aleyrodes pruinosa* Bemis. Often present in enormous quantities on undersurface of Christmasberry (toyon) leaves, causing serious smutting in central and southern California. The pupa is yellow to dark brown with a frosty white covering. Adults have yellow bodies with brown markings, 2 dusky spots on each fore wing.

Rhododendron Whitefly*, *Dialeurodes chittendeni* Laing. Yellowish mottling on upper side of leaves together with rolling of margins is caused by flat, oval, greenish, almost transparent larvae. There is much honeydew accompanied by sooty mold. Only rhododendrons with smooth underleaf surfaces are infested. In the Pacific Northwest spraying with 2 per cent white oil emulsion in fall before frost has been effective. In Rhode Island spraying twice in June with DDT has been satisfactory, with lindane and nicotine sulfate giving almost as good control.

Strawberry Whitefly*, *Trialeurodes packardi* (Morrill). A not too important pest of strawberries.

Sweetpotato Whitefly*, *Bemisia tabaci* (Gennadius). Destructive to sweetpotatoes in Florida, especially late planted vines. Larvae are 1/12 inch long, flat, thin, nearly round, very inconspicuous on underside of leaves. Their honeydew encourages black mold. Spray with malathion.

Woolly Whitefly*, *Aleurothrixus floccosus* (Maskell). Probably native to Florida on seagrape, later infesting citrus. The pupa is covered with white woolly filaments of wax, which gives the common name. Eggs are brown, curved, laid in circles as the female revolves around her inserted beak. The 1st larval stage is green, the others brown with a wide fringe of white wax. Adults are yellowish, do not fly much. There are 4 broods. There are several parasites and this species is not of much economic importance.

WIREWORMS

Wireworms are the larvae of click beetles, order Coleoptera, family Elateridae. They occur throughout North America and over most of the world as destructive pests of corn, small grains, grasses, potatoes, beets, carrots, and other root crops. They may also injure other vegetables, beans, peas, lettuce, radish and onions in particular, and flowers such as asters, dahlia, gladiolus, and phlox. Injury is usually most extensive in land recently taken over from sod, but in some sections wireworms are numerous in soil continuously under cultivation. They eat seed, resulting in almost total loss of a planting of corn or peas; they feed on underground stems, causing death of seedlings; they eat the small roots of larger plants; they burrow into potatoes, carrots, beets, or bulbs. They are entirely soil pests, working on underground plant parts.

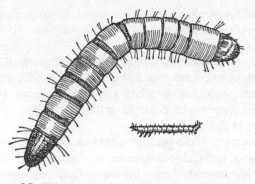

95. Wireworm, larva of a click beetle.

The larvae are smooth, wiry worms, first white with dark jaws, but after feeding and molting several times they are hard, jointed, and shiny, dark yellow to brown, with the last segment of the body pronged or forked, ¼ to ¾ inch long (Plate XXIII). Adults are hard shelled, tapering beetles, gray brown to black, with the joint in front of the wing covers loose and flexible. When they are placed or fall on their backs, they right themselves with a sharp click.

The adults winter in soil cells, emerge in spring when soil temperature warms up, and crawl over the surface or make short flights to lay their eggs, in damp soil 1 to 6 inches deep. The larvae feed little and do not cause much injury until their 2nd season. They sometimes change to white pupae in a year, but more often 2 or 3 years—sometimes 5 or 6 years—pass before they make a small cell 3 to 8 inches below soil surface and pupate. The pupa changes to the adult in 3 weeks but the latter does not emerge until spring. Due to overlapping of generations, wireworms of all sizes and ages are present in the soil at the same time. A few representative species are listed here, followed by general control measures.

Abbreviated Wireworm*, *Hypolithus abbreviatus* (Say).

Columbia Basin Wireworm*, *Limonius subauratus* LeConte. A robust, slate gray to nearly black beetle, larva pale yellow, somewhat flattened. It is a root pest of potato, corn, grains, with the adults feeding on buds and petals of wild rose and apple. It is particularly injurious in Washington, Oregon, and Idaho, is present in California, Arizona, New Mexico, and eastern states.

Dry-land Wireworm*, *Ctenicera glauca* (Germar). Reported in the Northwest on wheat and potatoes.

Eastern Field Wireworm*, *Limonius agonus* (Say). Probably the most common eastern species, found even on land which has been under cultivation for many years. It is a serious pest in the tobacco areas along the Connecticut River and in upstate New York, attacking potatoes, beets, carrots, radishes, onions; most injurious in early spring.

Great Basin Wireworm*, *Ctenicera pruinina* (Horn). Found in dry areas east of the Cascades in Washington, Oregon, Idaho. The beetle is black, slender, the larva yellow.

Gulf Wireworm*, *Conoderus amplicollis* (Gyllenhal). A most important subterranean pest of sweetpotatoes in the Gulf States, its punctures followed by rots. It is also important on white potatoes. Treating soil with lindane, aldrin, or dieldrin two weeks prior to setting slips has given good control with no off-flavor in the potatoes.

Oregon Wireworm*, *Melanotus oregonensis* (LeConte). Common on the West Coast, Oregon, and California, at roots of grapes and figs.

Pacific Coast Wireworm*, *Limonius canus* LeConte. Infesting bulbs along with other root crops. Wedgewood iris bulbs have been protected with benzene hexachloride or dieldrin included with thiram in a 10-minute preplanting dip.

Plains False Wireworm*, *Eleodes opaca* (Say). Found between the Mississippi River and the Pacific Coast; preferring wheat but also attacking grasses, oats, corn, sugar beets, beans, and other garden crops. The beetle is black with a flat back sparsely clothed with white hairs. It cannot fly and when disturbed elevates the hind part of its body, keeping its head on the ground. The larvae are brown or yellow, prominently jointed. Treating wheat seed with a mixture of benzene hexachloride and phenyl mercury has given increased yields.

Puget Sound Wireworm*, *Ctenicera aeripennis aeripennis* (Kirby).

Sand Wireworm*, *Horistonotus uhleri* Horn. A southern pest, on cotton, corn, and peanuts.

Southern Potato Wireworm, *Conoderus falli* Lane. The most abundant species in commercial potato-producing areas in the Southeast, sometimes a pest of sweetpotatoes.

Sugar-beet Wireworm*, *Limonius californicus* (Mannerheim). Common in California and north to Washington. The adult is a small, elongate click beetle, ⅜ inch long, light or dark brown, with coarse punctures on the back. The larvae, typical shiny, yellow-brown hard worms, feed mostly on roots of young plants, asters, chrysanthemums and other flowers as well as sugar beets, beans, and corn.

Tobacco Wireworm*, *Conoderus vespertinus* (Fabricius). Spotted Click Beetle. Common in cornfields as well as a tobacco pest. The larva is hard, thick, ½ inch long, more destructive in dry than in wet soils.

Western Field Wireworm*, *Limonius infuscatus* Motschulsky. Associated with the sugar-beet wireworm on the West Coast, particularly injurious to potatoes in sandy river-bottom land.

Wheat Wireworm*, *Agriotes mancus* (Say). Pest of potato, corn, wheat, and a wide variety of plants across the country.

Control. The soil can be fumigated, treated with insecticides, or seeds and bulbs can be treated before planting. Fumigation gives immediate control, killing the wireworms present, but has no long residual action. Treatment is for fallow soil only and planting should be delayed at least 2 weeks after treatment. Punch holes in the soil 1 foot apart and at least 6 inches deep and pour in ½ to 1 teaspoon of a 10 per cent solution of ethylene dibromide or 1 to 2 teaspoons D-D mixture and close the holes with soil. Special applicators are available for large plots. Both fumigants are poisonous to man; do not breathe the vapors; wash off immediately any liquid spilled on the skin. Ethylene dibromide is combustible.

Soil insecticides are easier to apply than fumigants and have a long-lasting effect, though the initial kill may be slow. Aldrin, dieldrin or heptachlor at 2 to 3 pounds per acre, or chlordane at 4 to 6 pounds, can be applied to the soil surface and disked in before planting. Or lesser amounts can be used along rows.

Seeds treated with lindane, heptachlor, aldrin, dieldrin, or endrin will kill most of the wireworms attracted to germinating seeds.

Cultural measures include crop rotation, clean summer fallowing of the land every 2 or 3 years, shallow tillage, proper drainage.

Chapter VI

HOST PLANTS AND THEIR PESTS

In this section there are sorted out under their different host plants (the plants they live or feed on) the nearly 1900 garden pests included in Chapter V. Some have been dismissed in a line or two; some have been treated in detail. The list is by no means complete, but I hope it covers the major insect pests to be found in the various sections of continental United States. It has only a few references to Hawaii because I have had no personal experience with the exotic possibilities there.

Some of the pests are limited to one or two hosts, others may attack several hundred different kinds of plants. In the latter case, the more important food plants are given as I have observed them in my own practice or have found in the literature. I have been greatly aided, in making up this Check List, by the *Cooperative Economic Insect Report* that comes weekly from the Plant Pest Control Division of the United States Department of Agriculture, as well as by the publications from various state institutions.

The pests are listed under each host alphabetically according to the groups under which they are described in the pest section, Chapter V, which is also in alphabetical order. The group name, **Aphid, Beetle, Borer, Bug, Caterpillar,** and so on, is given in boldface. For instance, under ABUTILON we have **Beetle,** Fuller Rose, which means that you find BEETLES in Chapter V and then run down **Fuller Rose Beetle** as if you were using a dictionary. So far as they are available, the common names are those presently approved by the Committee on Common Names of the Entomological Society of America. Where an insect does not have a common name officially designated, I have supplied one that will aid in finger-tip reference. Approved names are marked with an asterisk. Other names frequently used as common names are given with the descriptions of the pests in Chapter V and also in the Index. See pages 45, 46 for further help in finding the particular pest that is worrying you at the moment.

The list of insects under certain host plants is appallingly long, but don't let it be hopelessly discouraging. Many insects can be safely ignored; many will never appear in your particular region; and of those that may be a problem in your state, few will be disastrous in any one season. Some of the more important pests are singled out by a brief comment.

Having noted some of the possibilities, check back to Chapter V for a more complete description of the damage, the life history or the pest and treatment. Always read the introduction to each group of pests as well as the text on a particular species. If typical life histories and control measures are given for the group as a whole, the details are not repeated under every species.

Remember also that control measures and particularly the chemicals recommended are constantly changing. They vary from state to state as well as year to year. For fruits, vegetables, and ornamentals be sure to ask for help from your local County Agent or State Experiment Station. They have free bulletins and spray schedules that are constantly being revised to keep up with our advancing knowledge. This book is definitely not the last word!

ABELIA
Nematode, Northern Root-knot; Southern Root-knot.
Scale, Florida Wax; Greedy; Latania; Lesser Snow; White Peach.

ABUTILON (Flowering Maple)
Beetle, Fuller Rose (feeds from leaf margins).
Bollworm, Pink. **Mealybugs. Mites** (red spiders).
Moth, Abutilon (looper caterpillar chews foliage).
Nematode, Root-knot.
Scale, Black Araucaria; Brown Soft; Cottony Taxus; Lesser Snow.
Weevil, Imported Long-horned (feeds from edge of leaf).
Whitefly, Greenhouse (minute white flies on underside of leaves).

ACACIA
Beetle, Fuller Rose. **Borer,** Branch and Twig.
Caterpillar, Omnivorous Looper; Orange Tortrix.
Mealybug, Citrus; Ground (white, powdery, on roots); Mexican.
Psyllid, Acacia.
Scale, Black Thread; California Red; Cottony-cushion; Cyanophyllum; Dictyospermum; Fern; Florida Red; Florida Wax; Greedy; Lesser Snow; Long Soft; Mimosa; Mining; Oleander; Pustule; Quohog-shaped; Rufous; San Jose; White Peach.
Spittlebugs. Whitefly, Acacia.

ACALYPHA (Copper-leaf; Chenille Plant)
Mealybug, Long-tailed; Mexican; Striped.
Scale, Black; Brown Soft; Cottony-cushion; Cottony Taxus; Cyanophyllum; Florida Red; Green Shield; Long Soft; Parlatorialike; Pyriform.

ACANTHOPANAX (Five-leaf Aralia)
Bug, Four-lined Plant (dark, depressed circular spots in leaves).

ACONITE, Monkshood (*Aconitum*)

Bug, Four-lined Plant (dark, depressed spots in leaves).
Leaf Miner, Larkspur (tan blotches on foliage).
Mite, Cyclamen (leaves, buds, deformed, blackened).

ACTINIDIA

Scale, Lesser Snow; San Jose.

AECHEMIA

Scale, Aechemia; Boisduval's; Latania; Pineapple.

AFRICAN-VIOLET (*Saintpaulia*)

Aphid, Foxglove.
Mealybug, Citrus (white cottony masses at leaf axils).
Mite, Broad (leaves glassy); Cyclamen (leaves deformed; stems twisted).
Nematode, Carolina Spiral; Peanut Root-knot; Spring-crimp (brown areas in leaves); West African Spiral.
Scale, Fern.

AGAPANTHUS (African-lily; Lily-of-the Nile)

Scale, Latania. **Thrips,** Banded Greenhouse.

AGAVE (see Century Plant)

AGERATUM

Beetle, Oriental. **Budworm,** Tobacco (feeds on buds).
Earworm, Corn (eats buds or foliage).
Leaf Tier, Celery (feeds inside rolled leaves).
Mite, Cyclamen (leaves, flowers deformed); Two-spotted (leaves white).
Whitefly, Greenhouse (common in late summer; leaves stippled white).

AGRIMONY (*Agrimonia*)

Aphid, Potato.

AILANTHUS (Tree-of-Heaven)

Borer, Brown Wood (brown beetle, yellow larva, winding galleries).
Moth, Cynthia (large green caterpillar). **Scale,** Oystershell.
Webworm, Ailanthus (brown caterpillars in fine webs).
Whitefly, Citrus.

AJUGA (Bugleweed)

Mite, Bugle Bud.

AKEBIA
Scale, San Jose (small, round, grayish).

AKEE (*Blightia sapinda*)
Scale, Black; Green Shield; Pustule.

ALBIZZIA (see Mimosa)

ALDER (*Alnus*)
Aphid, Alder; Hop; Woolly Alder (common, goes over to maple).
Beetle, Alder Bark; Alder Flea (steel-blue, may defoliate); Elm Calligrapha.
Borer, Banded Alder; California Prionus; Pacific Flat-headed; Poplar-and-Willow.
Bug, Alder Lace. **Butterfly,** Western Swallowtail.
Casebearer, Birch.
Caterpillar, Chain-spotted Geometer; Omnivorous Looper; Western Tent.
Leaf Miner, European Alder. **Leaf Skeletonizer,** Birch.
Mite, Fruit-tree; Yellow Spider.
Moth, Gypsy; Smeared Dagger; Spotted Tussock.
Psyllid, Alder. **Sawfly,** Striped Alder.
Scale, Black; Brown Soft; Cottony Maple; European Fruit Lecanium; Green Shield; Oystershell; San Jose; Willow Scurfy.
Spittlebug, Alder.

ALFALFA (*Medicago*)
Aphid, Alfalfa; Pea; Spotted Alfalfa.
Armyworm, Western Yellow-striped.
Beetle, Alfalfa Snout; Pale-striped; Striped Blister.
Bug, Alfalfa Plant; Rapid Plant; Superb Plant.
Butterfly, Orange Sulfur.
Caterpillar, Alfalfa; Alfalfa Looper; Green Cloverworm.
Curculio, Clover Root. **Leaf Roller,** Omnivorous.
Mite, Strawberry Spider. **Moth,** Pine Tortrix.
Nematode, Cobb's Meadow; Corn Meadow; Godfrey's Meadow.
Rootworm, Western Corn. **Spittlebug,** Meadow.
Treehopper, Three-cornered Alfalfa.
Webworm, Alfalfa; Garden.
Weevil, Alfalfa; Clover Head; Sweetclover.

ALLAMANDA
Mealybug, Long-tailed.
Scale, Black; Cyanophyllum; Dictyospermum; Florida Red; Hemispherical; Mining; Purple; Pyriform; Tesselated; White Peach.
Whitefly, Citrus.

ALMOND (*Prunus communis*)

Aphid, Black Peach; Waterlily (winter host for).
Beetle, Western Striped Cucumber; Tobacco Flea.
Borer, American Plum; California Prionus; Peach Twig; Shot-hole; Western Peach Tree.
Bug, Boxelder; Consperse Stink.
Casebearer, California.
Caterpillar, California Tent; Filbertworm; Navel Orangeworm; Omnivorous Looper; Red-humped.
Leafhopper, Plum (transmits yellows). **Leaf Roller,** Fruit-tree.
Mite, Clover; European Red; Pacific Spider; Silver; Texas Citrus; Two-spotted.
Nematode, Root-knot; Walnut Meadow.
Scale, Black; Coconut; Cottony-cushion; European Fruit Lecanium; Forbes; Greedy; Green Shield; Hemispherical; Howard; Olive; Oystershell; San Jose; Walnut.
Thrips, Citrus.

ALOE

Scale, Brown Soft; California Red; Florida Red; Hemispherical; Oleander (pale yellow).

ALSTROEMERIA

Thrips, Banded Greenhouse.

ALTERNANTHERA

Scale, Parlatorialike.

ALYSSUM (Madwort, Basket-of-Gold)
and SWEET ALYSSUM (*Lobularia maritima*)

Beetle, Red Turnip.
Caterpillar, Imported Cabbageworm.
Leafhopper, Six-spotted (transmits aster yellows).
Moth, Diamondback (green caterpillar).
Nematode, Cabbage Cyst.

AMARANTH (*Amaranthus*)

Aphid, Potato. **Beetle,** Carrot.
Leafhopper, Southern Garden.
Nematode, Cobb's Meadow; De Man's.
Scale, Cottony-cushion; Green.

AMARYLLIS (*Hippeastrum,* other Genera)
Beetle, Black Blister.
Caterpillar, Convict (black with white bands). **Cutworm,** Climbing.
Fly, Bulb (one maggot inside); Lesser Bulb (several maggots).
Mealybug, Citrus. **Mite,** Bulb (in rotting bulbs).
Nematode, Scribner's Meadow; Stem and Bulb (dark rings in bulb).
Scale, Brown Soft; Hemispherical.
Thrips, Banded Greenhouse; Gladiolus (foliage, flowers streaked); Greenhouse; Sugar-beet.

AMAZON-LILY (*Eucharis*)
Mealybug, Pineapple.
Scale, Dictyospermum.

AMPELOPSIS
Beetle, Rhabdopterus.
Scale, Barnacle; Hemispherical.
Weevil, Black Vine.

ANCHUSA
Leafhopper, Six-spotted. **Mites,** Spider.

ANDIRA (Angelin-tree; Cabbage-tree)
Scale, Black Thread; Latania; Mining.

ANDROMEDA (*Pieris,* other genera)
Bug, Andromeda lace (foliage of *Pieris japonica* stippled white).
Caterpillar, Azalea.
Mite, Two-spotted (foliage yellow). **Nematode,** Tesselate Stylet.
Scale, Florida wax (waxy white tinged with pink); Cottony Maple; Latania; Nigra.

ANEMONE (Windflower)
Aphid, Crescent-marked Lily; other species.
Beetle, Black Blister (devours foliage, flowers of Japanese anemone).
Cutworms. Leaf Tier, Celery (webs foliage).
Nematode, Spring Crimp (dark blotches on leaves); Stem and Bulb.
Thrips, Pear.

ANISE-TREE (*Illicium floridanum*)
Scale, Brown Soft; Cottony-cushion; Florida Red; Purple.

ANTHERICUM (St.-Bernards-Lily)
Scale, Cyanophyllum; Dictyospermum; Florida Red; Hemispherical.

ANTHURIUM
Scale, Brown Soft; Boisduval's; Dictyospermum; Fern; Green Shield; Hemispherical; Proteus.
Mealybugs. Mites.

ANTIDESMA (Tropical Currant)
Scale, Black; Brown Soft; Cottony-cushion; Green; Green Shield; Pyriform.

APPLE (*Pyrus malus*)
Aphid, Apple; Apple Grain; Clover; Hawthorn; Hop; Potato; Rosy Apple (curls leaves); Spirea; Woolly Apple.

Beetle, Apple Flea; Apple Twig; Bumbling Flower; Cherry Leaf; Fig; Fuller Rose; Grape Colaspis; Grape Flea; Green June; Imbricated Snout; Japanese; Potato Flea; Rose Chafer; Rose Leaf; Strawberry Leaf; Syneta Leaf; Western Striped Cucumber.

Borer, American Plum; Apple Twig; Broad-necked Root; Brown Wood; California Prionus; Flatheaded Apple Tree; Pacific Flatheaded; Pigeon Tremex; Roundheaded Apple Tree; Shot-hole; Western Peach Tree.

Bud Moth, Eye-spotted.

Bug, Apple Red; Boxelder; Dark Apple Red; Green Stink; Lygus; Pear Plant; Tarnished Plant.

Butterfly, Western Swallowtail.

Cankerworm, Fall; Spring.

Casebearer, California, Cherry, Cigar, Pistol.

Caterpillar, Azalea; California Tent; Eastern Tent; Forest Tent; Linden Looper; Orange Tortrix; Palmerworm; Red-humped; Saddled Prominent; Schizura; Stinging Rose; Unicorn; Walnut; Western Tent; Western Tussock; Yellow-necked.

Cicada, Periodical.   **Cricket,** Black-horned; Snowy Tree.

Curculio, Apple; Larger Apple; Plum.

Fruitworm, Green; Lesser Appleworm.   **Leaf Crumpler.**

Leafhopper, Apple; Grape; Japanese; Mountain; Potato; Rose; Three-banded; Virginia-creeper; White Apple.

Leaf Miner, Apple Leaf Blotch; Apple Trumpet; Basswood; Spotted Tentiform; Unspotted Tentiform.

Leaf Roller, Fruit-tree; Oblique-banded; Red-banded.

Leaf Skeletonizer, Apple; Apple-and-thorn.

Maggot, Apple (common cause of wormy apples).

Mealybug, Apple; Citrophilus; Comstock; Grape; Taxus.

Midge, Apple Leaf-curling.

Mite, Clover; European Red (serious problem, foliage sickly); Four-spotted; Fruit-tree; McDaniel Spider; Pacific Spider; Pear Leaf Blister; Pear Rust; Strawberry Spider; Two-spotted; Willamette; Yellow Spider.

Moth, American Dagger; Apple Fruit; Brown-tail; Codling (most important apple pest; wormy deformed fruit); Crinkled Flannel; Ermine; Gypsy; Hickory Tussock; Leopard; Oriental; Oriental Fruit; Resplendent Shield Bearer; Rusty Tussock; Spotted Tussock; Western Tussock; White-lined Sphinx; White-marked Sphinx.

Nematode, Christie's Spiral; Cobb's Meadow; De Man's; Steiner's Spiral; Tesselate Stylet.

Psyllid, Apple Sucker. **Rootworm,** Strawberry.

Sawfly, Dock; European Apple.

Scale, Acuminate; Black; Brown Soft; California Red; Cottony-cushion; Cottony Maple; Cottony Peach; European Fruit Lecanium; Florida Red; Florida Wax; Forbes; Greedy; Green Shield; Howard; Italian Pear; Olive Parlatoria; Oystershell; Putnam; San Jose; Scurfy; Walnut.

Spanworm, Cleft-headed.

Termites, Subterranean. **Thrips,** Madroña; Pear.

Treehopper, Buffalo.

Wasp, Apple Chalcid. **Webworm,** Fall.

Weevil, Apple Flea; Bronze Apple Tree; New York; Pea Leaf.

Wireworm, Columbia Basin.

Farmers have to apply a dozen or more combination sprays to obtain marketable fruit. Every state and county provides spray schedules for commercial growers and others for home gardeners, tailored to local pests and conditions. Combination fruit-tree sprays are available for home gardeners, and sometimes 5 properly timed applications will produce fruit fairly free from pests. The schedule usually calls for a dormant or delayed dormant spray for scale insects and aphids; a pink spray when buds show color, for caterpillars and other chewing insects, as well as apple scab; a petal-fall or calyx spray when most of the petals have fallen (very important for controlling codling moth); and at least 2 cover sprays for codling moth. A summer spray may be needed for apple maggot. If DDT is used in the all-purpose spray, a miticide should be included.

APRICOT (*Prunus armeniaca*)

Aphid, Black Peach; Green Peach; Mealy Plum (slits and smudges fruit, stunts tree); Thistle; Waterlily.

Beetle, Fig; Fuller Rose; Green June; Plum Gouger; Western Spotted Cucumber (eats holes in fruits, spreads brown rot).

Borer, American Plum; Branch and Twig; (small holes at base of buds, fruit spurs); Carpenterworm; Flatheaded Apple Tree; Pacific Flatheaded; Peach Tree; Peach Twig; Shot-hole; Western Peach Tree.

Butterfly, Western Swallowtail.
Cankerworm, Fall; Spring.
Caterpillar, California Tent; Orange Tortrix; Red-humped; Yellow-necked.
Curculio, Plum. **Earwig,** European.
Fruitworm, Green. **Leafhopper,** Plum.
Leaf Roller, Fruit-tree; Oblique-banded.
Mealybug, Grape.
Mite, Clover; Fruit-tree; Pacific Spider; Two-spotted; Willamette.
Moth, Codling, Oriental Fruit; Western Tussock.
Nematode, Walnut Meadow.
Sawfly, Cherry Fruit.
Scale, Black; Brown Soft; Cottony-cushion; European Fruit Lecanium; Forbes; Italian Pear; Olive Parlatoria; Oystershell; San Jose; Walnut; White Peach.
Termites. Thrips, Citrus; Pear; Western Flower.

ARABIS (Rockcress)
Aphid, Crescent-marked Lily (yellow and black).

ARALIA
Aphid, Ivy (oleander).
Caterpillar, Imported Cabbageworm; Omnivorous Looper.
Leafhopper, Japanese. **Leaf Miner,** Serpentine.
Mealybug, Citrus; Long-tailed.
Scale, Black; Brown Soft; Dictyospermum; Cottony-cushion; Florida Red; Green; Green Shield; Hemispherical; Japanese Wax; Pyriform; Red Wax.
Thrips, Banded Greenhouse; Sugar-beet.

ARAUCARIA (Monkeypuzzle; Norfolk-Island-pine)
Mealybug, Citrus; Cypress; Golden (covered with yellow wax).
Scale, Araucaria (white); Black Araucaria (very dark); Brown Soft; Chaff; Dictyospermum; Florida Red; Proteus.
Thrips, Greenhouse.

ARBORVITAE (*Thuja*)
Aphid, Arborvitae (brown with white bloom).
Bagworm, (common, small bags on twigs).
Beetle, Northern Cedar Bark (twigs wilt, hang down); Western Cedar Bark.
Borer, Cedar Tree (brown beetle; may girdle trees).
Caterpillar, Hemlock Looper.
Leaf Miner, Arborvitae (tips of twigs light-colored).
Mite, Spruce Spider (common, serious; foliage brown); Tip-dwarf; Two-spotted.

Nematode, Cobb's Meadow; De Man's; Tesselate Stylet.
Psyllid, Tomato. **Sawfly,** Arborvitae.
Scale, Dictyospermum; European Fruit Lecanium; Fletcher; Glover; Juniper; Latania; Newstead's; San Jose.
Spittlebugs.
Weevil, Arborvitae; Lilac; Strawberry Root.

ARBUTUS (see Madrona; Strawberry-tree)

ARDISIA

Orthezia, Greenhouse.
Scale, Brown Soft; Cottony Taxus; Cyanophyllum; Dictyospermum; Fern; Florida Wax; Hemispherical; Latania; Lesser Snow; Yellow.

ARTEMISIA (Wormwood; Sagebrush)

Aphid, Artemisia; Pale Chrysanthemum.
Beetle, Gray Leaf; Goldenrod. **Grasshoppers.**
Mealybug, Yucca.
Midge, Artemisia Gall. **Mite,** Artemisia Gall.
Psyllid, Artemisia; Knotweed.
Scale, Black Araucaria; Artemisia (large white sacs); Black.
Thrips, Artemisia.

ARTICHOKE, GLOBE (*Cynara scolymus*)

Aphid, Bean (black); Oleaster-thistle (pale yellow to green).
Earworm, Corn.
Moth, Artichoke Plume (yellow caterpillar in stems, heads).
Slug, Gray Garden; Greenhouse.
Termites, Western Subterranean.

ARTICHOKE, JERUSALEM (*Helianthus tuberosus*)

Aphid, Sunflower.

ARTILLERY PLANT (*Pilea*)

Scale, Lesser Snow.

ASCLEPIAS (see Butterfly Weed)

ASH (Fraxinus)

Aphid, Leaf-curl Ash.
Borer, Apple Twig; Ash; Banded Alder; Brown Wood; California Prionus; Carpenterworm; Flatheaded Apple Tree; Lilac (common, in wood, scar tissue on trunk); Pacific Flatheaded; Red-headed Ash.
Bug, Ash Lace; Ash Plant; California Ash Mirid; Sycamore Lace.

Butterfly, Tiger Swallowtail.
Cankerworm, Fall.
Caterpillar, California Tent; Forest Tent; Great Basin Tent; Hickory Horned Devil.
Cricket, Snowy Tree (may injure bark in egg laying).
Fruitworm, Green.   **Leaf Miner,** Lilac (blotches in leaves).
Leaf Roller, Fruit-tree; Oblique-banded (caterpillars in rolled leaves).
Mite, Ash Flower-gall; Privet.
Moth, Brown-tail; Great Ash Sphinx; Leopard; Polyphemus; Promethea (large green caterpillar).
Sawfly, Black-headed Ash; Brown-headed Ash (may defoliate).
Scale, Brown Soft; Cottony Maple; European Fruit Lecanium; Howard; Olive; Osborn's; Oystershell (often injurious); Putnam; San Jose; Scurfy; Terrapin; White Peach.
Webworm, Fall.
Whitefly, Citrus.

ASPARAGUS

Aphid, Bean; Crescent-marked Lily; Melon; Potato.
Beetle, Asparagus (feeds on shoots, foliage); Japanese (on foliage); Spotted Asparagus (larvae eat berries); Spotted Cucumber.
Bug, Garden Fleahopper; Say Stink; Harlequin.
Caterpillar, Orange Tortrix; Yellow Woollybear.
Centipede, Garden Symphylan (injures shoots, serious in California).
Cutworms.
Leaf Miner, Asparagus (maggots may girdle stems).
Mite, Bulb (may injure underground stems).
Nematode, De Man's; Godfrey's Meadow; Steiner's Spiral.
Scale, Black Thread, Dictyospermum; Latania; Lesser Snow.

ASPARAGUS FERN, "SMILAX" (*Asparagus plumosus*)

Aphid, Crescent-marked Lily.
Armyworm, Beet.
Bug, Garden Fleahopper; Rapid Plant.
Cutworm, Variegated (climbs plants, clips stems).
Mite, Two-spotted (mealy webs, loss of color).
Scale, Black; Chaff; Coconut; Hemispherical; Lesser Snow; Oleander.
Thrips, Onion (silvering, curling of leaves; brown corky spots).

ASPEN (see Poplar)

ASPIDISTRA

Scale, California Red; Dictyospermum; Fern (white, conspicuous); Florida Red; Lesser Snow; Proteus; Pyriform.

ASSONIA (Dombeya)

Scale, Black, Brown Soft; Chaff; Latania; Lesser Snow; Long Soft; Pustule.

ASTER, CHINA (*Callistephus*)

Aphid, Brown Ambrosia; Corn Root; Crescent-marked Lily; Green Peach; Leaf-curl Plum; Lettuce Root; Melon; Potato; Solanum Root; Sugar-beet Root; Western Aster Root; White Aster Root.

Beetle, Asiatic Garden; Black Blister (common on flowers); Clematis Blister; June (grubs injure roots); Margined Blister; Potato Flea; Spotted Cucumber; Striped Cucumber.

Borer, European Corn; Stalk.

Bug, Chrysanthemum Lace; Four-lined Plant; Tarnished Plant.

Centipede, Garden Symphylan.

Leafhopper, Six-spotted (transmits aster yellows); Red-banded; Southern Garden. **Leaf Miner,** Wild Parsnip.

Leaf Roller, Oblique-banded. **Leaf Tier,** Celery.

Mealybug, Solanum; Yucca. **Mite,** Broad.

Nematode, Chrysanthemum Foliar.

Scale, Black (not common); Green.

Thrips, Banded Greenhouse; Gladiolus.

Whitefly, Greenhouse. **Wireworm,** Sugar-beet.

ASTER, Perennial

Aphid, Aster (green, clustered thick on flower stems); Grindelia; Little Black-lined Aster.

AUCUBA (Golddust Plant)

Aphid, Aucuba (greenish).

Scale, California Red (yellow strain, making wounds for leaf-spot fungi); Chaff; Cyanophyllum; Dictyospermum; Latania; White Peach.

Walkingstick, Two-striped.

ASTILBE

Beetle, Japanese (descends on flowers and foliage in hordes).

AUSTRALIAN-PINE (*Casuarina*)

Borer, Australian-pine.

Mealybug, Citrus; Long-tailed.

Scale, Barnacle; Brown Soft; Cottony-cushion; Dictyospermum; Latania; Long Soft; Mining (grayish, mines partly in bark).

AUSTRALIAN SILK-OAK (see Grevillea)

AVOCADO (*Persea americana*)

Ant, Argentine; Fire.

Aphid, Bean; Melon; Spirea.

Beetle, Ambrosia; Banded Flea; Blossom Anomala; Bronze Willow Flea; Darkling Ground; Fuller Rose; June (on young trees); Rhabdopterus.

Borer, Branch and Twig; Avocado Tree Girdler; Shot-hole.

Bug, Avocado Lace; False Chinch; Harlequin; Lygus.

Butterfly, Western Swallowtail.

Caterpillar, Avocado (Amorbia; skeletonizes leaves, scars fruit); Omnivorous Looper; Orange Tortrix.

Cricket, Snowy Tree. **Cutworm,** Variegated (on young trees).

Mealybug, Citrophilus; Citrus; Coconut; Coleman's; Long-tailed.

Leaf Roller, Avocado.

Mite, Avocado Brown; Avocado Bud; Avocado Red; Broad; Pallid; Platanus; Six-spotted.

Nematode, Godfrey's Meadow; Stubby Root; Walnut Meadow.

Scale, Acuminate; Barnacle; Black; Brown Soft; Camphor; California Red; Cottony Maple; Cyanophyllum; Dictyospermum (important in Florida); European Fruit Lecanium; Florida Red; Florida Wax; Greedy; Green Shield; Hemispherical; Latania (gray to yellow, serious pest); Lesser Snow; Oleander; Oriental; Parlatorialike; Purple; Pyriform (serious in Florida); Red Bay; Rufous; Tea; Terrapin; Tesselated; Tuliptree.

Snail, Brown Garden.

Thrips, Avocado Blossom; Bean; Greenhouse (important, fruit scarred); Red-banded.

Weevil, Adaleres; Citrus Root.

Whitefly, Avocado; Greenhouse.

AZALEA (*Rhododendron*)

Aphid, Azalea.

Beetle, Asiatic Garden; Fuller Rose.

Borer, Azalea Stem (yellow grub in twigs); Rhododendron (in wood near base); Raspberry Cane.

Bug, Azalea Lace (most common and serious pest); Rhododendron Lace.

Caterpillar, Azalea. **Leaf Miner,** Azalea.

Mealybug, Citrophilus; Long-tailed; Striped.

Mite, Azalea; Cyclamen; Privet; Southern Red (causes defoliation); Two-spotted.

Moth, White-lined Sphinx.

Nematode, American Dagger; Christie's Stubby Root; Cobb's Meadow; Cotton Root-knot; De Man's; Fig Pin; Javanese Root-knot; Steiner's Spiral; Sting; Tesselate; Thorne's Lance.

Planthopper, Citrus Flatid.

Scale, Acuminate; Azalea Bark (white cotton, black mold on twigs); Camellia Mining; Camphor; Cyanophyllum; Florida Red; Greedy; Latania; Oleander; Peony (serious in South; brown humps, white circles in branches); Pyriform; Red Bay; Soft Azalea (resembles Azalea Bark); Walnut.

Thrips, Greenhouse (leaves pale, covered with black dots); Madroña.

Walkingstick, Two-striped.

Weevil, Black Vine (grubs injure roots; beetles notch leaves at night; girdle stem); Japanese; Strawberry Root.

Whitefly, Mulberry; Rhododendron.

Spraying to control azalea lace bug is almost always necessary. Bark and peony scales, thrips, and mites are more of a problem in warm climates.

BALSAM-APPLE (*Momordica balsamina*)

Scale, Green; Hemispherical; Lesser Snow.

BALSAM, GARDEN (*Impatiens balsamina*)

Aphid, Impatiens; Spirea.

Beetle, Spotted Cucumber (eats holes in blossoms).

Bug, Tarnished Plant (blackens new shoots).

Mealybug, Citrus. **Nematode,** Peanut Root-knot.

BALSAM FIR (see Fir)

BALSAM-ROOT (*Balsamorhiza*)

Bug, Distinct Lace. **Fly,** in flower head.

Mite, Balsam-root.

BAMBOO (*Bambusa*)

Aphid, Bamboo (yellow with black markings).

Mite, Bamboo.

Scale, Bamboo; Cottony Bamboo (white sacs at leaf axils); Cottony-cushion; Dictyospermum; Green; Hemispherical; Proteus.

BANANA (*Musa*)

Aphid, Banana.

Borer, Banana Root.

Mealybug, Citrus; Long-tailed; Pineapple; Yucca.

Nematode, Burrowing; Southern Root-knot; West African Spiral.

Scale, Acuminate; Black; Boisduval's; Brown Soft; California Red; Coconut; Cyanophyllum; Dictyospermum; Fern; Florida Red; Green; Hemispherical; Latania; Oleander; Oriental; Pyriform; Rufous; Tesselated.

Whitefly, Avocado; Citrus.

BANANA-SHRUB (*Michelis fuscata*)
Scale, Tuliptree. **Whitefly,** Citrus.

BANKSIA (Australian Honeysuckle)
Scale, Black Araucaria; Purple.

BANYAN (*Ficus benghalensis*)
Mealybug, Long-tailed.
Scale, Black; Chinese Obscure; Green Shield; Mining.

BARBERRY (*Berberis*)
Aphid, Barberry (small, yellow-green, on new shoots).
Beetle, Asiatic Garden.
Moth, Eight-spotted Forester. **Nematode,** Northern Root-knot.
Scale, Barberry (convex, reddish brown, soft); Florida Wax.
Webworm, Barberry (webs over twigs).
Weevil, Japanese. **Whitefly,** Barberry; Greenhouse.

BASSWOOD (see Linden)

BAUHINIA (Mountain Ebony, Orchid Tree)
Beetle, Cuban May. **Mealybug,** Citrus; Long-tailed.
Scale, Acuminate; Black; Black Thread; Brown Soft; Cottony-cushion; Cyanophyllum; Dictyospermum; Fern; Florida Red; Latania; Lesser Snow; Long Soft; Mining; Pustule; Proteus; Pyriform; Quohog-shaped; Rufous; White Peach.

BAY, LOBLOLLY (*Gordonia lasianthus*)
Beetle, Rhabdopterus.

BAY, SWEET (*Laurus*—see Laurel)

BAY, SWEET (*Magnolia*—see Sweetbay)

BAYBERRY, WAX-MYRTLE (*Myrica cerifera*)
Beetle, Pine Colaspis.
Caterpillar, Chain-spotted Geometer; Red-humped; Stinging Rose.
Moth, Crinkled Flannel.
Mealybug, Long-tailed; Striped.
Scale, Acuminate; Black; Barnacle; Dictyospermum; Florida Red; Florida Wax; Glover; Green Shield; Hemispherical; Long Soft; Latania; Nigra; Purple; Pustule; Pyriform; Tesselated.

BEAN, LIMA BEAN (*Phaseolus*)

Aphid, Bean (small, black); Cowpea; Melon; Pea; Potato; Solanum Root; Turnip.

Armyworm, Fall; Yellow-striped.

Beetle, Banded Cucumber; Bean Leaf; Fuller Rose; Grape Colaspis; June; Mexican Bean (yellow with black spots, the most serious bean pest); Oriental; Pale-striped Flea; Potato Flea; Red Turnip; Rose Chafer; Spotted Cucumber; Striped Blister; Striped Cucumber; Western Striped Cucumber; White-fringed.

Borer, European Corn; Lesser Cornstalk; Lima-bean Pod; Lima-bean Vine.

Bug, Garden Fleahopper; Green Stink; Harlequin; Leaf-footed; Lygus; One-spot Stink; Pumpkin; Rapid Plant; Say Stink; Tarnished Plant.

Caterpillar, Alfalfa; Green Cloverworm; Salt-marsh; Yellow Woollybear.

Cricket, Field. **Curculio,** Cowpea.

Cutworm, Western Bean. **Earworm,** Corn (feeds on pods).

Leafhopper, Beet; Potato.

Leaf Miner, Serpentine.

Leaf Roller, Bean; Oblique-banded; Omnivorous.

Leaf Skeletonizer, Bean. **Leaf Tier,** Celery.

Maggot, Seed-corn (tunnels in sprouting seeds).

Mealybug, Grape. **Millipedes.**

Mite, Pacific Spider; Strawberry Spider; Tumid Spider; Two-spotted.

Nematode, American Dagger; Awl; California Dagger; Clover Cyst; Cobb's Meadow; Cotton Root-knot; De Man's; Fig Pin; Javanese Root-knot; Northern Root-knot; Peanut Root-knot; Southern Root-knot; Sting; Tarjan's Sheath; Tesselate Stylet.

Springtail, Garden. **Termites.**

Thrips, Bean; Onion; Western Flower.

Treehopper, Three-cornered Alfalfa.

Webworm, Beet; Garden.

Weevil, Bean (grubs in stored beans); Bean Stalk; Citrus Root; Japanese (on lima bean).

Whitefly, Glacial; Greenhouse.

Wireworm, Plains False; Sugar-beet.

Most gardeners have to spray or dust for Mexican bean beetles; often the other pests can be ignored.

BEARBERRY (*Arctostaphylos*)

Aphid, Manzanita Leaf-gall; Rose and Bearberry.

Whitefly, Bearberry.

BEAUTY-BUSH (*Kolkwitzia*)

Scale, Purple.

BEAUTY-LEAF (*Calophyllum*)

Mealybug, Coconut.
Scale, Coconut; Cottony-cushion; Florida Red; Tesselated.

BEECH (*Fagus*)

Aphid, Beech; Beech Blight (white, woolly); Giant Bark.
Beetle, Birch Bark; Grape Flea.
Borer, Brown Wood; Flatheaded Apple Tree; Oak Timberworm; Pacific Flatheaded; Pigeon Tremex; Two-lined Chestnut.
Bug, Birch Lace.
Cankerworm, Fall; Spring.
Caterpillar, Eastern Tent; Hemlock Looper; Red-humped Oakworm; Saddled Prominent; Walnut; Yellow-necked.
Leaf Cutter, Maple. **Leafhopper,** Grape. **Leaf Tier,** Beech.
Mite, Beech; Oak.
Moth, Gypsy; Imperial; Io; Leopard; Luna; Rusty Tussock.
Scale, Beech (circular, pale yellow with wax, associated with Nectria disease); Black; Cottony-cushion; Cottony Maple; European Fruit Lecanium; Osborn's; Oystershell; Putnam; San Jose.
Spanworm, Elm. **Weevil,** New York.

BEET (Beta)

Aphid, Bean; Corn Root; Green Peach; Melon; Solanum Root; Sugar-beet Root.
Armyworm, Beet.
Beetle, Asiatic Garden; Beet Leaf; Carrot (works on roots); Hop Flea; Oriental; Pale-striped Flea; Potato Flea (minute, black, makes pinholes in leaves); Rose Chafer; Spinach Carrion; Spinach Flea; Spotted Cucumber; Striped Blister; Toothed Flea; Western Striped Cucumber.
Borer, European Corn.
Bug, Alfalfa Plant; False Chinch; Garden Fleahopper; Harlequin; Tarnished Plant.
Caterpillar, Cabbage Looper; Celery Looper; Yellow Woollybear.
Cutworm, Pale Western.
Leafhopper, Beet (important as vector of curly-top disease).
Leaf Miner, Beet; Serpentine; Spinach (common).
Maggot, Cabbage; Seed-corn.
Moth, White-lined Sphinx.
Nematode, Christie's Stubby Root; False Root-knot of Sugar Beet; Javanese Root-knot; Peanut Root-knot; Sugar-beet Root-knot.
Springtail, Garden (occasional injury to seedlings).
Termites. Thrips, Onion.
Webworm, Alfalfa; Cabbage; Garden; Southern Beet; Spotted Beet.
Weevil, Vegetable (injurious in the Gulf States).
Wireworm, Eastern Field.

BEGONIA
Aphid, Melon. **Beetle,** Fuller Rose.
Caterpillar, Orange Tortrix (rolls leaves).
Mealybug, Citrus (common: white cotton at leaf axils); Long-tailed.
Mite, Broad (leaves glassy); Cyclamen (plants stunted); Two-spotted.
Nematode, Spring Crimp (dark areas in leaves).
Scale, Brown Soft; Cyanophyllum; Fern; Florida Red; Hemispherical; Latania. **Termites.**
Thrips, Banded Greenhouse; Greenhouse; Sugar-beet.
Weevil, Black Vine (grubs destroy roots; serious on tuberous begonia).
Whitefly, Greenhouse (very common).

BERGAMOT (*Citrus bergamia*)
Scale, Hemispherical; Purple.

BIGNONIA (Cross Vine; Trumpet Flower)
Mealybug, Citrus.
Scale, Barnacle; Hemispherical; Lesser Snow.
Whitefly, Greenhouse.

BILLBERGIA
Scale, Boisduval's; Cyanophyllum; Dictyospermum; Latania; Pineapple; Proteus.

BIRCH (*Betula*)
Aphid, Birch; European Birch; Giant Bark; Spiny Witchhazel Gall; Witchhazel Leaf Gall.
Beetle, Birch Bark; Japanese; June; Pitted Ambrosia.
Borer, Bronze Birch (kills from the top down); Sapwood Timberworm.
Bug, Alder Lace; Birch Lace.
Butterfly, Tiger Swallowtail.
Cankerworm, Fall; Spring. **Casebearer,** Birch; Birch Tubemaker.
Caterpillar, Chain-spotted Geometer; Eastern Tent; Forest Tent; Hemlock Looper; Linden Looper; Red-humped; Saddled Prominent; Variable Oak Leaf; Yellow-necked.
Leaf Cutter, Maple.
Leaf Miner, Birch (serious, nearly half of each leaf blighted, brown).
Leaf Roller, Oblique-banded. **Leaf Skeletonizer,** Birch.
Mite, Oak.
Moth, American Dagger; Cecropia; Crinkled Flannel; Elm Sphinx; Gypsy; Io; Leopard; Imperial; Oriental; Polyphemus; Rusty Tussock; Spotted Tussock.
Sawfly, Birch; Dusky Birch.
Scale, Greedy; European Fruit Lecanium; Oystershell; San Jose; Terrapin.

Spanworm, Bruce; Elm.
Wasp, Giant Hornet.   **Webworm,** Fall.   **Weevil,** Willow Flea.

BIRD-OF-PARADISE (see Strelitzia)

BISHOPWOOD (*Bischofia*)

Scale, Acuminate; Florida Red; Pyriform; Tesselated.

BITTERSWEET (*Celastrus*)

Aphid, Bean (black, common); Spirea (green).
Scale, Euonymus (almost always encrusting vines, covering leaves; Oyster-shell; San Jose.

BLACKBERRY (*Rubus*)

Aphid, Blackberry.
Beetle, Fuller Rose; Green June; Imbricated Snout; Rose Chafer; Rose Leaf; White-fringed.
Borer, Currant; Pacific Flatheaded; Raspberry Cane; Raspberry Crown; Red-necked Cane; San Jose.
Bud Moth, Eye-spotted.
Bug, Consperse Stink; Negro (bad taste in berries).
Caterpillar, Red-humped; Saddled Prominent; Yellow-necked; Yellow Woolly-bear.
Cricket, Black-horned; Snowy Tree.   **Horntail,** Raspberry.
Leaf Miner, Apple Trumpet; Blackberry.
Leaf Roller, Fruit-tree; Oblique-banded; Strawberry.
Maggot, Raspberry Cane (tips wilt).
Mealybug, Citrophilus; Coleman's.
Mite, Dryberry; Pacific Spider; Redberry; Two-spotted.
Moth, Io; Strawberry Crown; Western Tussock.
Nematode, Cobb's Meadow.
Psyllid, Blackberry (occasional distortion, stunting).
Rootworm, Strawberry.
Sawfly, Blackberry (leaves eaten by blue-green larvae).
Scale, Cottony Maple; European Fruit Lecanium; Parlatorialike; Rose; San Jose.
Wasp, Blackberry Knot-gall.
Weevil, Apple Flea; Black Vine; Cribrate; Pea Leaf; Strawberry; Strawberry Root.
Whitefly, Glacial; Greenhouse.

BLACKBERRY-LILY (*Belamcanda*)

Aphid, Tulip Bulb.   **Borer,** Iris.
Scale, Florida Red.

BLEEDING-HEART (*Dicentra*)
Scale, Latania; Quohog-shaped.

BLADDERNUT (*Staphylea*)
Scale, Putnam.

BLUEBERRY (*Vaccinium corymbosum*)
Beetle, Blueberry Flea; Green June; Pitted Ambrosia; Rhabdopterus.
Borer, Azalea Stem; Blueberry Crown Girdler; Rhododendron.
Caterpillar, Azalea; Chain-spotted Geometer; Forest Tent; Hemlock Looper; Yellow-necked.
Curculio, Plum. **Cutworm,** Black Army.
Fruitworm, Cherry; Cranberry (wormy berries).
Leafhopper, Sharp-nosed (vector of stunt disease).
Maggot, Apple (common cause of worms in berries).
Mite, Blueberry; Yellow Spider.
Nematode, Awl; Christie's Stubby Root; Cobb's Meadow; De Man's; Northern Root-knot; Steiner's Spiral; Tesselate Stylet; Zimmerman's Spiral.
Scale, Azalea Bark; Barnacle; Cottony Maple; European Fruit Lecanium; Florida Wax; Japanese Wax; Oak Eriococcus; Oleander; Oystershell; Parlatorialike; Putnam; Red Bay; Terrapin.
Spanworm, Currant. **Spittlebug,** Dogwood.
Thrips, Blueberry (curls, deforms buds and leaves).
Wasp, Blueberry Stem Gall. **Webworm,** Fall. **Weevil,** Blossom; Cranberry.

BOEHMERIA (Chinese Silk-plant)
Nematode, Thames Root-knot.
Scale, Florida Red.

BOTTLE-BRUSH (*Callistemon*)
Mealybug, Citrus.
Scale, Acuminate; Black; Black Thread; Brown Soft; Coconut; Cottony-cushion; Cyanophyllum; Dictyospermum; Florida Red; European Fiorinia; Florida Wax; Green Shield; Long Soft; Latania; Proteus; Pyriform; Tea; Tesselated.

BOUGAINVILLEA (*Buginvillaea*)
Caterpillar, Bougainvillea. **Mealybug,** Long-tailed.
Orthezia, Greenhouse.
Scale, Brown Soft; Cottony-cushion; Cyanophyllum; Florida Red; Hemispherical; Latania; Mining; Pustule; Quohog-shaped.

BOUVARDIA
Mealybug, Citrus.
Nematode, Spring Crimp.

BOYSENBERRY (*Rubus*)
Leaf Roller, Omnivorous.   **Scale,** Latania; Long Soft.
Whitefly, Glacial.
See Blackberry, Raspberry for other possible pests.

BOXELDER (*Acer negundo*)
Aphid, Boxelder (green, hairy, with conspicuous honeydew).
Bagworm.   Beetle, Sweetpotato Flea.
Borer, Boxelder Twig; Flatheaded Apple Tree; Pacific Flatheaded.
Bug, Boxelder (a common nuisance); Green Stink.
Caterpillar, Forest Tent; Green-striped Mapleworm; Omnivorous Looper.
Leaf Roller, Boxelder; Fruit-tree; Oblique-banded.
Mite, Willamette.
Moth, American Dagger; Cecropia; Smeared Dagger; Spotted Tussock.
Nematode, Cobb's Meadow.   **Psyllid,** Boxelder.
Scale, Brown Soft; California Red; Cottony Maple; European Fruit Leca-
nium; Gloomy; Oystershell; Terrapin; Walnut.
Webworm, Fall.

BOXWOOD (*Buxus*)
Leaf Miner, Boxwood (common, injurious; blisters in leaves).
Mealybug, Comstock; Ground.
Mite, Boxwood (leaves grayish); Two-spotted.
Nematode, American Dagger; Boxwood Spiral; De Man's; Fig Pin; Northern
Root-knot; Steiner's Spiral; Tesselate Stylet; Walnut Meadow; Zimmer-
man's Spiral.
Planthopper.   Psyllid, Boxwood (terminal leaves curled into cups).
Scale, California Red; Camellia Mining; Chaff; Coconut; Cottony-cushion;
Cottony Maple; Dictyospermum; European Fruit Lecanium; Florida Red;
Florida Wax; Glover; Greedy; Japanese; Lesser Snow; Oleander; Oyster-
shell; Proteus; Pyriform; Walnut; White Peach.
Wasp, Giant Hornet (tears bark).   **Webworm,** Boxwood.

BRAZILIAN PEPPER-TREE (*Schinus terebinthifolius*)
Scale, Acuminate; Barnacle; Black; Black Thread; Brown Soft; Chaff; Cot-
tony-cushion; Florida Wax; Green Shield; Hemispherical; Mango Shield;
Mining; Lesser Snow; Olive; Parlatorialike; Proteus; Purple; Pyriform;
Quohog-shaped; White Peach.

BREADFRUIT (*Artocarpus*)
Mealybug, Long-tailed.
Scale, California Red; Latania; Red Wax.

BROADBEAN (*Vicia faba*)
Weevil, Broad-bean.

BROCCOLI (*Brassica oleracea*)
Aphid, cabbage (common; grayish lice on leaves, flower heads); Turnip.
Beetle, Potato Flea (shot holes in leaves).
Caterpillar, Cabbage Looper; Imported Cabbageworm.
Leafhopper, Flavescent.
Maggot, Cabbage (seedlings wilt; very common).
Nematode, Cabbage Cyst; De Man's; Sugar-beet Root-knot; Tesselate Stylet.
See Cabbage for other possible pests.

BROMELIAD (Air Plant)
Scale, Boisduval's; Brown Soft; Latania; Pineapple; Proteus.

BROOM (*Genista*)
Aphid, Bean (black).   **Caterpillar,** Genista.
Scale, Greedy (gray, convex); Oleander (round, flat, yellow).

BROOM, SCOTCH (*Cytisus*)
Scale, White Peach.

BROUSSONETIA (Paper Mulberry)
Scale, White Peach.

BROWALLIA
Aphid, Corn Root; Western Aster Root.
Leafhopper, Six-spotted.

BRUNFELSIA (Raintree)
Scale, Barnacle; Mining; Oleander; Pyriform; Rufous.

BRUSSELS SPROUTS (*Brassica oleracea* var. *gemmifera*)
Aphid, Cabbage.
Beetle, Western Striped Flea.   **Bug,** Harlequin.
Caterpillar, Cabbage Looper; Imported Cabbageworm.
Maggot, Cabbage.
Nematode, Cabbage Cyst.
See also Cabbage.

BUCKEYE (*Aesculus*)
Beetle, Striped Cucumber.
Caterpillar, Omnivorous Looper.

Mealybug, Grape.   Moth, White-marked Tussock.
Scale, Cottony-cushion; Cottony Maple.
   See also Horsechestnut.

BUCKTHORN (*Rhamnus*)
Aphid, Buckthorn; Melon.
Moth, Oriental.
Scale, Barnacle; Florida Wax; Gloomy; Long Soft; San Jose; Terrapin.

BUDDLEIA (Butterfly Bush)
Beetle, Japanese.   Butterfly, Checker Spot.
Moth, Buddleia.   Nematode, Root-knot.
Scale, Latania; White Peach.
Thrips, Banded Greenhouse.

BUFFALOBERRY (*Shepherdia*)
Aphid, Oleaster-thistle; Russian-olive; Polygonum.

BUMELIA (False Buckthorn)
Fly, Bumelia Fruit.
Scale, Cottony-cushion; Cottony Maple; Florida Wax; Proteus; Pyriform;
   Terrapin.

BUTTERCUP (*Ranunculus*)
Aphid, Corn Root; Poplar Folded Leaf.
Thrips, Small.

BUTTERFLY-PEA (*Clitoria*)
Orthezia, Greenhouse.
Scale, Lesser Snow; Pustule.

BUTTERFLY WEED (*Asclepias*)
Aphid, Melon; Oleander.
Beetle, Argus Tortoise.   Bug, Small Milkweed.
Butterfly, Monarch (greenish caterpillar with dark bands).
Leaf Miner, Serpentine (winding tunnels in leaves).
Mealybug, Citrus.
Scale, Cyanophyllum; Pustule; San Jose.
Thrips, Western Flower.

BUTTERNUT (*Juglans cinerea*)
Beetle, Hickory Saperda; June.
Borer, Painted Hickory.   Bug, Walnut Lace.
Caterpillar, Hickory Horned Devil; Walnut; Yellow Woollybear.

Curculio, Butternut; Hickory Nut.
Moth, Hickory Tussock; Imperial; Luna; Walnut Sphinx.
Rootworm, Strawberry (beetle makes minute holes in foliage).
Sawfly, Butternut Woollyworm (leaves eaten; hairy larvae).
Scale, European Fruit Lecanium; Oystershell; Walnut (round, gray).
Treehopper, Two-marked.

BUTTONBUSH (*Cephalanthus*)
Scale, Green; Pyriform; San Jose; Tuliptree; White Peach.

CABBAGE (*Brassica oleracea*)
Aphid, Cabbage (gray lice, numerous on underside of leaves); Turnip.
Armyworm, Fall.
Beetle, Argus Tortoise; Black Blister; Cabbage Flea; Hop Flea; Imbricated
    Snout; Potato Flea; Red Turnip; Rose Chafer; Sinuate Flea; Spotted Cu-
    cumber; Striped Flea; Western Black Flea; Western Striped Flea; White-
    fringed; Yellow-margined Leaf.
Bug, False Chinch; Green Stink; Harlequin (red and black, southern);
    Horned Squash; Tarnished Plant.
Caterpillar, Cabbage Looper; Cross-striped Cabbageworm; Gulf White Cab-
    bageworm; Imported Cabbageworm; Purple-backed Cabbageworm; South-
    ern Cabbageworm; Yellow Woollybear.
Curculio, Cabbage (ash-gray weevil); Cabbage Seedstalk.
Cutworms. Earworm, Corn.
Leaf Miner, Serpentine. **Leaf Tier,** Celery.
Maggot, Cabbage (wilts seedlings); Seed-corn.
Millipedes. Moth, Diamondback (green caterpillar).
Nematode, Cabbage Cyst; Christie's Stubby Root; Cobb's Meadow; Cotton
    Root-knot; Javanese Root-knot; Peanut Root-knot; Sting; Sugar-beet.
Slugs (several species make holes in leaves, enter heads).
Termites. Thrips, Onion.
Webworm, Beet; Cabbage. **Weevil,** Vegetable.

CACTUS
Aphid, Tulip Bulb (on roots). **Beetle,** Fig.
Mealybug, Citrus; Ground (may kill plants); Long-tailed; Striped.
Midge, Cactus Fruit Gall.
Mite, Desert Spider; Two-spotted (plants gray, webby).
Nematode, Cactus Cyst; False Root-knot of Sugar Beet.
Orthezia, Greenhouse (dark with white wax).
Scale, Boisduval's; Cactus; Cottony Cochineal; Cyanophyllum; Dictyosper-
    mum; Greedy; Latania; Lesser Snow; Oleander; Oriental; Pineapple;
    Proteus; Pyriform; Tesselated; Walnut.
Thrips, Date palm.

Use sprays on cacti with some caution. A pointed stick or stiff brush will help to remove scales and mealybugs. For ground mealybugs on roots, wash off all soil and repot.

CAESALPINIA

Scale, Dictyospermum; Quohog-shaped.

CAJEPUT (*Melaleuca leucadendra*)

Scale, Acuminate; Black; Black Thread; Brown Soft; Chaff; Coconut; Dictyospermum; Fern; Florida Red; Florida Wax; Green Shield; Pyriform; Tea; Tesselated.
Mealybug, Citrus.

CALADIUM

Mealybug, Pineapple.
Scale, Boisduval's; Brown Soft; Cottony-cushion; Florida Red; Lesser Snow.

CALABASH (*Crescentia cujete*)

Orthezia, Greenhouse. **Scale,** Black Thread.

CALATHEA

Nematode, Cotton Root-knot; Steiner's Spiral.
Scale, Cyanophyllum.

CALCEOLARIA

Aphid, Geranium; Crescent-marked Lily; Green Peach.
Nematode, Chrysanthemum Foliar; Spring Crimp.
Whitefly, Greenhouse.

CALENDULA

Aphid, Bean (black, common); Crescent-marked Lily; Green Peach; Western Aster Root.
Beetle, Black Blister; Spotted Cucumber.
Borer, Stalk. **Bug,** Tarnished Plant. **Butterfly,** Painted Lady.
Caterpillar, Yellow Woollybear; Cabbage Looper.
Leafhopper, Red-banded; Six-spotted (transmits aster yellows).
Mealybug, Mexican.
Scale, Ground Pearls.
Thrips, Composite (in flower head). **Whitefly,** Greenhouse.

CALIFORNIA CHRISTMASBERRY,
TOYON (*Photinia arbutifolia*)

Aphid, Rose and Bearberry; Woolly Hawthorn.
Borer, California Buprestid; Pacific Flatheaded.
Bug, Toyon Lace (common; leaves lose color, have brown flecks).
Caterpillar, California Tent; Omnivorous Looper.
Mite, Platanus. **Moth,** Western Tussock.
Scale, Black; European Fruit Lecanium; Italian Pear (shiny dark gray, sunken in bark; associated with lichens); Oystershell; San Jose.
Thrips, Greenhouse; Toyon.
Weevil, Black Fruit Tree.
Whitefly, Crown, Inconspicuous, Iridescent; Pruinose.

CALIFORNIA COFFEEBERRY (*Rhamnus californica*)

Aphid, Buckthorn (?).
Borer, Flatheaded Cherry Tree; Pacific Flatheaded.
Butterfly, Eurymedon.
Leaf Miner, Nepticula.
Moth, Ceanothus Silk; Western Tussock.
Thrips, Robust.
Whitefly, Crown; Glacial; Greenhouse; Inconspicuous; Iridescent.

CALIFORNIA-LAUREL (*Umbellularia californica*)

Aphid, California-laurel; Crescent-marked Lily.
Borer, Banded Alder; Branch and Twig.
Caterpillar, Omnivorous Looper (yellow, green or pink, striped).
Leaf Miner, Cameraria Gall.
Nematode, Northern Root-knot.
Scale, Brown Soft; Greedy.
Thrips, Onion; Pear.
Whitefly, Inconspicuous; Iridescent; Laurel.

CALIFORNIA-NUTMEG (*Torreya californica*)

Scale, Black; Pine Leaf.

CALIFORNIA-POPPY (*Eschscholzia californica*)

Mealybug, Grape.

CALLA (*Zantedeschia*)

Aphid, Crescent-marked Lily; Geranium.
Beetle, Grapevine Hoplia.
Caterpillar, Yellow Woollybear.
Leaf Tier, Omnivorous.

Mealybug, Grape; Long-tailed. **Mite,** Bulb; Two-spotted.
Scale, Brown Soft.
Thrips, Banded Greenhouse; Greenhouse; Onion; Sugar-beet.

CALLIANDRA (Powder-puff).
Scale, Parlatorialike; Pustule.
Treehopper, Thornbug.

CALLICARPA (Beauty-berry; French Mulberry)
Mealybug, Citrus.
Scale, Black; Brown Soft; Florida Wax; Green Shield; Latania; Pustule; White Peach.

CALYCANTHUS (Sweetshrub)
Scale, Dictyospermum; Florida Red; Latania.

CAMELLIA
Aphid, Black Citrus (curls new leaves); Melon; Green Peach; Ornate.
Beetle, Fuller Rose; Rhabdopterus; Grape Colaspis.
Caterpillar, Omnivorous Looper; Orange Tortrix; Western Parsley.
Curculio, Cambium.
Leaf Roller, Fruit-tree. **Leaf Tier,** Celery.
Mealybug, Citrus; Long-tailed.
Mite, Camellia Bud; Camellia Rust (rusty foliage); Southern Red.
Nematode, American Dagger; Cotton Root-knot; Steiner's Spiral.
Planthopper, Citrus Flatid.
Rootworm, Cranberry.
Scale, Black; Black Thread; Brown Soft; Camellia (brown, leaves may drop, important in Southeast); Camellia Mining; Camellia Parlatoria (common on Pacific Coast); Camphor; Chaff; Cottony-cushion; Cottony Taxus; Cyanophyllum; Degenerate; Dictyospermum; European Fiorinia; Fern; Florida Red; Florida Wax; Greedy; Green Shield; Hemispherical; Japanese Wax; Latania; Mining; Oleander; Oystershell; Parlatorialike; Peony (white circles on branches, sometimes serious); Proteus; Purple; Pyriform; Quohog-shaped; Tea (the worst pest in Gulf States; white filaments on underside of leaves); San Jose.
Weevil, Black Vine; Cribrate; Japanese; Strawberry Root.
Whitefly, Citrus; Greenhouse.
DDT should not be used on camellias; it injures certain varieties. An oil spray spring and fall has been standard for control of scales but phosphates are now popular, with dimethoate relatively safe and particularly effective for tea scale.

CAMPANULA (Bluebell, Canterbury Bells)

Aphid, Foxglove. **Nematode,** Stem.
Slugs. Thrips, Onion.

CAMPHOR-TREE (*Cinnamomum camphora*)

Mite, Avocado Red (leaves turn reddish); Platanus; Southern Red.
Scale, Brown Soft; Camphor (convex, dark brown, may cause death); Chaff; Cyanophyllum; Dictyospermum; Fern; Florida Red; Florida Wax; Greedy; Latania; Lesser Snow; Oystershell; Parlatorialike; Pyriform; Red Bay; Tesselated.
Thrips, Camphor (most injurious, buds, branches die; bark cracks).

CANDLENUT, CANDLEBERRY-TREE (*Aleurites moluccana*)

Mealybug, Long-tailed.
Scale, Florida Red; Latania; Lesser Snow.

CANDYTUFT (*Iberis*)

Moth, Diamondback. **Nematode,** Cabbage Cyst.

CANNA

Beetle, Fuller Rose; Goldsmith; Japanese (common on flowers); Spotted Cucumber.
Caterpillar, Saddleback; Yellow Woollybear.
Earworm, Corn.
Leaf Roller, Larger Canna (green caterpillar rolls leaves); Lesser Canna.
Leaf Tier, Celery.
Mealybug, Citrus; Pineapple.
Scale, Coconut; Dictyospermum; Florida Red; Green Shield; Latania (small, gray, convex); Oriental; Pineapple (white and gray).

CANTALOUPE (see Melon)

CAPE-HONEYSUCKLE (*Tecomaria*)

Scale, Black Thread; Barnacle; Brown Soft; Latania; Mining; Quohog-shaped.

CAPE-JASMINE (see Gardenia)

CAPE-MARIGOLD (*Dimortheca*)

Leafhopper, Six-spotted.

CARAGANA (Pea-tree)

Beetle, Caragana Blister. **Bug,** Caragana Plant.

CARAWAY (*Carum*)

Aphid, Willow.
Caterpillar, Celeryworm (green, black-banded).

CARDINAL-FLOWER (*Lobelia cardinalis*)

Bug, Negro (red to black; southern). **Leaf Roller,** Red-banded.
Nematode, Root-knot. **Wireworms.**

CARISSA (Natal-plum)

Scale, Black; Barnacle; Chaff; Cyanophyllum; Dictyospermum; Florida Red;
Green Shield; Hemispherical; Latania; Lesser Snow; Oriental; Proteus;
Purple; Pustule; Pyriform; Quohog-shaped; Tesselated; Yellow.
Thrips, Greenhouse.

CARNATION (*Dianthus caryophyllus*)

Aphid, Green Peach. **Armyworm,** Beet.
Beetle, Fuller Rose.
Caterpillar, Cabbage Looper; Salt-marsh.
Cutworm, Spotted (climbs stems).
Leaf Miner, Carnation.
Leaf Roller, Oblique-banded; Omnivorous. **Leaf Tier,** Celery.
Maggot, Carnation; Carnation Tip. **Mealybug,** Grape.
Mite, Carnation; Carnation Bud; Two-spotted (leaves pale, dusty).
Nematode, Carnation Pin; Clover Cyst; Crown-headed Lance; Javanese
Root-knot; Peanut Root-knot.
Scale, Brown Soft; Oriental; Parlatorialike.
Thrips, Gladiolus; Onion; Western Flower.

CAROB (*Ceratonia siliqua*)

Borer, Carpenterworm. **Caterpillar,** Navel Orangeworm.
Mealybug, Citrus; Long-tailed; Mexican.
Scale, Brown Soft; California Red; Greedy; Latania; Long Soft; Lesser Snow;
Oleander.

CARROT (*Daucus carota*)

Ants, Pavement.
Aphid, Bean; Corn Root (white, powdery at roots); Green Peach; Honey-
suckle and Parsnip; Leaf-curl Plum; Lettuce Root; Solanum Root; Tulip
Bulb; Willow.
Beetle, Asiatic Garden; Black Blister; Carrot; Pale-striped Flea; Potato Flea.
Bug, Rapid Plant. **Butterfly,** Western Parsley.
Caterpillar, Celeryworm (green, black-banded); Yellow Woollybear.
Fly, Carrot Rust (rusty tunnels in roots); Onion Bulb.

Leafhopper, Six-spotted; Mountain.
Millipedes. Mite, Desert Spider.
Nematode, Cotton Root-knot; Cobb's Meadow; De Man's Meadow; False Root-knot of Sugar Beet; Javanese Root-knot; Northern Root-knot; Peanut Root-knot; Southern Root-knot.
Termites. Thrips, Onion.
Webworm, Alfalfa; Beet.
Weevil, Carrot (tunnels in roots); Vegetable (eats foliage at night).
Wireworm, Eastern Field; Western Field; other species.

CASHEW (*Anacardium*)

Scale, Acuminate.

CASSAVA (*Manihot esculenta*)

Mealybug, Coconut. **Mite,** Two-spotted.
Scale, Black; Cassava; Lesser Snow.

CASSIA (Golden-shower)

Beetle, Cuban May.
Bug, Eggplant Lace (brown and yellow). **Caterpillar.** Species?
Mite, Texas Citrus. **Nematode,** Root-knot.
Scale, Black, Brown Soft; Cottony-cushion; Florida Red; Dictyospermum; Latania; Lesser Snow; Long Soft; Oleander; Oriental; Pustule; Pyriform; White Peach.

CASTOR-BEAN (*Ricinus*)

Armyworm, Southern (may defoliate and kill).
Bug, Alfalfa Plant.
Leafhopper, Potato. **Leaf Miner,** Serpentine.
Mite, Lewis Spider; Texas Citrus; Two-spotted.
Scale, Cottony-cushion; Green; Lesser Snow.
Webworm, Garden.

CATALINA CHERRY (*Prunus lyoni*)

Borer, Pacific Flatheaded. **Caterpillar,** Filbertworm.
Leaf Miner, Apple. **Moth,** Catalina Cherry (caterpillars in seeds).
Scale, European Fruit Lecanium.
Whitefly, Black Aleyrodid; Kellogg's (looks like small white flower).

CATALPA

Aphid, Melon. **Bug,** Green Stink.
Mealybug, Comstock (white fluffs in bark crevices; serious).
Midge, Catalpa (small brown spots in leaves).
Moth, Catalpa Sphinx (large dark caterpillar, defoliates).

Nematode, Root-knot. **Planthopper.**
Scale, San Jose; White Peach.

CATNIP (*Nepeta*)
Leafhopper, Grape. **Webworm,** Small Beet.

CATTAIL (*Typha*)
Aphid, Mealy Plum; Melon; Waterlily.
Borer, Potato Tuberworm.
Grasshoppers. Mites.

CAULIFLOWER (*Brassica oleracea* var. *botrytis*)
Aphid, Cabbage; Turnip.
Beetle, Striped Flea; Western Black Flea; Western Striped Flea.
Bug, Harlequin; Tarnished Plant.
Caterpillar, Cabbage Looper; Imported Cabbageworm; Yellow Woollybear.
Curculio, Cabbage (weevil attacking seedlings).
Leaf Tier, Celery.
Maggot, Cabbage (seedlings wilt). **Moth,** Diamondback.
Nematode, Cabbage Cyst; Zimmerman's Spiral.
Springtail, Garden (on seedlings). **Thrips,** Onion.
Webworm, Cabbage. **Weevil,** Vegetable.
  See Cabbage for other possible pests.

CEANOTHUS
Aphid, Ceanothus (red-brown to black); Crescent-marked Lily.
Borer, Flatheaded Cherry Tree; Pacific Flatheaded.
Bug, Ceanothus Lace (black and brown; leaves whitened; common).
Butterfly, California Tortoise-shell.
Caterpillar, California Tent; Great Basin Tent.
Mealybug, Yucca. **Mite,** Lewis Spider.
Moth, Douglas-fir Tussock; Ramosia.
Scale, Greedy; San Jose; Scurfy; Willow.
Spittlebug, Alder. **Thrips,** Madroña.

CEDAR (*Cedrus*)
  Deodar (*Cedrus deodara*) and Cedar of Lebanon (*C. libanotica*)
Aphid, Bow-legged Fir.
Beetle, Cedar Bark; Northern Cedar Bark; Pine Colaspis; Western Cedar
  Bark.
Borer, Black-horned Pine; Cedar Tree; Western Cedar.
Horntail, Western.
Mealybug, Grape; Juniper; Taxus.
Nematode, Cobb's Meadow; Zimmerman's Spiral.

Sawfly, Cedar Cone; Red-headed Pine.
Scale, Black; Brown Soft; Cottony-cushion; Florida Red; Florida Wax; Newstead's; Pine; Pine Needle.
Weevil, Deodar.

CEDAR, INCENSE (*Libocedrus*)

Beetle, Cypress Bark. **Mealybug,** Cypress.
Scale, Cypress; Juniper; Pine Needle; Putnam.

CELERIAC (*Apium graveolens* var. *rapaceum*)

Fly, Carrot Rust. **Nematode,** Cobb's Meadow.

CELERY (*Apium graveolens* var. *dulce*)

Aphid, Crescent-marked Lily; Green Peach; Honeysuckle and Parsnip; Leafcurl Plum; Melon; Rhodes Grass; Willow.
Armyworm, Southern.
Beetle, Carrot; Potato Flea. **Borer,** European Corn.
Bug, Garden Fleahopper; Negro; Tarnished Plant. **Butterfly,** Western Parsley.
Caterpillar, Cabbage Looper; Celery Looper; Celeryworm (green with black bands); Yellow Woollybear.
Fly, Carrot Rust (plants wilt; outer leaves turn yellow).
Leafhopper, Beet; Six-spotted. **Leaf Roller,** Oblique-banded; Omnivorous.
Leaf Tier, Celery (major pest, webbing foliage, mining in hearts).
Maggot, Cabbage. **Mite,** Desert Spider; Tumid Spider; Two-spotted.
Nematode, Awl; Christie's Stubby Root; Cobb's Meadow; Cotton Root-knot; Fig Pin; Sting; Tarjan's Sheath.
Thrips, Onion. **Webworm,** Parsnip. **Weevil,** Carrot.

CENTURY PLANT (*Agave*)

Borer, Stalk. **Mealybug,** Grape.
Scale, Black Thread; Brown Soft; California Red; Chaff; Dictyospermum; Fern; Florida Red; Lesser Snow; Oleander; Proteus; Pustule.
Thrips, Dracaena. **Weevil,** Yucca (black billbug).

CEPHALOTAXUS (Plum-yew)

Scale, Dictyospermum.

CERIMAN (*Monstera deliciosa*)

Mealybug, Long-tailed.
Scale, Acuminate; Black; Black Thread; Brown Soft; Chaff; Florida Red; Green Shield; Proteus; Pyriform.

CEROPEGIA

Mite, Privet.

CHALICE-VINE (*Solandra*)
Scale, Chaff; Green Shield; Pineapple.

CHAMAECYPARIS (see Retinospora)

CHASTE-TREE (*Vitex*)
Scale, Barnacle; Latania; White Peach.

CHAYOTE (*Sechium edule*)
Mealybug, Citrus. **Nematode,** Christie's Stubby Root.

CHERIMOYA (*Annona cherimola*)
Mealybug, Coconut.
Scale, Cyanophyllum, Coconut; Hemispherical; Oleander; Pyriform.
Thrips, Greenhouse.

CHERRY (*Prunus avium; P. cerasus*)
Aphid, Black Cherry (prevalent on young shoots, curls leaves); Green Peach; Malaheb Cherry; Oat Bird-cherry; Red and Black Cherry; Waterlily.
Beetle, Asiatic Garden; Cherry Leaf; Japanese; Imbricated Snout; Peach Bark; Plum Gouger; Rose Chafer; Syneta Leaf.
Borer, American Plum; Apple Twig; Brown Wood; California Prionus; Flat-headed Apple Tree; Flatheaded Cherry Tree; Lesser Peach Tree; Peach Tree; Shot-hole.
Bud Moth, Eye-spotted.
Bug, Boxelder; Green Stink; Harlequin.
Butterfly, Tiger Swallowtail; Western Swallowtail.
Cankerworms, Fall; Spring. **Casebearer,** California; Cherry; Cigar.
Caterpillar, California Tent; Eastern Tent; Forest Tent; Omnivorous Looper; Orange Tortrix; Palmerworm; Phigalia Looper; Red-humped; Saddle-back; Saddled Prominent; Ugly Nest; Western Tent; Yellow-necked; Yellow Woollybear.
Cricket, Snowy Tree.
Curculio, Apple; Cherry; Plum (wormy cherries).
Fly, Black Cherry Fruit; Cherry Fruit (maggots in fruit).
Fruitworm, Green. **Leaf Crumpler.**
Leafhopper, Privet. **Leaf Miner,** Spotted Tentiform.
Leaf Roller, Fruit-tree; Oblique-banded; Red-banded.
Leaf Skeletonizer, Apple-and-thorn.
Maggot, Apple. **Mealybug,** Citrophilus.
Mite, Clover, Fruit-tree; McDaniel Spider; Pacific Spider; Pear Rust; Willamette.
Moth, Apple Fruit; Brown-tail; Codling; Crinkled Flannel; Ermine; Oriental; Oriental Fruit; Western Tussock.

Nematode, Cobb's Meadow; De Man's; Northern Root-knot; Tesselate Stylet.

Sawfly, Cherry Fruit; Pear-slug.

Scale, Barnacle; Calico; Cottony Maple; Dictyospermum; European Fruit Lecanium; Florida Red; Forbes; Glover; Greedy; Hemispherical; Latania; Pustule; Putnam; Pyriform; San Jose; Scurfy; Terrapin; Walnut; White Peach.

Termites, Subterranean. **Thrips,** Onion; Pear.

Treehopper, Buffalo (curved slits in bark).

Webworm, Fall. **Whitefly,** Citrus.

CHERRY, ORIENTAL FLOWERING, JAPANESE (*Prunus* spp.)

Aphid, Waterlily (when tree is near ponds).

Beetle, Japanese.

Cankerworm, Fall; Spring. **Caterpillar,** Eastern Tent; other species.

Planthopper.

See Cherry for other possible pests.

CHERRY, SAND (*Prunus pumila*)

Bug, Green Stink.

Sawfly, Plum Web-spinning; **Scale,** San Jose.

Thrips, Greenhouse.

CHERRY-LAUREL, LAUREL-CHERRY (*Prunus laurocerasus*)

Aphid, Spirea.

Scale, Black Thread; Brown Soft; Cottony-cushion; Chaff; Dictyospermum; Cyanophyllum; European Fruit Lecanium; Florida Red; Florida Wax; Glover; Latania; Mining; Pyriform; San Jose; Terrapin; Walnut; White Peach.

Whitefly, Citrus.

CHESTNUT (*Castanea*)

Although the American chestnut was practically exterminated by blight, Asiatic chestnuts are being grown, hybrids are being produced, and there is still the native chinquapin in the South.

Aphid, Giant Bark (large, gray).

Beetle, Japanese (very fond of Chestnut foliage).

Borer, Broad-necked Root; Brown Wood; Chestnut Bark; Chestnut Timberworm; Dogwood; Flatheaded Apple Tree; Oak Sapling; Oak Timberworm; Tile-horned Prionus; Twig Pruner; Two-lined Chestnut.

Cankerworms.

Caterpillar, California Oakworm; Filbertworm; Omnivorous Looper; Stinging Rose.

Moth, Brown-tail; Gypsy; Imperial; Leopard; Luna.

Scale, Dictyospermum; European Fruit Lecanium; Mining; Obscure; Oyster-shell; Putnam; San Jose; Terrapin.

Webworm, Fall.

Weevil, Asiatic Oak; Large Chestnut; Small Chestnut.

CHICK-PEA (*Cicer*)

Earworm, Corn.

CHINABERRY (*Melia azedarach*)

Mite, Pacific Spider (yellowing foliage).

Scale, Black; California Red; European Fruit Lecanium; Chaff; Greedy; Green Shield; Latania; Lesser Snow; Oleander; Oriental; Pustule; Pyriform; White Peach.

Whitefly, Citrus (breeds profusely on this tree).

CHINESE EVERGREEN (*Aglaeonema simplex*)

Mealybug, Comstock; Pineapple.

CHINESE LANTERN (*Physalis*)

Beetle, Striped Cucumber (devours foliage; transmits mosaic).

Bug, Four-lined. **Weevil,** Imported Long-horned.

CHOISYA (Mexican Orange)

Mealybug, Citrophilus; Grape.

Whitefly, Citrus.

CHIONODOXA (Glory-of-the-snow).

Nematode, Stem and Bulb.

CHOKEBERRY (*Aronia*)

Beetle, Rhabdopterus. **Borer,** Roundheaded Apple Tree.

Scale, San Jose.

CHOKECHERRY (*Prunus virginiana*)

Aphid, Chokecherry. **Beetle,** Birch Bark.

Borer, Roundheaded Apple Tree.

Caterpillar, Chain-spotted Geometer; Eastern Tent (almost inevitable); Hemlock Looper; Schizura; Stinging Rose; Ugly Nest.

Fly, Black Cherry Fruit; Cherry Fruit.

Leaf Crumpler. Leaf Miner, Apple Blotch; Unspotted Tentiform.

Moth, Cynthia; Io; Lappet; Polyphemus; Promethea; Resplendent Shield Bearer; Spotted Tussock.

Scale, Barnacle; Black; Cottony-cushion; Florida Wax; Green Shield; Masked; Walnut.

Spittlebugs. Walkingstick. Webworm, Fall.

CHRYSANTHEMUM

Aphid, Chrysanthemum; Foxglove; Geranium; Goldenglow; Green Peach; Leaf-curl Plum; Melon; Myrtle; Pale Chrysanthemum; Thistle.

Armyworm, Beet.

Beetle, Asiatic Garden; Black Blister; European Chafer; Fuller Rose; Goldsmith; Rose Chafer; Spotted Cucumber; White-fringed.

Borer, European Corn; Stalk.

Bug, Alfalfa Plant; Chrysanthemum Lace; Four-lined (round, depressed, tan spots in leaves); Garden Fleahopper; Harlequin; Tarnished Plant.

Caterpillar, Cabbage Looper; Yellow Woollybear; Zebra.

Leafhopper, Six-spotted. **Leaf Miner,** Chrysanthemum.

Leaf Roller, Red-banded. **Leaf Tier,** Celery.

Mealybug, Citrus; Ground; Mexican (serious in greenhouses).

Midge, Chrysanthemum Gall (conical galls in stem, leaf, and bud).

Mite, Broad; Cyclamen; Privet; Two-spotted.

Nematode, Chrysanthemum Foliar (brown wedges in leaves; serious); Cobb's Meadow; Corn Meadow; De Man's; Fig Pin; Spring Crimp.

Orthezia, Greenhouse.

Scale, Black; Cottony-cushion; Hemispherical; Latania.

Slugs. Spittlebug, Meadow (common). **Termites.**

Thrips, Banded Greenhouse; Chrysanthemum; Greenhouse.

Weevil, Cocklebur; Imported Long-horned; Japanese.

Whitefly, Greenhouse. **Wireworm,** Sugar-beet.

Tip cuttings, rather than crown divisions, reduce spread of leaf nematodes.

CHUFA (*Cyperus*)

Beetle, White-fringed.

CINERARIA

Aphid, Geranium; Green Peach; Leaf-curl Plum; Melon; Potato.

Caterpillar, Cabbage Looper; Orange Tortrix.

Cutworms. Leafhopper, Six-spotted.

Leaf Miner, Chrysanthemum. **Leaf Tier,** Celery.

Mealybug, Citrus; Long-tailed. **Mite,** Two-spotted.

Slug, Spotted Garden; Greenhouse. **Whitefly,** Greenhouse.

CINNAMON-TREE (*Cinnamomum zeylandicum*)
Scale, Chaff; Dictyospermum; Fern; Florida Red; Florida Wax; Lesser Snow; Pyriform; Tesselated.

CINNAMON VINE (*Dioscorea batatas*)
Scale, Pyriform; Tesselated.

CINQUEFOIL (*Potentilla*)
Aphid, Rose (small, green). **Weevil,** Strawberry.

CISSUS (Kangaroo Vine; Marine Ivy)
Aphid, Grapevine. **Beetle,** Fuller Rose.
Mealybug, Citrus. **Scale,** Greedy; Lesser Snow.

CITRON (*Citrus medica*)
Beetle, Fuller Rose.
Scale, California Red; Cottony-cushion.

CITRUS FRUITS
(Calamondin, Citron, Grapefruit, Kumquat, Lemon, Orange, Tangerine)
Ant, Argentine (disseminates scales, mealybugs, aphids); Fire; Little Fire.
Aphid, Black Citrus; Cowpea; Green Peach; Melon; Potato; Spirea.
Bagworm.
Beetle, Citrus Root; Darkling Ground; Fuller Rose; Spotted Cucumber; Tobacco Flea; Western Spotted Cucumber.
Borer, Branch and Twig; California Prionus.
Bug, Cotton Stainer; Green Stink; Harlequin; Leaf-footed; Southern Green Stink; Tarnished Plant; Western Leaf-footed.
Butterfly, Western Parsley.
Caterpillar, Garden Tortrix; Navel Orangeworm; Omnivorous Looper; Orange-dog; Orange Tortrix (bores in rind of fruit); Pink Scavenger; Puss.
Cutworms. Fly, Mediterranean Fruit.
Grasshoppers. Katydids.
Leafhopper, Potato. **Leaf Roller,** Fruit-tree; Omnivorous.
Mealybug, Citrophilus; Citrus; Fruit; Grape; Japanese; Long-tailed.
Mite, Broad; Citrus Bud; Citrus Flat; Citrus Red (purple mite in Florida, leaves grayish); Citrus Rust (fruit rusty, dry, rough); European Red; Lewis Spider; Omnivorous; Pacific Spider; Six-spotted; Texas Citrus; Two-spotted; Yuma Spider.
Moth, Raisin; Western Tussock.
Nematode, American Dagger; Burrowing (serious in Florida); Citrus; Citrus Ring; Citrus Spine; Crown-headed Lance; Godfrey's Meadow; Walnut Meadow.
Planthopper, Citrus Flatid.

Scale, Barnacle; Black; Brown Soft; California Red; Camphor; Chaff; Citricola; Citrus Snow; Cottony-cushion; Dictyospermum; Fern; Florida Red; Florida Wax; Glover; Greedy; Green; Green Shield; Hemispherical; Japanese Wax; Lesser Snow; Mango Shield; Mining; Nigra; Oleander; Purple (major pest); Putnam; Rufous; San Jose; Tea; Yellow.

Snail, European Brown.   **Slug,** Banded; Gray Garden; Greenhouse.

Termites.

Thrips, Bean; Citrus (scars fruit); Cotton; Florida Flower; Flower; Greenhouse; Orchid.

Weevil, Citrus Root.

Whitefly, Avocado; Citrus (trees devitalized, covered with sooty mold); Cloudy-winged; Woolly.

It is impossible to suggest a citrus spray schedule that would be generally applicable. The citrus whitefly so troublesome in Florida is not a problem in California. Conditions vary within a state; the citrus grower must have a program tailored for his own location. For the homeowner, using citrus trees as ornamentals, a cleanup spray in May or June with a summer oil is perhaps most important. Malathion aids in control of whiteflies and many scales.

CLARKIA

Leafhopper, Six-spotted.

CLEMATIS

Beetle, Black Blister (devours flowers, foliage); Clematis Blister.

Borer, Clematis (works in roots).

Bug, Tarnished Plant.

Caterpillar, Omnivorous Looper.

Mite, Two-spotted (webby, yellow foliage).

Nematode, Spring Crimp; Northern Root-knot (may kill vines).

Scale, Brown Soft; Oystershell.

Weevil, Japanese.   **Whitefly,** Glacial; Inconspicuous.

CLERODENDRUM (Glory-Bower)

Mealybug, Citrus; Long-tailed.   **Orthezia,** Greenhouse.

Scale, Black; Brown Soft; Green Shield; Hemispherical; Latania; Pustule.

CLOVER (*Trifolium*)

Aphid, Clover; Corn Root; Cowpea; Hawthorn; Pea; Spotted Alfalfa; Sweetclover; Yellow Clover.

Armyworm, Fall.

Beetle, Beet Leaf; Grape Colaspis; Imbricated Snout; Pale-striped Flea; Potato Flea.

Borer, Clover Root; Clover Stem.

Bug, Alfalfa Plant. **Butterfly,** Clouded Sulfur.
Caterpillar, Clover Head; Clover Looper; Green Cloverworm.
Curculio, Clover Root. **Earworm,** Corn.
Leafhopper, Corn.
Mite, Clover; Strawberry Spider. **Moth,** Pine Tortrix.
Nematode, American Dagger; Citrus Spine; Cobb's Meadow; Godfrey's Meadow; Northern Root-knot; Scribner's Meadow; Steiner's Spiral; Tesselate Spiral; Zimmerman's Spiral.
Wasp, Clover Seed Chalcid. **Webworm,** Garden.
Weevil, Alfalfa; Clover Head; Clover Leaf; Clover Seed; Lesser Clover Leaf; Sweetclover.

COCKSCOMB (*Celosia*)

Mite, Two-spotted; other species (mealy webs; serious in hot weather).
Scale, Latania.

COCONUT (see Palms)

COFFEE (*Coffea*)

Mealybug, Citrus; Long-tailed. **Orthezia,** Greenhouse.
Scale, Black; Black Thread; Camellia; Cyanophyllum; Green; Green Shield; Hemispherical; Pyriform; Tesselated.
Whitefly, Citrus.

COFFEEBERRY (see California Coffeeberry)

COLEUS

Caterpillar, Yellow Woollybear.
Mealybug, Citrus; Grape; Long-tailed (white fluffs at leaf axils).
Mite, Privet; Two-spotted.
Nematode, Cotton Root-knot; Southern Root-knot; Spring Crimp.
Orthezia, Greenhouse (dark scale with white wax).
Scale, Parlatorialike. **Slug,** Greenhouse.
Weevil, Imported Long-horned (gray snout beetle).
Whitefly, Greenhouse (common problem).

COLLARDS (*Brassica oleracea* var. *acephala*)

Aphid, Cabbage; Turnip (grayish lice, common).
Beetle, White-fringed; Yellow-margined Leaf.
Bug, Horned Squash; Harlequin; Southern Squash.
Caterpillar, Cabbage Looper; Imported Cabbageworm.
Moth, Diamondback; White-lined Sphinx.
Webworm, Cabbage.
   See Cabbage for other pests.

COLUMBINE (*Aquilegia*)

Aphid, Black-backed Columbine (pink-and-green); Columbine (cream-colored, abundant); Crescent-marked Lily; Foxglove; Melon; Potato; Spirea.
Beetle, Asiatic Garden.
Borer, Columbine (salmon caterpillar in crown); Stalk.
Budworm, Rose. **Bug,** Red-and-black Stink. **Butterfly,** Columbine Skipper.
Curculio, Cambium.
Leaf Miner, Columbine (white winding tunnels); Wild Parsnip.
Mealybug, Citrophilus; Grape. **Mites.**
Moth, White-lined Sphinx.
Weevil, Imported Long-horned. **Whitefly,** Glacial.

CONFEDERATE-JASMINE (*Trachelospermum*)

Scale, Black Thread; Acuminate; Camphor; Chaff; Dictyospermum; Florida Red; Florida Wax; Latania; Pustule; Pyriform; Quohog-shaped.
Whiteflies.

CONFEDERATE-ROSE (*Hibiscus mutabilis*)

Scale, Chaff; Pustule.

COOPERIA (Rainlily; Prairielily)

Fly, Narcissus Bulb.

CORAL BEAN, CORAL TREE (*Erythrina*)

Beetle, Cuban May. **Mealybug,** Striped.
Scale, Lesser Show.

CORALBELLS (*Heuchera*)

Mealybugs (occasional).
Nematode, Spring Crimp (brown blotches in leaves).
Weevil, Strawberry Root (grubs at roots).

CORALBERRY (*Symphoricarpos*)

Scale, Barnacle; Black; Cottony-cushion; Green Shield; Latania; Lesser Snow; Pustule; San Jose; Walnut.

CORAL-PLANT, BELLYACHE BUSH (*Jatropha*)

Mealybug, Long-tailed; Mexican; Striped.
Scale, Brown Soft; Dictyospermum; Hemispherical; Latania; Lesser Snow; Oleander; Purple.

CORAL-VINE (*Antigonon*)

Scale, Black; Brown Soft; Black Thread; Cottony-cushion; Hemispherical; Latania; Lesser Snow.

COREOPSIS (Tickseed)

Aphid, Coreopsis.
Beetle, Chrysomela Leaf; Spotted Cucumber.
Bug, Four-lined Plant. **Leafhopper,** Six-spotted.

CORK TREE (*Phellodendron*)

Scale, Lesser Snow; Pustule.

CORN (*Zea mays*)

Ant, Cornfield.
Aphid, Bean; Corn Leaf; Corn Root (woolly white lice at roots; distributed by ants); English Grain; Greenbug; Potato; Rusty Plum.
Armyworm, Beet; Fall.
Beetle, Asiatic Garden; Argus Tortoise; Bean Leaf; Blister; Bumble Flower; Carrot; Cereal Leaf; Corn Flea; Corn Sap; Corn Silk; Desert Corn Flea; Dusky Sap; Green June; Imbricated Snout; Japanese; Pale-striped Flea; Potato Flea; Rose Chafer; Seed-corn; Spotted Cucumber (southern corn rootworm); Striped Blister; Striped Cucumber; Sweetpotato Flea; Toothed Flea; Western Black Flea; Western Spotted Cucumber; Western Striped Cucumber; White-fringed.
Borer, European Corn (cream-colored caterpillars at base of ears and in stalks; Elder; Lesser Cornstalk; Southern Cornstalk; Stalk (dark, striped caterpillar); Sugar-cane.
Billbug, Maize; Southern Corn.
Bug, Chinch; Garden Fleahopper; Green Stink; Harlequin; Negro; Southern Green Stink.
Caterpillar, Range; Yellow Woollybear.
Cutworm, Bronzed; Clayback; Pale-sided; Western Bean; Western W-marked.
Earworm, Corn (dark caterpillars at tips of ears; common).
Leaf Miner, Corn Blotch. **Maggot,** Seed-corn.
Millipedes. Mite, Desert Spider.
Nematode, American Dagger; Bean; California Dagger; Christie's Stubby Root; Cobb's Meadow; Corn Meadow; Cotton Root-knot; Crown-headed Lance; De Man's; Javanese Root-knot; Peanut Root-knot; Pine Sting; Scribner's Meadow; Southern Root-knot; Steiner's Spiral; Sting; Tarjan's Sheath; Tesselate Stylet; Zimmerman's Spiral.
Planthopper, Corn.
Rootworm, Northern Corn; Western Corn.
Termites. Thrips, Grass.
Webworm, Corn Root. **Weevil,** Corn Stem.
Wireworm, Columbia Basin; Plains False; Sand; Sugar-beet; Tobacco; Wheat.
 The two most important pests are the European corn borer, with control started when plants are young, and the corn earworm, treated just after silking.

CORNFLOWER, BACHELORS-BUTTON (*Centaurea*)

Aphid, Western Aster Root; other species.
Borer, Stalk.
Leafhopper, Six-spotted. **Leaf Tier,** Omnivorous.
Scale, Hemispherical.

COSMOS

Aphid, Coreopsis; Bean (black); Western Aster Root; Potato.
Beetle, Asiatic Garden; Japanese; Spotted Cucumber (on flowers).
Borer, European Corn (cream-colored); Stalk (dark, striped).
Bug, Four-lined Plant; Tarnished Plant.
Leafhopper, Six-spotted (transmits aster yellows).
Mite, Two-spotted (plant yellow or gray, mealy).
Termites, Subterranean.

COSTMARY (*Chrysanthemum balsamita*)

Aphid, Artemisia.

COTONEASTER

Aphid, Apple. **Borer,** Sinuate Pear.
Bug, Hawthorn Lace (leaves stippled gray, rusty flecks underneath).
Leafhopper, Privet.
Mite, Pear Leaf Blister (small, reddish-brown blisters); Platanus.
Scale, Acuminate; Dictyospermum; Florida Wax; Greedy; Latania; Olive;
   Oystershell; Quohog-shaped; San Jose; White Peach.
Webworm, Cotoneaster (webbing ends of branches).

COTTONWOOD (see Poplar)

COWPEA (*Vigna sinensis*)

Aphid, Bean (black, common); Cowpea.
Armyworm, Fall.
Beetle, Bean Leaf; Blister; Grape Colaspis; Mexican Bean; White-fringed.
Borer, Lesser Cornstalk.
Bug, Green Stink; Harlequin; Garden Fleahopper; Leaf-footed; Pumpkin.
Caterpillar, Green Cloverworm; Velvetbean.
Cricket, Camel. **Curculio,** Clover Root; Cowpea.
Cutworms. Leaf Miner, Serpentine.
Treehopper, Three-cornered Alfalfa. **Webworm,** Garden.
Weevil, Cowpea; Sweetclover. **Wireworms.**

CRABAPPLE, ORNAMENTAL (*Pyrus* spp.)

Aphid, Apple; Apple Grain.
Borer, Flatheaded Apple Tree; Roundheaded Apple Tree.

Bug, Alder Lace; Apple Red. **Cankerworms.**
Caterpillar, Eastern Tent. **Curculio,** Apple.
Leaf Crumpler.
Leaf Miner, Apple Blotch; Spotted Tentiform; Unspotted Tentiform.
Maggot, Apple. **Moth,** Codling.
Rootworm, Strawberry. **Sawfly,** European Apple.
Scale, San Jose. **Weevil,** Apple Flea.
See Apple for other possible pests.

CRANBERRY (*Vaccinium macrocarpon*)

Beetle, Cranberry; Rhabdopterus.
Borer, Cranberry Girdler.
Budworm, Cranberry Blossomworm.
Caterpillar, Blackheaded Fireworm; Yellowheaded Fireworm (berries webbed); Chain-spotted Geometer.
Fruitworm, Cranberry; Sparganothis.
Leafhopper, Blunt-nosed (vector of false-blossom disease).
Midge, Cranberry Tipworm.
Moth, Gypsy; Crinkled Flannel; Tussock.
Nematode, Christie's Stubby Root; Steiner's Spiral; Tesselate Stylet; Zimmerman's Spiral.
Rootworm, Cranberry.
Scale, Cranberry; Oystershell; Putnam.
Spanworm, Cranberry. **Termites.**
Weevil, Black Vine; Cranberry; Strawberry Root.

CRANBERRY, HIGH-BUSH (*Viburnum opulus*)

Aphid, Bean.

CRAPEMYRTLE (*Lagerstroemia*)

Aphid, Crapemyrtle (profuse honeydew with sooty mold).
Beetle, Colaspis; Fuller Rose.
Mealybug, Citrus.
Scale, Black; Camellia Mining; Coconut; Cyanophyllum; Florida Red; Florida Wax; Green Shield; Hemispherical; Latania; Pustule; Pyriform.

CRASSULA

Mealybug, Citrus (white woolly bodies congested on stems).
Mite, Cyclamen (plants deformed).
Nematode, Spring Crimp. **Scale,** Latania; Lesser Snow.

CRESS, GARDEN (*Lepidium*)

Beetle, Western Black Flea. **Bug,** Harlequin.
Leaf Miner, Serpentine. **Maggot,** Cabbage.
Nematode, Cabbage Cyst; Northern Root-knot.

CROCUS
Aphid, Crescent-marked Lily; Green Peach; Tulip Bulb.
Mite, Bulb.

CROSSANDRA
Mealybug, Mexican. **Orthezia,** Greenhouse.
Scale, Barnacle.

CROTON (*Codiaeum*)
Mealybug, Citrus; Long-tailed; Striped.
Mite, Texas Citrus. **Orthezia,** Greenhouse.
Scale, Black; Brown Soft; Coconut; Cottony-cushion; Dictyospermum; Fern; Florida Red; Florida Wax; Glover; Green Shield; Hemispherical; Latania; Lesser Snow; Long Soft; Oriental; Purple; Pyriform; Quohog-shaped; Rufous.
Thrips, Greenhouse.

CROTALARIA
Mite, Two-spotted; other species.
Scale, Black; Cyanophyllum; Dictyospermum; Florida Red; Lesser Snow; Pustule; White Peach.

CUCUMBER (*Cucumis sativus*)
Aphid, Green Peach; Melon (carries bacteria-causing wilt).
Armyworm, Fall.
Beetle, Banded Cucumber; Hop Flea; Imbricated Snout; Potato Flea; Spotted Cucumber (green with 12 black spots); Striped Cucumber (yellow-green with 3 black stripes); Western Spotted; Western Striped.
Borer, Squash Vine.
Bug, Garden Fleahopper; Horned Squash; Squash; Southern Green Stink; Tarnished Plant.
Caterpillar, Melonworm; Pickleworm (small, greenish, in blossom, fruit).
Centipede, Garden Symphylan. **Cricket,** Field. **Cutworms.**
Leafhopper, Beet (transmits curly top).
Leaf Tier, Celery. **Maggot,** Seed-corn.
Mite, Desert Spider; Two-spotted.
Nematode, Cobb's Meadow; Corn Meadow; Cotton Root-knot; Northern Root-knot; Southern Root-knot.
Springtail, Garden. **Thrips,** Onion; Western Flower.
Whitefly, Greenhouse. **Weevil,** Strawberry Root.
Start plants under Hotkaps, later changing to cheesecloth or wire screening to protect young vines from aphids and cucumber beetles spreading disease. Start spraying or dusting as soon as plants are too large for covering.

CUNNINGHAMIA (China-fir)

Scale, Cottony-cushion; Florida Wax.

CUPHEA (Cigarflower; Cigarette Plant)

Beetle, Pine Colaspis.
Scale, Black; Brown Soft; Cottony-cushion; Florida Wax; Latania; Lesser Snow; Pustule.

CURRANT (*Ribes*)
(Including Flowering Currant)

Aphid, Currant (leaves crinkled, cupped down, green lice in pockets); Dogberry; Ornamental Currant; Potato; Variable Currant; Chrysanthemum.
Beetle, Fuller Rose.
Borer, Currant (canes die back); Currant Stem Girdler; Flatheaded Apple Tree; Pacific Flatheaded.
Bug, Four-lined Plant (circles in leaves).
Caterpillar, California Tent; Western Tent; Yellow Woollybear.
Fly, Currant Fruit (maggots in fruit).
Fruitworm, Gooseberry.
Leafhopper, Grape; Privet; White Apple.
Leaf Roller, Fruit-tree; Oblique-banded.
Mealybug, Ground.
Mite, Currant Bud; McDaniel Spider; Two-spotted.
Moth, Io; White-lined Sphinx.
Sawfly, Imported Currantworm (green with black spots).
Scale, Chaff; Cottony Maple; European Fruit Lecanium; Forbes; Green Shield; Oystershell; Putnam; San Jose; Scurfy; Walnut.
Spanworm, Currant (looper Caterpillar).
Weevil, Currant Fruit.
Cut out canes with borers. Spray for aphids and sawfly larvae.

CUSTARD-APPLE (*Annona reticulata*)

Mealybug, Coconut.
Scale, Florida Wax; Hemispherical; Latania; Long Soft; Quohog-shaped.

CYCAD, SAGO PALM (*Cycas*)

Mealybug, Citrus; Long-tailed.
Scale, Araucaria; Black; Black Thread; Brown Soft; California Red; Chaff; Coconut; Cyanophyllum; Dictyospermum; European Fiorinia; Fern; Florida Red; Green Shield; Hemispherical (brown, convex, common); Latania; Oleander (yellow); Oriental; Proteus; Purple; Red Bay; Tesselated; White Peach.

CYCLAMEN

Aphid, Crescent-marked Lily; Melon.
Beetle, Oriental. **Mealybug,** Citrus.
Mite, Broad; Cyclamen (plants deformed, stunted, buds black).
Nematode, Root-knot; Spring Crimp (foliar).
Thrips, Greenhouse.
Weevil, Black Vine (grubs on roots may kill plants).

Use insecticides cautiously on Cyclamen; some may be phytotoxic. Rotenone is relatively safe.

CYNOGLOSSUM

Aphid, Leaf-curl Plum.

CYPRESS (*Cupressus*)

Aphid, Arborvitae (brown); Cypress (large green).
Beetle, Cedar Bark; June; Pine Colaspis.
Borer, Western Cedar. **Horntail,** Western.
Mealybug, Citrus; Cypress; Long-tailed; Redwood.
Midge, Monterey-pine.
Mite, Cypress; Date; Platanus; Southern Red.
Moth, Cypress Cone; Cypress Tip; Cypress Webber; Imperial; White-marked Tussock.
Sawfly, Cypress.
Scale, Cottony-cushion; Cypress Bark (serious on Monterey cypress); Dictyospermum; Juniper; Latania; Newstead's; Red Bay.
Thrips, Greenhouse.

CYPRESS, BALD (*Taxodium*)

Moth, Cypress. **Scale,** Taxodium.

CYPRESS-VINE (*Quamoclit*)

Scale, Black; Green Shield.

DAHLIA

Aphid, Bean (black, common); Green Peach; Leaf-curl Plum.
Bee, Leaf-cutter.
Beetle, Asiatic Garden; Black Blister; Carrot; Grape Colaspis; Japanese; Rose Chafer; Spotted Cucumber (eats petals); Western Spotted Cucumber; White-fringed.
Borer, Burdock; European Corn; Stalk.
Bug, Four-lined Plant; Tarnished Plant (new shoots blackened).
Caterpillar, Saddleback; Yellow Woollybear.
Leaf Cutter, Morning-glory.

Leafhopper, Potato (prevalent, serious; leaves curl, brown at margins; plants stunted); Southern Garden.
Leaf Tier, Celery. **Mealybug,** Citrus.
Mite, Cyclamen; Two-spotted (mealy webs).
Nematode, Chrysanthemum Foliar; Scribner's Meadow.
Planthopper.
Scale, Black; Cottony-cushion; Florida Wax.
Thrips, Flower; Greenhouse; Onion (transmits spotted-wilt virus).
Wasp, Giant Hornet (may tear stalks).
Weevil, Cocklebur. **Wireworms.**

DAISY, OXEYE (*Chrysanthemum leucanthemum*)
Aphid, Artemisia. **Beetle,** White-fringed.
Bug, Daisy Plant (punctures leaves, flower buds).
Caterpillar, Omnivorous Looper.
Leaf Miner, Chrysanthemum. **Leaf Tier,** Celery.
Mealybug, Ground (works at roots).

DAISY, SHASTA (*Chrysanthemum maximum*)
Aphid, Myrtle.
Beetle, Spotted Cucumber (very common on flowers).
Bug, Daisy Plant; Four-lined Plant; Tarnished Plant.
Butterfly, Checker Spot.
Leaf Miner, Chrysanthemum (irregular light mines in leaves).

DAPHNE
Aphids, several species. **Mealybug,** Citrus.
Scale, Citricola; Cottony-cushion; Dictyospermum; Greedy; Yellow.

DATE PALM (*Phoenix dactylifera*)
Beetle, Corn Sap; Dried Fruit; Fig.
Bug, Western Leaf-footed (large, with leaflike legs).
Mealybug, Grape.
Mite, Date (webs leaves together; scars fruit).
Scale, Brown Soft; Oriental; Parlatoria Date (small, gray and white, presumably eradicated); Red Date.
Thrips, Banded Greenhouse.

DATURA (Angel's Trumpet)
Leafhopper, Beet. **Mite,** Tomato Russet.
Psyllid, Tomato.
Scale, Cottony Taxus; Latania.

DAYLILY (*Hemerocallis*)
Aphid, Sand Lily.
Nematode, Cotton Root-knot; Southern Root-knot.
Scale, Coconut.
Thrips, Flower; other species (blossoms streaked, foliage silvered).
Weevil, Imported Long-horned.

DELPHINIUM (Larkspur)
Aphid, Delphinium (red, on underside of cupped-down leaves); Green Peach; Crescent-marked Lily.
Beetle, Asiatic Garden; Black Blister; Japanese (rare on delphinium).
Borer, Burdock; Stalk. **Budworm,** Rose.
Bug, Four-lined Plant. **Cutworms.**
Leaf Miner, Larkspur (tan blotches in leaves).
Millipedes.
Mite, Broad (leaves glassy); Cyclamen (the most important pest; plants stunted, leaves deformed, flower buds black); Two-spotted.
Nematode, Chrysanthemum Foliar; De Man's Meadow; Steiner's Spiral; Root-knot; Stem.
Slugs. Sowbugs. Thrips, Gladiolus.

DEUTZIA
Aphid, Bean; Cowpea; Currant (leaves crinkled); Melon.
Beetle, Fuller Rose (leaves notched from margins).
Leaf Miner, Lilac (tan blotches in leaves).
Nematode, Root-knot. **Scale,** White Peach.

DEWBERRY (*Rubus flagellaris*)
Borer, Red-necked Cane.
Leaf Roller, Oblique-banded; Strawberry.
Maggot, Raspberry Cane. **Sawfly,** Dewberry; Raspberry.
Scale, Rose. **Weevil,** Strawberry.
See Blackberry and Raspberry for other pests.

DIANTHUS (Garden Pink)
Aphid, Green Peach. **Beetle,** Black Blister.
Nematode, Spring Crimp.

DICHONDRA (Grass)
Cutworm, Granulate. **Weevil,** Vegetable.

DIEFFENBACHIA
Mealybug, Long-tailed. **Scale,** Mango Shield.

DILL (*Anethum graveolens*)
Aphid, Honeysuckle and Parsnip; Willow.
Caterpillar, Celeryworm. **Weevil,** Carrot.

DOCK (*Rumex*)
Aphid, Dock. **Sawfly,** Dock. **Scale,** Green.

DOGWOOD (*Cornus*)
Aphid, Dogwood; Melon; Sunflower.
Beetle, Pitted Ambrosia.
Borer, Azalea Stem; Dogwood (kills branches); Dogwood Cambium; Dogwood Twig; Flatheaded Apple Tree (injures young trees); Pecan.
Bug, Green Stink.
Caterpillar, Phigalea Looper; Red-humped; Stinging Rose.
Cicada, Periodical (injures twigs by egg laying).
Leafhopper, Rose (foliage commonly stippled white); Eight-lined.
Leaf Miner, Locust. **Leaf Roller,** Oblique-banded.
Midge, Dogwood Club Gall.
Nematode, American Dagger; De Man's Meadow; Godfrey's Meadow; Tesselate Stylet.
Sawfly, Dogwood.
Scale, Cottony Maple; Cyanophyllum; Dogwood; Florida Wax; Forbes; Obscure; Oystershell; Oleander; Purple; Putnam; San Jose; Tea; Tesselated; Tuliptree; Walnut; White Peach; Willow Scurfy.
Whitefly, Mulberry (round, black with white fringe).

DORONICUM (Leopards-bane)
Aphid, Crescent-marked Lily.
Nematode, Spring Crimp (transparent to dark spots in leaves).

DOUGLAS-FIR (*Pseudotsuga*)
Aphid, Cooley Spruce Gall (alternate host for); Douglas-fir; Monterey-pine.
Beetle, Douglas-fir; Douglas-fir Engraver; Golden Buprestid; Obtuse Sawyer; Silver Fir.
Borer, California Prionus; Cedar Tree (may girdle and kill); Fir Flatheaded; Sculptured Pine; Western Larch Roundheaded; White-pine Shoot.
Bud Moth, Larch. **Budworm,** Spruce (serious).
Butterfly, Pine (green, white-striped caterpillar; may defoliate).
Caterpillar, Phantom Hemlock Looper; Western Hemlock Looper.
Horntails.
Midge, Balsam Gall; Douglas-fir Cone.
Moth, Douglas-fir Cone; Douglas-fir Pitch; Douglas-fir Tussock; Pine Cone; Sequoia Pitch; Silver-spotted Tiger; Zimmerman Pine.
Nematode, De Man's Meadow.

Scale, Black Pine Leaf; Hemlock; Pine Needle.
Weevil, Douglas-fir Twig; Strawberry Root.

DRACAENA
Beetle, Fuller Rose.
Mealybug, Citrus; Long-tailed.
Nematode, Tarjan's Sheath.
Scale, Boisduval's; Brown Soft; Cyanophyllum; Dictyospermum; Fern; Hemispherical; Long Soft; Pyriform; Tesselated.
Thrips, Banded Greenhouse; Dracaena.

DURANTA (Golden Dewdrop)
Orthezia, Greenhouse.
Scale, Acuminate; Black; Black Thread; Cottony-cushion; Dictyospermum; Florida Red; Florida Wax; Hemispherical; Latania; Mining; Long Soft.

DUTCHMANS-PIPE (*Aristolochia*)
Butterfly, Pipevine Swallowtail (brown caterpillar).
Mealybug, Long-tailed. Scale, Hemispherical.

ECHEVERIA
Nematode, Root-knot.
Scale, Lesser Snow. Weevil, Black Vine.

EGGFRUIT (*Lucuma nervosa*)
Scale, Green; Lesser Snow; Mining; Pyriform; Tesselated.

EGGPLANT (*Solanum melongena* var. *esculentum*)
Aphid, Green Peach; Melon; Potato.
Beetle, Asiatic Garden; Blister; Colorado Potato (yellow with black stripes); Eggplant Flea (tiny shot holes in leaves); Pale-striped Flea; Potato Flea (injurious to seedlings); Spotted Cucumber; Tobacco Flea.
Borer, Potato Stalk; Potato Tuberworm.
Bug, Cotton Stainer; Eggplant Lace; Green Stink; Garden Fleahopper; Harlequin; One-spot Stink; Pumpkin; Southern Green Stink.
Caterpillar, Yellow Woollybear. Cutworms.
Hornworm, Tobacco; Tomato.
Leafhopper, Potato. Leaf Miner, Eggplant.
Maggot, Pepper (occasional; worms in fruit).
Mite, Strawberry Spider; Two-spotted.
Nematode, Cobb's Meadow; Golden; Javanese Root-knot; Northern Root-knot; Southern Root-knot.
Whitefly, Greenhouse (common on plants started in greenhouses).

ELAEAGNUS (Russian-olive)

Aphid, Oleaster-thistle (yellow and green).
Scale, Brown Soft; Chaff; Cyanophyllum; Dictyospermum; Florida Red; Florida Wax; Hemispherical; Latania; Lesser Snow; Oleander; Olive; Olive Parlatoria; Oriental; Proteus; Purple; Pustule; San Jose; Walnut; White Peach.

ELDER (*Sambucus*)

Aphid, Elder; Bean.
Beetle, Potato Flea; Rose Chafer.
Borer, Currant; Elder; Elder Shoot.   **Bug,** Green Stink.
Caterpillar, Omnivorous Looper.   **Cricket,** Black-horned Flea.
Mealybug, Citrus; Grape.   **Moth,** American Dagger.
Scale, Black; Brown Soft; Green; Green Shield; Hemispherical; Walnut.
Thrips, Madroña.

ELDER, YELLOW (*Stenolobium*)

Mealybug, Citrus.   **Orthezia,** Greenhouse.
Scale, Acuminate; Black; Green Shield; Hemispherical; Lesser Snow; Mining; Proteus; Quohog-shaped.

ELM (*Ulmus*)

Aphid, Elm Cockscomb Gall; Elm Leaf; Elm Sack Gall; Giant Bark; Woolly Apple; Woolly Elm; Woolly Elm Bark; Woolly Hawthorn; Woolly Pear.
Beetle, Carrot; Elm Calligrapha; Elm Flea; Elm Leaf (serious; leaves skeletonized, may drop); Grape Flea; Japanese (chews leaves to lace); June; Larger Elm Leaf; Native Elm Bark; Red Elm Bark; Rose Chafer; Smaller European Elm Bark (transmits Dutch Elm disease); Striped Cucumber.
Borer, Azalea Stem; Brown Wood; Carpenterworm; Dogwood Twig; Elm; Flatheaded Apple Tree (injurious to new transplants); Flatheaded Cherry Tree; Oak Timberworm; Pacific Flatheaded; Pigeon Tremex; Painted Hickory; Twig Girdler; Twig Pruner.
Bug, Alder Lace; Elm Lace.
Butterfly, Mourning-cloak (spiny caterpillar).
Cankerworm, Fall; Spring (important; may defoliate).
Casebearer, Elm.
Caterpillar, Eastern Tent; Hemlock Looper; Omnivorous Looper; Red-humped Oakworm; Puss; Variable Oak Leaf.
Cricket, Black-horned Tree.
Leafhopper, White-banded Elm (transmits phloem necrosis); Virginia-creeper.
Leaf Miner, Elm; Locust.   **Leaf Roller,** Fruit-tree.
Mealybug, Striped.

Mite, Avocado Red; European Red; Four-spotted; Oak; Two-spotted.
Moth, Brown-tail; American Dagger; Cecropia; Elm Sphinx; Gypsy; Leopard (borer); Polyphemus; White-lined Sphinx; White-marked Tussock.
Nematode, American Dagger; Root-knot. **Sawfly,** Elm.
Scale, Calico; Camphor; Citricola; Cottony Maple; Dictyospermum; Elm Scurfy (important); European Elm; European Fruit Lecanium; Gloomy; Green Shield; Japanese Wax; Latania; Obscure; Oystershell; Putnam; Pyriform; San Jose; Scurfy; Walnut; White Peach.
Spanworm, Elm. **Treehopper,** Buffalo. **Webworm,** Fall.
Weevil, Apple Flea; Black Elm Bark; Japanese; Red Elm Bark.

DDT is very effective against bark beetles and elm leaf beetles but increases mites, Putnam scale and elm leaf aphids.

ENDIVE (*Cichorium*)

Aphid, Bean (black); Brown Ambrosia; Pea (large, green).
Nematode, Root-knot.

EPILOBIUM

Aphid, Evening Primrose; Green Gooseberry; Malaheb Cherry.

ERIOPHYLLUM

Mealybug, Yucca.

ERYTHRINA

Mealybug, Striped. **Scale,** Lesser Snow.

ERYTHRONIUM

Aphid, Green Peach.

ESCAROLE

Nematode, Northern Root-knot; Peanut Root-knot.

EUCALYPTUS

Aphid, Cowpea.
Borer, California Prionus; Nautical; Pacific Flatheaded.
Bug, Lygus.
Caterpillar, California Oakworm; Omnivorous Looper; Orange Tortrix.
Mealybug, Long-tailed.
Mite, Avocado Red; Platanus; Southern Red.
Scale, Acuminate; Black; California Red; Cottony-cushion; Dictyospermum; Florida Red; Greedy; Latania; Lesser Snow; Oleander; Oriental; Purple; Pyriform; San Jose.
Thrips, Greenhouse.

EUGENIA
Mealybug, Citrus; Long-tailed; Mexican.
Scale, Black; Acuminate; Chaff; Coconut; Dictyospermum; Florida Red; Florida Wax; Mango Shield; Masked; Proteus; Purple; Pustule; Pyriform; Tesselated.
Thrips, Greenhouse.

EUONYMUS
Aphid, Bean; Ivy.
Scale, Araucaria; Barnacle; Black; Brown Soft; California Red; Chaff; Cottony Maple; Cyanophyllum; Dictyospermum; Euonymus (males thin, white, conspicuous; females brown; common and injurious); Florida Red; Florida Wax; Glover; Greedy; Latania; Proteus; Parlatorialike; Purple; Pyriform; San Jose; Tea; Yellow.
Euonymus Scale is the chief problem.

EUPATORIUM (Mistflower)
Aphid, Brown Ambrosia; Coreopsis; Leaf-curl Plum.
Fly, Eupatorium Gall.   **Leaf Miner,** Chrysanthemum.
Scale, Cassava; Cyanophyllum; Green; Latania.

EUPHORBIA (Crown-of-Thorns)
Scale, Cyanophyllum; Dictyospermum; Florida Red; Latania; Long Soft; Oriental; Proteus.

EUPHORBIA (Snow-on-the-mountain)
Scale, Brown Soft.

EUPHORBIA (Spurge)
Aphid, Lettuce Root; Potato.
Scale, Cyanophyllum; Dictyospermum; Long Soft.

EURYA
Scale, Barnacle; Citrophilus; Cottony-cushion; Camellia; Florida Red; Florida Wax; Latania; Tea.

EVENING PRIMROSE (*Oenothera*)
Aphid, Oenothera; White Aster Root.
Beetle, Steel-blue Flea.   **Mealybug,** Yucca.
Nematode, Stem.   **Weevil,** Cocklebur.

FATSHEDERA
Scale, Florida Red; Pyriform.

FATSIA
Scale, Florida Red; Green Shield; Pyriform.

FEIJOA
Scale, Acuminate; Bamboo; Barnacle; Black; Brown Soft; Chaff; Dictyospermum; Florida Red; Florida Wax; Green Shield; Pyriform; Latania; Red Bay; Tesselated.

FERNS
Aphid, Crescent-marked Lily; Fern (black); Latania.
Beetle, Japanese (feeds on some types).
Caterpillar, Florida Fern (feeds at night); Orange Tortrix (rolls leaves); Yellow Woollybear.
Mealybug, Citrus; Long-tailed; Coconut.
Crickets. Cutworms. Grasshoppers. Millipedes.
Nematode, Cobb's Meadow; Spring Crimp (black or brown bands).
Scale, Acuminate; Barnacle; Black; Black Thread; Brown Soft; Coconut; Cottony-cushion; Chaff; Dictyospermum; Fern (white); Florida Red; Florida Wax; Green; Green Shield; Hemispherical (brown); Latania; Lesser Snow; Long Soft; Oleander (flat, yellow, common); Parlatoria-like; Proteus; European Fiorinia; Oriental.
Orthezia, Greenhouse.
Slug, Gray Field. **Snail,** Fern (eats from lower leaf surface).
Weevil, Black Vine (on maidenhair fern); Japanese.
Whitefly, Citrus; Fern; Greenhouse.
Use insecticides on ferns with caution; they are subject to chemical injury.

FETTERBUSH (*Lyonia lucida*)
Scale, Azalea Bark.

FIG, CREEPING (*Ficus pumila*)
Mealybug, Citrophilus.
Scale, Dictyospermum; Cottony-cushion; Pyriform.
Whitefly, Citrus. **Thrips,** Cuban-laurel.

FIG, STRANGLER (*Ficus aurea*)
Orthezia, Greenhouse.
Scale, Black; Brown Soft; Chinese Obscure; Florida Red; Florida Wax; Green; Green Shield; Hemispherical; Pustule; Pyriform; Long Soft; Tesselated.

FIG, TREE (*Ficus carica*)
Beetle, Dried Fruit; Fig; Green June; Darkling Ground.
Borer, Branch and Twig (black-and-brown beetle bores in twigs).

Caterpillar, Navel Orangeworm.
Mealybug, Citrophilus; Fruit; Long-tailed (prevalent); Mexican.
Mite, Dried Fruit; Fig Rust; Pacific Spider; Texas Citrus.
Nematode, California Dagger; Christie's Stubby Root; Fig Cyst; Fig Pin; Walnut Meadow; Root-knot.
Scale, Black; Cottony-cushion; Dictyospermum; Fig (oyster-shaped, purple or brown); Florida Wax; Green Shield; Japanese Wax; Latania; Lesser Snow; Mining; Oriental; Oystershell; San Jose; White Peach; Pustule.
Thrips, Cuban-laurel. **Wireworm,** Oregon.

FILBERT (*Corylus*)

Caterpillar, Filbertworm. **Mealybug,** Apple.
Mite, Filbert Bud. **Weevil,** Filbert.

FIR (*Abies*)

Aphid, Balsam Twig; Balsam Woolly; Bow-legged Fir; Flocculent Fir.
Bagworm.
Beetle, Fir Engraver; Lion; Mountain Pine; Obtuse Sawyer; Oregon Fir Sawyer; Silver Fir; Western Balsam Bark.
Borer, California Prionus; Flatheaded Cone; Flatheaded Fir; Roundheaded Fir; Sculptured Pine.
Budworm, Black-headed; Spruce. **Bud Moth,** Larch.
Caterpillar, Chain-spotted Geometer; Fir Cone Looper; False Hemlock Looper; Hemlock Looper.
Horntails. Leaf Miner, White-fir Needle.
Midge, Balsam Gall. **Mite,** Spruce Spider (needles cobwebby).
Moth, Douglas-fir Tussock; Fir Seed; Pine Tube Cone; Silver-spotted Tiger; Spotted Tussock.
Sawfly, Balsam-fir. **Scale,** Oystershell; Pine Needle.

FLACOURTIA (Governors-plum)

Mite, Texas Citrus.
Scale, Acuminate; Brown Soft; Latania; Purple; Pustule; White Peach.

FLAME VINE (*Pyrostegia*)

Mealybug, Citrus. **Orthezia,** Greenhouse.
Scale, Black Thread; Barnacle; Brown Soft; Cyanophyllum; Chaff; Florida Wax; Green Shield; Lesser Snow; Mining; Proteus; Pustule; Parlatorialike; Pyriform.

FORGET-ME-NOT (*Myosotis*)

Aphid, Forget-me-not; Green Peach.
Beetle, Potato Flea (small, black; pinholes in leaves).
Butterfly, Painted Beauty (purple, yellow and green caterpillars).
Leaf Tier, Celery.

FORSYTHIA
Bug, Four-lined Plant (occasional; tan circles in leaves).
Nematode, Northern Root-knot; Tesselate Stylet; Walnut Meadow.
Scale, Latania; Purple; San Jose; Walnut.
Weevil, Japanese.

FOXGLOVE (*Digitalis*)
Aphid, Foxglove; Crescent-marked Lily.
Beetle, Asiatic Garden; Japanese; Rose Chafer.
Mealybug, Citrophilus.   **Nematode,** Stem.
Scale, Cottony-cushion.   **Thrips,** Onion.

FRANGIPANI (*Plumeria*)
Mealybug, Long-tailed.
Scale, Acuminate; Black; Brown Soft; Coconut; Cottony-cushion; Cyano-
   phyllum; Green; Green Shield; Hemispherical; Latania; Lesser Snow;
   Oriental; Pyriform.

FRANKLINIA (*Gordonia alatamaha*)
Scale, Red Bay; Walnut.   **Wasp,** Giant Hornet.

FREESIA
Aphid, Crescent-marked Lily; Green Peach; Tulip Bulb.
Mite, Bulb (in rotting bulbs).
Nematode, Root-knot.   **Thrips,** Gladiolus.

FRINGE-TREE (*Chinonanthus*)
Scale, White Peach; Rose.

FRITILLARIA
Scale, Latania.

FUCHSIA
Aphid, Crescent-marked Lily; Ornate; Potato.
Beetle, Fuller Rose; Strawberry Flea.
Caterpillar, Yellow Woollybear.
Mealybug, Citrus; Long-tailed.
Mite, Broad; Privet (pits underside of leaves); Cyclamen; Two-spotted.
Moth, White-lined Sphinx.   **Nematode,** Root-knot.
Scale, Barnacle; Black; California Red; Greedy.
Thrips, Greenhouse (foliage with "pepper-and-salt" effect).
Whitefly, Greenhouse (prevalent; injurious); Iris.

FURCRAEA
Scale, Brown Soft; Hemispherical.

GAILLARDIA
Bug, Four-lined Plant.
Beetle, Asiatic Garden; Japanese.
Nematode, False Root-knot of Sugar Beet. **Mites.**
Scale, Cottony-cushion.
Thrips, Flower; Onion. **Wireworms.**

GALLBERRY (*Ilex glabra*)
Scale, Acuminate; Florida Wax; Gloomy; Latania; Oak Eriococcus; Purple; Walnut.

GALTONIA
Fly, Narcissus Bulb.

GARDENIA (Cape-jasmine)
Aphid, Melon.
Beetle, Fuller Rose (notches leaves at night).
Mealybug, Citrus; Long-tailed.
Nematode, Cotton Root-knot; Peanut Root-knot; Reniform; Southern Root-knot; Steiner's Spiral.
Orthezia, Greenhouse.
Scale, Acuminate; Barnacle; Black; Brown Soft; Dictyospermum; Florida Red; Florida Wax; Green; Green Shield; Hemispherical; Long Soft; Mango Shield; Mining; Proteus; Pustule; Pyriform; Quohog-shaped; Tesselated; Tea; Tuliptree.
Thrips, Banded Greenhouse; Flower.
Weevil, Black Vine.
Whitefly, Citrus (very common; accompanied by much sooty mold).

GARLIC (*Allium sativa*)
Nematode, Stem and Bulb.

GAURA
Scale, Barnacle.

GAYFEATHER (*Liatris*)
Nematode, Cobb's Meadow; Walnut Meadow.

GEIGER-TREE (Cordia)
Scale, Black; Brown Soft; Coconut; Green Shield; Hemispherical; Latania; Lesser Snow; Pyriform.

GERANIUM (Wild)
Aphid, Wild Geranium.

GERANIUM (*Pelargonium*)
Aphid, Geranium; Green Peach; Potato.
Beetle, Fuller Rose; Rose Chafer.
Budworm, Tobacco. **Cankerworm,** Fall.
Caterpillar, Cabbage Looper; Omnivorous Looper; Orange Tortrix.
Earworm, Corn.
Leaf Roller, Beet; Oblique-banded; Red-banded.
Leaf Tier, Celery. **Mealybug,** Citrus; Mexican.
Mite, Broad; Cyclamen (young leaves curl); Two-spotted.
Moth, Geranium Plume.
Nematode, American Dagger; Northern Root-knot; Southern Root-knot; Spring Crimp.
Scale, Cottony-cushion; Fern; Lesser Snow; Pustule; Rose; White Peach.
Weevil, Black Vine; Imported Long-horned; Japanese.
Whitefly, Greenhouse (almost inevitable on indoor geraniums).

GERBERA (African-daisy)
Aphid, Leaf-curl Plum. **Mealybug,** Citrus; Mexican.
Mite, Broad; Cyclamen.
Scale, Black; Brown Soft; Coconut; Cottony-cushion; Dictyospermum; Green Shield; Hemispherical; Latania; Mango Shield; Oriental; Pyriform.
Thrips, Banded Greenhouse.

GERMANDER (*Teucrium*)
Nematode, Northern Root-knot.
Mite, Germander Leaf Crinkle.

GINGER-LILY (*Hedychium*)
Mealybug, Pineapple. **Scale,** Tesselated.

GINKGO
Caterpillar, Omnivorous Looper.
Mealybug, Grape. **Scale,** Peach Lecanium.

GINSENG (*Panax*)
Mealybug, Long-tailed.
Scale, Hemispherical; Oystershell.

GLADIOLUS
Aphid, Crescent-marked Lily; Foxglove; Melon; Potato; Tulip Bulb.
Beetle, Asiatic Garden; Black Blister; European Chafer; June; White-fringed.

Borer, European Corn; Stalk. **Bug,** Garden Fleahopper; Tarnished Plant.
Caterpillar, Zebra. **Cutworms. Earworm,** Corn.
Leafhopper, Red-banded. **Leaf Tier,** Omnivorous.
Maggot, Seed-corn.
Mite, Bulb (in corms); Desert Spider; Two-spotted.
Nematode, Cobb's Meadow; De Man's Meadow; Northern Root-knot.
Scale, Florida Red; Latania.
Thrips, Gladiolus (universal pest; leaves and flowers streaked); Banded
  Greenhouse; Greenhouse; Western Flower.
Weevil, Imported Long-horned. **Wireworms.**
  DDT remains an excellent control for gladiolus thrips.

GLOBETHISTLE (*Echinops*)
Aphid, Bean; Green Peach (leaves curl down).
Bug, Four-lined Plant (small, circular tan spots in leaves).

GLORYBUSH (*Tibouchina*)
Scale, Florida Wax; Hemispherical.

GLOXINIA
Aphid, Crescent-marked Lily; Green Peach.
Mite, Cyclamen. **Nematodes,** Foliar.
Thrips, Greenhouses; Onion. **Weevil,** Black Vine.

GOLDENCHAIN (*Laburnum*)
Aphid, Bean; Cowpea (infests ends of branches).
Mealybug, Grape. **Nematode,** Northern Root-knot.

GOLDENGLOW (*Rudbeckia*)
Aphid, Goldenglow (common; bright red on stems).
Beetle, Asiatic Garden; Fuller Rose.
Borer, Burdock; Stalk.
Bug, Four-lined Plant; Tarnished Plant.
Mite, Two-spotted.
Sawfly, Goldenglow. **Slugs.**

GOLDENRAIN-TREE (*Koelreuteria*)
Scale, Lesser Snow; Mining; White Peach.

GOLDENROD (*Solidago*)
Aphid, Goldenglow; Leaf-curl Plum; Sugar-beet Root.
Beetle, Goldenrod; Black Blister. **Borer,** Locust.
Bug, Chrysanthemum Lace.
Caterpillar, Orange Tortrix. **Fly,** Gall.

Leafhopper, Mountain.
Scale, Cottony-cushion; Black; Florida Wax; Green; Goldenrod.
Thrips. Treehopper, Buffalo.

GOOSEBERRY (*Ribes grossularia; R. hirtellum*)

Aphid, Currant (crinkled leaves); Dogberry; Gooseberry Witchbroom; Green Gooseberry.
Beetle, Imbricated Snout.
Borer, Currant; Pacific Flatheaded.
Bug, Four-lined Plant.
Caterpillar, Yellow Woollybear. **Fly,** Currant.
Fruitworm, Gooseberry. **Leafhopper,** White Apple.
Leaf Roller, Fruit-tree; Oblique-banded.
Mealybug, Grape; Ground. **Moth,** White-lined Sphinx.
Sawfly, Imported Currantworm (green, black-spotted larvae).
Scale, Cottony Maple; European Fruit Lecanium; Oystershell; Peach Lecanium; Putnam; San Jose; Scurfy.
Spanworm, Currant.

GOURD (*Cucurbita*)

Aphid, Melon. **Beetle,** Spotted Cucumber; Striped Cucumber.
Borer, Squash Vine. **Bug,** Squash.
Whitefly, Cloudy-winged; Greenhouse (very common pest).

GRAPE (*Vitis*)

Aphid, Grapevine; Grape Phylloxera.
Armyworm, Western Yellow-striped.
Beetle, Bumbling Flower; Darkling Ground; Fig; Grape Bud; Grape Colaspis; Grape Flea; Grapevine Hoplia; Japanese (serious on foliage); Green June; Rose Chafer; Rose Leaf; Small Darkling Ground; Spotted Grapevine; Steel-blue Flea.
Borer, Apple Twig; Branch and Twig; Broad-necked Root; Grape Cane Gall Maker; Grape Root; Grape Trunk.
Bug, Boxelder; Consperse Stink; False Chinch; Harlequin.
Caterpillar, Yellow Woollybear.
Cricket, Black-horned Tree. **Curculio,** Grape.
Cutworm, Brassy; Greasy; Variegated.
Earworm, Corn. **Grasshoppers. Leaf Folder,** Grape.
Leafhopper, Grape; Southern Garden; Three-banded; Variegated; Virginia-creeper.
Leaf Miner, Grape. **Leaf Skeletonizer,** Grape; Western Grape.
Mealybug, Comstock; Fruit; Grape; Ground; Long-tailed.
Midge, Grape Blossom; Grape Gall; Grapevine Tomato Gall.
Mite, Erineum; Grape Bud; Grape Rust; Pacific Spider; Willamette.

Moth, Abbott's Sphinx; Achemon Sphinx; Eight-spotted Forester; Grape Berry (wormy berries, clusters webbed together); Grape Plume; Virginia-creeper; White-lined Sphinx.

Nematode, California Dagger; California Meadow; Citrus; Cotton Rootknot; Tesselate Stylet.

Planthopper (on wild grape).

Rootworm, Grape (chains of holes in leaves); Strawberry; Western Grape.

Sawfly, Grape.

Scale, Black; Brown Soft; California Red; Camphor; Cottony-cushion; Cottony Maple; Cyanophyllum; European Fruit Lecanium; Florida Red; Grape (round, gray, on old canes); Greedy; Green; Lesser Snow; Obscure; Olive; Osborn's; Oystershell; Peach; Pustule; Quohog-shaped; White Peach; Ground Pearls.

Spittlebugs. Termites.

Treehopper, Two-marked (on wild grape).

Thrips, Bean; Citrus; Grape; Greenhouse; Pear; Western Flower.

Wasp, Grape Seed Chalcid.

Whitefly, Grape; Greenhouse; Woolly. **Wireworms.**

Most spray schedules are planned primarily for control of the grape berry moth.

GRAPEFRUIT

Beetle, Fuller Rose. **Mealybug,** Long-tailed.

Mite, Citrus Red; Citrus Rust.

Scale, Black; California Red; Cottony-cushion.

Thrips, Citrus.

See Citrus Fruits for many other pests.

GRAPE-HYACINTH (*Muscari*)

Nematode, Northern Root-knot.

GRASS (see Lawn Grasses)

GREVILLEA (Australian Silk-oak)

Budworm, Tobacco.

Caterpillar, Omnivorous Looper.

Mealybug, Citrophilus; Grape.

Mite, Avocado Red; Grevillea.

Scale, Black; Brown Soft; Chaff; Coconut; Cottony-cushion; Cyanophyllum; Dictyospermum; Florida Red; Greedy; Green Shield; Latania; Lesser Snow; Long Soft; Mining; Oleander; Pustule; Pyriform; Quohog-shaped.

GRINDELIA

Aphid, Grindelia.

GROUNDCHERRY (*Physalis*)
Aphid, Potato.
Beetle, Colorado Potato; Potato Flea; Tobacco Flea.
Borer, Potato Stalk.   **Budworm,** Tobacco.
Hornworm, Tobacco; Tomato.   **Maggot,** Pepper.
Mite, Tomato Russet.   **Mealybugs.**

GROUNDSEL (*Senecio*)
Aphid, Green Peach.   **Butterfly,** Painted Beauty.
Caterpillar, Omnivorous Looper.

GROUNDSELBUSH, SEAMYRTLE (*Baccharis*)
Scale, Acuminate; Black; Cyanophyllum; Florida Wax; Goldenrod; Green
   Shield; Green; Hemispherical; Latania; Pyriform.

GUAVA (*Psidium*)
Beetle, Rhabdopterus.   **Fly,** Mexican Fruit (only in part of Texas).
Mealybug, Citrus; Long-tailed; Mexican; Striped.
Mite, Broad; False Spider.
Scale, Barnacle; Black; Brown Soft; Chaff; Coconut; Cottony-cushion; Cot-
   tony Taxus; Dictyospermum; Florida Red; Florida Wax; Greedy; Green;
   Green Shield; Hemispherical; Latania; Nigra; Oriental; Parlatorialike;
   Pyriform; Tesselated.
Termites.   Thrips, Greenhouse; Red-banded.
Whitefly, Avocado; Woolly.

GUMBO-LIMBO (*Bursera simaruba*)
Scale, Black; Brown Soft; Coconut; Cottony-cushion; Florida Wax; Japanese
   Wax; Pustule; Latania; Rufous.

GYPSOPHILA
Leafhopper, Six-spotted.

HABRANTHIS
Fly, Narcissus Bulb.

HACKBERRY (*Celtis*)
Beetle, Hackberry Engraver.
Borer, Live-oak Root; Painted Hickory; Twig Pruner.
Bug, Hackberry Lace; Southern Green Stink.
Butterfly, Hackberry Empress.   **Caterpillar,** Puss.
Mite, Hackberry Witches' Broom.   **Moth,** Oriental.
Psyllid, Hackberry Nipple-gall.
Orthezia, Greenhouse.

Scale, Camphor; Citricola; Cottony-cushion; Cottony Maple; Cyanophyllum; Elm Scurfy, European Fruit Lecanium; Gloomy; Green Shield; Lesser Snow; Obscure; Oystershell; Pustule; Putnam; San Jose; Walnut.
Spittlebug, Blueberry. **Whitefly,** Mulberry.

HAMELIA (Firebush, Scarletbush)
Mealybug, Citrus. **Orthezia,** Greenhouse.
Scale, Black; Green Shield; Hemispherical; Lesser Snow; Mining; Parlatoria-like.

HAWTHORN (*Crataegus*)
Aphid, Apple; Apple Grain; Clover; Four-spotted Hawthorn; Grapevine; Hawthorn; Rosy Apple (curls young leaves); Spirea; Woolly Apple (white on branches); Woolly Hawthorn.
Beetle, Larger Elm Leaf; Striped Cucumber; Japanese.
Borer, Apple Bark; Flatheaded Apple Tree; Roundheaded Apple Tree; Shot-hole; Sinuate Pear Tree.
Bud Moth, Eye-spotted.
Bug, Apple Red; Hawthorn Lace (stippled foliage).
Cankerworm, Fall; Spring. **Casebearer,** Cigar.
Caterpillar, Eastern Tent (common); Forest Tent; Red-humped; Variable Oak Leaf; Western Tent; Walnut.
Leafhopper, Poplar.
Leaf Miner, Apple Blotch; Apple Trumpet; Spotted Tentiform; Unspotted Tentiform.
Leaf Roller, Oblique-banded. **Leaf Skeletonizer,** Apple-and-thorn.
Mite, Two-spotted.
Moth, Brown-tail; Codling; Gypsy; Oriental Fruit; Western Tussock.
Planthopper. Sawfly, Pear-slug.
Scale, Barnacle; Brown Soft; Cottony Maple; European Fruit Lecanium; Florida Red; Florida Wax; Forbes; Latania; Putnam; San Jose; Scurfy; Terrapin; Walnut.
Weevil, Apple Flea.

HAZELNUT (*Corylus*)
Beetle, Larger Elm Leaf; Pitted Ambrosia.
Bug, Alder Lace.
Caterpillar, California Tent; Filbertworm; Palmerworm; Yellow-necked.
Leafhopper, Japanese. **Leaf Roller,** Oblique-banded.
Scale, European Fruit Lecanium; Oystershell.
Weevil, Apple Flea; Hazelnut. **Whitefly,** Hazel.

HEATH (*Erica*)
Scale, Greedy; Oleander; Oystershell.

HEATHER (*Calluna*)
Beetle, Japanese. **Leaf Tier,** Omnivorous.
Mite, Two-spotted. **Scale,** Greedy; Mining; Oystershell.

HELENIUM (Sneezeweed)
Beetle, Helenium Snout.

HELIOPSIS
Bug, Four-lined Plant; Garden Fleahopper.

HELIOTROPE
Aphid, Crescent-marked Lily; Green Peach; Leaf-curl Plum.
Bug, Four-lined Plant. **Leaf Tier,** Celery.
Mealybug, Citrophilus; Citrus. **Mite,** Two-spotted.
Orthezia, Greenhouse. **Termites.**
Whitefly, Greenhouse (common, even outdoors).

HEMLOCK (*Tsuga*)
Aphid, Hemlock Woolly. **Bagworm.**
Beetle, Asiatic Garden (on seedlings); Fir Engraver; Lion; Mountain Pine.
Borer, Black-horned Pine; Flatheaded Cone; Flatheaded Fir; Hemlock (destructive); Roundheaded Western Larch.
Caterpillar, False Hemlock Looper; Hemlock Looper (may defoliate); Phantom Hemlock Looper; Western Hemlock Looper (serious).
Leaf Miner, Spruce Needle. **Leaf Roller,** Red-banded.
Mite, Spruce Spider (important, needles turn white); Two-spotted.
Moth, Cypress; Gypsy.
Nematode, Cobb's Meadow; Tesselate Stylet.
Sawfly, Hemlock.
Scale, Black Pine Leaf; Cottony-cushion; Florida Wax; Hemlock (gray, circular); Lesser Snow; Pine Needle (white); Latania; Red Bay.
Webworm, Hemlock. **Weevil,** Strawberry Root.

HIBISCUS (Rose-mallow)
Aphid, Bean; Melon.
Beetle, Cuban May; Fuller Rose; Japanese.
Bollworm, Pink. **Bug,** Cotton Stainer. **Katydids** (large holes in foliage).
Earworm, Corn. **Moth,** Abutilon (green caterpillar).
Nematode, Cotton Root-knot; Scribner's Meadow; Southern Root-knot.
Scale, Black; Brown Soft; California Red; Cottony-cushion; Chaff; Cyanophyllum; Fern; Florida Red; Florida Wax; Hemispherical; Japanese Wax; Latania; Lesser Snow; Long Soft; Nigra; Oleander; Oriental; Parlatoria-like; Pineapple; Pustule; Quohog-shaped; San Jose; Tesselated.
Weevil, Boll; Hibiscus. **Whitefly,** Greenhouse.

HICKORY (*Carya*)

Aphid, Black-margined; Giant Bark (large, gray and black).

Beetle, Hickory Bark; Hickory Saperda; June.

Borer, Banded Hickory; Brown Wood; Flatheaded Apple Tree; Painted Hickory; Pecan Carpenterworm; Red-headed Ash; Tiger Hickory; Twig Girdler; Twig Pruner.

Bug, Hickory Plant; Sycamore Lace.

Cankerworms. Casebearer, Cigar; Pecan.

Caterpillar, Hickory Horned Devil; Hickory Shuckworm; Linden Looper; Red-humped; Stinging Rose; Walnut; Yellow-necked.

Cicada, Periodical. **Curculio,** Hickory-nut.

Leaf Roller, Fruit-tree; Hickory. **Mite,** Oak.

Moth, Gypsy; Hickory Tussock; Imperial; Lappet; Luna; Oriental.

Sawfly, Butternut Woollyworm.

Scale, Cottony Maple; European Fruit Lecanium; Grape; Hickory; Latania; Osborn's; Obscure; Putnam; Scurfy; Tesselated.

Treehopper, Three-cornered Alfalfa; Two-marked.

Walkingstick. Webworm, Fall. **Weevil,** New York; Pecan.

HOGPLUM (*Spondias*)

Mealybug, Striped.

Scale, Florida Wax; Mimosa; Obscure; Rufous; Walnut.

HOLLY (*Ilex*)

Aphid, Black Citrus.

Beetle, Black Blister; Potato Flea; Rhabdopterus.

Bud Moth, Holly. **Caterpillar,** Saddleback.

Leaf Miner, Holly (blotch mines, very common); Native (serpentine mines).

Leaf Tier, Holly. **Mealybug,** Comstock.

Mite, Southern Red (serious; leaves turn grayish).

Moth, Gypsy; Lappet.

Nematode, Cobb's Meadow; De Man's Meadow; Tesselate Stylet.

Scale, Acuminate; Barnacle; Black; Brown Soft; California Red; Camellia Mining; Chaff; Cottony Maple; Cyanophyllum; Dictyospermum; Florida Red; Greedy; Green Shield; Hemispherical; Holly; Japanese; Japanese Wax; Oleander; Oystershell; Parlatorialike; Peach; Pustule; Pyriform; Red Bay; Tea (white, common on Chinese holly); Terrapin; Tesselated; Walnut; White Peach.

Spittlebugs. Whitefly, Citrus; Mulberry.

Spraying is usually necessary for holly leaf miner.

HOLLYHOCK (*Althaea rosea*)

Aphid, Bean; Hollyhock; Potato.

Beetle, Japanese (common on flowers); Oriental; Rose Chafer; Spotted Cucumber.

Borer, Burdock; European Corn; Stalk.
Bug, Hollyhock Plant; Tarnished Plant.
Butterfly, Painted Beauty; Painted Lady.
Caterpillar, Yellow Woollybear.
Leaf Roller, Red-banded. **Leaf Skeletonizer,** Cotton Leaf Perforator.
Mealybug, Mexican. **Mite,** Two-spotted.
Moth, Abutilon. **Nematode,** Cotton Root-knot.
Scale, Brown Soft; Latania; Lesser Snow.
Slug, Spotted Garden (large holes in leaves).
Thrips, Gladiolus; Hollyhock. **Weevil,** Boll; Hollyhock.

HONEYLOCUST (*Gleditsia*)
Beetle, Ash-gray Blister.
Borer, Honeylocust; Painted Hickory; Twig Girdler.
Caterpillar, Walnut. **Leaf Roller,** Locust.
Midge, Honeylocust Pod Gall. **Mite,** Honeylocust Spider.
Moth, Oriental. **Scale,** Black; Cottony Maple.
Webworm, Mimosa (very common and injurious). **Whitefly,** Greenhouse.

HONEYSUCKLE (*Lonicera*)
Aphid, Honeysuckle and Parsnip; Woolly Honeysuckle.
Beetle, Fuller Rose; Potato Flea.
Bug, Four-lined Plant.
Caterpillar, Omnivorous Looper.
Leaf Roller, Oblique-banded; European Honeysuckle; Red-banded.
Mealybug, Comstock; Long-tailed.
Moth, Snowberry Clearwing; White-lined Sphinx.
Sawfly, Honeysuckle.
Scale, Camphor; Cottony-cushion; Chaff; Coconut; Cyanophyllum; Dictyospermum; Greedy; Green Shield; Hemispherical; Latania; Lesser Snow; Mining; Oystershell; Parlatorialike; Pyriform; Quohog-shaped; San Jose; Walnut; White Peach.
Webworm, Fall. **Whitefly,** Greenhouse; Iris.

HOP-HORNBEAM (*Ostrya*)
Bug, Birch Lace.

HOP-TREE (*Ptelea*)
Scale, White Peach. **Treehopper,** Two-marked.

HORNBEAM (*Carpinus*)
Scale, Maple Phenacoccus; Sour-gum.

HORSECHESTNUT (*Aesculus*)

Bagworm.
Beetle, Japanese (very destructive); Potato Flea.
Borer, Flatheaded Apple Tree.
Caterpillar, Omnivorous Looper.
Leaf Roller, Fruit-tree; Oblique-banded.
Mealybug, Comstock; Grape.
Mite, Four-spotted. **Moth,** White-marked Tussock.
Scale, Cottony Maple; Maple Phenacoccus; Oystershell; Putnam; Scurfy; Walnut.
Spanworm, Elm.
See also Buckeye.

HORSERADISH (*Armoracia*)

Aphid, Western Aster Root.
Beetle, Horseradish Flea; Western Black Flea.
Bug, Harlequin.
Caterpillar, Cabbage Looper; Imported Cabbageworm.
Curculio, Cabbage. **Moth,** Diamondback.
Nematode, Cobb's Meadow; Fig Pin; De Man's Meadow.
Webworm, Cabbage.

HOSTA (Plantain Lily)

Scale, Florida Wax.

HUCKLEBERRY (*Gaylussacia*)

Scale, Azalea Bark; False Cottony Maple; Latania; Oak Eriococcus; Putnam; Red Bay.

HUCKLEBERRY (*Vaccinium*)

See Blueberry.

HYACINTH (*Hyacinthus*)

Caterpillar, Yellow Woollybear.
Fly, Lesser Bulb; Narcissus Bulb (large maggot in rotting bulb).
Mite, Bulb (minute, white, in rotting bulbs).
Nematode, Stem and Bulb (dark rings in bulb).

HYDRANGEA

Aphid, Crescent-marked Lily; Melon.
Beetle, Rose Chafer. **Bug,** Tarnished Plant.
Leaf Tier, Hydrangea (leaves tied around flower bud).
Mite, Two-spotted. **Nematode,** Spring Crimp.
Thrips, Banded Greenhouse. **Scale,** Cottony Taxus.

HYMENOCALLIS (Spider-lily)
Caterpillar, Convict. **Fly,** Narcissus Bulb.
Scale, Boisduval's; Lesser Snow. **Thrips,** Banded Greenhouse.

HYPERICUM (St.-Johns-wort)
Scale, Hypericum; Latania; San Jose; White Peach.

HYSSOP
Scale, Black Araucaria.

IMPATIENS (*I. sultana*)
Aphid, Impatiens. **Nematode,** Javanese Root-knot.
Mite, Two-spotted (serious pest on indoor plants).

INDIA-HAWTHORN (*Raphiolepis*)
Scale, Brown Soft; Cottony-cushion; Camellia; Florida Red; Florida Wax;
Dictyospermum.

INDIAN-LAUREL (*Ficus nitida*)
Scale, Black; Black Thread; Chinese Obscure; Cyanophyllum; Dictyospermum; Florida Red; Florida Wax; Green Shield; Proteus; Rufous.

INDIAN-PAINTBRUSH (*Castileja*)
Mealybug, Coleman's.

INKBERRY (see Gallberry)

IRESINE
Scale, Green.

IRIS
Aphid, Crescent-marked Lily; Potato; Tulip Bulb (white, cottony).
Beetle, Carrot; Blister; Oriental; Rose Chafer; Rose Leaf; White-fringed.
Borer, Burdock; Iris (chief pest, producing ragged leaves, hollow rhizomes); Stalk.
Bud Moth, Verbena (green caterpillars on seed pods).
Fly, Lesser Bulb. **Caterpillar,** Zebra.
Leaf Tier, Omnivorous. **Mites.**
Nematode, Cotton Root-knot; Fig Pin; Stem and Bulb.
Scale, Black Thread; Florida Red. **Slug,** Spotted Garden; other species.
Thrips, Gladiolus; Flower; Iris (prevalent on Japanese iris).
Weevil, Iris (in seed pods). **Wireworm,** Pacific Coast.

IRONWOOD (*Ostrya virginiana*)
Aphid, Melon. **Beetle,** Pitted Ambrosia.
Borer, Two-lined Chestnut. **Scale,** Cottony-cushion; Latania.

IVY, BOSTON (*Parthenocissus tricuspidata*)
Beetle, Japanese (serious).
Leafhopper, Grape; Virginia-creeper (foliage white in summer).
Moth, Eight-spotted Forester.
Scale, Calico; Cottony-cushion.
Weevil, Imported Long-horned.

IVY, ENGLISH (*Hedera helix*)
Aphid, Bean; Green Peach; Ivy.
Beetle, Black Blister.
Caterpillar, Cabbage Looper; Omnivorous Looper; Puss.
Leaf Tier, Celery. **Hornworms.**
Mealybug, Citrus; Grape; Mexican.
Mite, Privet; Two-spotted (very common; leaves gray, mealy).
Moth, Eight-spotted Forester.
Scale, Brown Soft; Cottony-cushion; Cottony Maple; Cottony Taxus; Dictyospermum; Florida Red (round, reddish brown); Green; Glover; Greedy; Florida Wax; Ivy or Oleander (yellow, flat); Oak Eriococcus; Olive; Oriental; Parlatorialike; Peach Lecanium; Pineapple; Pit; Pustule; Proteus; Pyriform; Red Bay; Tesselated.

IXORA
Aphid, Black Citrus. **Beetle,** Pine Colaspis.
Mealybug, Long-tailed. **Moth,** Io.
Scale, Acuminate; Barnacle; Black; Black Thread; Brown Soft; Cottony-cushion; Cyanophyllum; Florida Red; Florida Wax; Green; Green Shield; Hemispherical; Mango Shield; Mining; Oriental; Parlatorialike; Pustule; Pyriform; Tesselated.

JACARANDA
Aphid, Spirea. **Orthezia,** Greenhouse.
Scale, Black; Cottony-cushion; Hemispherical; Lesser Snow; Long Soft; Purple; Pustule; Quohog-shaped; Rufous.

JACOBINIA
Orthezia, Greenhouse.
Scale, Hemispherical; Mining; Parlatorialike; Proteus; Pustule.

JACQUEMONTIA
Nematode, Reniform.

JAMAICA-APPLE, CUSTARD-APPLE (*Annona reticulata*)
Mealybug, Coconut.
Scale, Hemispherical; Latania; Long Soft; Quohog-shaped.

JAPANESE PAGODA-TREE (*Sophora*)
Scale, Cottony-cushion; Long Soft.

JAPANESE QUINCE (*Chaenomeles*)
Aphid, Hawthorn; Melon; Spirea. **Beetle,** Japanese.
Bug, Hawthorn Lace. **Mealybug,** Grape.
Scale, Black; Greedy; Florida Wax; Japanese Wax; Peach; San Jose; White
Peach.

JASMINE (*Jasminum*)
Mealybug, Citrus; Long-tailed. **Orthezia,** Greenhouse.
Scale, Acuminate; Barnacle; Black; Black Thread; Brown Soft; California
Red; Camphor; Chaff; Camellia; Cyanophyllum; Dictyospermum; Flor-
ida Red; Florida Wax; Green; Green Shield; Hemispherical; Japanese
Wax; Latania; Lesser Snow; Long Soft; Mimosa; Mining; Oleander;
Olive; Oriental; Parlatorialike; Pineapple; Proteus; Purple; Pustule; Pyri-
form; Quohog-shaped; Rufous; Terrapin; Tesselated.
Termites. Whitefly, Citrus; Jasmine.

JERUSALEM-CHERRY (*Solanum pseudocapsicum*)
Aphid, Potato. **Caterpillar,** Orange Tortrix (rolls leaves).
Scale, White Peach. **Thrips,** Flower; Onion.
Whitefly, Greenhouse.

JESSAMINE (*Cestrum*)
Mealybug, Citrus; Long-tailed. **Orthezia,** Greenhouse.
Scale, Acuminate; Black; Black Thread; Brown Soft; Cyanophyllum; Chaff;
Dictyospermum; Florida Red; Florida Wax; Green Shield; Hemispherical;
Latania; Lesser Snow; Mining; Oleander; Oriental; Parlatorialike; Pine-
apple; Pustule; Pyriform; Quohog-shaped; Rufous; Tesselated.

JESSAMINE, YELLOW (*Gelsemium*)
Mealybug, Long-tailed. **Scale,** Terrapin.

JOBS-TEARS (*Coix lacryma-jobi*)
Caterpillar, Orange Tortrix.

JUNEBERRY (see Shadbush)

JUNIPER, REDCEDAR (*Juniperus*)

Aphid, Arborvitae; Redcedar; Rocky Mountain Juniper; American Juniper.
Bagworm, (spindle-shaped bags on twigs; common).
Beetle, Cedar Bark; Gold Buprestid.
Borer, Black-horned Pine; Flatheaded Cone.
Caterpillar, Redcedar Tortrix.
Mealybug, Juniper.   **Midge,** Juniper.
Mite, Spruce Spider (foliage gray, webby); Two-spotted.
Moth, Imperial; Juniper.   **Sawfly,** Arborvitae.
Scale, Dictyospermum; Juniper (small, round, white, foliage yellow);
   Latania; Newstead's; Pine Needle; Red Bay.
Spittlebugs.   Webworms, Juniper; Pale Juniper.
Weevil, Arborvitae; Deodar; Strawberry Root.

JUSTICIA

Mealybug, Citrus.   **Scale,** Black Thread.

KALANCHOE (*Bryophyllum*)

Aphids.   Mite, Cyclamen.
Scale, Lesser Snow.

KALE (*Brassica oleracea* var. *acephala*)

Aphid, Cabbage; Turnip.
Caterpillar, Cabbage Looper; Imported Cabbageworm.
Leaf Tier, Celery.   **Moth,** Diamondback.
Nematode, Cabbage Cyst; Northern Root-knot.
Webworm, Cabbage.
   See Cabbage for other pests.

KENTUCKY COFFEE-TREE (*Gymnocladus*)

Scale, Olive.

KERRIA

Beetle, Japanese (prevalent on this host).

KOHLRABI (*Brassica caulorapa*)

Aphid, Cabbage; Turnip.   **Beetle,** Asiatic Garden.
Bug, Harlequin.
Caterpillar, Cabbage Looper; Imported Cabbageworm.
Nematode, Cabbage Cyst.
   See Cabbage for other pests.

KUDZU (*Pueraria*)

Beetle, Japanese.   **Caterpillar,** Velvetbean.
Scale, Brown Soft; Oleander; White Peach.

KUMQUAT
Thrips, Citrus.
See Citrus for other pests.

LANCEWOOD (*Ocotea*)
Scale, Acuminate; Black Thread; Cottony-cushion; Latania; Pyriform; Tesselated.

LANTANA
Caterpillar, Orange Tortrix. **Fly,** Lantana Gall.
Leaf Tier, Celery.
Mealybug, Citrus; Mexican; Yucca. **Mite,** Broad; Cyclamen.
Moth, Lantana Plume. **Nematode,** Spring Crimp.
Orthezia, Greenhouse.
Scale, Brown Soft; Chaff; Cottony-cushion; Green; Latania; Lesser Snow; Mango Shield; Mining; Pustule; Pyriform.
Whitefly, Greenhouse.

LARCH (*Larix*)
Aphid, Spruce Gall; Woolly Larch.
Bagworm (may defoliate).
Beetle, Douglas-fir; Eastern Larch; Douglas-fir Engraver; Japanese.
Borer, Flatheaded Fir; Western Larch Roundheaded.
Bud Moth, Eye-spotted; Larch. **Budworm,** Spruce.
Casebearer, Larch (leaves mined, used as cases).
Caterpillar, False Hemlock Looper.
Moth, Douglas-fir Pitch; Gypsy; White-marked Tussock.
Sawfly, Larch (green larvae may strip trees); Red-headed Pine.
Weevil, Pales.

LARKSPUR, ANNUAL (*Delphinium*)
Aphid, Delphinium (red, common on flower heads).
Borer, Stalk. **Leafhopper,** Mountain.
Leaf Miner, Larkspur. **Mealybug,** Ground.
Mite, Cyclamen. **Nematode,** De Man's Meadow.

LAUREL (*Laurus*)
Bud Moth, Eye-spotted. **Mealybug,** Ground. **Psyllid,** Laurel.
Scale, Brown Soft; Chaff; Cottony-cushion; Dictyospermum; Florida Red; Florida Wax; Greedy; Green Shield; Glover; Latania; Purple; Pyriform; San Jose; Tesselated; Walnut; White Peach.

LAURESTINUS (*Viburnum tinus*)
Scale, Dictyospermum; Parlatorialike; White Peach.
Thrips, Greenhouse.

LAVATERA (Tree-mallow)

Psyllid, Lavatera.   **Scale,** Greedy.

LAVENDER

Butterfly, West Coast Lady.   **Bug,** Four-lined Plant.
Caterpillar, Orange Tortrix; Yellow Woollybear.

LAWN GRASSES

Ant, Argentine; Cornfield; Pavement; other species (mounds in lawns).
Aphid, Apple Grain; Chokeberry; Chokecherry; Corn Root; Elm Cockscomb Gall; Elm Sack Gall; English Grain; Lettuce Root; Mealy Plum; Rose Grass; Rusty Plum; Solanum Root.
Armyworm, Fall; Lawn (on Bermuda grass).
Beetle, Asiatic Garden; Cuban May (on St. Augustine); European Chafer; Japanese; June; Northern Masked Chafer; Oriental; Southern Masked Chafer; Rose Chafer (all the preceding have grubs working at grass roots); Pale-striped Flea; Sweetpotato Flea.
Billbug, Bluegrass.   **Borer,** Cranberry Girdler.
Bug, Chinch; False Chinch; Hairy Chinch (grass turns brown in patches); Say Stink; Western Chinch.
Cricket, Changa; Mormon; Northern Mole; Southern Mole.
Cutworm, Bronzed; Glassy; Yellow-headed.   **Earthworms.**
Fly, Australian Sod; Frit.   **Grasshoppers.**
Leafhopper, Mountain; Painted; Yellow-headed.
Mealybug, Ground.   **Millipedes.**
Mite, Banks Grass; Bermuda Grass; Clover.
Nematode, American Dagger; Bent Grass; Christie's Spiral; Christie's Stubby Root; Cobb's Meadow; Cobb's Stubby Root; Corn Meadow; Crownheaded Lance; De Man's Meadow; Godfrey's Meadow; Grass Cyst; Grass Sheath; Northern Root-knot; Reniform; Seinhorst Stubby Root; Steiner's Spiral; Sting; Thorne's Meadow; Tesselate Stylet; Zimmerman's Spiral.
Scale, Ground Pearls; Rhodes Grass.   **Slugs. Snails.**
Spittlebugs. Termites. Thrips, Flower; Grass.
Walkingstick, Prairie.   **Wasp,** Cicada killer (holes, mounds in lawns).
Webworm, Sod; Vagabond Crambus (silken nests).
Weevil, Strawberry Root; Cribrate.
Wireworm, Eastern Field; Plains False.

The usual treatments are for beetle grubs, chinch bugs, sod webworms, sometimes nematodes, with spot treatment for ants.

LEMON (*Citrus limonia*)

Beetle, Fuller Rose.
Mealybug, Grape; Long-tailed; Yucca.

Mite, Citrus Bud; Citrus Rust; Lewis Spider; Strawberry Spider; Yuma Spider.
Scale, Black; California Red; Cottony-cushion; Oleander.
Thrips, Citrus.
See Citrus Fruits for other pests.

LESPEDEZA
Nematode, Soybean Cyst.
Webworm, Lespedeza. **Weevil,** Imported Long-horned.

LETTUCE (*Lactuca sativa*)
Aphid, Bean; Brown Ambrosia; Goldenglow; Green Peach; Lettuce Root; Potato; Turnip; White Aster Root.
Beetle, Pale-striped Flea; Potato Flea.
Bug, Garden Fleahopper; Harlequin; Pitted Lygaeid; Tarnished Plant.
Caterpillar, Cabbage Looper; Celery Looper; Imported Cabbageworm.
Centipede, Garden Symphylan. **Earworm,** Corn.
Leafhopper, Six-spotted; Potato.
Leaf Roller, Omnivorous. **Leaf Tier,** Celery.
Nematode, Cobb's Meadow; Cotton Root-knot; De Man's Meadow; False Root-knot of Sugar Beet; Northern Root-knot; Tesselate Stylet.
Millipedes. Slugs. Thrips, Tubulifera.
Weevil, Vegetable. **Whitefly,** Vegetable.

LEUCOJUM (Snowflake)
Fly, Narcissus Bulb.

LIGNUM-VITAE (*Guaiacum*)
Scale, Barnacle; Florida Red.

LIGUSTRUM (see Privet)

LILAC (*Syringa*)
Aphid, Melon.
Beetle, Rhinoceros (occasionally feeds on roots, kills bushes).
Borer, Lilac (common; holes in trunk, protruding sawdust).
Butterfly, Tiger Swallowtail. **Caterpillar,** Hickory Horned Devil.
Leaf Miner, Chrysanthemum; Lilac (tan or brown blotches).
Leaf Roller, Oblique-banded.
Moth, Cynthia; Great Ash Sphinx; Leopard; Polyphemus; Promethea.
Nematode, Citrus; De Man's Meadow; Tesselate Stylet.
Scale, Cottony Maple; Euonymus; Florida Red; Latania; Olive; Oystershell; (may completely encrust and kill branches); Purple; San Jose; Scurfy; White Peach.

Wasp, Giant Hornet (tears off bark around branches).
Weevil, Japanese; Lilac. Whitefly, Citrus.
A dormant spray is often advisable for scales.

LILY (*Lilium*)

Aphid, Crescent-marked Lily; Foxglove; Green Peach; Melon (dark green to brown; transmits mosaic); Purple-spotted Lily; Tulip Bulb.
Beetle, Carrot; Fuller Rose; White-fringed. Borer, Stalk.
Caterpillar, Convict; Saddleback; Yellow Woollybear; Zebra.
Fly, Narcissus Bulb (large white maggot).
Mealybug, Long-tailed; Citrus. Mite, Bulb.
Nematode, Spring Crimp. Planthopper.
Scale, Black Thread; Cyanophyllum; Dictyospermum; Florida Red; Hemispherical; Lesser Snow; Proteus.
Thrips, Lily Bulb. Weevil, Lily.

LILY-OF-THE-VALLEY (*Convallaria*)

Nematode, Root-knot. Weevil, Lily-of-the-valley.

LIME (*Citrus aurantifolia*)

Bug, Western Leaf-footed.
Mealybug, Yucca. Mite, Citrus Rust.
Scale, Cottony-cushion; Dictyospermum; Terrapin.
Thrips, Citrus.
See also Citrus Fruits.

LINDEN, LIME, BASSWOOD (*Tilia*)

Aphid, Giant Bark; Linden (yellow and black, abundant).
Bagworm.
Beetle, Elm Calligrapha; Japanese (serious); Native Elm Bark.
Borer, American Plum; Brown Wood; Flatheaded Apple Tree; Linden.
Bug, Green Stink; Basswood Lace; Walnut Lace.
Cankerworm, Fall; Spring.
Caterpillar, Linden Looper; Variable Oak Leaf; Red-humped Oakworm; Yellow-necked.
Leaf Miner, Basswood. Leaf Roller, Basswood; Oblique-banded.
Mealybug, Taxus. Mite, Four-spotted.
Moth, American Dagger; Cynthia; Cecropia; Elm Sphinx; Gypsy; White-marked Tussock.
Sawfly, Elm.
Scale, Brown Soft; Cottony Maple; European Fruit Lecanium; Latania; Long Soft; Oystershell; Putnam; San Jose; Terrapin; Tesselated; Tuliptree; Walnut; White Peach.
Walkingstick. Whitefly, Mulberry (dark with white fringe).

LIPSTICK TREE (*Bixa*)
Scale, Mining; Quohog-shaped.

LIRIOPE (Lily-turf)
Scale, Cyanophyllum; Dictyospermum; Fern; Florida Red; Lesser Snow; Proteus.

LIZARDS-TAIL (*Saururus*)
Mealybug, Coleman's.

LOBELIA
Aphid, Leaf-curl Plum. **Bug,** Negro.
Leafhopper, Six-spotted. **Leaf Roller,** Red-banded.
Leaf Tier, Celery. **Nematode,** Root-knot.

LOCUST (*Robinia*)
Aphid, Cowpea; Locust. **Bagworm.**
Beetle, Sweetpotato Leaf; Ten-lined June.
Borer, Brown Wood; Carpenterworm; Lima-bean Pod; Locust (serious on black locust; young trees killed); Locust Twig; Painted Hickory; Twig Pruner.
Bug, Harlequin. **Butterfly,** Silver-spotted Skipper.
Caterpillar, Red-humped; Velvetbean.
Leaf Miner, Locust (foliage looks "blighted"; very common).
Leaf Roller, Fruit-tree; Locust.
Mite, European Red. **Moth,** Crinkled Flannel; Io.
Scale, Black; Brown Soft; Cottony-cushion; Cottony Maple; European Fruit Lecanium; Greedy; Oystershell; Putnam; San Jose; Walnut; White Peach.
Spanworm, Cleft-headed.
Treehopper, Buffalo; Three-cornered Alfalfa; Two-marked.
Walkingstick, Two-striped.

LOGANBERRY (*Rubus loganobacchus*)
Aphid, European Raspberry. **Beetle,** Fuller Rose.
Bug, Consperse Stink. **Cricket,** Black-horned Tree; Snowy Tree.
Fruitworm, Western Raspberry. **Horntail,** Raspberry.
Leaf Roller, Fruit-tree; Oblique-banded.
Maggot, Raspberry Cane. **Nematode,** Walnut Meadow.
Sawfly, Raspberry. **Scale,** Rose.
Whitefly, Glacial; Greenhouse.
See Raspberry for other possible pests.

LOQUAT (*Eriobotrya japonica*)
Aphid, Apple; Melon.
Beetle, Flea; Western Striped Cucumber; Western Spotted Cucumber.

Borer, Pacific Flatheaded; Shot-hole.
Bug, Harlequin.   **Mealybug,** Citrus.
Mite, Platanus; Southern Red.   **Moth,** Codling.
Scale, Acuminate; Barnacle; Cyanophyllum; Florida Red; Florida Wax; Mining; Latania; Olive; Pyriform; San Jose.

LOTUS (*Nelumbium*)
Aphid, Melon; Waterlily.

LUPINE (*Lupinus*)
Aphid, Essig's Lupine; Lupine (green with white wax; abundant).
Borer, Lima-bean Pod.   **Bug,** Four-lined Plant.
Butterfly, Painted Lady.   **Fly,** Lupine.
Weevil, Lupine (eats half moons out of leaves).
Whitefly, Greenhouse.

LYCHEE (*Litchi chinensis*)
Beetle, Rhabdopterus.   **Bug,** Southern Green Stink.
Mite, Avocado Red; Litchi.
Scale, Black; Barnacle; Cottony-cushion; Dictyospermum; Florida Red; Florida Wax; Green Shield; Lesser Snow; Long Soft; Latania; Pyriform; Quohog-shaped; Tesselated.
Thrips, Florida Flower; Greenhouse.

MACADAMIA
Caterpillar, Navel Orangeworm.   **Mealybug,** Grape.
Scale, Araucaria; Dictyospermum; Greedy; Latania; Mining; Oleander.
Thrips, Greenhouse.

MADRONA (*Arbutus menziesi*)
Aphid, Rose and Bearberry.
Borer, Branch and Twig; California Prionus; Flatheaded Cherry Tree; Nautical.
Caterpillar, California Tent.   **Leaf Miners.**
Moth, Madroña Shield Bearer; Polyphemus.
Scale, Brown Soft.   **Thrips,** Madroña; Pear.
Whitefly, Kellogg's; Iridescent; Madroña; Manzanita.

MAGNOLIA
Borer, Root Collar.   **Caterpillar,** Omnivorous Looper; Saddleback.
Mealybug, Comstock; Long-tailed; Striped.
Scale, Acuminate; Black; Brown Soft; Camellia; Chaff; Coconut; Cottony-cushion; Cyanophyllum; Dictyospermum; European Fruit Lecanium; Florida Red; Florida Wax; Glover; Greedy; Lesser Snow; Latania; Japanese

Wax; Magnolia (soft, brown, convex); Oleander; Parlatorialike; Purple; Red Bay; Tuliptree; White Peach.
Weevil, Sassafras. **Whitefly,** Citrus.

MAHOGANY (Swietenia)
Beetle, Cuban May. **Caterpillars,** Species?
Scale, Black; Black Thread; Coconut; Latania; Lesser Snow.
See also Mountain-mahogany.

MAHONIA (Oregon-grape; Grape-holly)
Aphid, Barberry. **Scale,** Greedy; Latania.
Whitefly, Barberry; Inconspicuous.

MALLOW (Malva)
Beetle, Japanese. **Bollworm,** Hibiscus; Pink.
Butterfly, Painted Beauty; Painted Lady.
Mealybug, Citrophilus. **Moth,** Abutilon.
Whitefly, Greenhouse.

MALPIGHIA (Barbados-cherry)
Mealybug, Striped.
Scale, Black; Barnacle; Coconut; Florida Wax; Dictyospermum; Hemispherical; Masked; Pyriform.

MANDEVILLA
Thrips, Greenhouse.

MANGO (Mangifera indica)
Beetle, Rhabdopterus.
Fly, Mexican Fruit (in Texas); Papaya Fruit; West Indian Fruit.
Leafhopper, Potato.
Mealybug, Citrus; Coconut; Long-tailed; Striped.
Mite, Avocado Red; Broad; Tumid Spider.
Scale, Acuminate; Black; Black Thread; Brown Soft; California Red; Chaff; Coconut; Dictyospermum; Florida Red; Florida Wax; Glover; Green Shield; Hemispherical; Latania; Lesser Snow; Mango Shield; Mining; Nigra; Oleander; Oriental; Purple; Pustule; Pyriform; Quohog-shaped; Tesselated; Tea.
Thrips, Greenhouse; Red-banded.

MANGROVE (Rhizophora)
Borer, Australian-pine. **Scale,** Green; Red Bay.

MANZANITA

Aphid, Manzanita Leaf-gall. **Borer,** Pacific Flatheaded.
Butterfly, California Tortoise-shell. **Moth,** Western Tussock.
Scale, Brown Soft; Greedy.
Whitefly, Crown; Inconspicuous; Manzanita.

MAPLE (*Acer*)

Aphid, American Maple; Boxelder; European Birch; Giant Bark; Norway-maple; Painted Maple; Sycamore; Woolly Alder.
Bagworm. Beetle, Columbian Timber; Potato Flea.
Borer, Brown Wood; American Plum; Carpenterworm; Flatheaded Apple Tree; Gall-making Maple; Maple; Maple Callus; Maple Petiole; Pacific Flatheaded; Pigeon Tremex; Sugar Maple; Twig Pruner.
Bug, Birch Lace; Boxelder; Green Stink.
Cankerworm, Fall; Spring.
Caterpillar, Eastern Tent; Forest Tent; Green-striped Mapleworm; Hemlock Looper; Linden Looper; Omnivorous Looper; Orange-humped Mapleworm; Phigalia Looper; Puss; Red-humped Oakworm; Saddled Prominent.
Cricket, Black-horned Tree. **Fruitworm,** Green.
Leaf Cutter, Maple.
Leafhopper, Grape; Japanese Maple; Norway-maple.
Leaf Roller, Oblique-banded. **Leaf Skeletonizer,** Maple Trumpet.
Mealybug, Comstock; Taxus. **Mite,** Maple Bladder Gall; Oak.
Moth, American Dagger; Brown-tail; Cecropia; Gypsy; Io; Leopard; Oriental; Pale Tussock; Polyphemus; Spotted Tussock; White-marked Tussock.
Nematode, Cobb's Meadow; De Man's Meadow; Tesselate Stylet.
Sawfly, Elm.
Scale, Black; Brown Soft; Calico; Chaff; Cottony-cushion; Cottony Maple; Cyanophyllum; European Fruit Lecanium; False Cottony Maple; Florida Wax; Gloomy; Greedy; Japanese; Lesser Snow; Maple Phenacoccus; Obscure; Oystershell; Putnam; San Jose; Scurfy; Terrapin; Walnut.
Spanworm, Bruce; Elm. **Thrips,** Bean; Pear.
Whitefly, Inconspicuous; Mulberry.
Maples seldom have as many pests as this list indicates but aphids are a common nuisance, dropping honeydew. Use oil sprays with caution; avoid on sugar maple. Japanese maple is sensitive to DDT.

MARANTA

Mite, Tumid Spider. **Mealybug,** Citrus.
Scale, Boisduval's; Cyanophyllum; Florida Red; Latania; Long Soft; Proteus.

MARGUERITE (*Chrysanthemum frutescens*)

Aphid, Leaf-curl Plum.
Leaf Miner, Chrysanthemum (Marguerite Fly). **Leaf Tier,** Omnivorous.
Mealybug, Ground. **Mite,** Broad; Cyclamen.

MARIGOLD (*Tagetes*)

Beetle, Japanese (prevalent on African, seldom on French marigolds);
White-fringed.
Borer, Stalk. **Bug,** Garden Fleahopper; Tarnished Plant.
Caterpillar, Yellow Woollybear. **Cutworms.**
Leafhopper, Potato; Red-banded; Six-spotted.
Mealybug, Citrus; Mexican. **Mite,** Broad; Cyclamen; Two-spotted.
Nematode, Northern Root-knot. **Slug,** Greenhouse; Spotted Garden.
Thrips, Composite. **Weevil,** Imported Long-horned.

MARLBERRY (*Ardisia paniculata*)

Scale, Acuminate; Green; Green Shield; Florida Wax.

MATRIMONY VINE (*Lycium chinense*)

Aphid, Crescent-marked Lily. **Borer,** Potato Tuberworm.
Scale, Latania.

MELON, CANTALOUPE (*Cucumis melo*)

Aphid, Melon (green to brown or black; curls leaves; transmits mosaic).
Armyworm, Western Yellow-striped.
Beetle, Fig; Grape Colaspis; Imbricated Snout; Pale-striped Flea; Potato
Flea; Squash; Spotted Cucumber; Striped Blister; Striped Cucumber; West-
ern Striped Cucumber.
Borer, Squash Vine (vines wilt).
Bug, Squash (large, brown, shield-shaped); Horned Squash.
Caterpillar, Melonworm; Pickleworm; Yellow Woollybear.
Leafhopper, Beet (transmits curly-top virus); Southern Garden.
Leaf Roller, Omnivorous. **Maggot,** Seed-corn. **Millipedes.**
Mite, Desert Spider; Southern Two-spotted; Strawberry Spider; Two-spotted.
Nematode, American Dagger; Cotton Root-knot; De Man's; Northern Root-
knot; Peanut Root-knot.
Termites. Thrips, Onion; Western Flower.
Whitefly, Greenhouse.

Start melons under protective Hotkaps or screens. Most melons are sensitive to sulfur; some varieties can take it.

MESEMBRYANTHEMUM (*Ice-Plant*)

Mealybug, Yucca. **Orthezia,** Greenhouse.
Scale, Green Shield; Lesser Snow. **Thrips,** Greenhouse.

MESQUITE (*Prosopis glandulosa*)

Borer, Huisache Girdler; Nautical; Pacific Flatheaded; Roundheaded Mesquite.
Bug, Green Stink. **Grasshoppers.**
Leafhopper, Sugar-beet. **Moth,** Gall-making Clearwing.
Termites. Treehopper, Modest.

MIGNONETTE (*Reseda*)

Beetle, Potato Flea.
Caterpillar, Cabbage Looper; Imported Cabbageworm.
Earworm, Corn. **Leafhopper,** Six-spotted.
Mite, Two-spotted. **Thrips,** Onion.

MIGNONETTE-TREE (*Lawsonia inermis*)

Scale, Black; Coconut; Cyanophyllum; Green Shield; Latania; Pyriform; Quohog-shaped; Rufous.

MIMOSA, SILK-TREE (*Albizzia julibrissin*)

Beetle, Blister.
Mealybug, Citrus.
Scale, Acuminate; Cottony-cushion; Dictyospermum; Chaff; Latania; Long Soft.
Webworm, Mimosa (very common and injurious).

MINT (*Mentha*)

Aphid, Mint. **Beetle,** Mint Flea; June.
Bug, Four-lined Plant (common, dark spots in leaves).
Leaf Cutter, Morning-glory. **Mealybug,** Citrus.
Nematode, Thorne's Needle.
Weevil, Strawberry Root.

MOCK-ORANGE (*Philadelphus*)

Aphid, Bean; Green Peach.
Nematode, Cobb's Meadow; Northern Root-knot.

MONKEYFLOWER (*Mimulus*)

Butterfly, Checker Spot. **Mealybug,** Yucca.
Mite, Desert Spider; Two-spotted. **Thrips,** Banded Greenhouse.

MONKEYPUZZLE (see Araucaria)

MOONFLOWER (*Calonyction*)

Beetle, Argus Tortoise (holes in leaves); Black-legged Tortoise.
Mealybug, Citrus; Long-tailed. **Nematode,** Spring Crimp.
Orthezia, Greenhouse. **Thrips,** Banded Greenhouse.

MORINDA (Indian Mulberry)
Scale, Cyanophyllum; Green. **Whitefly,** a Jasmine.

MORNING-GLORY (*Convolvulus*)
Aphid, Melon; Myrtle.
Beetle, Argus Tortoise; Golden Tortoise; Mottled Tortoise; Spotted Cucumber; Striped Tortoise; Sweetpotato Flea; White-fringed.
Bug, Four-lined Plant; Garden Fleahopper.
Leaf Cutter, Morning-glory. **Leaf Miner,** Morning-glory.
Mealybug, Long-tailed; Citrus. **Nematode,** Northern Root-knot.
Scale, Black; Brown Soft; Green; Latania; Lesser Snow.
Weevil, Sweetpotato. **Whitefly,** Greenhouse; Inconspicuous.

MOUNTAIN-ASH (*Sorbus*)
Aphid, Rosy Apple; Woolly Apple. **Beetle,** Japanese.
Borer, American Plum; Apple Bark; Ash; Flatheaded Apple Tree; Lilac; Pacific Flatheaded; Roundheaded Apple Tree; Shot-hole; Sinuate Pear Tree.
Bug, Birch Lace. **Mite,** European Red; Pear Leaf Blister.
Moth, Apple Fruit; Rusty Tussock. **Rootworm,** Strawberry.
Sawfly, Mountain-ash (eats all of leaf except veins); Pear-slug.
Scale, Black; Cottony Maple; Oystershell; San Jose; Scurfy.

MOUNTAIN EBONY (see Bauhinia)

MOUNTAIN-HOLLY (*Nemopanthus*)
Scale, Greedy; Hemispherical; Oystershell.

MOUNTAIN-LAUREL (*Kalmia*)
Beetle, Strawberry Flea.
Borer, Azalea Stem; Rhododendron.
Bug, Rhododendron Lace (leaves stippled gray).
Scale, Azalea Bark; Dictyospermum; Chaff; Latania.
Weevil, Japanese. **Whitefly,** Mulberry (dark with white fringe)

MOUNTAIN-MAHOGANY (*Cercocarpus*)
Beetle, Pitted Ambrosia.
Borer, California Buprestid; Flatheaded Cherry Tree; Pacific Flatheaded.

MUEHLENBECKIA
Scale, California Red; Dictyospermum; Florida Wax; Green Shield; Latania; Proteus; Tesselated.

MULBERRY (*Morus*)

Bug, Southern Green Stink; Sycamore Lace.
Mealybug, Comstock; Long-tailed. **Mite,** Southern Two-spotted.
Nematode, Northern Root-knot. **Planthopper.**
Scale, Black; Brown Soft; California Red; Cottony Maple; Cottony Taxus; Dictyospermum; European Fruit Lecanium; Florida Red; Florida Wax; Gloomy; Glover; Greedy; Green Shield; Japanese Wax; Olive; Latania; Lesser Snow; Peach; Pustule; Quohog-shaped; San Jose; Terrapin; White Peach.
Whitefly, Mulberry (dark with white fringe).

MUSTARD (*Brassica*)

Aphid, Turnip.
Beetle, Horseradish Flea; Western Black Flea; Western Striped Flea; Yellow-margined Leaf.
Bug, Green Stink; Harlequin.
Caterpillar, Cabbage Looper; Imported Cabbageworm.
Curculio, Cabbage. **Maggot,** Cabbage.
Mealybug, Citrophilus. **Nematode,** Cabbage Cyst; Northern Root-knot.
Weevil, Cabbage Seedpod; Cribrate; Vegetable.

MYRTLE (*Myrtus*)

Aphid, Clover; Crescent-marked Lily; Myrtle.
Leafhopper, Privet. **Nematode,** Northern Root-knot.
Mealybug, Long-tailed; Striped.
Scale, Acuminate; Barnacle; Black; Cottony Maple; Dictyospermum; Florida Red; Florida Wax; Glover; Greedy; Green Shield; Hemispherical; Latania; Long Soft; Nigra; Obscure; Purple; Pustule; Pyriform; Tesselated.
Thrips, Greenhouse.

MYRTLE, PERIWINKLE (see Vinca)

MYRTLE, WAX (see Bayberry)

NANDINA

Scale, Cottony-cushion.

NARCISSUS (Daffodil)

Aphid, Tulip Bulb. **Caterpillar,** Convict.
Fly, Lesser Bulb (several maggots); Narcissus Bulb (1 large maggot).
Mealybug, Citrus; Solanum. **Millipedes.**
Mite, Bulb; Bulb Scale; Two-spotted.
Nematode, De Man's; Stem and Bulb (dark rings in bulb).
Slug, Introduced. **Thrips,** Flower; Gladiolus.

NASTURTIUM (*Tropaeolum*)

Aphid, Bean (black, inevitable); Buckthorn; Crescent-marked Lily; Green Peach.
Beetle, Flea. **Bug,** Tarnished Plant.
Caterpillar, Cabbage Looper; Imported Cabbageworm. **Earworm,** Corn.
Leafhopper, Beet. **Leaf Miner,** Serpentine (serious in the South).
Leaf Tier, Celery. **Mite,** Two-spotted.
Thrips, Greenhouse.

NECTARINE (see Peach)

NEMESIA

Aphid, Melon.

NEPHTHYTIS (see Syngonium)

NERINE

Thrips, Banded Greenhouse.

NEW JERSEY TEA (*Ceanothus americanus*)

Beetle, Rose Chafer. **Scale,** Oystershell.

NICOTIANA (Flowering Tobacco)

Beetle, Colorado Potato; Poatato Flea; Tobacco Flea; White-fringed.
Cutworms. Hornworms. Whiteflies.

NINEBARK (*Physocarpus*)

Borer, Dogwood. **Whitefly,** Glacial; Iris.

NOLINE (*Nolina*)

Scale, Black Thread; Chaff; Fern; Dictyospermum; Latania; Lesser Snow; Proteus.

OAK (*Quercus*)

Aphid, Giant Bark; Oak.
Beetle, Carrot; Goldsmith; Fuller Rose; Japanese; June.
Borer, Banded Hickory; Broad-necked Root; California Prionus; Carpenterworm; Chestnut Bark; Chestnut Timberworm; Flatheaded Apple Tree; Little Carpenterworm; Live-oak Root; Nautical; Oak Sapling; Oak Timberworm; Pacific Flatheaded; Pecan Carpenterworm; Pigeon Tremex; Red-headed Ash; Sycamore; Tiger Hickory; Tile-horned Prionus; Twig Girdler; Twig Pruner; Two-lined Chestnut.
Bud Moth, Eye-spotted. **Bug,** Oak Lace (leaves whitened).
Cankerworm, Fall; Spring (may defoliate in peak years).

Caterpillar, Azalea; Blue-sided Tent; California Oakworm; California Tent; Chain-spotted Geometer; Eastern Tent; Forest Tent; Green-striped Mapleworm; Hemlock Looper; Linden Looper; Orange-striped Oakworm; Orange Tortrix; Palmerworm; Phigalia Looper; Pink-striped Oakworm; Puss; Red-humped Oakworm; Saddleback; Saddled Prominent; Spiny Oakworm; Stinging Rose; Ugly Nest; Variable Oak Leaf; Western Oak Looper; Yellow-necked.

Cicada, Periodical (twigs hang down, turn brown).

Leaf Miner, Basswood; Gregarious Oak; Solitary Oak Leaf.

Leaf Roller, Fruit-tree; Oak; Oblique-banded.

Leaf Skeletonizer, Oak.   **Leaf Tier,** Oak.

Mite, Avocado Red; Oak; Platanus; Southern Red; Willamette.

Moth, American Dagger; Brown-tail; Buck; Cecropia; Crinkled Flannel; Gypsy (favors oak); Imperial; Io; Lappet; Leopard; Nevada Buck; Oriental; Polyphemus; Satin; Spotted Tussock; Western Tussock.

Nematode, Fig Pin; Oak Sheathoid; Pacific Dagger; Zimmerman's Spiral.

Sawfly, Pin-oak (leaves skeletonized).

Scale, California Red; Cottony-cushion; Cottony Maple; Dictyospermum; European Fruit Lecanium; Florida Wax; Golden Oak; Greedy; Lesser Snow; Oak Eriococcus; Oak Kermes; Oak Lecanium; Obscure; Osborn's; Oystershell; Pit; Putnam; Purple; Pustule; Red Bay; Terrapin; Tesselated; Walnut.

Treehopper, Oak; Three-cornered Alfalfa.

Walkingstick, Two-striped.   **Wasp,** Oak Gall (many species).

Webworm, Fall; Oak.   **Weevil,** Asiatic Oak; Japanese; New York.

Whitefly, Citrus; Crown; Glacial; Inconspicuous.

Oaks often require a dormant spray for scale insects and a foliage spray for cankerworms, the latter often taking care of other caterpillars.

OKRA (*Hibiscus esculentus*)

Aphid, Melon.

Beetle, Flea; Grape Colaspis; Japanese; Striped Cucumber.

Bug, Green Stink; Harlequin; Pumpkin; Southern Green Stink.

Earworm, Corn.   **Mite,** Tumid Spider; Two-spotted.

Moth, Abutilon (Okra Caterpillar).

Nematode, Southern Root-knot.   **Weevil,** Boll.   **Whiteflies.**

OLEANDER (*Nerium*)

Aphid, Bean; Green Peach; Oleander (yellow and black).

Caterpillar, Oleander.   **Leaf Roller,** Omnivorous.

Mealybug, Citrus; Long-tailed; Striped.

Nematode, Peanut Root-knot.

Scale, Araucaria; Black; Brown Soft; Chaff; Cottony-cushion; Dictyospermum; Florida Red; Florida Wax; Green; Hemispherical; Latania; Lesser

Snow; Oleander; Olive; Oriental; Parlatorialike; Peach; Pustule; Pyriform; Rufous; Tesselated.
Termites, Subterranean.

OLIVE (*Olea*)
Beetle, Olive Bark. **Borer,** American Plum; Branch and Twig.
Caterpillar, Omnivorous Looper. **Mealybug,** Long-tailed.
Mite, Lewis Spider; Olive Leaf. **Nematode,** Citrus.
Scale, Araucaria; Black; California Red; Dictyospermum; Florida Red; Florida Wax; Greedy; Hemispherical; Mining; Oleander; Olive; Oriental; Pineapple; Purple; Red Bay; White Peach.
Thrips, Bean; Citrus. **Whitefly,** Citrus.

ONION (*Allium*)
Armyworm, Fall.
Beetle, Blister; Imbricated Snout; Oriental.
Bug, Onion Plant. **Cutworms.**
Fly, Lesser Bulb; Onion Bulb. **Leaf Miner,** Pea.
Maggot, Onion (may kill seedlings); Seed-corn. **Mite,** Bulb.
Nematode, Christie's Stubby Root; Cobb's Meadow; De Man's Meadow; Fig Pin; Southern Root-knot; Stem and Bulb.
Thrips, Onion (leaves silvered, distorted).
Weevil, Vegetable. **Wireworm,** Eastern Field.

OPHIOPOGON, WHITE LILYTURF (*Mondo*)
Scale, Brown Soft; Cyanophyllum; Dictyospermum; Fern; Florida Red; Hemispherical; Lesser Snow; Proteus.

ORANGE (*Citrus*)
Beetle, Fuller Rose.
Bug, Cotton Stainer; Green Stink; Leaf-footed; Western Leaf-footed.
Caterpillar, Navel Orangeworm; Omnivorous Looper; Orange Tortrix.
Katydid, Angular-winged.
Mealybug, Grape; Ground; Japanese; Long-tailed.
Mite, Citrus Red; Citrus Rust; Lewis Spider.
Scale, Black; Camphor; California Red; Cottony-cushion; Greedy; Oleander; San Jose; Tea.
Thrips, Bean; Citrus.
See also Citrus Fruits.

ORCHIDS
Aphid, Orchid. **Beetle,** Chinese Rose.
Borer, Dendrobium; Orchid Bulb.
Bug, Orchid Plant.

Fly, Orchid (maggots in brown buds, small black flies).

Mealybug, Citrus; Long-tailed.   **Midge,** Cattleya.

Mite, Omnivorous; Oncidium; Phalenopsis; Two-spotted.

Nematode, Chrysanthemum Foliar; Scribner's Meadow; Stem and Bulb.

Scale, Araucaria; Black; Boisduval's; Brown Soft; Cactus; Chaff; Coconut; Cyanophyllum; Dictyospermum; Fern; Florida Red; Florida Wax; Hemispherical; Latania; Lesser Snow; Newstead's; Oleander; Orchid; Oriental; Oystershell; Parlatorialike; Proteus; Pineapple; Pustule; Purple; Red Bay; Tea; Tesselated; White Peach.

Slugs. Snails.

Thrips, Greenhouse; Lily Bulb; Orchid.

Weevil, Cattleya; Orchid.

DDT has been used for many orchid pests.

ORCHID-TREE (see Bauhina)

OSAGE-ORANGE (*Maclura*)

Mealybug, Citrus.

Scale, Cottony-cushion; Cottony Maple; European Fruit Lecanium; Putnam; San Jose.

Whitefly, Citrus.

OSMANTHUS (Sweetolive; Tea Olive)

Scale, Acuminate; Brown Soft; Camellia; Black Thread; Chaff; Dictyospermum; Florida Red; Latania; Parlatorialike; Red Bay; White Peach; Oleander.

OXALIS

Aphid, Potato.

PACHYSANDRA (Spurge)

Mite, Two-spotted (serious when plants are crowded).

Nematode, Zimmerman's Spiral.

Scale, Euonymus (thin, white, common); Florida Red; Oystershell; Purple; San Jose.

PALMETTO (*Sabal*)

Leaf Skeletonizer, Palm (major pest in Florida).

Scale, Black Thread; Boisduval's; Coconut; Dictyospermum; Florida Red; Glover; Green; Oriental; Palmetto; Parlatorialike; Red Bay.

Whitefly, Citrus.

PALMS
Aphid, Latania; Green Peach; Palm.
Beetle, Fuller Rose. **Bug,** Royal Palm. **Caterpillar,** Saddleback.
Leaf Skeletonizer, Palm (serious; leaves webbed).
Mealybug, Citrus; Coconut; Coleus; Grape; Long-tailed; Palm.
Mite, Banks Grass; Privet; Tumid Spider. **Moth,** Fan Palm.
Nematode, American Dagger; Steiner's Spiral. **Orthezia,** Greenhouse.
Scale, Araucaria; Black; Black Thread; Boisduval's; Brown Soft; California
  Red; Chaff; Coconut; Cottony-cushion; Cyanophyllum; Dictyospermum;
  Fern; Florida Red; Florida Wax; Glover; Greedy; Green Shield; Hemi-
  spherical; Latania; Oleander; Olive; Oriental; Palmetto; Parlatorialike;
  Pineapple; Purple; Pustule; Pyriform; Red Bay; Rufous; Tesselated; White
  Peach.
Thrips, Banded Greenhouse; Dracaena; Greenhouse.

PANDANUS (see Screwpine)

PANSY (*Viola*)
Aphid, Foxglove; other species. **Beetle,** Flea.
Caterpillar, Yellow Woollybear. **Cutworms.**
Leafhopper, Beet. **Mealybug,** Solanum.
Mite, Two-spotted. **Nematode,** Northern Root-knot.
Sawfly, Violet. **Slugs. Sowbugs. Termites. Wireworms.**

PAPAYA (*Carica papaya*)
Fly, Papaya Fruit. **Leafhopper,** Papaya. **Nematode,** Root-knot.
Scale, Coconut; Cottony-cushion; Mining; Nigra; Parlatorialike; Pyriform.
Webworm, Papaya. **Whitefly,** Avocado; Papaya.

PARKINSONIA (Jerusalem-thorn)
Mealybug, Citrus.
Scale, Barnacle; Brown Soft; Chaff; Cottony-cushion; Dictyospermum; Florida
  Wax; Latania; Long Soft; Lesser Snow; Quohog-shaped.

PARSLEY (*Petroselinum*)
Aphid, Western Aster Root. **Butterfly,** Western Parsley.
Caterpillar, Cabbage Looper; Celeryworm.
Fly, Carrot Rust. **Leaf Tier,** Celery.
Mite, Strawberry Spider. **Nematode,** Fig Pin.

PARSNIP (*Pastinaca*)
Aphid, Bean; Honeysuckle and Parsnip; Willow.
Beetle, Asiatic Garden; Carrot; Pale-striped Flea.

Butterfly, Western Parsley.
Caterpillar, Celeryworm; Yellow Woollybear.
Fly, Carrot Rust (tunnels in roots).   **Leafhopper,** Six-spotted.
Leaf Miner, Parsnip (blotch mines).   **Millipedes.**
Nematode, Cobb's Meadow; De Man's Meadow; Northern Root-knot; Scribner's Meadow.
Webworm, Parsnip.   **Weevil,** Carrot.

PASSION-FLOWER (*Passiflora*)

Butterfly, Gulf Fritillary; Passion-vine; Zebra.
Caterpillar, Omnivorous Looper.   **Leaf Tier,** Celery.
Mealybug, Citrus; Grape; Long-tailed.   **Orthezia,** Greenhouse.
Scale, Barnacle; California Red; Greedy; Green Shield; Latania; Lesser Snow; Purple; Proteus; Pustule.

PAWPAW (*Asimina triloba*)

Butterfly, Zebra Swallowtail.   **Caterpillar,** Stinging Rose.

PEA (*Pisum*)

Aphid, Bean; Pea (large, green; important); Potato.
Armyworm, Beet.
Beetle, Bean Leaf; Imbricated Snout; Pale-striped Flea; Spotted Cucumber; Striped Blister; Striped Cucumber; Western Striped Cucumber.
Borer, Clover Root; Lesser Cornstalk; Lima-bean Pod.
Bug, Garden Fleahopper; Green Stink; Say Stink.
Caterpillar, Alfalfa; Cabbage Looper; Green Cloverworm; Yellow Woolly-bear.
Centipede, Garden Symphylan.   **Earworm,** Corn.
Leaf Miner, Pea.   **Leaf Tier,** Celery, Omnivorous.
Maggot, Seed-corn.   **Millipedes.**
Mite, Tumid Spider; Two-spotted (serious in dry weather).
Moth, Pea (small caterpillars in pods).
Nematode, Corn Meadow; De Man's Meadow; Peanut Root-knot.
Thrips, Onion; Western Flower.   **Webworm,** Beet.
Weevil, Broad Bean; Pea; Pea Leaf.   **Whitefly,** Greenhouse.

PEACH (*Prunus persica*)
(Including Nectarine, smooth-skinned peach)

Aphid, Black Cherry; Black Peach; Green Peach; Hop; Mealy Plum; Rusty Plum.
Beetle, Asiatic Garden; Bumbling Flower; Cherry Leaf; Fig; Fuller Rose; Green June; Japanese (prevalent, serious); Peach Bark; Plum Gouger; Red-legged Flea; Rose Chafer; Rose Leaf.
Borer, Branch and Twig; California Prionus; Flatheaded Apple Tree; Lesser

Peach Tree; Nautical; Pacific Flatheaded; Peach Tree (common, serious; gum at base of trunk); Peach Twig; Roundheaded Apple Tree; Shothole; Western Peach Tree.

Bug, Boxelder; Dusty Stink; Green Stink (catfaces fruit); Leaf-footed; Southern Green Stink; Tarnished Plant (new shoots black).

Cankerworm, Fall; Spring. **Casebearer,** California.

Caterpillar, Eastern Tent; Forest Tent; Walnut; Yellow-necked.

Cicada, Periodical. **Cricket,** Black-horned; Snowy Tree.

Curculio, Peach; Plum (common cause of wormy fruit).

Earworm, Corn. **Fly,** Mexican Fruit (in Texas).

Leafhopper, Mountain; Plum; Privet; Saddled.

Leaf Roller, Oblique-banded; Red-banded.

Mealybug, Citrophilus; Comstock; Ground.

Mite, Clover; European Red; Fruit Tree; Peach Silver; Strawberry Spider; Two-spotted.

Moth, Codling (wormy fruit); Oriental Fruit (blackens shoots).

Nematode, American Dagger; Christie's Stubby Root; Cobb's Meadow; Cobb's Ring; De Man's Meadow; Fig Pin; Scribner's Meadow; Southern Root-knot; Steiner's Spiral; Tesselate Stylet; Walnut Meadow.

Rootworm, Strawberry. **Sawfly,** Cherry Fruit; Peach.

Scale, Brown Soft; Cottony-cushion; Cottony Maple; Cottony Peach; European Fruit Lecanium; Florida Wax; Forbes; Grape; Howard; Latania; Italian Pear; Lesser Snow; Peach Lecanium; Pustule; Putnam; Pyriform; Rose; San Jose; Scurfy; Walnut; White Peach.

Thrips, Pear; Western Flower.

Treehopper, Buffalo. **Webworm,** Fall.

Peach spray schedules are timed primarily for control of brown rot and some other diseases with, usually, a dormant spray for scale insects, seasonal insecticides for plum curculio, Oriental fruit moth, and Japanese beetles, and late summer treatment for peach tree borers.

PEANUT (*Arachis hypogea*)

Armyworm, Fall.

Beetle, Elongate Flea; Pale-striped Flea; Spotted Cucumber; White-fringed.

Billbug, Southern Corn. **Borer,** Lesser Cornstalk.

Caterpillar, Red-necked Peanutworm; Velvetbean (serious in Gulf States); Yellow Woollybear.

Cutworm, Granulate. **Earworm,** Corn.

Leafhopper, Potato (causes peanut "pouts"); Southern Garden.

Leaf Miner, Locust. **Mealybug,** Solanum. **Moth,** Bella.

Nematode, European Dagger; Godrey's Meadow; Northern Root-knot; Peanut Root-knot; Reniform; Steiner's Spiral; Sting.

Scale, Cottony-cushion. **Termites.**

Thrips, Tobacco (terminal buds black). **Wireworm,** Sand.

PEAR (*Pyrus communis*)

Aphid, Apple; Apple Grain; Clover; Cowpea; Hawthorn; Rosy Apple; Spirea; Woolly Apple; Woolly Pear.

Beetle, Fig; Fuller Rose; Green June; Pale-striped Flea; Rose Chafer; Rose Leaf; Syneta Leaf.

Borer, Apple Bark; Apple Twig; Brown Wood; Branch and Twig; Carpenterworm; Flatheaded Apple Tree; Pacific Flatheaded; Pear Fruit; Pigeon Tremex; Roundheaded Apple Tree; Shot-hole; Sinuate Pear Tree; Twig Girdler; Twig Pruner.

Bud Moth, Eye-spotted; Pecan.

Bug, Apple Red; Consperse Stink; Pear Plant; Tarnished Plant.

Casebearer, California; Cigar.

Caterpillar, Eastern Tent; Forest Tent; Palmerworm; Red-humped; Stinging Rose; Yellow-necked.

Cricket, Snowy Tree. **Curculio,** Apple; Plum; Quince (wormy fruit).

Earworm, Corn. **Fly,** Black Cherry Fruit; Cherry Fruit.

Fruitworm, Green. **Leaf Crumpler.**

Leaf Roller, Fruit-tree; Oblique-banded. **Leaf Skeletonizer,** Apple and Thorn.

Mealybug, Citrophilus; Comstock; Grape. **Midge,** Pear; Pear Leaf.

Mite, Clover; European Red; Fruit-tree; Pacific Spider; Pear Leaf Blister (serious; dark blisters in leaves); Pear Rust; Strawberry Spider; Willamette.

Moth, Apple Fruit; Brown-tail; Codling; Hickory Tussock; White-lined Sphinx.

Nematode, California Meadow; Cobb's Meadow.

Psyllid, Pear Psylla (leaves, fruit black; defoliation; tree decline).

Sawfly, California Pear-slug; European Apple; Pear-slug.

Scale, Barnacle; Black; Brown Soft; Calico; Cottony Maple; Cottony-cushion; Dictyospermum; European Fruit Lecanium; Florida Wax; Forbes; Greedy; Howard; Italian Pear; Japanese Wax; Latania; Olive; Oystershell; Peach Lecanium; Pustule; Putnam; San Jose; Scurfy; Walnut; White Peach.

Thrips, Bean; Pear (blossoms appear burned).

Treehopper, Buffalo. **Webworm,** Beet.

Weevil, New York. **Whitefly,** Citrus.

The apple spray schedule often includes pears. Special treatment may be required for pear leaf blister mite and pear psylla.

PECAN (*Carya pecan*)

Aphid, Black-margined; Black Pecan; Giant Bark; Hickory; Pecan Leaf Phylloxera; Pecan Phylloxera.

Beetle, Cuban May; June.

Borer, American Plum; Apple Bark; Apple Twig; Dogwood; Flatheaded Apple Tree; Live-oak Root; Pecan; Pecan Carpenterworm; Shot-hole; Twig Girdler; Twig Pruner.

Bud Moth, Pecan.   **Bug,** Leaf-footed; Southern Green Stink.

Casebearer, Pecan Cigar; Pecan Leaf; Pecan Nut.

Caterpillar, Hickory Horned Devil; Hickory Shuckworm (most serious pest); Omnivorous Looper; Walnut.

Curculio, Hickory Nut.   **Mite,** Avocado Red; Hickory; Pecan Leaf Roll.

Nematode, American Dagger.   **Sawfly.**

Scale, Camphor; Cottony-cushion; Cottony Maple; Dictyospermum; European Fruit Lecanium; Florida Red; Forbes; Greedy; Hickory; Latania; Obscure; Osborn's; Purple; Putnam; San Jose; Walnut; White Peach.

Spittlebug, Pecan.   **Termites.**

Webworm, Fall.   **Weevil,** Pecan (worms in nuts; serious).

PELARGONIUM (see Geranium)

PENSTEMON (Beard-tongue)

Aphid, Crescent-marked Lily; Foxglove; Potato.

Beetle, Fuller Rose.   **Bug,** Red-and-black Stink.

Butterfly, Checker Spot.   **Caterpillar,** Orange Tortrix.

PENTAS

Caterpillar, Orange Tortrix.

Scale, Black; Pustule; Cottony-cushion; Parlatorialike.

PEONY (*Paeonia*)

Ants (in buds, not injurious except as spreading Botrytis spores).

Beetle, Japanese (rare); Rose Chafer (common on flowers); Rose Leaf.

Bug, Four-lined Plant (tan circles in leaves); Tarnished Plant.

Curculio, Rose.

Nematode, Cobb's Meadow; De Man's Meadow; Northern Root-knot; Spring Crimp.

Scale, Oystershell; San Jose (present when old stalks not removed).

Thrips, Flower; Greenhouse (petals turn brown).

PEPEROMIA

Nematode, Steiner's Spiral.

PEPPER (*Capsicum*)

Aphid, Green Peach; Melon; Potato.

Armyworm, Beet.

Beetle, Asiatic Garden; Blister; Colorado Potato; Potato Flea; Rose Chafer; Spotted Cucumber; Tobacco Flea.

Borer, European Corn; Stalk.

Bug, Leaf-footed; Pumpkin; Southern Green Stink; Garden Fleahopper.

Cutworm, Granulate; Pale-sided.

Earworm, Corn. **Hornworm,** Tobacco; Tomato.

Leafhopper, Beet. **Leaf Miner,** Serpentine.

Maggot, Pepper. **Mealybug,** Ground.

Mite, Broad; Cyclamen; Two-spotted.

Nematode, American Dagger; Awl; Cobb's Meadow; Cotton Root-knot; Northern Root-knot; Peanut Root-knot; Southern Root-knot; Tesselate Stylet; Zimmerman's Spiral.

Orthezia, Greenhouse. **Psyllid,** Tomato.

Scale, Cottony-cushion. **Weevil,** Pepper. **Whitefly,** Greenhouse.

PEPPER-TREE (*Schinus molle*)

Caterpillar, Omnivorous Looper. **Mealybug,** Citrophilus.

Scale, Black (common); Barnacle; Chaff; Fern; Greedy; Green Shield; Hemispherical; Lesser Snow; Mining; Oleander; Parlatorialike; Purple; Quohog-shaped.

Thrips, Citrus.

PERSIMMON (*Diospyros*)

Beetle, Fuller Rose.

Borer, Flatheaded Apple Tree; Persimmon; Red-headed Ash; Twig Girdler (important in the East).

Caterpillar, Hickory Horned Devil; Red-humped; Variable Oak Leaf.

Mealybug, Citrus; Mexican. **Moth,** Luna.

Nematode, Citrus. **Psyllid,** Persimmon.

Scale, Acuminate; Bamboo; Barnacle; Black; Brown Soft; Camphor; Cottony Maple; European Fruit Lecanium; Florida Red; Florida Wax; Green Shield; Japanese Wax; Latania; Lesser Snow; Oleander; Osborn's; Oriental; Pustule; Putnam; San Jose; Tesselated; Walnut; White Peach.

Thrips, Greenhouse. **Whitefly,** Citrus.

PETUNIA

Beetle, Asiatic Garden; Colorado Potato; Potato Flea (tiny shot holes in leaves); Spotted Cucumber.

Bug, Garden Fleahopper; Tarnished Plant.

Caterpillar, Yellow Woollybear. **Grasshoppers.**

Hornworm, Tobacco, Tomato. **Leafhopper,** Six-spotted.

Mealybug, Ground. **Mite,** Tomato Russet (transmits mosaic); Two-spotted. **Moth,** White-lined Sphinx.

Nematode, Cotton Root-knot. **Orthezia,** Greenhouse.

PHACELIA

Aphid, Leaf-curl Plum.

PHELLODENDRON (Cork Tree)
Scale, Lesser Snow; Pustule.

PHILODENDRON
Mealybug, Citrus; Long-tailed. **Millipedes.**
Mite, Southern Two-spotted.
Nematode, Burrowing; Steiner's Spiral.
Scale, Black Thread; Brown Soft; Boisduval's; Dictyospermum; Fern; Latania; Orchid; Proteus; Red Wax.
Thrips, Banded Greenhouse.

PHLOX
Beetle. Asiatic Garden; Black Blister; Golden Tortoise; June; Oriental; Potato Flea.
Borer, Stalk.
Bug, Four-lined Plant; Phlox Plant (reddish orange; deforms buds).
Earworm, Corn. **Leafhopper,** Six-spotted.
Mite, Two-spotted (very common; leaves yellow, webby).
Nematode, Chrysanthemum Foliar; Cobb's Meadow; Corn Meadow; Stem and Bulb (plants deformed, stems twisted).
Scale, Black; Brown Soft; Pyriform.

PHOTINIA
Beetle, Rhabdopterus.
Scale, Acuminate; Chaff; Dictyospermum; Florida Red; Florida Wax; Olive; San Jose; Walnut; White Peach.
See also California Christmasberry.

PHYSOSTEGIA
Aphid, Foxglove. **Bud Moth,** Verbena.

PIERIS
Bug, Andromeda Lace (on *Pieris japonica*).
Nematode, Cobb's Meadow; De Man's Meadow; Fig Pin; Godfrey's Meadow; Zimmerman's Spiral.
See also Andromeda.

PINE (*Pinus*)
Aphid, Monterey-pine; Pine Bark (white fluffs on bark); Pine Leaf; Spruce Gall; Powdery Pine; White-pine; Woolly Pine Needle.
Bagworm.
Beetle, Asiatic Garden (on seedlings); Black Hills; Black Turpentine; Coarse-writing; Engelmann Spruce; Five-spined Ips; Golden Buprestid; Jeffrey Pine; June; Lion; Lodgepole Pine; Monterey-pine Cone; Monterey-

pine Engraver; Mountain Pine; Northeastern Sawyer; Obtuse Sawyer; Oregon Fir Sawyer; Pine Chafer; Pine Colaspis; Pine Engraver; Pinyon Cone; Ponderosa-pine; Roundheaded Pine; Red Turpentine; Red-winged Pine; Smaller Mexican Pine; Southern Pine; Southwestern Pine; Spotted Pine; Sugar-pine Cone; Western Pine; White-pine Cone.

Borer, Black-horned Pine; Broad-necked Root; Brown Wood; Cedar Tree; California Prionus; Flatheaded Cone; Flatheaded Fir; Pitch Mass; Ponderosa Pine Bark; Roundheaded Cone; Sculptured Pine; Turpentine; Western Larch Roundheaded; White-pine Shoot.

Budworm, Spruce. **Butterfly,** Pine.

Caterpillar, Hemlock Looper; Monterey-pine Looper; Orange Tortrix; Pine Looper.

Horntail, California; Western.

Leaf Miner, Lodgepole Pine; Pine Needle; Pine Needle-sheath.

Mealybug, Comstock; Cypress; Golden; Loblolly.

Midge, Gouty Pitch Gall; Monterey-pine; Monterey-pine Resin.

Mite, Pine Bud; Spruce Spider.

Moth, Cypress Tip; European Pine Shoot (common on ornamentals; tip yellow, crooked); Gypsy; Imperial; Monterey-pine Tip; Nantucket Pine Tip; Pandora; Pine Cone; Pine Tortrix; Pine Tube; Pine Tussock; Pitch Blister; Pitch Twig; Sequoia Pitch; Silver-spotted Tiger; Zimmerman Pine.

Nematode, American Dagger; Cobb's Meadow; Crown-headed Lance; De Man's Meadow; Fig Pin; Godfrey's Meadow; Pine Cystoid; Pine Sheathoid; Pine Sting; Tesselate Stylet; Zimmerman's Spiral.

Sawfly, Balsam Fir; European Pine (serious; denudes branches); Introduced Pine; Jack-pine; Loblolly-pine; Lodgepole-pine; Monterey-pine; Red-headed Pine; Red-pine; Swaine Jack-pine.

Scale, Barnacle; Black Pine Leaf; Brown Soft; Cottony-cushion; Cottony Pine; Florida Wax; Hemlock; Matsucoccus; Pine-needle (white, pear-shaped, common); Newstead's; Pine Tortoise; Pinyon Needle; Prescott; Red Bay; Red-pine; Rufous; Walnut.

Spittlebug, Pine; Saratoga.

Webworm, Pine; Pine False (needles webbed together).

Weevil, Deodar; Douglas-fir Twig; Lodgepole Terminal; Monterey-pine; Pales; Pine Gall; Pine Reproduction; Pine Root Collar; White-pine (leader dies back); Yosemite Bark.

A dormant spray of oil or lime-sulfur for scales and later treatment with DDT or lead arsenate for sawfly larvae takes care of many problems. Use lindane for bark aphids; remove tips with shoot moths.

PINEAPPLE (*Ananas*)

Mealybug, Pineapple. **Nematode,** Godfrey's Meadow.

Scale, Boisduval's; Pineapple.

PISTACHIO (*Pistacia*)

Scale, California Red.

PITHECELLOBIUM

Orthezia, Greenhouse.
Scale, Cottony-cushion; Long Soft; Latania; Pustule.
Treehopper, Thornbug.

PITTOSPORUM

Aphid, Green Peach. **Mealybug,** Citrophilus.
Mite, Tumid Spider; Two-spotted. **Nematode,** Root-knot.
Scale, Black; Brown Soft; Camellia; Cottony-cushion (common); Chaff; Cyanophyllum; Florida Red; Florida Wax; Greedy; Green; Green Shield; Latania; Lesser Snow; Pit; Purple; Pustule; Pyriform.
Weevil, Cribrate.

PLUM, PRUNE (*Prunus domestica;* other species)

Aphid, Black Peach; Green Peach; Green June; Hop; Leaf-curl Plum; Mealy Plum; Rusty Plum; Thistle; Waterlily.
Beetle, Cherry Leaf; Fuller Rose; Grape Flea; Japanese; Plum Gouger; Rose Leaf; Syneta Leaf.
Borer, American Plum; California Prionus; Flatheaded Apple Tree; Lesser Peach Tree; Pacific Flatheaded; Peach Tree; Peach Twig; Roundheaded Apple Tree; Shot-hole; Western Peach Tree.
Bud Moth, Eye-spotted. **Bug,** Boxelder; Harlequin.
Cankerworm, Fall; Spring. **Casebearer,** California; Cigar.
Caterpillar, California Tent; Eastern Tent; Forest Tent; Orange Tortrix; Palmerworm; Puss; Red-humped; Stinging Rose; Yellow-necked.
Cricket, Snowy Tree. **Curculio,** Plum (important).
Fly, Black Cherry Fruit; Cherry Fruit.
Leaf Crumpler. Leafhopper, Grape; Plum; Privet; Prune.
Leaf Miner, Spotted Tentiform; Unspotted Tentiform.
Leaf Roller, Fruit-tree; Oblique-banded; Red-banded.
Leaf Skeletonizer, Apple. **Maggot,** Apple.
Mealybug, Citrophilus; Ground; Long-tailed.
Mite, Clover; European Red; Four-spotted; McDaniel Spider; Pacific Spider; Plum Rust.
Moth, Apple Fruit; Brown-tail; Artichoke Plume; Codling; Cynthia; Leopard; Oriental; Oriental Fruit; Western Tussock; White-lined Sphinx; White-marked Tussock.
Nematode, Cobb's Meadow; Fig Pin; Walnut.
Sawfly, Cherry Fruit; European Apple; Pear-slug; Plum Web-spinning.
Scale, Black; Brown Soft; Cottony Maple; Cottony Peach; European Fruit Lecanium; Florida Red; Florida Wax; Forbes; Green Shield; Howard;

Italian Pear; Japanese Wax; Latania; Long Soft; Mimosa; Obscure; Olive; Oriental; Oystershell; Peach Lecanium; Purple; Pustule; Putnam; Quohog-shaped; San Jose; Terrapin; Walnut; White Peach.

Thrips, Pear; Western Flower. **Weevil,** Cribrate.

For plums as for peaches the spray schedule is timed for the control of brown rot. Methoxychlor is safe to use in home gardens for the control of plum curculio.

PLUMBAGO (Leadwort)
Beetle, Fuller Rose.
Mealybug, Citrus. **Orthezia,** Greenhouse.
Scale, Cottony-cushion; Florida Red; Pustule.

PODOCARPUS
Scale, California Red; Dictyospermum; Florida Red; Florida Wax; Glover; Japanese Wax; Latania; Long Soft; Purple.

POINCIANA
Beetle, Cuban May.
Scale, Coconut; Cottony-cushion; Latania; Lesser Snow; Long Soft; Pustule; Quohog-shaped.

POINCIANA, ROYAL (*Delonix regia*)
Scale, Black; Cottony-cushion; Latania; Lesser Snow; Long Soft.

POKER-PLANT (*Kniphofia*)
Thrips, Gladiolus.

POINSETTIA (*Euphorbia pulcherrima*)
Aphid, Root. **Mealybug,** Citrus; Mexican; Long-tailed; Striped.
Mite, Lewis Spider.
Scale, Barnacle; Black; Brown Soft; Coconut; Cottony-cushion; Dictyospermum; Florida Red; Florida Wax; Lesser Snow; Long Soft; Nigra; Oleander; Pustule.
Termites.

POMEGRANATE (*Punica granatum*)
Aphid, Melon. **Bug,** Western Leaf-footed.
Caterpillar, Navel Orangeworm. **Mealybug,** Citrus.
Mite, Pomegranate Leafroll.
Scale, Acuminate; Barnacle; Black; Citricola; Cottony-cushion; Cyanophyllum; Florida Wax; Greedy; Latania; Mining; Olive; Rufous.
Thrips, Citrus; Greenhouse. **Weevil,** Cribrate. **Whitefly,** Citrus.

PONDAPPLE (*Annona glabra*)
Scale, Coconut; Oriental.

POPLAR, ASPEN, COTTONWOOD (*Populus*)

Aphid, Poplar Petiole Gall; Poplar Twig Gall; Poplar Vagabond; Sugar-beet Root.
Beetle, Alder Flea; American Aspen; Aspen Leaf; Cottonwood Leaf; Goldsmith; Gray Willow Leaf; Imported Willow Leaf; June.
Borer, Broad-necked Root; Bronze Birch; Bronze Poplar; California Prionus; Carpenterworm; Flatheaded Apple Tree; Linden; Pacific Flatheaded; Poplar; Poplar and Willow (small beetle may girdle trees); Sapwood Timberworm; Twig Girdler.
Bug, Ash Lace.
Butterfly, Mourning-cloak (spiny elm caterpillar); Tiger Swallowtail; Viceroy.
Caterpillar, California Tent; Chain-spotted Geometer; Forest Tent; Great Basin Tent; Poplar Tent Maker; Red-humped; Saddled Prominent.
Cutworm, Western W-marked. **Leafhopper,** Poplar.
Leaf Miner, Aspen; Aspen Blotch; Cottonwood; Poplar.
Leaf Roller, Fruit-tree; Oblique-banded.
Mealybug, Comstock. **Mite,** Four-spotted.
Moth, Cecropia; Hornet; Io; Leopard; Nevada Buck; Oriental; Polyphemus; Satin; Smeared Dagger; Rusty Tussock; White-marked Tussock.
Sawfly, Willow; Willow Shoot.
Scale, Black; Brown Soft; Cottony Maple; European Fruit Lecanium; Greedy; Latania; Oystershell; San Jose; Scurfy; Terrapin; Walnut; Willow Scurfy; White Peach.
Spanworm, Bruce; Cleft-headed.
Thrips, Pear. **Treehopper,** Buffalo.
Wasp, Giant Hornet. **Webworm,** Fall. **Weevil,** Willow Flea.

POPPY (*Papaver*)

Aphid, Bean (black, common); Green Peach; Melon.
Beetle, Rose Chafer. **Bug,** Four-lined Plant; Tarnished Plant.
Leafhopper, Six-spotted. **Mealybug,** Grape.

PORTULACA

Bug, Garden Fleahopper. **Moth,** White-lined Sphinx.

POTATO (*Solanum tuberosum*)

Aphid, Buckthorn; Crescent-marked Lily; Foxglove; Green Peach; Potato; Solanum Root.
Armyworm, Fall; Southern; Yellow-striped.
Beetle, Ash-gray Blister; Banded Flea; Black Blister; Carrot; Colorado

Potato (convex striped beetle devours foliage); Eggplant Flea; Eggplant Tortoise; False Potato; Fuller Rose; Hop Flea; Imbricated Snout; Margined Blister; Pale-striped Flea; Potato Flea (tiny, black; minute holes in foliage); Spotted Cucumber; Strawberry Leaf; Striped Blister; Three-lined Potato; Tobacco Flea; Tuber Flea; Western Potato Flea; Western Spotted Cucumber; Western Striped Cucumber; White-fringed; Yellow-margined Leaf.

Borer, European Corn; Potato Stalk; Potato Tuberworm; Stalk; Tobacco Stalk.

Bug, Alfalfa Plant; Big-legged Plant; Eggplant Lace; False Chinch; Four-lined Plant; Garden Fleahopper; Harlequin; Leaf-footed; Pumpkin; Rapid Plant; Say Stink; Southern Green Stink; Tarnished Plant; Western Plant.

Caterpillar, Cabbage Looper; Yellow Woollybear.

Cricket, Changa; Jerusalem; Northern Mole; Southern Mole.

Cutworm, Black; Dingy; Glassy; Pale Western; Spotted; Variegated.

Earwig, European. **Earworm,** Corn. **Fly,** Potato Scab Gnat.

Grasshopper, Clear-winged; Differential; Lesser Migratory; Red-legged; Two-striped.

Hornworm, Tobacco; Tomato.

Leafhopper, Arid; Beet; Clover; Potato (very injurious, rolls and burns leaves); Southern Garden; Six-spotted; Western Potato.

Leaf Miner, Serpentine. **Maggot,** Seed-corn; Seed-potato.

Mealybug, Apple; Citrophilus; Grape; Solanum.

Millipedes. Mite, Tomato Russet.

Nematode, Cobb's Meadow; Corn Meadow; Cotton Root-knot; De Man's Meadow; Godfrey's Meadow; Golden (quarantine against); Javanese Root-knot; Northern Root-knot; Peanut Root-knot; Potato Rot; Scribner's Meadow; Sting; Tesselate Stylet.

Psyllid, Potato. **Scale,** Cottony-cushion.

Slug, Gray Garden; Spotted Garden. **Springtail,** Garden.

Termites. Webworm, Beet; Garden.

Weevil, Vegetable. **Whitefly,** Greenhouse; Iris.

Wireworm, Columbia Basin; Corn; Dry-land; Eastern Field; Gulf; Pacific Coast; Prairie Grain; Southern Potato; Sugar-beet; Wheat.

DDT usually takes care of the more important potato pests, such as Colorado potato beetle, potato flea beetle, and potato leafhopper.

POTENTILLA (Cinquefoil)

Aphid, Potato; Strawberry. **Weevil,** Strawberry Root.

POTHOS

Nematode, Burrowing. **Mealybug,** Long-tailed.

Scale, Brown Soft; Florida Red; Latania; Proteus.

PRICKLY-ASH (*Zanthoxylum americanum*)
Scale, Barnacle; Black; Brown Soft; European Fruit Lecanium; Florida Wax; Howard; Lesser Snow; Pyriform; Scurfy; Walnut; White Peach.

PRIMROSE (*Primula*)
Aphid, Corn Root; Cowpea; Foxglove; Green Peach; White Aster Root.
Beetle, Fuller Rose (leaves chewed in from margin); Potato Flea; Steel-blue Flea; Strawberry Flea; Yellow-margined Leaf.
Mealybug, Long-tailed; Yucca.
Mite, Two-spotted (foliage always turns yellow in summer).
Nematode, Spring Crimp; Stem and Bulb.
Slug, Spotted Garden (large holes in leaves).
Weevil, Black Vine (grubs work on roots).
Whitefly, Greenhouse.

PRIVET (*Ligustrum*)
Aphid, Privet.
Beetle, Sweetpotato Leaf; Ten-lined June.
Borer, Mountain-ash. **Caterpillar,** Omnivorous Looper.
Leafhopper, Privet. **Leaf Miner,** Lilac; Privet.
Mealybug, Citrophilus; Ground.
Mite, Citrus Flat; Privet (leaves dusty); Privet Rust; Tuckerellid.
Nematode, Northern Root-knot; Steiner's Spiral. **Planthopper.**
Scale, Black; Black Thread; California Red; Camphor; Chaff; Coconut; Cyanophyllum; Dictyospermum; Forbes; Florida Red; Florida Wax; Forbes; Glover; Hemispherical; Japanese; Latania; Lesser Snow; Mining; Oleander; Green Shield; Olive; Pit; Privet; Proteus; Purple; Pyriform; Quohog-shaped; Red Bay; Rufous; San Jose; White Peach; Yellow.
Thrips, Privet (common, serious; leaves grayish).
Walkingstick, Two-striped.
Weevil, Cribrate; Japanese; Lilac.
Whitefly, Citrus (very common in southern gardens); Greenhouse.

PRUNE (see Plum)

PUMPKIN (*Cucurbita*)
Aphid, Melon; Potato.
Beetle, Blister; Pale-striped Flea; Potato Flea; Spinach Carrion; Squash; Striped Cucumber; Western Striped Cucumber.
Borer, Squash Vine. **Bug,** Garden Fleahopper; Squash.
Caterpillar, Melonworm; Yellow Woollybear.
Earworm, Corn. **Mealybug,** Citrus.
See Squash for other pests.

PYRACANTHA (Firethorn)

Aphid, Apple; Rose. **Beetle,** Rhabdopterus.

Bug, Hawthorn Lace (leaves stippled gray; more serious in South).

Mite, Platanus; Southern Red.

Scale, Acuminate; Barnacle; Brown Soft; Cottony-cushion; Dictyospermum; Florida Red; Florida Wax; European Fruit Lecanium; Greedy; Latania; Olive; San Jose; Walnut.

Webworm, Pyracantha (leaves, twigs, webbed; prevalent in Southwest).

Weevil, Cribrate.

QUINCE (*Cydonia*)

Aphid, Apple; Apple Grain; Clover; Woolly Apple.

Beetle, Grape Flea; Japanese (serious).

Borer, Roundheaded Apple Tree. **Casebearer,** Cigar.

Caterpillar, Eastern Tent; Forest Tent; Yellow-necked.

Curculio, Apple; Quince (wormy fruit).

Leaf Crumpler. Leafhopper, Privet.

Leaf Miner, Spotted Tentiform; Unspotted Tentiform.

Leaf Roller, Fruit-tree. **Leaf Skeletonizer,** Apple.

Moth, Oriental Fruit; Codling; Rusty Tussock; White-marked Tussock.

Sawfly, Pear-slug.

Scale, Barnacle; California Red; Cottony-cushion; Cottony Maple; European Fruit Lecanium; Florida Wax; Greedy; Japanese Wax; Oystershell; Putnam; San Jose; Scurfy.

Treehopper, Buffalo; Quince. **Weevil,** Apple Flea.

A spray schedule can be adapted from one for apples. Japanese beetles may be a problem in midsummer.

QUISQUALIS (Rangoon Creeper)

Scale, Brown Soft; Cyanophyllum; Latania; Mining; Proteus.

RADISH (*Raphanus sativus*)

Aphid, Cabbage; Green Peach; Turnip.

Beetle, Black Blister; Pale-striped Flea; Potato Flea; Red Turnip; Sinuate Flea; Striped Blister; Western Black Flea; Western Striped Flea; Yellow-margined Leaf.

Bug, Harlequin.

Caterpillar, Cabbage Looper; Imported Cabbageworm; Yellow Woollybear.

Centipede, Garden Symphylan. **Curculio,** Cabbage.

Leaf Miner, Serpentine. **Maggot,** Seed-corn; Cabbage (seedlings wilt).

Nematode, Cabbage Cyst; Cotton Root-knot; Peanut Root-knot; Sugar-beet.

Moth, Diamondback. **Springtail,** Garden.

Webworm, Cabbage. **Weevil,** Vegetable; Cabbage Seedpod.

Wireworm, Eastern Field; other species.

See Cabbage for other possible pests.

RANDIA
Scale, Black Thread.

RASPBERRY (*Rubus*)

Aphid, Blackberry; European Raspberry; Potato; Spotted-winged.
Beetle, Alfalfa Snout; Argus Tortoise; Fuller Rose; Green June; Imbricated Snout; Japanese (serious); Potato Flea; Rose Chafer; Rose Leaf; Sweet-potato Flea.
Borer, Flatheaded Apple Tree; Raspberry Cane; Raspberry Crown; Red-necked Cane; Rose Stem Girdler.
Bug, Negro (bad taste to berries); Consperse Stink.
Caterpillar, Green Cloverworm; Orange Tortrix; Yellow Woollybear.
Cricket, Black-horned Tree.
Fruitworm, Raspberry; Western Raspberry (beetle may injure buds).
Horntail, Raspberry.
Leafhopper, Grape; White Apple.   **Leaf Miner,** Apple Trumpet.
Leaf Roller, Fruit-tree; Oblique-banded; Raspberry; Strawberry.
Maggot, Raspberry Cane (tips die back).
Mealybug, Citrophilus; Citrus.
Mite, Clover; McDaniel Spider; Willamette; Yellow.
Moth, Crinkled Flannel; Strawberry Crown.
Nematode, Cobb's Meadow; De Man's Meadow; Scribner's Meadow; Tesselate Stylet; Walnut Meadow.
Sawfly, Raspberry.
Scale, Brown Soft; Latania; Oystershell; Parlatorialike; Rose; Scurfy.   **Spittlebug,** Strawberry.
Weevil, Black Vine; Pea Leaf; Strawberry; Strawberry Root.
Whitefly, Glacial.
So far as possible, cut out infested canes. Use rotenone for Japanese beetles when berries are ripening.

REDBUD, JUDAS TREE (*Cercis*)

Beetle, Rhabdopterus.   **Caterpillar,** California Tent.
Leaf Folder, Grape.   **Leaf Roller,** Redbud.
Mite, Grevillea.
Scale, Brown Soft; Cottony-cushion; European Fruit Lecanium; Greedy; Latania; Oleander; Parlatorialike; Pyriform; Terrapin; Walnut; White Peach.
Trehopper, Two-marked.   **Whitefly,** Greenhouse.

REDWOOD (*Sequoia*)

Beetle, Redwood Bark.
Borer, Cedar Tree; California Prionus.   **Horntail,** Western.
Mealybug, Cypress; Redwood; Yucca.   **Moth,** Sequoia Pitch.
Scale, Black Araucaria; Brown Soft; Greedy; Oleander; Redwood.

RETINOSPORA (*Chamaecyparis*)

Aphid, Arborvitae.   **Scale,** Newstead's; Red Bay.
Weevil, Arborvitae; Black Vine.

RHODODENDRON

Aphid, Rhododendron.
Beetle, Asiatic Garden; Pitted Ambrosia; Rhabdopterus.
Borer, Azalea Stem; Broad-necked Root; Rhododendron (common).
Bug, Rhododendron Lace (foliage yellow, stippled).
Mealybug, Taxus.   **Midge,** Rhododendron Tip.
Nematode, Tesselate Stylet.   **Rootworm,** Cranberry.
Scale, Azalea Bark; Oleander; Rhododendron; Soft Azalea.
Thrips, Greenhouse; Madroña; Onion.
Weevil, Black Vine; Japanese.
Wasp, Giant Hornet.   **Whitefly,** Rhododendron.
   Lace bugs and borers are most important.

RHUBARB (*Rheum*)

Aphid, Bean.   **Armyworm,** Western Yellow-striped.
Beetle, Alfalfa Snout; Hop Flea; Japanese; Oriental; Potato Flea.
Borer, European Corn; Stalk.
Caterpillar, Yellow Woollybear.   **Curculio,** Rhubarb (important).
Leafhopper, Potato.   **Mealybug,** Citrophilus; Citrus.
Nematode, Root-knot; Zimmerman's Spiral.
Scale, Black.   **Termites.**

RIBBON-BUSH (*Homalocladium*)

Scale, Tesselated.

RICEPAPER-PLANT (*Tetrapanax*)

Mealybug, Citrus.
Scale, Green Shield; Latania; Purple; Pyriform; Tesselated.

ROCK-ROSE (*Cistus*)

Scale, Barnacle.

ROSARY-PEA (*Abrus precatorius*)

Scale, Brown Soft.

ROSE (*Rosa*)

Aphid, Black-and-red Rose; Crescent-marked Lily; Green Peach; Hairy
   Rose; Melon; Potato (pink and green, common); Rose (green); Rose and
   Bearberry; Rose Grass; Small Rose; Small Green Rose; Strawberry;
   Yellow Rose.

Bee, Small Carpenter (borer in pith); Leaf-cutter (ovals and circles cut from leaf margins).

Beetle, Asiatic Garden; Chinese Rose; Fuller Rose; Grape Colaspis; Grapevine Hoplia; Green Rose Chafer; Japanese (major pest; eats flower, foliage); Oriental; Rhabdopterus; Rose Chafer (on flowers); Rose Leaf; Spotted Cucumber (on flowers); Strawberry Leaf.

Borer, Flatheaded Apple Tree; Pacific Flatheaded; Pigeon Tremex; Raspberry Cane; Rose Stem Girdler; Red-necked Cane.

Budworm, Rose.

Bug, Four-lined Plant; Harlequin; Tarnished Plant.

Cankerworms.

Caterpillar, Eastern Tent; Forest Tent; Omnivorous Looper; Orange Tortrix; Puss; Red-humped; Saddleback; Schizura; Stinging Rose; Western Tent; Yellow Woollybear.

Curculio, Rose. **Earwig,** European (on flowers).

Earworm, Corn. **Grasshoppers. Horntail,** Raspberry.

Leafhopper, Apple (foliage white); Potato (brown tips, margins); Redbanded; Rose (coarse white stippling); Virginia-creeper; White Apple.

Leaf Roller, Fruit-tree; Oblique-banded; Omnivorous; Red-banded.

Leaf Tier, Celery. **Maggot,** Raspberry Cane. **Mealybug,** Citrophilus.

Midge, Rose (small buds turn black; occasional but serious).

Mite, European Red; Four-spotted; Southern Red; Two-spotted (leaves webby, yellow, may drop).

Moth, Brown-tail; Io.

Nematode, American Dagger; California Dagger; Cobb's Meadow; De Man's Meadow; European Dagger; Fig Pin; Northern Root-knot; Scribner's Meadow; Steiner's Spiral; Walnut Meadow; other species.

Sawfly, Bristly Rose-slug; Curled Rose; Rose-slug (leaves skeletonized); Rose Stem.

Scale, Black; Brown Soft; California Red; Camphor; Cottony-cushion; Cottony Maple; Dictyospermum; European Fruit Lecanium; Florida Red; Greedy; Green Shield; Latania; Long Soft; Masked; Oleander; Olive; Oriental; Oystershell; Peach Lecanium; Pustule; Rose (round, white); Rose Palaeococcus; Rufous; San Jose; Walnut.

Thrips, Florida Flower; Flower (buds ball; petals turn brown); Greenhouse; Onion; Tobacco; Western Flower.

Treehopper, Buffalo (curved slits in bark).

Walkingstick, Northern. **Webworm,** Fall.

Weevil, Cribrate; Imported Long-horned; Japanese; Pea Leaf.

Whitefly, Greenhouse. **Wireworm,** Columbia Basin.

Most rose pests can be controlled with a single combination fungicide-insecticide-miticide spray, applied weekly from the time roses come into full leaf until hard frost. The more common problems are aphids, leafhoppers, rose-slugs, beetles, and spider mites but sprays are timed primarily to control rose blackspot.

ROSE-OF-SHARON, ROSE-ACACIA (*Robinia hispida*)

Aphid, Cowpea (dark, numerous at tips); Melon.
Beetle, Japanese (on flowers; foliage). **Bug,** Four-lined Plant.
Bollworm, Pink. **Mealybug,** Mexican.
Scale, Black; Brown Soft; Japanese; Latania; Lesser Snow; Mining; Quohog-shaped; San Jose.

RUBBER PLANT (*Ficus elastica*)

Mealybug, Citrus; Long-tailed. **Nematode,** Steiner's Spiral.
Scale, Black; Black Thread; Brown Soft; Chinese Obscure; Chaff; Cyano-phyllum; Dictyospermum; Florida Red; Florida Wax; Green Shield; Japanese Wax; Latania; Lesser Snow; Nigra; Oleander; Oriental; Proteus; Pustule; Pyriform; Rufous; Tesselated.
Thrips, Banded Greenhouse; Cuban Laurel; Dracaena; Greenhouse.

RUDBECKIA (Coneflower)

Aphid, Brown Ambrosia; Goldenglow; Crescent-marked Lily.
Bug, Garden Fleahopper. **Leafhopper,** Six-spotted.
Scale, Quohog-shaped.

RUSSIAN-OLIVE (see Elaeagnus)

RUTABAGA (see Turnip)

SAGE, BLACK, WHITE (*Audibertia*)

Mealybug, Yucca. **Scale,** Olive; Greedy.
Whitefly, Glacial; Greenhouse; Iridescent.

SAGE, SCARLET, BLUE (*Salvia*)

Aphid, Foxglove. **Beetle,** Asiatic Garden.
Borer, Stalk. **Bug,** Tarnished Plant.
Leafhopper, Grape. **Leaf Tier,** Celery.
Mealybug, Citrus. **Mites. Nematode,** Spring Crimp.
Orthezia, Greenhouse. **Planthopper.**
Scale, Black; Brown Soft; Cottony-cushion; Cassava; Greedy; Latania; Mining; Olive; Pit.
Whitefly, Glacial Greenhouse.

SALAL (*Gaultheria*)

Caterpillar, Western Hemlock Looper. **Leaf Miner,** Blotch.

SALSIFY (*Tragopogon*)
Aphid, Western Aster Root. **Bug,** Tarnished Plant.
Caterpillar, Yellow Woollybear. **Nematode,** False Root-knot.

SANCHEZIA
Mealybug, Citrus; Long-tailed. **Scale,** Barnacle; Latania.

SANDALWOOD (*Santalum*)
Scale, Black.

SAND-LILY (*Leucocrinum*)
Aphid, Sand-lily.

SANSEVIERIA
Scale, Lesser Snow.

SAPODILLA (*Achras sapota=Manilkara zapotilla*)
Beetle, Cuban May.
Mealybug, Citrus; Coconut. **Mite,** Texas Citrus.
Scale, Barnacle; Black; Acuminate; Cottony-cushion; Coconut; Dictyospermum; Florida Wax; Greedy; Green Shield; Hemispherical; Japanese Wax; Latania; Lesser Snow; Mining; Masked; Proteus; Pustule; Pyriform; Rose Palaeococcus; Rufous.
Thrips, Greenhouse.

SAPOTE, WHITE (*Casimiroa*)
Mealybug, Long-tailed.
Scale, Black; Brown Soft; Florida Red; Florida Wax; Green Shield; Japanese Wax; Latania; Lesser Snow; Mining; Oriental; Pyriform.

SASSAFRAS
Beetle, Japanese (important); Pitted Ambrosia.
Butterfly, Spicebush Swallowtail.
Caterpillar, Hickory Horned Devil; Phigalia Looper.
Leaf Roller, Fruit-tree.
Moth, Gypsy; Io; Polyphemus; Promethea.
Scale, European Fruit Lecanium; Florida Wax; Oystershell; Pyriform; San Jose.
Weevil, Sassafras.

SATINLEAF (*Chrysophyllum*)
Mealybug, Coconut.
Scale, Chaff; Coconut; Cottony-cushion; Florida Red; Green; Latania; Mining; Tesselated.

SAUSAGE-TREE (*Kigelia pinnata*)
Scale, Black.

SAXIFRAGE (*Saxifraga*)
Rootworm, Grape. **Slug,** Spotted Garden.

SCABIOSA
Beetle, Fuller Rose. **Bug,** Chrysanthemum Lace; Garden Fleahopper.
Leafhopper, Six-spotted. **Nematode,** Spring Crimp.

SCHEFFLERA
Nematode, Cotton Root-knot.
Scale, Acuminate; Black; Barnacle; Florida Red; Latania; Pustule; Pyriform.

SCHEMEA
Scale, Boisduval's.

SCHIZANTHUS (Butterfly-flower)
Leafhopper, Six-spotted. **Nematode,** Stem and Bulb.

SCINDAPSUS
Nematode, Thames Root-knot.

SCREWPINE (*Pandanus*)
Mealybug, Long-tailed.
Scale, Black Thread; Boisduval's; Chaff; Coconut; Cyanophyllum; Dictyospermum; Fern; Florida Red; Latania; Lesser Snow; Nigra; Proteus; Rufous.

SEAGRAPE (*Coccolobis uvifera*)
Aphid, Black Citrus; Melon. **Borer,** Seagrape.
Mealybug, Citrus; Comstock; Coconut; Striped.
Scale, Black; Brown Soft; Chaff; Cyanophyllum; Florida Red; Florida Wax; Green; Green Shield; Hemispherical; Latania; Lesser Snow; Long Soft; Masked; Oleander; Pustule; Pyriform.
Whitefly, Woolly.

SEAKALE (*Crambe maritima*)
Nematode, Cabbage Cyst.

SEDUM
Aphid, Sedum; Green Peach; Melon. **Scale,** Greedy.

SERISSA
Scale, Cottony-cushion; Cyanophyllum; Florida Wax; Latania; Pyriform; Quohog-shaped.

SEVERINIA (Boxorange)
Mealybug, Citrus.
Scale, Black Thread; Chaff; Cottony-cushion; Dictyospermum; Florida Red; Florida Wax; Hemispherical; Latania; Lesser Snow; Proteus; Purple.

SHADBUSH, SERVICEBERRY (*Amelanchier*)
Aphid, Woolly Elm; Woolly Hawthorn.
Borer, Apple Bark; Lesser Peach; Roundheaded Apple Tree; Shot-hole.
Butterfly, California Tortoise-shell. **Curculio,** Apple.
Leaf Miner, Shadbush. **Mite,** Pear Leaf Blister; Willamette.
Moth, Apple Fruit; Gypsy. **Sawfly,** Pear-slug.
Scale, Oystershell; San Jose; Willow Scurfy.

SHALLOT (*Allium ascalonicum*)
Fly, Lesser Bulb.
See Onion for other pests.

SHAVING-BRUSH TREE (*Pachira fastuosa*)
Beetle, Cuban May.

SILVER LACE-VINE, FLEECE-VINE (*Polygonum aubertii*)
Aphid, Corn Root. **Beetle,** Flea; Japanese.

SHRIMP-PLANT (*Beloperone*)
Orthezia, Greenhouse.

SILVER-TREE (*Leucadendron argenteum*)
Scale, Greedy.

SILVER-VINE (*Actinidia polygama*)
Orthezia, Greenhouse. **Scale,** Lesser Snow; San Jose.

SMILAX (Greenbrier)
Scale, Chaff; Cyanophyllum; Green; Green Shield; Dictyospermum; Latania; Parlatorialike; Pustule; Red Bay; Smilax.
For the Smilax of florists see Asparagus Fern.

SMOKE-TREE (*Cotinus coggygria*)
Leaf Roller, Oblique-banded. **Scale,** San Jose.

SNAPDRAGON (*Antirrhinum*)

Aphid, Green Peach; Melon.   **Beetle,** Asiatic Garden.
Borer, Stalk.   **Budworm,** Rose; Verbena.
Bug, Four-lined Plant; Red-and-black Stink; Snapdragon Lace; Tarnished Plant.
Caterpillar, Yellow Woollybear.   **Centipede,** Garden Symphylan.
Leaf Tier, Celery.   **Mite,** Broad; Cyclamen; Two-spotted.
Moth, Snapdragon Plume.   **Nematode,** Javanese Root-knot.   **Slugs.**

SNOWBALL (See Viburnum)

SNOWBERRY (*Symphoricarpos*)

Aphid, Crescent-marked Lily; Honeysuckle and Parsnip; Pulverulent Snowberry; Snowberry.
Borer, Flatheaded Cherry Tree.   **Maggot,** Apple.
Mealybug, Coleman's.   **Moth,** Snowberry Clearwing.
Scale, Green; Green Shield; San Jose.   **Whitefly,** Glacial.

SOAPBERRY (*Sapindus*)

Scale, Black; Gloomy; Green Shield; Obscure; Quohog-shaped.

SOURGUM (see Tupelo)

SOURSOP (*Annona muricata*)

Mealybug, Coconut.
Scale, Black; Coconut; Florida Red; Green; Green Shield; Hemispherical; Latania; Long Soft; Lesser Snow; Tesselated.

SOYBEAN (*Glycine max*)

Armyworm, Yellow-striped.
Beetle, Banded Cucumber; Japanese (makes lace of foliage); Mexican Bean; Striped Blister.
Bug, Brown Stink; Rapid Plant.
Caterpillar, Green Cloverworm; Velvetbean (may defoliate).
Curculio, Clover Root.   **Grasshopper,** Red-legged.
Leaf Miner, Locust.   **Mite,** Strawberry Spider.
Nematode, American Dagger; Clover Cyst; Cobb's Meadow; Corn Meadow; Cotton Root-knot; De Man's; Fig Pin; Godfrey's Meadow; Northern Root-knot; Scribner's Meadow; Soybean Cyst; Steiner's Spiral; Sting; Tesselate Stylet; Zimmerman's Spiral.
Rootworm, Western Corn.   **Thrips,** Bean.
Webworm, Garden.   **Weevil,** Sweetclover.

SPANISH BAYONET (*Yucca aloifolia*)
Citrus, Mealybug. **Orthezia,** Greenhouse.
Scale, Black; Chaff; Cyanophyllum; Lesser Snow; Oleander; Purple.

SPANISH DAGGER (*Yucca gloriosa*)
Scale, Cyanophyllum; Lesser Snow; Purple.

SPANISH-LIME (*Melicocca bijuga*)
Beetle, Cuban May.
Scale, Barnacle; Black; Dictyospermum; Florida Wax; Green Shield; Latania; Lesser Snow; Mining; Rufous.

SPANISH-NEEDLES (*Bidens*)
Caterpillar, Yellow Woollybear.
Mealybug, Citrus Mexican. **Orthezia,** Greenhouse.
Scale, Black; Brown Soft; Cottony-cushion; Chaff; Green; Green Shield; Mango Shield; Hemispherical.
Thrips, Florida Flower.

SPARKLEBERRY (*Vaccinium arboreum*)
Mealybug, Long-tailed.
Scale, Cyanophyllum; Dictyospermum; Florida Wax; Latania; Pyriform; Red Bay; Terrapin.

SPICEBUSH (*Benzoin aestivale*)
Butterfly, Spicebush Swallowtail.
Scale, Brown Soft; Cottony-cushion; Dictyospermum; Florida Red; Lesser Snow; Pyriform.

SPINACH (*Spinacia*)
Aphid, Bean; Green Peach; Melon. **Armyworm,** Fall.
Beetle, Beet Leaf; Blister; Potato Flea; Spinach Carrion; Spinach Flea.
Caterpillar, Cabbage Looper. **Cutworms. Grasshoppers.**
Leafhopper, Beet. **Leaf Miner,** Serpentine; Spinach.
Leaf Tier, Celery. **Maggot,** Seed-corn.
Nematode, Clover Cyst; Cobb's Meadow; De Man's Meadow.
Springtail, Garden.
Webworm, Beet; Southern Beet. **Weevil,** Vegetable.

SPINACH, NEW ZEALAND (*Tetragonia expansa*)
Nematode, Cotton Root-knot.

SPIREA (*Spiraea*)
Aphid, Brown Spirea; Spirea (green; common).

Caterpillar, Saddled Prominent. **Leafhopper,** Privet.
Leaf Roller, Oblique-banded. **Mite,** Yellow.
Nematode, Northern Root-knot.
Scale, Black; Cottony-cushion; Cottony Maple; Florida Red; Florida Wax; Latania; Oystershell; San Jose; Spirea; Walnut; White Peach.

SPREKELIA
Fly, Narcissus Bulb. **Thrips,** Banded Greenhouse.

SPRUCE (*Picea*)
Aphid, Balsam Twig; Black Polished Spruce; Bow-legged Fir; Cooley Spruce Gall (galls at tips of blue spruce twigs); Dark Brown Spruce; Eastern Spruce Gall (gall at base of Norway-spruce twigs); Green Spruce; Light Brown Spruce; Pine Leaf; Powdery Spruce; Spruce; Woolly Larch.
Beetle, Alaska; Allegheny Spruce; Black Turpentine; Douglas-fir; Douglas-fir Engraver; Eastern Spruce; Engelmann Spruce; European Spruce; Fir Engraver; Golden Buprestid; Lodgepole Pine; Mountain Pine; Northeastern Sawyer; Pine Colaspis; Pine Engraver; Red Turpentine; Sitka-spruce; Southern Pine; White-pine Cone.
Borer, Black-horned Pine; Flatheaded Fir; Hemlock; Pitch Mass; Western Larch Roundheaded.
Budworm, Blackheaded; Spruce (very serious; needles webbed together, die); **Bud Moth,** Larch; Spruce.
Caterpillar, False Hemlock Looper; Hemlock Looper; Phantom Hemlock Looper; Western Hemlock Looper.
Leaf Miner, Spruce (needles webbed together). **Midge,** Spruce Gall.
Mite, Spruce Spider (common, injurious; needles gray, webby).
Moth, Douglas-fir; Pitch; Gypsy; Imperial; Pine Cone; Silver-spotted Tiger; Spruce Epizeuxis.
Nematode, De Man's Meadow.
Sawfly, Balsam Fir; European Spruce; Greenheaded Spruce; Yellow-headed Spruce.
Scale, Hemlock; Pine Needle; Spruce Bud. **Spittlebug,** Pine.
Weevil, Engelmann Spruce; Pales; Sitka-spruce; Strawberry Root; White-pine.
Spruce budworm is very important in forests, spruce mite and gall aphids in home plantings.

SQUASH (*Cucurbita maxima*)
Aphid, Bean; Melon (common; curls leaves); Potato.
Beetle, Imbricated Snout; Spinach Carrion; Spotted Cucumber; Squash; Striped Cucumber; Tobacco Flea; Western Striped.
Borer, Squash Vine (common, serious; vines wilt).
Bug, Garden Fleahopper; Harlequin; Horned Squash; Squash.

Caterpillar, Melonworm; Pickleworm; Yellow Woollybear.
Earworm, Corn. **Leafhopper,** Beet.
Nematode, Cotton Root-knot. **Springtail,** Garden. **Termites.**
Thrips, Onion; Western Flower.
Whitefly, Greenhouse (often abundant).
Many squash varieties are sensitive to sulfur and DDT.

SQUILL (*Scilla*)
Aphid, Tulip Bulb.

STAGGERBUSH (*Lyonia*)
Scale, Azalea Bark; Florida Wax; Oak Eriococcus; Red Bay.

STEPHANOTIS
Mealybug, Citrus; Long-tailed.
Scale, Black; Cottony-cushion; Brown Soft; Cyanophyllum; Hemispherical; Pustule.

STAR-APPLE (*Chrysophyllum cainito*)
Mealybug, Coconut; Long-tailed.
Scale, Cottony-cushion; Green Shield; Latania; Mining; Tesselated.

STOCK (*Mathiola*)
Beetle, Striped Flea; Western Black Flea; Western Striped Flea.
Mealybug, Mexican. **Moth,** Diamondback.
Spittlebug, Meadow. **Springtail,** Garden.
Weevil, Imported Long-horned.

STATICE (Sea-pink; Thrift)
Thrips, Greenhouse.

STRAWBERRY (*Fragaria*)
Aphid, Melon; Strawberry; Strawberry Root; Yellow Rose.
Beetle, Alfalfa Snout; Asiatic Garden; Darkling; European Chafer; Grape Colaspis; Hoplia; Oriental; Pale-striped Flea; Rose Chafer; Rose Leaf; Strawberry Flea; Strawberry Leaf; Ten-lined June; White-fringed.
Borer, Strawberry Crown; Lesser Cornstalk.
Bug, Leaf-footed; False Chinch; Lygus; Negro; Pameras (hard berries); Tarnished Plant.
Caterpillar, Green Cloverworm; Garden Tortrix; Salt Marsh; Woollybear.
Centipede, Garden Symphylan.
Cricket, Field; Northern Mole; Southern Mole.
Curculio, Cowpea. **Cutworms. Earwig,** European.
Leaf Miner, Strawberry Crown.

Leaf Roller, Oblique-banded; Omnivorous; Strawberry; Western Strawberry.
Leaf Tier, Celery; Omnivorous.
Mealybug, Grape; Ground.   **Millipedes.**
Mite, Cylamen (serious); Desert Spider; Strawberry Spider; Two-spotted.
Moth, Strawberry Crown.
Nematode, American Dagger; Chamber's Dagger; Christie's Stubby Root; Cobb's Meadow; De Man's; European Dagger; Fig Pin; Godfrey's Meadow; Northern Root-knot; Scribner's Meadow; Spring Crimp; Summer Dwarf; Tesselate Stylet; Walnut Meadow; Zimmerman's Spiral.
Rootworm, Strawberry.   **Sawfly,** Strawberry.
Scale, Brown Soft; Rose; San Jose;   **Slugs. Snails. Sowbugs.**
Spittlebug, Meadow; Strawberry.
Thrips, Florida Flower; Western Flower.   **Webworm,** Garden.
Weevil, Black Vine (grubs on roots); Citrus Root; Imported Long-horned; Japanese; Pea Leaf; Strawberry; Strawberry Root.
Whitefly, Greenhouse; Iris; Strawberry.   **Wireworms.**
Buy certified strawberry plants and so start with clean stock. Cyclamen mite and nematodes are serious problems.

STRAWBERRY-TREE (*Arbutus unedo*)
Aphid, Rose and Bearberry.
Scale, Black; Brown Soft; Greedy.

STRAWFLOWER (*Helichrysum bracteatum*)
Beetle, Asiatic Garden.   **Leafhopper,** Six-spotted.
Scale, Ground Pearls.

STRELITZIA (Bird-of-Paradise)
Mealybug, Citrus; Long-tailed.
Scale, Boisduval's; Dictyospermum; Florida Red; Green; Greedy; Lesser Snow; Latania; Oriental; Pyriform.

STROBILANTHES (Lavenderbell)
Mealybug, Mexican.   **Orthezia,** Greenhouse.
Scale, Barnacle; Black; Cottony-cushion; Black Thread; Florida Wax; Hemispherical; Latania; Mining; Nigra; Pustule; Tesselated.

SUGAR-APPLE (*Annona squamosa*)
Mealybug, Citrus; Coconut; Striped.
Scale, Barnacle; Brown Soft; Coconut; Cottony-cushion; Dictyospermum; Florida Red; Florida Wax; Hemispherical; Latania; Lesser Snow; Long Soft; Oriental; Mining; Pustule; Rose Palaeococcus; Rufous.

SUGAR-BUSH (*Rhus ovata*)
Thrips, Toyon.

SUMAC (*Rhus*)

Aphid, Monell's Sumac; Sumac Gall. **Beetle,** Potato Flea.
Borer, Currant.
Caterpillar, Hickory Horned Devil; Omnivorous Looper; Walnut.
Leaf Roller, Oblique-banded. **Psyllid,** Sumac.
Scale, Black; Cottony Maple; Green; Lesser Snow; Pustule; Pyriform; Walnut; White Peach.

SUNFLOWER (*Helianthus*)

Aphid, Brown Ambrosia; Dogwood or Sunflower; Goldenglow; Hop; Leafcurl Plum; Melon; Potato; White Aster Root.
Beetle, Asiatic Garden; Carrot; Pale-striped Flea; Potato Flea; Sunflower; Western Striped Cucumber; White-fringed.
Bug, Big-legged; Four-lined Plant; Garden Fleahopper; Harlequin; Leaffooted; Say Stink; Tarnished Plant.
Butterfly, Painted Lady. **Caterpillar,** Yellow Woollybear.
Earworm, Corn. **Leaf Cutter,** Morning-glory.
Leaf Roller, Oblique-banded. **Maggot,** Sunflower.
Mealybug, Citrophilus; Mexican. **Midge,** Sunflower Seed.
Mite, Desert Spider. **Moth,** Banded Sunflower; Sunflower.
Rootworm, Northern Corn.
Scale, Cottony-cushion; Hemispherical; Lesser Snow; Latania.
Spittlebug, Sunflower. **Weevil,** Cocklebur.

SURINAM-CHERRY (*Eugenia uniflora*)

Mealybug, Citrus.
Scale, Black; Florida Red; Florida Wax; Dictyospermum.

SWEETBAY (*Magnolia virginiana*)

Scale, Brown Soft; Cyanophyllum; Dictyospermum; Florida Red; Florida Wax; European Fiorinia; Green Shield; Lesser Snow; Nigra; Oleander; Oriental; Parlatorialike; Red Bay; Terrapin; Tesselated; Tuliptree.

SWEETFERN (*Comptonia asplenifolia*)

Caterpillar, Chain-spotted Geometer. **Moth,** Crinkled Flannel.
Spanworm, Cleft-headed. **Spittlebug,** Saratoga.

SWEETGUM (*Liquidambar*)

Bagworm. Borer, Twig Pruner.
Caterpillar, Forest Tent; Hickory Horned Devil; Red-humped.
Leaf Tier, Sweetgum.
Moth, Azalea Sphinx; Luna; Polyphemus; Promethea.
Scale, Cottony-cushion; Cyanophyllum; Gloomy; Latania; Sweetgum; Terrapin; Tuliptree; Walnut. **Webworm,** Sweetgum.

SWEETPEA (*Lathyrus odoratus*)

Aphid, Corn Root; Pea; Potato; Solanum Root.
Beetle, Spotted Cucumber; Western Spotted Cucumber.
Bug, Four-lined Plant. **Caterpillar,** Zebra.
Centipede, Garden Symphylan.
Leaf Miner, Serpentine. **Leaf Tier,** Celery.
Mite, Desert Spider; Two-spotted (common; leaves yellow, mealy).
Moth, Pea. **Nematode,** Root-knot. **Sowbugs.**
Thrips, Banded Greenhouse; Onion; Western Flower.

SWEETPOTATO (*Ipomoea batatas*)

Aphid, Potato. **Armyworm,** Fall; Southern; Yellow-striped.
Beetle, Argus Tortoise; Blister; Golden Tortoise; Mottled Tortoise; Potato
  Flea; Striped Tortoise; Sweetpotato Flea; Sweetpotato Leaf; White-fringed.
Caterpillar, Yellow Woollybear. **Cutworm,** Granulate.
Fly, Onion Bulb. **Hornworm,** Sweetpotato.
Leafhopper, Bean; Southern Garden.
Leaf Miner, Morning-glory; Sweetpotato.
Maggot, Seed-corn. **Mealybug,** Citrus; Grape; Mexican.
Mite, Tumid Spider.
Nematode, American Dagger; Cobb's Meadow; Crownheaded Lance; De
  Man's Meadow; Southern Root-knot.
Scale, Lesser Snow. **Termites. Thrips,** Banded Greenhouse.
Weevil, Sweetpotato. **Whitefly,** Sweetpotato.
Wireworm, Gulf; Southern Potato.

SWEET-WILLIAM (*Dianthus barbatus*)

Leafhopper, Six-spotted. **Mites. Nematode,** Stem and Bulb.
Scale, Brown Soft.

SWISS CHARD (*Beta*)

Bug, Tarnished Plant. **Leaf Miner,** Spinach.
Nematode, Cotton Root-knot. **Weevil,** Vegetable.
  See also Beet for other possible pests.

SYCAMORE, PLANE (*Platanus*)

Aphid, Beech Blight; Giant Bark; Sycamore. **Bagworm.**
Borer, American Plum; Flatheaded Apple Tree; Flatheaded Cherry Tree;
  Pacific Flatheaded; Pigeon Tremex; Sycamore.
Bug, Sycamore Lace; Sycamore Plant.
Caterpillar, Hickory Horned Devil; Omnivorous Looper; Puss.
Leaf Miner, Sycamore.
Mite, Platanus; Southern Red; Willamette.

Moth, Cynthia; Imperial; Io; Oriental; Sycamore Tussock; White-marked Tussock.
Scale, Barnacle; Black; Brown Soft; Cottony Maple; Grape; Latania; Oyster-shell; Putnam; Sycamore (serious on oriental plane); Terrapin.
Treehopper, Two-marked. **Weborm,** Fall. **Whitefly,** Mulberry.

SYNGONIUM (*Nephthytis*)
Mealybug, Long-tailed. **Nematode,** Cotton Root-knot.
Scale, Hemispherical; Latania. **Thrips,** Greenhouse.

TABEBUIA
Aphid, Melon. **Scale,** Mining.

TABERNAEMONTANA
Scale, Acuminate; Barnacle; Brown Soft; Cyanophyllum; Florida Red; Green Shield; Hemispherical; Latania; Mining; Oriental; Pustule; Par-latorialike; Tesselated.

TAMARIND (*Tamarindus*)
Scale, Latania; Mining; Oriental; Quohog-shaped; Rufous.
Treehopper, Thornbug.

TAMARISK, SALT CEDAR (*Tamarix*)
Leafhopper, Southern Garden. **Mealybug,** Citrus.
Scale, Cottony-cushion; Florida Wax; Oystershell.

TANGERINE (*Citrus nobilis*)
Beetle, Fuller Rose. **Bug,** Leaf-footed.
Mite, Yuma Spider. **Scale,** California Red. **Thrips,** Citrus.
See also Citrus Fruits.

TEA (*Thea sinensis*)
Scale, Acuminate; Chaff; Dictyospermum; Florida Red; Florida Wax; Cyanophyllum; Latania; Oleander; Proteus; Tea.

TEASEL (*Dipsacus*)
Aphid, Goldenglow. **Nematode,** Stem and Bulb.

TECOMA
Caterpillar, Omnivorous Looper. **Mealybug,** Long-tailed.
Scale, Barnacle; Black; Florida Wax; Green Shield; Lesser Snow; Mining; Oleander.

TERNSTROEMIA
Scale, Florida Red; Camellia.

THEVETIA (Yellow Oleander)

Scale, Acuminate; Black; Brown Soft; Cyanophyllum; Florida Red; Florida Wax; Latania; Proteus; Pyriform; Tesselated.

THISTLE (*Cirsium*)

Aphid, Melon; Oleaster-thistle; Thistle.
Bug, Alfalfa Plant.   **Butterfly,** Painted Lady; Painted Beauty.
Leaf Roller, Oblique-banded.   **Leaf Tier,** Celery.
Moth, Artichoke Plume.   **Scale,** Green.

THORN, THORNAPPLE (see Hawthorn)

THUNBERGIA (Clockvine)

Mealybug, Citrus.   **Orthezia,** Greenhouse.
Scale, Acuminate; Black; Green Shield; Lesser Snow; Purple; Proteus; Pyriform; Tesselated; White Peach.

THYME (*Thymus*)

Mealybug, Ground.

TOMATILLO (*Physalis ixocarpa*)

Mite, Tomato Russet.

TOMATO (*Lycopersicon esculentum*)

Aphid, Green Peach; Potato (both common).
Armyworm, Beet; Fall; Western Yellow-striped.
Beetle, Black Blister; Colorado Potato; Darkling; Fig; Hop Flea; Pale-striped Flea; Potato Flea (common; minute holes in foliage); Spotted Cucumber; Striped Blister; Tobacco Flea; Western Potato Flea.
Borer, Potato Stalk; Potato Tuberworm.
Bug, Eggplant Lace; Garden Fleahopper; Green Stink; Leaf-footed; One-spot Stink; Pumpkin.
Caterpillar, Cabbage Looper; Tomato Pinworm.
Centipede, Garden Symphylan.   **Cricket,** Camel; Field.
Cutworm, Granulate; Pale-sided.   **Earworm,** Corn (tomato fruitworm).
Hornworm, Tobacco; Tomato (large green caterpillars).
Leafhopper, Beet.   **Maggot,** Pepper.   **Millipedes.**
Mealybug, Solanum.   **Mite,** Tomato Russet; Cyclamen; Two-spotted.
Moth, White-lined Sphinx (hornworm caterpillar).
Nematode, Awl; Cobb's Meadow; Corn Meadow; Cotton Root-knot; Crown-headed Lance; De Man's Meadow; Fig Pin; Godfrey's Meadow; Golden; Javanese Root-knot; Northern Root-knot; Peanut Root-knot; Reniform; Southern Root-knot; Soybean Cyst; Steiner's Spiral; Tesselate Stylet; Tobacco Cyst; Thames Root-knot.

Psyllid, Potato or tomato (plants deformed, appear diseased).
Scale, Lesser Snow. **Slugs. Springtail,** Garden.
Thrips, Banded Greenhouse; Flower; Onion; Western Flower.
Treehopper, Three-cornered Alfalfa. **Weevil,** Vegetable.
Whitefly, Greenhouse (tiny white "moths" on underside of leaves).
Tomato pests vary in different sections. Flea beetles and cutworms are rather general.

TRAVELERS-TREE (*Ravenala madagascariensis*)
Mealybug, Coconut; Long-tailed.
Scale, Boisduval's; Brown Soft; Black Thread; Coconut; Dictyospermum; Florida Red; Green Shield; Latania; Lesser Snow; Nigra; Proteus; Tesselated.

TRUMPET VINE (*Campsis radicans*)
Planthopper.
Scale, Olive; Oriental; Pyriform; Quohog-shaped; Tesselated. **Whitefly,** Citrus.

TUBEROSE (*Polianthes tuberosa*)
Caterpillar, Convict. **Nematode,** Root-knot.

TULIP (*Tulipa*)
Aphid, Green Peach; Potato; Tulip Bulb; Tulip Leaf.
Fly, Lesser Bulb; Narcissus Bulb. **Millipedes.**
Mite, Bulb; Two-spotted. **Nematode,** Stem and Bulb. **Scale,** Black.

TULIPTREE (*Liriodendron*)
Aphid, Tuliptree (green, secreting much honeydew, with sooty mold).
Beetle, June. **Borer,** Sapwood Timberworm.
Moth, Promethea. **Nematode,** Tesselate Stylet.
Scale, Oystershell; Putnam; Tuliptree (serious); Walnut; Willow Scurfy.
Weevil, Sassafras.

TUNG-OIL-TREE (*Aleurites fordii*)
Scale, Chaff; Cyanophyllum; Latania; Lesser Snow; Cottony-cushion; Oleander; Olive; White Peach.

TUPELO, SOURGUM (*Nyssa sylvatica*)
Borer, Twig Girdler. **Leaf Miner,** Tupelo (cuts pieces from leaves).
Moth, Azalea Sphinx. **Scale,** San Jose; Sour-gum.

TURKS-CAP, SLEEPING HIBISCUS (*Malvaviscus arboreus*)
Katydids, (large holes in foliage). **Moth,** Abutilon.

Mealybug, Citrus; Long-tailed; Mexican.
Scale, Black; Brown Soft; Hemispherical; Japanese Wax; Latania; Nigra.

TURNIP (*Brassica rapa*)

Aphid, Cabbage; Potato; Turnip. **Armyworm,** Fall.
Beetle, Asiatic Garden; Pale-striped Flea; Red Turnip; Sinuate Flea; Striped Blister; Western Black Flea; Western Striped Flea; White-fringed; Yellow-margined Leaf.
Borer, Lesser Cornstalk.
Bug, Green Stink; Harlequin; Tarnished Plant.
Caterpillar, Cabbage Looper; Imported Cabbageworm; Yellow Woollybear.
Curculio, Cabbage. **Leaf Miner,** Serpentine.
Maggot, Cabbage; Seed-corn. **Millipedes.**
Moth, Diamondback; White-lined Sphinx.
Nematode, Cobb's Meadow; Cotton Root-knot; Sting; Sugar-beet.
Termites. Thrips, Onion.
Weevil, Cabbage Seedpod; Vegetable.

TURQUOISE VINE (*Ampelopsis brevipedunculata*)

Beetle, Japanese (very fond of this vine).

UMBRELLA PLANT (*Cyperus*)

Mealybug, Citrus; Long-tailed. **Scale,** Oleander.
Thrips, Citrus. **Whitefly,** Citrus.

UMBRELLA-TREE (*Magnolia tripetala*)

Mite, Four-spotted. **Scale,** Greedy; Lesser Snow; Oleander.
Thrips, Citrus. **Whitefly,** Citrus.

VALLOTA (Scarboro-lily)

Fly, Narcissus Bulb.

VELVETBEAN (*Stizolobium*)

Beetle, White-fringed. **Caterpillar,** Velvetbean. **Mite,** Texas Citrus.

VERBASCUM (Mullein)

Bug, Red-and-black Stink.

VERBENA

Aphid, Foxglove; Geranium; Green Peach; Melon.
Beetle, Clematis Blister. **Bud Moth,** Verbena.
Bug, Snapdragon Lace; Tarnished Plant; Garden Fleahopper.
Caterpillar, Omnivorous Looper; Yellow Woollybear.

Leaf Miner, Verbena (light blotches in leaves; common).
Leaf Roller, Oblique-banded. **Mite,** Broad; Cyclamen; Two-spotted.
Nematode, Chrysanthemum Foliar. **Orthezia,** Greenhouse.
Scale, Brown Soft; Cottony-cushion; Latania; Oleander.
Thrips, Flower; Greenhouse. **Webworm,** Garden. **Whitefly,** Greenhouse.

VERBESINA (Crownbeard)
Mealybug, Citrus.

VETCH (*Vicia*)
Borer, Lima-bean pod. **Earworm,** Corn. **Moth,** Pea.
Nematode, Soybean Cyst. **Weevil,** Broad-bean; Vetch Brucid.

VIBURNUM (Snowball)
Aphid, Bean; Currant; Grapevine; Ivy; Snowball; Spirea; Viburnum.
Beetle, Asiatic Garden; Potato Flea. **Borer,** Dogwood Twig.
Bug, Tarnished Plant. **Caterpillar,** Schizura.
Hornworm, Tobacco; Tomato. **Mealybug,** Citrus; Long-tailed.
Nematode, American Dagger; De Man's Meadow; Northern Root-knot;
    Peanut Root-knot.
Planthopper, Citrus Flatid.
Scale, Barnacle; Brown Soft; Camellia Mining; Chaff; Cottony-cushion; Cottony Maple; Cyanophyllum; Dictyospermum; Florida Red; Florida Wax; Hemispherical; Japanese Wax; Latania; Obscure; Olive; Oystershell; Parlatorialike; Pyriform; Putnam; San Jose; Tesselated; Walnut.
Thrips, Flower; Greenhouse.
Treehopper, Three-cornered Alfalfa; Two-marked.
Whitefly, Citrus; Greenhouse.
The foliage of common snowball is usually curled up with aphids.
Viburnum carlesii is sensitive to sulfur and DDT.

VINCA (Myrtle; Periwinkle)
Aphid, Green Peach; Melon; Potato; Solanum Root.
Beetle, Fuller Rose. **Leafhopper,** Six-spotted.
Mealybug, Citrus; Long-tailed. **Nematode,** Northern Root-knot.
Orthezia, Greenhouse.
Scale, Brown Soft; Dictyospermum; Florida Red; Florida Wax; Hemispherical; Latania; Olive; Oleander; Proteus.

VIOLET (*Viola*)
Aphid, Crescent-marked Lily; Foxglove; Green Peach; Red Violet; Violet.
Beetle, Asiatic Garden; Potato Flea; White-fringed.
Caterpillar, Omnivorous Looper; Yellow Woollybear.
Leaf Cutter, Morning-glory. **Leaf Roller,** Red-banded.

Leaf Tier, Celery. **Midge,** Violet Gall.

Mite, Cyclamen; Two-spotted (prevalent; leaves yellow).

Nematode, Spring Crimp; Root-knot.

Sawfly, Violet (blue-black larvae feed at night).

Scale, Fern. **Slug,** Spotted Garden (large holes in leaves).

Avoid nicotine on violets.

VIRGINIA-CREEPER (*Parthenocissus quinquefolia*)

Aphid, Rusty Plum.

Beetle, Grape Flea; Japanese (serious); Rose Chafer.

Caterpillar, Grapevine Looper. **Hornworm,** Tobacco; Tomato.

Leaf Folder, Grape.

Leafhopper, Grape; Three-banded; Virginia-creeper (foliage gray).

Moth, Abbott's Sphinx; Achemon Sphinx; Eight-spotted Forester; Virginia-creeper.

Scale, Brown Soft; Calico; Cottony-cushion; Cottony Maple; Cyanophyllum; Florida Red; Green; Latania; Olive; Oystershell; Peach Lecanium; San Jose.

Weevil, Imported Long-horned.

WALLFLOWER (*Cheiranthus*)

Aphid, Crescent-marked Lily.

Beetle, Red Turnip; Western Black Flea; Western Striped Flea.

Moth, Diamondback. **Nematode,** Cabbage Cyst.

WALNUT (*Juglans*)

Aphid, Black-margined; Dusky-veined Walnut; European Walnut; Giant Bark; Walnut.

Borer, Brown Wood; California Prionus; Nautical; Pacific Flatheaded; Painted Hickory; Tiger Hickory; Twig Pruner.

Bug, False Chinch; Walnut Lace. **Casebearer,** Pecan Cigar.

Caterpillar, Filbertworm; Hickory Horned Devil; Navel Orangeworm; Omnivorous Looper; Orange Tortrix; Red-humped; Variable Oak Leaf; Walnut (black with white hairs); Yellow-necked.

Curculio, Black Walnut; Butternut. **Fly,** Walnut Husk.

Leaf Roller, Fruit-tree. **Mealybug,** Citrophilus; Grape.

Mite, European Red; Pacific Spider; Platanus; Southern Red; Strawberry Spider; Two-spotted; Walnut Blister.

Moth, Codling; Hickory Tussock; Leopard; Luna; Walnut Sphinx; Western Tussock.

Nematode, American Dagger; California Sessile; Persian Walnut; Walnut Meadow.

Rootworm, Strawberry. **Sawfly,** Butternut Woollyworm.

Scale, Black; Calico; California Red; Citricola; Cottony-cushion; Dictyospermum; European Fruit Lecanium; Frosted; Greedy; Italian Pear; Obscure; Oystershell; Purple; Putnam; San Jose; Scurfy; Tuliptree; Walnut; White Peach.

Spanworm, Elm; Walnut. **Termites. Webworm,** Fall.

The walnut aphid and the codling moth are serious problems of commercial growers.

WANDERING-JEW (*Tradescantia*)

Caterpillar, Orange Tortrix. **Leaf Cutter,** Morning-glory.
Leaf Tier, Celery. **Mealybug,** Citrus; Long-tailed.
Nematode, Peanut Root-knot. **Scale,** Chaff.

WATERCRESS (*Nasturtium officinale*)

Aphid, Bean; Spinach.
Beetle, Watercress Leaf; Western Black Flea; Western Striped Flea.
Moth, Diamondback. **Sowbugs.**

WATERLILY (*Nymphaea*)

Aphid, Corn Leaf; Waterlily. **Beetle,** Waterlily Leaf.
Leaf Cutter, Waterlily. **Midge,** False Leaf-mining.

WATERMELON (*Citrullus vulgaris*)

Aphid, Melon (common; serious).
Beetle, Hop Flea; Imbricated Snout; Potato Flea; Squash; Spotted Cucumber; Striped Cucumber.
Bug, Horned Squash; Western Leaf-footed.
Caterpillar, Melonworm; Pickleworm. **Cricket,** Camel.
Leaf Miner, Serpentine. **Millipedes.**
Nematode, Cotton Root-knot; Southern Root-knot.
Scale, Black; California Red.
Treehopper, Three-cornered Alfalfa.
Whitefly, Greenhouse. **Wireworms.**

See Melon for other pests.

WATER PRIMROSE (*Jussiaea peruviana*)

Mealybug, Citrus. **Scale,** Black Thread.

WEIGELA

Bug, Four-lined Plant. **Mealybug,** Comstock. **Nematode,** Steiner's Spiral.
Scale, Barnacle; Cottony-cushion; Latania.
Weevil, Japanese.

WILLOW (*Salix*)

Aphid, Black Willow; Giant Bark; Giant Willow; Green-and-pink Willow; Little Black and Green Willow; Willow.

Beetle, Alder Flea; Cottonwood Flea; Elm Calligrapha; Goldsmith; Gray Willow Leaf; Imported Willow Leaf (skeletonizes leaves, especially weeping willow; small, metallic-blue beetle); June; Pacific Willow Leaf; Rose Leaf; Striped Cucumber; Willow Flea.

Borer, Banded Alder; Bronze Birch; Brown Wood; Carpenterworm; Cottonwood; Flatheaded Apple Tree; Pacific Flatheaded; Poplar and Willow (may be serious).

Bug, Mountain Ash; Willow Lace.

Butterfly, Mourning-cloak; Viceroy; Western Swallowtail.

Casebearer, California.

Caterpillar, California Tent; Chain-spotted Geometer; Eastern Tent; Forest Tent; Hemlock Looper; Omnivorous Looper; Orange Tortrix; Poplar Tent Maker; Red-humped; Schizura; Unicorn; Walnut.

Leafhopper, Poplar; Southern Garden. **Mealybug,** Grape.

Midge, Willow Beaked Gall. **Mite,** Platanus; Yellow.

Moth, American Dagger; Brown-tail; Buck; Cecropia; Cottonwood Dagger; Gypsy; Douglas-fir Tussock; Hornet; Io; Leopard (borer); Luna; Nevada Buck; Oriental; Rusty Tussock; Satin; Smeared Dagger; Spotted Tussock; Western Tussock; White-marked Tussock.

Nematode, Cotton Root-knot; Southern Root-knot; Tesselate Stylet.

Sawfly, Willow; Willow Red-gall; Willow Shoot.

Scale, Black; Brown Soft; California Red; Cottony-cushion; Cottony Maple; Dictyospermum; European Fruit Lecanium; Greedy; Green; Nigra; Obscure; Oleander; Putnam; San Jose; Scurfy; Terrapin; Willow Scurfy.

Spanworm. Cleft-headed. **Spittlebug,** Saratoga.

Thrips, Citrus; Pear. **Treehopper,** Two-marked.

Wasp, Giant Hornet. **Webworm,** Fall. **Weevil,** Cribrate; Willow Flea.

WISTERIA (*Wistaria*)

Aphid, Melon.

Beetle, Rose Chafer; Sweetpotato Leaf; Ten-lined June.

Butterfly, Silver-spotted Skipper. **Leaf Roller,** Honeylocust.

Mealybug, Long-tailed; Citrus; Mexican. **Planthopper.**

Scale, Brown Soft; Cottony-cushion; European Fruit Lecanium; Florida Red; Lesser Snow; Mining; Peach Lecanium.

Weevil, Black Vine. **Webworm,** Fall.

WITCH-HAZEL (*Hamamelis*)

Aphid, Witch-hazel Leaf Gall; Spiny Witch-hazel Gall.

Caterpillar, Saddled Prominent.

YAM (*Dioscorea*)

Nematode, West African Spiral. **Whitefly,** Cloudy-winged.

YARROW (*Achillea*)

Aphid, Artemisia; Lettuce Root; Leaf-curl Plum; Sugar-beet Root.
Nematode, Cobb's Meadow. **Thrips.**

YAUPON (*Ilex vomitoria*)

Beetle, Rhabdopterus.
Scale, Acuminate; Cottony Maple; False Cottony Maple; Florida Wax; Japanese Wax; Latania; Parlatorialike; Red Bay; Tea; Tesselated.

YEW (*Taxus*)

Beetle, Asiatic Garden. **Mealybug,** Taxus. **Mite,** Taxus Bud.
Nematode, De Man's Meadow; Steiner's Spiral; Tesselate; Zimmerman's Spiral.
Scale, Cottony-cushion; Cottony Taxus; California Red; Dictyospermum; Fletcher; Hemlock; Oleander; Purple.
Termites.
Weevil, Black Vine (grubs at roots; plants die); Strawberry Root.

YUCCA

Bug, Yucca Plant. **Borer,** Stalk.
Mealybug, Citrus; Yucca. **Moth,** Yucca (effects pollination).
Scale, Black; Boisduval's; Brown Soft; California Red; Cassava; Chaff; Cyanophyllum; Dictyospermum; Florida Wax; Latania; Mining; Lesser Snow; Oleander; Oystershell; Purple; Red Bay.
Thrips, Flower. **Weevil,** Yucca.

ZAMIA

Mealybug, Striped.
Scale, Brown Soft; Cyanophyllum; Chaff; Dictyospermum; Fern; Florida Red; Hemispherical; Latania; Lesser Snow; Oleander; Oriental; Parlatorialike; Proteus; Purple; Red Bay; Zamia.

ZEPHYRANTHES (Zephyr-lily; Rain-lily)

Fly, Narcissus Bulb. **Scale,** Brown Soft.

ZINNIA

Aphid, Bean; Corn Root.
Beetle, Asiatic Garden; Black Blister; Japanese (serious); Spotted Cucumber; White-fringed.
Borer, European Corn; Stalk.
Bug, Four-lined Plant; Garden Fleahopper; Tarnished Plant.
Leaf Cutter, Morning-glory. **Leafhopper,** Beet; Red-banded.
Leaf Roller, Red-banded. **Mealybug,** Long-tailed.

Mite, Broad; Cyclamen; Desert Spider; Two-spotted.
Nematode, Chrysanthemum Foliar; Spring Crimp.

ZIZYPHUS (Jujube)

Mealybug, Citrus.   **Mite,** Texas Citrus.
Scale, Lesser Snow; Cottony-cushion; Mining; Oriental; Pustule.

ZOYSIA

Nematode, Crownheaded Lance; Zoysia Spine.

LIST OF AGRICULTURAL EXPERIMENT
STATIONS IN THE UNITED STATES

Alabama: *Auburn*
Alaska: *Palmer*
Arizona: *Tucson*
Arkansas: *Fayetteville*
California: *Berkeley* 4
  Davis
  Riverside
Colorado: *Fort Collins*
Connecticut: *New Haven* 4
Delaware: *Newark*
Florida: *Gainesville*
Georgia: *Griffin*
Hawaii: *Honolulu* 10
Idaho: *Moscow*
Illinois: *Urbana*
Indiana: *Lafayette*
Iowa: *Ames*
Kansas: *Manhattan*
Kentucky: *Lexington* 29
Louisiana: *Baton Rouge* 3
Maine: *Orono*
Maryland: *College Park*
Massachusetts: *Amherst*
Michigan: *East Lansing*
Minnesota: *St. Paul* 8
Mississippi: *State College*
Missouri: *Columbia*

Montana: *Bozeman*
Nebraska: *Lincoln* 1
Nevada: *Reno*
New Hampshire: *Durham*
New Jersey: *New Brunswick*
New Mexico: *State College*
New York: *Geneva*
  Ithaca
North Carolina: *Raleigh*
North Dakota: *Fargo*
Ohio: *Wooster*
Oklahoma: *Stillwater*
Oregon: *Corvallis*
Pennsylvania: *University Park*
Puerto Rico: *Rio Piedras*
Rhode Island: *Kingston*
South Carolina: *Clemson*
South Dakota: *Brookings*
Tennessee: *Knoxville* 7
Texas: *College Station*
Utah: *Logan*
Vermont: *Burlington*
Virginia: *Blacksburg*
Washington: *Pullman*
West Virginia: *Morgantown*
Wisconsin: *Madison* 6
Wyoming: *Laramie*

GLOSSARY

Abdomen. The third, posterior, division of the insect's body.

Aerosol. An atomized fluid with very small particles, usually appearing as a fog or smoke.

Alternate Host. A second type of plant required for the completion of the life cycle of an insect.

Amphid. Sensory organ near the mouth of a nematode.

Antenna (pl. *antennae*). Paired segmented appendages, one on each side of the head, sometimes called "feelers."

Anus. The posterior opening of the alimentary tract.

Apterous. Wingless.

Asymmetrical. Not alike on the two sides.

Beak. The protruding mouth-part structure of a sucking insect; proboscis.

Bilateral Symmetry. With parts arranged more or less symmetrically on either side of a median vertical plane.

Brood. Individuals which hatch from the eggs laid by one mother, or individuals which hatch and normally mature at about the same time.

Buccal. Related to the cavity of the mouth; used for nematodes.

Bulb. Chief pumping-and-sucking structure of the nematode esophagus.

Caterpillar. Immature form—larva—of a moth, butterfly, or sawfly, having cylindrical body, well-developed head, thoracic legs, and abdominal prolegs.

Caudal. Near the tail.

Cephalothorax. United head and thorax, found in the Arachnida and Crustacea.

Cercus (pl. *cerci*). One of a pair of appendages at the end of the abdomen.

Chitin. A colorless, nitrogenous substance occurring in the outer layer of the body wall of arthropods.

Chrysalis (pl. *chrysalids*). The pupa of a butterfly.

Class. A subdivision of a phylum, containing a group of related orders.

Clypeus. A hardened plate on the lower part of the face, just above the labrum or upper lip.

Cocoon. A silken case inside which the pupa is formed.

Compatible. A material that can be used with another without counteracting or changing its effect.

Compound Eye. An eye composed of many individual elements, each represented externally by a facet.

Contact Poison. One which is effective on contact, as contrasted with a poison that must be swallowed.

Constricted. Narrowed.

Corium. The elongate, usually thickened, basal portion of the front wing, found in the Hemiptera.

Cornicle. One of a pair of dorsal tubes on the posterior part of the abdomen of aphids, secreting a waxy liquid.

Coxa (pl. *coxae*). The basal segment of the leg, by which it is joined to the body.

Crawler. The first active instar of a scale insect.

Crotchets. Hooked spines at tip of prolegs of caterpillars.

Cuticle. The non-cellular outer layer of the body wall.

Cyst. A sac or vesicle with an outer membrane but no opening; a resting stage of certain nematodes.

Deciduous. Having a part or parts that may fall off or be shed.

Diapause. A period of arrested development or suspended animation.

Diluent. Inert material used in the preparation of a spray or dust.

Dormant. Inactive, usually in winter; the term is applied to the host plant, the insect, or to the spray applied during the inactive period.

Dorsal. Pertaining to the back or upper side.

Dust. A finely divided or pulverized powder, applied dry.

Ectoparasite. A parasite that lives on the outside of its host.

Elytra (pl.). The thickened, leathery, or horny front wings of beetles, occasionally other insects.

Emergence. The act of an adult insect leaving the pupal case or last nymphal skin.

Endoparasite. A parasite that lives inside its host.

Esophagus. The narrow portion of the alimentary canal posterior to the mouth cavity.

Exoskeleton. A skeleton or supporting structure on the outside of the body.

Exuviae (always used in the plural). The cast skins of an arthropod.

Family. Subdivision of an order containing a group of related genera. Family names end in *idae*.

Femur (pl. *femora*). The third leg segment, between the trochanter and the tibia.

Filiform. Hairlike or threadlike.

Frass. Sawdust or wood fragments, made by a wood-boring insect, mixed with excrement.

Furcula. The forked springing apparatus of the Collembola, springtails.

Fusiform. Spindle-shaped; tapering at each end.

Gall. Abnormal growth of plant tissues caused by stimulus of an animal or another plant.

Gaster. Rounded part of the abdomen of an ant.

Generation. From any given stage in the life cycle to the same stage in the offspring.

Genus (pl. *genera*). A group of closely related species; the first capitalized name in a scientific binomial.

Glabrous. Smooth, without hairs.

Globose. Spherical or nearly so.

Gregarious. Living in groups.

Grub. Immature form—larva—of a beetle; thick-bodied with well-developed head, thoracic legs but no prolegs.

Haltère (or *halter*). A small, knobbed structure in place of the hind wings in the order Diptera, flies.

Head. The anterior body region, bearing eyes, antennae and mouth parts.

Hermaphroditic. Possessing both male and female sex organs.

Hibernation. A period of suspended animation in animals during seasonal low temperatures.

Honeydew. A sweet substance discharged from the anus of aphids, mealybugs, scales, and whiteflies.

Host Plant. Plant attacked by, or supporting, insects or diseases.

Hyperparasite. A parasite whose host is another parasite.

Inactivated. Made inactive or inefficient.

Instar. The form of an insect between successive molts. The first instar is the stage between hatching and the first molt.

Integument. The outer covering of the body.

Labium. The lower lip.

Labrum. The upper lip, just under the clypeus.

Lanceolate. Spear-shaped, tapering at each end.

Larva (pl. *larvae*). Immature form of an insect having complete metamorphosis. The name is also applied to the six-legged first instar of mites (Acarina).

Lateral. On or pertaining to the side.

Maggot. A legless wormlike larva, without a well-developed head; immature state of Diptera, flies.

Mandibles. The first or anterior pair of jaws.

Maxillae (sing. *maxilla*). The second pair of jaws, immediately posterior to the mandibles.

Mesothorax. The middle or second segment of the thorax.

Molt. A process of shedding the skin.

Nocturnal. Active at night, flying or feeding.

Nymph. The immature stage of an insect with incomplete metamorphosis, one that does not have a pupal stage; also the eight-legged immature stage of Acarina.

Ocellus (pl. *ocelli*). The simple eye of an insect or other arthropod.

Order. Subdivisions of a class, containing a group of related families.

Oviparous. Reproducing by laying eggs.

Ovipositor. Specialized organ in the female for depositing eggs.

Ovisac. An egg sac, conspicuous in mealybugs and some scale insects.

Palpus (pl. *palpi*). A segmented process borne by the maxillae or labium.

Parasite. An animal that lives in or on the body of another living animal, at least during part of its life cycle. Also, a plant living on or in another plant.

Parthenogenesis. Reproduction by development of unfertilized eggs.

Pedicel. The "waist," or stem, of the abdomen (between thorax and gaster) in ants; also second segment of the antenna.

Phasmid. Cuticular pouch near the posterior end of nematodes.

Phylum (pl. *phyla*). One of the major divisions of the animal kingdom.

Plumose. Featherlike.

Posterior. Hind or rear.

Predator. An animal which attacks and feeds on another animal.

Proboscis. Extended beaklike mouth parts.

Proleg. One of the fleshy "false" abdominal legs of a caterpillar.

Prothorax. First segment of the thorax.

Protonymph. Second instar of a mite.

Pubescent. Downy, covered with short fine hairs.

Pulvillus (pl. *pulvilli*). A soft pad or lobe beneath each tarsal claw.

Punctate. Pitted, with punctures.

Pupa (pl. *pupae*). Stage between the larva and adult in insects with complete metamorphosis; non-feeding, usually inactive.

Puparium (pl. *puparia*). The thickened, hardened last larval skin in which the pupa is formed in the Diptera, flies.

Pupate. Transform to a pupa.

Scavenger. An animal that feeds on dead plants or animals or decaying material.

Segment. A subdivision of the body or an appendage between joints.

Seta (pl. *setae*). A bristle.

Sessile. Attached directly without stem or petiole, incapable of moving from place to place.

Species. A group of individuals similar in structure and physiology, capable of interbreeding and producing fertile offspring, and differentiating in structure and physiology from other such groups.

Spinneret. Organ used in certain insects in making silk or spinning webs.

Spiracle. A breathing pore, external opening of the tracheal system.

Spiral. Winding, like the head of a screw.

Spray. A liquid dispersed in fine drops.

Stem Mother. Female aphid giving birth to living young without fertilization.

Stipe. A short stalk or support.

Striate. With grooves or depressed lines.

Stylet. A needlelike structure; in nematodes a protrusible spear used to puncture plants.

Systemic Insecticides. Compounds which, applied to soil or foliage, are absorbed by the plant, or translocated within it, rendering the sap toxic to certain insects.

Tarsus (pl. *tarsi*). The part of the leg beyond the tibia, consisting of one or more segments, bearing at the apex claws and pulvilli of the insect "foot."

Tegmina. Hard fore wings of grasshoppers.

Thorax. The body region behind the head, bearing legs and wings.

Tibia (pl. *tibiae*). The fourth segment of the leg, between the femur and the tarsus.

Tolerance. The amount of a spray or dust that can be left as residue on harvested fruits or vegetables without danger when they are used as food.

Trachea (pl. *tracheae*). A spirally ringed internal elastic air tube in insects, part of the respiratory system.

Trap Crop. A crop, usually planted in advance, to lure insects so they can be destroyed before attacking the desired crop.

Triungulin. The first instar larva of a blister beetle.

Trochanter. The second segment of the leg, between the coxa and femur.

Tubercle. A small rounded or knoblike protuberance.

Tympanum. A vibrating auditory membrane or eardrum; in grasshoppers.

Vector. A carrier of disease-producing fungi, bacteria, or viruses.

Vein. A thickened line in the wing.

Ventral. Pertaining to the lower side of the body.

Viviparous. Giving birth to living young, not egg-laying.

Vulva. Opening to the reproductive system in the female nematode.

SELECTED BIBLIOGRAPHY

Anderson, Roger F. *Forest and Shade Tree Entomology.* 428 pp. John Wiley &
Sons, Inc., New York, 1960.

Arnett, Ross H., Jr. *An Introduction to the Study of Beetles.* 40 pp. The Catholic
University of America Press, Washington, D.C., 1963.

Borror, Donald J., and Dwight M. DeLong. *An Introduction to the Study of Insects.* 1030 pp. Rinehart and Company, New York, 1954.
A fine textbook, not too complicated for the serious gardener.

Brues, Charles T., A. L. Melander, and Frank M. Carpenter. *Classification of In-
sects.* Bulletin of the Museum of Comparative Zoology at Harvard College,
Vol. 108. 917 pp. Cambridge, Mass., 1954.
For the taxonomic entomologist.

Cairns, E. J., Chairman. *Plant Nematology Notes* from Workshops at North Carolina State College in 1954 and Alabama Polytechnic Institute in 1955. 2nd
edition. Southern Regional Nematode Project (S-19), Auburn, Alabama,
1958.

Chitwood, B. G., and W. Birchfield. *Nematodes, their Kinds and Characteristics.*
49 pp. State Plant Board of Florida Vol. II, Bull. 9. Gainesville, 1956.

Clausen, C. P. *Biological Control of Insect Pests in the Continental United
States.* 151 pp. U. S. Department of Agriculture Tech. Bull. 1139. U. S.
Government Printing Office, Washington, D.C., 1956.

Christie, Jesse R. *Plant Nematodes, their Bionomics and Control.* 256 pp. Agricultural Experiment Stations, University of Florida, Gainesville, 1959.

Connecticut Agricultural Experiment Station. *Plant Pest Handbook.* Bull. 600.
194 pp. New Haven, Conn., 1956.

Conover, Herbert S. *Grounds Maintenance Handbook.* 2nd edition, 501 pp. F. W.
Dodge Corporation, New York, 1958.

Craighead, E. C. et al. *Insect Enemies of Eastern Forests.* U. S. Department of
Agriculture Misc. Publ. 657. 679 pp. U. S. Government Printing Office,
Washington 25, D.C., 1950.

Dimock, A. W. et al. *1963 Cornell Recommendations for Commercial Floriculture Crops.* 68 pp. New York State College of Agriculture, Ithaca, N.Y.,
1963.

Dowden, Philip B. *Parasites and Predators of Forest Insects Liberated in the
United States through 1960.* U. S. Department of Agriculture Agricultural
Handbook 226. 70 pp. U. S. Government Printing Office, Washington 25,
D.C., 1962.

Eberling, Walter. *Subtropical Fruit Pests.* 436 pp. University of California, Berkeley, Cal., 1959.

Essig, E. O. *Insects of Western North America.* 1035 pp. The Macmillan Company, New York, 1926.

My copy is dog-eared from constant use. The 1958 edition, *Insects and Mites of Western North America,* is not in my personal library.

Felt, Ephraim Porter. *Plant Galls and Gall Makers.* 364 pp. Comstock Publishing Company, Inc., Ithaca, N.Y., 1940.

Fisher, E. H., editor. *Entoma, a Directory of Pesticide Materials—Equipment—Services.* 335 pp. Entomological Society of America, Madison, Wisconsin, 14th edition, 1962.

Frear, D. E. H., editor. *Pesticide Index,* 193 pp. College Science Publishers, State College, Pa., 1961.

———. *Pesticide Handbook,* 312 pp. College Science Publishers, State College, Pa., 15th edition, 1963.

This edition lists 9487 pesticides.

Goetsch, Wilhelm. *The ants.* 173 pp. University of Michigan Press, Ann Arbor, Mich., 1957.

Graham, Kenneth. *Concepts of Forest Entomology.* 388 pp. Reinhold Publishing Corporation, New York, 1963.

Harding, Wallace C., Jr., and Warren T. Johnson. *Controlling Insects of Ornamental Shrubs and Trees.* University of Maryland Extension Service Bull. 168. 28 pp. College Park, Md., 1960.

Hopper, Bruce E., and Eldon J. Cairns. *Taxonomic Keys to Plant, Soil and Aquatic Nematodes.* Southern Regional Nematode Project (S-19). Auburn, Alabama, 1959.

Hutchison, M. T. et al. Plant Parasitic Nematodes of New Jersey. N. J. Agricultural Experiment Station Bull. 796. 32 pp. New Brunswick, N.J., 1961.

Jenkins, W. R., W. F. Mai, and G. J. Stessel. *A Review of Plant Nematology in the Northeastern United States,* 1956 to 1963. 30 pp. New Jersey Agricultural Experiment Station Bull. 805, New Brunswick, N.J., 1963.

Jenkins, W. R., et al. *Nematodes Associated with Crop Plants in Maryland.* University of Maryland Agricultural Experiment Station Bull. A-89. 25 pp. College Park, Md., 1957.

Keen, E. P. *Insect Enemies of Western Forests.* U. S. Department of Agriculture Misc. Publ. 273. 280 pp. U. S. Government Printing Office, Washington 25, D.C., 1952.

Kenaga, Eugene E. *Commercial and Experimental Organic Insecticides* (1963 Revision). Bull. of the Entomological Society of America Vol. 9, No. 2:67–103. 1963.

Klots, Alexander B., and Elsie B. Klots. *Living Insects of the World.* 304 pp. Doubleday & Company, Garden City, N.Y., 1959. Marvelous color photographs, fascinating text.

Laffoon, Jean L. *Common Names of Insects Approved by the Entomological Society of America.* Bulletin of the Entomological Society of America Vol. 6, No. 4:175–211. 1960.

Leonard, Mortimer Demarest. *A List of Aphids of New York.* Proceedings of Rochester Academy of Science Vol. 10, No. 6:289–432, Rochester, N.Y., 1963.

Lutz, Frank E. *Field Book of Insects.* 510 pp. G. P. Putnam's Sons, New York, 1935.

Mai, W. F., H. W. Chittenden, and W. R. Jenkins. *Distribution of Stylet-bearing Nematodes in the Northeastern United States.* New Jersey Agricultural Experiment Station Bull. 795. 62 pp. New Brunswick, N.J., 1961.

Mason, Hamilton. *Your Garden in the South.* 358 pp. D. Van Nostrand Company, Inc., Princeton, N.J., 1961.

Maxwell, Lewis S. *Handbook of Florida Insects and their Control.* 106 pp. Great Outdoors Publishing Co., Inc., St. Petersburg, Florida, 1959.

Merrill, G. B. A. *A Revision of the Scale-Insects of Florida.* State Plant Board of Florida Bulletin 1. 143 pp. Gainesville, Florida, 1953.

Metcalf, C. L. and W. P. Flint, rev. by R. L. Metcalf. *Destructive and Useful Insects.* 4th edition, 1087 pp. McGraw-Hill Book Company, Inc., New York, 1962.
Even more useful, if possible, than previous editions.

New England Section, Society of American Foresters. *Important Tree Pests of the Northeast.* 2nd edition, 191 pp. Evans Printing Company, Concord, N.H., 1952.

Palmer, Miriam A. *Aphids of the Rocky Mountain Region.* 452 pp. Thomas Say Foundation. Vol. V, 1952.

Pirone, Pascal P., Bernard O. Dodge, and Harold W. Rickett. *Diseases and Pests of Ornamental Plants.* 3rd edition, 775 pp. The Ronald Press Company, New York, 1960.
Helpful to gardeners and to those who advise them.

Pirone, P. P. Tree Maintenance. 483 pp. Oxford University Press, New York, 1959.

Pratt, Robert M. *Florida Guide to Citrus Insects, Diseases and Nutritional Disorders in Color.* 191 pp. Agricultural Experiment Station, Gainesville, Fla., 1958.

Pritchard, A. Earl, and Edward W. Baker. *Revision of the Spider Mite Family Tetranychidae,* 472 pp. Pacific Coast Entomological Society, San Francisco, Cal., 1955.

Reed, L. B., and S. P. Doolittle. *Insects and Diseases of Vegetables in the Home Garden.* U. S. Department of Agriculture Home and Garden Bulletin No. 46. 48 pp. U. S. Government Printing Office, Washington 25, D.C., Rev. 1963.

Riddick, Eloise. *A List of Florida Plants and the Scale-Insects Which Infest Them.* State Plant Board of Florida Bulletin 7. 78 pp. Gainesville, Fla., 1955.

Rutgers, the State University. *1963 Pesticides for New Jersey.* 122 pp. College of Agriculture, New Brunswick, N.J., 1963.

Schuder, Donald L. *Insect Pests of Shade Trees and Shrubs.* Purdue University Mimeo E–41. 36 pp. Lafayette, Ind., 1962.

Smith, Floyd F. *Controlling Insects on Flowers.* U. S. Department of Agriculture Agric. Inf. Bull. 237. 78 pp. U. S. Government Printing Office, Washington 25, D.C., 1962.

————. *Control of Insect Pests of Greenhouse Vegetables.* U. S. Department of Agriculture Handbook 142. 25 pp. U. S. Government Printing Office, Washington 25, D.C., 1959.

Steiner, G. *Plant Nematodes the Grower Should Know.* State of Florida Department of Agriculture Bull. 131. 47 pp. Tallahassee, Fla., 1956.

Swain, Ralph B. *The Insect Guide*. 261 pp. Doubleday & Company, Inc., Garden City, N.Y., 1952.

U. S. Department of Agriculture. *Insects*. The Yearbook of Agriculture, 1952. 780 pp. U. S. Government Printing Office, Washington 25, D.C., 1952.

————. *Insecticide Recommendations of the Entomology Division for the Control of Insects Attacking Crops and Livestock*. Agric. Handbook 120. 152 pp. U. S. Government Printing Office, Washington 25, D.C., 1963.

————. Forest Insect Conditions in the United States; in 1960; in 1961. Forest Service, U. S. Department of Agriculture, Washington, D.C., 1961; 1962.

Watkins, John V., and Herbert S. Wolfe. *Your Florida Garden*. 319 pp. University of Florida Press, Gainesville, Fla., 1954.

Weidhaus, John A., et al. *Cornell Recommendations for Trees and Shrubs*. 31 pp. New York State College of Agriculture, Ithaca, N.Y., 1962.

Weigel, C. A., and L. G. Baumhofer. *Handbook on Insect Enemies of Flowers and Shrubs*. U. S. Department of Agriculture Misc. Publ. 626. 115 pp. U. S. Government Printing Office, Washington 25, D.C., 1948.

Westcott, Cynthia. *Are You Your Garden's Worst Pest?* 305 pp. Doubleday & Company, Inc., Garden City, N.Y., 1961.

————, ed. *Handbook on Pests and Diseases*. 96 pp. Brooklyn Botanic Garden. Brooklyn, N.Y., 1955.

————. *Handbook on Biological Control of Plant Pests*. 97 pp. Brooklyn Botanic Garden, Brooklyn 25, N.Y.

Zim, Herbert S., and Clarence Cottam. *Insects*. 160 pp. Golden Press, N.Y., Rev., 1956.

A useful paperback with 225 species in full color.

The publications that come regularly to my desk include: *Agricultural Chemicals; American Fruit Grower; Arborist's News; Bulletin of the Entomological Society of America; Cooperative Economic Insect Report* (from the Plant Pest Control Division of the U. S. Department of Agriculture); *Farm Journal; Farm Research* (New York Agricultural Experiment Station); *Frontiers of Plant Science* (Connecticut Agricultural Experiment Station); *The Garden Journal* (New York Botanical Garden); *Journal of Economic Entomology; NAC News* (National Agricultural Chemicals Association); *National Gardener* (National Council of State Garden Clubs); *National Shade Tree Conference Proceedings* (the Conference is now International); *New Jersey Agriculture;* New Jersey *Insect-Disease Newsletter;* New York *Insect & Disease Report; Plant Disease Reporter* (from U. S. Department of Agriculture, Crops Research Division); *Plants & Gardens* (Brooklyn Botanic Garden); *The Exchange* (formerly Florist's Exchange); and *Trees Magazine*. I also receive most of the popular garden magazines, publications from state garden clubs, from manufacturing chemists, and from many state experiment stations and universities. I have made extensive use of material from the State Plant Board of Florida and the University of Florida, from the University of California, Cornell University, Rutgers, the State University (New Jersey), Purdue University (Indiana), and the University of Maryland.

I am indebted to many individuals in the U. S. Department of Agriculture, but I am particularly grateful to Kelvin Dorward of the Plant Pest Control Division through whose good offices I receive the weekly *Cooperative Economic Insect Report*. This has been of great assistance in deciding which pests are important enough to be included in the *Bug Book*, in keeping me up-to-date on new insects and on the frequent changes in insect names. More help on names has come from Louise M. Russell, W. H. Anderson, and E. W. Baker of the Entomology Research Division. For many years Floyd Smith, also of this division, has patiently answered my questions on insects of ornamental plants; A. L. Taylor, of the Crops Research Branch, has kept me well supplied with literature on nematodes; and Elizabeth Mason has sent pertinent publications from the U. S. Forest Service. I have also made good use of hundreds of popular bulletins and circulars ordered from the U. S. Government Printing Office.

Although my graduate work was at Cornell University (not in Entomology) and I continue to ask help from many friends there, during my many years in New Jersey, Rutgers became a more constant source of information. I can single out here for special thanks only Bailey B. Pepper, head of the Department of Entomology, and W. R. Jenkins, nematologist, who has kindly reviewed the nematode section of this manual. More thanks go to Neely Turner, John C. Schread, and Raimon L. Beard of the Connecticut Experiment Station for publications and aid over many years.

The final tribute goes to my editor, Clara Claasen, for persuading Doubleday & Company that yet another edition of the *Bug Book* is justified.

INDEX

Boldface numerals indicate line drawings; plate numbers refer to color illustrations following pages 290 and 314.

Abbott's sphinx, 294
Abbreviated wireworm, 433
Abelia, 437
Abies, 490
Abrus precatorius, 538
Abutilon, 437
  moth, 294
Acacia, 437
  psyllid, 334
  whitefly, 428
Acalymma trivittata, 131
  vittata, 127
Acalypha, 437
Acanthocinus spectabilis, 151
Acantholyda erythrocephala, 413
Acanthomyops claviger, 51
Acanthopanax, 437
Acanthoscelides obtectus, 416
Acaridae, 279
Acer, 514
  negundo, 456
Aceratagallia sanguinolenta, 242
Aceria ajugae, 281
  camelliae, 282
  caryae, 287
  erinea, 291
  essigi, 288
  fagerinea, 280
  ficus, 284
  fraxinivorus, 279
  granati, 288
  litchii, 286
  mangiferae neocynodonis, 280

  paradianthi, 282
  sheldoni, 281
  vaccinii, 280
Achatodes zeae, 141
Achemon sphinx, 294
Acheta assimilis, 210
Achillea, 559
Achras sapota, 541
Acleris minuta, 205
  variana, 159
Aconite, 438
Aconitum, 438
Acrididae, 232
Acrobasis betulella, **185**
  caryae, 186
  indigenella, 239
  juglandis, 186
  vaccinii, 230
Acronicta americana, 294
  lepusculina, 297
  oblinita, 309
Acrosternum hilare, 170
Actebia fennica, 217
Actias luna, 304
Actinidia, 438
Actinidia polygama, 543
Aculus atlantazaleae, 280
  cornutus, 287
  fockeui, 288
  lycopersici, 290
  schlectendali, 279
  teucrii, 285
Acuminate scale, 350
Acyrthosiphon barri, 69
  dirhodum, 75
Adaleres weevil, 415
Adalia bipunctata, 114
Adelphocoris lineolatus, 163

  rapidus, 174
  superbus, 176
Adenophorea, 316
Adephaga, 88
Adoretus sinicus, 97
Adoxus obscurus, 338
Aechemia, 438
Aegeria apiformis, 302
Aegeriidae, 292
Aeolothripidae, 395
Aerosol bomb, 26, **27**
Aesculus, 457, 502
African-daisy, 493
African-lily, 438
African-violet, 438
Agapanthus, 438
Agasphaerops nigra, 422
Agave, 438, 467
Ageratum, 438
Aglaeonema simplex, 470
Agonoderus lecontei, 122
Agrimonia, 438
Agrimony, 438
Agrilus anxius, 137
  bilineatus, 158
  cephalicus, 141
  cristatus, 177
  difficilis, 144
  liragus, 138
  rubicola, 153
  ruficollis, 153
  sinuatus, 155
Agriotes lineatus, 115
  mancus, 434
Agromyza artemisiae, 256
  parvicornis, 251
Agromyzidae, 223
Agrotis gladiaria, 217
  ipsilon, 217

malefida, 217
  orthogonia, 217
Ailanthus, 438
  webworm, 410
Air plant, 457
Ajuga, 438
Akebia, 439
Akee, 439
Alaska spruce beetle, 92
Alaus oculatus, 102
Albizzia, 439
Albizzia julibrissin, 516
Alcathoe caudata, 139
Alder, 439
  aphid, 55
  bark beetle, 92
  blight aphid, 55, 81
  flea beetle, 92
  lace bug, 163
  psyllid, 334
  spittlebug, 391
Aldrin, 11
Alebra albostriella, 243
Aleurites fordii, 553
  moluccana, 463
Aleurocanthus woglumi, 428
Aleuroplatus berbericola, 428
  coronatus, 429
Aleyrodes inconspicua, 431
  kelloggi, 431
  nephrolepidis, 429
  pruinosa, 432
Aleyrodidae, 427
Alfalfa, 439
  aphid, 55
  butterfly, 181
  caterpillar, 188
  looper, 188
  plant bug, 163
  snout beetle, 92
  webworm, 410
  weevil, 415
Allamanda, 439
Allantus cinctus, 340
Allegheny spruce beetle, 92
Allethrin, 11
Allium, 521
  ascalonicum, 543
  sativa, 492

Almond, 440
  mite, 282
Alniphagus aspericollis, 92
Alnus, 439
Aloe, 440
Alsophila pometaria, 183
Alstroemeria, 440
Alternanthera, 440
Althaea rosea, 500
Altica ambiens, 92
  canadensis, 120
  chalybea, 105
  ignita, 126
  sylvia, 96
  torquata, 126
  ulmi, 101
Alypia octomaculata, 298
Alyssum, 440
Amaranth, 440
Amaranthus, 440
Amaryllis, 441
Amathes C-nigrum, 218
Amazon-lily, 441
Ambrosia beetles, 92
Ambush bugs, 163
Amelanchier, 543
Ameloeca myron, 310
American aspen beetle, 92
American dagger moth, 294
American dagger nematode, 318
American grasshopper, 233
American maple aphid, 55
American plum borer, 135
American poplar bark aphid, 73
American walnut aphid, 80
Ametastegia glabrata, 341
  pallipes, 349
Amorbia essigana, 188
Ampeloglypter ater, 144
  aesostris, 144
Ampelopsis, 441
Ampelopsis brevipedunculata, 554
Amphicercidus flocculosus, 68
  pulverulens, 76
Amphicerus bicaudatus, 136

Amphidasis cognataria, 389
Amphimallon majalis, 102
Amphorophora crataegi, 68
  crystelae, 68
  geranii, 64
  nervata, 75
  ribiella, 61, 71
  rubi, 74
  rufomaculatum, **71**
  sonchi, 76
Anabrus simplex, 210
Anacampsis fragariella, 260
Anacardium, 465
Anagrapha falcifera, 190
Ananas, 530
Anarsia lineatella, 150
Anasa armigera, 172
  tristis, 175
Anastrepha ludens mombinpraeoptans, 230
Anavitrinella pampinaria, 389
Ancanthomyops interjectus, 50
Anchusa, 441
Ancylis comptana fragariae, 259
Andira, 441
Andromeda, 441
  lace bug, 164
Anemone, 441
Anethum graveolens, 484
Angelin-tree, 441
Angels-trumpet, 482
Anguina, 316
  agrostis, 318
  tritici, 331
Angular-winged katydid, **237**
Anise-tree, 441
Anisomorpha buprestoides, 405
Anisota rubicunda, 194
  senatoria, 198
  stigma, 202
  virginiensis, 200
Annelida, 219
Annona cherimola, 468
  glabra, 533

muricata, 544
reticulata, 480, 505
squamosa, 548
Annual cicada, 207
Anobiidae, 119
Anomala oblivia, 118
orientalis, 44, 117
Anomis erosa, 294
Anophothrips obscurus, 399
Anoplodera nitens, 139
Ant(s), 43, 46, **47**
Allegheny mound, 48
Argentine, 48
big-headed, 48
black carpenter, 48
California harvester, 49
cornfield, 49
crazy, 49
fire, 49
Florida carpenter, 49
Florida harvester, 49
imported fire, 49
larger yellow, 50
little black, 50
little fire, 50
odorous house, 50
pavement, 50
pharaoh, 50
pyramid, 50
red harvester, 50
silky, 51
smaller yellow, 51
southern fire, 51
Texas leaf-cutting, 51
thief, 51
western harvester, 51
western thatching, 51
Antheraea polyphemus, 307
Anthericum, 442
Anthicidae, 88
Anthocoridae, 162
Anthonomus eugenii, 424
grandis, 417
thurberiae, 426
hirsutus, 424
musculus, 419
scutellaris, 119
signatus, 425
Anthophila paraiana, 260
Anthurium, 442

Anticarsia gemmatilis, 204
Antidesma, 442
Antigonum, 475
Antirrhimum, 544
Antispila nysaefoliella, 256
Antlered maple caterpillar, 202
Ant-lion, **46**
Antonina crawi, 357
graminis, 378
Anuraphis bakeri, 59
cardui, 79
helichrysi, 68
maidiradicis, 60
persicaeniger, 57
rosea, 75
tulipae, 79
viburnicola, 76
viburniphila, 79
Aonidia shastae, 383
Aonidiella aurantii, 354
citrina, 384
orientalis, 373
taxus, 350
Apamea amputatrix, 218
Aphelenchidae, 316
Aphelenchoidea, 316
Aphelenchoides, 316
besseyi, 330
fragariae, 327
olesistus, 327
oryza, 330
ritzema-bosi, 320
Aphelenchus, 316
Aphid(s), 51, **52, 54**
alder, 55
alder blight, 55
American maple, 55
American poplar bark, 73
American walnut, 80
apple, 55
apple grain, 55
arborvitae, 55
artemisia, 55
artichoke, 71
aster, 55
aucuba, 56
azalea, 56
balsam woolly, 56
bamboo, 56
banana, 56

barberry, 56
bean, 56, Plate **I**
beech, 56
beech blight, 57
birch, 57
black and red rose, 74
blackberry, 57
black cherry, 57
black citrus, 57
black cloudy-winged poplar, 73
black-margined, 57
black peach, 57
black pecan, 58
black polished spruce, 77
black willow, 81
bow-legged fir, 58
boxelder, 58
brown ambrosia, 58, 69
brown spirea, 77
buckthorn, 58
cabbage, 58
California-laurel, 59
Canadian fleabane, 59
ceanothus, 59
chokecherry, 59
chrysanthemum, 59
clear-winged aspen, 73
clear-winged cottonwood leaf, 73
cloudy-winged cottonwood leaf, 73
clover, 59
columbine, 59
Cooley spruce gall, 59, 60, Plate **II**
coreopsis, 60
corn leaf, 60
corn root, 60
cotton, 69
cowpea, 61
crapemyrtle, 61
crescent-marked lily, 61
currant, 61
cypress, 61
dark brown spruce, 77
delphinium, 62
dock, 62
dogberry, 62
dogwood, 62
Douglas-fir, 62

574 INDEX

eastern spruce gall, 62, 63, Plate II
elder, 63
elm cockscomb gall, 63
elm leaf, 63
elm sack gall, 64
English grain, 64
evening primrose, 71
European birch, 57
European raspberry, 74
European walnut, 80
geranium, 64
giant bark, 64
giant willow, 65
Gillette's blue grass, 65
goldenglow, 65
goldenrod, 65
gooseberry witchbroom, 65
grape phylloxera, 65
grapevine, 66
green and brown pine needle, 72
greenbug, 66
green and pink willow, 67
green gooseberry, 66
green peach, 66, 67
green spruce, 67
grindelia, 67
hairy rose, 75
hawthorn, 67
hawthorn, 67
hemispherical juniper, 68
hemlock woolly, 67
hickory, 64
hollyhock, 67
honeysuckle and parsnip, 67
hop, 68
horsemint, 68
ivy, 68
juniper, 68
larch, 68
larkspur, 62
leaf-curl ash, 68
leaf-curl plum, 68
lettuce, 69
lettuce root, 69
light brown spruce, 77
lily, 69
linden, 69

little black-and-green willow, 81
little black-veined aster, 69
locust, 69
long-beaked clover, 67
lupine, 69
malaheb cherry, 69
manzanita leaf-gall, 69
maple leaf, 81
mealy plum, 69
melon, 69, Plate I
mint, 70
Monell's sumac, 70
Monterey-pine, 70
Norway-maple, 70
oak, 71
oat bird-cherry, 71
oenothera, 71
oleander, 71
oleaster-thistle, 71
orchid, 71
ornamental currant, 61, 71
ornate, 71
painted maple, 71
pale chrysanthemum, 71
palm, 71
pea, 71
pine, 72
pine bark, 72
pine leaf, 72
polygonum, 75
poplar, 73
poplar leaf-petiole gall, 73
poplar leaf-purse, 73
poplar petiole gall, 72
poplar sugar-beet root, 73
poplar twig gall, 73
poplar vagabond, 73
potato, 73, Plate II
powdery pine needle, 72
powdery spruce, 77
privet, 74
pulverulent snowberry, 76
purple-spotted lily, 74
raspberry, 74
red and black cherry, 74
reddish brown poplar, 73

rhododendron, 74
Rocky Mountain juniper, 68
Russian-olive, 75
rusty plum, 75
sand lily, 75
sedum, 76
small green rose, 74
snowball, 76, Plate II
snowberry, 76
solanum root louse, 76
sowthistle, 76
spinach, 66
spiny witch-hazel gall, 81
spirea, 77
spotted alfalfa, 77
spotted poplar, 73
spotted spruce, 77
spotted-winged raspberry, 74
spruce, 77
spruce gall, 53
strawberry, 78
sugar-beet root, 78
sumac gall, 78
sunflower, 62, 78
sweetclover, 78
sycamore, 79
thistle, 79
tulip leaf, 79
tuliptree, 79
turnip, 79
variable currant, 61
viburnum 79
violet, 80
walnut, 62, 80
waterlily, 80
western aster root, 80
white-pine, 80
wild geranium, 64
willow, 80
witch-hazel leaf gall, 81
woolly alder, 81
woolly apple, 81
woolly elm, 82
woolly elm bark, 82
woolly hawthorn, 82
woolly honeysuckle, 82
woolly larch, 82
woolly pear, 82
woolly pine needle, 72

yellow clover, 82
yellow rose, 82
Aphididae, 52
Aphinae, 52
Aphis abbreviata, 58
  abietina, 77
  asterensis, 69
  ceanothi, 59
  cerasifoliae, 59
  coreopsidis, 60
  cornifoliae, 62
  craccivora, 61
  debilicornis, 78
  fabae, 56
  feminea, 74
  forbesi, 78
  gossypii, 69
  hederue, 68
  helianthi, 62
  illinoisensis, 66
  impatientis, 68
  maculatae, 73
  medicaginis, 61
  nasturtii, 58
  neogillettei, 62
  nerii, 71
  oenotherae, 71
  pomi, 55
  pseudohederae, 68
  ribiensis, 61
  ribi-gillettei, 61
  rociadae, 62
  rubicola, 74
  rubifolii, 57, 74
  rumicis, 62
  saliceti, 67
  sambucifoliae, 63
  sanborni, 66
  sedi, 76
  sensoriata, 74
  solidaginifoliae, 65
  spiraecola, 77
  spiraephila, 77
  varians, 61
Aphrophora parallela, 392
  saratogensis, 392
Apion longirostre, 420
  ulicis, 420
Apium graveolens var.
    dulce, 467
    var. *rapaceum*, 467
Apocrita, 406

Apple, 442
  -and-thorn skeletonizer,
    260
  aphid, 55
  bark borer, 136
  curculio, 212
  flea weevil, 415
  fruit fly, 264
  fruit moth, 294
  grain aphid, 55
  leaf blotch miner, 247
  leaf-curling midge, 273
  leafhopper, 241
  leaf skeletonizer, 260
  leaf trumpet miner, 247
  maggot, 264, Plate XXV
  mealybug, 268
  red bug, 164
  rust mite, 279
  seed chalcid, 407
  sucker, 334
  twig beetle, 92
  twig borer, 136
  worm, 298
Apricot, 443
Aquilegia, 475
Argus tortoise beetle, 92
Argyrotaenia citrana, 198
  juglandana, 258
  mariana, 258
  pinatubana, 307
  velutinana, 259
Arabis, 444
Arachis hypogea, 525
Arachnida, 39, 278
Aradidae, 162
Aralia, 444
Aramite, 11
Arathane, 16
Araucaria, 444
  scale, 350
Arborvitae, 444
  aphid, 55
  sawfly, 339
  soft scale, 363
  weevil, 415
Arbutus, 445
  menziesi, 512
  unedo, 548
Archips argyrospila, 257
  cerasivoranus, 203
  fervidanus, 413

  rosaceanus, 258
Archodontes melanopsis,
    147
Arctiidae, 292
Arctostaphylos, 451
Arcythosiphon pelargonni,
    64
Ardisia, 445
Ardisia paniculata, 515
Argentine ant, 48
Argentine ant bait, 48
Arge pectoralis, 339
Argyresthia conjugella,
    294
  cupressella, 298
  thuiella, 247
*Argyrotoxa semipurpu-
    rana*, 258
Arion ater, 385
Aristolochia, 485
Arizona pine beetle, 92
Armadillidium vulgare, 388
Armoracia, 502
Army cutworm, 216
Armyworm(s), 82, 83
  beet, 83
  fall, **83**
  lawn, 84
  semitropical, 84
  southern, 84
  western yellow-striped,
    84
  yellow-striped, 84
Aroga websteri, 202
Arrhenodes minutus, 148
Artemisaphis artemisicola,
    55
Artemisia, 445
  aphid, 55
  gall midges, 274
  scale, 350
Arthropoda, 38
Artichoke, globe, 445
Artichoke, Jerusalem, 445
Artichoke aphid, 71
  plume moth, 295
Artocarpus, 456
Ascia omonuste, 195
Asciodes gordialis, 189
Asclepias, 445, 458
Ash, 445
  bark beetle, 92

borer, 136, 146
flower-gall mite, 279
lace bug, 164
plant bug, 165
tingid, 164
Ash-gray blister beetle, 92
Asiatic beetle, 117
Asiatic garden beetle, 44,
  Plate IX
Asiatic oak weevil, 416
Asiatic red scale, 350
Asilidae, 223
Asimina triloba, 524
Asiphum pseudo-byrsum,
  73
Asparagus, 446
  beetle, 93, Plate III
  miner, 247
Asparagus fern, 446
  caterpillar, 83
Asparagus plumosus, 446
Aspen, 533
  blotch miner, 248
  leaf beetle, 94
  leaf miner, 248
Asphondylia opuntiae, 274
Aspidiotus ancylus, 377
  brittanicus, 368
  californicus, 352
  camelliae, 365
  cyanophylli, 359
  destructor, 356
  forbesi, 364
  hederae, 372
  howardi, 368
  ithacae, 368
  juglans-regiae, 384
  lataniae, 369
  osborni, 373
  ostreaeformis, 362
  oxycoccus, 359
  perniciosus, 379
  pseudospinosus, 379
  uvae, 365
Aspidistra, 446
Assassin bugs, 163
Assonia, 447
Aster, aphid, 55, 71
  leafhopper, 245
Aster, China, 447
  perennial, 447

Asterolecanium arabidis,
  376
  bambusae, 351
  minus, 376
  pustulans, 377
  puteanum, 368
  variolosum, 365
Astilbe, 447
Atarsos grindelliae, 67
Atomizer sprayer, **26**
Atteva aurea, 410
Atylenchus, 316
Aucuba, 447
  aphid, 56
Audibertia, 540
Augomonoctenus libocedri,
  340
Aulacaspis rosae, 379
Australian honeysuckle,
  450
Australian lady beetle, 5,
  113
Australian-pine, 447
  borer, 136
Australian silk-oak, 447,
  496
Australian sod fly, 224
Autographa californica, 188
Automeris io, 303
Autoplusia egena, 261
Autoserica castanea, 44, 93
Avocado, 448
  brown mite, 279
  caterpillar, 188
  leaf roller, 256
  mealybug, 270
  red mite, 280
  whitefly, 428
Awl nematodes, 318
Azalea, 448
  aphid, 56
  bark scale, 350
  caterpillar, 188
  lace bug, **165**
  leaf miner, 248
  leaf roller, 248
  mealybug, 268
  mite, 280
  stem borer, 136
  whitefly, 428
Azobenzene, 11

Baccharis, 497
Bachelors-button, 477
Bacillus thuringiensis, 5, 11
Bagworm(s), 84, 85, Plate
  III
  moths, 294
Bait, Argentine ant, 48
  cutworm, 216
Baker's mealybug, 271
Baliosus ruber, 248
Balsam, garden, 449
Balsam-apple, 449
Balsam-fir, 449
  sawfly, 339
Balsam gall midge, 274
  twig aphid, 56
  woolly aphid, 56
Balsamorhiza, 449
Balsam-root, 449
  root mite, 280
Bamboo, 449
  aphid, 56
  mite, 280
  scale, 351
Bambusa, 449
Banana, 449
  aphid, 56
  root borer, 136
Banana-shrub, 450
Banded alder borer, 136
Banded cucumber beetle,
  94
Banded greenhouse thrips,
  396
Banded hickory borer, 137
Banded sunflower moth,
  295
Banded thrips, 395
Banded-wing whitefly, 428
Banded wood snail, 386
Banded woollybear, 188,
  Plate XX
Banks grass mite, 280
Banksia, 450
Banyan, 450
Barbados-cherry, 513
Barbara colfaxiana, 298
Barberry, 450
  aphid, 56
  scale, 351
  webworm, 410
  whitefly, 428

Baris confinis, 107
Bark beetle(s), 91, Plate X
  alder, 92
  cedar, 96
  coarse-writing, 119
  hickory, 107
  native elm, 116, Plate X
  northern cedar, 117
  olive, 117
  smaller European elm,
    Plate X
  western balsam, 130
  western cedar, 130
Barnacle scale, 351
Barthrin, 11
Basket-of-gold, 440
Basswood, 450, 510
  lace bug, 166
  leaf miner, 248
  leaf roller, 256
  looper, 196
Bauhinia, 450
Bay, loblolly, 450
  sweet, 450
Bayberry, 450
Bean, 451
  aphid, 56
  jassid, 243
  leaf beetle, 94
  leaf roller, 257
  leaf skeletonizer, 261
  thrips, 396
  stalk weevil, 416
  weevil, 416, Plate
    XXXV
Bearberry, 451
Beard-tongue, 527
Beauty-berry, 462
Beauty-bush, 451
Beauty-leaf, 452
Bedellia orchilella, **255**
  somnulentella, 253
Bee(s), 43, 85
  carpenter, 86
  leaf-cutter, **86**
  small carpenter, **86,** 87
Beech, 452
  aphid, 56
  blight aphid, 57
  leaf tier, 262
  mite, 280
  scale, 351

Beet, 452
  armyworm, 83
  leaf beetle, 94
  leafhopper, 241, Plate
    XXIV
  leaf miner, 248
  mite, 280
  webworm, 410
Beetle(s), 87, **88**
Alaska spruce, 92
  alder bark, 92
  alder flea, 92
  alfalfa snout, 92
  Allegheny spruce, 92
  American aspen, 92
  argus tortoise, 92
  Arizona pine, 92
  ash bark, 92
  ash-gray blister, 92
  Asiatic garden, Plate IX
  asparagus, 93, Plate IV
  aspen leaf, 94
  Australian lady, **113**
  banded cucumber, 94
  bark, 91
  bark-gnawing, 91
  bean leaf, 94
  beet leaf, 94
  birch bark, 94
  black-bellied clerid, 94
  black blister, **94,** 95
  Black Hills, 95
  black lady, 95
  black-legged tortoise, 96,
    Plate XI
  black turpentine, 96
  blister, 90
  blueberry flea, 96
  bumble flower, 96
  cabbage flea, 96
  California five-spined ips,
    96
  caragana blister, 96
  carrion, 91
  carrot, 96
  cedar bark, 96
  cereal leaf, 97
  checkered, 89
  cherry leaf, 97
  Chinese rose, 97
  clematis blister, 97, Plate
    V

  click, 90, 432
  Colorado pine, 97
  Colorado potato, 97
  Columbian timber, 98
  convergent lady, **113,**
    114
  corn flea, 98
  corn sap, 98
  corn silk, 98
  cottonwood leaf, 98
  cranberry, 99
  Cuban May, 99
  darkling, 91, 99
  desert corn flea, 99
  diabrotica, 99
  Douglas-fir, 99
  Douglas-fir engraver, 99
  dried-fruit, 100
  dusky sap, 100
  eastern larch, 100
  eastern spruce, 100
  eggplant flea, 100, Plate
    VII
  elephant, 121
  elm calligrapha, **100**
  elm flea, 101
  elm leaf, **100,** 101, Plate
    VI
  Engelmann spruce, 102
  engraver, 91
  European chafer, 102
  European ground, 102
  European spruce, 102
  eyed click, 102
  false potato, 102
  false powder post, 89
  fig, 103
  fir engraver, 103
  flat bark, 89
  flea, 103
  flower, 91
  fruitworm, 89
  Fuller rose, **104**
  fungus, 89
  giant stag, 105
  golden buprestid, 105
  golden tortoise, 105
  goldsmith, 105
  grain, 91
  grape bud, 105
  grape colaspis, 105

grape flea, 105, Plate VII
grapevine hoplia, 108
gray willow leaf, 106
green June, 106, Plate XI
green rose chafer, 106
ground, 88, 102, **106**
hackberry engraver, 107
helenium snout, 107
hickory bark, 107
hickory saperda, 108
hister, 90
imbricated snout, 108
imported willow leaf, 108, Plate XI
iris blister, 109
Japanes, **109**, Plate VIII
Jeffrey pine, 111
June, 111, Plate VIII
Kapra, 112
Kalamath weed, 112
lady, 89, 112, **113**
ladybird, 112
larger elm leaf, 114
leaf, 89
linden leaf, **100**
lined click, 115
lion, 115
lizard, 90
lodgepole cone, 115
lodgepole-pine, 115
long-horned, 89
margined blister, 115, Plate V
May, 111
mealybug destroyer, 114
Mexican bean, 115, Plate IX
mint flea, 116
Monterey-pine cone, 116
Monterey-pine engraver, 116
mottled tortoise, 116
mountain pine, 116
native elm bark, 116, Plate X
net-winged, 90
northeastern sawyer, 116
northern cedar, 117
northern masked chafer, 117

obtuse sawyer, 117
oedermerid, 91
olive bark, 117
Oregon fir sawyer, 117
oriental, 117
owl, 102
Pacific willow leaf, 118
pale-striped flea, **104**, 118, Plate VII
peach bark, 118
pine chafer, 118
pine colaspis, 118
pine engraver, 118
piñon cone, 119
pitted ambrosia, 119
plum gouger, 119
potato flea, **104**, 119, Plate VII
powder post, 90, 119
prairie flea, 120
red-legged flea, 120
red milkweed, 120
red spider destroyer, 120
red turnip, 120
red turpentine, 120
red-winged pine, 120
rhabdopterus, 120
rhinoceros, 121, Plate XI
rose chafer, 121, Plate XI
rose leaf, 122
roundheaded pine, 122
rove, 91
sap, 90
scarab, 91
seed, 89
seed-corn, 122
silver fir, 122
sinuate-striped flea, 122
Sitka spruce, 122
skin, 90
smaller European elm bark, 122 Plate X
smaller Mexican pine, 123
snout, 89
soldier, 89
southern masked chafer, 117
southern pine, 123

southern pine sawyer, 124
southwestern pine, 124
spinach carrion, 124
spinach flea, 124, Plate VII
spotted asparagus, 124, Plate IV
spotted blister, 125
spotted cucumber, **125**, Plate XII
spotted grapevine, 126
spotted pine, 126
squash, 126
stag, 90
steel-blue flea, 126
steel-blue lady, 126
strawberry flea, 126
striped ambrosia, 127
striped blister, 127, Plate V
striped cucumber, **125**, 127, Plate XII
striped flea, 128, Plate VII
striped tortoise, 128
sugar-pine cone, 128
sunflower, 128
sweetpotato leaf, 128
syneta leaf, 128
ten-lined June, 128
three-lined potato, 128
three-striped blister, 129
tiger, 88
tobacco flea, 129
toothed flea, 129
tortoise, **129**
transverse lady, 129
tuber flea, 129
tumbling flower, 90
twice-stabbed lady, 114
two-spotted lady, 114
watercress leaf, 130
waterlily leaf, 130
unicorn, 121
western balsam bark, 130
western black flea, 130
western cedar bark, 130
western fruit, 128
western pine, 130, Plate X

western potato flea, 131
western spotted cucumber, 131
western striped cucumber, 131
western striped flea, 131
white-banded ash, 92
white-fringed, **131**
white-pine cone, 132
white-spotted sawyer, 132
yellow-margined leaf, 132
Begonia, 453
Belamcanda, 454
Beleodorus, 316
Bella moth, 295
Bellows duster, **35**, 36
Belonolaimus, 314, 329
gracilis, 325, 329
longicaudatus, 329
Beloperone, 543
Bellyache bush, 475
Bembecia marginata, 152
Bemisia tabaci, 432
Bentgrass nematode, 318
Benzene hexachloride, 11, 16
Benzoin aestivale, 545
Berberis, 450
Bergamot, 453
Bermuda grass mite, 280
Bermuda-grass scale, 352
Berytidae, 162
Beta, 452, 550
Betula, 453
BHC, 11
Bichloride of mercury, 11
Bidens, 545
Bidrin, 11
Big-headed ant, 48
Big-legged plant bug, 166
Bignonia, 453
Billbergia, 453
Billbug(s), 133
bluegrass, 133
maize, 133
southern corn, 133
Binapacryl, 11
Biological control, 4
Birch, 453
aphids, 57

bark beetle, 94
casebearer, 185
lace bug, 166
leaf miner, **248**, 249
sawfly, 339
skeletonizer, 261
tube maker, 185
Bird-of-paradise, 454, 548
Bischofia, 454
Bishopwood, 454
Bittersweet, 454
Bixa, 511
Black and red rose aphid, 74
Black araucaria scale, 352
Black army cutworm, 217
Black-bellied clerid, 94
Blackberry, 454
aphid, 57
bud mite, 280, 284
knot-gall wasp, 454
leaf miner, 249
mite, 288
psyllid, 334
sawfly, 339
Blackberry-lily, 454
Black blister beetle, 44, **94, 95**
Black carpenter ant, 48
Black cherry aphid, 57
Black cherry fruit fly, 224
Black citrus aphid, 57
Black cloudy-winged poplar aphid, 73
Black cutworm, 217
Black elm bark weevil, 416
Blackfly, citrus, 428
Black-headed ash sawfly, 340
Black-headed budworm, 159
Black-headed fireworm, 189
Black Hills beetle, 95
Black-horned pine borer, 137
Black-horned tree cricket, 209
Black lady beetle, 95
Black Leaf 40, 12, 18
Black-legged tortoise beetle, 96, Plate XI

Black-margined aphid, 57
Black peach aphid, 57
Black pecan aphid, 58
Black pine leaf scale, 352
Black polished spruce aphid, **77**
Black scale, 352
Black swallowtail, 191
Black thread scale, 353
Black turpentine beetle, 96
Black vine weevil, 416, Plate XXXV
Bladafume, 12
Bladan, 12
Bladdernut, 455
Blaniulus guttulatus, 278
Bleeding-heart, 455
Blennocampa caryae, 346
Blighia sapinda, 439
Blissus leucopterus, 167
hirtus, 170
insularis, 170
Blister beetles, 90. *See also under* Beetle(s)
Blister mites, 279
Bluebell, 463
Blueberry, 455
bud mite, 280
flea beetle, 96
leaf roller, 232
spittlebug, 391
stem-gall wasp, 408
thrips, 396
Bluegrass billbug, 133
Bluegrass webworm, 411, 414
Blue horntail, 235
Blue sage, 540
Blue-sided tent caterpillar, 190
Blunt-nosed cranberry leafhopper, 242
Boehmeria, 455
Boisduval's scale, 353
Boll weevil, 417
Bollworm(s), 133
pink, 133
Bomb, aerosol, 26, **27**
Boreal mite, 280, 291
Borer(s), 45, 134
American plum, 135
apple bark, 136

580 INDEX

apple twig, 136
ash, 136
Australian-pine, 136
azalea stem, 136
banana root, 136
banded alder, 136
banded hickory, 137
black horned pine, 137
boxelder twig, 137
branch and twig, 137
broad-necked root, 137
bronze birch, 137
bronze poplar, 138
burdock, 138
California   flatheaded,
    138
carpenterworm, **138,** 139
cedar tree, 139
chestnut bark, 139
chestnut   timberworm,
    139
clematis, 139
clover root, 139
clover stem, 140
columbine, 140
cottonwood, 140
cranberry girdler, 140
currant, 140
currant stem, 140
dendrobium, 140
dogwood, 140
dogwood cambium, 141
dogwood twig, 141
elder, 141
elder shoot, 141
elm, 141
European   corn,   Plate
    XIII
flatheaded   apple   tree,
    142, 143, Plate XIV
flatheaded   cherry   tree,
    143
flatheaded cone, 143
flatheaded fir, 143
gall-making maple, 144
giant apple, 138
grape cane gall marker,
    144
grape cane girdler, 144
grape root, 144
grape trunk, 144
hemlock, 144

honeylocust, 144
iris, 144, Plate XV
larger shot-hole, 145
lesser cornstalk, 145
lesser peach tree, 145
lilac, 146, Plate XV
lima-bean pod, 146
lima-bean vine, 146
linden, 146
little   carpenterworm,
    147
live-oak root, 147
locust, 147
mangrove, 136
maple, 148
maple callus, 148
maple petiole, 148
nautical, 148
oak sapling, 148
oak timberworm, 148
orchid bulb, 148
Pacific flatheaded, 148
painted hickory, 149
peach tree, 149, Plate
    XVI
peach twig, 150
pear fruit, 150
pecan, 150
pecan   carpenterworm,
    150
persimmon, 150
pigeon tremex, 150
pitch mass, 150
ponderosa-pine   bark,
    151
poplar, 151
poplar-and-willow, 151
potato stalk, 151
potato tuberworm, 151
raspberry cane, 152
raspberry crown, 152
red-headed ash, 153
red-necked cane, 153
rhododendron, 153
root collar, 153
rose stem girdler, 153
roundheaded apple tree,
    153, Plate XIV
roundheaded cone, 154
roundheaded fir, 154
roundheaded wood, 89
rustic, 154

sapwood   timberworm,
    154
sculptured pine, 154
seagrape, 154
shot-hole, **155**
sinuate pear tree, 155
southwestern corn, 156
squash vine, 156, Plate
    XVI
stalk, 156
strawberry crown, 157
sugarcane, 157
sugar-maple, 157
sweetpotato root, 426
sycamore, 158
tiger hickory, 158
tile-horned prionus, 158
tobacco stalk, 158
turpentine, 158
twig girdler, 158
twig pruner, 158
two-lined chestnut, 158
western cedar, 159
western larch round-
    headed, 159
western peach tree, 159
white-pine shoot, 159
wood, 89
Boston ivy, 504
Bostrichidae, 89, 119
Bothynus gibbosus, 96
Bottle-brush, 455
Bougainvillea, 455
    caterpillar, 189
Bourletiella hortensis, 393
    Bouvardia, 455
Bow-legged fir aphid, 58
Boxelder, 456
    aphid, 58
    bug, **166,** 167
    leaf roller, 257
    psyllid, 334
    twig borer, 137
Boxorange, 543
Boxwood, 456
    leaf miner, **249**
    mite, 280
    psyllid, **335**
    spiral nematode, 318
    webworm, 411
Boysenberry, 456

Brachyrhinus cribricollis, 420
ligustici, 92
meridionalis, 422
ovatus, 425
sulcatus, 416
Brachystola magna, 233
Braconidae, 406
Braconids, **406**
Bramble leafhopper, 242
Branch and twig borer, 137
Brentidae, 89, 148
Brentid beetles, 80
Brassica, 518
canlorapa, 506
oleracla, 457
var. *acephala,* 474, 506
var. *botrytis,* 466
var. *gemmifera,* 457
rapa, 554
Brazilian pepper-tree, 456
Breadfruit, 456
Brevicoryne brassicae, 58
symphoricari, 76
Brevipalpus californicus, 286
lewisi, 282
obovatus, 288
orchidii, 286
phoenicis, 282
Bristly cutworm, 217
Bristly rose-slug, 340, Plate XXXII
Broadbean, 457
weevil, 418
Broad mite, 281
Broad-necked root borer, 137
Broad-winged katydid, 237
Broad-winged thrips, 395
Broccoli, 457
Bromeliad, 457
Bromethane, 18
Bromofume, 12
Bronze apple tree weevil, 418
Bronze birch borer, 137
Bronzed cutworm, 217
Bronze poplar borer, 138

Broom, 457
Broom, Scotch, 457
Broussonetia, 457
Browallia, 457
Brown ambrosia aphid, 58, 69
Brown garden snail, 386
Brown-headed ash sawfly, 340
Brown mite, 282
Brown soft scale, 353
Brown spirea aphid, 77
Brown stink bug, 167
Brown-tail moth, 295
Brown wood borer, 138
Bruce spanworm, 389
Bruchophagus gibbus, 408
Bruchus brachialis, 426
pisorum, 423
rufimanus, 418
Brunfelsia, 457
Brussels sprouts, 457
Bryobia praetiosa, 282
rubrioculus, 285
Bryophyllum, 506
Bucculatrix ainsliella, 261
canadensisella, 261
Bucket pump, 29
Buckeye, 457
Buck moth, 295
Buckthorn, 458
aphid, 58
Bud and leaf nematode, 320
Buddleia, 458
moth, 296
Bud moth(s), 159
eye-spotted, 159
holly, 160
larch, 160
lesser, 160
pecan, 160
spruce, 160
verbena, 162
Budworm (s), 45, 159
black-headed, 159
Jack-pine, 160
rose, 160
spruce, **161**
tobacco, 161
Buffaloberry, 458
Buffalo treehopper, **403**

Bug(s), 162
ambush, 163
andromeda lace, 164
apple red, 164
assassin, 163
boxelder, **166,** 167
chinch, 167, Plate XVII
consperse stink, 168
coreid, 162
cotton stainer, 168
damsel, 163
dark apple red, 164
false chinch, 168
flat, 162
flower, 162
four-lined plant, 168, **169**
fungus, 162
garden fleahopper, 169, Plate VII
hairy chinch, 170, Plate XVII
harlequin, **171**
lace, 163, **165**
leaf, 163
leaf-footed, **172**
lygaeid, 163
lygus, 172
masked hunter, 173
minute pirate, 162
negro, 173
pameras, 173
plant, 163
royal palm, 175
small milkweed, 175
spined soldier, 175
squash, 175, Plate XII
stilt, 162
stink, 163
tarnished plant, 176, Plate V
western chinch, 177
western leaf-footed, 177
wheel, 177
Buginvillaea, 455
Bugle bud mite, 281
Bugleweed, 438
Bulan, 12
Bulb and stem nematode, 328
Bulb mite, 281
Bulb scale mite, 281

Bumble flower beetle, 96
Bumelia, 458
  fruit fly, 224
Buprestidae, 89
Buprestis aurulenta, 105
  apricans, 158
Burdock borer, 138
Burrowing nematode, 318
Bursera simaruba, 497
Buttercup, 458
Butterfly(flies), 43, 178
  California tortoise-
    shell, 179
  checker-spot, 179
  clouded sulfur, 180
  hackberry empress, 180
  harvester, 180
  monarch, 180
  mourning-cloak, **180**
  orange sulfur, 181
  painted beauty, 181
  painted lady, 181
  pine, 181
  pipevine swallowtail, 181
  red-admiral, 181
  spice-bush   swallowtail,
    182
  tiger swallowtail, 182
  viceroy, 182
  western parsley, 182
  western swallowtail,
    182
  zebra, 182
  zebra swallowtail, 182
Butterfly bush, 458
Butterfly-flower, 542
Butterfly-pea, 458
Butternut, 458
  curculio, 212
  woollyworm, 340
Buttonbush, 459
Buxus, 456
Byturidae, 89
Byturus bakeri, 232
  rubi, 231

Cabbage, 459
  aphid, 58
  curculio, 213
  cyst nematode, 319
  flea beetle, 96
  looper, 189

  maggot,   264,   Plate
    XXVI
  seedpod weevil, 418
  seedstalk curculio, 213
  webworm, 411
Cabbage-tree, 441
Cacopaurus, 314
  epacris, 319
  pestis, 325
Cactus, 459
  cyst nematode, 319
  fruit gall midge, 274
  scale, 354
Caenurgina   crassiuscula,
    191
Caesalpinia, 460
Cajeput, 460
Calabash, 460
Caladium, 460
Calaphis betulella, 57
  betulae-colens, 57
Calathea, 460
Calceolaria, 460
Calcium arsenate, 12
Calcium cyanide, 12
Calendula, 460
Calico scale, 354
California ash mirid, 165
California casebearer, 185
California Christmasberry,
    461
California coffeeberry, 461
California dagger nema-
    tode, 319
California five-spined ips,
    96
California flatheaded bor-
    er, 138
California green lacewing,
    239
California harvester ant,
    49
California horntail, 235
California-laurel, 461
  aphid, 59
  borer, 137
California meadow nema-
    tode, 319
California-nutmeg, 461
California oakworm, 189,
    190
California pear-slug, 340

California   pepper-tree
  chalcid, 408
California-poppy, 461
California red scale, 354
California sessile nema-
    tode, 319
California tent caterpillar,
    190
California   tortoise-shell,
    179
Caliroa cerasi, 346
  lineata, 346
Calla, 461
Calliandra, 462
Callicarpa, 462
Callidium antennatum var.
  hesperum, 137
Calligrapha scalaris, 100
Callipus lactarius, 278
Callistemon, 455
Callistephus, 447
Callisto geminatella, 256
Callopistris floridensis, 193
Callosamia promethea, 307
Callosobruchus maculatus,
    419
Calluna, 499
Calomel, 12
Calomycterus setarius, 421
Calonyction, 516
Calophya californica, 337
  flavida, 337
  nigripennis, 337
  triozomima, 337
Calopitrimerus vitis, 285
Calosoma candidum, 102
  frigidum, 107
  sycophanta, 102
Calophyllum, 452
Calpodes ethlius, 258
Calycanthus, 462
Cambala annulata, 278
Cambium curculio, 213
Camel cricket, 209
Camellia, 462
  bud mite, 282
  mining scale, 355
  parlatoria, 355
  scale, 355
Cameraria   cincinnatiella,
    252
  hamadryadella, 254

Camnula pellucida, 233
Camphor scale, 355
  thrips, 396
Camphor-tree, 463
Camponotus abdominalis floridanus, 49
  ferrugineus, 50
  pennsylvanicus, 48
Campsis radicans, 553
Campylenchia latipes, 404
Canadian fleabane aphid, 59
Candleberry-tree, 463
Candlenut, 463
Candytuft, 463
Cankerworm(s), 182
  fall, **183**, Plate XVIII
  spring, **183**, 184
Canna, 463
Cantaloupe, 463
Canterbury bells, 463
Cantharidae, 89
Cape-honeysuckle, 463
Cape-jasmine, 463, 492
Cape-marigold, 463
Capitophorus braggii, 71
  hippophaes, 75
  ribis, 61
  shepherdiae, 75
Capsicum, 527
Carabidae, 106
Caragana, 463
  blister beetle, 96
  plant bug, 167
Caraway, 464
Carbaryl, 12
Carbon disulfide, 12
Carbon tetrachloride, 12
Carbophenothion, 12
Cardinal-flower, 464
Carica papaya, 523
Carissa, 464
Carnation, 464
  maggot, 265
  mite, 282
  pin nematode, 319
  tip maggot, 265
Carnocephala flaviceps, 247
Carob, 464
Carolina grasshopper, 233
Carolina mantis, 267

Carolina spiral nematode, 319
Carpenter bee, 86, 87
Carpenterworm, **138**, 139
  moths, 292
Carpinus, 501
Carpocapsa pomonella, 296
Carpoglyphidae, 279
Carpoglyphus lactis, 284
Carpophilus dimidiatus, 98
  hemipterus, 100
  lugubris, 100
Carrion beetles, 91
Carrot, 464
  beetle, 96
  rust fly, 224
  weevil, 418
Carya, 500
  pecan, 526
Casebearer(s), 184, 185, 292
  birch, 185
  birch tube maker, 185
  California, 185
  cherry, 185
  cigar, 185
  larch, 185
  pecan cigar, 186
  pecan leaf, 186
  pecan nut, 186
  pistol, 186, **187**
Cashew, 465
Casimiroa, 541
Cassava, 465
  scale, 356
Cassia, 465
Cassida bivittata, 128
Castanea, 469
Castileja, 503
Castor-bean, 465
Casuarina, 447
Catalina cherry, 465
  moth, 193
Catalpa, 465
  midge, 274
  mealybug, 270
  sphinx, 296
Caterpillar(s), 43, 45, **187**
  alfalfa, 188
  alfalfa looper, 188

  avocado, 188
  azalea, 188
  banded woollybear, 188, Plate XXV
  black-headed fireworm, 189
  blue-sided tent, 190
  bougainvillea, 189
  cabbage looper, 189
California oakworm, 189, **190**
  California tent, 190
  celery looper, 190
  celeryworm, 191, Plate XIX
  chain-spotted geometer, 191
  clover head, 191
  clover looper, 191
  convict, 191
  cross-striped cabbage-worm, 192
  eastern tent, 192, Plate XVIII
  false hemlock looper, 192
  filbertworm, 193
  fir cone looper, 193
  Florida fern, 193
  forest tent, 193
  garden tortrix, 198
  genista, 194
  grapevine looper, 194
  Great Basin tent, 194
  green cloverworm, 194
  green-striped maple-worm, 194
  Gulf white cabbage-worm, 195
  hemlock looper, 195
  hickory horned devil, 195
  hickory shuckworm, 195
  imported cabbageworm, 196, Plate XXVI
  large aspen tortrix, 196
  linden looper, 196
  melonworm, 196, Plate XXXVI
  Monterey-pine looper, 197
  navel orangeworm, 197
  okra, 294

oleander, 197
omnivorous, 197
orange-dog, 198
orange-humped maple-worm, 198
orange-striped oakworm, 198
orange tortrix, 198
palmerworm, 199
phantom hemlock, 199
phigalia looper, 199
pickleworm, 199, Plate XXXVI
pine looper, 200
pink scavenger, 200
pink-striped oakworm, 200
poplar tent maker, 200
prairie tent, 200
pumpkin, 200
purple-backed cabbage-worm, 200
puss, 200
range, 201
red-humped, 201, Plate XX
red-necked peanutworm, 201
saddleback, 202
saddled prominent, 202
sagebrush, 202
salt-marsh, 202
Schizura, 202
southern cabbageworm, 202
spiny elm, **180**, 181
spiny oakworm, 202
stinging rose, 203
striped garden, 203
sweetpotato, 84
tent, 293
tomato pinworm, 203
ugly-nest, 204
unicorn, 203
variable oak leaf, 203
velvetbean, 204
walnut, 204
western hemlock looper, 204
western oak looper, 204
western tent, 205

yellow-headed fireworm, 205
yellow-necked, 205
yellow woollybear, 205
zebra, 205
Catnip, 466
Cattail, 466
Cattleya fly, 229
midge, 274
weevil, 419
Cauliflower, 466
Caulocampus acericaulis, 148
Cavariella aegopodii, 81
essigi, 81
Ceanothus, 466
aphid, 59
clearwing, 296
lace bug, 167
spittlebug, 391
Ceanothus americanus, 519
Cecidomyia balsamicola, 274
catalpae, 274
psilaspis, 290
resinicoloides, 276
ribis, 283
viticola, 275
Cecidomyiidae, 223
Cecropia moth, 296
Cedar, 466
bark beetle, 96
cone sawfly, 340
tree borer, 139
Cedar, incense, 467
Cedrus, 466
Celastrus, 454
Celeriac, 467
Celerio lineata, 310
Celery, 467
leaf tier, 262
looper, 190
Celeryworm, 191
Celosia, 474
Celtis, 497
Centaurea, 477
Centipede (s), 39, **206**
garden, 39, **206**
Century plant, 467
Cepaea nemoralis, 386
Cephalanthus, 459
Cephalosporium lecanii, 350

Cephalotaxus, 467
Cephidae, 234, 339
Ceramica picta, 205
Cerambycidae, 89
Cerasphorus albofasciatus, 144
cinctus, 137
Cerataphis lataniae, 68
orchidearum, 68, 71
variabilis, 68, 71
Ceratina spp., 87
Ceratitis capitata, 226
Ceratomia amyntor, 299
catalpae, 296
Cercis, 537
Cercocarpus, 517
Cercopidae, 390
Cereal leaf beetle, 97
Ceriman, 467
Ceropegia, 467
Ceroplastes cirripediformis, 351
floridensis, 364
rubens, 378
Cerotoma trifurcata, 94
Cestrum, 505
Ceutorhynchus assimilis, 418
quadridens, 213
rapae, 213
Chaenomeles, 505
Chaetanaphorthrips orchidii, 401
Chaetocnema ectypa, 99
pulicaria, 98
Chaff scale, 356
Chain-spotted geometer, 191
Chaitophorus populifoliae, 73
populellus, 73
viminalis, 81
Chalcididae, 406
Chalcidoidea, 406
Chalcids, 406
Chalcodermus aeneus, 213
Chalcophora angulicollis, 154
Chalice-vine, 468
Chamaecyparis, 468, 538
Chamber's dagger nema-tode, 320
Changa, 210

Chaste-tree, 468
Chayote, 448
Checkered beetle, 89
Checker-spot butterfly, 179
Cheiranthus, 556
Chelymorpha cassidea, 92
Chemicals, 5, 8, 9, 22
Chenille plant, 437
Cherimoya, 468
Chermes abietis, 62
  cooleyi, 59
  laricatus, 78
  piceae, 56
  strobilobius, 78, 82
  tsugae, 67
Chermidae, 52, 53
Cherminae, 53
Cherry, 468
  casebearer, 185
  curculio, 213
  fruit fly, 224
  fruit sawfly, 340
  fruitworm, 230
  leaf beetle, 97
  maggot, 265
  slug, 346
Cherry, flowering, 469
  Japanese, 469
  sand, 469
Cherry-laurel, 469
Cherry-tree tortrix, 203
Chestnut, 469
  bark borer, 139
  timberworm, 139
Chick pea, 470
Chilocorus stigma, 114
Chilopoda, 39, 206
China aster, 447
Chinaberry, 470
China-fir, 480
Chinch bug, 167, Plate
  XVII
Chinese evergreen, 470
Chinese lantern, 470
Chinese mantis, 267
Chinese rose beetle, 97
Chinese silk-plant, 455
Chionanthus, 491
Chionaspis americana, 360
  caryae, 368
  corni, 360
  furfura, 380
  quercus, 372

salicis-nigrae, 384
Chion cinctus, 137
Chionodoxa, 470
Chlorbenside, 12
Chlordane, 12
Chlorobenzilate, 12
Chlorochroa sayi, 175
Chloropicrin, 12, 231
Chloropidae, 223
Choisya, 470
Chokecherry, 470
  aphid, 59
Cholus cattleyae, 419
Choristoneura conflictana,
  196
  fumiferana, 161
  pinus, 160
Chorizagrotis auxiliaris,
  216
Chortophaga viridifasciata,
  233
Christie's spiral nematode,
  320
Christie's stubby root nem-
  atode, 320
Chromaphis juglandicola,
  80
Chryptophagidae, 89
Chrysanthemum, 471
  aphid, 59
  foliar nematode, 320
  gall midge, 274, Plate
  XXVIII
  lace bug, 168
  leaf miner, 250
  thrips, 397
Chrysanthemum balsamita,
  477
  frutescens, 515
  leucanthemum, 482
  maximum, 482
Chrysididae, 406
Chrysidoidea, 406
Chrysobothris femorata,
  143
  mali, 148
  tranquebarica, 136
Chrysolina spp., 112
Chrysomela crotchi, 94
  scripta, 98
Chrysomelidae, 89, 103
Chrysomphalus aonidum,
  363

dictyospermi, 359
  mimosae, 371
  obscurus, 372
  perseae, 378
  personatus, 370
  rossi, 352
  tenebricosus, 365
Chrysopa californica, 239
  oculata, 238
Chrysophana placida var.
  conicola, 143
Chrysophyllum, 541
  cainito, 547
Chrysopidae, 238
Chufa, 471
Cicada(s), 207
  dogday, 207
  periodical, 208
Cicada killer, 408
Cicadellidae, 241
Cicadidae, 207
Cicer, 470
Cichorium, 487
Cicindellidae, 88
Cigar casebearer, 185
Cigarette plant, 480
Cigarflower, 480
Cimbex americana, 341
Cimbicidae, 339
Cimbicid sawflies, 339
Cinara spp., 72
  braggi, 77
  curvipes, 58
  engelmanniensis, 77
  fornacula, 67
  occidentalis, 64
  palmerae, 77
  piceicola, 77
  pseudotaxifoliae, 62
  sabinae, 68
  splendens, 62
  strobi, 80
  tujafilina, 55
Cineraria, 471
Cinerin I, II, 13, 20
Cingilia catenaria, 191
Cinnamomum camphora,
  463
  zeylandicum, 472
Cinnamon-tree, 472
Cinnamon vine, 472
Cinquefoil, 472, 534
Circulifer tenellus, 241

Cirsium, 552
Cistus, 538
Citheronia regalis, 195
Citheroniidae, 292
Citricola scale, 356
Citron, 472
Citrophilus mealybug, 268
Citrullus vulgaris, 557
Citrus, 472
  blackfly, 428
  bud mite, 281
  flatid planthopper, 333
  flat mite, 282
  mealybug, **269**
  nematode, 320
  red mite, 282
  ring nematode, 321
  root weevil, 419
  rust mite, 282
  snow scale, 356
  spine nematode, 321
  thrips, 397
  tree snail, 386
  whitefly, 428
Citrus aurantifolia, 510
  bergamia, 453
  limonia, 508
  medica, 472
  nobilis, 551
Cladius isomerus, 340
Clarkia, 473
Clastoptera achatina, 391
  arborina, 392
  arizona, 392
  elongatus, 392
  lawsoni, 392
  obtusa, 391
  proteus, 391
  vittata, 391
  xanthocephala, 392
Clay-back cutworm, 217
Clear-winged aspen aphid, 73
Clear-winged cottonwood leaf aphid, 73
Clear-winged grasshopper, 233
Clearwing moths, 292
Cleft-headed spanworm, 389
Clematis, 473

blister beetle, 97, Plate XXVIII
  borer, 139
Clepsis peritana, 198
Cleridae, 89
Clerodendrum, 473
Click beetles, 90, 432
Climbing cutworm, 218
Clitoria, 458
Clivina impressifrons, 122
Cloaked knotty horn, 141
Clockvine, 552
Clouded sulfur, 180
Cloudy-winged cottonwood leaf aphid, 73
Cloudy-winged whitefly, 429
Clover, 473
  aphid, 59
  cutworm, 217
  cyst nematode, 321
  head caterpillar, 191
  leafhopper, 242
  leaf weevil, 419
  looper, 191
  mite, 282
  root borer, 139
  root curculio, 213
  rootworm, 105
  seed chalcid, 408
  seed weevil, 419
  stem borer, 140
  weevil, 419
Cnephasia longana, 263
Cnidocampa flavescens, 306
Coarse-writing bark beetle, 119
Cobb's awl nematode, 321
Cobb's lance nematode, 321
Cobb's meadow nematode, 321
Cobb's ring nematode, 321
Cobb's spiral nematode, 321
Cobb's stubby root nematode, 321
Coccidae, 349
Coccinella transversoguttata, 129
Coccinellidae, 89, 112
Coccolobis uvifera, 542

Coccus acuminatus, 350
  elongatus, 370
  hesperidum, 352
  pseudomagnoliarum, 356
  viridis, 366
Cocklebur billbug, 133, 419
Cocklebur weevil, 419
Cockscomb, 474
Coconut, 474
  mealybug, 270
  scale, 356
Codiaeum, 479
Codling moth, 2, 296, Plate XXV
Coffea, 474
Coffee, 474
Coffeeberry, 474
Coffeeberry, California, 461
Coiled rose worm, 340
Coix lacryma-jobi, 505
Coleman's mealybug, 270
Coleophora caryaefoliella, 186
  laricella, 185
  limosipennella, 185
  malivorella, 186
  occidentis, 185
  pruniella, 185
  sacramenta, 185
  salmani, 185
Coleophoridae, 184, 292
Coleoptera, 43, 88, 212, 415, 432
Coleus, 474
Colias eurytheme, 188
  philodice, 180
  eurytheme, 181
Collandonus clitellarius, 245
  montanus, 243
Collembola, 43, 392
Colopha ulmicola, 63
Coloradia pandora, 306
Colorado pine beetle, 97
Colorado potato beetle, 8, 97, Plate IV
Columbia Basin wireworm, 433
Columbian timber beetle, 98

Columbine, 475
 aphid, 59
 borer, 140
 leaf miner, 250, **251**
 skipper, 179
Common milkweed bug, 175
Composite thrips, 397
Compressed air sprayer, **26**, 28
Comptonia asplenifolia, 549
Comstock mealybug, 270
Conoderus falli, 434
 vespertinus, 434
Coneflower, 540
Confederate jasmine, 475
Confederate rose, 475
Conifer sawflies, 339
Coniodes plumogeraria, 390
Coniontis subpubescens, 99
Conoderus amplicollis, 434
Conopthorus coniperda, 132
 contortae, 115
 edulis, 119
 lambertianae, 128
 ponderosae, 119
 radiatae, 116
Conotrachelus affinis, 213
 anaglypticus, 213
 crataegi, 215
 juglandis, 212
 nenuphar, 214
 retentus, 212
Consperse stink bug, 168
Continuous sprayer, 28
Contarinia johnsoni, 275
 juniperina, 275
 oregonensis, 275
 pyrivora, 276
Control methods, 4, 5, 6, 8
Convallaria, 510
Convergent lady beetle, **113**, 114
Convict caterpillar, 191
Convolvulus, 517
 leaf miner, 253

Cooley spruce gall aphid, 59, **60**, Plate II
Cooperia, 475
Copper-leaf, 437
Coptodisca arbutiella, 304
 slendoriferella, 308
Coral bean, 475
Coralbells, 475
Coralberry, 475
Coral-plant, 475
Coral tree, 475
Coral-vine, 475
Cordia, 492
Coreidae, 162
Coreid bugs, 162
Coreopsis, 476
 aphid, 60
Corimelaena pulicaria, 173
Cork tree, 476, 529
Corn, 476
 blotch leaf miner, 251
 earworm, 221, Plate XIII
 flea beetle, 98
 leaf aphid, 60
 leafhopper, 333
 meadow nematode, 321
 planthopper, 333
 root aphid, 60
 root webworm, 411
 sap beetle, 98
 silk beetle, 98
 spindleworm, 141
 stem weevil, 419
Cornaphis populi, 73
Cornfield ant, 49
Cornflower, 477
Cornus, 484
Corrosive sublimate, 13, 17
Corylus, 490, 498
Coryhucha arcuata, 173
 celtidis, 170
 ciliata, 176
 cydoniae, 171
 incurvata, 177
 juglandis, 177
 marmorata, 168
 mollicula, 178
 obliqua, 167
 pallipes, 166
 pergandei, 163

ulmi, 168
Corythylus columbianus, 98
 punctatissimus, 119
Cosmopepla bimaculata, 174
Cosmopolites sordidus, 136
Cosmopterygidae, 292
Cosmos, 477
Cossidae, 292
Cossula magnifica, 150
Costmary, 477
Cotalpa lanigera, 105, 174
Cotinus coggyria, 543
 nitida, 106
 texana, 103
Cotoneaster, 477
 webworm, 411
Cotton aphid, 61, 69
 bollworm, 221
 cutworm, 84
 leaf perforator, 261
 root-knot nematode, 321
 stainer, 168
Cottonwood, 477, 533
 borer, 140
 dagger moth, 297
 leaf beetle, 98
Cottony bamboo scale, 357
Cottony cochineal scale, 357
Cottony-cushion scale, 2, 4, **357**
Cottony maple scale, 358, Plate XXXIV
Cottony peach scale, 358
Cottony pine scale, 358
Cottony taxus scale, 358
Coulee cricket, 210
Cowpea, 477
 aphid, 61
 curculio, 213
 pod-weevil, 213
 weevil, 419
Crabapple, ornamental, 477
Crambidae, 292
Crambus spp., 414
 bonifatellus, 414
 caliginosellus, 411
 maritima, 542
 sperryellus, 414
 teterellus, 411, **414**

topiarius, 140
vulvivagellus, 414, 415
Cranberry, 478
  beetle, 99
  fruitworm, 230
  girdler, 140
  rootworm, 337
  spanworm, 398
  sparganothis, 232
  spittlebug, 391
  tipworm midge, 275
  weevil, 419
  worm, 189, 205
Cranberry, high-bush, 478
Crank duster, 34
Crapemyrtle, 478
  aphid, 61
Craponius inaequalis, 213
Crassula, 478
Crataegus, 498
Crazy ant, 49
Creeping fig, 489
Cremona cotoneaster, 411
Crescentia cujete, 460
Crescent-marked lily aphid, 61
Cress, garden, 478
Cressonia juglandis, 310
Cribrate weevil, 420
Cricket(s), 43, 209
  black-horned tree, 209
  camel, 209
  changa, 210
  coulee, 210
  field, 210
  four-spotted tree, 210
  Jerusalem, 210
  Mormon, 210
  northern mole, 211, Plate XXI
  snowy tree, 211, Plate XXI
  southern mole, 212
Criconema, 325, 314
  civellae, 321
  decalineatum, 323
  spinalineatum, 331
Criconematidae, 314, 318, 325, 327, 329
Criconemoides, 314, 325
  citri, 321
  ornatus, 275

similis, 321
Crimp, 330
Crinkled flannel moth, 297
Crioceris asparagi, 93
  duodecimpunctata, 124
Crocus, 479
Croesus latitarsus, 341
Crophius bohemani, 173
Cross-striped cabbage-worm, 192
Cross vine, 453
Crotalaria, 479
Croton, 479
Crownbeard, 555
Crown-headed lance nematode, 322
Crown-of-thorns, 488
Crown whitefly, 429
Crustacea, 39, 388
Crymodes devastator, 217
Cryolite, 13
Cryptococcus fagi, 351
Cryptolaemus montrouzieri, 114
Crytophyllaspis liquidambaris, 381
Ctenicera aeripennis aeripennis, 434
  glauca, 433
  pruinina, 434
Cuban-laurel thrips, 397
Cuban May beetle, 99
Cube, 13
Cuckoo wasps, 406
Cucujidae, 89
Cucumber, 479
Cucumis melo, 515
  sativus, 479
Cucurbita, 495, 535
  maxima, 546
Cue-lure, 13
Cultural control, 6
Cunninghamia, 480
Cuphaea, 480
Cupressus, 481
Curculio(s), 89, 212
  apple, 212
  black walnut, 212
  butternut, 212
  cabbage seedstalk, 213
  cambium, 213
  cherry, 213

clover root, 213
cowpea, 213
grape, 213
hickory-nut, 213
plum, 214, Plate XXII
quince, 215
rhubarb, 215
rose, 215, Plate XI
Curculio auriger, 425
  obtusus, 420
  proboscideus, 422
  uniformis, 420
Curculionidae, 89, 212, 415
Curled rose sawfly, 340, Plate XXXII
Curlew bug, 133
Currant, 480
  aphid, 61
  borer, 140
  bud mite, 283
  fruit fly, 225
  fruit weevil, 420
  spanworm, 389
  stem borer, 140
Custard-apple, 480, 505
Cutworm(s), 215, **216**
  army, 216
  black, 217
  black army, 217
  bristly, 217
  bronzed, 217
  clay-back, 217
  clover, 217
  cotton, 84
  dark-sided, 217
  dingy, 217, Plate XXIII
  glassy, 217
  granulate, 217
  pale-sided, 217
  pale western, 217
  red-backed, 218
  spotted, 218
  striped, 218
  variegated, 218, Plate XXIII
  western bean, 218
  western W-marked, 218
  W-marked, 218
  yellow-headed, 218
Cutworm bait, 216
Cyanogas, 13

Cyanophyllum scale, 359
Cycad, 480
Cycas, 480
Cyclamen, 481
  grub, 416
  mite, 283, Plate XXV
Cyclethrin, 13
Cyclocephala borealis, 117
  immaculata, 117
Cydonia, 536
Cygon, 13, 14
Cylas formicarius elegantulus, 425
Cylindrocopturus eatoni, 424
  furnissi, 420
Cynara scolymus, 445
Cynem, 13
Cynipidae, 406
Cynipodea, 406
Cynoglossum, 481
Cynthia moth, 297
Cyperus, 471, 554
Cypress, 481
  aphid, 61
  bark scale, 359
  cone moth, 297
  mealybug, 270
  mites, 284
  moth, 297
  sawfly, 341
  tip moth, 298
  webber, 298
Cypress, bald, 481
Cypress-vine, 481
Cyrtepistomus castaneus, 416
Cyst nematode, 322
Cytisus, 457

Dactylopius confusus, 357
Dactynotus ambrosiae, 58
  erigeronensis, 59
  rudbeckiae, 65
Dacus dorsalis, 229
  oleae, 228
Daffodil, 518
Dagger nematodes, 322
Dahlia, 481
Daihinia brevipes, 209
Daisy, oxeye, 482
  Shasta, 482

Damsel bugs, 163
Danaidae, 178
Danus plexippus, 180
Daphne, 482
Dark apple red bug, 164
Dark brown spruce aphid, 77
Darkling beetles, 91, 99
Dark-sided cutworm, 217
Dasychira plagiata, 307
Dasyneura gleditschiae, 275
  mali, 273
  pyri, 276
  rhodophaga, 276
  vaccinii, 274
Datana integerrima, 204
  major, 188
  ministra, 205
Date mite, 280
Date palm, 482
Datura, 482
Daucus carota, 464
  cucurbitae, 227
Daw bugs, 111
Daylily, 483
  aphid, 62
DBCP, 331
DDD, 21
D-D Mixture, 13, 331
DDT, 22, 13
DDVP, 14, 22
Delnav, 14
Deloyala guttata, 116
Delonix regia, 532
Delphinium, 483, 507
  aphid, 62
De Man's meadow nematode, 322
Demeton, 14
Dendrobium borer, 140
  weevil, 422
Dendroctonus approximatus, 97
  arizonicus, 92
  barberi, 124
  borealis, 92
  brevicomis, 130
  convexifrons, 122
  engelmanni, 102
  frontalis, 123
  jeffreyi, 111
  mexicanus, 123

micans, 102
monticolae, 116
murrayanae, 115
obesus, 122
parallelocollis, 97
piceaperda, 100
ponderosae, 95
pseudotsugae, 99
punctatus, 92
rufipennis, 120
simplex, 100
terebrans, 96
valens, 120
Deodar, 465
  weevil, 420
Depressaria heracliana, 413
Dermaptera, 43, 220
Dermestidae, 90
Deroceras reticulatum, 386
Derocrepis erythropus, 120
Derris, 14, 20
Desert corn flea beetle, 99
Desert dampwood termite, 395
Desert spider mite, 284
Desmia funeralis, 240
Desmocerus palliatus, 141
Deutzia, 483
Devastating grasshopper, 233
Dewberry, 483
Diabrotica balteata, 94
  longicornis, 338
  undecimpunctata howardi, 125
    punctata, 131
  virgifera, 338
Diabrotica beetles, 99
Diacrisia virginica, 205
Dialeurodes chittendeni, 432
  citri, 428
  citrifolii, 429
  kirkaldyi, 431
Diamondback moth, 298
Dianthus, 483
  barbatus, 550
  caryophyllus, 464
Diaphania hyalinata, 196
  indica, 200
  nitidalis, 199

590 INDEX

Diapheromera femorata, 405
  velii, 405
Diarthronomyia artemisiae, 274
  chrysanthemi, 274
Diaspis boisduvalli, 353
  bromeliae, 375
  carueli, 369
  echinocacti, 354
  zamiae, 384
Diatraea crambidoides, 156
  saccharalis, 157
Diazinon, 14
Dibrom, 14, 18
Dicapthon, 14
Dicentra, 455
Dicerca divaricata, 143
Diceroprocta apache, 209
Dichelonyx backi, 106
Dichloroethyl ether, 14
Dichomeris ligulella, 199
  marginella, 412
Dichondra, 483
Dictyospermum scale, 359
Dieffenbachia, 483
Dieldrin, 14
Digger wasp, 408
Digitalis, 491
Dilan, 14
Dill, 484
Dilopoda, 39
Dilution table, 31
Dimecron, 14, 19
Dimefox, 14
Dimetan, 14
Dimethoate, 14
Dimethrin, 15
Dimetilan, 15
Dimite, 15
Dimortheca, 463
Dinex, 15
Dingy cutworm, 217, Plate XXIII
Dinitrobutylphenol, 15
Dinitrocresol, 15
Dinitrocyclohexylphenol, 15
Dinoseb, 15
Dioptidae, 292
Dioryctria abietella, 307
  zimmermani, 312

Diorymerellus laevimargo, 422
Dioscorea, 558
  batatas, 472
Diospyros, 528
Diplolepis radicum, 410
  rosae, 409
Diplopoda, 277
Diprion hercyniae, 343
  rohweri, 346
  similis, 344
Diprionidae, 339
Dipsacus, 551
Diptera, 44, 223, 273
Disonycha xanthomelas, 124
Dissoteira carolina, 233
  longipennis, 233
Distrophus nebulosus, 407
Di-Syston, 15
Ditylenchus, 316
  destructor, 325
  dipsaci, 328
DNBP, 15
DN Dry Mix, 15
DNSOBP, 15
DN-289, 15
Dock, 484
  aphid, 62
  sawfly, 341
Dogberry aphid, 62
Dogday cicada, 207
Dogwood, 484
  aphid, 62
  borer, 140
  cambium borer, 141
  club-gall midge, 275
  sawflies, 341
  scale, 360
  spittlebug, 391
  thrips, 397
  twig borer, 141
Dolichodorus, 315
  heterocephalus, 318, 321
  obtusus, 318
Dolichopodiae, 223
Dombeya, 447
Donacia spp., 130
Dooryard sowbug, 388
Doronicum, 484
Dorylaimida, 316

Dorylaimidae, 316, 322, 329, 330
Dorylaimus, 317
Dorymyrmex pyramicus, 50
Douglas-fir, 484
  aphid, 62
  beetle, 99
  cone midge, 275
  cone moth, 298
  engraver, 99
  pitch moth, 298
  tussock moth, 298
  twig weevil, 420
Dowfume MC-2, 331
Dowfume N, 13
Dowfume W-85, 331
Dracaena, 486
Drepanaphis acerifolia, 71
Drepanosiphum braggii, 58
  platanoides, 79
Drepanothrips reuteri, 399
Dried-fruit beetle, 100
Dried-fruit mite, 279, 284
Drosophilidae, 223
Dryberry mite, 284
Dry-land wireworm, 433
Drymaeus dormani, 386
Dryocoetes betulae, 94
  confusus, 130
Drywood termite, 395
Duranta, 485
Dusky birch sawfly, 341
Dusky sap beetle, 100
Dusky stink bug, 168
Dusky-veined walnut aphid, 62
Dusters, 34, 35, 36
Dust guns, 34, **35**
Dusting, 34
Dusts, 34
Dutchmans-pipe, 485
Dynastes tityrus, 121
Dynastinae, 121
Dysdercus suturellus, 168
Dysmicoccus obesus, 271

Eacles imperialis, 303
Earthworms, 219
Earwig(s), 43, **220**
  European, **220**
  ring-legged, 221

southern, 221
Earworm, corn, 221, Plate XIII
Eastern field wireworm, 433
Eastern flatheaded hemlock borer, 144
Eastern katydid, 238
Eastern larch beetle, 100
Eastern lubber grasshopper, 233
Eastern raspberry fruitworm, 231
Eastern spruce gall aphid, 62, **63**, Plate II
Eastern subterranean termite, 394
Eastern tent caterpillar, 192, Plate XVIII
Ecdytolopha insiticiana, 147
Echeveria, 485
Echinops, 494
EDB, 15
Eelworm, wheat, 331
Eggfruit, 485
Egg parasites, 407
Eggplant, 485
  flea beetle, 100, Plate VII
  lace bug, 168
  leaf miner, 251
Ehrhornia cupressi, 359
Eight-spotted forester, 298
Elaeagnus, 486
  aphid, 63
Elaphidion villosum, 158
Elasmopalpus lignosellus, 145
Elateridae, 90, 432
Elder, 486
  aphid, 63
  borer, 141
  shoot borer, 141
Elder, yellow, 486
Eleodes opaca, 434
Elephant beetle, 121
Elgetol, 15
Elm, 486
  borer, 141
  calligrapha, **100**
  casebearer, 185

cockscomb gall aphid, **63**
flea beetle, 101
lace bug, 168
leaf aphid, 63
leaf beetle, **100**, 101, Plate VI
leaf miner, 251
sack gall aphid, 64
sawfly, **341**
scurfy scale, 360
spanworm, 389
sphinx, 299
twig girdler, 141
Empoasca abrupta, 246
  fabae, 243
  maligna, 241
  solana, 246
Enchinopa binotata, 404
Endelomyia aethiops, 348
Endive, 487
Endosulfan, 15
Endothenia hebesana, 162
Endothion, 15
Endria inimica, 243
Endrin, 15
Engelmann spruce beetle, 102
Engelmann spruce weevil, 420
English grain aphid, 64
English ivy, 504
Engraver beetles, 91
Ennomos subsigniarius, 389
Enocleris lecontei, 94
Entomological Society of America, 1, 44
Entomologists, 1
Entomoscelis americana, 120
Eotetranychus lewisi, 286
  libocedri, 284
  multidigituli, 285
  sexmaculatus, 288
  uncatus, 285
  willamettei, 284
Epargyreus clarus, 181
Epicaerus imbricatus, 108
Epicauta cinera, 97
  fabricii, 92
  lemniscata, 129
  maculata, 125

pennsylvanica, 44, 95
pestifera, 115
subglabra, 96
vittata, 44, 127
Epicnaptera americana, 303
Epidiaspis piricola, 368
Epilachna borealis, 126
Epilobium, 487
Epinotia subviridis, 298
Epitrimerus pyri, 287
Epitrix cucumeris, 119
  hirtipennis, 129
  subcrinita, 131
  tuberis, 129
Epizeuxis aemula, 309
EPN, 15
Epochra canadensis, 225
Erannis tiliaria, 196
Erica, 498
Eriobotrya japonica, 511
Eriococcus araucariae, 350
  artemisiae, 350
  azaleae, 350
  borealis, 381
Eriophyes sp., 285
  gracilis, 280
  pyri, 287
  thujae, 290
  vitis, 285
Eriophyidae, 279
Eriophyllum, 487
Eriosoma americanum, 82
  crataegi, 82
  lanigerum, 81
  pyricola, 82
  rileyi, 82
Eriosomatinae, 53
Ermine moth, 299
Erynephala puncticollis, 94
Erynnis lucilius, 179
Erythaspides vitis, 344
Erythrina, 475, 487
Erythroneura comes, 242
  elegantula, 242
  tricincta, 246
  variabilis, 242
  ziczac, 246
Erythronium, 487
Escarole, 487
Eschscholzia californica, 461

Essigella california, 70
    fusca, 72
Essig's lupine aphid, 69
Estigmene acrea, 202
Ethion, 15
Ethylene bromide, 15
Ethylene chlorobromide, 15
Ethylene dibromide, 331
Ethylene dichloride, 15
Ethylene oxide, 15
Etiella zinckenella, 146
Euboriella annulipes, 221
Eucactophagus weissi, 148
Eucalymnatus tessellatus, 383
Eucalyptus, 487
Eucharis, 441
Eucosma gloriola, 159
Eugenia, 488
Eugenia uniflora, 549
Eugenol, 15
Eulachnus agilus, 72
Eumargarodes laingi, 367
Eumegastigmus transvaalensis, 408
Eumerus strigatus, 288
    tuberculatus, 225
Euonymus, 488
    scale, 360, Plate **XXXIII**
Eupatorium, 488
    gall fly, 225
Euphorbia, 488
Euphorbia pulcherrima, 532
Euphoria inda, 96
Euphydryas chalcedona, 179
Eupithecia spermaphaga, 193
European alder leaf miner, 251
European apple sawfly, 342
European birch aphid, 57, 64
European chafer, 102
European corn borer, 141, Plate **XIII**
European dagger nematode, 322
European earwig, **220**
European elm scale, 361

European fiorinia scale, 361
European fruit lecanium, **361,** 362
European fruit scale, 362
European ground beetle, 102
European honeysuckle leaf roller, 257
European hornet, 409
European mantis, 267
European pine sawfly, **342**
European pine shoot moth, 299, Plate **III**
European raspberry aphid, 64, 74
European red mite, 284
European rose-slug, 348
European spruce beetle, 102
European spruce sawfly, 343
European walnut aphid, 80
Eurya, 488
Eurytetranychus buxi, 280
Eurytoma orchidearum, 229
Eurytomidae, 407
Euschistus conspersus, 168
    servus, 167
    tristignus, 168
Eutetranychus banksii, 290
    carpini borealis, 291
Eutreta xanthochaeta, 225
Euxoa messoria, 217
    tessellata, 218
    ochrogaster, 218
Euzophera ostricolorella, 153
    semifuneralis, 135
Evening primrose, 488
    aphid, 71
Evergestis pallidata, 200
    rimosalis, 192
Evergreen bagworm, 85
Evoxysoma vitis, 409
Exartema permundanum, 259
Exclusion, 5
Exoteleia pinifoliella, 254
Eyed click beetle, 102
Eye-spotted bud moth, 159

Fagus, 452
Fall armyworm, **83**
Fall cankerworm, **183,** Plate XVIII
Fall webworm, 411, Plate XVIII
False buckthorn, 458
False cabbage aphid, 79
False chinch bug, 168
False cottony maple scale, 362
False hemlock looper, 192
False leaf mining midge, 275
False potato beetle, 102
False powder post beetles, 89
False root-knot nematode, 323
False tarnished plant bug, 173
False spider mites, 279
Fan palm moth, 299
Fascista cercerisella, 259
Fatshedera, 488
Fatsia, 489
Federal Food, Drug and Cosmetic Act, 8, 9
Federal Insecticide, Fungicide and Rodenticide Act, 8, 9
Federal Plant Pest Act, 2, 5
Feijoa, 489
Feltia subgothica, 217
Feniseca tarquinius, 180
Fenusa dohrnii, 251
    pusilla, 249
    ulmi, 251
Fern(s), 489
    aphid, 64
    nematode, 323, 327
    scale, **362**
    whitefly, 429
Fetterbush, 489
Ficus aurea, 489
    carica, 489
    benghalensis, 450
    nitida, 503
    pumila, 489
Fidia viticida, 337
Fieberiella florii, 244

Field cricket, 210
Fiery hunter, 102
Fig beetle, 103
  cyst nematode, 323
  mite, 284
  pin nematode, 323
  rust mite, 284
  scale, 363
  spine nematode, 323
Fig, creeping, 489
  strangler, 489
  tree, 489
Filbert, 490
  big-bud, 285
  bud mite, 285
  weevil, 420
Filbertworm, 193
Fiorinia externa, 368
  theae, 381
Fire ant, 49
Fireflies, 90, 103
Fir, 490
  cone looper, 193
  engraver, 103
  seed moth, 103
Firebush, 498
Firethorn, 536
Five-leaf aralia, 437
Flacourtia, 490
Flame vine, 490
Flannel moths, 293
Flat bugs, 162
Flatheaded apple tree
  borer, 141, **142**, Plate
  XIV
Flatheaded cherry tree
  borer, 143
Flatheaded cone borer, 143
Flatheaded fir borer, 143
Flea beetle(s), 103
  cabbage, 96
  corn, 98
  desert corn, 99
  elm, 101
  mint, 116
  pale-striped, **104**, 118
  potato, **104**, 119
  prairie, 120
  red-legged, 120
  sinuate-striped, 122
  steel-blue, 126
  strawberry, 126

  striped, 128
  tobacco, 129
  toothed, 129
  tuber, 129
  western black, 130
  western potato, 131
  western striped, 131
Fleahopper, garden, 169
Fleece-vine, 543
Fletcher scale, 363
Flocculent fir aphid, 64
Florida carpenter ant, 49
Florida fern caterpillar,
  193
Florida flower thrips, 397
Florida harvester ant, 49
Florida red scale, **363**
Florida wax scale, 364
Flower beetles, 88, 90, 91,
  96
Flower bugs, 162
Flowering cherry, 469
Flowering currant, 480
Flowering maple, 437
Flowering tobacco, 519
Flower thrips, **398**
Fly (flies):
  Australian sod, 224
  black cherry fruit, 224
  carrot rust, 224
  cattleya, 229
  cherry fruit, 224
  currant fruit, 225
  Eupatorium gall, 225
  flower, 223, 229
  frit, 225
  fruit, 223, 224
  Hessian, 225
  lantana gall, 225
  leaf miner, 223
  lesser bulb, 225
  lupine, 226
  Mediterranean fruit, **226**
  Melon, 227
  Mexican fruit, 227
  mushroom, 227
  narcissus bulb, 228
  olive fruit, 228
  onion bulb, 228
  oriental fruit, 229
  papaya fruit, 229
  pomace, 223

  robber, 223
  rust, 223
  soldier, 223
  syrphid, 223, 229
  tachinid, 224
  vinegar, 223
  walnut husk, 230
  West Indian fruit, 230
Folded-leaf poplar aphid,
  73
Forbes scale, 364
Forda olivacea, 65
Forest tent caterpillar, 193
Forficula auricularia, 220
Forget-me-not, 490
Fork-tailed bush katydid,
  237
Formica exsectoides, 48
  fusca, 51
  obscuripes, 51
Forsythia, 491
Four-lined plant bug, 168,
  169
Four-spotted hawthorn
  aphid, 64
Four-spotted spider mite,
  285
Four-spotted tree cricket,
  210
Foxglove, 491
  aphid, 64
Fragaria, 547
Frangipani, 491
Frankliniella bispinosa, 397
  fusca, 402
  moultoni, 402
  occidentale, 402
  tritici, 398
  vaccinii, 396
Fraxinus, 445
Freesia, 491
French mulberry, 462
Fringe-tree, 491
Fritillaria, 491
Frosted scale, 365
Fruit flies, 223, 224
Fruit mealybug, 270
Fruit tree bark beetle, 155
Fruit-tree leaf roller, 257
Fruit-tree mite, 285
Fruit tree pulvinaria, 358
Fruitworm(s), 89, 230

cherry, 230
cranberry, 230
eastern raspberry, 231
gooseberry, 231
green, **231**
sparganothis, 232
strawberry, 263
western raspberry, 232
Fuchsia, 491
Fulgoridae, 333
Fulgorids, 333
Fuller rose beetle, **104**
Fumazone, 16, 18
Fungi, in insect control, 5
Fungivoridae, 223
Fungus beetles, 89
Fungus bugs, 162
Fungus gnats, 223, 227
Furcaspis biformis, 373
Furcraea, 492
Furethrin, 16

Gaillardia, 492
Galasa nigrinodis, 411
Galerucella carbo, 118
cavicollis, 97
decora, 106
luteola, 101
notata, 128
nymphaeae, 130
Gall aphids, 77, 53
Gallberry, 492
Gall-making maple borer, 144
Gall mites, 279
Gall wasps, 406
Galtonia, 492
Garden balsam, 449
Garden centipede, **206**
Garden cress, 478
Garden fleahopper, 169, Plate VII
Garden pink, 483
Garden slug, 386
Garden springtail, **393**
Garden symphylan, **206**
Garden tortrix, 198
Garden webworm, 412
Gardenia, 492
Gargaphia solani, 168
tiliae, 166
Garlic, 492

Garman spider mite, 285
Gastropda, 385
Gaultheria, 540
Gaura, 492
Gayfeather, 492
Gaylussacia, 502
Geiger-tree, 492
Gelechiidae, 292
Gelechiid moths, 292
Gelsemium, 505
Genicide, 16
Genista, 457
caterpillar, 194
moth, 194
Genite, 16
Geometridae, 182, 292
Geometrid moths, 292
Geranium, 493
aphid, 64
plume moth, 299
Geranium, wild, 493
Gerbera, 493
Germander, 493
leaf crinkle mite, 285
Geshna cannalis, 258
Ghost moths, 293
Giant American sawfly, 341
Giant apple borer, 138
Giant bark aphid, 64
Giant hornet, **409**
Giant slug, 387
Giant stag beetle, 105
Giant walkingstick, 405
Giant willow aphid, 65
Giardomyia rhododendri, 276
Gillette's blue grass aphid, 65
Ginger-lily, 493
Ginkgo, 493
Ginseng, 493
Glacial whitefly, 430
Gladiolus, 493
thrips, 398, Plate XXV
Glassy cutworm, 217
Gleditsia, 501
Globe artichoke, 445
Globe thistle, 494
Globose scale, 365
Gloomy scale, 365
Glory-bower, 473

Glorybush, 494
Glory-of-the-snow, 470
Glossonotus crataegi, 404
Glover scale, 365
Glowworms, 103
Gloxinia, 494
Glycine max, 544
Glycobius speciosus, 157
Gnat, fungus, 223, 227
potato scale, 229
Gnorimoschema opercu-lella, 152
Godfrey's meadow nema-tode, 323
Goes tesselatus, 148
tigrinus, 158
Goldbugs, 129
Golddust plant, 447
Golden buprestid, 105
Goldenchain, 494
Golden dewdrop, 486
Golden-eye lacewing, **238**
Goldenglow, 494
aphid, 65
sawfly, 343
Golden mealybug, 270
Golden nematode, 323
Golden oak scale, 365
Goldenrod, 494
aphid, 65
Golden-shower, 465
Goldsmith beetle, 105
Gonioctena americana, 92
Gooseberry, 495
fruitworm, 231
witchbroom aphid, 65
Gordonia alatamaha, 491
lasianthus, 450
Gorse weevil, 420
Gossyparia spuria, 361
Gourd, 495
Gouty pitch gall midge, 275
Governors-plum, 490
Gracilaria azaleella, 248
cuculipennella, 254
negundella, 257
perseae, 256
syringella, 253
Gracilariidae, 293
Granulate cutworm, 217
Grape, 495

berry moth, 300
blossom midge, 275
bud beetle, 105
bud mite, 285
cane gall maker, 144
cane girdler, 144
colaspis, 105
curculio, 213
erineum mite, 285
flea beetle, 105, Plate VII
gall midge, 275
leaf folder, 240
leafhopper, 242
leaf miner, 251
mealybug, 271
phylloxera, 2, 65
plume moth, 300
root borer, 144
rootworm, 337
rust mite, 285
sawfly, 344
scale, 365
seed chalcid, 409
thrips, 399
trunk borer, 144
whitefly, 430
Grapefruit, 496
Grape holly, 513
Grape-hyacinth, 496
Grapevine aphid, 66
hoplia, 108
looper, 194
tomato gall midge, 275
Graphocephala coccinea, 244
Graphognathus spp., 131
Grapholitha interstinctana, 191
molesta, 305
packardii, 230
Grasshopper(s), 43, 232
American, 233
Carolina, 233
clear-winged, 233
devastating, 233
eastern lubber, 233
green-striped, 233
High Plains, 233
long-horned, 237
lubber, 233
migratory, 234

Packard, 234
red-legged, 234
Rocky Mountain, 234
two-striped, 234
Grass, lawn, 496, 508
cyst nematode, 324
moths, 292
nema, 318
sheath nematode, 324
snail, 386
thrips, 399
Gray-banded leaf roller, 258
Gray field slug, 386
Gray garden slug, 386
Gray willow leaf beetle, 106
Great ash sphinx, 300
Great Basin tent caterpillar, 194
Great Basin wireworm, 434
Greedy scale, 365
Green and brown pine needle aphid, 72
Green and pink willow aphid, 67
Green apple aphid, 55
Green apple bug, 173
Greenbrier, 543
Greenbug, 66
Green citrus aphid, 66, 77
Green cloverworm, 194
Green fruit beetle, 103
Green fruitworm, 231
Green gooseberry aphid, 66
Green-headed spruce sawfly, 344
Greenhouse leaf tier, 262
Greenhouse orthezia, 332, 333
Greenhouse slug, 333
Greenhouse snails, 387
Greenhouse thrips, 399
Greenhouse whitefly, 430
Green June beetle, 106, Plate XI
Green peach aphid, 66, 67
Green rose chafer, 106
Green scale, 366
Green shield scale, 366

Green spruce aphid, 67
Green stink bug, 170
Green-striped grasshopper, 233
Green-striped mapleworm, 194
Gregarious oak leaf miner, 252
Gretchena bolliana, 160
Grevillea, 496
mite, 285
Grindelia, 496
aphid, 67
Ground beetles, 88, 102, 106
Groundcherry, 497
Ground mealybug, 271
Ground pearls, 366
Groundsel, 497
Groundselbush, 497
Grub, 43
Gryllacrididae, 209
Gryllidae, 209
Gryllotalpa gryllotalpa, hexadactyla, 211
Guava, 497
Gulf white cabbageworm, 195
Gulf wireworm, 434
Gumbo-limbo, 497
Guthion, 16
Gymnocladus, 506
Gynaikothrips ficorum, 397
Gyplure, 16
Gypsophila, 497
Gypsy moth, 300, Plate VI

Habranthis, 497
Hackberry, 497
empress, 180
engraver, 107
lace bug, 170
nipple-gall psyllid, 335
witches-broom mite, 285
Hag moth, 302
Hairy chinch bug, 170, Plate XVII
Hairy rose aphid, 75
Halisodota argentata, 308
caryae, 302
harrisii, 310
maculata, 309

tesselaris, 306
Hall scale, 367
Halticotoma valida, 178
Halticus bracteatus, 169
Hamamelis, 558
Hamelia, 498
Haplothrips clarisetis, 402
Harlequin bug, **171**
Harpalus pennsylvanicus, 106
Harpipteryx xylostella, 257
Harrisina brillians, 262
Hartigia cressoni, 235
  trimaculata, 235, 348
Harvester, 180
Harvesterman, 207
Harvest mites, 279
Hawk moths, 294
Hawthorn, 498
  aphid, 67
  lace bug, 171
Hazelnut, 498
  weevil, 420
HCN, 16
Heath, 498
Heather, 499
Hedera helix, 504
Hedychium, 493
Helenium, 499
  snout beetle, 107
Helianthus, 549
  tuberosus, 445
Helichrysum bracteatum, 548
Heliconius charithonius, 182
Helicotylenchus, 315, 327
  multicinctus, 321
  nannus, 328
Heliopsis, 499
Heliothis virescens, 161
  zea, 221
Heliothrips dracaenae, 397
  haemorrhoidalis, 399
Heliotrope, 499
Heliozelidae, 293
Helix aspersa, 386
Hellula rogatalis, 411
Hemadas nubilipennis, 408
Hemaris diffinis, 309
Hemerobiidae, 238
Hemerobius pacificus, 239

Hemerocallis, 483
Hemerocampa leucostigma, 311
  pseudotsugata, 298
  vetusta, 310
Hemichroa crocea, 348
Hemicriconemoides, 314
  biformis, 324
  floridensis, 325
  wessoni, 331
Hemicycliophora, 314, 327
  parvana, 330
Hemileuca maia, 295
  nevadensis, 305
  oliviae, 201
Hemiptera, 43, 162, 207, 241, 267, 334, 349, 390, 403, 427
Hemispherical juniper aphid, 68
Hemispherical scale, **367**
Hemitarsonemus latus, 281
Hemlock, 499
  borer, 144
  looper, 195
  sawfly, 344
  scale, 368
  woolly aphid, 67
Hepialidae, 293
Heptachlor, 16
Hercinothrips femoralis, 396
Hercothrips fasciatus, 396
Hesperiidae, 178
Hessian fly, 225
Heterocampa guttivitta, 202
  manteo, 203
Heterocordylus malinus, 164
Heterodera, 315, 322
  cacti, 319
  cruciferae, 319
  fici, 323
  glycines, 327
  göttingiana, 324
  marioni, 325
  punctata, 324
  rostochiensis, 323
  schactii, 329
  tabacum, 330
  trifolii, 321

Heteroptera, 43, 162
Heuchera, 475
Hexapoda, 39
Hexeris enhydris, 154
Hibiscus, 499
  weevil, 420
Hibiscus, sleeping, 553
Hibiscus esculentus, 520
  mutabilis, 475
Hickory, 500
  aphid, 64
  bark beetle, 107
  cossid, 150
  horned devil, 195
  leaf roller, 258
  nut curculio, 213
  plant bug, 172
  saperda, 108
  scale, 368
  shuckworm, 195
  tiger moth, 302
  tussock moth, 302
High Plains grasshopper, 233
Hippeastrum, 441
Hippodamia convergens, 114
Hister beetles, 90
Histeridae, 90
Hog-plum, 500
Holly, 500
  bud moth, 160
  leaf miner, **252**
  leaf tier, 263
  mite, 288
  scale, 368
Hollyhock, 500
  aphid, 67
  leaf skeletonizer, 261
  plant bug, 172
  thrips, 400
  weevil, 420
Holocampa cookei, 340
Holochlora japonica, 238
Homadaula albizziae, 413
Homaledra sabalella, 261
Homalocladium, 538
Homoeosoma electellum, 310
Homoptera, 43, 207, 241, 267, 349, 403, 427
Honeylocust, 501

borer, 144
pod gall midge, 275
spider mite, 285
Honeysuckle, 501
sawfly, 344
Honeysuckle and parsnip
aphids, 67
Hop aphid, 68
flea beetle, 108
plant bug, 172
Hop-hornbeam, 501
Hoplia beetles, 108
Hoplia oregona, 108
Hoplocampa testudinea,
342
*Hoplochairophorus quer-
cicola*, 71
Hoplolaimidae, 315, 322,
325, 327, 329
Hoplolaimus, 315
coronatus, 322
tylenchiformis, 322
uniformis, 330
Hop-tree, 501
Horistonotus uhleri, 434
Hormaphis hamamelidis,
81
Hormorus undulatus, 422
Hornbeam, 501
Horned squash bug, 172
Hornet(s), 407
giant, **409**
vespa, 409
Hornet moth, 302
Horntail(s), 234, **235**
blue, 235
California, 235
raspberry, 235
raspberry, 235
western, 235
Hornworm(s), 236
southern, 236
sweetpotato, 236
tobacco, 236
tomato, 236, **406**, Plate
XIX
Horsechestnut, 502
Horsemint aphid, 68
Horseradish, 502
flea beetle, 108
Hose-end sprayer, **27**, 29
Hosta, 502

Hover flies, 229
Howardia biclavis, 371
Howard scale, 368
Huckleberry, 502
Hunter's butterfly, 181
Hyacinth, 502
Hyacinthus
Hyalophora cecropia, 296
Hyalopterus pruni, 69
Hydrangea, 502
leaf tier, **263**
Hydrogen cyanide, 16
Hylastinus obscurus, 139
Hylecoetus lugubris, 154
Hylemya antiqua, 265
brassicae, 264
brunnescens, 265
cchinata, 265
floralis, 266
lupini, 226
Hylobius pales, 423
radicis, 424
Hylurgopinus rufipes, 116
Hymenia perspectalis, 414
Hymenocallis, 503
Hymenoptera, 43, 85, 150,
234, 339, 405
Hypera meles, 419
nigrirostris, 422
postica, 415
punctata, 419
Hypericum, 503
Hyperus humilis, 419
Hyphantria cunea, 411
Hypolithus abbreviatus,
433
Hyponomeuta padella, 299
Hyponomeutidae, 293
Hyssop, 503
Hysteroneura setariae, 75

Iberis, 463
Ice-plant, 516
Icerya purchasi, 357
Ichneumonidae, 407
Ichneumonoidea, 406
Ichneumons, 407
Ichthyura inclusa, 200
Idiocerus pallidus, 243
scurra, 243
Idiopterus nephrolepidis,
64

Ilex, 500
glabra, 492
vomitoria, 559
Illicium floridanum, 441
Imbricated snout beetles,
Impatiens, 503
Impatiens balsamina, 449
sultana, 503
Imperial moth, 303
Imported cabbageworm,
196, Plate XXVI
Imported currantworm,
344, Plate XXXII
Imported fire ant, 49
Imported long-horned wee-
vil, **421**
Imported willow leaf bee-
tle, 108, Plate XI
Incense cedar, 467
Inchworms, 182
Inconspicuous whitefly,
431
Incurvariidae, 293
India-hawthorn, 503
Indian-laurel, 503
Indian mulberry, 517
Indian-paintbrush, 503
Inkberry, 503
Insecta, 39
Insects, beneficial, 2
common names of, 44
control of, 4
as disseminators of dis-
ease, 3
numbers of, 3
parts of, **39, 40**
Insect Pest Act, 5
Instars, **42, 43**
Intermittent sprayer, 28
Introduced pine sawfly,
344, Plate XXXI
Io moth, 303
Ipidae, 91
Ipomoea batatas, 550
Ips calligraphus, 119
pini, 118
radiatae, 116
Iresine, 503
Iridomyrmex humilis, 48
Iridothrips iridis, 400
Iris, 503
blister beetle, 109

borer, 144, Plate XV
root aphid, 68
thrips, 400
weevil, 421
Ironwood, 504
Ischnaspis longirostris, 353
Iscothan, 16
Isia isabella, 188
Isolan, 16
Isoptera, 43, 393
Italian pear scale, 368
Itame ribearia, 389
Ithycerus novaboracensis,
422
Itonidae, 223
Itycorsia sp., 345
Ivy aphid, 68
scale, 372
Ivy, Boston, 504
English, 504
Ixora, 504

Jacaranda, 504
Jack-pine budworm, 160
sawfly, 345
Jacobinia, 504
Jacquemontia, 504
Jamaica-apple, 505
Janus abbreviatus, 349
integer, 140
Japanese beetle, **109,** Plate
VIII
Japanese broad-winged,
katydid, 238
Japanese cherry, 469
Japanese leafhopper, 243
Japanese maple leafhopper,
243
Japanese mealybug, 271
Japanese pagoda-tree, 505
Japanese quince, 505
Japanese root-knot nema-
tode, 324
Japanese scale, 369
Japanese wax scale, 369
Japanese weevil, 421
Japanus hyalinus, 243
Jasmine, 505
whitefly, 431
Jasminum, 505
Jatropha, 475
Jeffrey pine beetle, 111

Jerusalem artichoke, 445
Jerusalem-cherry, 505
Jerusalem cricket, 210
Jerusalem-thorn, 523
Jessamine, 505
Jessamine, yellow, 505
Jewel wasps, 505
Jointworms, 407
Jonthonota nigripes, 96
Judas tree, 537
Juglans, 556
cinerea, 458
Jujube, 560
June beetle, 111, Plate VIII
ten-lined, 128
Juneberry, 505
Juniper, 506
aphids, 68
mealybug, 271
midge, 275
moth, 303
scale, 369, Plate XXXIII
webworm, 412
Juniperus, 506
Jussiaea peruviana, 557
Justicia, 506

Kakimia cynosbati, 62
houghtonensis, 65
Kalanchoe, 506
Kale, 506
Kalmia, 517
Kalotermes minor, 395
Kangaroo vine, 472
Karathane, 16
Katydid(s), 43, **237**
angular-winged, **237**
broad-winged, 237
fork-tailed bush, 237
Japanese broad-winged,
238
northern, 238
Keiferia glochinella, 251
lycopersicella, 203
Kellogg's whitefly, 431
Kelthane, 16
Kentucky coffee-tree, 506
Keonolla spp., 247
Kermes pubescens, 371
Kerria, 506
Khapra beetle, 112
Kigelia pinnata, 542

Klamath weed beetle, 112
Knapsack duster, 36
Knapsack sprayer, **26,** 28
Kniphofia, 532
Kohlrabi, 506
Kolkwitzia, 451
Kuanaspis hikosani, 351
Kudzu, 506
Kumquat, 507

Label, regulations for, **9**
Labidura riparia, 221
Labopidea allii, 173
Laburnum, 494
Lace bug(s), 163
alder, 163
andromeda, 164
ash, 164
azalea, **165**
basswood, 166
birch, 166
ceanothus, 167
chrysanthemum, 168
eggplant, 168
elm, 168
hackberry, 170
hawthorn, 171
lantana, 172
oak, 173
rhododendron, 174
sycamore, 176
toyon, 177
walnut, 177
willow, 178
Lacewing(s), **238**
California green, 239
golden-eye, **238**
Pacific brown, 239
slender brown, 239
Lachnus rosae, 75
salignus, 65
Lacinipolia renigera, 217
Lactuca sativa, 509
Lady beetle(s), 89, 112
Australian, **113**
black, 95
convergent, **113,** 114
steel-blue, 126
transverse, 129
twice-stabbed, 114
two-spotted, **113,** 114
vedalia, 113

Ladybugs, 112, **113**
Lagerstroemia, 478
Lambdina athasaria athasaria, 195
　　pelluscidaria, 200
fiscellaria, 195
　　somniaria, 204
　　lugubrosa, 204
Lampetia equestris, 228
Lampyridae, 90, 103
Languria mozardi, 140
Languriidae, 90
Lancewood, 507
Lantana, 507
　aphid, 68
　gall fly, 225
　lace bug, 172
　plume moth, 303
Lanternflies, 333
Laphygma frugiperda, 83
Lappet moth, 303
Larch, 507
　aphid, 68
　bud moth, 160
　casebearer, 185
　sawfly, 345
Large aspen tortrix, 196
Large chestnut weevil, 422
Larger canna leaf roller, 258
Larger elm leaf beetle, 114
Larger Mexican pine beetle, 97
Larger shot-hole borer, 145
Larger yellow ant, 50
Laricobius erichsoni, 56
Larix, 507
Larkspur, 483
　aphid, 62, 68
　leaf miner, 253
Larkspur, annual, 507
Larvacide, 16, 331
Lasiocampidae, 293
Lasioptera vitis, 275
Lasius alienus, 49
Laspeyresia bracteatana, 299
　caryana, 195
　cupressana, 297
　nigricana, 306
　youngana, 309
Latania scale, 369

Lathyrus odoratus, 550
Laurel, 507
　psyllid, 335
Laurel-cherry, 469
Laurestinus, 507
Laurus, 450, 507
Lavatera, 508
Lavender, 508
Lavenderbell, 548
Lawn grasses, 508
Lawn armyworm, 84
Lawsonia inermis, 516
Lead arsenate, 1, 16, 23
Leadwort, 532
Leaf beetle(s), 89
　cereal, 97
　cherry, 97
　cottonwood, 98
　elm, 101
　rose, 122
　Syneta, 128
　watercress, 130
　waterlily, 130
　yellow-margined, 132
Leaf blotch miners, 293
Leaf bugs, 163
Leaf crumpler, 239
Leaf-curl ash aphid, 68
Leaf-curl plum aphid, 68
Leaf cutter(s), 240
　maple, 240
　morning-glory, 240
　waterlily, 240
Leaf-cutter bee, **86**
Leaf folder, 240
　grape, 240
Leaf-footed bug, **172**
Leafhopper(s), 241
　apple, 241
　aster, 245
　beet, 241, Plate XXIV
　blunt-nosed cranberry, 242
　bramble, 242
　clover, 242
　grape, 242
　Japanese, 243
　Japanese maple, 243
　mountain, 243
　Norway-maple, 243
　painted, 243
　plum, 243

poplar, 243
potato, 243, Plate XIV
privet, 244
prune, 244
red-banded, 244
rose, 244, **245**
saddled, 245
sharp-nosed, 245
six-spotted, 245, Plate XXIV
southern garden, 246
three-banded, 246
Virginia-creeper, 246
western potato, 246
white apple, 246
white-banded elm, 246
willow, 247
yellow-headed, 247
Leaf miner(s), 247
　apple blotch, 247
　apple trumpet, 247
　arborvitae, 247
　asparagus, 247
　aspen blotch, 248
　aspen leaf, 248
　azalea, 248
　basswood, 248
　beet, 248
　birch, **248**, 249
　blackberry, 249
　boxwood, **249**
　chrysanthemum, 250
　columbine, 250, **251**
　corn blotch, 251
　eggplant, 251
　elm, 251
　European alder, 251
　grape, 251
　gregarious oak, 252
　holly, **252**
　larkspur, 253
　lilac, 253
　locust, 253
　lodgepole needle, 253
　morning-glory, 253
　native holly, 252
　pea, 254
　pine needle, 254
　pine needle-sheath, 254
　privet, 254
　serpentine, 254
　solitary oak leaf, 254

spinach, 254
spotted tentiform, 255
spruce needle, 255
strawberry crown, 255
sweetpotato, 255
tupelo, 256
unspotted tentiform, 256
verbena, 256
white-fir needle, 256
wild parsnip, 256
Leaf roller(s), 256
avocado, 256
basswood, 256
bean, 257
boxelder, 257
European honeysuckle, 257
fruit tree, 257
gray-banded, 258
hickory, 258
larger canna, 258
lesser canna, 258
locust, 258
oak, 258
oblique-banded, 258
omnivorous, 259
raspberry, 259
red-banded, 259
redbud, 259
strawberry, 259
sweetpotato, 260
three-lined, 260
western strawberry, 260
Leaf skeletonizer(s), 260
apple, 260
apple-and-thorn, 260
bean, 261
birch, 261
cotton leaf perforator, 261
palm, 261
western grape, 262
Leaf tier(s), 262
beech, 262
celery, 262
greenhouse, 262
holly, 263
hydrangea, 263
oak, 263
omnivorous, 263
sweetgum, 263
Lecaniodiaspis, 351

Lecanium cerasorum, 354
  corni, 362
  fletcheri, 363
  nigrofasciatum, 382
  persicae, 374
  pruinosum, 365
  prunastri, 365
  quercifex, 372
Leconte's sawfly, 347
Lema trilineata, 128
Lemon, 508
Leopard moth, **303**, 304
Leopards-bane, 484
Lepidium, 478
Leperisinus aculeatus, 92
  californicus, 117
  fasciatus, 92
Lepidoptera, 43, 178, 292
Lepidosaphes alba, 356
  beckii, 376
  camelliae, 355
  ficus, 363
  gloverii, 365
  newsteadi, 371
  ulmi, 373
Leptinotarsa juncta, 102
Leptocoris trivittatus, 167
Leptoglossus phyllopus, 172
  zonatus, 177
Leptophya minor, 164
Leptoterna dolabratus, 173
Lespedeza, 509
  webworm, 412
Lesser bud moth, 160
Lesser bulb fly, 225
Lesser canna leaf roller, 258
Lesser clover leaf weevil, 422
Lesser cornstalk borer, 145
Lesser peach tree borer, 145
Lesser snow scale, 369
Lethane, 16, 60
Lettuce, 509
  aphids, 69
  root aphid, 69
Leucadendron argenteum, 543
Leucaspis indica, 370
  japonica, 369

Leucocrinum, 541
Leucojum, 509
Lewis spider mite, 286
Liatris, 492
Libocedrus, 467
Lichnanthe vulpina, 99
Light brown spruce aphid, 77
Lightning bugs, 90, 103
Lightning leafhoppers, 333
Lignum-vitae, 509
Ligustrum, 509, 535
  weevil, 422
Lilac, 509
  borer, 146, Plate XV
  leaf miner, 253
  leaf roller, 253
  weevil, 422
Lilium, 510
Lily, 510
  aphids, 69
  bulb thrips, 400
  weevil, 422
Lily-of-the-Nile, 438
Lily-of-the-valley, 510
  weevil, 422
Lily-turf, 511
Lima bean, 451
  pod borer, 146
  vine borer, 146
Limax flavus, 387
  maximus, 387
Lime, 510
Limentis archippus, 182
Lime-sulfur, 8, 16
Lime-tree looper, 196
Limonius agonus, 433
  californicus, 434
  canus, 434
  infuscatus, 434
  subauratus, 433
Lindane, 16
Linden, 510
  aphid, 69
  borer, 146
  leaf beetle, 100
  looper, 196
Lined click beetle, 115
Lined spittlebug, 391
Lion beetle, 115
Lipstick tree, 511
Liquidambar, 549

Liriodendron, 553
scale, 383
Liriomyza brassicae, 254
langei, 254
Liriope, 511
Liriothrips floridensis, 396
vaneecki, 400
varicornis, 400
Listroderes costirostris obliquus, 426
Listronotus oregonensis, 418
Litchi chinensis, 512
Litchi mite, 286
Lithocolletis tremuloidiella, 248
Lithophane antennata, 231
Little black-and-green willow aphid, 81
Little black ant, 50
Little black-veined aster aphid, 69
Little carpenterworm, 147
Little fire ant, 50
Lizard beetles, 90
Lizards-tail, 511
Live-oak root borer, 147
Lixus concavus, 215
Lobelia, 511
Lobelia cardinalis, 464
Loblolly bay, 450
Loblolly mealybug, 271
pine sawfly, 345
Locust, 511
aphid, 69
borer, 147
leaf beetle, 253
leaf miner, 253
leaf roller, 258
twig borer, 147
Locustidae, 232
Locusts, 207
Lodgepole-pine beetle, 115
Lodgepole cone beetle, 115
Lodgepole needle miner, 253
Lodgepole sawfly, 345
Lodgepole terminal weevil, 422
Loganberry, 511
Lonchocarpus, 17, 20
London purple, 17

Long-beaked clover aphid, 67
Long-horned grasshoppers, 237
Longidorus, 317
sylphus, 330
Longistigma caryae, 64
Longitarsus waterhousei, 116
Long-legged flies, 223
Long soft scale, 370
Long-tailed mealybug, **269,** 272
Lonicera, 501
Lopidea dakota, 167
davisi, 174
Loquat, 511
Lotus, 512
Loro, 17
Loxagrotis albicosta, 218
Loxostege commixtalis, 410
obliteralis, 240
similalis, 412
sticticalis, 410
Lubber grasshopper, 233
Lucanus elaphus, 105
Lucuma nervosa, 485
Luna moth, 304
Luperodes brunneus, 98
Lupine, 512
aphid, 69
fly, 226
Lupinus, 512
Lycaenidae, 179
Lychee, 90
Lychium chinensis, 515
Lycidae, 90
Lycopersicon esculentum, 552
Lyctidae, 90, 119
Lygaeidae, 163
Lygaeid bugs, 163
Lygaeus kalmii, 175
reclivatus, 175
Lygidea mendax, 164
Lygris diversilineata, 194
Lygus bugs, 172
Lygus elisus, 172
hesperis, 172
lineolaris, 176
Lymacodidae, 293

Lymantriidae, 293
Lyonia, 547
lucida, 489
Lytta cyanipennis, 109

Macadamia, 512
Maclura, 522
Macremphytus subspinosus, 121
tarsatus, 341
varianus, 341
Macronoctua onusta, 144
Macrophya intermedia, 343
simillima, 343
Macropsis trimaculata, 243
Macrosiphoniella sanborni, 59
Macrosiphum albifrons, 69
anomalae, 55
artemisiae, 55
asterifoliae, 55
aucubae, 56
breviscriptum, 55
coweni, 55
creelii, 55
eocssigi, 67
euphorbiae, 73
fascifrons, 245
granarium, 64
impartiensicolens, 68
impatientis, 68
lilii, 74
liriodendri, 79
nigromaculosum, 75
pisi, 71
pseudodirhodum, 75
rhododendri, 74
rosae, 74
Macrosteles fascifrons, 245
Madrona, 512
shield bearer, 304
thrips, 400
whitefly, 431
Madwort, 440
Maecolaspis favosa, 118
flavida, 105
pini, 118
Magdalis armicollis, 424
barbita, 416
senescens, 418
Maggot(s), 43, 264
apple, 264, Plate XXV

cabbage, 264, Plate XXVI
carnation, 265
carnation tip, 265
onion, 265
pepper, 265
raspberry cane, 266
seed-corn, 266
sunflower, 266
turnip, 266
Magicicada septemdecim, 207
Magnesium arsenate, 17
Magnolia, 450, 512
scale, 370
Magnolia tripetala, 554
virginiana, 549
Mahogany, 513
Mahonia, 513
Maize billbug, 133
Malacosoma californicum, 190
constrictum, 190
disstria, 193
fragile, 194
lutescens, 200
pluviale, 205
Maladera castanea, 93
Malaheb cherry aphid, 69
Malathion, 17
Mallow, 513
Malphigia, 513
Malva, 513
Malvaviscus arboreus, 553
Manatee snail, 386
Mandevilla, 513
Mangifera indica, 513
Mango, 513
bud mite, 286
scale, 370
Mangrove, 513
borer, 136
Manihot esculenta, 465
Manilkara zapotilla, 541
Mantidae, 266
Mantids, 43, 266
Mantis, Carolina, 267
Chinese, 267
European, 267
narrow-winged, 267
Mantis religiosa, 267
Manzanita, 514

leaf-gall aphid, 69
whitefly, 431
Maple, 514
bladder-gall mite, 286
border, 148
callus borer, 148
leaf aphid, 81
leaf cutter, 240
petiole borer, 148
phenacoccus, 370
sesian, 148
Maranta, 514
Margarodes meridionalis, 366
rileyi, 367
Margined blister beetle, 115, Plate V
Marguerite, 515
Marigold, 515
Marine ivy, 472
Marlberry, 515
Marlate, 17
Masked hunter, 173
Masked scale, 370
Mathiola, 547
Matrimony vine, 515
Matsucoccus spp. 375
acalyptus, 376
gallicolus, 375
paucicatrices, 375
resinosae, 378
vexillorum, 376
May beetles, 111
McDaniel spider mite, 286
Meadow plant bug, 173
Meadow spittlebug, 391
Mealybug(s), 267, **269**
apple, 268
citrophilus, 268
citrus, **269**
coconut, 270
Coleman's, 270
Comstock, 270
cypress, 270
destroyer, 114
fruit, 270
golden, 270
grape, 271
ground, 271
Japanese, 271
juniper, 271
loblolly, 271

long-tailed, **272**
Mexican, 272
pineapple, 272
redwood, 272
solanum, 272
striped, 273
taxus, 273
yucca, 273
Mealy flata, 333
Mealy plum aphid, 69
Measurements, of chemicals, 30
Measuring worms, 182, 292
Mediterranean fruit fly, **226**
Megachile spp., 86
Megacyllene caryae, 149
robiniae, 147
Megalopyge crispata, 297
opercularis, 200
Megalopygidae, 293
Megaphasma dentricus, 405
Melaleuca leucadendra, 460
Melalgus confertus, 137
Melanagromyza simplex, 247
Melanocallis caryaefoliae, 58
Melanophila drummondi, 144
fulvoguttata, 144
Melanoplus bivittatus, 234
devastator, 233
femurrubrum, 234
packardii, 234
sanguinipes, 234
spretus, 234
Melanotrichus althaeae, 172
Melanotus oregonensis, 434
Melaphis rhois, 78
Melissopus latiferreanus, 193
Melia azedarach, 470
Melicocca bijuga, 545
Melittia cucurbitae, 156
Melittoma sericeum, 139
Meloidae, 90

Meloidera, 315
  floridensis, 325
Meloidogyne, 315, 325
  arenaria, 324
    thamesii, 330
  hapla, 324
  incognita acrita, 131
    incognita, 327
  javanica, 327
Melon, 515
  aphid, 69, Plates **I, II**
  fly, 227
Melonworm, 196, Plate
  XXXVI
Membracidae, 403
Menazon, 17
Mentha, 516
Mercuric chloride, 17
Mercurous chloride, 17
Merothripidae, 396
Merothrips morgani, 396
Mesembryanthemum, 515
Mesquite, 516
Metacide, 17
Metaldehyde, 17
Metallus rubi, 249
Metamorphosis, 41, **42**
Metaponia rubriceps, 224
Metaponium abnorme, 99
Metapside, 17
Meta-Systox, 18
Metcalfa pruinosa, 333
Metepa, 17
Methiotepa, 17
Methotrexate, 17
Methoxychlor, 17
Methyl apholate, 18
Methyl bromide, 18, 331
Methyl chloride, 18
Methyl demeton, 18
Methyl parathion, 18
Methyl Trithion, 18
Metriona bicolor, 105
Mexican bean beetle, Plate
  IX
Mexican fruit fly, 227
Mexican mealybug, 272
Mexican orange, 470
Mexican wax scale, 371
Miccotrogus picirostris,
  419
Michaelis fuscata, 450

Microbial insecticides, **5**
Microcentrum retinerve,
  237
  rhomifolium, 237
*Microcephalothrips ab-
  dominalis,* 397
Microlarinus spp., 424
Micromyzus violae, 80
Microtheca ochroloma,
  132
Midge(s), 273
  apple leaf-curling, 273
  artemisia gall, 274
  balsam gall, 274
  cactus fruit gall, 274
  catalpa, 274
  cattleya, 274
  chrysanthemum gall,
    Plate XXVII
  cranberry tipworm, 275
  dogwood club-gall, 275
  Douglas-fir cone, 275
  false leaf mining, 275
  gouty pitch gall, 275
  grape blossom, 275
  grape gall, 275
  grapevine tomato gall,
    275
  honeylocust pod gall,
    275
  juniper, 275
  Monterey-pine, 275
  Monterey-pine resin, 276
  pear, 276
  pear leaf, 276
  rhododendron tip, 276
  rose, **276,** Plate XXVII
  spruce gall, 277
  sunflower seed, 277
  violet gall, 277
  willow beaked-gall, 277
Mignonette, 516
Mignonette-tree, 516
Migratory grasshopper,
  234
Milax gagates, 386
Mildex, 16
Miller amendment, 9
Millipedes, 39, 277, **278,**
  Plate XXIX
Mimosa, 516
  scale, 371

  webworm, 413
Mimulus, 516
Mindarus abietinus, 56
Mining scale, 371
Mint, 516
  aphid, 70
  flea beetle, 116
Minute pirate bugs, 162
Mipafox, 18
Mirex, 18
Miridae, 163
Mistflower, 488
Mite(s), 278
  acarid, 279
  almond, 282
  apple rust, 279
  ash flower-gall, 279
  avocado brown, 279
  avocado red, 280
  azalea, 288
  balsam root, 280
  bamboo, 280
  Banks grass, 280
  beech, 280
  beet, 280
  Bermuda grass, 280
  blackberry bud, 280, 284
  blister, 279
  blueberry bud, 280
  bugle bud, 281
  bulb, 281
  bulb scale, 281
  boxwood, 280
  broad, 281
  brown, 282
  camellia bud, 282
  carnation, 282
  citrus bud, 281
  citrus flat, 282
  citrus red, 282
  citrus rust, 282
  clover, 282
  currant bud, 283
  cyclamen, 283, Plate
    XXX
  cypress, 284
  date, 280
  desert spider, 284
  dried-fruit, 279, 284
  dryberry, 284
  European red, 284
  false spider, 279

fig, 284
filbert bud, 285
four-spotted spider, 285
fruit-tree, 285
gall, 279
Garman spider, 285
Germander leaf crinkle, 285
grape bud, 285
grape erineum, 285
grape rust, 285
hackberry witches-broom, 285
harvest, 279
holly, 288
honeylocust spider, 285
Lewis spider, 286
litchi, 286
mango bug, 286
maple bladder-gall, 286
McDaniel spider, 286
oak, 286
olive leaf, 286
omnivorous, 286
oncidium, 286
pallid, 283
peach rust, 287
peach silver, 287
pear leaf blister, 287
pear rust, 287
pecan leafroll, 287
phaelenopsis, 287
pine bud, 287
platanus, 288
plum rust, 288
pomegranate leafroll, 288
privet, 288
redberry, 288
Schoene spider, 288
six-spotted, 288
soft-bodied, 279
southern red, 288
southern two-spotted, 289
spider, 279
spruce spider, 289
strawberry crown, 283
strawberry spider, 290
taxus bud, 290
Texas citrus, 290
tip-dwarf, 290

tomato russet, 290
tumid spider, 290
two-spotted spider, Plate XXVII
walnut blister, 291
Willamette, 291
yellow spider, 291
Mitox, 11
Mock-orange, 516
Mole crickets, 43, 211
Mollusca, 385
Mollusks, 385
Momordia balsamina, 449
Monarch butterfly, 180
Monarthropalpus buxi, 249
Mondo, 521
Monellia caryae, 80
Monellis sumac aphid, 70
Monkeyflower, 516
Monkeypuzzle, 444, 516
Monkshood, 438
Monocesta coryli, 114
Monochamus maculosus, 126
    notatus, 116
    obtusus, 117
    oregonensis, 117
    scutellatus, 132
    titillator, 124
Monoctenus melliceps, 339
Monomorium minimum, 50
    pharaonis, 50
Mononychus vulpeculus, 421
Monophadnoides geniculatus, 347
Monoptilota pergratialis, 146
Monstera deliciosa, 467
Monterey-pine midge, 275
Monterey-pine resin midge, 276
Monterey-pine sawfly, 345
Monterey-pine tip moth, 304
Monterey-pine weevil, 422
Monterey-pine aphid, 70
Monterey-pine cone beetle, 116
Monterey-pine engraver, 116

Monterey-pine looper, 197
Moonflower, 516
Mordellidae, 90
Mordwilkoja vagabunda, 73
Morinda, 517
Mormon cricket, 210
Morning-glory, 517
    leaf cutter, 240
    leaf miner, 253
Morocide, 11
Morus, 518
Morzid, 18
Mossy rose-gall wasp, 409
Moth(s), 43, 45, 292
    Abbott's sphinx, 294
    abutilon, 294
    American dagger, 294
    apple fruit, 294
    artichoke plume, 295
    bagworm, 294
    banded sunflower, 295
    bella, 295
    brown-tail, 295
    buck, 295
    bud, 159
    buddleia, 296
    carpenterworm, 292
    catalpa sphinx, 296
    ceanothus clearwing, 296
    cecropia, 296
    clearwing, 292
    codling, 296, Plate XXV
    cottonwood dagger, 297
    crinkled flannel, 297
    Cynthia, 297
    cypress, 297
    cypress cone, 297
    cypress tip, 298
    diamondback, 298
    Douglas-fir cone, 298
    Douglas-fir pitch, 298
    Douglas-fir tussock, 298
    eight-spotted forester, 298
    elm sphinx, 299
    ermine, 299
    European pine shoot, 299, Plate III
    fan palm, 299
    flannel, 293
    gelechiid, 292

geometrid, 292
geranium plum, 299
ghost, 293
grape berry, 300
grape plume, 300
great ash sphinx, 300
gypsy, 300, Plate VI
hag, 302
hawk, 294
hickory tiger, 302
hickory tussock, 302
hornet, 302
imperial, 303
Io, 303
juniper, 303
lantana plume, 303
lappet, 303
leopard, 303, 304
luna, 304
madrona shield bearer, 304
Monterey-pine tip, 304
Nantucket pine tip, 304
Nevada buck, 305
noctuid, 293
oriental, 306
oriental fruit, 305
owlet, 293
pale tussock, 306
pandora, 306
pea, 306
pine cone, 307
pine tortrix, 307
pine tube, 307
pitch blister, 307
pitch twig, 307
plutellid, 293
promethea, 307
pyralid, 294
red-cedar tortrix, 308
regal, 308
resplendent shield bearer, 308
royal, 292
rusty tussock, 308
satin, 308
sequoia pitch, 308
silkworm, 294
silver-spotted tiger, 308
smeared dagger, 309
snout, 294

snowberry clearwing, 309
snow-white linden, 389
sphinx, 294
spotted tussock, 309
spruce epizeuxis, 309
spruce seed, 309
strawberry crown, 309
sunflower, 360
tiger, 292
tussock, 293
walnut sphinx, 310
western tussock, 310
white-lined sphinx, 310
white-marked tussock, 311
yucca, 293, 312
Zimmerman pine, 312
Mottled tortoise beetle, 116
Mountain-ash, 517
sawfly, 345
Mountain ebony, 450, 517
Mountain-holly, 517
Mountain-laurel, 517
Mountain leafhopper, 243
Mountain pine beetle, 116
Mourning-cloak butterfly, 180
Mouth parts, insect, 40
Muehlenbeckin, 517
Mulberry, 518
whitefly, 431
Mullein thrips, 400
Murgantia histrionica, 171
Musa, 449
Muscari, 496
Mushroom flies, 227
Mustard, 518
Mycetophilidae, 223
Mycodiplosis alternata, 275
Mylone, 331
Myosotis, 490
Myrica cerifera, 450
Myrmelon, 46
Myrmeleon, 46
Myrmeleontidae, 46
Myrtle, 518, 555
Myrtle, wax, 518
Myrtus, 518
Myzaphis bucktoni, 75
rosarum, 74

Myzocallis arundinariae, 56
discolor, 71
robiniae, 69
tiliae, 69
ulmifoliae, 63
Myzus cerasi, 57
leucocrini, 75
ligustri, 74
lythri, 69
monardi, 68
ornatus, 71
persicae, 66
porosus, 82

Nabidae, 163
Naccobus, 315
Naled, 18
Names, insect, 44, 45
Nandina, 518
Nantucket pine tip moth, 304
Naphthalene, 18
Narcissus, 518
bulb fly, 228
Narrow-winged mantis, 267
Nasturtium, 519
Nasturtium officinale, 557
Natal-plum, 464
Native elm bark beetle, 116, Plate X
Native holly leaf miner, 252
Natriphene, 18
Natural control, 4
Nautical borer, 148
Navel orangeworm, 197
Nectarine, 519, 524
Nectria coccinea var. faginata, 351
Negro bug, 173
Neididae, 162
Nelumbium, 512
Nemagon, 18, 331
Nemaphos, 13
Nematoda, 312, 314
Nematode(s), 312, 313, 317, 318, 326
American dagger, 318
bentgrass, 318
boxwood spiral, 318
bud and leaf, 320

burrowing, 318
cabbage cyst, 319
cactus cyst, 319
California dagger, 319
California meadow, 319
California spiral, 319
carnation pin, 319
Chamber's dagger, 320
Christie's spiral, 320
Christie's stubby root, 320
Chrysanthemum foliar, 317, 320
citrus, 320
citrus ring, 321
citrus spine, 321
clover cyst, 321
Cobb's awl, 321
Cobb's lance, 321
Cobb's meadow, 321
Cobb's ring, 321
Cobb's spiral, 321
corn meadow, 321
cotton root-knot, 321
crown-headed lance, 322
De Man's meadow, 322
European dagger, 322
false root-knot of sugar beets, 323
fern, 317, 327
fig cyst, 323
fig pin, 323
fig spine, 323
Godfrey's meadow, 323
golden, 323
grass, 318
grass cyst, 324
grass sheath, 324
northern root-knot, 324
oak sheathoid, 324
Pacific dagger, 324
pea cyst, 324
peanut root-knot, 324
Persian sessile, 325
pine cystoid, 325
pine sheathoid, 325
pine sting, 325
potato rot, 325
reniform, 325
Scribner's meadow, 326
Seinhorst stubby root, 327

sheath, 327
smooth-headed meadow, 327
southern root-knot, 327
soybean cyst, 327
spiral, 327
spring crimp, 327
Steiner's spiral, 328
stem and bulb, 328
sting, 329
strawberry dwarf, 327
stubby root, 329
stunt, 329
stylet, 329
sugar-beet, 329
sugarcane dwarf, 330
sugarcane stylet, 330
Tarjan's sheath, 330
teasel, 328
tesselate stylet, 330
Thames' root-knot, 330
Thorne's lance, 330
Thorne's meadow, 330
Thorne's needle, 330
tobacco cyst, 330
walnut meadow, 330
Wesson's sheathoid, 331
West African spiral, 331
wheat, 331
Zimmerman's spiral, 331
Zoysia spine, 331
Nematus bozemani, 346
proximus, 349
ribesii, 433
ventralis, 349
Nemesia, 519
Nemopanthus, 517
Neoborus amoenus, 165
Neoclytus acuminatus, 153
Neodiprion abietis, 339
americanum, 345
burkei, 345
excitans, 346
lecontei, 347
nanulus contortae, 346
nanulus, 348
pratti banksianae, 345
sertifer, 342
swainei, 349
taedae linearis, 346
tsugae, 344

Neolecanium cornuparvum, 370
Neolygus communis, 173
Neomyzus circumflexus, 61
Neophasia menapia, 181
Neotran, 18
Neotylenchus, 316
Nepeta, 466
Nephelodes emmedonia, 217
Nephopteryx rubrizonella, 150
subcaesiella, 258
uvinella, 263
Nephthytis, 519, 551
Nepticulidae, 293
Nepytia canosaria, 192
phantasmaria, 199
umbrosaria, 197
Nerine, 519
Nerium, 520
Net-winged beetles, 90
Neuroptera, 43, 46, 238
Neurotoma inconspicua, 346
Nevada buck moth, 305
New Jersey tea, 519
Newstead's scale, 371
New York weevil, 422
New Zealand spinach, 545
Nezara viridula, 175
Nialate, 15, 18
Nicotiana, 519
Nicotine, 18
Nicotine sulfate, 8, 18
Nigra scale, 371
Nilotaspis halli, 367
Ninebark, 519
Nitulidae, 90
Noctuidae, 140, 215, 293
Nodonota puncticollis, 122
Nolina, 519
Noline, 519
Nomius pygmaeus, 126
Norfolk-Island-pine, 444
Norma dietsiana, 263
Northeastern sawyer, 116
Northern brenthian, 148
Northern cedar bark beetle, 117
Northern corn rootworm, 338

Northern katydid, 238
Northern masked chafer, 117
Northern mole cricket, 211
  Plate XXI
Northern peanut nematode, 324
Northern root-knot nematode, 324
Northern walkingstick, 40
Norway-maple aphid, 70
  leafhoppers, 243
Nothotylenchus, 316
Notodontidae, 293
Nygmia phaeorrhoea, 295
Nymphaea, 557
Nymphalidae, 179
Nymphalis antiopa, 180
  californica, 179
Nymphs, 43
Nysius ericae, 168
Nyssa sylvatica, 553

Oak, 519
  aphids, 71
  cossid, 150
  eriococcus, 371
  gall wasps, 409
  gall scale, 371
  kermes, 371
  lace bug, 173
  leaf roller, 258
  leaf tiers, 263
  lecanium, 372
  mite, 286
  sapling borer, 148
  scale, 372
  sheathoid nematode, 324
  timberworm, 148
  treehoppers, 403
  twig pruner, 158
  webworm, 413
Oak bird-cherry aphid, 71
Oakworm, orange-striped, 198
  pink-striped, 200
  red-humped, 201
  spiny, 202
Oberea bimaculata, 152
  myops, 136
  tripunctata, 141

Oblique-banded leaf roller, 258
Obtuse sawyer, 117
Obtuse scale, 372
Ocotea, 507
Odonaspis ruthae, 352
Odontopus calceatus, 424
Odorous house ant, 50
Oecanthus nigricornis nigricornis, 209
  quadripunctatus, 210
  niveus, 211
Oecophoridae, 293
Oedermeridae, 91
Oenothera, 488
  aphid, 71
Oestlundiella flava, 55
Oils, 8, 18
Okanagana, 209
Okra, 520
  caterpillar, 294
Olea, 521
Oleander, 520
  aphid, 71
  caterpillar, 197
  scale, 372
Oleaster-thistle aphid, 71
Olethreutidae, 137, 293
Oligonychus bicolor, 286
  coniferarum, 284
  ilicis, 288
  platani, 288
  pratensis, 280
  punicae, 279
  ununguis, 289
  yothersi, 280
Olive, 521
  bark beetle, 117
  fruit fly, 228
  leaf mite, 286
  parlatoria, 372
  scale, 372
Omnivorous leaf roller, 259
Omnivorous leaf tier, 263
Omnivorous looper, 197
Omnivorous mite, 286
OMPA, 20
Omphalocera dentosa, 410
Oncideres cingulata, 158
Oncidium mite, 286
One-spot stink bug, 173
Onion, 521

bulb fly, 228
  maggot, 265
  plant bug, 173
  thrips, 400
Operophthera bruceata, 389
Ophiopogon, 521
Orange, 521
Orange-dog, 198
Orange-humped mapleworm, 198
Orange-striped oakworm, 198
Orange sulfur butterfly, 181
Orange tortrix, 198
Orchid(s), 521
  aphid, 71
  bulb borer, 148
  plant bug, 173
  scale, 373
  thrips, 401
  weevil, 422
Orchidfly, 229
Orchid-tree, 450
Orcus chalybeus, 126
Oregon fir sawyer, 117
Oregon-grape, 513
Oregon wireworm, 434
Orgyria antiqua, 308
Oriental beetle, 44, 117
Oriental cherry, 469
Oriental earthworm, 219
Oriental fruit fly, 229
Oriental moth, 306
Oriental fruit moth, **305**
Oriental scale, 373
Orientus ishidae, 243
Ormenis pruinosa, 333
  septentrionalis, 334
Ornamental currant aphid, 71
Ornate aphid, 71
Orthezia, 332, **333**
  greenhouse, 332, **333**
Orthezia insignis, 332
Orthomorpha gracilis, 278
Orthoptera, 43, 209, 232, 237, 404
Osage-orange, 522
Osborniellus borealis, 244
Osborn's scale, 373
Oscinella frit, 225

Osmanthus, 522
Ostomatidae, 91
Ostrinia nubilalis, 141
Ostrya, 501
  virginiana, 504
Oulema melanopa, 97
Ovatus crataegarius, 70
Ovex, 19
Ovotran, 19
Owl beetle, 102
Owlet moths, 293
Oxalis, 522
Oxeye daisy, 482
Oxychilus spp., 387
Oxypleurites maxwelli, 286
Oystershell scale, 373, Plate
  XXXIV

Pachira fastuosa, 543
Pachnaeus litus, 419
Pachybrachius bilobata,
  173
Pachypsylla celtidis-
  mamma, 335
Pachysandra, 522
Pachyzancla bipunctalis,
  414
Pacific brown lacewing,
  239
Pacific Coast wireworm,
  434
Pacific dagger nematode,
  324
Pacific flatheaded borer,
  148
Pacific spider mite, 286
Pacific willow leaf beetle,
  118
Packard grasshopper, 234
Paeonia, 527
Painted beauty, 181
Painted hickory borer, 149
Painted lady, 181
Painted leafhopper, 243
Painted maple aphid, 71
Paleacrita vernata, 184
Palaeococcus rosae, 379
Pale chrysanthemum aphid,
  71
Pale juniper webworm, 413
Pales weevil, 423
Pale-sided cutworm, 217

Pale-striped flea beetle,
  104, 118, Plate VII
Pale tussock moth, 306
Pale western cutworm, 217
Palinaspis quohogiformis,
  378
Pallid mite, 283, 287
Palm(s), 482, 523
  aphid, 71
  leaf miner, 261
  leaf skeletonizer, 261
  mealybug, 270
  scale, 383
Palmerworm, 199
Pameras, 173
Palmetto, 522
  scale, 374
Pamphilidae, 339
Pamphilius dentatus, 339
  persicus, 345
Panaphis juglandis, 62, 80
Panax, 493
Pandanus, 523, 542
Pandemis limitata, 260
Pandora moth, 306
Panonychus citri, 282
  ulmi, 284
Pansy, 523
Pantographa limata, 256
Pantomorus godmani, 104
Papaipema cataphracta,
  138
  nebris, 156
  purpurifascia, 140
Papaya, 523
  fruit fly, 229
Paper mulberry, 457
Papilio cresphontes, 198
  glaucus, 182
  polyxenes asterius, 191
  rutulus, 182
  troilus, 182
  zelicaon, 182
Papilionidae, 179
Paracide, 19
Paraclemensia acerifo-
  liella, 240
Para-dichlorobenzene, 19
Parallelodiplosis cattleyae,
  274
Paralobesia viteana, 300
Paramyelois transitella, 197

Parandra brunnea, 138
Paraneotermes simplici-
  cornis, 395
Para-oxon, 19
Parasa indetermina, 203
Parathion, 19
Paratimia conicola, 154
Paratrechina longicornis,
  49
Paratrioza cockerelli, 336
Paratylenchus, 314, 325
  dianthus, 319
  hamatus, 323
Paria fragariae, 338
Paris green, 8, 19
Parkinsonia, 523
Parlatoria camelliae, 355
  chinensis, 356
  oleae, 372
  pergandii, 356
  pyri, 376
Parlatoria date scale, 374
Parlatorialike scale, 374
Parsley, 523
Parsleyworm, 191
Parsnip, 523
  webworm, 413
Parthenocissus quinque-
  folia, 556
  tricuspidata, 504
Passiflora, 524
Passion-flower, 524
Pastinaca, 523
Paurodontus, 316
Pavement ant, 50
Pawpaw, 524
Pea, 524
  aphid, 71
  cyst nematode, 324
  leaf miner, 254
  leaf weevil, 423
  moth, 306
  weevil, 423
Pea-tree, 463
Peach, 524
  bark beetle, 118
  beetle, 103
  lecanium, 374
  rust mite, 287
  sawfly, 345
  silver mite, 287

tree borer, 149, Plate XVI
twig borer, 150
Pealius azaleae, 428
Peanut, 525
  root-knot nematode, 324
Pear, 546
  borer, 136
  fruit borer, 150
  leaf blister mite, 287
  leaf midge, 276
  midge, 276
  plant bug, 173
  psylla, 335, Plate XXII
  rust mite, 287
  thrips, 401
Pear-slug, 346
  California, 340
Pecan, 526
  borer, 150
  bud moth, 160
  carpenterworm, 150
  cigar casebearer, 186
  leaf casebearer, 186
  leaf phylloxera, 72
  leafroll mite, 287
  nut casebearer, 186
  phylloxera, 72
  shuckworm, 195
  spittlebug, 391
  weevil, 423
Pectinophora gossypiella, 133
Pegomya betae, 248
  hyoscyami, 254
  rubivora, 266
Pelargonium, 493, 527
  aphid, 64
Pelicinidae, 407
Pelidnota punctata, 126
Pemphigus balsamiferae, 73
  betae, 78
  brevicornis, 69
  bursarius, 69
  populitransversus, 72
Penstemon, 527
Pentac, 19
Pentalonia nigronervosa, 56
Pentas, 527
Pentatomidae, 163

Pentatrichopus fragarae-folii, 78
Peony, 527
  scale, 374
Peperomia, 527
Pepper, 527
  maggot, 265
  weevil, 424
Pepper-tree, 528
Peranbrus scabricollis, 210
Peregrinus maidis, 333
Peretima hupeiensis, 219
Pergandeidia trirhoda, 59
Peridroma saucia, 218
Perilampidae, 407
Perillus bioculatus, 177
Periodical cicada, 207, 208
Periphyllus americanus, 55
  bruneri, 73
  lyropictus, 70
  negundinis, 58
  salicorticis, 81
Periploca nigra, 303
Periwinkle, 518, 555
Persea americana, 448
Persian sessile nematode, 325
Persimmon, 528
  borer, 150
  psylla, 336
Perthane, 19
Pestox III, 19, 20
Petroselinum, 523
Petrova albicapitana, 307
  comstockiana, 307
Petunia, 528
Phaedon aeruginosus, 130
Phalacridae, 91
Phalaenidae, 215, 293
Phalenopsis mite, 287
Phalonia hospes, 295
  rutilana, 413
Phaloniidae, 293
Phantom hemlock looper, 199
Pharoah ant, 50
Phaseolus, 451
Phasmatidae, 404
Phasmidia, 314
Pheidole megacephala, 48
Phellodendron, 529

Phenacaspis nyssae, 381
  pinifoliae, 375
Phenacoccus acericola, 370
  aceris, 268
  colemanni, 270
  gossypii, 272
Phenothiazine, 19
Phigalia looper, 199
Phigalia titea, 199
Philadelphus, 516
Philaenus leucophthalmus, 391
  spumarius, 391
Philodendron, 529
Phloeosinus canadensis, 117
  cupressi, 96
  dentatus, 96
  punctatus, 90, 130
Phloeothripidae, 396
Phloeotribus liminaris, 118
Phlox, 529
  plant bug, 174
Phobetron pithecium, 302
Phoenicoccus marlatti, 378
Phoenix dactylifera, 482
Pholus achemon, 294
Phorate, 19
Phorodon humuli, 68
  menthae, 70
Phosdrin, 19
Phosphamidon, 19
Phostex, 19
Photinia, 529
Photinia arbutifolia, 461
Phryganidia californica, 189
Phycitidae, 184, 293
Phyllaphis fagi, 56
Phyllocnistis populiella, 248
  vitigenella, 251
Phyllocoptes gracilis, 284
Phyllocoptruta oleivora, 282
Phyllonorycter crataegella, 247, 255
  felinella, 256
  malifoliella, 247
Phyllophaga spp., 111
  bruneri, 99
Phyllotreta armoraciae, 108

cruciferae, 96
pusilla, 130
ramosa, 131
striolata, 128
zimmermanni, 122
Phylloxera, grape, 65
pecan, 72
pecan leaf, 72
Phylloxera devastatrix, 72
notabilis, 72
vitifoliae, 65
Phylloxerinae, 53
Phymatidae, 163
Physalis, 470, 497
ixocarpa, 552
Physocarpus, 519
Physokermes piceae, 381
Physostegia, 529
Phytomyza albiceps, 256
atricornis, 250
delphiniae, 253
ilicicola, 252
ilicis, 252
minuscula, 250
Phytophaga piceae, 277
rigidae, 277
violicola, 277
Phytoptipalpidae, 279
Phytoptus avellanae, 285
pini, 287
Picea, 546
Picfume, 331
Pickleworm, 199, Plate
XXXVI
Pieridae, 179
Pieris, 441, 529
Pieris protodice, 202
rapae, 196
Pigeon tremex, 150
Pikonema alaskensis, 349
dimmockii, 344
Pilea, 445
Pillbugs, 388
Pilocrocis tripunctata, 260
Pine, 529
aphids, 72
bark aphid, 72
bud mite, 287
butterfly, 181
chafer, 118
colaspis, 118
cone moth, 307

cystoid nematode, 325
engraver, 118
false webworm, 413
gall weevil, 424
leaf aphid, 72
looper, 200
needle miner, 254
needle scale, 375, Plate
XXXIII
needle-sheath miner,
254
pyralid, 414
reproduction weevil, 424
root collar weevil, 424
sawflies, 346
sawyer, 116
scales, 375
sheathoid nematode, 325
spittlebug, 392
sting nematode, 325
tortoise scale, 375
tortrix, 307
tube moth, 307
tussock moth, 307
webworm, 414
Pineapple, 530
mealybug, 272
scale, 375
Pineus floccus, 77
pinifoliae, 72
similis, 77
strobi, 72
Pink bollworm, 133
Pink scavenger caterpillar,
200
Pink-striped oakworm, 200
Pinnaspis aspidistrae, 362
strachani, 369
Pin nematodes, 325
Pin-oak sawfly, 346
Pinon cone beetle, 119
Pinus, 529
Pinworm, tomato, 203
Pinyon needle scale, 376
Piperonyl butoxide, 19
Piperonyl cyclonene, 20
Pipevine swallowtail, 181
Pissodes engelmanni, 420
nemorensis, 420
radiatae, 422
sitchensis, 424
strobi, 426

terminalis, 422
yosemite, 427
Pistachio, 531
Pistacia, 531
Pistol casebearer, 186, 187
Pistol-grip duster, 35
Pisum, 524
Pitch blister moth, 307
Pitch mass borer, 150
Pitch twig moth, 307
Pithecellobium, 531
Pit scales, 376
Pitted ambrosia beetle,
119
Plagiodera versicolora, 108
Plagiognathus albatus, 176
Plains false wireworm, 434
Plane, 550
Plantain lily, 502
Plant bug(s), 163, 173
alfalfa, 163
ash, 165
big-legged, 166
caragana, 167
four-lined, 168, 169
hickory, 172
hollyhock, 172
hop, 172
meadow, 173
onion, 173
orchid, 173
phlox, 174
rapid, 174
superb, 176
sycamore, 176
tarnished, 176
yucca, 178
Planthopper(s), 333, 334
citrus flatid, 33
corn, 333
Plant Quarantine Act, 2, 5
Platanus, 550
Platanus mite, 288
Plathypena scabra, 194
Platycotis quadvittata, 403
vittata, 403
Platynotus stultana, 259
Platyptilia antirrhina, 309
carduidactyla, 295
pica, 299
pusilodactyla, 303
Platypus, 92

Plectrodera scalator, 140
Plum, 531
  curculio, 2, 214, Plate
    XXII
  gouger, 119
  leafhopper, 243
  nursery mite, 288
  rust mite, 288
  web-spinning sawfly,
    346
Plumbago, 532
Plumeria, 491
Plum-yew, 467
Plunger duster, 34
Plutella maculipennis, 298
Plutellid moths, 293
Podapion gallicola, 424
Podisus maculiventris, 175
Podocarpus, 532
Podosesia syringae, 136
       syringae, 146
Poecilocapsus lineatus, 168
Pogonomyrmex badius, 49
  barbatus, 50
  californicus, 49
  occidentalis, 51
Poinciana, 532
Poinsettia, 532
Poker-plant, 532
Pole borer, 138
Polia legitima, 203
Polianthes tuberosa, 553
Polycaon confertus, 137
Polyhedrosis virus, 5
Polygonum aphid, 75
Polygonum aubertii, 543
Polyphaga, 88
Polyphemus moth, 307
Polyphylla decemlineata,
  128
Pomace flies, 223
Pomegranate, 532
  leafroll mite, 288
Pondapple, 533
Ponderosa-pine bark borer,
  151
  cone beetle, 119
Popillia japonica, 109
Poplar, 533
  aphids, 73
  borer, 151
  leaf-folding sawfly, 346

leafhopper, 243
leaf-petiole gall aphid,
  73
leaf-purse aphid, 73
petiole gall aphid, 72
sawfly, 346
sugar-beet root aphid,
  73
tent maker, 200
twig gall aphid, 73
vagabond aphid, 73
Poplar-and-willow borer,
Poppy, 533
Populus, 533
Porcellio laevis, 388
Porthetria dispar, 300
Portulaca, 533
Potato, 533
  aphid, 73, Plate II
  beetle, 97, 128
  flea beetle **104**, 119,
    Plate VII
  leafhopper, 243, Plate
    XIV
  psyllid, 336
  rot nematode, 325
  scab gnat, 229
  stalk borer, 151
  tuberworm, 152
Potentilla, 472, 534
Pothos, 534
Powder post beetles, 90,
  119
Powder-puff, 462
Powdery pine needle aphid,
  72
Powdery spruce aphid, 77
Power sprayer, **27**, 30
Prairie flea beetle, 120
Prairielily, 475
Prairie tent caterpillar, 200
Prairie walkingstick, 405
Pratyenchoides, 315
Pratylenchus, 315
  brachyurus, 323
  coffeae, 321
  leiocephalus, 323
  minyus, 319
  penetrans, 321
  pratensis, 322
  scribneri, 326
  thornei, 330

  vulnus, 330
  zeae, 331
Praying mantis, 266, 267
Prescott scale, 376
Prickly-ash, 535
Primrose, 535
Primula, 535
Prionoxystus robiniae, 139
Prionus californicus, 138
  imbricornis, 158
  laticollis, 137
Pristiphora californica, 340
  erichsonii, 345
  geniculata, 345
Privet, 535
  aphid, 74
  leafhopper, 244
  leaf miner, 254
  mite, 288
  scale, 376
  thrips, 401
Procecidochares utilis, 225
Prociphilus corrugatus, 82
  erigeronensis, 80
  fraxinifolii, 68
  imbricator, 57
  tessellatus, 81
  xylostei, 82
Prodenia eridania, 84
  ornithogalli, 84
  praefica, 84
Prodoxidae, 293
Promethea moth, 307
Prominents, 293
Propyl isome, 20
Prosapia bicincta, 392
Prosopis glandulosa, 516
Proteoteras willingana, 137
Protoparce quinquemacu-
  lata, 236
  sexta, 236
Protopulvinaria pyrifor-
  mis, 377
Pruinose whitefly, 432
Prune, 531, 535
  leafhopper, 244
Prunus armeniaca, 443
  avium, 468
  cerasus, 468
  communis, 440
  domestica, 531
  laurocerasus, 467

lyoni, 465
persica, 523
pumila, 469
virginiana, 470
Pseudaletia unipuncta, 83
Pseudanthonomus validus, 420
Pseudaonidia clavigera, 355
duplex, 355
paeoniae, 374
Pseudaulacaspis pentagona, 384
Pseudococcidae, 267
Pseudococcus adonidum, 272
aurilanatus, 270
brevipes, 272
citri, 269
comstocki, 270
cuspidatae, 273
gahani, 268
juniperi, 271
krauhniae, 271
malacearum, 270
maritimus, 271
nipae, 270
ryani, 270
sequoiae, 272
solani, 272
wistariae, 273
Pseudocneorhinus bifasciatus, 421
Pseudodacus pallens, 224
Pseudohylesinus grandis, 122
granulatus, 122
Pseudoparlatoria parlatorioides, 374
Pseudophilippia quaintancii, 358
Pseudotsuga, 485
Psidium, 497
Psila rosae, 224
Psilenchus, 316
Psilidae, 223
Psilocorsis faginella, 262
quercicella, 263
reflexella, 263
Psorosina hammondi, 260
Psychidae, 294
Psylla floccosa, 334

mali, 334
negundinis, 334
pyricola, 335
uncatoides, 334
Psylla, pear, 335, Plate XXII
persimmon, 336
Psyllid(s), 334
acacia, 334
alder, 334
apple sucker, 334
blackberry, 334
boxelder, 334
boxwood, **335**
hackberry nipple-gall, 335
laurel, 335
potato, 336
sumac, 337
tomato, 336
willow, 337
Psylliodes punctulata, 108
Ptelea, 501
Pteridae, 179
Pterocomma bicolor, 81
pseudo-populea, 73
smithiae, 81
Pteromalidae, 407
Pterophoridae, 294
Pterophorus periscelidactylus, 300
Pterophylla camellifolia, 238
Ptinidae, 119
Pueraria, 506
Puerto Rican mole cricket, 210
Puget Sound wireworm, 434
Pulverulent snowberry aphid, 76
Pulvinaria acericola, 362
amygdali, 358
ericicola, 381
floccifera, 358
innumerabilis, 358
psidii, 366
Pumpkin, 535
caterpillar, 206
Puncturevine weevil, 424
Punica granatum, 532
Puparium, 43

Purple-backed cabbageworm, 200
Purple scale, **376**
Purple-spotted lily aphid, 74
Puss caterpillar, 200
Pustule scale, 377
Putnam scale, 377
Puto yuccae, 273
Pyracantha, 536
Pyralidae, 294
Pyralid moths, 294
Pyramid ant, 50
Pyramidobela angelarum, 296
Pyrethrin, I, II, 20, 21
Pyrethrum, 20
Pyriform scale, 377
Pyrostegia, 490
Pyroderces rileyi, 200
Pyrrhia umbra, 160
Pyrrhocoridae, 163
Pyrus spp., 477
communis, 526
malus, 442

Quamoclit, 481
Quercus, 519
Quince, 536
curculio, 215
treehopper, 404
Quisqualis, 536
Quohog-shaped scale, 378

Radish, 536
Radopholus, 315
oryzae, 325
similis, 318
Railroad worm, 264
Rain, effect on spray, 32
Rainlily, 475
Rain-lily, 559
Raintree, 457
Ramosia bibionipennis, 309
mellinipennis, 296
resplendens, 158
rhododendri, 153
tipuliformis, 140
Randia, 537
Range caterpillar, 201
Rangoon creeper, 536
Ranunculus, 458

Raphanus sativus, 536
Raphiolepis, 503
Rapid plant bug, 174
Raspberry, 537
  aphids, 74
  cane borer, 152
  cane maggot, 266
  crown borer, 152
  horntail, 235
  leaf roller, 259
  root borer, 152
  sawfly, 347
Ravenala madagascariensis, 553
Recurvaria apictripunc-tella, 297
  milleri, 253
  nanella, 160
Red-admiral, 181
Red and black cherry aphid, 74
Red-and-black stink bug, 174
Red-backed cutworm, 218
Red-banded leafhopper, 244
Red-banded leaf roller, 259
Red-banded thrips, 402
Red bay scale, 378
Redberry mite, 288
Redbud, 537
  leaf roller, 259
Red bugs, 163
Red carpenter ant, 50
Redcedar, 506
  tortrix, 308
Red date scale, 378
Reddish brown poplar aphid, 73
Red elm bark weevil, 424
Red harvester ant, 50
Red-headed ash borer, 153
Red-headed pine sawfly, 347, Plate XXXI
Red-humped appleworm, 201
Red-humped caterpillar, 201, Plate XV
Red-humped oakworm, 201
Red-legged flea beetle, 120
Red-legged grasshopper, 234

Red milkweed beetle, 120
Red-necked cane borer, 153
Red-necked peanutworm, 201
Red-pine sawfly, 348
Red-pine scale, 378
Red spider destroyer, 120
Red spiders, 279, 290
Red turnip beetle, 120
Red turpentine beetle, 120
Reduviidae, 163
Reduvius personatus, 173
Red wax scale, 378
Red-winged pine beetle, 120
Redwood, 537
  mealybug, 272
  scale, 383
Regal moth, 195, 308
Reniform nematode, 325
Reseda, 516
Resistant varieties, 6
Resplendent shield bearer, 308
Reticulitermes flavipes, 394
  hesperus, 394
Retinodiplosis inopsis, 275
Retinospora, 538
Rhabdopterus beetles, 120
Rhabdopterus bowditchi, 120
  deceptor, 120
  picipes, 120, 337
  praetexus, 120
Rhagoletis cingulata, 224
  completa, 230
  fausta, 224
  pomella, 264
Rhamnus, 458
  californica, 461
Rheum, 538
Rhinoceros beetle, 121, Plate XI
Rhizobius ventralis, 95
Rhizoecus falcifer, 271
  kondonis, 271
Rhizogloephus echinopus, 281
  sagittae, 280
  tarsalis, 280
Rhizophera, 513

Rhodes-grass scale, 378
Rhodobaenus tredecim-punctatus, 419
Rhododendron, 448, 538
  aphid, 74
  borer, 153
  lace bug, 174, Plate XVII
  scale, 379
  tip midge, 276
  whitefly, 432
Rhopalandrothrips corni, 397
Rhopalosiphoninus tuli-paella, 79
Rhopalosiphum conii, 67
  fitchii, 55
  maidis, 60
  nymphaeae, 80
  padi, 71
  poae, 65
  pseudobrassicae, 79
  rhois, 70
Rhopobota naevana, 189
  ilicifoliana, 160
Rhothane, 20, 21
Rhubarb, 538
  curculio, 215
  weevil, 215
Rhus, 549
  ovata, 548
Rhyacionia buoliana, 299
  frustrana, 304
  pasadena, 304
Rhynchaenus pallicornis, 415
  rufipes, 427
Rhynchites bicolor, 215
Rhyncothrips ilex, 402
Ribautiana tenerrima, 242
Ribbon-bush, 538
Ribes, 480
  grossularia, 495
  hirtellum, 495
Ricepaper-plant, 538
Rice-root nematode, 325
Rice white-tip nematode, 325
Rice white top, 330
Ricinus, 465
Riley's ground pearl, 367

614 INDEX

Ring-legged earwig, 221
Ring nematodes, 325
Robber flies, 223
Robinia, 511
 hispida, 540
Rockcress, 444
Rock-rose, 538
Rocky Mountain grasshopper, 234
Rocky Mountain juniper aphid, 68
Rodolia cardinalis, 113
Roly-poly, 388
Romalea microptera, 233
Root collar borer, 153
Root-knot nematodes, 325
Root mealybug, 271
Rootworm(s), 337
 clover, 105
 cranberry, 337
 grape, 337
 northern corn, 338
 strawberry, 338
 western corn, 338
 western grape, 338
Rosa, 538
Rosalia funebris, 136
Rosary-pea, 538
Rose, 538
 aphid, 74, 75
 budworm, 160
 bug, 121
 chafer, 121, Plate XI
 curculio, 215, Plate XI
 grass aphid, 75
 leaf beetle, 122
 leafhopper, 244, 245
 leaf tier, 258
 midge, 276, Plate XXVII
 palaeococcus, 379
 root-gall wasp, 410
 scale, 379
 snout beetle, 215
 stem girdler, 153
 stem sawfly, 348
Rose-acacia, 540
Rose-mallow, 499
Rose-of-Sharon, 540
Rose-slug, 348
 bristly, 340
Rosy apple aphid, 75, Plate II

Rotary duster, 35, 36
Rotenone, 20
Rotylenchulus, 315
 reniformis, 325
Rotylenchus, 327, 315
 blaberus, 331
 brachyurus, 319
 buxophilus, 318
 robustus, 330
Roundheaded apple tree borer, 153, Plate XIV
Roundheaded cone borer, 154
Roundheaded fir borer, 154
Roundheaded pine beetle, 122
Rove beetles, 91
Royal moths, 292
Royal palm bug, 175
Royal poinciana, 532
Rubber plant, 540
Rubus, 454, 456, 537
 flagellaris, 483
 loganobacchus, 511
Rudbeckia, 494, 540
Rufous scale, 379
Rumex, 484
Russet-colored larkspur aphid, 75
Russian-olive, 486, 540
 aphid, 75
Rust flies, 223
Rustic borer, 154
Rusty plum aphid, 75
Rusty tussock moth, 308
Rutabaga, 540
Ryania, 20

Sabadilla, 20
Sabal, 522
Sabulodes caberata, 197
Saddleback caterpillar, 202
Saddled leafhopper, 245
Saddled prominent, 202
Safety measures, 10, 23
Sage, black, 540
 blue, 540
 scarlet, 540
 white, 540
Sagebrush, 445
 defoliator, 202
Sago palm, 480

St.-Bernards-lily, 442
St.-Johns-wort, 503
Saintpaulia, 438
Saissetia hemisphaerica, 367
 nigra, 371
 oleae, 352
Salal, 540
Salebria afflictella, 415
Salix, 557
Salsify, 541
Salt cedar, 551
Salt-marsh caterpillar, 202
Salvia, 540
Sambucus, 486
Samia cynthia, 297
Sanchezia, 541
Sandalwood, 541
Sand cherry, 469
 weevil, 424
Sand cricket, 210
Sand-lily, 541
 aphid, 75
Sand wireworm, 434
San Jose scale, 379, Plate XXXIV
Sannina uroceriformis, 150
Sanninoidea exitiosa, 149
 graefi, 159
Sansevieria, 541
Santalum, 541
Sap beetles, 90
Saperda calcarata, 151
 candida, 153
 discoidea, 108
 tridentata, 141
 vestita, 146
Sapindus, 544
Sapodilla, 541
Sapote, white, 541
Sapwood timberworm, 154
Saratoga spittlebug, 392
Sassafras, 541
 weevil, 424
Satinleaf, 541
Satin moth, 308
Saturniidae, 294
Satyridae, 179
Saururus, 511
Sausage-tree, 542
Sawfly(flies), 43, 339
 arborvitae, 339

balsam-fir, 339
birch, 339
blackberry, 339
black-headed ash, 340
bristly rose-slug, 340, Plate XXXII
brown-headed ash, 340
butternut woollyworm, 340
California pear-slug, 340
cedar cone, 340
cherry fruit, 340
cimbicid, 339
conifer, 339
curled rose, 340, Plate XXXII
cypress, 341
dock, 341
dogwood, 341
dusky birch, 341
elm, **341**
European apple, 342
European pine, **342**
European spruce, 343
goldenglow, 343
grape, 344
green-headed spruce, 344
hemlock, 344
honeysuckle, 344
imported currantworm, 344, Plate XXXII
introduced pine, 344, Plate XXXI
Jack-pine, 345
larch, 345
loblolly pine, 345
lodgepole, 345
Monterey-pine, 345
mountain-ash, 345
peach, 345
pear-slug, 346
pine, 346
pin-oak, 346
plum web-spinning, 346
poplar, 346
poplar leaf-folding, 346
raspberry, 347
red-headed pine, **347,** Plate XXXI
red-pine, 348
rose-slug, **348**
rose stem, 348

stem, 339
striped alder, 348
Swaine Jack-pine, 349
violet, 349
web-spinning, 339
willow, 349, Plate XXXI
willow red-gall, 349
willow shoot, 349
yellow-headed spruce, 349
Saxifraga, 542
Saxifrage, 542
Say stink bug, 175
Scabiosa, 542
Scale(s), 349
  acuminate, 350
  araucaria, 350
  arborvitae soft, 363
  Asiatic red, 350
  azalea bark, 350
  bamboo, 351
  barberry, 351
  barnacle, 351
  beech, 351
  Bermuda-grass, 352
  black, 352
  black araucaria, 352
  black pine leaf, 352
  black thread, 353
  Boisduval's, 353
  brown soft, 353
  cactus, 354
  calico, 354
  California red, 354
  camellia, 355
  camellia mining, 355
  camellia parlatoria, 355
  camphor, 355
  cassava, 356
  chaff, 356
  Chinese obscure, 356
  citricola, 356
  citrus snow, 356
  coconut, 356
  cottony bamboo, 357
  cottony cochineal, 357
  cottony-cushion, **357**
  cottony maple, 358, Plate XXXIV
  cottony peach, 358
  cottony pine, 358
  cottony taxus, 358

cranberry, 359
cyanophyllum, 359
cypress bark, 359
dictyospermum, 359
dogwood, 360
elm scurfy, 360
euonymus, 360, Plate XXXIII
European elm, 361
European fiorinia, 361
European fruit, 362
European fruit lecanium, **361,** 362
false cottony maple, 362
fern, **362**
fig, 363
Fletcher, 363
Florida red, **363**
Florida wax, 364
Forbes, 364
frosted, 365
globose, 365
gloomy, 365
Glover, 365
golden oak, 365
grape, 365
greedy, 365
green, 366
green shield, 366
ground pearls, 366
hall, 367
hemispherical, **367**
hemlock, 368
hickory, 368
holly, 368
Howard, 368
ivy, 372
Japanese, 369
Japanese wax, 369
juniper, 369, Plate XXXIII
latania, 369
lesser snow, 369
long soft, 370
magnolia, 370
mango, 370
maple phenacoccus, 370
masked, 370
Mexican wax, 371
mimosa, 371
mining, 371
Newstead's, 371

oak, 372
oak eriococcus, 371
oak lecanium, 372
obscure, 372
olive, 372
orchid, 373
oriental, 373
Osborn's, 373
oystershell, 373, Plate XXXIV
palm, 383
palmetto, 373
parlatoria date, 374
parlatorialike, 374
peach lecanium, 374
peony, 374
pineapple, 375
pine needle, 375, Plate XXXIII
pine tortoise, 375
pinyon needle, 376
pit, 376
Prescott, 376
privet, 376
purple, 376
pustule, 377
Putnam, 377
pyriform, 377
quohog-shaped, 378
red bay, 378
red date, 378
red-pine, 378
red wax, 378
Rhodes-grass, 378
rhododendron, 379
rose, 379
rose palaeococcus, 379
rufous, 379
San Jose, 379, Plate XXXIV
scurfy, 380, Plate XXXIV
soft azalea, 381
sour-gum, 381
Spanish red, 360
spirea, 381
spruce bud, 381
sweetgum, 381
sycamore, 381
tea, 381, 382
terrapin, 382
tesselated, 383

tuliptree, 383
Utah cedar, 383
walnut, 384
white peach, 384
willow scurfy, 384
yellow, 384
zamia, 384
Scalecide, 8
Scaphoideus luteolus, 246
Scaphytopius magdalensis, 245
Scapteriscus acletus, 212
vicinus, 210
Scarabaeidaei, 91
Scarab beetles, 91
Scarboro-lily, 554
Scarletbush, 498
Scarlet sage, 540
Scelionidae, 407
Schefflera, 542
Schemea, 542
Schinus molle, 528
terebinthifolius, 456
Schizanthus, 542
Schizaphis graminum, 66
Schizolachnus pineti, 72
piniradiatae, 72
Schizotetranychus celarius, 280
Schizura badia, 202
concinna, 201
ipomoeae, 202
letonoides, 202
unicornis, 203
Schizura caterpillars, 202
Schoene spider mite, 288
Schradan, 20
Sciara spp., 327
Scilla, 547
Scindapsus, 542
Scirtothrips citri, 397
Scleroacus vaccinii, 242
Scolioidea, 406
Scolytidae, 91, 139
Scolytus mali, 145
multistriatus, 122
muticus, 107
quadrispinosus, 107
rugulosus, 45, 155
unispinosus, 99
ventralis, 103
Scotch broom, 457

Scotogramma trifolii, 217
Screening, of chemicals, 9
Screwpine, 542
Scribner's meadow nematode, 326
Sculptured pine borer, 154
Scudderia furcata, 237
Scurfy scale, 380, Plate XXXIV
Scutellonema, 315, 327
blaberum, 331
brachyurum, 319
christiei, 320
Scutigerella immaculata, 206
Scyphophorus yuccae, 427
Seagrape, 542
borer, 154
Seakale, 542
Seamyrtle, 497
Sea-pink, 547
Secernentea, 314
Sechium edule, 468
Sedum, 542
aphid, 76
Seed beetles, 89
Seed chalcids, 407
Seed-corn beetle, 122
Seed-corn maggot, 266
Seinhorst stubby root nematode, 327
Selenaspidus articulatus, 379
Selenium, 20
Selenothrips rubrocinctus, 402
Semitropical armyworm, 84
Senecio, 497
Sequoia, 537
pitch moth, 308
Sericothrips variabilis, 396
Serissa, 543
Serpentine leaf miner, 254
Serviceberry, 543
Sesamex, 20
Sesamin, 20
Sesamolin, 20
Severinia, 543
Sevin, 12, 20
Shadbush, 543
Sharp-nosed leafhopper, 245

Shallot, 543
Shasta daisy, 482
Shaving-brush tree, 543
Sheath nematodes, 327
Shepherdia, 458
Shield bearers, 293
Shistocerca americana, 233
Shot-hole borer, 45, **155**
Shrimp-plant, 543
Sibine stimulea, 202
Siglure, 21
Silk-tree, 516
Silkworm moths, 294
Silky ant, 51
Silpha bituberosa, 124
Siphidae, 91
Silver fir beetles, 122
Silver lace-vine, 543
Silver-spotted skipper, 181
Silver-spotted tiger moth, 308
Silver-tree, 543
Silver-vine, 543
Sinuate pear tree borer, 155
Sinuate-striped flea beetle, 122
Siphonatrophia cupressi, 61
   gravida, 68
Sirex aerolatus, 235
   californicus, 235
   cyaneus, 235
Siricidae, 150, 234
Sitka-spruce beetle, 122
Sitka-spruce weevil, 424
Sitona cylindricollis, 425
   hispidula, 213
   lineata, 423
Six-spotted leafhopper, 245, Plate XXIV
Six-spotted mite, 288
Skin beetles, 90
Skipper(s), 43, 179
   columbine, 179
   silver-spotted, 181
Sleeping hibiscus, 553
Slender brown lacewing, 239
Slide sprayer, 29
Slug(s), 385, Plate XXIX
   giant, 387

gray field, 386
gray garden, 386
greenhouse, 386
spotted garden, **387**
tawny garden, 388
Slug caterpillars, 293
Small carpenter bee, **86, 87**
Small chestnut weevil, 425
Small darkling ground beetle, 99
Smaller European elm bark beetle, 122, Plate X
Smaller Mexican pine beetle, 123
Smaller yellow ant, 51
Small green rose aphid, 74
Small milkweed bug, 175
Smeared dagger moth, 309
Smilax, 446, 543
Smoke-tree, 543
Smooth-headed meadow nematode, 327
Smynthurodes betae, 76
Snail(s), 385
   banded wood, 386
   brown garden, 386
   citrus tree, 386
   grass, 386
   greenhouse, 387
   Manatee, 386
   subulina, 388
   white garden, 388
Snapdragon, 544
   plume moth, 309
Sneezeweed, 499
Snout beetles, 89
Snout moths, 294
Snowball, 544, 555
   aphid, **76**, Plate II
Snowberry, 544
   aphid, 76
   clearwing, 309
Snowflake, 509
Snow-on-the-mountain, 488
Snow-white linden moth, 389
Snowy tree cricket, 211, Plate XXI
Soapberry, 544
Social wasps, 407
Sodium arsenate, 21

Sodium arsenite, 21
Sodium fluoride, 21
Sodium fluosilicate, 21
Sodium selenate, 21
Sod webworms, 414
Soft azalea scale, 381
Soft-bodied mites, 279
Soft brown scale, 353
Soft scale, 353
Solandra, 468
Solanum mealybug, 272
   root louse, 76
Solanum melongena var. *esculentum*, 485
   pseudocapsicum, 505
   tuberosum, 533
Soldier beetles, 89
Soldier flies, 223
Solenopsis geminata, 49
   molesta, 51
   richteri, 49
   xyloni, 51
Solidago, 494
Solitary oak leaf miner, 254
Solitary wasps, 407
Somatium oviformis, 120
Sophora, 505
Sorbus, 517
Sourgum, 544, 553
   casecutter, 256
   scale, 381
Soursop, 544
Southern armyworm, 84
Southern beet webworm, 414
Southern cabbageworm, 202
Southern corn billbug, 133
Southern corn rootworm, 338
Southern cornstalk borer, 156
Southern earwig, 221
Southern fire ant, 51
Southern garden leafhopper, 246
Southern green stink bug, 175
Southern hornworm, 236
Southern masked chafer, 117

Southern mole cricket, 212
Southern pine beetle, 123
Southern pine sawyer, 124
Southern potato wireworm, 434
Southern red mite, 288
Southern root-knot nematode, 327
Southern squash bug, 172
Southern two-spotted mite, 289
Southwestern corn borer, 156
Southwestern pine beetle, 124
Sowbug(s), 388, Plate XXIX
  dooryard, 388
Sowthistle aphid, 76
Soybean, 544
  cyst nematode, 327
Spaelotis clandestina, 218
  havilae, 218
Spanish bayonet, 545
Spanish dagger, 545
Spanish-lime, 545
Spanish-needles, 545
Spanish red scale, 360
Spanworm(s), 389
  Bruce, 389
  cleftheaded, 389
  cranberry, 389
  currant, 389
  elm, 389
  walnut, 390
Sparganothis fruitworm, 232
Sparganothis sulphuriana, 232
Sparkleberry, 545
Sphaeronema, 315
Sphecidae, 407
Sphecodina abbotti, 294
Sphecoidea, 406
Sphenophorus callosus, 133
  maidis, 133
  parvulus, 133
  phoeniciensis, 133
Sphingidae, 236, 294
Sphinx achemon, 294
  chersis, 300
Sphinx moths, 236, 294

Spicebush, 545
  swallowtail, 182
Spider-lily, 503
Spider mites, 279
Spider wasps, 407
Spilonota ocellana, 159
Spinach, 545
  aphid, 66
  carrion beetle, 124
  flea beetle, 124, Plate VII
  leaf miner, 254
Spinach, New Zealand, 545
Spinacia, 545
Spindleworm, corn, 141
Spined soldier bug, 175
Spiny elm caterpillar, 180
Spiny oakworm, 202
Spiny witch-hazel gall aphid, 81
Spiraea, 545
Spiral nematodes, 327
Spirea, 545
  aphid, 77
  scale, 381
Spirobolus marginatus, 278
Spissistilus festinus, 404
Spittlebug(s), 390, 391
  alder, 391
  ceanothus, 391
  cranberry, 391
  dogwood, 391
  lined, 391
  meadow, 391
  pecan, 391
  pine, 392
  Saratoga, 392
  sunflower, 392
Spodoptera exigua, 83
  mauritia acronyctoides, 84
Spondias, 500
Spotted alfalfa aphid, 77
Spotted asparagus beetle, 124, Plate IV
Spotted beet webworm, 414
Spotted blister beetle, 125
Spotted cucumber beetle, 125, Plate XII
Spotted cutworm, 218
Spotted garden slug, 387

Spotted grapevine beetle, 126
Spotted hemlock borer, 144
Spotted pine sawyer, 126
Spotted poplar aphid, 73
Spotted spruce aphid, 77
Spotted tentiform leaf miner, 255
Spotted tussock moth, 309
Spotted-winged raspberry aphid, 74
Sprayers, 25, 26, 27, 28, 29
Spraying, 25, 30, 32
Spreader-sticker, 23
Sprekelia, 546
Spring cankerworm, 183, 184
Spring crimp nematode, 327
Spring dwarf, 327
Springtail(s), 43, 392
  garden, 393
Spruce, 546
  aphids, 77
  bud moth, 160
  bud scale, 381
  budworm, 161
  epizeuxis, 309
  gall aphids, 53, 59, 60, 62, 63, 77
  gall midge, 277
  needle miner, 255
  seed moth, 309
  spider mite, 289
Spurge, 488, 522
Squash, 546
  beetle, 126
  bug, 175, Plate XII
  vine borer, 156, Plate XVI
Squill, 547
Stag beetles, 90
Staggerbush, 547
Stagomantis carolina, 267
Stainers, 163
Stalk borer, 156
Staphylea, 455
Staphylinidae, 91
Star-apple, 547
Statice, 547
Steel-blue flea beetle, 126

Steel-blue lady beetle, 126
Stegasta bosqueella, 201
Stegophylla quercicola, 71
Stem and bulb nematode, 328
Steiner's spiral nematode, 328
Stem sawflies, 234, 339
Steneotarsonemus laticeps, 281
  pallidus, 283
Stenolobium, 486
Stenopelmatus fuscus, 210
Stephanitis globulifera, 164
  pyrioides, 165
  rhododendri, 174
Stephanoderes obscurus, 92
Stephanotis, 547
Sternechus paludatus, 416
Sternochetus lapathi, 151
Stictocephala bubalus, 403
Stilpnotia salicis, 308
Stilt bugs, 162
Stinging rose caterpillar, 203
Sting nematodes, 329
Stink beetle, 126
Stink bug(s), 163
  brown, 167
  dusky, 168
  green, 170
  one-spot, 173
  Say, 175
  southern green, 175
  two-spotted, 177
Stizolobium, 554
Stock, 547
Stomacoccus platani, 381
Strangler fig, 489
Strategus, 121
Stratiomyidae, 223
Strauzia longipennis, 266
Strawberry, 547
  aphid, 78
  bud nematode, 330
  crown borer, 157
  crown miner, 255
  crown mite, 283
  crown moth, 309
  dwarf nematode, 327, 330
  flea beetle, 126

fruitworm, 263
leaf roller, 259
root weevil, 425
rootworm, 338
spider mite, 290
weevil, 425
whitefly, 432
Strawberry-tree, 548
Strawflower, 548
Strelitzia, 548
Strepsistera, 91
Striped alder sawfly, 348
Striped ambrosia beetle, 127
Striped blister beetle, 44, 127, Plate V
Striped cucumber beetle, 125, 127, Plate XII
Striped cutworm, 218
Striped flea beetle, 128, Plate VII
Striped garden caterpillar, 203
Striped mealybug, 273
Striped tortoise beetle, 128
Strobilanthes, 548
Stubby root nematode, 329
Stunt nematodes, 329
Stylet nematodes, 329
Stylommatophora, 385
Stylopidae, 91
Subulina octona, 388
Subulina snail, 388
Sugar-apple, 548
Sugar-beet nematode, 329
  root aphid, 78
  wireworm, 434
Sugar-bush, 548
Sugarcane borer, 157
  stylet nematode, 330
Sugar-maple borer, 157
Sugar-pine cone beetle, 128
Sulfotepp, 21
Sulfoxide, 21
Sulfur, 21, 22
Sulphenone, 21
Sumac, 549
  gall aphid, 78
  psyllid, 337
Summer dwarf nematode, 330

Sunflower, 549
  aphid, 62, 78
  beetle, 128
  maggot, 266
  moth, 310
  peacock fly, 266
  seed midge, 277
  spittlebug, 392
Superb plant bug, 176
Surinam-cherry, 549
Susanna cupressi, 341
Swaine Jack-pine sawfly, 349
Sweet alyssum, 440
Sweetbay, 549
Sweet bay, 450
Sweetclover aphid, 78
  weevil, 425
Sweetfern, 549
Sweetgum, 549
  leaf tier, 263
  scale, 381
  webworm, 415
Sweetolive, 522
Sweetpea, 550
Sweetpotato, 550
  beetles, 129
  caterpillar, 84
  hornworm, 236
  leaf beetle, 128
  leaf miner, 255
  leaf roller, 260
  root borer, 426
  weevil, 425
  whitefly, 432
Sweetshrub, 462
Sweet-william, 550
Swietenia, 513
Swifts, 293
Swiss chard, 550
Sycamore, 550
  aphid, 79
  borer, 158
  leaf miner, 256
  plant bug, 176
  scale, 381
  tussock moth, 310
Sylvora acerni, 148
Symmerista albicosta, 201
  albifrons, 201
  leucitys, 198

Sympherobius angustus, 239
Symphoricarpos, 475, 544
Symphyla, 39, 206
Symphylan(s), **206**
  garden, **206**
Synanthedon pictipes, 145
Synclita obliteralis, 240
Syneta leaf beetle, 128
Syngonium, 551
Syntomedia epilais jucundissima, 197
Syringa, 509
Syrphidae, 223
Syrphid flies, 223, 229
Systena blanda, 118
Syston, 15
Systox, 14, 21

Tabebuia, 551
Tabernaemontana, 551
Tachinidae, 224, 229
Tachinid flies, 224, 229
Tachypterellus consors, 212
  cerasi, 213
  quadrigibbus, 212
  magnus, 212
Taedia hawleyi, 172
Taeniothrips inconsequens, 401
  simplex, 398
Tagetes, 515
Tamalia coweni, 69
Tamarind, 551
Tamarindus, 551
Tamarisk, 551
Tamarix, 551
Tangerine, 551
Taniva albolineana, 255
Tapinonema sessile, 50
Tarjan's sheath nematode, 330
Tarnished plant bug, 176
Tarsonemidae, 279
Tartar emetic, 21
Tawny garden slug, 388
Taxodium, 481
Taxus, 559
Taxus bud mite, 290
  mealybug, 273

weevil, 416
TDE, 21
Tea, 551
Tea olive, 522
Tear gas, 331
Tea scale, 381, **382**
Teasel, 551
  nematode, 328
Tecoma, 551
Tecomaria, 463
Tedion, 21
Tegeticula yuccasella, 312
Teleonemia scrupulosa, 172
Telone, 21, 332
Tenebrionidae, 91
Ten-lined June beetle, 128
Tenodera angustipennis, 267
  aridifolia sinensis, 267
Tent caterpillars, 293
Tenthecoris bicolor, 173
Tenthredinidae, 339
Tenuipalpidae, 279
Tenuipalpus pacificus, 287
Tephritidae, 224
TEPP, 21
Terebrantia, 395
Termite(s), 43, 393, **494**
  desert dampwood, 395
  drywood, 395
  eastern subterranean, 394
Ternstroemia, 551
Terrapin scale, 382
Tesselated scale, 383
Tesselate stylet nematode, 330
Tethida cordigera, 340
Tetradifon, 21
Tetra ethyl pyrophosphate, 21
Tetragonia expansa, 545
Tetraleurodes acaciae, 428
  mori, 431
Tetralopha asperatella, 413
  melanogramma, 415
  robustella, 414
  scortealis, 412
Tetramorium caespitum, 50
Tetranychidae, 279
Tetranychus atlanticus, 290
  canadensis, 285

cinnabarinus, 289
desertorum, 284
mcdanieli, 286
pacificus, 286
schoeni, 288
telarius, 290
Tetraopes tetrophthalmus, 120
Tetrapanax, 538
Tetropium abietis, 154
  velutinum, 159
Tettigoniidae, 209, 237
Tetylenchus, 316
Teucrium, 493
Texas citrus mite, 290
Texas leaf-cutting ant, 51
Thames' root-knot nematode, 330
Thamnosphecia pyri, 136
  scitula, 140
Thea sinensis, 551
Theba pisana, 388
Thecabius populiduplifolius, 73
  populi-monilis, 73
Thecodiplosis pini-radiatae, 275
Therioaphis bellus, 71
  maculata, 77
  riehmi, 78
  trifolii, 82
Thevetia, 552
Thief ant, 51
Thimet, 19, 22
Thiodan, 15, 22
Thistle, 552
  aphid, 79
  butterfly, 181
Tholeria reversalis, 194
Thoraphis umbellulariae, 59
Thorn, 552
Thornapple, 552
Thornbug, 404
Thorne's lance nematode, 330
Thorne's meadow nematode, 330
Thorne's needle nematode, 330
Three-banded leafhopper, 246

Three-cornered alfalfa hopper, 404
Three-lined leaf roller, 260
Three-lined potato beetle, 128
Three-striped blister beetle, 129
Thrift, 547
Thripidae, 396
Thrips, 43, 385
  banded greenhouse, 396
  bean, 396
  blueberry, 396
  camphor, 396
  chrysanthemum, 397
  citrus, 397
  composite, 397
  Cuban-laurel, 397
  dogwood, 397
  Florida flower, 397
  flower, **398**
  gladiolus, 398, Plate XXX
  grape, 399
  grass, 399
  greenhouse, 399
  hollyhock, 400
  iris, 400
  mullein, 400
  onion, 400
  orchid, 401
  pear, 401
  privet, 401
  red-banded, 402
  tobacco, 402
  toyon, 402
  western flower, 402
  wheat, 398
Thrips madroni, 400
  nigropilosus, 397
  tabaci, 400
Thuja, 444
Thunbergia, 552
Thurberia weevil, 426
Thuricide, 11, 22
Thyme, 552
Thymus, 552
Thyridopteryx ephemerae-formis, 85
Thysanoptera, 43, 395
Tibicen linnei, 207
Tibouchina, 494

Tickseed, 476
Tiger beetles, 88
Tiger hickory borer, 158
Tiger moths, 292
Tiger swallowtail, 182
Tile-horned prionus, 158
Tilia, 510
Tingidae, 163
Tip-dwarf mite, 290
Tiphiidae, 407
Tiphiid wasps, 407
Tischeria malifoliella, 247
Tobacco budworm, 161, 221
  cyst nematode, 330
  flea beetle, 129
  hornworm, 236
  stalk borer, 158
  thrips, 402
  wireworm, 434
Tolerance, 9
Tolype velleda, 303
Tomatillo, 552
Tomato, 552
  fruitworm, 221, 232
  hornworm, 236, **406**
  pinworm, 203
  psyllid, 336
  russet mite, 290
Toothed flea beetle, 129
Torreya californica, 461
Tortoise beetle(s), 92, **129**
  black-legged, 96
  golden, 105
  mottled, 116
Tortricidae, 294
Tortrix cocherellana, 308
  pallorana, 307
Torymidae, 407
Torynus druparum, 407
Toumeyella liriodendri, 383
  numismaticum, 375
Toxaphene, 22
Toxoptera aurantii, 57
Toxotrypana curvicauda, 229
Toyon, 461
  lace bug, 177
  thrips, 402
Trachelospermum, 475
Trachykele blondeli, 159

Tradescantia, 557
Tragopogon, 541
Transverse lady beetle, 129
Travelers-tree, 553
Treehopper(s), 403
  buffalo, **403**
  oak, 403
  quince, 404
  three-cornered, 404
  two-marked, 404
  wide-footed, 404
Tree-mallow, 508
Tree-of-heaven, 438
Tremex columba, 150
Trialeurodes abutilonea, 428
  floridensis, 428
  glacialis, 430
  madroni, 431
  merlini, 431
  packardi, 432
  vaporarium, 430
  vittatus, 430
Trichiocampus viminalis, 346
Trichobaris mucorea, 158
  trinotata, 151
Trichodorus, 317, 329
  christiei, 320
  pachydermis, 327
Trichogrammatidae, 407
Trichoplusia ni, 189
Tridactylidae, 209
Trifidaphis radicicola, 76
Trifolium, 473
Trimedlure, 22
Trioxys pallidus, 80
Trioza alacris, 335
  diospyri, 336
  maura, 337
  tripunctata, 334
Trogoderma granarium, 112
Trombidiidae, 279
Trombone sprayer, **26**
Tropaeolum, 519
Trophonema, 315
Trophotylenchulus, 315
Tropical currant, 442
Tropidostreptes amoenus, 165
  illitus, 165

pacificus, 165
Trumpet flower, 453
Trumpet vine, 553
Trypetidae, 224
Trypodendron lineatum, 127
Tsuga, 499
Tuber flea beetle, 129
Tuber moth, 152
Tuberose, 553
Tubulifera, 396
  thrips, 402
Tuckerellid mite, 285, 290
Tulip, 553
  bulb aphid, 79
  leaf aphid, 79
Tulipa, 553
Tuliptree, 553
  aphid, 79
  scale, 383
Tumid spider mite, 290
Tung-oil-tree, 553
Tupelo, 553
  leaf miner, 256
Turks-cap, 553
Turnip, 554
  aphid, 79
  louse, 79
  maggot, 266
Turpentine borer, 158
Turquoise vine, 554
Tussock moths, 293
Twice-stabbed lady beetle, 114
Twig girdler, 158
Twig pruner, 159
Twisted-wing insects, 91
Two-lined chestnut borer, 158
Two-marked treehopper, 404
Two-spotted lady beetle, **113**, 114
Two-spotted spider mite, 290, Plate XXVII
Two-spotted stink bug, 177
Two-striped grasshopper, 234
Two-striped walkingstick, 405
Tydeus californicus, 287
Tylenchida, 314

Tylenchidae, 316
Tylenchoidea, 314
Tylenchorhynchus, 315, 329
  claytoni, 330
  martini, 330
Tylenchulidae, 315
Tylenchulus, 315
  semipenetrans, 320
Tylenchus, 316
Tyloderma fragariae, 157
Typha, 466
Typophorus nigritus viridi-cyaneus, 128
Tyroglyphidae, 279

Udea rubigalis, 262
Ugly-nest caterpillar, 203
Ulmus, 486
Ulochaetes leoninus, 115
Umbellularia californica, 461
Umbonia crassicornis, 404
Umbrella plant, 554
Umbrella-tree, 554
Unaspis citri, 356
  euonymi, 360
Unicorn beetle, 121
Unicorn caterpillar, 203
Uniform State Act, 9
Unspotted tentiform leaf miner, 256
Urbanus proteus, 257
Urocerus californicus, 235
Utah cedar scale, 383
Utetheisa bella, 295

Vaccinium, 502
  arboreum, 545
  corymbosum, 455
  macrocarpon, 478
Vagabond crambus, 414
Vallonia pulchella, 386
Vallota, 554
Vanessa atalanta, 181
  cardui, 181
  virginiensis, 181
Vapam, 22, 332
Vapona, 22
Variable currant aphid, 61
Variable oak leaf caterpillar, 203

Variegated cutworm, 218, Plate XXIII
Variegated leafhopper, 242
Vasates quadripedes, 286
V-C-13 Nemacide, 22, 332
Vedalia, 4, **113**
Vegetable weevil, 426
Velvetbean, 554
  caterpillar, 204
Verbascum, 554
Verbena, 554
  bud moth, 162
  leaf miner, 256
Verbesina, 555
Vesiculaphis caricis, 56
Vespa crabro germana, 409
Vespa hornet, 409
Vespamina novarroensis, 298
  pini, 150
  sequoiae, 308
Vespidae, 407
Vespoidea, 406
Vetch, 555
  bruchid, 426
Viburnum, 555
  aphid, 79
Viburnum opulus, 478
  tinus, 507
Viceroy, 182
Vicia, 555
  faba, 457
Vigna sinensis, 477
Vinca, 555
Vinegar flies, 223
Viola, 523, 555
Violet, 555
  aphid, 80
  gall midge, 277
  sawfly, 349
Virginia-creeper, 556
  leafhopper, 246
  sphinx, 310
Virginia tiger moth, 205
Vitacea polistiformis, 144
Vitex, 468
Vitis, 495

Walkingstick(s), 43, 404, **405**
  giant, 405
  prairie, 405

two-striped, 405
Wallflower, 556
Walnut, 556
  aphids, 80
  blister mite, 291
  caterpillar, 204
  husk fly, 230
  lace bug, 177
  meadow nematode, 330
  scale, 384
  spanworm, 390
  sphinx, 310
  weevil, 213
Wandering-Jew, 557
WARF, 22
Wasmannia auropunctata, 50
Wasp(s), **54**, 405, **406**
  apple seed chalcid, 407
  blackberry knot-gall, 407
  blueberry stem-gall, 408
  California pepper-tree chalcid, 408
  cicada-killer, **408**
  clover seed chalcid, 408
  digger, **408**
  giant hornet, **409**
  grape seed chalcid, 409
  mossy rose-gall, 409
  oak gall, 409
  rose root-gall, 410
Watercress, 557
  leaf beetle, 130
Waterlily, 557
  aphid, 80
  leaf beetle, 130
  leaf cutter, 240
Watermelon, 557
Water primrose, 557
Wax-myrtle, 450
Web-spinning sawflies, 339
Webworm(s), 293, 410
  ailanthus, 410
  alfalfa, 410
  barberry, 410
  beet, 410
  cabbage, 411
  corn root, 411
  bluegrass, 414
  boxwood, 411
  cotoneaster, 411
  fall, 411, Plate XVIII

garden, 412
juniper, 412
lespedeza, 412
mimosa, 413
oak, 413
pale juniper, 413
parsnip, 413
pine, 414
pine false, 413
sod, 414
southern beet, 414
spotted beet, 414
sweetgum, 415
vagabond crambus, 414
Weevil(s), 43, 89, 415
  adaleres, 415
  alfalfa, 415
  arborvitae, 415
  Asiatic oak, 416
  bean, 416, Plate XXXV
  bean stalk, 416
  black elm bark, 416
  black vine, 416, Plate XXXV
  boll, 417
  broadbean, 418
  cabbage seedpod, 418
  carrot, 418
  cattleya, 419
  citrus root, 419
  clover, 419
  clover leaf, 419
  clover seed, 419
  cocklebur, 419
  corn stem, 419
  cowpea, 419
  cranberry, 419
  cribrate, 420
  currant fruit, 420
  dendrobium, 422
  deodar, 420
  Douglas-fir twig, 420
  Engelmann spruce, 420
  filbert, 420
  gorse, 420
  hazelnut, 420
  hibiscus, 420
  hollyhock, 420
  imported long-horned, **421**
  iris, 421
  Japanese, 421

large chestnut, 422
lesser clover leaf, 422
ligustrum, 422
lilac, 422
lily, 422
lily-of-the-valley, 422
lodgepole terminal, 422
Monterey-pine, 422
New York, 422
orchid, 422
pales, 422
pea, 423
pea leaf, 423
pecan, 423
pepper, 424
pine gall, 424
pine reproduction, 424
pine root collar, 424
puncturevine, 424
red elm bark, 424
sand-cherry, 424
sassafras, 424
Sitka-spruce, 424
small chestnut, 425
strawberry, 425
strawberry root, 425
sweetclover, 425
sweetpotato, 425
thurburia, 426
vegetable, 426
vetch bruchid, 426
white-pine, 426
willow flea, 427
yosemite bark, 427
yucca, 427
Weigela, 557
Wesson's sheathoid nematode, 331
West African spiral nematode, 331
Western aster root aphid, 80
Western balsam bark beetle, 130
Western bean cutworm, 218
Western black flea beetle, 130
Western cedar bark beetle, 97, 130
Western cedar borer, 159
Western chinch bug, 177

Western corn rootworm, 338
Western field wireworm, 434
Western flower thrips, 402
Western fruit beetle, 128
Western grape leaf skeletonizer, 262
Western grape rootworm, 338
Western harvester ant, 51
Western hemlock looper, 204
Western horntail, 235
Western larch roundheaded borer, 159
Western leaf-footed bug, 177
Western oak looper, 204
Western parsley swallowtail, 182
Western peach tree borer, 159
Western pine beetle, 130, Plate X
Western potato flea beetle, 131
Western potato leafhopper, 246
Western raspberry fruitworm, 232
Western spotted cucumber beetle, 125, 131
Western strawberry leafroller, 260
Western striped cucumber beetle, 131
Western striped flea beetle, 131
Western subterranean termite, 394
Western swallowtail, 182
Western tent caterpillar, 205
Western tussock moth, 310
Western W-marked cutworm, 218
Western yellow-striped armyworm, 84
West Indian fruit fly, 230
West Indian mole cricket, 210

Wheat eelworm, 331
Wheat gall nematode, 331
Wheat nematode, 331
Wheat thrips, 398
Wheat wireworm, 434
Wheelbarrow sprayer, 26, 29
Wheel bug, 177
White apple leafhopper, 246
White-banded ash beetle, 92
White-banded elm leafhopper, 246
White fir needle miner, 256
Whitefly(flies), 427
  acacia, 428
  avocado, 428
  azalea, 428
  banded wing, 428
  barberry, 428
  citrus, 428
  cloudy-winged, 429
  crown, 429
  fern, 429
  glacial, 430
  grape, 430
  greenhouse, 430
  inconspicuous, 431
  jasmine, 431
  Kellogg's, 431
  madrona, 431
  mulberry, 431
  pruinose, 432
  rhododendron, 432
  strawberry, 432
  sweetpotato, 432
  woolly, 432
White-fringed beetles, 131
White garden snail, 388
White lilyturf, 521
White-lined sphinx, 310
White-marked tussock moth, 311
White oak borer, 158
White peach scale, 384
White-pine aphid, 80
  cone beetle, 132
  shoot borer, 159
  shoot moth, 312
  weevil, 426
White-spotted sawyer, 132

Wide-footed treehopper, 404
Wild geranium aphid, 64
Wild parsnip leaf miner, 256
Willamette mite, 291
Willow, 557
  aphids, 80
  beaked-gall midge, 277
  flea beetle, 132
  flea weevil, 427
  lace bug, 178
  leafhoppers, 247
  psyllid, 337
  red-gall sawfly, 349
  sawfly, 349, Plate XXI
  scurfy scale, 384
  shoot sawfly, 349
Windflower, 441
Wireworm(s), 90, 432, 433, Plate XXIII
  abbreviated, 433
  Columbia Basin, 433
  dry-land, 433
  eastern field, 433
  Great Basin, 434
  Gulf, 434
  Oregon, 434
  Pacific Coast, 434
  Plains false, 434
  Puget Sound, 434
  sand, 434
  southern potato, 434
  sugar-beet, 434
  tobacco, 434
  western field, 434
  wheat, 434
Wistaria, 558
Wisteria, 558
Witch-hazel, 558
  leaf gall aphid, 81
W-marked cutworm, 218
Wood borers, 89
Wood wasps, 234
Woolly alder aphid, 81
Woolly apple aphid, 81, Plate II
Woolly balsam aphid, 56
Woolly beech aphid, 82
Woolly elm aphid, 82
Woolly elm bark aphid, 82
Woolly hawthorn aphid, 82

Woolly honeysuckle aphid, 82
Woolly larch aphid, 82
Woolly pear aphid, 82
Woolly pine needle aphid, 82
Woolly whitefly, 432
Wormwood, 445

Xanthopastis timais, 191
Xenochalepus dorsalis, 253
Xiphinema, 316
  americanum, 318
  chambersi, 320
  diversicaudatum, 322
  index, 319
  radicicola, 324
Xiphydria maculata, 148
Xiphydriidae, 148
Xylastodoris luteolus, 175
Xyleborus, 92
  morigerus, 140
Xylocopa virginica, 86
Xyloryctes satyrus, 121
Xylotrechus aceris, 144
  colonus, 154
  nauticus, 148

Yam, 558
Yankee bug, 95
Yarrow, 559
Yaupon, 559
Yellow clover aphid, 82

Yellow elder, 486
Yellow-headed cutworm, 218
Yellow-headed fireworm, 205
Yellow-headed leafhopper, 247
Yellow-headed spruce sawfly, 349
Yellow jessamine, 505
Yellow-margined leaf beetle, 132
Yellow-necked caterpillar, 205
Yellow oleander, 552
Yellow rose aphid, 82
Yellow scale, 384
Yellow-spider mite, 291
Yellow-spotted willow slug, 349
Yellow-striped armyworm, 84
Yellow woollybear, 205
Yew, 559
Yosemite bark weevil, 427
Yucca, 559
  mealybug, 273
  moth, 293, 312
  plant bug, 178
  spider mite, 291
  weevil, 427
Yucca aloifolia, 545
  gloriosa, 545

Zamia, 559
  scale, 384
Zantedeschia, 461
Zanthoxylum americanum, 535
Zaraea inflata, 344
Zeadiatraea grandiosella, 156
Zea mays, 476
Zebra butterfly, 182
Zebra caterpillar, 205
Zebra swallowtail, 182
Zectran, 22
Zeiraphera griseana, 160
  ratzeburgiana, 160
Zelleria haimbachi, 254
Zephyranthes, 559
Zephyr-lily, 559
Zeuzera pyrina, 304
Zimmerman pine moth, 312
Zimmerman's spiral nematode, 331
Zinnia, 559
Zinophos, 13
Zizyphus, 560
Zonosemata electa, 265
Zophodia convolutella, 231
Zoysia, 560
  spine nematode, 331
Zygaenidae, 294
Zygospila exclamationis, 128